AR

# ANNUAL REVIEW OF NUTRITION

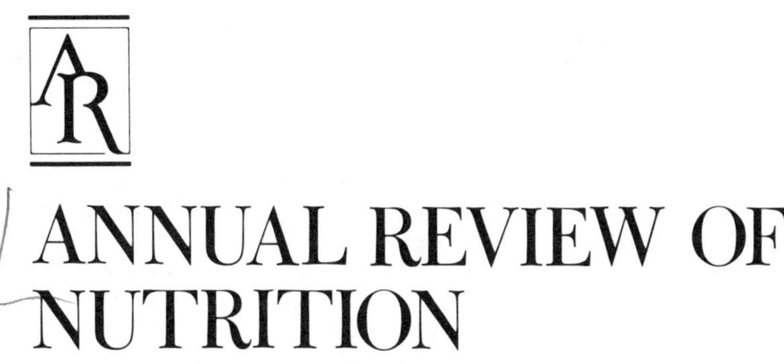

# ANNUAL REVIEW OF NUTRITION

VOLUME 6, 1986

ROBERT E. OLSON, *Editor*
State University of New York, Stony Brook

ERNEST BEUTLER, *Associate Editor*
Scripps Clinic and Research Foundation

HARRY P. BROQUIST, *Associate Editor*
Vanderbilt University

ANNUAL REVIEWS INC. 4139 EL CAMINO WAY P.O. BOX 10139 PALO ALTO, CALIFORNIA 94303-0897

ANNUAL REVIEWS INC.
Palo Alto, California, USA



*International Standard Serial Number: 0199–9885*
*International Standard Book Number: 0–8243–2806-X*



Typesetting by Kachina Typesetting Inc., Tempe, Arizona; John Olson, President
Typesetting coordinator, Janis Hoffman

PRINTED AND BOUND IN THE UNITED STATES OF AMERICA

# PREFACE

The *Annual Review of Nutrition,* in conformity with the goals of Annual Reviews Inc., provides a systematic, periodic examination of scholarly advances in nutrition through "critical, authoritative surveys of the recent original literature describing the current developments in the science of nutrition."

The purpose of a critical review is not only to summarize a topic, but to root out errors of fact or concept and to provoke discussion that will lead to vigorous new research activity. The critical review is as essential a part of the overall scientific method as the original experiments and is part of a continuing peer-review process. The experimenter creates a hypothesis, plans an experiment, records his data, and evaluates his hypothesis. In due time he publishes a paper that is reviewed by peers in the field for adequacy of materials and methods, originality, and soundness of its conclusions. As other papers accumulate, however, it is necessary to take a second look at the published record to see what new scientific discoveries have been made and corroborated, what new areas have been opened, and which research should be encouraged. Fallacies and questionable hypotheses must also be combatted in these reviews in order to limit research in less promising directions. No human judgment, of course, is infallible, but the overall scientific effort depends upon a critical review at each stage in the development of a scientific report, from the experimental plan to the integration of the results into a broader field of science. This is particularly important for nutrition science at this time because of two major threats to the integrity, stability, and funding of the nutritional sciences. These factors apply to all science to an extent but it appears to me at the moment that nutrition science is particularly vulnerable.

The first factor is the turf battle between nutrition scientists and nutrition politicians for control of the data base that underlies food and health policy. Nutrition scientists depend upon the scientific method for their data base. Nutrition politicians, on the other hand, lean on descriptive epidemiology and anecdotal evidence, influenced by their particular beliefs about foods and by those of their constituents (consumerists, corporate interests, the media, and the public). It is regrettable that some scientists have joined these politicians in supporting unsound programs in nutrition education. Critical reviews play an important role in separating nutrition fact from fancy.

In addition, the tightening of the Federal Budget under such political phenomena as the Gramm-Rudman-Hollings Anti-deficit Act creates a gloomy financial future for the NIH and the NSF, particularly in the biological sciences. Such constraints in Federal funding make it extremely important that the most imaginative ideas in the hands of the most productive scientists be supported. Again, the critical review can be of value in guiding the assessment of grant

*(continued)* 

applications, so that the scientific study of nutrition can grow. Such study is crucial, not only in clarifying the function of nutrients but also in elucidating the interactions of genetics, metabolism, and nutrition in the pathogenesis and prevention of the chronic degenerative diseases.

The *Annual Review of Nutrition* strives to cover the wide range of subjects that constitute the field of nutrition. Nutrition is not a single discipline; it draws from a variety of disciplines in both the basic and clinical areas. In the first six volumes, 50% of the pages deal with basic and experimental nutrition, 33% are devoted to clinical nutrition, and the remainder are related to epidemiology, anthropology, and public health nutrition.

The present issue, Volume 6, begins with a prefatory chapter by Dr. Hamish Munro of the Massachusetts Institute of Technology. He pleads for application of the modern disciplines of molecular and cell biology to problems in nutrition science. Nutrition science is not in any sense limited by its past or present technologies but must demand the application of new technologies and concepts to the study of nutrient requirements, metabolism, function, and the relationship of nutritional status to health.

This issue also includes reviews on the energetics of ethanol, the role of sugars in nutrition, the regulation of cholesterol biosynthesis, the metabolism of sulfur-containing amino acids, and the function of inositol phospholipids. The biochemical function of vitamins C and D, metabolism of carotenoids, and the function of carnitine in humans are also reviewed.

In clinical nutrition, Volume 6 includes reviews of the physiological adaptation to lower intakes of energy and protein; nutrition and infection; calcium and hypertension; mutagens and carcinogens in foods; labile methyl groups in the promotion of cancer; and inheritable disorders of biotin metabolism. In comparative nutrition we have essays on the nutrition of fish and of ruminants and an article on the role of gastrointestinal microflora in mammals. In the field of nutritional anthropology we present chapters on the impact of culture on food habits; diet and human behavior; and food likes and dislikes.

I would like to thank my associates on the Editorial Committee, the consultants who aided us in assembling the reviews, and the authors who have provided such excellent reviews for Volume 6. Our work has been ably complemented by that of Ms. Margot Platt, the Production Editor of the *Annual Review of Nutrition* in Palo Alto.

ROBERT E. OLSON, EDITOR

Annual Review of Nutrition
Volume 6, 1986

# CONTENTS

PREFATORY ESSAY

Back to Basics: An Evolutionary Odyssey With Reflections on the Nutrition Research of Tomorrow, *Hamish N. Munro* 1–12

CARBOHYDRATES

Monosaccharides in Health and Disease, *Rachmiel Levine* 211–24

ENERGY METABOLISM

Alcohol and Nutrition: Caloric Value, Bioenergetics, and Relationship to Liver Damage, *Mack C. Mitchell and H. Franklin Herlong* 457–74

LIPIDS

Regulation of Cholesterol Biosynthesis, *Harry Rudney and Russell C. Sexton* 245–72

PROTEINS, PEPTIDES, AND AMINO ACIDS

Metabolism of Sulfur-Containing Amino Acids, *Martha H. Stipanuk* 179–209

Protein and Amino Acid Requirements of Fishes, *Robert P. Wilson and John E. Halver* 225–44

VITAMINS

The Biochemical Functions of Ascorbic Acid, *Sasha Englard and Sam Seifter* 365–406

Vitamin D Receptors: Nature and Function, *Mark R. Haussler* 527–62

INORGANIC NUTRIENTS

Biochemical Basis for the Manifestations of Iron Deficiency, *Peter R. Dallman* 13–40

Mutagens and Carcinogens in Foods, *Chie Furihata and Taijiro Matsushima* 67–94

Metabolism, Nutrition, and Function of Carotenoids, *T. W. Goodwin* 273–97

*(continued)* 

Other Food Components

Metabolism and Function of *myo*-Inositol and Inositol Phospholipids, *Bruce J. Holub* 563–97

Clinical Nutrition

Carnitine Metabolism and Function in Humans, *Charles J. Rebouche and Dennis J. Paulson* 41–66

Nutrition and Infection, *Gerald T. Keusch and Michael J. G. Farthing* 131–54

The Pathophysiology of Anorexia Nervosa and Bulimia Nervosa, *Regina C. Casper* 299–316

Inheritable Biotin-Treatable Disorders and Associated Phenomena, *Lawrence Sweetman and William L. Nyhan* 317–43

Labile Methyl Groups and the Promotion of Cancer, *Paul M. Newberne and Adrianne E. Rogers* 407–32

Calcium and Hypertension, *Njeri Karanja and David A. McCarron* 475–94

Metabolic Adaptation to Low Intakes of Energy and Protein, *J. C. Waterlow* 495–526

Microorganisms

Gastrointestinal Microflora in Mammalian Nutrition, *Dwayne C. Savage* 155–78

Nutritional Anthropology

Diet and Human Behavior: How Much Do They Affect Each Other?, *Markus J. P. Kruesi and Judith L. Rapoport* 113–30

The Impact of Culture on Food-Related Behavior, *M. L. Axelson* 345–63

Food Likes and Dislikes, *P. Rozin and T. A. Vollmecke* 433–56

Comparative Nutrition

Somatic Nutrient Requirements of Ruminants, *J. M. Asplund* 95–112

Indexes

Author Index 599–630

Subject Index 631–43

Cumulative Index of Contributing Authors, Volumes 2–6 644–45

Cumulative Index of Chapter Titles, Volumes 2–6 646–49

## SOME RELATED ARTICLES IN OTHER *ANNUAL REVIEWS*

From the *Annual Review of Biochemistry,* Volume 55 (1986):

Beta-Amino Acids: Mammalian Metabolism and Utility as Alpha-Amino Acid Analogues, *O. Griffith*

Metallothionein, *D. H. Hamer*

Arachidonic Acid Metabolism, *P. Needleman, J. Turk, B. A. Jakschik, A. R. Morrison, and J. B. Lefkowith*

Molecular Aspects of Sugar: Ion Cotransport, *J. K. Wright, R. Seckler, and P. Overath*

Taurine: Biological Update, *C. E. Wright, H. H. Tallan, Y. Y. Lin, and G. E. Gaull*

From the *Annual Review of Physiology,* Volume 48 (1986):

Inositol Phospholipid Metabolism in the Kidney, *D. A. Troyer, D. W. Schwertz, J. I. Kreisberg, and M. A. Venkatachalam*

Functional Activities of Hepatic Lipoprotein Receptors, *R. J. Havel*

Prostaglandin Biosynthesis and Its Compartmentation in Vascular Smooth Muscle and Endothelial Cells, *W. L. Smith*

Antioxidant Defenses in the Lung, *I. Fridovich and B. Freeman*

From the *Annual Review of Psychology,* Volume 37 (1986):

The Neurochemistry of Behavior, *J. Panksepp*

From the *Annual Review of Public Health,* Volume 7 (1986):

Carcinogenesis Modeling: From Molecular Biology to Epidemiology, *S. H. Moolgavkar*

Obesity and Body Weight Standards, *A. P. Simopoulos*

The Importance of Obesity in the Development of Coronary Risk Factors and Disease: The Epidemiological Evidence, *H. B. Hubert*

Dietary Aspects of the Treatment of Hypertension, *N. M. Kaplan*

Public Health Approaches to Obesity and Its Management, *K. D. Brownell*

Anorexia Nervosa and Bulimia, *J. H. Autry, E. S. Stover, N. Reatig, and R. Casper*

ANNUAL REVIEWS INC. is a nonprofit scientific publisher established to promote the advancement of the sciences. Beginning in 1932 with the *Annual Review of Biochemistry,* the Company has pursued as its principal function the publication of high quality, reasonably priced *Annual Review* volumes. The volumes are organized by Editors and Editorial Committees who invite qualified authors to contribute critical articles reviewing significant developments within each major discipline. The Editor-in-Chief invites those interested in serving as future Editorial Committee members to communicate directly with him. Annual Reviews Inc. is administered by a Board of Directors, whose members serve without compensation.

Hamish N. Munro

Ann. Rev. Nutr. 1986. 6:1–12

# BACK TO BASICS: An Evolutionary Odyssey With Reflections on the Nutrition Research of Tomorrow[1]

*Hamish N. Munro*

USDA Human Nutrition Research Center on Aging at Tufts, Boston, Massachusetts 02111

CONTENTS

PRELUDE ........ 1
THE HISTORICAL BACKGROUND OF NUTRITIONAL SCIENCE ........ 2
INTERMISSION ........ 5
NUTRITION AND THE EVOLUTION OF ANIMALS ........ 5
THE CHALLENGE FOR TOMORROW'S NUTRITION SCIENTIST ........ 9

## PRELUDE

The *Annual Review of Nutrition* provides the rare opportunity and challenge of reflecting on the status of nutrition research within the family of Life Sciences. I shall argue that, like other applied biological sciences, nutrition research needs to be continuously enriched by concepts and techniques developed in the course of basic biological research. This implies that some in the community of nutrition scientists must maintain lively contact with the rapidly moving front in basic biological sciences. Hence the phrase "back to basics" in my title. Not only will this have a beneficial effect on nutrition research, but it will also improve credibility for nutritionists among their basic science colleagues.

The mature scientist always appears to be a more or less autonomous individualist. Yet there are encounters along the way that determine our career patterns. Looking back on my own progress, I can identify several such factors that, without my seeking them out, have conspired to steer my own progress into basic directions. In its own way, each displays an aspect of evolution, whether it be the evolution of a species or of a scientific discipline.

First, I have always had an interest in history, an interest I share with other prefatory essayists in this *Annual Review* series. In editing the first volume in a series on protein metabolism in the 1960s (21, 22), I decided to explore the history of this area for an introductory chapter, and found that I and the people I had worked with early in my career came from a scientific lineage going back two hundred years to the beginning of modern chemistry, like a family tree that progressively evolves in sophistication.

Second, in continuation of the same series on protein metabolism, I concluded that it needed a section on the role of nutrition as a central factor in the evolution of *animals,* which, I was able to show, share a distinctive common pattern of nutrient needs not found in other life forms, a pattern that can only be satisfied by a supply of food. This need distinguishes unicellular animals from unicellular plants or molds, while multicellular animals can be shown to have made evolutionary adaptations to accommodate their needs for nutrients. In particular, mammals, the class we most often deal with experimentally, show an inverse relationship between body weight and daily intake of nutrients per unit of body weight.

Third, during the past decade it has become possible to explore these evolutionary changes at the level of the genome and this has provided me and others with the exciting possibility of observing both conservation of functional components of proteins along with new adaptations as evolution progresses.

The final molding effect on my career has been my good fortune in being associated with the development of the USDA Human Nutrition Research Center on Aging at Tufts University. It offers the possibility of determining how nutritional and other environmental factors cooperate to allow the human to optimize his or her genomic potential throughout the life span and to ameliorate the gradual aging process.

## THE HISTORICAL BACKGROUND OF NUTRITIONAL SCIENCE

Scientific research is an evolutionary process in which the present builds on the past, often without recognition of the latter. In the words of Carl Voit in 1865 [cited in translation by Lusk (17)]: "The man of science ought to realise the factors which have given him the vantage which he holds. But there are textbooks on the animal mechanism which do not even mention the name of Liebig. This anomaly is possible only for those who do not understand history and hold only the new to be worthy of consideration." Here, I want to illustrate how my early association with the nutritional sciences was predestined from the succession of previous investigators whose work pointed in that direction.

I have written elsewhere (23) about the development of protein metabolism and nutrition. Modern chemical science began with the discovery of carbon dioxide by the Edinburgh physician Joseph Black in 1756 (4). That discovery was rapidly followed by the identification of oxygen and nitrogen in the atmosphere. The biological importance of these gases was appreciated from the beginning. Nitrogen was first recognized by its inability to sustain the life of a mouse (35), a property commemorated in the French word for nitrogen, *azote* (Greek "without life"). In France, Black's contemporary Lavoisier developed the first systematic modern chemistry that included gasometric volume determinations for many compounds. In 1790, he wrote to Black to tell him that his gasometric measurements showed that respiration is accompanied by the disappearance of some oxygen and its replacement by carbon dioxide in the expired air, and that this exchange is accelerated some 50% after meals and several-fold by exercise (23). Thus modern chemistry was born in an atmosphere of physiological function, including measurement of the energy needs of different states. It may be noted that energy needs is as good a place as any to start nutritional research. It remains a major field of nutritional research.

Although Lavoisier did not survive the French Revolution, his school of chemistry flourished and provided fertile ground in which the biological sciences could develop. In 1817, the French physiologist Magendie issued his *Elementary Compendium of Physiology* (18), the first modern text on this discipline. In the preceding century, Haller had published an eight-volume text on physiology written in turgid Latin, and without benefit of the new chemistry. With Magendie, we step from the primeval forests of mystery and speculation created by Haller's *Elementa Physiologiae* (12) into the bright sunshine of scientific observation and deductive reasoning displayed in Magendie's book. Because of his Parisian contemporaries, who had been trained in chemistry in the school of Lavoisier, Magendie was able to state that "the proximate principles of animals are divided into nitrogenous and non-nitrogenous. The nitrogenous principles of animals are: albumen, fibrin, gelatin, mucus, casein, urea, uric acid, red-colouring matter of blood. The non-nitrogenous principles are: olein, stearin, fatty matter of the brain, acetic, benzoic, lactic, formic, oxalic acids, as well as sugar of milk, sugar of diabetic urine, colouring matter of bile." Magendie went on to demonstrate that essential dietary constituents included nitrogenous organic compounds, later to receive the unifying name of "protein" by Mulder (20) in 1839.

Another scientist who benefited from the Lavoisier school of chemistry was Liebig, a German scientist who spent the years 1823–1824 in Paris. He carried the new chemistry to Giessen in Germany, where he applied organic chemistry to the study of animal metabolism. From this emerged his book *Animal*

*Chemistry or Organic Chemistry in its Applications to Physiology and Pathology* (15) in 1840, which laid the foundations of metabolic principles. In 1852, Liebig transferred from Giessen to Munich, where he established a vigorous school of metabolic studies from which emerged Carl Voit, later to be Liebig's successor in Munich. Although balance studies of carbon, hydrogen, oxygen, and nitrogen had been carried out on cattle by Boussingault (5) in 1844, it was Voit who raised the technique of nitrogen balance to fine precision (3). He taught these skills to various foreign workers who went back to their own countries to perpetuate the science of nutrition: Atwater and Lusk to the US, Rubner to Germany, and Cathcart to Britain, the last-named to be the teacher of the present author.

Voit may be regarded for other reasons as the father of modern nutritional experimentation. In 1853 and again in 1865, Playfair (33), professor of chemistry at Edinburgh University, had surveyed the diets of different classes in the British population and had concluded that the daily diet of the average man contained 119 g protein, 51 g fat, and 530 g carbohydrate. In 1881, Voit (38) summarized these surveys and others, including his own, and assessed the needs of the average working man to be 118 g protein, 56 g fat, and 500 g of carbohydrate. At the time, these intakes were also regarded as desirable quantities of each nutrient class needed to maintain health, but were challenged at the turn of the century by Sivén (37), Chittenden (8), and Hindhede (14). The low intakes of protein advocated by these investigators were later rejected by many who had observed impaired resistance to disease on diets low in protein. Thus Voit and his immediate successors had begun to ask the questions with which we still struggle in the field of nutrition, and which are reflected in another chapter in the present volume (39). It may be noted that, through his long-term role as editor of the *Zeitschrift für Biologie,* Carl Voit identified himself as a generalist in biology.

From this brief history, it will not have escaped the reader that science is made up of a series of successive small steps in which skills in laboratory techniques, and practice in both deductive and inductive reasoning that lead to new concepts, are passed on from the older to the younger investigator. In my own case, I first studied protein metabolism in 1934 with D. P. Cuthbertson (later Sir David Cuthbertson, Director of the Rowett Institute, Aberdeen), who at that time was in the Department of Physiology at Glasgow University headed by Cathcart. Cathcart had also acted as a preceptor for Boyd Orr, the founder of the Rowett Institute and later of the Food and Agricultural Organization in post–World War II Rome. Thus, through Cuthbertson and Cathcart, I learned the concepts developed by Voit, who in turn was influenced by the teachings of Liebig, based on the organic chemistry he had learned from the French school of Lavoisier in Paris. Thus the mature investigator is not an island unto himself, but is part of an ongoing process in the evolution of scientific knowledge!

## INTERMISSION

The period of my life from the mid-1930s until the mid-1950s was punctuated by a teaching position in clinical medicine, a war, and other changing events. However, the basic allure of studying nutritional and other factors in protein metabolism persisted. Under the guidance of Dr. Cuthbertson, the relationship of energy intake to protein utilization was extensively explored between the years 1936 and 1952 and it still provides basic data. Indeed, my most recent publication (11) on this topic was in 1979 with John Kinney's surgical metabolism group in Columbia College of Medicine and deals with the influence of energy intake on nitrogen balance in surgical cases. But slowly the desire to delve deeper became irresistible. There was a perceived need to integrate the metabolic events that make protein metabolism the wild ballet that it is, with whirling metabolites answering to the orchestration of the endocrine system as they shuttle among the tissues. To reduce this to order, there followed a period of examining the principles on which protein metabolism is accomplished in different mammals. This was consolidated by an in-depth survey of the evolution of animals, seen from the viewpoint of their nutritional needs and their metabolic responses.

## NUTRITION AND THE EVOLUTION OF ANIMALS

A defensible case can be made for the view that the main driving force in the evolution of animals from the most primitive forms onward has been the supply of nutrients in the environment (24). It can be presumed that primitive unicellular organisms evolved from non-nucleated (prokaryotic) forms into nucleated (eukaryotic) unicellular forms, such as molds, which still retain the general prokaryotic property of synthesizing all organic compounds required for metabolism. However, it seems likely that, in the early history of the Earth as the fluid surrounding the colonies of such organisms became enriched with their metabolites, it was possible for some mutant cells that had lost the capacity to make certain metabolic pathways to find enough of the missing metabolites to survive. In this way, cells that had eliminated metabolic pathways could multiply even faster than their better-endowed neighbors who had to divert energy to the synthesis of these metabolites. Zamenhof & Eichhorn (40) showed with a histidine-deficient mutant of *B. subtilis* that, in the presence of histidine, this mutant grows faster than the wild type, which continues to make this amino acid and thus has to divert energy to its synthesis.

Eventually, cell populations must have emerged with a stable inheritance of DNA lacking the synthetic pathways for eight to ten amino acids, the B vitamins, and some other essential cell components. These were the first animal cells. Thus the animal kingdom became distinguishable because such cells lacked the capacity to make a full spectrum of organic compounds. Ever after, evolution of animals was to recapitulate this pattern. For example, a fundamental feature of all animals, from unicellular protozoa up to man, is firmly established to be the dietary requirement for essentially the same series of amino acids whose synthetic pathways were deleted from the DNA of the first animal cells (25).

Nutrition then is a central environmental requirement for the survival and evolution of animal species, in which individual nutrients have to be conserved.

In the case of iron, this element circulates in the blood attached to transferrin. In the mammal, this carrier protein is about 80,000 daltons in size and consists of two nearly identical sequences. However, there was a period in the early evolution of animals when transferrin consisted of only one of these sequences of molecular weight 41,000. It appears that, when the kidney first evolved in *Urochordates,* duplication of the molecule was favored because it then became large enough not to filter through the semipermeable glomerular membrane, whereas the 41,000-dalton transferrin would do so (19). This illustrates how evolution has to adapt nutrient availability to increasing physiological complexity.

In the case of vitamin A, the retinol-binding protein (RBP) is small enough to be filtered through the mammalian kidney and destroyed, but is protected by binding to the much larger pre-albumin of plasma. In fish and tadpoles, RBP lacks the pre-albumin-binding site, since proteins filtered through the kidney are reabsorbed intact into the blood (36). Higher vertebrates obviously adapted by developing the pre-albumin-binding site. The results strongly suggest that the piscine retinol-binding protein is a prototype of the specific vitamin A–transporting protein in plasma of the vertebrates, but was modified later in evolution during phylogenetic development of the vertebrates to acquire a binding site for pre-albumin on the molecule.

Perhaps the evolutionary progression most relevant to us occurred in mammals, where an inverse relationship between mature body size and the intensity of metabolism can be demonstrated. This is expressed by the allometric equation

$$\log M = \log a + b \log W, \qquad \text{or } M = aW^b,$$

where $M$ is the metabolic measurement (e.g. energy needs), $W$ is the weight of the adult animal, $a$ is a constant and $b$ is an exponent of weight expressing the effect of body size on the intensity of metabolism. The exponent $b$ thus tells how body size of mammals affects the metabolic or nutritional measurement. This has been well documented for a range of metabolic processes (25), many of which are related through the 0.75 power of body weight, implying that a 200-g rat has five times the intensity of metabolism of a 70-kg man. For example, the basal energy metabolism of different mammals is related to the 0.75 power of their body weights. This relationship includes the requirements for essential amino acids, which on the basis of daily needs per kg body weight decline by five-fold between the rat and man. Not surprisingly, protein turnover decreases in parallel, so that, for example, the half-life of plasma albumin becomes longer and longer, being 1.2 days for the mouse, 2.5 days for the rat, 5.7 for the rabbit, 8.2 for a large dog, 18 days for man, and 20.7 days for the cow, a progression related to the 0.66 power of body weight.

Analysis of the livers of these mammals (28) showed a similar decline in RNA content per cell. Thus the machinery for intracellular protein synthesis is geared to metabolic intensity. Others have consequently used the RNA content of tissues to predict the intensity of protein synthesis in organs and tissues, and have confirmed the relationship of concentration of RNA to intensity of protein synthesis. Along with the larger body size of most mammals goes a longer life span. Cutler (9) recently demonstrated that the brain and the kidneys of animals of increasing body size show progressively reduced rates of in vitro peroxidation of lipids. Peroxidation is one putative cause of aging, and these findings thus provide an attractive explanation for the different life spans of mammals.

Since the liver is intimately related to metabolism of incoming nutrients, it is not surprising to find that the relative slowing of metabolism in large animals is correlated with reduction in liver size in relation to body weight, from 6% of body weight in the shrew to 1% in the elephant. However, not all tissues share this proportionate decrease. In the slim young adult animal of any size, muscle remains a little below half of body weight. This means that, in larger animals such as man, muscle assumes a more important role relative to the liver and other viscera in the total metabolism of the body. At the time in the late 1960s when we were examining these effects of mammalian evolution on metabolism, new findings were emerging on exchange of metabolites between tissues, notably between muscle and liver. It is thus becoming possible to provide a complex and quantitative picture of metabolism built into the evolution of mammals. This is not restricted to the well-established meal-related surge of branched-chain amino acids from liver to muscle, and the return of amino groups from muscle to the viscera in the form of alanine and glutamine (26, 27). Evidence from our laboratory and elsewhere is emerging to show that incoming dietary carbohydrates follow an equally elaborate path in which they are reduced to three-carbon compounds in the peripheral tissues for return to the liver in order to provide hepatic glycogen deposition through gluconeogenesis.

The unifying features of structure and metabolism in mammals of different size do not extend to the interface between mother and fetus, namely the placenta (30). In evolutionary terms, the placenta is of recent origin and evolution is probably still experimenting with its structure. Fortunately, despite the wide divergence in the architectural features of placentas, they can be functionally divided for nutrient transport into two types, depending on whether the placental villi are in direct contact with the maternal blood supply (the hemochorial placentas of higher primates and of rodents) or whether nutrients must first pass from maternal blood through a layer of uterine cells before being transferred to the placental villi (the epitheliochorial and syndesmochorial placentas of the sheep, pig, cow, and horse). In the latter case, the surrounding uterine wall imposes a barrier that has to be crossed. For example, in the pig, iron is taken up into the uterine cells from transferrin in the maternal plasma; these cells then synthesize a second iron carrier protein, uteroferrin, which transports the iron into the placenta in order to reach the fetus (34). Uteroferrin belongs to the class of purple acid phosphatases, an example of evolutionary adaptation to provide a new function related to nutrition.

The special reproductive system of the mammal includes the secretion of milk by the mammary gland, which is believed to have developed from the sweat glands of the skin (16). The milk protein α-lactalbumin bears a structural similarity to lysozyme, an antibacterial glycosidic enzyme present in sweat (6). Lactalbumin is responsible for ensuring synthesis of lactose by modifying the action of galactosyl transferase. This enzyme normally adds galactose to the growing carbohydrate chains of glycoproteins. In the presence of α-lactalbumin, glucose becomes the preferred acceptor for galactose and, as a consequence, milk contains lactose in proportion to its lactalbumin content (7).

This brief survey of the role of nutrition in the evolution of animals emphasizes that molecular changes are constantly at work, adapting the species to the environment. To understand the nature of the nutritional factors in this process, one must answer questions demanding analysis of genomic structure and control of its expression. Some years ago, I became involved in studies of the iron-storage protein ferritin, which is unusual in being an enzyme that stores its product, namely oxidized iron (29). In mammals, the ferritin protein shell is made up of subunits of two sizes. Comparison of the amino acid sequences of the two subunits of human ferritin (10) showed that they were only fifty percent similar in sequences. However, the three-dimensional structure showed preservation of the five helical regions in each subunit protein, resulting in similarity of their gross structures. When amino acid sequences of ferritin were compared in different mammals, it was found that they had diverged by 0.16% for each million years of evolution, implying that the two ferritin subunits probably evolved from a single ancestral protein about $350 \times 10^6$ years ago (31), which is about the time of divergence of the α- and β-globins from a single globin chain such as occurs in the hemoglobin of the lamprey.

In the case of hemoglobin, it is well established that the two globin chains are associated with improved capacity to take up and release oxygen as compared to the single-chain hemoglobin of the lamprey. The advantage of the two subunits of ferritin has not been precisely identified, but must relate to efficiency of iron storage, since free ions of iron in the cell can cause peroxidative damage to unsaturated fatty acids in membranes, to proteins, and to DNA (13). The structure of the messenger RNAs for the two ferritin subunits reflects the importance of this protective function. In the rat, these were found to be stored in the cell cytoplasm in an inactive form that can be rapidly transferred into polyribosome form for active protein synthesis when iron enters the cell (2). In this way, the balance between the need for iron and the risk of peroxidation is achieved by varying the proportion of ferritin messenger that is in the active form. We (31) now have reason to believe that this regulation is achieved through certain features of the secondary structure of the ferritin messenger that make it sensitive to the free iron content of the cell (J. K. Vass and H. N. Munro, unpublished information).

It appears to me that the application of modern techniques for studying genomic function will provide an increasingly deep understanding of the role of nutrients, singly and in combination, on the long-term function and health of animals and man.

## THE CHALLENGE FOR TOMORROW'S NUTRITION SCIENTIST

In most sciences, individual scientists are specialists in narrow areas of their discipline that are advancing so rapidly that it is academically suicidal to be other than expert in their own specialized area. Nutritional research tends to impose the need for integration of much biochemical data to meaningful terms for whole animals, so that the generalist is more common. This finds a market because nutritionists are often called upon to make pronouncements on the overall effect of diet on health and disease.

The challenge of integrating an imperfect background of widely diverse but pertinent knowledge was impressed on me by my experiences in developing a program to explore the role of nutrition in the aging process. Nutrition may interact with aging in three ways—first, as a potential means to ameliorate the continuous loss of organ function throughout adult life; second to influence the onset of age-related degenerative diseases; and third, to provide guidelines for intakes of nutrients at different ages, especially for the elderly (32).

I want to emphasize how difficult it is to make judgments in broad fields in which no one view prevails. For example, osteoporosis is an important degenerative condition in which the only agreement seems to be that the loss of bone strength associated with it can be extensive enough to predispose to fracture (32). Is calcium intake an important factor in osteoporosis? If so, would a high intake be most important in ensuring extensive deposition of bone calcium during adolescence or during middle life, and can it contribute to restoring bone strength after fracture? What is the importance of dietary protein in causing osteoporotic calcium loss from bone and can this be prevented by raising the phosphorus content of the diet through natural foods? What is the importance of vitamin D and its metabolic derivatives in age-related metabolic bone disease? Is there any role for fluoride or for fiber in the prevention of osteoporosis? How much does exercise contribute to maintaining bone strength? Should estrogens be used to prevent post-menopausal osteoporosis, and does supplementary calcium reduce the effective dose of the steroid? Some of these measures, such as raising calcium intake, could be public health options affecting the general population, whereas others, such as administration of estrogens or even of vitamin D metabolites, might be regarded as involving medical decisions for individuals.

To solve nutritional problems of this kind requires an integrated approach for which research training programs in nutrition have in the past usually not provided the appropriate mixture of disciplines. Indeed, university departments of nutrition have often become extinct or nearly extinct, as if after the departure of their leaders nutrition was an aberration in the college's offerings. Fortunately, the interest in nutrition as a health factor that characterized the 1970s was instrumental in triggering government action, one consequence being the establishment of five nutrition research centers working within the Department of Agriculture. This cluster of research centers and the establishment of clinical nutrition core units under the Department of Health and Human Services are solid evidence of government commitment to answering important questions involving human nutrition. In the case of the five USDA centers, the primary objective is to identify human nutrient requirements that will optimize the genetic potential of the individual at all stages of life, as expressed in official objective Number 5 of the Agricultural Research Service Program Plan (1): "To develop the means for promoting optimum human health and well-being through nutrition and family resource management."

The present is clearly an appropriate time for encouraging a renaissance of nutritional science, provided that it can take full advantage of the exciting advances in the basic sciences, as have many other applied sciences.

We must emulate the spirit of Drs. Goldstein and Brown on hearing of their award of the Nobel Prize on October 15, 1985. Dr. Brown said on interview that, in their basic work on lipoprotein receptors, their goal has been to determine why diet has a determining role in atherosclerosis. No team of research workers could better demonstrate the resounding success of basic science as applied to a nutrition-related problem. Back to basics!

## *Literature Cited*


1. Agricultural Research Service. 1983. *Program Plan*. Misc. Publ. No. 1429. Washington, DC: US Dept. Agric.
2. Aziz, N., Munro, H. N. 1986. Both subunits of rat liver ferritin are regulated at a translational level by iron induction. *Nucleic Acids Res*. In press
3. Bischoff, T. L. W., Voit, C. 1860. *Die Gesetze der Ernährung des Fleischfressers*. Leipzig: Winter
4. Black, J. 1756. Experiments upon magnesia alba, quicklime, and some other alcaline substances. In *Essays and Observations, Physical and Literary,* 2:157. Edinburgh: Creech
5. Boussingault, J. B. 1844. *Économie rurale,* Vol. II. Paris: Bechet Jeune
6. Brew, K., Vanaman, T. C., Hill, R. L. 1967. Comparison of the amino acid sequence of bovine α-lactalbumin and hen's egg white lysosome. *J. Biol. Chem*. 242:3747–49
7. Brew, K., Vanaman, T. C., Hill, R. L. 1968. The role of α-lactalbumin and the A protein in lactose synthetase: a unique mechanism for the control of a biological reaction. *Proc. Natl. Acad. Sci. USA* 59:491–97
8. Chittenden, R. H. 1905. *Physiological Economy in Nutrition*. London: Heinemann; New York: Stokes
9. Cutler, R. G. 1985. Peroxide-producing potential of tissues: inverse correlation with longevity of mammalian species. *Proc. Natl. Acad. Sci. USA* 82:4798–4802
10. Dörner, M. H., Salfeld, J., Will, H., Leibold, E. A., Vass, J. K., Munro, H. N. 1985. Structure of human ferritin light subunit messenger RNA: comparison with heavy subunit message and functional implications. *Proc. Natl. Acad. Sci. USA* 82:3139–43
11. Elwyn, D., Gump, F. E., Munro, H. N., Iles, M., Kinney, J. M. 1979. Changes in nitrogen balance of depleted patients with infusions of glucose. *Am. J. Clin. Nutr*. 32:1597–1611
12. Haller, A. 1757–1765. *Elementa Physiologiae Corporis Humanae,* Vols. I–VIII. Lausanne: Bousquet
13. Halliwell, B., Gutteridge, J. M. C. 1984. Oxygen toxicity, oxygen radicals, transition metals and disease. *Biochem. J*. 219:1–14
14. Hindhede, M. 1913. *Protein and Nutrition*. London: Ewart Seymour
15. Liebig, J. von. 1840. *Animal Chemistry, or Organic Chemistry in its Application to Physiology and Pathology,* Transl. W. Gregory, in 1842. London: Taylor & Walton
16. Long, C. A. 1969. The origin and evolution of mammary glands. *BioScience* 19:519–23
17. Lusk, G. 1928. *The Science of Nutrition*. Philadelphia: Saunders. 4th ed.
18. Magendie, F. 1829. *An Elementary Compendium of Physiology for the Use of Students*. Transl. E. Mulligan. Edinburgh: Carfrae; London: Longmans, Green. 3rd ed.
19. Martin, A. W., Huebers, E., Huebers, H., Webb, J., Finch, C. A. 1984. A mono-sited transferrin from a representative deuterostome: the Ascidian *Pyura stolonifera* (subphylum *Urochordata*). *Blood* 64:1047–52
20. Mulder, G. J. 1839. *J. Prakt. Chem*. 16:129–42
21. Munro, H. N., Allison, J. B., eds. 1964. *Mammalian Protein Metabolism,* Vols. 1, 2. New York: Academic
22. Munro, H. N., ed. 1969–1970. *Mammalian Protein Metabolism,* Vols. 3, 4. New York: Academic
23. Munro, H. N. 1964. Historical introduction: The origin and growth of our present concepts of protein metabolism. See Ref. 21, 1:1–29
24. Munro, H. N. 1969. An introduction to protein metabolism during the evolution and development of mammals. See Ref. 22, 3:3–19
25. Munro, H. N. 1969. Evolution of protein metabolism in mammals. See Ref. 22, 3:133–82
26. Munro, H. N. 1982. Metabolic integration of organs in health and disease. Fifth Annual Jonathan E. Rhoads Lecture. *J. Paren. Enter. Nutr*. 6:271–79
27. Munro, H. N. 1982. Interaction of liver and muscle in the regulation of metabolism in response to nutritional and other factors. In *The Liver: Biology and Pathobiology,* ed. I. Arias, H. Popper, D. Schachter, D. A. Shafritz, pp. 677–91. New York: Raven
28. Munro, H. N., Downie, E. D. 1964. Relationship of liver composition to intensity of protein metabolism in different mammals. *Nature* 203:603–5
29. Munro, H. N., Linder, M. C. 1978. Ferritin: structure, biosynthesis and role in iron metabolism. *Physiol. Rev*. 58:317–97
30. Munro, H. N., Pilistine, S. J., Fant, M. E. 1983. The placenta in nutrition. *Ann. Rev. Nutr*. 3:97–124
31. Munro, H. N., Leibold, E. A., Vass, J.

K., Aziz, N., Rogers, J., et al. 1985. Ferritin gene structure and expression. In *Proteins of Iron Storage and Transport, Proc. 7th Int. Congr. Proteins of Iron Metabolism,* ed. G. Spik, J. Montreuil, R. R. Crichton, J. Mazurier, pp. 331–41. Amsterdam: Elsevier

32. Munro, H. N. 1986. Nutrition and metabolism during aging and in the elderly. In *Nutrition and Metabolism in Patient Care*, ed. J. M. Kinney, K. N. Jeejeebhoy, G. L. Hill, O. E. Owen. Philadelphia: Saunders. In press
33. Playfair, L. 1865. *Med. Times Gazette,* Vol. i, 459, 485, 511
34. Roberts, R. M., Raub, T. J., Bazer, F. W. 1986. Role of uteroferrin in transplacental iron transport in the pig. *Fed. Proc.* In press
35. Rutherford, D. 1772. *Dissertatio Inauguralis de Aero Fixo Dicto, aut Mephitico.* MD thesis. Univ. Edinburgh
36. Shidoji, Y., Muto, Y. 1977. Vitamin A transport in plasma of the non-mammalian vertebrates: isolation and partial characterization of piscine retinol-binding protein. *J. Lipid Res.* 18:679–91
37. Sivén, V. C. 1901. Zur Kenntnis des Stoffwechsels beim erwachsenen Menschen mit Berucksichtigung des Eiweissbedarfs. *Skand. Arch. Physiol.* 11:308–20
38. Voit, C. 1881. Physiologie des allgemeinen Stoffwechsels und der Ernährung. In *Handbuch der Physiologie,* ed. L. Hermann, 6:3. Leipzig: Vogel
39. Waterlow, J. 1986. Physiological adaptation to low intakes of energy and protein. *Ann. Rev. Nutr.* 6:495–526
40. Zamenhof, S., Eichhorn, H. H. 1967. Study of microbial evolution through loss of biosynthetic functions: Establishment of "defective" mutants. *Nature* 216:456–58

*Ann. Rev. Nutr. 1986. 6:13–40*


# BIOCHEMICAL BASIS FOR THE MANIFESTATIONS OF IRON DEFICIENCY

*Peter R. Dallman*[1]

Department of Pediatrics, School of Medicine, University of California, San Francisco, California 94143

---

CONTENTS

INTRODUCTION .......... 13
IRON COMPOUNDS IN THE BODY: DISTRIBUTION AND METABOLIC FUNCTION .......... 14
*Essential Iron Compounds* .......... 14
*Iron Storage and Transport Proteins* .......... 15
SYNTHESIS AND TURNOVER OF IRON COMPOUNDS .......... 16
STAGES OF IRON DEFICIENCY .......... 17
TISSUE IRON COMPOUNDS IN RELATION TO PROGRESSION OF ANEMIA .......... 18
DEFICIENCIES OF IRON COMPOUNDS ASSOCIATED WITH IMPAIRMENTS OF FUNCTION .......... 20
*Hemoglobin, Myoglobin, and Oxygen Transport* .......... 20
*Cytochromes and Iron-Sulfur Proteins in Relation to Energy Metabolism* .......... 20
*Altered Metabolism of Biogenic Amines as a Possible Basis for Changes in Behavior* 25
*The Immune Response: Bacterial Killing by Neutrophils and Activation of T Lymphocytes* .......... 30
*Cytochrome P-450 and the Defense of the Body Against Foreign Compounds* .......... 33
CONCLUDING REMARKS .......... 35

## INTRODUCTION

The prevention of iron deficiency anemia has attained a high priority among physicians, public health workers, and governmental health agencies. Iron

[1]Supported by NIH Grant # AM 13897.



0199-9885/86/0715-0013$02.00

deficiency tends to be singled out among other nutrient deficiencies because it is common, it is easily identified by laboratory measurements, its laboratory manifestations are readily corrected by iron treatment, and iron is one of the cheapest forms of medication available. However, the correction of laboratory abnormalities is only important if it is accompanied by an improvement in body function and well-being. A program to prevent or treat iron deficiency must ultimately be justified in terms of its physiological consequences. At present, it is easier to define iron deficiency by laboratory measurements on blood than it is to characterize it in terms of its impact on health and well-being (1, 2).

Numerous studies have been aimed at defining the consequences of iron deficiency on work performance, the immune response, and behavior; much of this work is covered in helpful reviews (3–8). These investigations have been stimulated by a better understanding of the biochemical consequences of iron deficiency, not only on the blood and bone marrow, but also on iron compounds in other organs and tissues (3–8). The biochemical abnormalities of iron deficiency also provide the most reliable basis for planning future studies of the manifestations of iron deficiency. It therefore seems useful to review the biochemical basis for the manifestations of iron deficiency, with a particular focus on iron compounds other than hemoglobin.

## IRON COMPOUNDS IN THE BODY: DISTRIBUTION AND METABOLIC FUNCTION (3, 4, 9)

The iron-containing compounds in the body are conveniently grouped into two categories (1, 2): those known to serve a metabolic or enzymatic function and those associated with iron storage and transport. The first category of so-called essential or functional iron compounds consists primarily of heme proteins, i.e. proteins with an iron-porphyrin prosthetic group. The function of all heme proteins is related to oxidative metabolism.

### *Essential Iron Compounds (9–11)*

*Hemoglobin* is the most abundant and easily sampled of the heme proteins and accounts for more than 65% of body iron (total body iron averages about 3.5 g in the adult male). The function of hemoglobin is to transport oxygen via the bloodstream from the lungs to the tissues. Hemoglobin is a tetramer made up of four globin chains, each of which is associated with a heme group that contains one iron atom. The total molecular weight is 66,000. Hemoglobin makes up more than 95% of the protein of the red cell and accounts for well over 10% of the weight of whole blood.

*Myoglobin,* the red pigment of muscle, transports and stores oxygen for use during muscle contraction. This protein accounts for about 10% of the total body iron. Myoglobin has a molecular weight of 17,800. Its structure is similar to the monomeric units of hemoglobin; i.e. it is made up of one globin chain attached to one heme group containing a single iron atom. The myoglobin concentration in human muscle is approximately 5 mg per gram of tissue.

*Cytochromes* are enzymes of electron transport and are located in the mitochondria as well as in other cellular membranes. Cytochromes a, b, and c are present within the cristae of mitochondria in all aerobic cells and are essential for the oxidative production of cellular energy in the form of adenosine triphosphate (ATP).

Cytochrome c, the most easily isolated and best characterized of the cytochromes, is a pink protein with a molecular weight of 13,000. Like myoglobin, it is made up of one globin chain and one heme group containing one atom of iron. Its concentration ranges from 5 to 100 μg per gram of tissue in humans and is somewhat higher in corresponding tissues in the rat. In both species, the highest concentrations are in tissues such as heart muscle that have a high rate of oxygen utilization.

Cytochrome P-450 is located primarily within the microsomal membranes of liver cells but also in the intestinal mucosa. It is involved in oxidative degradation of drugs and endogenous substrates. Cytochrome $b_5$ is also a component of liver microsomal membranes where it probably provides energy for protein synthesis. Cytochrome $b_5$ is also present within the cytoplasm of the red blood cell, where it functions as an intermediate in the reduction of methemoglobin. Other heme enzymes are catalase and peroxidase, including the myeloperoxidase of the granulocyte.

*Non-heme iron compounds* comprise another important group of iron enzymes involved in oxidative metabolism. In these compounds the iron is not in the form of heme. They include the iron-sulfur proteins and metalloflavoproteins, and they account for more iron in the mitochondria than do the cytochromes. Examples are reduced nicotinamide adenine dinucleotide (NADH) dehydrogenase, succinic dehydrogenase, and xanthine oxidase.

*Other iron-dependent enzymes,* such as tryptophan pyrrolase and phosphoenol-pyruvate carboxykinase, do not contain iron but require iron as a cofactor or activator. Finally, there are some enzymes that contain iron, such as α-glycerophosphate dehydrogenase, in which the form of iron is uncertain.

## *Iron Storage and Transport Proteins (12, 13)*

The major iron storage compounds are *ferritin* and *hemosiderin,* which are located primarily in the liver, reticuloendothelial cells, and erythroid precursors of the bone marrow. The total amount of storage iron can vary over a wide range without apparent impairment of body function. Storage iron may be almost entirely depleted before iron deficiency anemia begins to develop. Conversely, a more than 20-fold increase in iron stores may occur before there is evidence of tissue damage due to iron overload. The protein portion of ferritin, apoferritin, consists of 24 polypeptide chains, with a total molecular weight of 450,000. These 24 subunits form a spherical cluster around variable amounts of hydrated ferric phosphate contained within a central colloidal core. In hematologically normal adults, ferritin accounts for about half of the storage iron present in the liver, and hemosiderin makes up the other half. Hemosiderin is believed to represent ferritin in various stages of degradation, since hemosiderin will react with antibodies against ferritin. As liver iron stores become abnormally large, hemosiderin makes up an increasingly greater proportion of total iron.

The contribution of the two types of storage iron to total body iron can vary widely from less than 5% to more than 30%. Unless the stores are exhausted, their amount has no discernible influence on any physiologic or biochemical function other than iron absorption.

*Transferrin* accounts for only about 0.1% of the total body iron. It is protein with a molecular weight of 74,000 and is capable of binding two atoms of ferric iron. Its major role is to transport iron from the reticuloendothelial system and the intestine to the bone marrow for synthesis of hemoglobin in developing red blood cells. The rate at which transferrin delivers iron depends on the relative amount of mono- and diferric transferrin and on the rate of red cell production (14). A high proportion of diferric transferrin and a rapid rate of erythropoiesis both favor increased iron delivery to the cell. Intracellular iron transport involves a less well-defined group of iron compounds of low molecular weight.

Of all the iron compounds that have been discussed, only hemoglobin, serum iron (mostly transferrin-bound), and serum ferritin (which generally reflects the amount of storage iron) are commonly used to assess iron status. These categories account for well over 90% of body iron.

## SYNTHESIS AND TURNOVER OF IRON COMPOUNDS (3)

Hemoglobin has a finite life span that, in humans, approximates the roughly 120-day survival of the red cell in the circulation. In the rat, red cell life span is about 60 days. Thus a little less than 1% of the total red cell iron in man and 2% in the rat is released each day from senescent red cells. Because of the large size of the hemoglobin iron pool, this small percentage of iron nevertheless accounts for the major flux of iron within the body. The iron from hemoglobin breakdown can be almost completely re-utilized, as can the amino acids. Heme, on the other hand, is degraded to bilirubin and largely lost via the bile.

In contrast to hemoglobin in the red cell, heme proteins in long-lived cells, such as those of liver and skeletal muscle, do not appear to have a finite life span. Rather, they seem to be subject to random degradation at an exponential rate that is in accord with the rate of turnover of the subcellular structure with which they are associated. Skeletal muscle cytochrome c, for example, has a half-life of about six days in the rat (15). The implication of the dynamic state of most body iron constituents is that tissue deficits should be largely reparable by treatment with iron. However, the rates at which deficiencies of individual iron compounds are corrected will often differ markedly from the rate at which anemia is reversed (3). Correction is most rapid in rapidly replaced cell populations, such as intestinal mucosa. Deficiencies of muscle myoglobin and iron containing electron transport compounds are corrected more slowly than anemia (3); depleted brain non-heme iron in the rat is replenished at such an extremely slow rate that the abnormality may not be completely reversible (16, 17). In the case of some iron enzymes such as ribonucleotide reductase, a decrease in activity due to iron lack can probably be corrected within less than an hour when increased iron becomes available, without requiring the synthesis of the entire molecule (18).

In an individual with iron deficiency anemia, hemoglobin synthesis can increase several-fold, as indicated by the reticulocyte response and by the increase in hemoglobin concentration almost to the normal value within one month of starting iron treatment. In the rat, the compensatory increase in red cell production during iron treatment is proportionally even greater, and severe anemia can be reversed within one week.

## STAGES OF IRON DEFICIENCY (1, 2)

The progression from adequate iron balance to iron deficiency anemia develops in three overlapping stages. The first stage consists of a depletion of storage iron. In man, this stage is characterized by a decrease in the concentration of serum ferritin, which reflects the declining concentration of iron stores in the liver, spleen, and bone marrow. The second stage of iron deficiency consists of a decrease in transport iron and is likely to be transient. This is characterized by an increase in the iron-binding capacity as well as by declining concentration of serum iron. The term "latent iron deficiency" is sometimes used to refer to these first two pre-anemic stages of iron deficiency. The third stage of iron deficiency develops when the supply of transport iron decreases sufficiently to restrict the concentration of hemoglobin and/or other iron compounds that fulfill known physiologic functions. With the few exceptions discussed below, it is safe to assume that there are no harmful consequences of iron deficiency until the third stage, when it is defined in this manner. An alternative definition of the third stage is in terms of a hemoglobin concentration that has decreased sufficiently to fulfill the laboratory definition of anemia (a hemoglobin concentration below the 95% reference range for age and sex) (1). In addition to the effect on hemoglobin, the laboratory characteristics of the third stage include an elevation of erythrocyte protoporphyrin and microcytosis.

## TISSUE IRON COMPOUNDS IN RELATION TO PROGRESSION OF ANEMIA

A vast amount of information on iron metabolism and iron deficiency anemia in man has accumulated during the past 50 years (1, 2). Most of this work was based on studies of peripheral blood, bone marrow, liver, and spleen. In contrast, most of our information on the effects of iron deficiency on other tissues and iron compounds other than hemoglobin, ferritin, and hemosiderin is of more recent origin and has been largely derived from studies using the rat as an experimental model (3, 4, 6). These dual sources of information raise questions about the suitability of the rat as a model for iron deficiency in man (19).

The rat has been widely accepted as a model for iron deficiency because it mirrors iron metabolism in man in most respects (20). Experiments in the rat have several advantages: dietary iron can be made the only experimental variable, tissue can be sampled extensively, longitudinal studies are easier, and experimental manipulations can be made that could not be justified in man. Iron kinetics and the steps in the progression of iron deficiency are remarkably similar where comparable studies have been done in both species. Hemoglobin concentration, blood volume as a percentage of total body weight, and the amount of iron per kilogram of body weight are also virtually identical in the rat and in man.

The differences between the two species are primarily a matter of rate of progression and degree of iron deficiency. The rat is less mature at birth, grows rapidly, and has a relatively short life span of three years. During early postnatal development it doubles its body weight in about five days, in contrast to human infants, in whom body weight doubles in four months in early infancy. By three to four weeks of age, the developing rat can be weaned from its mother, and by 40 to 60 days of age it is sexually mature. This rapid rate of growth is naturally associated with a higher peak iron requirement than in man: roughly 6 mg/kg/day (21) in contrast to the high of 1 mg/kg/day in term infants (2). Among the other notable differences in iron metabolism are the differing susceptibilities to iron deficiency in males and females. The female rat has a much lower growth rate compared to the male and is also much less vulnerable to dietary iron deficiency. In contrast, after sexual maturity human females are at much greater risk of iron deficiency (due to menstrual blood loss) than are males. In respect to iron absorption, the rat also differs in that it absorbs dietary heme iron less well than non-heme iron; the opposite relationship is true in man.

Most studies using the rat as an experimental model have provided an iron-deficient diet starting shortly after weaning at 3–4 weeks of age, and then maintained for 2–8 weeks. This regimen takes advantage of the high iron

requirement imposed by the remarkably rapid growth of rats during this period. The rapid rate at which rats grow and develop severe anemia could conceivably exaggerate the degree of tissue iron deficiency in the rat in comparison to man.

Another issue to be considered is that there is usually some degree of growth suppression in rats (as in children) given an iron-deficient diet. In most recent studies, the dietary regimens have not depressed the growth of the iron-deficient rat by more than 10–25% compared to control animals, in contrast to many earlier studies in which the body weight of deficient rats was less than half that of the control group. Studies in which suppression of growth is so extreme raise concerns about secondary effects that might be more directly related to decreased food intake than to iron deficiency.

The concentration of hemoglobin provides the best frame of reference for severity of iron deficiency both in the rat and in man because it is the most easily measured essential iron compound. In the rat, some tissue iron compounds, such as skeletal muscle cytochrome c and myoglobin, become depleted to a similar degree as hemoglobin, not only with severe iron deficiency anemia but also when anemia is relatively mild (21). In terms of the sequence of development of tissue iron deficiency, the cytochrome c concentration of intestinal mucosa is depressed earlier and more profoundly than hemoglobin concentration (22). Presumably this is because the cells lining the intestinal mucosa have a much more rapid turnover than red blood cells, (2 days vs 60 days), which makes it possible for a decreased iron supply to influence the entire cell population more rapidly.

Because the rat's unusually rapid growth makes it particularly vulnerable to iron deficiency, it is pertinent to ask whether similarly impressive changes in tissue iron compounds occur in man. The best data relating to tissue iron compounds in man pertain to biopsies of endothelial tissue and to the neutrophils and lymphocytes sampled from peripheral blood. Humans with relatively mild iron deficiency anemia have a decreased activity of cytochrome oxidase in buccal mucosa (23) and the mucosal cells lining the intestinal villi (24). More quantitative evidence of tissue iron depletion comes from studies of neutrophils and lymphocytes. In neutrophils there is a decreased capacity of the cells to kill ingested bacteria (25–29), presumably because the oxidative burst is iron dependent. Lymphocytes, in most studies, have a decreased response to mitogens (26–28, 30–33), probably because of a decreased activity of the iron-containing enzyme, ribonucleotide reductase, that is required for the production of DNA and subsequent cell division (34). These few examples (discussed in more detail below) provide convincing evidence that tissue iron depletion is a feature of iron deficiency in man and not merely a characteristic of a possibly more vulnerable animal model.

## DEFICIENCIES OF IRON COMPOUNDS ASSOCIATED WITH IMPAIRMENTS OF FUNCTION

### *Hemoglobin, Myoglobin, and Oxygen Transport*

Hemoglobin plays the major role in transporting oxygen from the lungs to various tissues. As the concentration of hemoglobin declines, there are several adaptations that minimize the consequences of a decreased oxygen-carrying capacity (35, 36). Initially, the tissues simply extract oxygen from hemoglobin more completely, aided by a decrease in the oxygen affinity of hemoglobin. There is also a redistribution of blood flow that maintains the oxygen supply to the brain and myocardium at the expense of other tissues. As anemia becomes more severe, cardiac output increases, a change that is eventually reflected by cardiac hypertrophy. The effectiveness of these adaptive mechanisms probably accounts for the fact that chronically anemic patients are characteristically symptom-free at rest and that their handicap is only made evident by exercise. In the rat, even with exercise, the decrease in maximal oxygen consumption ($\dot{V}O_2$ max) is relatively modest until anemia becomes severe (37).

The degree to which anemia is responsible for the manifestations of iron deficiency can be distinguished from the role of other tissue iron compounds by experimentally using exchange transfusion to modify the hemoglobin concentration (38). When anemia in iron-deficient rats is corrected, performance in brief exercise tolerance tests is improved, and $\dot{V}O_2$ max returns to almost normal values (39). Recent evidence suggests that impaired ability to maintain body temperature in the cold is also reversed by transfusion (40). In each case, the conclusion is that these manifestations of iron deficiency are more closely linked to anemia than to the effects of iron deficiency on iron compounds other than hemoglobin.

Myoglobin serves an oxygen transport and storage function but one that is restricted to muscle. In the iron-deficient rat, skeletal muscle myoglobin is decreased in concentration (21, 38, 40, 41). Myoglobin deficiency is less marked when rats are subjected to exercise training (42). The important role of work load is supported by the maintenance of closer-to-normal or normal myoglobin concentrations in the myocardium (41–43). Heart hypertrophy in severely anemic rats is presumed to occur in response to an increased work load imposed by anemia (36). The maintenance of a nearly normal cardiac myoglobin concentration probably aids in the increased cardiac output that makes it possible to maintain oxygen delivery to tissues despite anemia.

### *Cytochromes and Iron-Sulfur Proteins in Relation to Energy Metabolism*

Most of the mitochondrial enzymes involved in the oxidative production of ATP contain iron. In cytochromes a, b, and c, iron is in the form of heme. The

NADH- and succinate-dehydrogenases contain iron as part of one or more iron-sulfur complexes. The degree to which the iron enzymes are affected in mitochondria from iron-deficient animals appears to correspond to where they are located in the electron transport chain. The iron-sulfur-containing dehydrogenases that are involved in the first reaction in the electron transport chain are the most severely depleted (41, 44). Cytochrome b and c, which are in the middle of the electron transport chain, are decreased to an intermediate degree and cytochrome a and cytochrome $a_3$, which comprise the last reaction, are least affected.

The oxidative capacity of the entire electron transport chain, estimated from the rate of oxidation of citric acid cycle intermediates, is as profoundly depressed as the activity of the iron-sulfur-containing dehydrogenases (44). This observation suggests that the deficiency of the iron-sulfur proteins may limit the rate of oxidation in the electron transport chain as a whole.

Although rates of oxidation of citric acid cycle intermediates are decreased in many tissues, the linkage between oxidation and phosphorylation remains normal (38, 44). Thus, the rate of ATP production is decreased in proportion to the diminution in rate of oxidation.

DIFFERENCES IN ORGAN SUSCEPTIBILITY There are large differences in the degree to which the iron-containing electron transport enzymes of the mitochondria are depleted in various organs. The most severely affected tissues are the skeletal muscle and intestinal mucosa (45).

*Skeletal muscle* Skeletal muscle is severely affected by iron deficiency (3, 38, 39, 41, 44, 45a,b, 46) and, because of the large mass of muscle in the body, the impaired capacity of skeletal muscle for oxidative metabolism probably has a major impact on the energy metabolism of the body as a whole. During the progression of iron deficiency, the depletion of the oxidative enzymes in skeletal muscle occurs more gradually than the development of anemia (22) but can eventually be of comparable or even greater severity (38, 39, 41, 44). Body growth and increase in oxidative capacity of muscle normally progresses at a very rapid rate during the post-weaning period (47) during which rats are usually made iron deficient. Undoubtedly, this rapid growth and differentiation predisposes muscle to the effects of iron deficiency. However, this is unlikely to be the only explanation since tissues such as liver and kidney, which also grow rapidly during this period, are far less affected (43, 48, 49).

Iron deficiency affects all fiber types in skeletal muscle (37, 41, 46). Muscle fiber types are categorized according to their biochemical and contractile characteristics (50). Fast-twitch white fibers are poor in oxidative enzymes. They engage in rapid movements that do not require sustained power and are dependent primarily on glycolysis as an energy source. Red muscle fibers, on the other hand, are rich in oxidative enzymes, which are their primary source of energy. In the rat, slow-twitch red muscle and fast-twitch red muscle have roughly three and five times the oxidative capacity, respectively, of fast-twitch white muscle.

Experiments in which iron-deficient rats were transfused to raise their hemoglobin concentration led to the conclusion that the major consequence of a decreased muscle capacity for energy metabolism was an impaired capacity for sustained exercise (39, 44). Even though $\dot{V}O_2$ max was virtually corrected by transfusion, the ability to run on a treadmill for a prolonged period remained severely impaired (39). When iron-deficient rats were treated with iron, the improvement in performance of prolonged exercise followed the same time course as correction of decreased muscle oxidative capacity, and was significantly slower than the reversal of anemia (44).

The conclusion that the effects of iron deficiency on muscle particularly impair the capacity for sustained exercise was also supported by experiments with the isolated and perfused hind limb muscles of the rat (45a). This preparation has the advantage of excluding variables unrelated to the direct effects of iron deficiency on muscle function. McLane and coworkers (45a) found that the effect of iron deficiency on contractile force varied with duration of electrical stimulation. During the first two minutes of stimulation there was little difference between iron-deficient and control animals. However, after four minutes, an increasing difference became discernible. After ten minutes of muscle contraction, the iron-deficient animals were only able to develop about 60% of the contractile force of the control animals.

There is an association between the obligatory work load and degree of impairment of oxidative capacity in muscle. Heart muscle, which has an increased work load associated with anemia, and diaphragmatic muscle, which has the continued work load of respiration, retained a much higher oxidative capacity than skeletal muscle compared to control animals (41, 43, 49, 51). Indeed there is little or no effect on cardiac muscle except in one study (52).

A cause-and-effect relationship between work load and oxidative capacity could be inferred in iron-deficient rats that were subjected to an exercise training regimen of four to six weeks (37). The skeletal muscle of trained animals had a far higher oxidative capacity than that of untrained iron-deficient rats. Indeed, the trained, iron-deficient rats achieve an oxidative capacity almost equivalent to that of sedentary animals fed an iron-sufficient diet. Concurrently there was an improvement in their capacity for prolonged exercise. However, neither oxidative capacity nor the ability to run for prolonged periods approached that of iron-sufficient animals that were given a similar exercise regimen. The mechanism of the improvement of the iron-deficient animals with training is uncertain, since training was also associated with a slightly milder anemia than that found in sedentary rats. The results nevertheless indicated that exercise training was effective in improving the performance of iron-deficient rats but that they remained handicapped when compared to similarly exercised animals fed a complete diet.

*Metabolic adaptations to a decreased capacity for oxidative metabolism in muscle* It is reasonable to anticipate some systemic changes in energy metabolism in response to the marked decrease in oxidative capacity of a tissue with so large a mass as skeletal muscle. Recent isotopic studies in the iron-deficient rat indicate that there are substantial alterations in glucose metabolism that allow muscle to utilize more glucose to produce ATP with less dependence on mitochondrial electron transport (52). This is made possible by an increased reconversion of lactate, the end-product of glycolysis, to glucose by the gluconeogenic pathway in the liver. Although hepatic recycling is costly in terms of ATP, this may not constitute a major handicap because the oxidative capacity for production of ATP in the liver is much less impaired by iron deficiency than that of skeletal muscle (41, 43, 49, 54). Glucose recycling in iron-deficient rats occurred at five times the control rate (53). Thus an increased muscle demand for glucose and an increased lactate release from muscle could be managed by the liver, in which mitochondrial oxidative capacity remains relatively high.

Some indication of the effectiveness of the circulatory and metabolic adaptations to iron deficiency can be obtained from studies of exercise performance in rats with iron deficiency of increasing severity (55). $\dot{V}O_2$ max during a brief, hard exercise declined only 16% with a decrease in hemoglobin concentration from 14 to 8 g/dl and fell sharply only below 7 g/dl. These results are in accord with the known effectiveness of compensatory mechanisms that help to maintain oxygen delivery to tissues until iron deficiency becomes severe. The time to exhaustion in a treadmill exercise of submaximal intensity (endurance) showed a different pattern. There was no significant change in performance in iron-deficient rats with a hemoglobin concentration as low as 10 g/dl, which indicates that metabolic reserve or adaptations are relatively effective in rats with mild iron deficiency anemia. However, endurance declined abruptly by 73% between a hemoglobin concentration of 10 and 8 g/dl. This sharp decrease indicates a threshhold of severity of iron deficiency beyond which metabolic adaptations may be adequate in sedentary animals but insufficient to maintain prolonged exercise.

*Intestinal mucosa* One obvious basis for the susceptibility of the intestinal mucosa to iron deficiency is its rapid cell turnover. Since the mucosal lining is completely replaced every two days in the rat and every three or four days in man, this tissue is particularly vulnerable to day-to-day fluctuations in the supply of iron. However, this rapid cell turnover also has the advantage of allowing for a rapid recovery following iron treatment. After the administration of iron to iron-deficient rats, mucosal cytochrome c concentration returns to normal values within two or three days (45). Histochemical studies of cytochrome oxidase activity show that young differentiating cells at the base of the villi are the first to restore their normal cytochrome oxidase activity after about 24 hours, following which there is a gradual progression of repair as the cells migrate toward the tip of the villi during the course of their maturation (45, 56).

Intestinal function is impaired in iron deficiency both in man and in the rat. Iron deficiency is often found to be associated with clinically significant intestinal blood loss in infants (57–59), but it is important in interpreting such studies to distinguish between cause and effect. An initial predisposing factor that leads to intestinal blood loss and to the secondary development of iron deficiency is the ingestion of fresh cows' milk (60–62). When the diet is changed from fresh milk to a heat-processed formula, the blood loss can be reversed in most instances (61, 62). Celiac disease also leads to intestinal blood loss and iron deficiency; however, some blood loss persisted for one or more years in patients for whom a gluten-free diet had been recommended (63). The degree of blood loss appeared to be greatest in patients with the greatest villous atrophy and intra-epithelial lymphocytosis and possibly in those with poorer adherence to dietary recommendations.

Dietary iron deficiency appears to be a primary cause of decreased intestinal disaccharide and of lactose malabsorption in children since both were reversed with iron treatment (64). Similar disaccharidase deficiency has been described in iron-deficient rats (65, 66). Absorption of disaccharides is an energy-requiring process, and its impairment may be linked to a decreased capacity for energy metabolism. Dietary iron deficiency was also thought to be primary in other studies that showed malabsorption of sugars (67) or of iron itself (68) because the abnormalities could be corrected by treatment with iron. A similar response to treatment has also been observed in the relatively rare cases of iron deficiency anemia accompanied by hypoproteinemia (69, 70).

*The fetus* The vulnerability of the fetus to maternal iron deficiency is very different in man and in the rat. In humans, mild iron deficiency during pregnancy has no detectable effect on hemoglobin concentration in the newborn and, at the most, a minor influence on serum ferritin (71–76). On the other hand, severe iron deficiency anemia does result in a decreased hemoglobin concentration in the offspring, but not as great as in the mother (77, 78). In the rat, the effect on the fetus is more profound. In severely iron-deficient, pregnant rats, the rate of fetal resorption is high and the survivors are also severely anemic (79). Biochemical studies of iron-deficient fetuses at 10 days of gestation show less than half of the normal mitochondrial NADH oxidase activity

(80). The apparent difference in susceptibility of the fetus in the two species may be explained by their relative iron requirements for pregnancy. In the rat, an amount of iron equivalent to about 25% of body iron must be transferred to the uterine contents over a 21-day period. In the human, the comparable requirement is only 15% of body iron, and it is spread out over a much longer period of 280 days. Consequently, the impact of iron deficiency during pregnancy is far more profound in the rat.

*Other tissues* The mitochondrial oxidative enzymes have been studied in other tissues of the iron-deficient rat: the liver (43, 47, 49, 81), kidney (47, 49), heart muscle (43, 49, 51, 52), and brain (16, 43, 82–84). These enzymes are less severely depleted in liver (as previously mentioned) and in kidney than they are in intestinal mucosa and skeletal muscle. Heart muscle (also discussed) and brain are least affected of all. Indeed brain cytochromes and oxidases are only affected under the most severe conditions of iron deficiency (83) or if the animal is made iron-deficient during early postnatal development when brain growth and development of mitochondrial energy metabolism are most rapid (82, 85).

*Possible reasons for differences in organ vulnerability* It was mentioned above that rapid growth, cell differentiation, and cell turnover are factors associated with the most profound deficits in oxidative capacity (3). In addition, an altered pattern of work load by organs and cells appears to influence the degree of impairment of oxidative capacity (3). It still remains to be explained how the priorities for production of iron-containing oxidative enzymes in various parts of the body are mediated in iron deficiency. Plasma iron that is bound to transferrin is delivered to all tissues. However, tissues differ substantially in their iron requirement and it is believed that the number of transferrin receptors on the surface of cell membranes can adjust the uptake of iron to the needs of the individual cell (86). The importance of this mechanism is brought out by a recent report of anemia in a patient who developed autoantibodies to the transferrin receptor and in whom incorporation of iron by developing red blood cells was impaired (87).

### *Altered Metabolism of Biogenic Amines as a Possible Basis for Changes in Behavior*

Children with severe iron deficiency were for many years characterized as irritable and uninterested in their surroundings. These manifestations often seemed to be rapidly reversed within a few days of iron treatment. Because such observations were not readily expressed in quantitative terms, it was difficult to distinguish whether they represented medical folklore or astute clinical observation. Scientific interest in the possibility of altered behavior ascribable to iron deficiency increased when it was reported a little more than a decade ago that iron-deficient rats had a decreased ability to catabolize systemically injected monoamines (88). Monoamine oxidase (MAO) is on the catabolic pathway of the neural mediators, serotonin (5HT), norepinephrine (NE), epinephrine (E), and dopamine (DA) and was thought to be an iron-containing enzyme. A few years later, children with iron deficiency anemia (but not other anemias) were found to have an elevated urinary NE that decreased to normal levels within a week of iron treatment (89). The elevation in urinary NE was considered to be a possible basis for the behavioral changes believed to characterize iron-deficient patients. The above-mentioned two papers stimulated numerous studies of the effects of iron deficiency on either behavior or on the metabolism of biogenic amines (catecholamines and serotonin). Because the studies of behavior are the subject of several recent reviews (8, 90, 91), the emphasis in this report is on the possible roles of iron in the metabolism of the biogenic amines.

Iron is involved at several steps in the synthesis and degradation of the biogenic amines. Although, iron deficiency appears to affect systemic catecholamine metabolism, the changes in the brain seem less profound. The notable exceptions, to be described in more detail, involve not synthesis or catabolism, but an impairment in the binding of DA to the $D_2$ receptor of the caudate nucleus (92) and of 5HT to brain synaptic vesicles (93).

BINDING OF BIOGENIC AMINES TO RECEPTOR SITES Dopamine plays an important role as the major neurotransmitter of the extrapyramidal system of the brain. Youdim and associates (92) investigated the effect of iron deficiency on DA binding sites in the caudate nucleus, an area of the extrapyramidal system that is iron-rich and in which DA receptors are concentrated. There are two types of DA receptors, one is linked to adenylcyclase (the $D_1$ receptor) and another is unrelated to activation of cyclic nucleotides (the $D_2$ receptor). In iron-deficient rats, $D_2$ binding sites, estimated by $^3$H-spiroperidol binding, were decreased to about half of the control number. When the rats were then given an iron-rich diet for two weeks, the anemia as well as the abnormality in binding were corrected. However, decreased binding did not appear to be caused by the anemia per se, because phenylhydrazine-induced hemolytic anemia did not result in any change in $^3$H-spiroperidol binding.

In contrast to the marked effect of iron deficiency on the $D_2$ binding site, there was no evidence of altered binding on the $D_1$ receptor: neither the basal activity of caudate nucleus DA-sensitive adenylcyclase nor its response to increasing concentrations of DA were affected by iron deficiency.

Analogous results for serotonin (5HT) were reported by Kaladhar & Rao (93). 5HT is also an important neurotransmitter whose function is linked to slow-wave sleep. Binding of 5HT by synaptic vesicles prepared from whole brain was about one-third lower in the iron-deficient compared to control rats;

this abnormality was corrected by one month of iron treatment. A plausible basis for the decreased binding of 5HT is the earlier observation that ferrous iron increases the rate of 5HT uptake by synaptic vesicles (94).

A relationship has been postulated between the decreased number of $D_2$ receptors for DA and an elevated pain threshold after administration of β-endorphin, morphine, or haloperidol (a blocker of DA receptors) to iron-deficient rats. Yehuda & Youdim (95) reported an increase in pain threshold in iron-deficient rats compared to control animals. In addition, there was a reversal of the normal circadian difference in pain threshold. In control rats, evidence of discomfort on a surface with a temperature of 58°C occurred more slowly when rats were tested during the 12-hour light period (when they are normally least active) than during the dark (their normal period of wakefulness and activity). This pattern was initially also observed in rats on the iron-deficient regimen. However, after 3 to 4 weeks of the dietary regimen, the iron-deficient rats had developed a marked delay in their pain response during the dark but not during the light period. This reversal in the light-dark response was even more evident after treatment with β-endorphin. Not only was the pain response markedly delayed over control values, but the delay was more prolonged during the dark than during the light period. Morphine and haloperidol produced a similarly greater delay in iron-deficient compared to control rats. After 25 days of iron treatment, all of these abnormalities were reversed.

It seems that the reversal of the circadian activity pattern may only occur under certain conditions of age and duration of diet. The altered circadian pattern of pain threshold in iron-deficient rats (96) seems in accord with the reversed pattern of eating and drinking and/or activity observed in another laboratory (97). However, other investigators have shown maintenance of the normal circadian pattern of nocturnal activity (98–100). This is a critical point to establish in future experiments in order to distinguish behavioral alterations that take place without an altered activity pattern from those that represent solely a change in diurnal pattern.

SYNTHESIS AND CATABOLISM OF BIOGENIC AMINES Two iron-dependent hydroxylases are on the direct synthetic pathways of the biogenic amines. Tyrosine hydroxylase catalyzes the hydroxylation of tyrosine to L-DOPA (3,4-dihydroxyphenylalanine), a precursor of the catecholamines NE and E. Tryptophan hydroxylase catalyzes the production of serotonin from tryptophan. Tryptophan hydroxylase activity in the brain of iron-deficient rats was either normal or only slightly decreased, even with very severe iron deficiency (84). Tyrosine hydroxylase could be inferred to retain normal activity from indirect evidence (84). In accord with these findings is the observation that brain concentrations of NE and DA were normal (84). The brain content of serotonin was found to be only slightly decreased by one group (84) but slightly increased by another (83).

The turnover and degradation of biogenic amines in brain also remained close to normal despite the fact that one or more of the catabolic steps is iron dependent (84). Aldehyde oxidase (or dehydrogenase) is an iron-dependent reaction. Mackler and associates (83) found the enzyme to be decreased in activity, and they interpreted this to be in accord with their finding of slightly increased brain concentrations of 5HT. However, these results were in disagreement with those of Youdim and coworkers (84), who found aldehyde dehydrogenase to be normal in activity and 5HT unchanged in concentration (84). Both groups agree that monamine oxidase (MAO) activity in brain is not altered by iron deficiency. MAO is now known not to contain iron. Nevertheless, MAO was found to be decreased in activity in the liver (though not by Mackler et al), heart, and adrenal of rats (84) and in the platelets of humans with iron deficiency (101). Intravenously injected synthetic monoamines were also catabolized at a less than normal rate in iron-deficient rats (88). From these findings, it has been inferred that iron may be involved in MAO synthesis even though it is not part of the MAO molecule (101).

Rats that become iron deficient within the first few weeks of postnatal development have a lower concentration of brain non-heme iron than do control animals (16, 84, 102). This deficit is unusual in that it cannot be reversed, even after other manifestations of iron deficiency have been corrected by iron treatment. The physiological implications of this finding remain uncertain since the relatively few other biochemical manifestations of iron deficiency in brain that have been described are reversed with iron administration (83, 92, 93).

Evidence for systemic alterations in catecholamine metabolism, aside from decreased MAO activity in the rat (88), is based primarily on increased blood and urine concentrations of NE in the rat (101, 103) and in man (89, 104). Since there is relatively little indication of substantial changes in synthesis and degradation of biogenic amines in brain, it seems more promising to seek systemic explanations for elevated blood and urine NE. Dillmann and coworkers determined the rate of disappearance of labelled NE from the blood after intravenous injection (105). Hemoglobin was first adjusted to an identical concentration of about 10 g/dl in the deficient and control groups by exchange transfusion. NE disappeared at a more rapid rate in the iron-deficient than in control rats. However the difference in disappearance rate was not interpreted as being great enough to account for the marked elevation in blood NE. It was proposed instead that the major factor was an increase in rate of production of NE in relation to impaired thermogenesis in the iron-deficient rat.

Iron-deficient rats (105–107) and humans (108) have been found to have an impaired capacity to maintain their body temperature in a cold environment. Two major systems are involved in maintaining body temperature, NE and thyroid hormone. Dillmann and coworkers (106) found that iron deficiency was associated with an impaired conversion of T4, the inactive precursor, to T3, the active thyroid hormone. They hypothesized that NE production was elevated in iron deficiency as a compensatory mechanism for an impaired thyroid hormone response.

More recent results from the same laboratory may require a modification of this hypothesis. Impaired thermogenesis in response to cold exposure was reversed when iron-deficient rats were transfused to correct their anemia (107). Similarly, the responses in T3 and thyroid stimulating hormone (TSH) to cold exposure could be modified by simply adjusting the hematocrit in iron-deficient or control rats. In either group, T3 and TSH responses were generally normal when the hematocrit was above 25% and were subnormal when the hematocrit was below 25%. Thus, the abnormalities in thermogenesis, T3, and TSH appeared to be a nonspecific consequence of anemia rather than a result of iron deficiency. Furthermore, the impaired TSH response provides evidence that not only iron deficiency, but anemia per se, can result in impaired pituitary and possibly central nervous system function. These conclusions require a reexamination of the earlier reports that NE elevation was characteristic of iron deficiency and not merely a consequence of anemia (105). If NE elevation in iron deficiency is indeed independent of anemia whereas the defect thermogenesis is anemia related, then it becomes difficult to attribute the NE elevation to a compensatory overproduction for maintenance of body temperature. Perhaps, after all, a decrease in NE catabolism is a more plausible explanation for blood and urine NE elevation.

The linkages between altered behavior and biogenic amine metabolism in iron deficiency remain tenuous. The review of Lozoff & Brittenham (8) emphasizes the useful distinction between behavioral changes that are primarily cognitive and those that are noncognitive. Cognitive functions include attention span, learning ability, and performance on IQ tests whereas spontaneous activity, apathy, responsiveness, alertness, apprehensiveness, and irritability are noncognitive characteristics (even though they can influence cognition). When considering possible biochemical bases for altered behavior it is also useful to make a distinction between primary alteration in brain metabolism and systemic changes, e.g. anemia and blood NE levels, that might influence behavior in a less direct manner.

Most of the studies of behavior in iron-deficient infants have used a single test, the Bailey Scale, that has both cognitive and noncognitive components (109–113). Despite the careful design of the studies, many of the reports have features that do not allow an unambiguous conclusion about the effects of iron deficiency on behavior. There is also disagreement whether (109, 111, 113) or not (108, 115) the behavioral abnormalities are reversed by treatment at the same rapid rate reported for the reversal of elevated blood and urine NE values.

None of the studies have followed the subjects for more than a month. Studies of older children, using IQ tests (114–116) and other measures of cognitive function (117), all indicated impaired performance associated with iron deficiency. Improvement with iron treatment was observed (115–117), but the possibility of long-term impairment was suggested by one report (114).

Lozoff & Brittenham (8) made cautious conclusions in their review of human and rat data. Studies in the iron-deficient rat did not demonstrate deficits in cognitive performance but did show differences in noncognitive factors such as responsiveness to environmental stimuli. Analysis of the human studies led to somewhat analogous conclusions. Although there were indicators of impaired cognitive function, there remains the possibility that the changes observed during testing could be due to noncognitive factors such as short attention span, fearfulness, and increased body tension and a striking increase in the maintenance of body contact between the iron-deficient infant and its mother.

## *The Immune Response: Bacterial Killing by Neutrophils and Activation of T Lymphocytes*

Two abnormalities in the response to infection have been relatively well documented in iron-deficient patients and in rats. One of these is the decreased capacity of neutrophils to kill ingested bacteria (25–29, 118) and the other is the impairment in T-cell proliferation in response to stimulation by mitogens (26, 27, 30–33) or by antigens.

NEUTROPHIL FUNCTION Neutrophils provide a major defense of the body against invasion by bacteria, as clearly demonstrated by the fact that profound deficiencies in neutrophil number or function are associated with a high rate of mortality from bacterial infections. Most studies of neutrophil function and enzyme activity in iron deficiency have used blood samples from humans. Although the results of human studies should be most conclusive, interpretation of the results was often complicated by the presence of additional nutritional deficiencies or concurrent or recent infections. Furthermore, the constraints imposed by small blood samples fostered the use of semiquantitative histologic tests of the oxidative function, such as reduction of the dye nitroblue tetrazolium (NBT), and the histochemical estimation of myeloperoxidase activity on blood smears. For these reasons, both animal and human data contribute to the evaluation of the immune response in iron deficiency.

There is general agreement that neutrophil number and ability to ingest bacteria by phagocytosis are normal or close to normal in iron-deficient patients (27, 32, 119) and rats (118). The major defect in iron deficiency is the capacity for killing certain types of bacteria once they have been ingested (25–29, 118). Bacterial killing involves a sharp increase in oxygen consumption that is known as the "respiratory burst" (120). The respiratory burst results from the activation of NADPH oxidase (presumably an iron-sulfur enzyme), which in turn produces $O_2^-$ and $H_2O_2$. The heme protein, cytochrome b, is associated with the respiratory burst but its precise role has not been defined. $H_2O_2$ and $O_2^-$ are then used as the starting materials for the production of oxidized halogens and hydroxyl radicals that are most effective in bacterial killing. The production of the oxidized halogens from $H_2O_2$ is catalyzed by the iron enzyme, myeloperoxidase which is located in the azurophilic granule of the neutrophil (121). The production of hydroxyl radical from $O_2^-$ is catalyzed by iron that is donated by lactoferrin, (122) an iron binding protein that is present in high concentration in the specific granule of the neutrophil (121). Consequently, there are at least two or three iron-dependent steps involved in bacterial killing.

In studies of iron-deficient patients, the results of the NBT dye test were decreased in some (25, 27) but normal in other (26, 29, 123) reports. Myeloperoxidase, estimated histochemically, was decreased in two studies (118, 124) but normal in two others (29, 123). These discordant results involving the presumed biochemical mechanisms are puzzling when there is virtual unanimity about the end result, bacterial killing. The confounding influences of additional nutrient deficiencies and the known stimulation of NBT reduction by infection could explain the disparity among various studies.

Two recent studies of iron-deficient rats provide additional information on the basis for impaired bacterial killing by neutrophils. Mackler and coworkers (125) measured the rate of oxygen consumption before and after activation in neutrophils that were isolated from iron-deficient and control rats. The baseline rates of respiration were similar in the two groups of animals but the maximum rate of oxygen consumption after activation in the iron-deficient group was less than half of the control value. The cytochrome b concentration of neutrophils was unaffected by iron deficiency. These results suggested that iron deficiency impaired the NADPH oxidase reaction and that the impairment was not attributable to cytochrome b. In the same study, myeloperoxidase was measured enzymatically. Its activity in the iron deficiency group was less than one third that of the control value. These results carry greater weight than the less quantitative histochemical data from other studies. Moore & Humbert (118) also studied neutrophil function in iron-deficient rats. NBT reduction and myeloperoxidase measured histochemically were decreased in iron deficiency.

An important factor in the ability of neutrophils to kill bacteria is whether the bacteria themselves contain catalase (118). Catalase-positive bacteria, such as *Staphylococcus aureus* and *Escherichia coli,* can break down $H_2O_2$ that the neutrophil has generated and consequently be more resistant to killing. These bacteria are not readily killed by neutrophils from iron-deficient rats and humans. With catalase-negative bacteria such as *Streptococcus pneumoniae,* $H_2O_2$ can be maintained at a high enough level to enhance bacterial killing by oxidized halogens and hydroxyl radical. Killing of this organism was unimpaired in neutrophils from iron-deficient rats.

ACTIVATION OF T LYMPHOCYTES A continuous supply of iron is required for the activity of mammalian ribonucleotide reductase (18), an obligatory step in the production of DNA (34). In fact, ribonucleotide reductase purified from calf thymus has an activity half-life of only 10 minutes when the supply of iron and oxygen are removed (18). For this reason iron appears to have an important regulatory role in DNA production.

The nearly normal growth of rats made iron deficient after weaning indicates sufficient availability of iron for DNA production under some circumstances. However, there may be a decreased capacity for maintaining an extremely rapid rate of DNA production. When rats are made iron deficient during the immediate postnatal period of lactation, there is a slower weight gain and a marked decrease in the concentration of DNA in thymus and spleen compared to normally nourished animals (128). Impaired DNA synthesis is also evident after partial hepatectomy in the iron-deficient rat (129) and in the decreased capacity of the T lymphocyte to respond to mitogens in iron-deficient children (as already discussed). It has also been shown more directly that deferoxamine, a potent chelator of iron, inhibits DNA production by human T and B lymphocytes and that this inhibition can be reversed by restoration of iron (130).

Studies of cell-mediated immunity in man yield some discordant data, as summarized in two recent reviews (5, 7) and in the article by Keusch & Farthing in this volume (131). As in the case of neutrophil function, there are the potential confounding influences of other nutritional deficiencies and concurrent or antecedent infections in the patient populations studied. Indeed, since infection results in many of the same laboratory abnormalities as iron deficiency (1, 2), it is possible that the anemia of infection was occasionally misdiagnosed as iron deficiency.

Resistance to intracellular invasion by bacteria, fungi, and viruses is mediated largely by thymus-dependent lymphocytes or T cells. T-cell function is most commonly estimated from the number of circulating T cells, the delayed hypersensitivity skin test response to antigens, and the in vitro lymphocyte response to mitogens such as phytohemagglutinin (PHA). Circulating T cells were decreased in three studies of patients (27, 28, 32). Skin reactivity to a variety of antigens was decreased in some but not all patients (26, 27, 31) and returned toward normal after iron treatment (26, 31). The in vitro response of lymphocytes from iron-deficient patients to PHA was decreased in most (26, 27, 32) but not all (132) studies. The group that reported negative results subsequently showed a T-cell-dependent impairment of delayed cutaneous hypersensitivity (133) as well as decreased splenic lymphocyte response to mitogens (134) in iron-deficient mice.

Humoral immunity has generally been considered normal in iron-deficient patients on the basis of IgG, IgA, and IgM concentrations (26, 27) and antibody production in response to T-cell-dependent and -independent antigens (27). However, studies in iron-deficient rats show a clear-cut deficit in antibody production to Salmonella and tetanus toxoid (135). Furthermore when nursing rats are made iron-deficient through maternal iron deficiency during pregnancy and lactation, there is a long-term deficit in antibody production that is not corrected by an iron-rich diet (136). The lack of accord between the human and rat studies of humoral immunity in iron deficiency makes this an area requiring further study.

Despite the many studies on the effects of iron deficiency on the immune response, the extent of the impairment remains unclear. As discussed in recent reviews (5, 7), serious flaws in experimental design make it difficult to draw any conclusions from two commonly cited studies that come to opposite conclusions regarding prevalence of infections in iron-deficient infants (126, 127). This is still an area that requires clarification. Differences in morbidity may be difficult to detect in industrialized countries where iron deficiency can be very mild (137), environmental sanitation is satisfactory, and antibiotic treatment readily available. Impaired resistance to infection might be easier to detect among populations in developing countries where none of the above conditions apply and where morbidity from infection is high. However, in those settings it is difficult to exclude the role of other nutrient deficiencies. Even if there were a clear-cut association between iron deficiency and infection, it might be difficult to determine cause and effect. Not only may iron deficiency lead to infection but infection can lead to iron deficiency by impairing iron absorption (138, 139).

An additional complicating factor is the protective role of the iron-binding proteins, transferrin and lactoferrin, in the defense against infection (139a). These proteins act by withholding iron from invading organisms that require it for their proliferation. This protective property can be lost as the iron-binding proteins become increasingly iron saturated with iron excess but could be modestly enhanced with decreased iron saturation in iron deficiency. However, the latter effect is likely to be counterbalanced by impairments of cellular and humoral immunity that have already been discussed. It will be a challenge to disentangle this in man.

### *Cytochrome P-450 and the Defense of the Body Against Foreign Compounds*

A large number of drugs, environmental pollutants, and other nonnutritive chemicals are readily absorbed but poorly eliminated from the body. Their elimination frequently involves oxidative transformation, primarily in the liver and intestine, to water-soluble products that are more readily excreted (140,

141). This oxidative transformation is mediated by a group of cytochrome-P-450-dependent mixed-function oxidations. In contrast to the oxidative production of cellular energy, which is localized in mitochondria, the mixed-function oxidations take place in the endoplasmic reticulum.

Among the iron-containing compounds involved in mixed-function oxidations are the group of heme proteins termed cytochrome P-450 (on the basis of their spectral absorption maximum) and cytochrome $b_5$. The response of these compounds to iron deficiency and its consequences for drug metabolism have been studied only in the rat. In the liver, where the mixed-function oxidation system is present in high concentration and has been best characterized, there was little or no effect of iron deficiency on the concentration of cytochrome P-450 (142–144) and no change in cytochrome $b_5$ (143, 144). Even the stimulation of cytochrome P-450 by barbiturate treatment was normal in iron deficiency (143). Rats with severe iron deficiency anemia, had the same fourfold increase in cytochrome P-450 in response to three days of phenobarbital as control animals. This normal response to phenobarbital treatment implies an unusually high priority for the limited amounts of iron from the deficient diet and/or the catabolism of hemoglobin and other iron proteins. In fact, the activity of several drug-metabolizing enzymes and the clearance of aniline and aminopyrine from the plasma were actually increased in iron deficiency (144).

In striking contrast to the situation in the liver is the marked vulnerability of intestinal cytochrome P-450 to iron deficiency (145, 146). An interesting feature of the production of intestinal cytochrome P-450 is its dependence on the day-to-day dietary supply of iron (and selenium), not on iron from systemic sources. As a consequence, the iron-replete rat with abundant storage iron nevertheless shows a decrease in intestinal cytochrome P-450 concentration within a day of starting an iron-deficient diet. Intestinal cytochrome $b_5$ and NADPH-cytochrome P-450 reductase were not affected. When intestinal cytochrome P-450 is acutely depleted by 1 to 3 days of a low-iron diet, drug oxidation by everted sacs of duodenum is impaired in acutely iron-deprived rats.

An important implication of the findings in respect to intestinal cytochrome P-450 is that day-to-day fluctuations in the diet can influence metabolic processes even when there is no systemic evidence of iron deficiency. This phenomenon is therefore an exception to the general rule that tissue abnormalities do not occur in iron deficiency until iron stores are depleted and hemoglobin production begins to be compromised. The applicability of the rat data to man remain to be demonstrated (147). Nevertheless, it seems quite possible that the response to drugs and other chemicals might vary considerably as a function of the day-to-day adequacy of a dietary nutrient such as iron.

## CONCLUDING REMARKS

In the past decade, there has been an increasing awareness of the role of non-hemoglobin iron compounds in the pathogenesis of iron deficiency. Indeed, the literature on this topic has become too large to encompass in a single review. The topics included for discussion in this review were selected because they are characterized by reasonable links between biochemical abnormalities and physiologic manifestations. In certain instances, including the immune response, there are many discordant data. In attempting to integrate and reconcile these studies, one runs the risk of oversimplification. Most of the topics that have been discussed bring to mind additional questions to be asked and studies to be performed. The rapid pace of progress in determining the subtle manifestations of iron deficiency is encouraging because it should provide a necessary perspective for planning measures to prevent, detect, and treat this common disorder.

### *Literature Cited*

1. Bothwell, T. H., Charlton, R. W., Cook, J. D., Finch, C. A. 1979. *Iron Metabolism in Man*. Oxford: Blackwell. 576 pp.
2. Dallman, P. R., Siimes, M. A., Stekel, A. 1980. Iron deficiency in infancy and childhood. *Am. J. Clin. Nutr.* 33:86–118
3. Dallman, P. R. 1974. Tissue effects of iron deficiency. In *Iron in Biochemistry and Medicine,* ed. A. Jacobs, M. Worwood, pp. 437–76. London: Academic
4. Beutler, E., Fairbanks, V. F. 1980. The effect of iron deficiency. See Ref. 10, pp. 394–425
5. Strauss, R. G. 1978. Iron deficiency, infections, and immune function: a reassessment. *Am. J. Clin. Nutr.* 31:660–66
6. Dallman, P. R. 1982. Manifestations of iron deficiency. *Semin. Hematol.* 19:19–30
7. Beisel, W. R. 1982. Single nutrients and immunity. *Am. J. Clin. Nutr.* 35:417–68
8. Lozoff, B., Brittenham, G. M. 1985. Behavioral aspects of iron deficiency. *Prog. Hematol.* In press
9. Worwood, M. 1977. The clinical biochemistry of iron. *Semin. Hematol.* 14: 3–30
10. Jacobs, A., Worwood, M., eds. 1980. *Iron in Biochemistry and Medicine*. London: Academic. 706 pp.
11. Saltman, P., Hegenauer, J., eds. 1982. *The Biochemistry and Physiology of Iron*. New York: Elsevier Science. 836 pp.
12. Hershko, C. 1977. Storage iron regulation. *Prog. Hematol.* 10:105–48
13. Deiss, A. 1983. Iron metabolism in reticuloendothelial cells. *Semin. Hematol.* 20:81–90
14. Huebers, H. A., Finch, C. A. 1984. Transferrin: physiologic behavior and clinical implications. *Blood* 64:763–67
15. Booth, F. W., Holloszy, J. O. 1977. Cytochrome c turnover in rat skeletal muscles. *J. Biol. Chem.* 252:416–19
16. Dallman, P. R., Siimes, M. A., Manies, E. C. 1975. Brain iron: persistent deficiency following short-term iron deprivation in the young rat. *Br. J. Haematol.* 31:209–15
17. Dallman, P. R., Spirito, R. A. 1977. Brain iron in the rat: extremely slow turnover in normal rats may explain long-lasting effects of early iron deficiency. *J. Nutr.* 107:1075–81
18. Thelander, L., Gräslund, A., Thelander, M. 1983. Continual presence of oxygen and iron required for mammalian ribonucleotide reduction: possible regulation mechanism. *Biochem. Biophys. Res. Commun.* 110:859–65
19. Crnic, L. S. 1984. Animal models of early malnutrition: A comment on bias, dependability, and human importance. In *Malnutrition and Behavior: Critical Assessment of Key Issues,* ed. J. Brozek, pp. 460–68. Lausanne: Nestle Found.

20. Morgan, E. H. 1980. Comparative iron metabolism. See Ref. 10, pp. 641–87
21. Siimes, M. A., Refino, C., Dallman, P. R. 1980. Manifestations of iron deficiency at various levels of dietary iron intake. *Am. J. Clin. Nutr.* 33:570–74
22. Dallman, P. R., Refino, C. A., Yland, M. J. 1982. Sequence of development of iron deficiency in the rat. *Am. J. Clin. Nutr.* 35:671–77
23. Jacobs, A. 1961. Iron-containing enzymes in the buccal epithelium. *Lancet* 2:1331–33
24. Dagg, J. H., Jackson, J. M., Curry, B., Goldberg, A. 1966. Cytochrome oxidase in latent iron deficiency (sideropenia). *Br. J. Haematol.* 12:331–33
25. Chandra, R. K. 1973. Reduced bactericidal capacity of polymorphs in iron deficiency. *Arch. Dis. Child.* 48:864–66
26. Macdougall, L. G., Anderson, R., McNab, G. M., Katz, J. 1975. The immune response in iron-deficient children: Impaired cellular defense mechanisms with altered humoral components. *J. Pediatr.* 86:833–43
27. Chandra, R. K. 1975. Impaired immunocompetence associated with iron deficiency. *J. Pediatr.* 86:899–902
28. Srikantia, S. G., Prasad, J. S., Bhaskaram, C., Krishnamachari, K. A.V. R. 1976. Anemia and immune response. *Lancet* 1:1307–9
29. Yetgin, S., Altay, C., Ciliv, G., Laleli, Y. 1979. Myeloperoxidase activity and bactericidal function of PMN in iron deficiency. *Acta Haematol.* 61:10–14
30. Vyas, D., Chandra, R. K. 1984. Functional implications of iron deficiency. In *Iron Deficiency in Infancy and Childhood,* ed. A. Stekel, pp. 45–69. New York: Raven
31. Joynson, D. H. M., Jacobs, A., Walker, D. M., Dolby, A. E. 1972. Defect of cell-mediated immunity in patients with iron-deficiency anaemia. *Lancet* 2:1058–59
32. Bhaskaram, C., Reddy, V. 1975. Cell-mediated immunity in iron and vitamin-deficient children. *Br. Med. J.* 3:522
33. Fletcher, J., Mather, J., Lewis, M. J., Whiting, G. 1975. Mouth lesions in iron-deficient anemia: Relationship to *Candida albicans* in saliva and to impairment of lymphocyte transformation. *J. Infect. Dis.* 131:44–50
34. Reichard, P., Ehrenberg, A. 1983. Ribonucleotide reductase—a radical enzyme. *Science* 221:514–19
35. Woodson, R. D., Wills, R. E., Lenfant, C. 1978. Effect of acute and established anemia on $O_2$ transport at rest, submaximal and maximal work. *J. Appl. Physiol.* 44:36–43
36. Varat, M. A., Adolph, R. J., Fowles, N. O. 1972. Cardiovascular effects of anemia. *Am. Heart J.* 83:415–26
37. Perkkiö, M. V., Jansson, L. T., Henderson, S., Refino, C., Brooks, G. A., Dallman, P. R. 1985. Work performance in the iron deficient rat: improved endurance with exercise training. *J. Appl. Physiol.* 249:E306–11
38. Finch, C. A., Miller, L. R., Inamdar, A. R., Person, R., Seiler, K., Mackler, B. 1976. Iron deficiency in the rat: physiological and biochemical studies of muscle dysfunction. *J. Clin. Invest.* 58:447–53
39. Davies, K. J. A., Donovan, C. M., Refino, C. J., Brooks, G. A., Packer, L., Dallman, P. R. 1984. Distinguishing effects of anemia and muscle iron deficiency on exercise bioenergetics in the rat. *Am. J. Physiol.* 246:E535–43
40. Beard, J., Green, W., Miller, L., Finch, C. A. 1984. Effect of iron-deficiency anemia on hormone levels and thermoregulation during cold exposure. *Am. J. Physiol.* 247:R114–19
41. McKay, R. H., Higuchi, D. A., Winder, W. W., Fell, R. D., Brown, E. B. 1983. Tissue effects of iron deficiency in the rat. *Biochim. Biophys. Acta* 757:352–58
42. McDonald, R., Hegenauer, J., Sucec, A., Saltman, P. 1984. Effects of iron deficiency and exercise on myoglobin. *Eur. J. Appl. Physiol.* 52:414–19
43. Dallman, P. R., Schwartz, H. C. 1965. Distribution of cytochrome and myoglobin in rats with dietary iron deficiency. *Pediatrics* 35:677–86
44. Davies, K. J. A., Maguire, J. J., Brooks, G. A., Dallman, P. R., Packer, L. 1982. Muscle mitochondrial bioenergetics, oxygen supply, and work capacity during dietary iron deficiency and repletion. *Am. J. Physiol.* 242:E418–27
45. Dallman, P. R., Schwartz, H. C. 1965. Myoglobin and cytochrome c response during repair of iron deficiency in the rat. *J. Clin. Invest.* 44:1631–38
45a. McLane, J. A., Fell, R. D., McKay, R. H., Winder, W. W., Brown, E. B., Holloszy, J. O. 1981. Physiological and biochemical effects of iron deficiency on rat skeletal muscle. *Am. J. Physiol.* 241:C47–54
45b. Ackrell, B. A. C., Maguire, J. J., Dallman, P. R., Kearney, E. B. 1984. Effect of iron deficiency on succinate and NADH-ubiquinone oxidoreductases in skeletal muscle mitochondria. *J. Biol. Chem.* 259:10053–59

46. Mackler, B., Grace, R., Finch, C. A. 1984. Iron deficiency in the rat: effects on oxidative metabolism in distinct types of skeletal muscle. *Pediatr. Res.* 18:499–500
47. Dallman, P. R., Schwartz, H. C. 1964. Cytochrome c concentration during rat and guinea pig development. *Pediatrics* 33:106–10
48. Beutler, E. 1957. Iron enzymes in iron deficiency. I cytochrome c. *Am. J. Med. Sci.* 234:517–27
49. Salmon, H. A. 1962. The cytochrome content of the heart, kidney, liver, and skeletal muscle of iron-deficient rats. *J. Physiol.* 164:17–30
50. Brooks, G. A., Fahey, T. H. 1984. *Exercise Physiology: Human Bioenergetics and Its Applications*. New York: Wiley
51. Goodman, J. R., Warshaw, J. B., Dallman, P. R. 1970. Cardiac hypertrophy in iron and copper deficiency: The quantitative contribution of mitochondrial enlargement. *Pediatr. Res.* 4:244–56
52. Blayney, L., Bailey-Wood, R., Jacobs, A., Henderson, A., Muir, J. 1976. The effects of iron deficiency on the respiratory function and cytochrome content of rat heart mitochondria. *Circ. Res.* 39: 744–48
53. Henderson, S. A., Dallman, P. R., Brooks, G. A. 1986. Glucose turnover and oxidation are increased in iron deficiency. *Am. J. Physiol.* In press
54. Ohira, Y., Hegenauer, J., Strause, L., Chen, S., Saltman, P., Beinert, H. 1982. Mitochondrial NADH dehydrogenase in iron-deficient and iron-repleted rat muscle: an EPR and work performance study. *Br. J. Haematol.* 52:623–30
55. Perkkiö, M. V., Jansson, L. T., Brooks, G. A., Refino, C. A., Dallman, P. R. 1984. Work performance in iron deficiency of increasing severity. *J. Appl. Physiol.* 58:1477–80
56. Dallman, P. R., Sunshine, P., Leonard, Y. 1967. Intestinal cytochrome response with repair of iron deficiency. *Pediatrics* 39:863–71
57. Rasch, C. A., Cotton, E. K., Harris, J. W., Griggs, R. C. 1960. Blood loss as a contributing factor in the etiology of iron-lack anemia in infancy. *Am. J. Dis. Child.* 100:627
58. Hoag, M. S., Wallerstein, R. O., Pollycove, M. 1961. Occult blood loss in iron deficiency anemia of infancy. *Pediatrics* 27:199–203
59. Elian, E., Bar-Shani, S., Liberman, A., Matoth, Y. 1966. Intestinal blood loss: A factor in calculation of body iron in late infancy. *J. Pediatr.* 69:215–19
60. Fomon, S. J., Ziegler, E. E., Nelson, S. E., Edwards, B. B. 1981. Cow milk feeding in infancy: gastrointestinal blood loss and iron nutritional status. *Pediatrics* 98:540–45
61. Wilson, J. F., Heiner, D. C., Lahey, M. E. 1964. Milk-induced gastrointestinal bleeding in infants with hypochromic microcytic anemia. *J. Am. Med. Assoc.* 189:568–72
62. Woodruff, C. W., Clark, J. L. 1972. The role of fresh cows milk in iron deficiency. I. Albumin turnover in infants with iron deficiency anemia. *Am. J. Dis. Child.* 124:18–23
63. Kosnai, I., Kuitonen, P., Siimes, M. A. 1979. Iron deficiency in children with celiac disease on treatment with gluten-free diet. Role of intestinal blood loss. *Arch. Dis. Child.* 54:375–78
64. Lanzkowsky, P., Karayalcin, G., Miller, F., Lane, B. P. 1981. Disaccharidase values in iron-deficient patients. *J. Pediatr.* 99:605–8
65. Sriratanaban, A., Thayer, W. R. 1971. Small intestinal disaccharidase activities in experimental iron and protein deficiency. *Am. J. Clin. Nutr.* 24:411–15
66. Buts, J.-P., Delacroix, D. L., Dekeyser, N., Paquet, S., Horsmans, Y., et al. 1984. Role of dietary iron in maturation of rat small intestine at weaning. *Am. J. Physiol.* 246:G725–31
67. Naiman, J. L., Oski, F. A., Diamond, L. K., Vawter, G. F., Schwachman, H. 1964. The gastrointestinal effects of iron deficiency anemia. *Pediatrics* 33:83–99
68. Kimber, C., Weintraub, L. R. 1968. Malabsorption of iron secondary to iron deficiency. *N. Engl. J. Med.* 279:453–59
69. Schubert, W. K., Lahey, M. E. 1959. Copper and protein depletion complicating hypoferric anemia of infancy. *Pediatrics* 24:710–33
70. Lundström, U., Perkkiö, M., Savilahti, E., Siimes, M. 1983. Iron deficiency anaemia with hypoproteinaemia. *Arch. Dis. Child.* 58:438–41
71. Sturgeon, P. 1959. Studies of iron requirements in infants. III. Influence of supplemental iron during normal pregnancy on mother and infant. B. The infant. *Br. J. Haematol.* 5:45–55
72. Shott, R. J., Andrews, B. F. 1972. Iron status of a medical high-risk population at delivery. *Am. J. Dis. Child.* 124:369–71
73. Jansson, L., Holmberg, L., Ekman, R. 1979. Variation of serum ferritin in low birth weight infants with maternal ferritin, birth weight and gestational age. *Acta Haematol.* 62:273–77
74. MacPhail, A. P., Charlton, R. W., Both-

well, T. H., Torrance, J. D. 1980. The relationship between maternal and infant iron status. *Scand. J. Haematol.* 25:141–50

75. Blot, I., Rey, A., Kaltwasser, J. P., Francoual, J., Papiernik, E., Tchernia, G. 1982. Folate and iron deficiencies in mothers and their newborn children. *Blut* 44:297–303
76. Wallenburg, H. C. S., van Eijk, H. G. 1984. Effect of oral iron supplementation during pregnancy on maternal and fetal iron status. *J. Perinat. Med.* 12:7–12
77. Sisson, T. R. C., Lund, C. J. 1958. The influence of maternal iron deficiency on the newborn. *Am. J. Clin. Nutr.* 6:376–84
78. Singla, P. N., Chand, S., Khanna, S., Agarwal, K. N. 1978. Effect of maternal anaemia on the placenta and the newborn infant. *Acta Paediatr. Scand.* 67:645–48
79. Finch, C. A., Huebers, H. A., Miller, L. R., Josephson, B. M., Shepard, T. H., Mackler, B. 1983. Fetal iron balance in the rat. *Am. J. Clin. Nutr.* 37:910–17
80. Mackler, B., Grace, R., Person, R., Shepard, T. H., Finch, C. A. 1983. Iron deficiency in the rat. Biochemical studies of fetal metabolism. *Teratology* 28:103–7
81. Bailey-Wood, R., Blayney, L. M., Muir, J. R., Jacobs, A. 1975. The effects of iron deficiency on rat liver enzymes. *Br. J. Exp. Pathol.* 56:193–98
82. Dallman, P. R. 1969. Iron restriction in the nursing rat: Early effects upon tissue heme proteins, hemoglobin, and liver iron. *J. Nutr.* 97:475–80
83. Mackler, B., Person, R., Miller, L. R., Inamdar, A. R., Finch, C. A. 1978. Iron deficiency in the rat: biochemical studies of brain metabolism. *Pediatr. Res.* 12:217–20
84. Youdim, M. B. H., Green, A. R., Bloomfield, M. R., Mitchell, B. D., Heal, D. J., Grahame-Smith, D. G. 1980. The effects of iron deficiency on brain biogenic monoamine biochemistry and function in rats. *Neuropharmacology* 19:259–67
85. Land, J. M., Booth, R. F. G., Berger, R., Clark, J. B. 1977. Development of mitochondrial energy metabolism in rat brain. *Biochem. J.* 164:339–48
86. Huebers, H. A., Finch, C. A. 1984. Transferrin: physiologic behavior and clinical implications. *Blood* 64:763–67
87. Larrick, J. W., Hyman, E. S. 1984. Acquired iron-deficiency anemia caused by an antibody against the transferrin receptor. *N. Engl. J. Med.* 311:214–18
88. Symes, A. L., Missala, K., Sourkes, T. L. 1971. Iron and riboflavin-dependent metabolism of a monoamine in the rat in vivo. *Science* 174:153–55
89. Voorhess, M. L., Stuart, M. J., Stockman, J. A., Oski, F. A. 1975. Iron deficiency anemia and increased urinary norepinephrine excretion. *J. Pediatr.* 86:542–47
90. Pollitt, E., Leibel, R. L., eds. 1982. *Iron Deficiency: Brain Biochemistry and Behavior,* p. 214. New York: Raven
91. Pollitt, E. 1985. Effects of iron deficiency with and without anemia on mental development among infants and preschool children. In *Nutritional Anthropology,* ed. F. E. Johnston. New York: Liss. In press
92. Ashkenazi, R., Ben-Shachar, D., Youdim, M. B. H. 1982. Nutritional iron and dopamine binding sites in the rat brain. *Pharmacol. Biochem. Behav.* 17(Suppl. 1):43–47
93. Kaladhar, M., Rao, B. S. N. 1982. Effects of iron deficiency on serotonin uptake in vitro by rat brain synaptic vesicles. *J. Neurochem.* 38:1576–81
94. Tamir, H., Klein, A., Rapport, M. M. 1976. Serotonin binding protein: enhancement of binding by $Fe^{2+}$ and inhibition of binding by drugs. *J. Neurochem.* 26:871–78
95. Yehuda, S., Youdim, M. B. H. 1984. The increased opiate action of β-endorphin in iron deficient rats: the possible involvement of dopamine. *Eur. J. Pharmacol.* 104:245–51
96. Youdim, M. B. H., Yehuda, S., Ben-Uriah, Y. 1981. Iron deficiency–induced circadian rhythm reversal of dopaminergic-mediated behaviors and thermoregulation in rats. *Eur. J. Pharmacol.* 74:295–301
97. Glover, J., Jacobs, A. 1972. Activity pattern of iron-deficient rats. *Br. Med. J.* 2:627–28
98. Edgerton, V. R., Bryant, S. L., Gillespie, C. A., Gardner, G. W. 1972. Iron deficiency anemia and physical performance and activity of rats. *J. Nutr.* 102:381–400
99. Martin J. C., Martin, D. C., Dillmann, E., Day, H. E., Sigman, G. 1980. Effects of ambient temperature upon diurnal activity in nutritionally iron-deficient rats. *Bull. Psychon. Soc.* 15:18–20
100. Dallman, P. R., Refino, C. A., Dallman, M. F. 1984. The pituitary-adrenal response to stress in the iron-deficient rat. *J. Nutr.* 114:1747–53
101. Youdim, M. B. H., Grahame-Smith, D. G., Woods, H. F. 1975. Some properties

of human platelet monamine oxidase in iron-deficiency anemia. *Clin. Sci. Mol. Med.* 50:479–85
102. Weinberg, J., Levine, S., Dallman, P. R. 1979. Long-term consequences of early iron deficiency in the rat. *Pharmacol. Biochem. Behav.* 11:631–38
103. Groeneveld, D., Smeets, H. G. W., Kabra, P., Dallman, P. R. 1985. Urinary catecholamines in iron-deficient rats at rest and following surgical stress. *Am. J. Clin. Nutr.* 42:263–69
104. Wagner, A., Fortier, N., Giroux, A., Lukes, J., Snyder, L. M. 1978. Catecholamines in adult iron deficient patients. *Experimentia* 35:102–3
105. Dillmann, E., Johnson, D. G., Martin, J., Mackler, B., Finch, C. A. 1979. Catecholamine elevation in iron deficiency. *Am. J. Physiol.* 237:R297–300
106. Dillmann, E., Gale, C., Green, W., Johnson, D. G., Mackler, B., Finch, C. A. 1980. Hypothermia in iron deficiency due to altered triiodothyronine metabolism. *Am. J. Physiol.* 239:R377–81
107. Beard, J., Green, W., Miller, L., Finch, C. 1984. Effect of iron-deficiency anemia on hormone levels and thermoregulation during cold exposure. *Am. J. Physiol.* 247:R114–19
108. Martinez-Torres, C., Cubeddu, L., Dillmann, E., Brengelmann, G. L., Leets, I., et al. 1984. Effect of exposure to low temperature on normal and iron-deficient subjects. *Am. J. Physiol.* 246:R380–83
109. Oski, F. A., Honig, A. S. 1978. The effects of therapy on the developmental scores of iron-deficient infants. *J. Pediatr.* 92:21–25
110. Lozoff, B., Brittenham, G. M., Viteri, F. E., Wolf, A. W., Urrutia, J. J. 1982. The effects of short-term oral iron therapy on developmental deficits in iron-deficient anemic infants. *J. Pediatr.* 100:351–57
111. Walter, T., Kovalskys, J., Stekel, A. 1983. Effect of mild iron deficiency on infant mental development scores. *J. Pediatr.* 102:519–22
112. Lozoff, B., Brittenham, G. M., Viteri, F. E., Wolf, A. W., Urrutia, J. J. 1982. Developmental deficits in iron-deficient infants: Effects of age and severity of iron lack. *J. Pediatr.* 101:948–52
113. Oski, F. A., Honig, A. S., Helu, B., Howanitz, P. 1983. Effect of iron therapy on behavior performance in nonanemic, iron-deficient infants. *Pediatrics* 71: 877–80
114. Palti, H., Pevsner, B., Adler, B. 1983. Does anemia in infancy affect achievement on developmental and intelligence tests? *Hum. Biol.* 55:189–94
115. Seshadri, S., Hirode, K., Naik, P., Malhotra, S. 1982. Behavioural responses to young anaemic Indian children to iron-folic acid supplements. *Br. J. Nutr.* 48:233–40
116. Pollitt, E., Soemantri, A. G., Yunis, F., Scrimshaw, N. S. 1985. Cognitive effects of iron-deficiency anaemia. *Lancet* 1:158
117. Pollitt, E., Viteri, F., Saco-Pollitt, C., Leibel, R. L. 1982. Behavioral effects of iron deficiency anemia in children. See Ref. 90, pp. 195–208
118. Moore, L. L., Humbert, J. R. 1984. Neutrophil bactericidal dysfunction towards oxidant radical-sensitive microorganisms during experimental iron deficiency. *Pediatr. Res.* 18:684–89
119. Kulapongs, P., Vithayasai, V., Suskind, R., Olson, R. E. 1974. Cell-mediated immunity and phagocytosis and killing function in children with severe iron-deficiency anaemia. *Lancet* 2:689–91
120. Babior, B. M. 1983. The respiratory burst of phagocytes. *J. Clin. Invest.* 73:599–601
121. Cramer, E., Pryzwansky, K. B., Villeval, J.-L., Testa, U., Breton-Gorius, J. 1985. Ultrastructural localization of lactoferrin and myeloperoxidase in human neutrophils by immunogold. *Blood* 65: 423–32
122. Ambruso, D. R., Johnson, R. B. Jr. 1981. Lactoferrin enhances hydroxyl radical production by human neutrophils, neutrophil particulate fractions, and an enzymatic generating system. *J. Clin. Invest.* 67:352–60
123. Higgs, J. M., Wells, R. S. 1972. Chronic mucocutaneous candidiasis: associated abnormalities on iron metabolism. *Br. J. Dermatol.* 86(Suppl. 8):88–102
124. Prasad, J. S. 1979. Leucocyte function in iron-deficiency anemia. *Am. J. Clin. Nutr.* 32:550–52
125. Mackler, B., Person, R., Ochs, H., Finch, C. A. 1984. Iron deficiency in the rat: effects on neutrophil activation and metabolism. *Pediatr. Res.* 18:549–51
126. Andelman, M. B., Sered, B. R. 1966. Utilization of dietary iron by term infants: A study of 1,048 infants from slow socioeconomic population. *Am. J. Dis. Child.* 111:45–55
127. Burman, D. 1972. Hemoglobin levels in normal infants aged 3–24 months and the effect of iron. *Arch. Dis. Child.* 47:261–71
128. Kochanowski, B. A., Sherman, A. R. 1985. Cellular growth in iron deficient

rats: effect of pre- and postweaning iron repletion. *J. Nutr.* 115:279–87

129. Siimes, M. A., Dallman, P. R. 1974. Iron deficiency: impaired liver growth and DNA synthesis in the rat. *Br. J. Haematol.* 28:453–62
130. Lederman, H. M., Cohen, A., Lee, J. W. W., Freedman, M. H., Gelfand, E. W. 1984. Deferoxamine: a reversible S-phase inhibitor of human lymphocyte proliferation. *Blood* 64:748–53
131. Keusch, G. T., Farthing, M. J. G. 1986. Nutrition and infection. *Ann. Rev. Nutr.* 6:131–54
132. Kulapongs, P., Vithayasai, V., Suskind, R., Olson, R. E. 1974. Cell-mediated immunity and phagocytosis and killing function in children with severe iron-deficiency anaemia. *Lancet* 2:689–91
133. Kuvibidila, S. R., Baliga, B. S., Suskind, R. M. 1981. Effects of iron deficiency anemia on delayed cutaneous hypersensitivity in mice. *Am. J. Clin. Nutr.* 34:2635–40
134. Kuvibidila, S., Nauss, K. M., Baliga, B. S., Suskind, R. M. 1983. Impairment of blastogenic response of splenic lymphocytes from iron-deficient mice: in vivo repletion. *Am. J. Clin. Nutr.* 37:15–25
135. Nalder, B. N., Mahoney, A. W., Ramakrishnan, R., Hendricks, D. G. 1971. Sensitivity of the immunological response to the nutritional status of rats. *J. Nutr.* 102:535–42
136. Kochanowski, B. A., Sherman, A. R. 1985. Decreased antibody formation in iron-deficient rat pups—effect of iron repletion. *Am. J. Clin. Nutr.* 41:278–84
137. Dallman, P. R., Yip, R., Johnson, C. 1984. Prevalence and causes of anemia in the United States, 1976–1980. *Am. J. Clin. Nutr.* 39:437–45
138. Beresford, C. H., Neale, R. J., Brooks, O. G. 1971. Absorption and pyrexia. *Lancet* 1:568–72
139. Bender-Götze, C., Ludwig, U., Schafer, K. H., Heinrich, H. C., Oppitz, K. H. 1976. Cytochemische knochenmarksbefunde und diagnostische $^{59}Fe^{2+}$-absorption wahrend des akuten und chronischen infektes im kindesalter. *Monatsschr. Kinderheilkd.* 124:305–7

139a. Weinberg, E. D. 1984. Iron withholding: a defense against infection and neoplasia. *Physiol. Rev.* 64:65–102

140. Remmer, H. 1970. Role of the liver in drug metabolism. *Am. J. Med.* 49:617–29
141. Gram, T. E., ed. 1980. *Extrahepatic Metabolism of Drugs and Other Foreign Compounds*. New York: SP Medical and Scientific. 601 pp.
142. Catz, C. S., Juchau, M. R., Yaffe, S. J. 1970. Effects of iron, riboflavin and iodine deficiencies on hepatic drug-metabolizing enzymes systems. *J. Pharmacol. Exp. Ther.* 174:197–205
143. Dallman, P. R., Goodman, J. R. 1971. The effects of iron deficiency on the hepatocytes: A biochemical and ultrastructural study. *J. Cell. Biol.* 48:79–90
144. Becking, G. C. 1972. Influence of dietary iron levels on hepatic drug metabolism in vivo and in vitro in the rat. *Biochem. Pharmacol.* 21:1585–93
145. Hoensch, H., Woo, C. H., Raffin, S. B., Schmid, R. 1976. Oxidative metabolism of foreign compounds in rat small intestine: cellular localization and dependence on dietary iron. *Gastroenterology* 70:1063–70
146. Pascoe, G. A., Correia, M. A. 1985. Structural and functional assembly of rat intestinal cytochrome P-450 isoenzymes. Effects of dietary iron and selenium. *Biochem. Pharmacol.* 34:599–608
147. O'Malley, K., Stevenson, I. H. 1972. Iron deficiency anemia and drug metabolism. *J. Pharm. Pharmacol.* 25:339–40

*Ann. Rev. Nutr. 1986. 6:41–66*


# CARNITINE METABOLISM AND FUNCTION IN HUMANS

*Charles J. Rebouche*

Department of Pediatrics, University of Iowa College of Medicine, Iowa City, Iowa 52242

*Dennis J. Paulson*

Department of Physiology, Chicago College of Osteopathic Medicine, Chicago, Illinois 60615

---

CONTENTS

INTRODUCTION .......... 42
FUNCTION .......... 42
BIOSYNTHESIS AND METABOLISM IN THE NORMAL ADULT .......... 43
*Biosynthesis* .......... 43
*Absorption* .......... 45
*Tissue Accretion and Turnover* .......... 45
*Renal Handling* .......... 46
THE ROLE OF CARNITINE IN PERINATAL ENERGY METABOLISM .......... 47
DISORDERS OF CARNITINE METABOLISM .......... 50
*Primary Genetic Carnitine Deficiency* .......... 50
*Deficiency Syndromes Secondary to Other Genetic or Acquired Disorders* .......... 52
THE ROLE OF CARNITINE IN OTHER ABNORMAL METABOLIC CONDITIONS .......... 55
*Myopathic Heart Disease* .......... 55
*Ischemic Heart Disease* .......... 57
*Hyperlipidemia* .......... 57
*Ketosis* .......... 58
SUMMARY AND CONCLUSIONS .......... 59



0199-9885/86/0715-0041$02.00

## INTRODUCTION

L-Carnitine [β-hydroxy-(γ-*N*-trimethylammonio)-butyrate] is a natural constituent of higher organisms and, in particular, cells of animal origin. Research on carnitine function and metabolism in humans has increased dramatically in the last 15 years, owing primarily to two important observations: Broquist and colleagues (71, 152) discovered that carnitine is ultimately derived from lysine, a limiting amino acid in diets of many third-world populations; and Engel and coworkers (43, 75) described human carnitine deficiency syndromes of apparent genetic origin. These observations provided impetus for extensive investigation into biosynthesis, metabolism, and functions of carnitine. These studies in turn led to identification of carnitine deficiency associated with a variety of genetic and acquired diseases and conditions, and to possible therapeutic uses of carnitine in human health and disease.

This review discusses recent research on carnitine metabolism and function in humans. Where appropriate, studies of experimental animals are described to provide clarification or substantiation of results obtained in human studies. This review is not intended to be exhaustive; the reader is directed to several recent reviews that discuss areas not covered here, or that provide greater detail (19, 22, 44, 57, 123, 147).

## FUNCTION

The role of carnitine in transport of long-chain fatty acids into the mitochondrial matrix has been well established in experimental animals for many years (see 22 for review). The work of Engel & Angelini (43), utilizing isolated mitochondria from a patient with muscle carnitine deficiency, verified that carnitine was necessary for transport of long-chain fatty acids into human mitochondria. Long et al (87) examined the relationship between concentration of carnitine and oxidation of oleate in homogenates prepared from human skeletal muscle, as well as from rat liver, kidney, and heart, and from rat and dog skeletal muscle. Carnitine content of these tissues varied widely, as did the carnitine concentration required for half-maximal rate of fatty acid oxidation in vitro. However, they concluded that for any given tissue the normal carnitine content was set at a level necessary for optimal rate of long-chain fatty acid oxidation.

Carnitine also participates in modulation of the intramitochondrial acyl-coenzyme A/coenzyme A ratio (13). Several mitochondrial pathways produce coenzyme A esters of short- and medium-chain organic acids. Under normal conditions these esters are further metabolized to regenerate free coenzyme A. Under conditions of stress, when one or more of these metabolic pathways produces large amounts of these esters, the organic acid may be transesterified to carnitine, freeing reduced coenzyme A to participate in other mitochondrial pathways, e.g. the tricarboxylic acid cycle. Under normal conditions the role of carnitine as a mitochondrial buffer for excess organic acids probably is minor. However, under abnormal conditions, such as diabetes, anoxia, or a defect of mitochondrial β-oxidation, this role may have major importance in maintaining mitochondrial function and viability of the cell. This process is discussed subsequently with regard to renal handling of carnitine, disorders of carnitine metabolism, and cardiac function.

## BIOSYNTHESIS AND METABOLISM IN THE NORMAL ADULT

### *Biosynthesis*

The pathway of carnitine biosynthesis has been studied most extensively in the rat. Virtually all available evidence indicates that the enzymatic pathways in rats and in humans are identical. The ultimate precursors of carnitine are lysine and methionine (115). S-Adenosylmethionine provides the methyl groups for enzymatic trimethylation of peptide-linked lysine (115, 116). Numerous proteins contain ε-*N*-trimethyllysine residues, including histones, cytochrome c, myosin and calmodulin (see 106 for a review). Attempts to demonstrate methylation of free lysine in human tissues or tissues of other mammalian species have been unsuccessful to date, and it is generally believed that this pathway does not exist in mammals. One caveat to this assumption follows from the study by Khan-Siddiqui & Bamji (78), in which they showed a significant rise in plasma carnitine concentration in human adults within six hours after oral administration of a bolus dose of lysine. The authors interpreted this result to indicate methylation of free lysine, because the process of protein synthesis, methylation of peptide-linked lysine residues, and turnover of these proteins would not be rapid enough to account for the observed rise in plasma carnitine.

ε-*N*-Trimethyllysine residues are released for carnitine biosynthesis by protein turnover (41, 80). ε-*N*-Trimethyllysine undergoes the following series of transformations: ε-*N*-trimethyllysine → β-hydroxy-ε-*N*-trimethyllysine → γ-trimethylaminobutyraldehyde → γ-butyrobetaine → L-carnitine. Regulation of this process in humans has not been studied. Henderson et al (68) have reviewed the enzymology of the pathway. The role of ascorbic acid in ε-*N*-trimethyllysine and γ-butyrobetaine hydroxylation is reviewed in this volume (47).

Enzymes for conversion of ε-*N*-trimethyllysine to γ-butyrobetaine were found in all human tissues studied (skeletal muscle, heart, liver, kidney, and brain) (120). However, γ-butyrobetaine hydroxylase activity was present in human liver, kidney, and brain, but not in skeletal muscle or heart.

Although all tissues studied contain ε-*N*-trimethyllysine hydroxylase activity, it is not known whether ε-*N*-trimethyllysine produced within a tissue is totally or partially metabolized within that tissue or whether it is released into the circulation for metabolism by other tissues. Normal circulating levels of ε-*N*-trimethyllysine are 0.3–0.5 μM (82). Renal clearance of this amino acid is similar to that of creatinine (82), i.e. it is poorly or not at all reabsorbed. Urinary output of ε-*N*-trimethyllysine in humans was estimated to be 30–92 μMol/g creatinine (73, 82, 88).

Exogenous ε-*N*-trimethyllysine administered intravenously is in large part (66–84%) excreted unchanged in urine within 48 hours of administration (121). Circulating ε-*N*-trimethyllysine destined for carnitine biosynthesis is primarily taken up by the kidney, where it is converted mostly to carnitine, although some γ-butyrobetaine is released for hydroxylation in other tissues (119).

Hydroxylation of γ-butyrobetaine has been the most intensely studied reaction of the pathway in humans. Lindstedt and coworkers (85) showed that the kinetic properties of human renal γ-butyrobetaine hydroxylase are similar to those of the enzyme in other species. Further, they identified multiple isoenzymes of γ-butyrobetaine hydroxylase in human kidney and liver (86). The enzyme was present in three forms, which are separable by chromatofocusing (isoelectric points of 5.6, 5.7, and 5.8). The specific activities of each form were identical, as were their molecular weights (64 kDaltons) and cofactor requirements. The three isoenzymes appeared to be dimeric combinations of two subunits differing in charge but not size, as isoenzyme 2 (isoelectric point = 5.7) was resolved into two protein bands by isoelectric focusing in polyacrylamide gels containing urea. Isoenzyme 1 contained only one of these bands and isoenzyme 3 the other.

Human liver γ-butyrobetaine hydroxylase is developmentally regulated. Enzyme activity in three infants was approximately 12% and in a 2.5-year-old boy 30% of the adult mean (120). By 15 years of age, hepatic enzyme activity was within the range of adult values. No data are currently available on the relative rates of renal γ-butyrobetaine hydroxylase in infants, children, and adults.

Carnitine is not considered to be an essential nutrient in the diet of adult humans, primarily because some human tissues are able to synthesize this amino acid. However, surprisingly little evidence is available to indicate that humans can synthesize sufficient quantities of carnitine to meet requirements. Studies from India (77) and Thailand (153) have shown that individuals consuming cereal-based diets very low in carnitine maintained plasma carnitine concentrations at or near levels typical of adults in Western nations, where carnitine is abundant in most diets. Adult surgical patients supported by carnitine-free total parenteral nutrition maintained normal plasma carnitine levels for twenty days, but subsequently a gradual decline of plasma carnitine concentration was observed (65). Although normal plasma carnitine levels are maintained in the human adult in the absence (or virtual absence) of dietary carnitine, the adequacy of plasma carnitine concentration as an indicator of carnitine status in humans has not been demonstrated. Thus, further investigation into the ability of endogenous carnitine biosynthesis to maintain body stores of carnitine in the absence of dietary sources of this amino acid is desirable. This question is particularly relevant for infants and children, in whom growth places extra demand for carnitine to supply newly synthesized tissue.

## *Absorption*

L-Carnitine is found in a variety of food sources; however, foods of animal origin are much more abundant in this amino acid than plant-derived foods (125). Red meats and dairy products are particularly rich sources of carnitine.

Absorption of carnitine from dietary sources has not been studied directly. Hamilton et al (67) studied carnitine transport across the human proximal small intestinal mucosa in vitro. They concluded that movement across this membrane was via an active process that depended on $Na^+$ cotransport. $K_T$ for the process was 974 μM and $V_{max}$ was 27.4 nmol/ml intracellular water/min. A passive, diffusional process was also identified, which may be important for absorption of large doses of carnitine. These results are similar to those reported by Gross & Henderson (61) and Gudjonsson et al (62), using live rats and isolated vascularly perfused intestine. These studies demonstrated relatively rapid transport of carnitine into intestinal mucosa from the lumen, acetylation of up to 50% of the carnitine accumulated in the tissue, and slower release of the free and acetylcarnitine into the circulation.

L-Carnitine in amounts normally found in the human diet was thought to be virtually totally absorbed. The basis for this assumption was the very small amount of carnitine normally found in human feces, i.e. less than 1% of that excreted in urine (125). Studies in humans (125) as well as in dogs (124) and rats (24, 31) have suggested that a small but significant amount of dietary carnitine is degraded in the gastrointestinal tract. Conclusive demonstration of the role of indigenous flora of the rat gastrointestinal tract in this process was recently reported (129), but similar studies in humans have not been described.

## *Tissue Accretion and Turnover*

Plasma total carnitine levels in normal adults 2–85 years old ranged from 30 to 89 μM (123). Mean values in males tended to be higher than in females: 59.3 ± 11.9 μM for males versus 51.5 ± 11.6 μM for females (mean ± S.D.; $N = 40$ for males, $N = 45$ for females). Skeletal muscle contains over 90% of total body carnitine in humans. Carnitine levels in skeletal muscle of normal humans ranged from 11 to 52 nmol/mg noncollagen protein (mean ± S.D.; 20.5 ± 8.4

for males, 20.1 ± 5.3 for females) (123). Thus the concentration of carnitine in skeletal muscle is approximately 70 times higher than in plasma. Similar but less steep carnitine concentration gradients are present between other tissues and extracellular fluid.

The steady-state rate of entry of carnitine into human muscle and heart, calculated by kinetic analysis, was 11.6 nmol/h/g tissue (125). This value is consistent with rates determined experimentally in isolated rat tissues (114, 159), and by kinetic analysis in dogs (124). Carnitine concentration in muscle is reduced by exercise, and the distribution of free and esterified carnitine is shifted toward increased esterification (83). Normal regulatory processes that maintain tissue carnitine gradients have not been identified, although hormonal interactions may be important (see the section on renal handling).

Using the technique of kinetic compartmental analysis, Rebouche & Engel (125) estimated turnover times for tissues, extracellular fluid, and whole-body carnitine. Turnover time for carnitine in skeletal muscle and heart was approximately 8 days, and for other tissues (thought to be primarily liver and kidney), 11.6 hours. Turnover time for carnitine in extracellular fluid was 1.13 hours and for the whole body, 66 days.

## *Renal Handling*

Carnitine is highly conserved in humans. At normal physiological concentrations in plasma, more than 90% of filtered carnitine is reabsorbed by the kidney (128). Several parameters have been used to describe the efficiency of the reabsorption process in humans (46, 126). In nine subjects ages 13 to 37, tubular maximum for carnitine reabsorption was 7.4 ± 0.44 μmol/dl glomerular filtrate (mean ± S.D.; range, 5.5–7.8 μmol/dl glomerular filtrate). Fractional reabsorption for a plasma total carnitine concentration of 65 μM was 90 ± 3.9% (mean ± S.D.; range, 84–95%). Even at very low plasma carnitine concentrations seen in some premature infants (see below) or patients with systemic carnitine deficiency, small amounts of carnitine are excreted in the urine. Thus a true renal plasma threshold for carnitine excretion cannot be determined. However, Engel et al (46) calculated an "apparent" renal plasma threshold for carnitine excretion. This value was estimated by plotting observed carnitine excretion versus plasma carnitine concentration and then extrapolating the curve to the abscissa for subjects infused over 3 hours with L-carnitine (0.25 μmol/min/kg body weight) (see Fig. 1 of Ref. 46). In six normal humans the apparent renal plasma threshold for carnitine excretion was 51 ± 7.4 μM (mean ± S.D.; range 45–59 μM) (46). In most individual subjects these values closely paralleled the plasma carnitine concentration (mean ± S.D., 53 ± 5.3 μM; range 46–59 μM). These results suggest that under normal conditions, plasma carnitine concentration is regulated, at least in part, by the kinetics of carnitine reabsorption by the kidney.

L-Carnitine formed intracellularly in the kidney may be partially secreted into the tubular lumen, either in free form (119) or as short-chain acylcarnitine esters (46). The significance of renal secretion of carnitine and carnitine esters is unclear. However, several investigators (32, 40, 148) have suggested that excretion of carnitine esters may be a mechanism for removing excess short- or medium-chain organic acids, particularly as they occur in excessive amounts in genetic diseases such as propionic acidemia and methylmalonic acidemia (see the section on disorders of carnitine metabolism). In this regard, it is noteworthy that the zenobiotic compound pivalic acid (2,2-dimethyl propionic acid), when administered orally as pivaloyl-1'-oxyethyl-(S)-3-(3,4-dihydroxyphenyl)-2-methylalaninate, was excreted almost entirely as pivaloylcarnitine in humans, but as the glucuronate conjugate in other species (160). Moreover, valproylcarnitine was identified in urine from two children undergoing chronic valproic acid therapy (94). Bieber & Kerner (14) demonstrated the presence of Δ6-octenoylcarnitine, Δ6-2-methyloctenoylcarnitine and 2-methyloctanoylcarnitine in human urine. The authors suggested that the acyl moieties were ingested from dietary dairy products and not synthesized de novo in humans. To date it is not known if these organic acids are conjugated with carnitine in the kidney or elsewhere in the body.

Several factors have been identified that affect carnitine excretion in human subjects, including serum thyroxine concentration (89). Hyperthyroidism markedly increased urinary carnitine excretion whereas hypothyroidism depressed urinary loss of carnitine. Because plasma carnitine levels were not reported in the study cited, it is not known if thyroxine induced release of carnitine from tissues, raising the plasma carnitine concentration, or if this hormone lowered the apparent plasma threshold for carnitine excretion. In another study (90) administration of $\beta^{1-24}$ACTH-Z to healthy subjects resulted in a six-fold increase in urinary carnitine excretion, and this increase was paralleled by a rise in plasma carnitine concentration.

Fasting for 36 hours in normal subjects decreased renal clearance of free carnitine but increased clearance of acylcarnitine esters (54). Total carnitine excretion was increased. Fasting decreased serum free carnitine (54, 70) but increased serum acylcarnitine ester and total carnitine concentrations (70). Urinary excretion of acylcarnitine esters increased parallel to rising plasma carnitine concentration (70). Ketoacidotic diabetics showed a similar increase in plasma acylcarnitine esters (55). This rise, both in fasting subjects and in diabetic ketoacidosis, was postulated to result from insulin deficiency (56).

## THE ROLE OF CARNITINE IN PERINATAL ENERGY METABOLISM

Glucose is the major metabolic fuel for the fetus (162). At parturition the infant must adapt to lipid as a major source of calories. Immediately at birth rapid elevation of blood free fatty acid and β-hydroxybutyrate levels occurs due to release of free fatty acids from adipose tissue (102). Later, high levels of free fatty acids in blood reflect intestinal absorption of fatty acids and triglycerides supplied by the diet (102). Human milk and many formula diets contain more than 40% of total calories as lipid. Fatty acids derived from these sources become the preferred fuel for heart and skeletal muscle (166). Thus, carnitine becomes an important cofactor for energy production in the neonate.

Human milk contains 28–95 nmol of total carnitine per ml (131, 162). Most milk-based formulas contain comparable or slightly higher levels of carnitine (20). However, formulas manufactured from soybean protein or casein and casein hydrolysate contain little or no carnitine (20, 162)[1]. Infants fed soy protein–based formula diets develop lower plasma carnitine concentrations than breast-fed infants or infants fed milk-based formula diets (102). Novak et al (99) studied a group of normal term infants, five of whom were fed an unsupplemented soy protein–based formula and seven of whom were fed the same formula, except supplemented with 50 μM of L-carnitine, from birth to five months. Plasma free carnitine was significantly increased at one, two, and three months of age, and plasma acylcarnitine esters were increased at two and three months in carnitine-supplemented infants. Plasma triglycerides at two and three months of age were significantly lower in infants given L-carnitine. Plasma free fatty acids were decreased significantly at three months of age in infants receiving L-carnitine. No difference in plasma β-hydroxybutyrate was found at one, two, or three months.

Clinical symptoms of carnitine deficiency in infants fed soy protein–based formulas are rare. However, subclinical consequences of mild to moderate carnitine deficiency, particularly relating to growth and development of the child, are unknown. The study by Novak et al (99) suggests differences in lipid metabolism in infants fed soy protein–based formulas with or without supplemental carnitine, but whether these differences have any short- or long-term clinical significance is at present a matter for speculation.

Plasma carnitine levels in preterm infants (less than 36 weeks gestational age) at birth are borderline normal or lower than normal (mean ± S.E., 29.0 ± 1.8 μM; $N = 53$; Ref. 139) with respect to levels in children and adults. These levels are maintained or increased by enteral feeding of milk-based formulas or human milk (110, 133). However, upon initiation of intravenous feeding with parenteral nutrition solutions (which to date are not routinely supplemented with carnitine), carnitine levels in blood fall to as low as 13 μM (110, 133). Further, Penn et al (109) reported that acid-soluble carnitine levels in heart and liver, but not in skeletal muscle, were significantly lower in premature infants fed intravenously for more than 15 days compared to premature or term infants

[1]At this writing, soy protein–based formula supplemented with L-carnitine is available from at least one commercial manufacturer.

fed intravenously for fewer than 36 hours. In a separate study, Shenai & Borum (138) demonstrated a positive correlation between gestational age and muscle carnitine concentration. Some infants of less than 30 weeks gestation had muscle carnitine levels considered borderline or deficient by criteria used to diagnose systemic carnitine deficiency (123).

Because exogenous carnitine is not provided by parenteral feeding solutions, it is reasonable to assume that, in the absence of excessive urinary carnitine excretion, the reduced carnitine levels result from the inability of endogenous biosynthesis to proceed at a rate sufficient to maintain "normal" concentrations in plasma and some tissues. Several investigators (64, 100, 138) have suggested that low (relative to adult levels) hepatic $\gamma$-butyrobetaine hydroxylase activity limits the rate of carnitine biosynthesis in infants. Rebouche & Lehman (127) demonstrated that carnitine biosynthesis in growing rats could be stimulated 100-fold by dietary $\epsilon$-*N*-trimethyllysine. In another study Rebouche (117) showed that in growing rats urinary output of carnitine was increased 65-fold (with concomitant increases in tissue carnitine levels) by addition of $\gamma$-butyrobetaine to a carnitine-free diet (as 0.1% of diet). Thus, because levels of hepatic $\gamma$-butyrobetaine hydroxylase activity in the rat and human are comparable, it is unlikely that even with a 10-fold reduction in activity of this enzyme (as occurs in human infants relative to adults) would the rate of this reaction be limiting for carnitine biosynthesis.

The question arises: Do reduced plasma and tissue carnitine levels in these infants hinder the utilization of lipid for energy production? It is well known that premature infants can tolerate only limited amounts of parenterally infused triglyceride (140). Infusion of the commercial lipid emulsion Intralipid® is generally considered safe at a rate of 150 mg/kg body weight/h or less. Lipid supplementation of parenteral feedings at 150 mg/kg body weight/h is considered adequate for lipid-derived caloric needs of the infant. However, it is not known if increased caloric intake, if tolerated, would improve growth performance and rate of development in parenterally fed premature infants.

To determine if low plasma and tissue levels of carnitine impair lipid utilization by premature infants, several investigators (104, 105, 134, 135, 165) have employed a lipid tolerance test (infusion of Intralipid at 1 g/kg body weight over 4–8 hours) with or without carnitine supplementation. Some studies were initiated shortly after birth (presumably before carnitine stores were depleted) or after 7 or more days of parenteral alimentation. In some studies normal feeding was continued during the course of the study, in others the infants received only the lipid emulsion. Various parameters were measured, including plasma free, acyl, and total carnitine; plasma free fatty acids, triglycerides, $\beta$-hydroxybutyrate, acetoacetate, and glycerol; and the plasma free fatty acid/$\beta$-hydroxybutyrate ratio.

Results of studies by Orzali et al (104, 105) suggest that glucose is the preferred substrate for energy production in the premature infant. Lipid is utilized only to the extent that glucose cannot meet the caloric needs of the individual. Under certain conditions, the effect of exogenous carnitine on the metabolism of bolus doses of triglycerides appeared to be an increase in the rate of oxidation of fatty acids either derived from the lipid infusion itself or from mobilization of adipose tissue (104, 135). In this regard, Novak et al (101) showed that carnitine enhances glycerol release from newborn subcutaneous adipose tissue in vitro. The positive correlation between plasma β-hydroxybutyrate and plasma total carnitine (134) suggests a carnitine-related enhancement of mitochondrial fatty acid oxidation.

Although some of these short-term studies with relatively high doses of lipid indicate a positive relationship between lipid utilization and carnitine concentration in plasma, they do not foretell the adequacy or extent of lipid utilization to provide energy for the parenterally alimented premature infant in a normal clinical setting. A recent study by Curran et al (38) bears directly on this issue. Premature, parenterally alimented infants of birth-weight between 800 and 1500 g (appropriate for gestational age) were divided into four groups: (*a*) infants given fat-free nutrition with carnitine (13 μmol/kg/day) or (*b*) without carnitine, and (*c*) infants given intravenous nutrition including Intralipid 20% (maximum 3 g/kg/day) with carnitine or (*d*) without carnitine. Amino acids and glucose were provided at 2.5 and 15 g/kg/day, respectively. Infants were maintained on this regimen for at least 5 days. The authors found no statistically significant differences in levels of plasma β-hydroxybutyrate (no evidence of increased ketogenesis) in any of the groups. There was a significant increase in free fatty acids in group (*c*) compared to group (*a*) after 12 days of the study, but no significant decrease in plasma free fatty acids when carnitine was provided to infants receiving Intralipid. Significant hypertriglyceridemia was not observed in infants receiving Intralipid. This study provides no evidence that carnitine supplementation alters the substrate preference for energy production in premature infants receiving total parenteral nutrition in a normal clinical situation. However, the parameters used in this study to detect alterations in substrate utilization are not unequivocal. Thus further study of this question is warranted.

## DISORDERS OF CARNITINE METABOLISM

### *Primary Genetic Carnitine Deficiency*

Primary carnitine deficiency syndromes are classified into two types, systemic and myopathic (123). The clinical features of these syndromes have been reviewed (123). Primary muscle carnitine deficiency, which has as its major clinical features mild to severe muscle weakness and variable excess of lipids in skeletal muscle fibers, was thought to arise from defective transport of carnitine into muscle (43). Direct evidence for this hypothesis has not been reported. However, Rebouche & Engel (125) showed, by kinetic compartmental analysis, that the rate of uptake of L-carnitine by a compartment identified as skeletal muscle was in one patient 43% of the mean of six normal subjects, and 40% lower than the lowest control. These results support the above hypothesis, but kinetic studies of this type and/or more direct measurements of carnitine transport in additional patients are required to substantiate the conclusion that carnitine transport is impaired in primary muscle carnitine deficiency.

Primary systemic carnitine deficiency is often associated with multiple episodes of metabolic encephalopathy, hypoglycemia, hypoprothrombinemia, hyperammonemia, and lipid excess in hepatocytes during acute attacks (123). In these respects it resembles Reye's syndrome. Theoretically, primary systemic carnitine deficiency could arise from one or more of the following: (*a*) a defect in carnitine biosynthesis; (*b*) abnormal renal handling of carnitine; (*c*) alterations in cellular mechanisms for carnitine transport, affecting uptake and/or release of carnitine from tissues; (*d*) excessive degradation of carnitine; or (*e*) defective intestinal absorption of carnitine (123).

No evidence for a defect in carnitine biosynthesis was found in three patients with primary systemic carnitine deficiency (118, 121). Indirect evidence from balance studies indicated that defective absorption or excessive degradation of carnitine did not contribute to the pathogenesis of this syndrome in four patients studied (125). Efficiency of reabsorption of carnitine by the renal tubule was reduced in five cases of systemic carnitine deficiency (46, 161)[2]. For four of these subjects fractional reabsorption of total carnitine at a plasma carnitine concentration of 65 μM was 60 ± 2.9% (mean ± S.D.; range 57–64%) compared to 90 ± 3.9% (range 84–95%) for nine normal subjects (126). However, fractional reabsorption of carnitine for one control subject with normal skeletal muscle carnitine concentration and no clinical symptoms of carnitine deficiency was 43 and 59% in two separate measurements (46). Thus it was concluded that decreased efficiency of carnitine reabsorption in the patients studied could not entirely account for the clinical presentation of systemic carnitine deficiency, but this abnormality may have contributed to the pathogenesis of the syndrome.

Kinetic measurements of carnitine transport into cultured skeletal muscle cells and skin fibroblasts of patients with systemic carnitine deficiency did not differ from those of normal subjects (122). Kinetic compartmental analysis of carnitine metabolism revealed a reduced rate of carnitine transport into muscle in each of four subjects with systemic carnitine deficiency[2], but the decreased rate was directly attributed to the reduced plasma carnitine concentration in

[2]Three of these cases subsequently were shown to be associated with medium-chain acyl-CoA dehydrogenase deficiency in skin fibroblasts or leukocytes (36).

these individuals (125). In the same study, markedly variable day-to-day plasma carnitine concentrations in these four subjects were reported. Mean coefficient of variation for consecutive daily measurements over 27–28 days was 0.35 (range 0.29–0.42) compared to 0.09 (range 0.05–0.11) for six normal subjects. These fluctuations suggested an abnormality in regulation of the muscle/plasma carnitine concentration gradient. To date, factors that regulate the flow of carnitine into and out of muscle have not been clearly defined.

Clinically, systemic carnitine deficiency is a heterogeneous syndrome. For example, age of onset (or recognition) has varied considerably. Some patients present with cardiomyopathy (see discussion below) whereas others do not (123). The response to treatment with supplemental carnitine has been variable (123). These observations suggest that heterogeneity in the etiology of different cases of this syndrome may also exist.

Two cases of clinically diagnosed dietary-dependent carnitine deficiency have been reported (48, 143). One child developed systemic carnitine deficiency after switching from a milk-based formula diet to a soy protein–based formula (143). Classical symptoms were observed: recurrent episodes of hypoglycemia and liver dysfunction, with very low plasma and urine carnitine levels. The child also developed marked dicarboxylic aciduria. After returning to a carnitine-enriched diet (beef and beef broth and milk-based formula) carnitine levels in plasma and urine increased, dicarboxylic aciduria subsided, and clinical evidence of systemic carnitine deficiency was absent. A similar case of diet-induced carnitine deficiency was reported in a 12-year-old child on a strict vegetarian diet (48). Supplementation of the child's diet with carnitine restored plasma carnitine levels to normal, improved muscle strength, and prevented further attacks of metabolic encephalopathy. The dramatic response of these patients to dietary carnitine suggests a possible error in carnitine biosynthesis. To date, no genetic defect in this process has been demonstrated.

## *Deficiency Syndromes Secondary to Other Genetic or Acquired Disorders*

Carnitine deficiency has also been recognized secondary to a variety of genetic defects of intermediary metabolism or other disorders and conditions (for reviews, see 45, 123).

ORGANIC ACIDURIA Of this heterogeneous group of disorders and conditions, the organic acidurias are of particular interest, because they suggest a new physiological role for carnitine in intermediary metabolism. Carnitine deficiency has been recognized in long- (66) and medium-chain acyl-CoA dehydrogenase deficiency (36, 145), isovaleric acidemia, glutaric aciduria, propionic and methylmalonic acidemia (32), and short-chain acyl-CoA dehydrogenase deficiency (157). Chalmers et al (32) have shown that total carnitine excretion in 23 of 35 patients with various organic acidurias was higher than the range of controls (greater than 255 nmol/mg creatinine). For all patients studied except one, urinary acylcarnitine ester concentration was more than twice that of free carnitine (the mean ratio was 1.45 in normal subjects) and for 25 of 35 patients the ratio was greater than 10. Oral supplementation with L-carnitine in three of the patients led to even greater levels of acylcarnitine esters in urine.

The results suggested that carnitine was being utilized as a means of removing excess organic acids, and they support the hypothesis of Bieber et al (13) that carnitine acts as an intramitochondrial buffer to remove excess acyl moieties, allowing regeneration of free CoA to be used to maintain normal metabolic functions of the mitochondrion. Presumably excess acylcarnitine esters are released from cells and preferentially excreted (i.e. they are reabsorbed less efficiently than free carnitine). Alternatively, in some patients plasma acylcarnitine concentration is not abnormally high; therefore, increased urinary acylcarnitine esters may arise from renal carnitine metabolism via secretion or passive diffusion into the urinary tract. In normal individuals carnitine lost as acylcarnitine esters is readily replaced by endogenous carnitine synthesis and from dietary sources. However, loss of extraordinarily large amounts of acylcarnitine esters in genetic disorders characterized by organic aciduria may lead to the observed secondary carnitine deficiency.

RENAL DISEASE Carnitine deficiency has been described in Fanconi syndrome, a condition characterized by excessive excretion of numerous substances that normally are efficiently reabsorbed (11, 13). Mean fractional excretion of free carnitine was 33% and of acylcarnitine esters 26% in 21 subjects with Fanconi syndrome, compared to 3 and 5%, respectively, in normal individuals (11). Total free carnitine excretion in Fanconi syndrome patients correlated with total amino acid excretion ($r = 0.76$). Plasma free carnitine levels in 19 affected children were very low (11.7 ± 4.0 μM; mean ± S.D.) compared to normal values (42.0 ± 9.0 μM). Muscle free and total carnitine levels in two patients were marginally low and biopsies revealed, in one case, a mild increase in lipid droplets, and in the other case, evidence of myopathy. In one patient a five-hour fast resulted in a normal increase in plasma β-hydroxybutyrate, which suggested that hepatic fatty acid oxidation was intact.

Hypercarnitinemia has been demonstrated in uremia (35). However, in 1974 Bohmer et al (18) first demonstrated that hemodialysis therapy for this condition reduced serum carnitine by 25% of the value occurring before dialysis. Later, the same group (17) showed that intermittent hemodialysis caused a dramatic loss of carnitine from skeletal muscle and plasma into the dialysate fluid. A number of studies have confirmed these results and it is now well established that chronic hemodialysis can induce muscle and possibly myocardial carnitine deficiency (15, 16, 108, 132). Usually plasma carnitine levels are restored within 8 hours after dialysis, presumably from increased hepatic synthesis (16, 108). This loss of carnitine has been related to the complications often accompanying intermittent hemodialysis, i.e. hyperlipidemia, cardiomyopathy, and skeletal muscle asthenia and cramps (post-dialysis syndrome). Treatment with oral carnitine has been shown to attenuate the loss of carnitine from plasma and skeletal muscle and improve some of the above symptoms (5, 7, 10, 12, 25, 28, 49, 50, 63, 79, 81, 151, 158).

Several studies have demonstrated a lipid-lowering effect of carnitine treatment in chronically uremic patients supported by maintenance hemodialysis. Administration of intravenous (12) or oral (28, 63, 81) DL-carnitine decreased mean serum triglyceride concentration and increased high-density lipoproteins (HDL). However, in some patients DL-carnitine evoked a myasthenia-like syndrome, with alterations in the electromyogram and decreased muscle action potentials (8). Administration of only the physiologically active L-isomer did not elicit this syndrome and was effective in reducing serum triglyceride and increasing HDL (7).

Three studies did not confirm the lipid-lowering effect of DL-carnitine (4, 33, 50), which suggests that some dialysis patients are not responsive to carnitine. This apparent discrepancy may be attributed to differences in the effective dose of carnitine required to produce a significant lipid-lowering effect. Vacha et al (158) demonstrated a lipid-lowering effect of carnitine (i.v. 20 mg/kg) in hemodialysis patients with hypertriglyceridemia and low HDL-cholesterol values; but in patients with hypertriglyceridemia and normal HDL-cholesterol levels a much higher dose of L-carnitine (60 mg/kg) was required to produce a significant lipid-lowering effect.

Only two studies have investigated the effects of carnitine supplementation on hemodialysis-induced muscle alterations (10, 50). In the study by Fagher et al (50), three patients on regular hemodialysis were supplemented with DL-carnitine (900 mg/day) for four weeks. Carnitine treatment was associated with improved heat production by skeletal muscle. Hepatic function was assessed using an intravenous galactose load test and was normalized by carnitine treatment. In a double-blind cross-over study, Bellinghieri et al (10) treated 14 uremic patients with L-carnitine (2 g/day) for 60 days and found a significant decrease in asthenia and cramps during and after dialysis. These improvements were associated with parallel increases in serum and muscle L-carnitine concentration. Except for one patient, alterations in muscle histology were not corrected with carnitine therapy.

Heart failure is a major cause of death in hemodialysis patients (25). Since myocardial carnitine deficiency has been associated with cardiomyopathy in other patients (123, 161), it is conceivable that the cardiomegaly in hemodialysis patients may be due to loss of carnitine from the heart into the dialysate. The effects of dialysis on myocardial carnitine content have not been investigated extensively. Only one study on the peritoneally dialyzed uremic rat demonstrated a significant reduction of carnitine in the heart (5). Another study in patients showed an inverse correlation between plasma carnitine and cardiomyopathy as assessed by the cardiothoracic ratio (79). Carnitine treatment of dialysis patients has been shown to enhance cardiac performance as evaluated by echocardiography (50) and to reduce arrhythmias significantly (151). However, a more recent study demonstrated that, in 28 randomly selected hemodialysis patients, L-carnitine administration did not improve left ventricular function, as monitored by echocardiography, electrocardiogram, phonocardiogram, and carotid pulse tracing (49).

The effect of peritoneal dialysis on plasma and muscle carnitine content appears to be different from that of intermittent hemodialysis (95, 96). As discussed above, a number of studies have shown that hemodialysis will decrease both plasma and skeletal muscle carnitine levels. In contrast, Moorthy et al (95) found that in patients receiving long-term peritoneal dialysis (either intermittent or continuous ambulatory peritoneal dialysis) normal plasma and muscle carnitine levels were maintained despite significant loss of carnitine into the dialysate. It was suggested that hemodialysis causes a rapid lowering of plasma carnitine, which triggers the release of carnitine from muscle stores, but in patients on peritoneal dialysis a much slower loss of carnitine into the dialysis fluid occurs and plasma and muscle carnitine levels are maintained, primarily by increased hepatic synthesis and/or dietary ingestion of carnitine. These results were recently confirmed in another 27 patients by the same group (96).

However, Bartel et al (5, 6) and Buoncristiani et al (26) reported that, in uremic rats or human subjects subjected to peritoneal dialysis, serum and muscle carnitine content declined sharply. These conflicting findings may be partially related to differences in the volume of dialysis fluid used during peritoneal dialysis and whether the kidneys of the patient were removed, but this information was not provided in the studies cited. Further investigation into the effects of peritoneal dialysis versus intermittent hemodialysis and the efficacy of carnitine therapy for dialysis patients is needed.

## THE ROLE OF CARNITINE IN OTHER ABNORMAL METABOLIC CONDITIONS

### *Myopathic Heart Disease*

In normal heart muscle approximately 60% of total energy metabolism comes from oxidation of fatty acids (103). Carnitine plays an essential role in transporting long-chain fatty acids into mitochondria (22); therefore adequate levels are required for normal fatty acid and energy metabolism in heart muscle.

Carnitine may also be of metabolic importance because of its role in buffering fluctuations in mitochondrial acetyl-CoA levels. Through the enzyme carnitine acetyltransferase, carnitine can provide an alternative metabolic pathway for excess acetyl units generated via β-oxidation or glycolysis.

Carnitine acetyltransferase is found in relatively large amounts in cardiac tissue and facilitates formation of acetylcarnitine from acetyl-CoA and carnitine (13). The acetylcarnitine formed in the mitochondrial matrix can rapidly exchange with free or acylcarnitine across the mitochondrial inner membrane. By this mechanism excess acetyl units produced in the mitochondrial matrix may be stored in the cytosol as acetylcarnitine. Under conditions of increased energy demand, the cytosolic acetylcarnitine can be transferred rapidly back into the mitochondrial matrix, providing an additional and readily available source of acetyl units for the citric acid cycle. This function of acetylcarnitine may be of particular importance to the heart, because a single heart beat consumes more than the intramitochondrial acetyl-CoA content existing at any given instant (97).

The carnitine acetyltransferase reaction may also indirectly regulate the rate of free fatty acid activation to long-chain acyl-CoA by controlling the amount of free coenzyme A available to the cytoplasmic thiokinase enzyme. An increase in cytoplasmic acetylcarnitine will also increase formation of cytoplasmic acetyl-CoA and free carnitine by the action of microsomal carnitine acetyltransferase. Consequently the amount of cytoplasmic free coenzyme A available for thiokinase-catalyzed activation of free fatty acids would be decreased. By equilibrating both the mitochrondrial and cytoplasmic ratios of acetyl-CoA/coenzyme A and acetylcarnitine/carnitine, activation of long-chain fatty acids is coupled to the rate of β-oxidation. In addition, by controlling the acetyl-CoA/coenzyme A ratio, carnitine may be involved in regulation of glucose utilization, since this ratio is an important regulator of pyruvate dehydrogenase activity (76). It has been proposed that carnitine, through other carnitine acyltransferase enzymes, may also be involved in metabolism of branched-chain amino acids and elimination of excess acyl units from the heart (13).

The importance of carnitine in cardiac metabolism and function is emphasized by the growing number of studies demonstrating a close association between systemic and myopathic carnitine deficiency and both hypertrophic and congestive cardiomyopathies (27, 29, 34, 37, 42, 59, 107, 123, 155, 156, 161). In most cases, oral carnitine treatment improved cardiac contractile function and morphology (29, 34, 39, 42, 107, 155, 156). The lack of a beneficial response to carnitine therapy in some patients may be due to a carnitine transport defect in the heart. This possibility is supported by the fact that only a few studies have demonstrated any significant increase in muscle carnitine after replacement therapy with carnitine in myopathic carnitine deficiency (156, 161). Cases of secondary carnitine deficiency induced by genetic defects of intermediary metabolism also have been associated with cardiomyopathy (3, 66, 146).

Myocardial carnitine deficiency is also found in a number of states and diseases such as aging (1), diabetes (93), diphtheria (23), and chronic heart failure (150). The correlation between carnitine deficiency and cardiomyopathy suggests that carnitine therapy may ameliorate alterations in cardiac contractile function associated with these conditions. A study in humans showed that carnitine administration to diphtheritic patients resulted in decreased incidence of heart failure, pacemaker implants, and lethality indices due to myocarditis (113). A few studies in experimental animals have indicated such an effect of carnitine in these diseases. At present no definite conclusion can be drawn concerning the efficacy of carnitine therapy for treatment of these conditions.

Cardiomyopathy may also be associated with elevated levels of carnitine in plasma and heart (156). The relationship between elevated plasma and tissue carnitine and cardiomyopathy is unclear.

### *Ischemic Heart Disease*

Although controversial, carnitine has been suggested as an agent for protecting the ischemic myocardium. The rationale for this is that myocardial ischemia causes a loss of total intracellular carnitine (84, 142) but an increase in intracellular long-chain acylcarnitine and coenzyme A esters (142, 163). It was suggested that carnitine therapy would prevent the loss of carnitine and would decrease the accumulation of lipid intermediates (particularly long-chain acylcarnitine esters), which are believed to be toxic to the heart (2, 141). Studies in humans have shown that carnitine improves exercise tolerance (74) and atrial pacing tolerance in patients with angina pectoris (51, 52, 154). However, studies in experimental animals have produced conflicting results with respect to the protective effect of L-carnitine in ischemia (53, 58, 84, 98, 149). Because of these conflicting findings, the efficacy of carnitine for treatment of ischemic heart disease in man is questionable and requires further study.

### *Hyperlipidemia*

Because of its essential role in fatty acid oxidation, carnitine may be an effective lipid-lowering agent. As discussed above, the effects of carnitine on lipid metabolism during hemodialysis and in newborn infants have been investigated (4, 12, 28, 33, 50, 63, 81, 99, 104, 105, 134, 135, 158, 162). A number of other studies have found a hypolipidemic effect of carnitine in other types of patients as well. Oral administration of carnitine to patients with Type IV hyperlipoproteinemia was shown to cause a pronounced reduction of serum triglycerides and free fatty acids without significantly changing total serum cholesterol (91, 111). Blood glucose levels were increased during carnitine administration (900 mg/day, 8 weeks), which suggests a shift from glucose to fatty acid oxidation in these patients. In Type II hyperlipoproteinemia patients, supplementation with oral carnitine (3 g/day, 40 days) resulted in a marked reduction of serum triglycerides and cholesterol and a normalized lipoprotein electrophoresis pattern (111). Another study revealed that oral carnitine administration (330 mg, 3 times per day for 8 to 250 days) to Type II and IV hyperlipoproteinemia patients significantly reduced plasma cholesterol and triglycerides (112). Similar results were found in hyperlipidemic diabetic patients given oral DL-carnitine (750 mg/day, 4–6 weeks) (9). Administration of L-carnitine (1 g/day, 10–15 weeks) to patients with normal serum triglycerides but low HDL caused a substantial decrease in serum triglycerides and an increase in HDL (130). Since high levels of HDL are associated with reduced risk of arteriosclerotic cardiovascular disease, the effect of carnitine on HDL levels may be of particular importance. However, the mechanism for this increase in HDL is unknown. In contrast, other studies have failed to demonstrate a significant lipid-lowering effect of carnitine in fasted (54), fat-loaded (30), or normal individuals (30), or in patients with jejunoileal bypass (136).

### *Ketosis*

Ketotic states are accompanied by an increase in carnitine content of liver (92) and an increased plasma-acylcarnitine-to-free-carnitine ratio (21, 54, 137). Carnitine stimulates ketogenesis in isolated perfused rat liver (92) and enhances the oxidation of acetoacetate by muscle and kidney mitochondria (72). These findings have led to speculation that carnitine has a regulatory role in both ketone body synthesis and utilization.

The effects of exogenous carnitine on blood ketone body levels vary considerably depending upon the metabolic state of the patient (60, 69, 161). Carnitine supplements were effective in lowering the β-hydroxybutyrate concentration of blood in fasted children (60) and in a patient with muscle carnitine deficiency (161). In contrast, other studies have shown that carnitine treatment stimulates ketosis. A recent study involving muscular dystrophy patients revealed that carnitine administration increased blood β-hydroxybutyrate concentration after an overnight fast (69). This effect was not observed in normal subjects under the same conditions. In some cases continuous carnitine treatment led to lethargy, irritability and caused personality changes that cleared after cessation of therapy (69). Another study reported that the beneficial effect of L-carnitine in a patient with medium-chain acyl-CoA dehydrogenase deficiency, secondary carnitine deficiency, and hypoglycemia was associated with increased ketone body levels (66).

The differential effect of carnitine may be explained partially in a study by Yeh (164). He found that in rats carnitine suppressed hyperketonemia induced by fasting, suckling, and fat feeding, but it did not alter production of $^{14}CO_2$

from [$^{14}$C]β-hydroxybutyrate. These findings provide presumptive evidence that carnitine does not affect ketone body utilization by peripheral tissues and strongly suggest that under some conditions carnitine can inhibit ketogenesis in the liver. This hypothesis is also supported by studies with isolated hepatocytes (164). In these cells high concentrations of carnitine inhibited ketone body production but at low concentrations ketone body production was stimulated. These results suggest that carnitine can be either ketogenic or antiketogenic depending on its concentration and the metabolic state of the subject. Thus, in patients receiving carnitine therapy it is advisable to monitor blood ketone body levels.

## SUMMARY AND CONCLUSIONS

It is apparent from the foregoing discussion that carnitine plays an essential role in human intermediary metabolism. The question of a dietary requirement for carnitine, particularly for the human infant, is of significant theoretical and practical interest. Aberrant carnitine metabolism resulting from abnormal genetic or acquired conditions may have serious consequences for the affected individual. At present many of the treatment modalities for carnitine deficiency are empirical. Further clarification of the mechanisms by which carnitine depletion is manifest in these conditions is essential for designing treatment programs. Moreover, therapeutic use of carnitine in several human diseases not involving carnitine deficiency per se has been indicated. Before such treatment becomes generally accepted, we must determine precisely the role of this amino acid in the biochemical and physiological events that participate in the pathogenesis of each disease.

### *Literature Cited*


1. Abu-Erreish, G. M., Neely, J. R., Whitmer, J. T., Whitman, V., Sanadi, D. R. 1977. Fatty acid oxidation by isolated perfused working hearts of aged rats. *Am. J. Physiol.* 232:E258–62
2. Adams, R. J., Cohen, D. W., Gupte, S., Johnson, J. D., Wallick, E. T., et al. 1979. In vitro effects of palmitylcarnitine on cardiac plasma membrane $Na^+$, $K^+$-ATPase, and sarcoplasmic reticulum $Ca^{2+}$ transport. *J. Biol. Chem.* 25: 12404–10
3. Allen, R. J., Hansch, D. B., Wu, H. L. C. 1982. Hypocarnitinaemia in disorders of organic acid metabolism. *Lancet* 2:500–1
4. Aubia, J., Masramon, J., Lloveras, J., Llorach, M., Andolz, P. 1980. Carnitine in haemodialysis patients. *Lancet* 2: 1028–29
5. Bartel, L. L., Hussey, J. L., Elson, C., Shrago, E. 1981. Depletion of heart and skeletal muscle carnitine in the normal rat by peritoneal dialysis. *Nutr. Res.* 1:261–66
6. Bartel, L. L., Hussey, J. L., Shrago, E. 1981. Perturbation of serum carnitine levels in human adults by chronic renal disease and dialysis therapy. *Am. J. Clin. Nutr.* 34:1314–20
7. Bazzato, G., Coli, U., Landini, S., Mezzina, C., Ciman, M. 1981. Myasthenia-like syndrome after D,L- but not L-carnitine. *Lancet* 1:1209
8. Bazzato, G., Mezzina, C., Ciman, M., Guarnieri, G. 1979. Myasthenia-like syndrome associated with carnitine in patients on long-term haemodialysis. *Lancet* 1:1041–42
9. Bekaert, J., Deltour, G. 1960. Effet de

la carnitine sur l'hyperlipidémie diabétique. *Clin. Chim. Acta* 5:177–80
10. Bellinghieri, L. G., Savica, V., Mallamace, A., DiStefano, C., Consolo, F., et al. 1983. Correlation between increased serum and tissue L-carnitine levels and improved muscle symptoms in hemodialyzed patients. *Am. J. Clin. Nutr.* 38:523–31
11. Bernardini, I., Rizzo, W. B., Dalakas, M., Bernar, J., Gahl, W. A. 1985. Plasma and muscle free carnitine deficiency due to renal Fanconi syndrome. *J. Clin. Invest.* 75:1124–30
12. Bertoli, M., Battistella, P. A., Vergani, L., Naso, A., Gasparotto, M. L., et al. 1981. Carnitine deficiency induced during hemodialysis and hyperlipidemia: effect of replacement therapy. *Am. J. Clin. Nutr.* 34:1496–1500
13. Bieber, L. L., Emaus, R., Valkner, K., Farrell, S. 1982. Possible functions of short-chain and medium-chain carnitine acyltransferases. *Fed. Proc.* 41:2858–62
14. Bieber, L. L., Kerner, J. 1985. Isolation and identification of α-methyloctenylcarnitines from human urine. *Fed. Proc.* 44(5):1415 (Abstr.)
15. Bizzi, A., Cini, M., Garattini, S., Mingardi, G., Licini, L., et al. 1983. L-Carnitine addition to haemodialysis fluid prevents plasma-carnitine deficiency during dialysis. *Lancet* 1:882
16. Bizzi, A., Mingardi, G., Codegoni, A. M., Mecca, G., Garattini, S. 1978. Accelerated recovery of post-dialysis plasma carnitine fall by oral carnitine. *Biomedicine* 29:183–84
17. Bohmer, T., Bergrem, H., Eiklid, K. 1978. Carnitine deficiency induced during intermittent haemodialysis for renal failure. *Lancet* 1:126–28
18. Bohmer, T., Rydning, A., Solberg, H. E. 1974. Carnitine levels in human serum in health and disease. *Clin. Chim. Acta* 57:55–61
19. Borum, P. R. 1983. Carnitine. *Ann. Rev. Nutr.* 3:233–59
20. Borum, P. R., York, C. M., Broquist, H. P. 1979. Carnitine content of liquid formulas and special diets. *Am. J. Clin. Nutr.* 32:2272–76
21. Brass, E. P., Hoppel, C. L. 1978. Carnitine metabolism in the fasting rat. *J. Biol. Chem.* 253:2688–93
22. Bremer, J. 1983. Carnitine—metabolism and functions. *Physiol. Rev.* 63:1420–80
23. Bressler, R., Wittels, B. 1965. The effect of diphtheria toxin on carnitine metabolism in the heart. *Biochim. Biophys. Acta* 104:39–45
24. Brooks, D. E., McIntosh, J. E. A. 1975. Turnover of carnitine by rat tissues. *Biochem. J.* 148:439–45
25. Brunner, F. P., Brynger, H., Chantler, C., Donckerwolcke, R. A., Hathaway, R. A., et al. 1978. Combined report on regular dialysis and transplantation in Europe IX. *Proc. Eur. Dial. Transplant. Assoc.* 16:3–82
26. Buoncristiani, U., DiPaolo, I. V., Carobi, C. 1981. Carnitine depletion with CAPD. In *Advances in Peritoneal Dialysis*, ed. G. M. Gahl, M. Kessel, K. D. Nolph, pp. 441–45. Amsterdam: Excerpta Medica. 508 pp.
27. Carroll, J. E., Brooke, M. H., DeVivo, D. C., Shumate, J. B., Kratz, R., et al. 1980. Carnitine "deficiency": lack of response to carnitine therapy. *Neurology* 30:618–26
28. Casciani, C. U., Caruso, U., Cravotto, E., Corsi, M., Pola, P., et al. 1980. Effect of L-carnitine on lipid pattern in haemodialysis. *Lancet* 2:1309–10
29. Cederbaum, S. D., Auestad, N., Bernar, J. 1984. Four-year treatment of systemic carnitine deficiency. *N. Engl. J. Med.* 310:1395–96
30. Cederblad, G. 1984. Fat metabolism following an intravenous bolus dose of a fat emulsion and carnitine. *Clin. Physiol.* 4:159–68
31. Cederblad, G., Lindstedt, S. 1976. Metabolism of labeled carnitine in the rat. *Arch. Biochem. Biophys.* 175:173–80
32. Chalmers, R. A., Roe, C. R., Stacey, T. E., Hoppel, C. L. 1984. Urinary excretion of L-carnitine and acylcarnitines by patients with disorders of organic acid metabolism: evidence for secondary insufficiency of L-carnitine. *Pediatr. Res.* 18:1325–28
33. Chan, M. K., Persaud, J. W., Varghese, Z., Baillod, R. A., Moorhead, J. F. 1982. Response patterns to DL-carnitine in patients on haemodialysis. *Nephron* 30:240–43
34. Chapoy, P. R., Angelini, C., Brown, W. J., Stiff, J. E., Shug, A. L., et al. 1980. Systemic carnitine deficiency—a treatable inherited lipid-storage disease presenting as Reye's syndrome. *N. Engl. J. Med.* 303:1389–94
35. Chen, S.-H., Lincoln, S. D. 1977. Increased serum carnitine concentration in renal insufficiency. *Clin. Chem.* 23:278–80
36. Coates, P. M., Hale, D. E., Stanley, C. A., Corkey, B. E., Cortner, J. A. 1985. Genetic deficiency of medium-chain acyl coenzyme A dehydrogenase: studies in cultured skin fibroblasts and peripheral

mononuclear leukocytes. *Pediatr. Res.* 19:671–76

37. Cruse, R. P., DiMauro, S., Towfighi, J., Trevisan, C. 1984. Familial systemic carnitine deficiency. *Arch. Neurol.* 41: 301–5
38. Curran, J. S., Williams, P. R., Kanarek, K. S., Novak, M., Monkus, E. F. 1983. An evaluation of orally supplemented L-carnitine in premature infants receiving Intralipid® 20%. *Acta Chir. Scand. Suppl.* 517:157–64
39. DiDonato, S., Pelucchetti, D., Rimoldi, M., Mora, M., Garavaglia, B., et al. 1984. Systemic carnitine deficiency: clinical, biochemical, and morphological cure with L-carnitine. *Neurology* 34:157–62
40. DiDonato, S., Rimoldi, M., Garavaglia, B., Uziel, G. 1984. Propionylcarnitine excretion in propionic and methylmalonic acidurias: a cause of carnitine deficiency. *Clin. Chim. Acta* 139:13–21
41. Dunn, W. A., Englard, S. 1981. Carnitine biosynthesis by the perfused rat liver from exogenous protein-bound trimethyllysine. Metabolism of methylated lysine derivatives arising from the degradation of 6-*N*-[*methyl*-$^3$H]lysine-labeled glycoproteins. *J. Biol. Chem.* 256:12437–44
42. Duran, M., de Klerk, J. B. C., Wadman, S. K., Scholte, H. R., Beekman, R. P., et al. 1984. Systemic carnitine deficiency: benefit of oral carnitine supplements vs. persisting biochemical abnormalities. *Eur. J. Pediatr.* 142:224–28
43. Engel, A. G., Angelini, C. 1973. Carnitine deficiency of human skeletal muscle with associated lipid storage myopathy: A new syndrome. *Science* 179:899–902
44. Engel, A. G., Rebouche, C. J. 1982. Pathogenetic mechanisms in human carnitine deficiency syndromes. In *Disorders of the Motor Unit,* ed. D. L. Schotland, pp. 643–55. New York: Wiley. 954 pp.
45. Engel, A. G., Rebouche, C. J. 1984. Carnitine metabolism and inborn errors. *J. Inherited Metab. Dis.* 7 (Suppl. 1):38–43
46. Engel, A. G., Rebouche, C. J., Wilson, D. M., Glasgow, A. M., Romshe, C. A., et al. 1981. Primary systemic carnitine deficiency. II. Renal handling of carnitine. *Neurology* 31:819–25
47. Englard, S., Seifter, S. 1986. The biochemical functions of ascorbic acid. *Ann. Rev. Nutr.* 6:365–406
48. Etzioni, A., Levy, J., Nitzan, M., Erde, P., Benderly, A. 1984. Systemic carnitine deficiency exacerbated by a strict vegetarian diet. *Arch. Dis. Child.* 59: 177–79
49. Fagher, B., Cederblad, G., Monti, M., Olsson, L., Rasmussen, B., et al. 1985. Carnitine and left ventricular function in haemodialysis patients. *Scand. J. Lab. Invest.* 45:193–98
50. Fagher, B., Thysell, H., Nilsson-Ehle, P., Monti, M., Olsson, L., et al. 1982. The effect of D,L-carnitine supplementation on muscle metabolism, neuropathy, cardiac and hepatic function in hemodialysis patients. *Acta Med. Scand.* 212:115–20
51. Ferrari, R., Cucchini, F., DiLisa, F., Raddino, R., Bolognesi, R., et al. 1984. The effect of L-carnitine (carnitene) on myocardial metabolism of patients with coronary artery disease. *Clin. Trials J.* 21:40–58
52. Ferrari, R., Cucchini, F., Visioli, O. 1984. The metabolical effects of L-carnitine in angina pectoris. *Int. J. Cardiol.* 5:213–16
53. Folts, J. D., Shug, A. L., Koke, J. R., Bittar, N. 1978. Protection of the ischemic dog myocardium with carnitine. *Am. J. Cardiol.* 41:1209–14
54. Frohlich, J., Seccombe, D. W., Hahn, P., Dodek, P., Hynie, I. 1978. Effect of fasting on free and esterified carnitine levels in human serum and urine: correlation with serum levels of free fatty acids and β-hydroxybutyrate. *Metabolism* 27:555–61
55. Genuth, S. M., Hoppel, C. L. 1979. Plasma and urine carnitine in diabetic ketosis. *Diabetes* 28:1083–87
56. Genuth, S. M., Hoppel, C. L. 1981. Acute hormonal effects on carnitine metabolism in thin and obese subjects: responses to somatostatin, glucagon, and insulin. *Metabolism* 30:393–401
57. Gilbert, E. F. 1985. Carnitine deficiency. *Pathology* 17:161–69
58. Gilmour, R. F. Jr., Williams, E. S., Farmer, B. B., Zipes, D. P. 1981. Effects of carnitine and atractyloside on canine cardiac electrical activity. *Am. J. Physiol.* 241:H505–12
59. Glasgow, A. M., Engel, A. G., Bier, D. M., Perry, L. W., Dickie, M., et al. 1983. Hypoglycemia, hepatic dysfunction, muscle weakness, cardiomyopathy, free carnitine deficiency and long-chain acylcarnitine excess responsive to medium-chain triglyceride diet. *Pediatr. Res.* 17:319–26
60. Gravina, E., Gravina-Sanvitale, G. 1969. Effect of carnitine on blood ace-

toacetate in fasting children. *Clin. Chim. Acta* 23:376–77
61. Gross, C. J., Henderson, L. M. 1984. Absorption of D- and L-carnitine by the intestine and kidney tubule in the rat. *Biochim. Biophys. Acta* 772:209–19
62. Gudjonsson, H., Li, B U. K., Shug, A. L., Olsen, W. A. 1985. In vivo studies of intestinal carnitine absorption in rats. *Gastroenterology* 88:1880–87
63. Gusmano, R., Oleggini, R., Perfumo, F. 1981. Plasma carnitine concentrations and dyslipidemia in children on maintenance hemodialysis. *J. Pediatr.* 99:429–32
64. Hahn, P. 1981. The development of carnitine synthesis from γ-butyrobetaine in the rat. *Life Sci.* 29:1057–60
65. Hahn, P., Allardyce, D. B., Frolich, J. 1982. Plasma carnitine levels during total parenteral nutrition of adult patients. *Am. J. Clin. Nutr.* 36:569–72
66. Hale, D. E., Batshaw, M. L., Coates, P. M., Frerman, F. E., Goodman, S. I., et al. 1985. Long-chain acyl coenzyme A dehydrogenase deficiency: an inherited cause of nonketotic hypoglycemia. *Pediatr. Res.* 19:666–71
67. Hamilton, J. W., Li, B U. K., Shug, A., Olsen, W. A. 1983. Studies of L-carnitine absorption in man. *Gastroenterology* 84(5, Pt. 2):1180 (Abstr.)
68. Henderson, L. M., Nelson, P. J., Henderson, L. 1982. Mammalian enzymes of trimethyllysine conversion to trimethylaminobutyrate. *Fed. Proc.* 41:2843–47
69. Hoganson, G. E., Chun, R., Berlow, D., Paulson, D. J., Traxler, J., et al. 1983. Ketogenic response to L-carnitine administration in Leigh's disease. *Am. J. Hum. Genet.* 35:135
70. Hoppel, C. L., Genuth, S. M. 1980. Carnitine metabolism in normal-weight and obese human subjects during fasting. *Am. J. Physiol.* 238:E409–15
71. Horne, D. W., Tanphaichitr, V., Broquist, H. P. 1971. Role of lysine in carnitine biosynthesis in *Neurospora crassa*. *J. Biol. Chem.* 246:4373–75
72. Hulsmann, W. C., Siliprandi, D., Ciman, M., Siliprandi, N. 1964. Effect of carnitine on the oxidation of α-oxoglutarate to succinate in the presence of acetoacetate or pyruvate. *Biochim. Biophys. Acta* 93:166–68
73. Kakimoto, Y., Akazawa, S. 1970. Isolation and identification of $N^G$,$N^G$- and $N^G$,$N'^G$-dimethylarginine, $N^\epsilon$-mono-, di-, and trimethyllysine, and glucosylgalactosyl- and galactosyl-δ-hydroxylysine from human urine. *J. Biol. Chem.* 245:5751–58
74. Kamikawa, T., Suzuki, Y., Kobayashi, A., Hayashi, H., Masumura, Y., et al. 1984. Effects of L-carnitine on exercise tolerance in patients with stable angina pectoris. *Jpn. Heart J.* 25:587–97
75. Karpati, G., Carpenter, S., Engel, A. G., Watters, G., Allen, J., et al. 1975. The syndrome of systemic carnitine deficiency. Clinical, morphological, biochemical and pathophysiologic features. *Neurology* 25:16–24
76. Kerbey, A. L., Randle, P. J., Cooper, R. H., Whitehouse, S., Pask, H. T., et al. 1976. Regulation of pyruvate dehydrogenase in rat heart. *Biochem. J.* 154:327–48
77. Khan-Siddiqui, L., Bamji, M. S. 1980. Plasma carnitine levels in adult males in India: effects of high cereal, low fat diet, fat supplementation, and nutritional status. *Am. J. Clin. Nutr.* 33:1259–63
78. Khan-Siddiqui, L., Bamji, M. S. 1983. Lysine-carnitine conversion in normal and undernourished adult men—suggestion of a nonpeptidyl pathway. *Am. J. Clin. Nutr.* 37:93–98
79. Kudoh, Y., Shoji, T., Oimatsu, H., Yoshida, S., Kikuchi, K., et al. 1983. The role of L-carnitine in the pathogenesis of cardiomegaly in patients with chronic hemodialysis. *Jpn. Circ. J.* 47:1391–97
80. LaBadie, J., Dunn, W. A., Aronson, N. N. Jr. 1976. Hepatic synthesis of carnitine from protein-bound trimethyl-lysine. Lysosomal digestion of methyl-lysine-labelled asialo-fetuin. *Biochem. J.* 160: 85–95
81. Lacour, B., Chanard, J., Haguet, M., Basile, C., Assan, R., et al. 1980. Carnitine improves lipid anomalies in haemodialysis patients. *Lancet* 2:763–65
82. Lange, H. W., Löwer, R., Hempel, S. 1973. Quantitative determination of $N^\epsilon$-methylated lysines in human plasma and urine. *Hoppe-Seyler's Z. Physiol. Chem.* 354:117–20
83. Lennon, D. L. F., Stratman, F. W., Shrago, E., Nagle, F. J., Madden, M., et al. 1983. Effects of acute moderate-intensity exercise on carnitine metabolism in men and women. *J. Appl. Physiol. Respirat. Environ. Exercise Physiol.* 55:489–95
84. Liedtke, A. J., Nellis, S. H., Whitesell, L. F. 1981. Effects of carnitine isomers on fatty acid metabolism in ischemic swine hearts. *Circ. Res.* 48:859–66
85. Lindstedt, G., Lindstedt, S., Nordin, I. 1982. γ-Butyrobetaine hydroxylase in human kidney. *Scand. J. Clin. Lab. Invest.* 42:477–85
86. Lindstedt, S., Nordin, I. 1984. Multiple

forms of γ-butyrobetaine hydroxylase (EC 1.14.11.1). *Biochem. J.* 223:119–27

87. Long, C. S., Haller, R. G., Foster, D. W., McGarry, J. D. 1982. Kinetics of carnitine dependent fatty acid oxidation: implications for human carnitine deficiency. *Neurology* 32:663–66
88. Lou, M. F., Siena, M. 1981. Quantitation of methylated basic amino acids in biological fluid. *Biochem. Med.* 25:309–14
89. Maebashi, M., Kawamura, N., Sato, M., Imamura, A., Yoshinaga, K., et al. 1977. Urinary excretion of carnitine in patients with hyperthyroidism and hypothyroidism: augmentation by thyroid hormone. *Metabolism* 26:351–56
90. Maebashi, M., Kawamura, N., Sato, M., Imamura, A., Yoshinaga, K., et al. 1977. Urinary excretion of carnitine and serum concentrations of carnitine and lipids in patients with hypofunctional endocrine diseases: involvement of adrenocorticoid and thyroid hormones in ACTH-induced augmentation of carnitine and lipids metabolism. *Metabolism* 26:357–61
91. Maebashi, M., Sato, M., Kawamura, N., Imamura, A., Yoshinaga, K. 1978. Lipid-lowering effect of carnitine in patients with type-IV hyperlipoproteinaemia. *Lancet* 2:805–7
92. McGarry, J. D., Robles-Valdes, C., Foster, D. W. 1975. Role of carnitine in hepatic ketogenesis. *Proc. Natl. Acad. Sci. USA* 72:4385–88
93. Mehlman, M. A., Kader, M. M. A., Therriault, D. G. 1969. Metabolism, turnover time, half-life, body pool of carnitine-$^{14}$C in normal, alloxan diabetic and insulin-treated rats. *Life Sci.* 8(Pt. II): 465–72
94. Millington, D. S., Bohan, T. P., Roe, C. R., Yergey, A. L., Liberato, D. J. 1985. Valproylcarnitine: a novel drug metabolite identified by fast atom bombardment and thermospray liquid chromatography-mass spectrometry. *Clin. Chim. Acta* 145:69–76
95. Moorthy, A. V., Rosenblum, M., Rajaram, R., Shug, A. 1983. A comparison of plasma and muscle carnitine in patients on peritoneal or hemodialysis for chronic renal failure. *Am. J. Nephrol.* 146:100–7
96. Moorthy, A. V., Shug, A. L. 1985. Plasma carnitine levels do not fall in patients on long-term CAPD. *Peritoneal Dialysis Bull.* 5:175–79
97. Neely, J. R., Denton, R. M., England, P. J., Randle, P. J. 1972. The effects of increased heart work on the tricarboxylate cycle and its interactions with glycolysis in the perfused rat heart. *Biochem. J.* 128:147–59
98. Neely, J. R., Garber, D., McDonough, K., Idell-Wenger, J. 1979. Relationship between ventricular function and intermediates of fatty acid metabolism during myocardial ischemia: effects of carnitine. In *Ischemic Myocardium and Antianginal Drugs,* ed. M. M. Winbury, Y. Abiko, pp. 225–34. New York: Raven
99. Novak, M., Monkus, E. F., Buch, M., Lesmes, H., Silverio, J. 1983. The effect of a L-carnitine-supplemented soybean formula on the plasma lipids of infants. *Acta Chir. Scand. Suppl.* 517:149–55
100. Novak, M., Monkus, E. F., Chung, D., Buch, M. 1981. Carnitine in the perinatal metabolism of lipids. I. Relationship between maternal and fetal plasma levels of carnitine and acylcarnitines. *Pediatrics* 67:95–100
101. Novak, M., Penn-Walker, D., Hahn, P., Monkus, E. F. 1975. Effect of carnitine on lipolysis in subcutaneous adipose tissue of newborns. *Biol. Neonate* 25:85–94
102. Novak, M., Wieser, P. B., Buch, M., Hahn, P. 1979. Acetylcarnitine and free carnitine in body fluids before and after birth. *Pediatr. Res.* 13:10–15
103. Opie, L. H. 1968. Metabolism of the heart in health and disease. Part 1. *Am. Heart J.* 76:685–98
104. Orzali, A., Donzelli, F., Enzi, G., Rubaltelli, F. F. 1983. Effect of carnitine on lipid metabolism in the newborn. I. Carnitine supplementation during total parenteral nutrition in the first 48 hours of life. *Biol. Neonate* 43:186–90
105. Orzali, A., Maetzke, G., Donzelli, F., Rubaltelli, F. F. 1984. Effect of carnitine on lipid metabolism in the neonate. II. Carnitine addition to lipid infusion during prolonged total parenteral nutrition. *J. Pediatr.* 104:436–40
106. Paik, W. K., Kim, S. 1980. *Protein Methylation,* pp. 8–25. New York: Wiley. 282 pp.
107. Parker, D., Root, A. W., Schimmel, S., Andriola, M., DiMauro, S. 1982. Encephalopathy and fatal myopathy in two siblings. *Am. J. Dis. Child.* 136:598–601
108. Penn, D., Schmidt-Sommerfeld, E. 1983. Carnitine and carnitine esters in plasma and adipose tissue of chronic uremic patients undergoing hemodialysis. *Metabolism* 32:806–9
109. Penn, D., Schmidt-Sommerfeld, E., Pascu, F. 1981. Decreased tissue carnitine concentrations in newborn infants receiving total parenteral nutrition. *J. Pediatr.* 98:976–78
110. Penn, D., Schmidt-Sommerfeld, E., Wolf, H. 1980. Carnitine deficiency in

premature infants receiving total parenteral nutrition. *Early Hum. Dev.* 4:23–34
111. Pola, P., Savi, L., Grilli, M., Flore, R., Serricchio, M. 1980. Carnitine in the therapy of dyslipidemic patients. *Curr. Ther. Res.* 27:208–16
112. Pola, P., Tondi, P., Dal Lago, A., Serricchio, M., Flore, R. 1983. Statistical evaluation of long-term L-carnitine therapy in hyperlipoprotein-aemias. *Drugs Exp. Clin. Res.* 9:925–34
113. Ramos, A. C. M. F., Elias, P. R. P., Barrucand, L., da Silva, J. A. F. 1984. The protective effect of carnitine in human diphtheric myocarditis. *Pediatr. Res.* 18:815–19
114. Rebouche, C. J. 1977. Carnitine movement across muscle cell membranes. Studies in isolated rat muscle. *Biochim. Biophys. Acta* 471:145–55
115. Rebouche, C. J. 1980. Comparative aspects of carnitine biosynthesis in microorganisms and mammals with attention to carnitine biosynthesis in man. In *Carnitine Biosynthesis, Metabolism, and Functions,* ed. R. A. Frenkel, J. D. McGarry, pp. 57–72. New York: Academic. 356 pp.
116. Rebouche, C. J. 1982. Sites and regulation of carnitine biosynthesis in mammals. *Fed. Proc.* 41:2848–52
117. Rebouche, C. J. 1983. Effect of dietary carnitine isomers and γ-butyrobetaine on L-carnitine biosynthesis and metabolism in the rat. *J. Nutr.* 113:1906–13
118. Rebouche, C. J., Engel, A. G. 1980. In vitro analysis of hepatic carnitine biosynthesis in human systemic carnitine deficiency. *Clin. Chim. Acta* 106:295–300
119. Rebouche, C. J., Engel, A. G. 1980. Significance of renal γ-butyrobetaine hydroxylase for carnitine biosynthesis in man. *J. Biol. Chem.* 255:8700–5
120. Rebouche, C. J., Engel, A. G. 1980. Tissue distribution of carnitine biosynthetic enzymes in man. *Biochim. Biophys. Acta* 630:22–29
121. Rebouche, C. J., Engel, A. G. 1981. Primary systemic carnitine deficiency. I. Carnitine biosynthesis. *Neurology* 31: 813–18
122. Rebouche, C. J., Engel, A. G. 1982. Carnitine transport in cultured muscle cells and skin fibroblasts from patients with systemic carnitine deficiency. *In Vitro* 18:495–500
123. Rebouche, C. J., Engel, A. G. 1983. Carnitine metabolism and deficiency syndromes. *Mayo Clin. Proc.* 58:533–40
124. Rebouche, C. J., Engel, A. G. 1983. Kinetic compartmental analysis of carnitine metabolism in the dog. *Arch. Biochem. Biophys.* 220:60–70
125. Rebouche, C. J., Engel, A. G. 1984. Kinetic compartmental analysis of carnitine metabolism in the human carnitine deficiency syndromes. Evidence for alterations in tissue carnitine transport. *J. Clin. Invest.* 73:857–67
126. Rebouche, C. J., Engel, A. G. 1984. Carnitine biosynthesis and metabolism in the primary carnitine deficiency syndromes. In *Neuromuscular Diseases,* ed. G. Serratrice, D. Cros, C. Desnuelle, J.-L. Gastaut, J.-F. Pellisier, et al., pp. 95–99. New York: Raven. 602 pp.
127. Rebouche, C. J., Lehman, L. J. 1985. Availability of dietary ε-*N*-trimethyllysine for carnitine biosynthesis in the growing rat. *Fed. Proc.* 44(3):763 (Abstr.)
128. Rebouche, C. J., Mack, D. L. 1984. Sodium gradient–stimulated transport of L-carnitine into renal brush border membrane vesicles: Kinetics, specificity, and regulation by dietary carnitine. *Arch. Biochem. Biophys.* 235:393–402
129. Rebouche, C. J., Mack, D. L., Edmonson, P. F. 1984. L-Carnitine dissimilation in the gastrointestinal tract of the rat. *Biochemistry* 23:6422–26
130. Rossi, C. S., Siliprandi, N. 1982. Effect of carnitine on serum HDL-cholesterol: report of two cases. *Johns Hopkins Med. J.* 150:51–54
131. Sandor, A., Pecsuvac, K., Kerner, J., Alkonyi, I. 1982. On carnitine content of the human breast milk. *Pediatr. Res.* 16:89–91
132. Savica, V., Bellinghieri, G., DiStefano, C., Corvaja, E., Consolo, F., et al. 1983. Plasma and muscle carnitine levels in haemodialysis patients with morphological-ultrastructural examination of muscle samples. *Nephron* 35:232–36
133. Schiff, D., Chan, G., Seccombe, D., Hahn, P. 1979. Plasma carnitine levels during intravenous feeding of the neonate. *J. Pediatr.* 95:1043–46
134. Schmidt-Sommerfeld, E., Penn, D., Wolf, H. 1982. Carnitine blood concentration and fat utilization in parenterally alimented premature newborn infants. *J. Pediatr.* 100:260–64
135. Schmidt-Sommerfeld, E., Penn, D., Wolf, H. 1983. Carnitine deficiency in premature infants receiving total parenteral nutrition: effect of L-carnitine supplementation. *J. Pediatr.* 102:931–35
136. Seccombe, D., Burget, D., Frolich, J., Hahn, P., Cleator, I., et al. 1984. Oral L-carnitine administration after jejunoileal by-pass surgery. *Int. J. Obesity* 8:427–33

137. Seccombe, D. W., Hahn, P., Novak, M. 1978. The effect of diet and development on blood levels of free and esterified carnitine in the rat. *Biochim. Biophys. Acta* 528:483–89
138. Shenai, J. P., Borum, P. R. 1984. Tissue carnitine reserves of newborn infants. *Pediatr. Res.* 18:679–81
139. Shenai, J. P., Borum, P. R., Mohan, P., Donlevy, S. C. 1983. Carnitine status at birth of newborn infants of varying gestation. *Pediatr. Res.* 17:579–82
140. Shennan, A. T., Bryan, M. H., Angel, A. 1977. The effect of gestational age on Intralipid tolerance in newborn infants. *J. Pediatr.* 91:134–37
141. Shug, A., Lerner, E., Elson, C., Shrago, E. 1971. The inhibition of adenine nucleotide translocase activity by oleoyl CoA and its reversal in rat liver mitochondria. *Biochem. Biophys. Res. Commun.* 43:557–63
142. Shug, A. L., Thomsen, J. H., Folts, J. D., Bittar, N., Klein, M. I., et al. 1978. Changes in tissue levels of carnitine and other metabolites during myocardial ischemia and anoxia. *Arch. Biochem. Biophys.* 187:25–33
143. Slonim, A. E., Borum, P. R., Tanaka, K., Stanley, C. A., Kasselberg, A. G., et al. 1981. Dietary-dependent carnitine deficiency as a cause of nonketotic hypoglycemia in an infant. *J. Pediatr.* 99:551–56
144. Spagnoli, L. G., Corsi, M., Villaschi, S., Palmieri, G., Maccari, F. 1982. Myocardial carnitine deficiency in acute myocardial infarction. *Lancet* 1:1419–20
145. Stanley, C. A., Hale, D. E., Coates, P. M., Hall, C. L., Corkey, B. E., et al. 1983. Medium-chain acyl-CoA dehydrogenase deficiency in children with non-ketotic hypoglycemia and low carnitine levels. *Pediatr. Res.* 17:877–84
146. Stanley, C. A., Hale, D. E., Whiteman, E. H., Coates, P. M., Yudkoff, M., et al. 1983. Systemic carnitine (carn) deficiency in isovaleric acidemia (IVA). *Pediatr. Res.* 17(4):296A (Abstr.)
147. Stumpf, D. A., Parker, W. D., Angelini, C. 1985. Carnitine deficiency, organic acidemias, and Reye's syndrome. *Neurology* 35:1041–45
148. Sugiyama, N., Morishita, H., Nagaya, S., Nakajima, T., Kawase, A., et al. 1984. Biochemical evidence of carnitine effect on propionate elimination. *J. Inherited Metab. Dis.* 7:137–38
149. Suzuki, Y., Kamikawa, T., Kobayashi, A., Masumura, Y., Yamazaki, N. 1981. Effects of L-carnitine on tissue levels of acyl carnitine, acyl coenzyme A and high energy phosphate in ischemic dog hearts. *Jpn. Circ. J.* 45:687–94
150. Suzuki, Y., Masumura, Y., Kobayashi, A., Yamazaki, N., Harada, Y., et al. 1982. Myocardial carnitine deficiency in chronic heart failure. *Lancet* 1:116
151. Suzuki, Y., Narita, M., Yamazaki, N. 1982. Effects of L-carnitine on arrhythmias during hemodialysis. *Jpn. Heart J.* 23:349–59
152. Tanphaichitr, V., Horne, D. W., Broquist, H. P. 1971. Lysine, a precursor of carnitine in the rat. *J. Biol. Chem.* 246:6364–66
153. Tanphaichitr, V., Lerdvuthisopon, N., Dhanamitta, S., Broquist, H. P. 1980. Carnitine status in Thai adults. *Am. J. Clin. Nutr.* 33:876–80
154. Thomsen, J. H., Shug, A. L., Yap, V. U., Patel, A. K., Karras, T. J., et al. 1979. Improved pacing tolerance of the ischemic human myocardium after administration of carnitine. *Am. J. Cardiol.* 43:300–6
155. Tripp, M. E., Katcher, M. L., Peters, H. A., Gilbert, E. F., Arya, S., et al. 1981. Systemic carnitine deficiency presenting as familial endocardial fibroelastosis. *N. Engl. J. Med.* 305:385–90
156. Tripp, M. E., Shug, A. L. 1984. Plasma carnitine concentrations in cardiomyopathy patients. *Biochem. Med.* 32:199–206
157. Turnbull, D. M., Bartlett, K., Stevens, D. L., Alberti, K. G. M. M., Gibson, G. J., et al. 1984. Short-chain acyl-CoA dehydrogenase deficiency associated with a lipid storage myopathy and secondary carnitine deficiency. *N. Engl. J. Med.* 311:1232–36
158. Vacha, G. M., Giorcelli, G., Siliprandi, N., Corsi, M. 1983. Favorable effects of L-carnitine treatment on hypertriglyceridemia in hemodialysis patients: decisive role on low levels of high-density lipoprotein-cholesterol. *Am. J. Clin. Nutr.* 38:532–40
159. Vary, T. C., Neely, J. R. 1982. Characterization of carnitine transport in isolated perfused adult rat hearts. *Am. J. Physiol.* 242:H505–92
160. Vickers, S., Duncan, C. A. H., White, S. D., Ramjit, H. G., Smith, J. L., et al. 1985. Carnitine and glucuronic acid conjugates of pivalic acid. *Xenobiotica* 15:453–58
161. Waber, L. J., Valle, D., Neill, C., DiMauro, S., Shug, A. 1982. Carnitine deficiency presenting as familial cardiomyopathy: A treatable defect in carnitine transport. *J. Pediatr.* 101:700–5
162. Warshaw, J. B., Curry, E. 1980. Comparison of serum carnitine and ketone

body concentrations in breast- and in formula-fed newborn infants. *J. Pediatr.* 97:122–25

163. Whitmer, J.-T., Idell-Wenger, J. A., Rovetto, M. J., Neely, J. R. 1978. Control of fatty acid metabolism in ischemic and hypoxic hearts. *J. Biol. Chem.* 253: 4305–9
164. Yeh, Y.-Y. 1981. Antiketonemic and antiketogenic actions of carnitine in vivo and in vitro in rats. *J. Nutr.* 111:831–40
165. Yeh, Y.-Y., Cooke, R. J., Zee, P. 1983. Plasma levels of free fatty acid, ketone bodies and carnitine during infusion of lipid emulsions in premature infants. *Pediat. Res.* 17(4, Pt. 2):343A (Abstr.)
166. Zierler, K. L. 1976. Fatty acids as substrates for heart and skeletal muscle. *Circ. Res.* 38:459–63

*Ann. Rev. Nutr. 1986. 6:67–94*


# MUTAGENS AND CARCINOGENS IN FOODS

*Chie Furihata and Taijiro Matsushima*

Department of Molecular Oncology, Institute of Medical Science, University of Tokyo, Tokyo 108, Japan

CONTENTS

INTRODUCTION ..... 67
HETEROCYCLIC AMINES AND RELATED COMPOUNDS ..... 68
*Mutagens-Carcinogens Produced by Pyrolysis of Amino Acids and Proteins and in Cooked Foods* ..... 68
*Genotoxicity of Pyrolysis Products in Mammalian Cells* in vitro ..... 68
*Genotoxicity of Pyrolysis Products* in vivo ..... 69
*Carcinogenicities* ..... 69
*Metabolic Pathways* ..... 69
*Amounts of Heterocyclic Amines in Cooked Foods* ..... 77
*Organic Syntheses of Heterocyclic Amines and Heterocyclic Imino Compounds* ..... 77
*Formation of MeIQx and DiMeIQx from Creatinine, Amino Acids, and Saccharides* 77
POLYNUCLEAR AROMATIC HYDROCARBONS ..... 81
*Mutagens-Carcinogens in Cooked Foods* ..... 81
*Mutagenicities* ..... 81
*Carcinogenicities* ..... 81
DICARBONYL COMPOUNDS ..... 86
*Methylglyoxal, Glyoxal, and Diacetyl* ..... 86

## INTRODUCTION

Epidemiological studies have shown that diets and life-styles are closely related to human cancer (12, 26). For instance, the incidences of stomach and colon cancers among Japanese immigrants in the second generation shifted away from the pattern in Japan to that in the country of residence (60); this reveals the importance of food habits in inducing cancers of the digestive tract. Foods contain both initiators and promoters (104) of carcinogenesis, and various types



0199-9885/86/0715-0067$02.00

of mutagens and carcinogens in foods are known. These include (*a*) naturally occurring mutagens and carcinogens, especially in edible plants or spices, such as pyrrolidine alkaloids, flavonoids, and anthraquinones (2, 23); (*b*) the nitrosamines and nitrosamides that are produced from food components and nitrite by nitrosation reaction either during cooking and food processing or in the stomach (9, 70); (*c*) mycotoxins produced by fungi contaminating in foods (14, 129); (*d*) heterocyclic amines and polycyclic aromatic hydrocarbons produced by pyrolysis of amino acids, proteins, and food components; (*e*) mutagenic dicarbonyl compounds produced by heating carbohydrates or by fermentation; (*f*) mutagens produced by the browning reaction (aminocarbonyl reactions) (127); (*g*) food additives and contaminants (8); and (*h*) others.

This paper reviews the mutagenic and carcinogenic activities of the structurally defined mutagens and carcinogens that are produced by heating foods; namely compounds of types (*d*) and (*e*) listed above.

## HETEROCYCLIC AMINES AND RELATED COMPOUNDS

### *Mutagens-Carcinogens Produced by Pyrolysis of Amino Acids and Proteins and in Cooked Foods*

In 1976 Sugimura et al (84, 106) found that broiled dried fish had mutagenic activity detectable by Ames' test (79) with *Salmonella typhimurium*. Since then, mutagenic activities have been widely found in pyrolysates of amino acids (61), peptides (74), and proteins (83) and in cooked foods (10, 57, 97, 101–103, 125). Harman (Har) and norharman (NorHar), compounds that were not themselves mutagenic but had comutagenic activity, were also found in pyrolysates of amino acids (Table 1) (73, 86, 87, 124). Up to the present, 14 new chemical compounds have been isolated from pyrolysates of amino acids and proteins and from cooked foods, as shown in Table 1. Although Har and NorHar are already known as alkaloids, they are also included. Table 1 shows the names, abbreviations, chemical structures, and mutagenic activities on *S. typhimurium* TA98 of these chemicals and the original materials from which they were isolated. Har, NorHar, and Lys-P-1 are heterocyclic imino compounds, but all the other chemicals are heterocyclic amines. AαC, MeAαC, 3AH, 3AN, Trp-P-1, Trp-P-2, Glu-P-1, Glu-P-2, Phe-P-1, and Orn-P-1 have a common 2-amino-pyridine structure, and IQ, MeIQ, and MeIQx have a common 2-amino-imidazole structure.

### *Genotoxicity of Pyrolysis Products in Mammalian Cells* in vitro

The in vitro effects on mammalian cells, including human cells, induced by pyrolysis products are summarized in Table 2. These pyrolysis products induced diphtheria toxin resistance (88), ouabain resistance (117), chromosomal aberration (98), sister chromatid exchange (98), and in vitro transformation (7, 113, 114) in mammalian cells. They also induced 8-azaguanine resistance (64–66), chromosomal aberration (98), and sister chromatid exchange (98, 119, 120) in human cells.

### *Genotoxicity of Pyrolysis Products* in vivo

Results were positive in somatic eye-color mutation (16) and the wing spot test (139) in *Drosophila melanogaster* and in the spot test in mice (54). Induction of ATPase-deficient foci in rat liver (50) was also reported (see Table 3).

### *Carcinogenicities*

At present 7 of 16 pyrolysis products have been demonstrated to be strongly carcinogenic. These seven carcinogenic chemicals are AαC (95), Glu-P-1 (95, 115), Glu-P-2 (95, 115), IQ (94, 116), MeAαC (95), Trp-P-1 (72, 116a), and Trp-P-2 (27, 72). Experimental results are summarized in Table 4. Oral administration of these seven chemicals to rats or mice induced hepatocellular carcinomas and tumors in some other organs.

### *Metabolic Pathways*

All these mutagens required metabolic activation by a liver microsomal fraction (S9 mix) in order to exert their mutagenic effects on *S. typhimurium* (109). Trp-P-2 was converted to the 2-hydroxyamino derivative (*N*-OH-Trp-P-2) in vitro (22, 135) by cytochrome P-448, which was purified from the liver of rats treated with polychlorinated biphenyls or 3-methylcholanthrene (49, 92, 128). Synthetic *N*-OH-Trp-P-2 with or without *O*-acetylation reacted with DNA, as shown in Figure 1 (22). Serine and seryl-tRNA synthetase from yeast (137), and proline and prolyl-tRNA synthetase from rat liver (136), enhanced the in vitro binding of *N*-OH-Trp-P-2 to DNA in a manner similar to the enhancement of activated 4-hydroxyaminoquinoline 1-oxide (112). IQ, MeIQ, AαC, MeAαC, Glu-P-1, Glu-P-2, Lys-P-1, Trp-P-1, and 3-acetyl-Trp-P-1 were also activated in vitro by cytochrome P-448 of rat liver microsomes induced by 3-methylcholanthrene, but not by cytochrome P-450 induced by phenobarbitone (128). Glu-P-1, AαC, and IQ are also activated to hydroxyamino derivatives (21, 92, 96). The hydroxyamino derivative of Glu-P-1 reacted with DNA only after *O*-acetylation and produced an adduct, 2-($C^8$-guanyl)amino-6-methylpyrido[1,2-*a*:3',2'-*d*]imidazole (21), as shown in Figure 2. Recently the ultimate forms of Glu-P-1, Glu-P-2, IQ, MeIQ, and MeIQx (but not of Trp-P-1, Trp-P-2, MeAαC, and AαC) in *Salmonella* were suggested to be sulfate esters of the *N*-hydroxy derivatives of these amines (82).

All these heterocyclic amines were quickly degraded and they also lost mutagenic activity on treatment with hypochlorite, which is usually present in

**Table 1** Pyrolysis products of amino acids and proteins and in cooked foods

| Name (abbreviation) | Structure | Mutagenic activity on *S. typhimurium* TA98 + S9 mix (revertants/μg) (109) | Original source |
|---|---|---|---|
| 1. 2-Amino-9*H*-pyrido[2,3-*b*]-indole (AαC) | 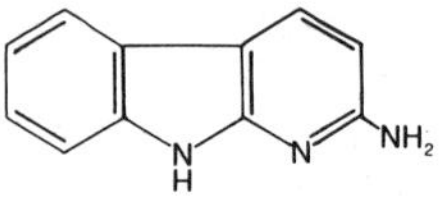 | 300 | Soybean globulin pyrolysate (140) |
| 2. 3-Amino-1-methyl-9*H*-pyrido[3,4-*b*]-indole (3AH) | 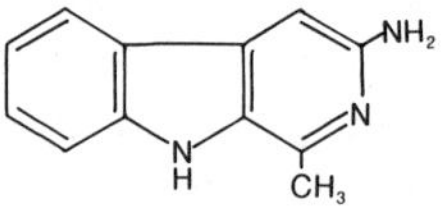 | 0[a,b] | L-Tryptophan pyrolysate (111) |
| 3. 3-Amino-9*H*-pyrido[3,4,-*b*]-indole (3AN) | 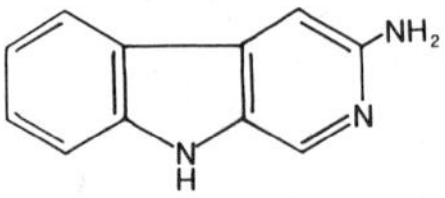 | 0.4[a] | L-Tryptophan pyrolysate (111) |
| 4. 2-Amino-6-methyl-dipyrido-[1,2-*a*:3',2'-*d*]-imidazole (Glu-P-l) | 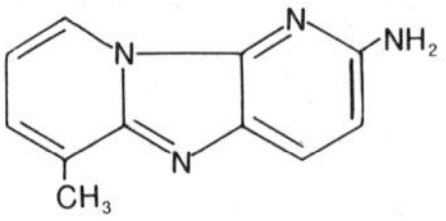 | 49,000 | L-Glutamic acid pyrolysate (134) |
| 5. 2-Aminodipyrido-[1,2-*a*:3',2'-*d*]-imidazole (Glu-P-2) | 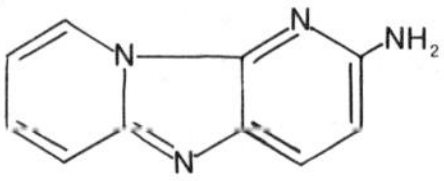 | 1,900 | L-Glutamic acid pyrolysate (134) |
| 6. 1-Methyl-9*H*-pyrido[3,4-*b*]-indole (Har) | 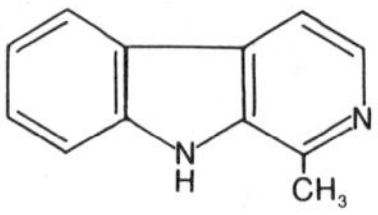 | 0 (comutagenic) (73) | L-Tryptophan pyrolysate (61) |
| 7. 2-Amino-3-methylimidazo-[4,5-*f*]quinoline (IQ) | 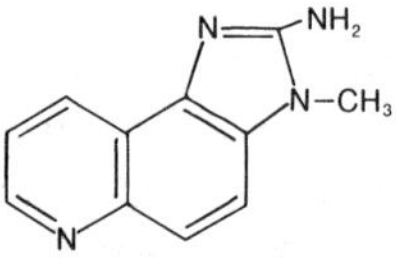 | 433,000 | Broiled sardine (56,59) |
| 8. 3,4-Cyclopenteno-pyrido[3,2-*a*]-carbazole (Lys-P-1) | 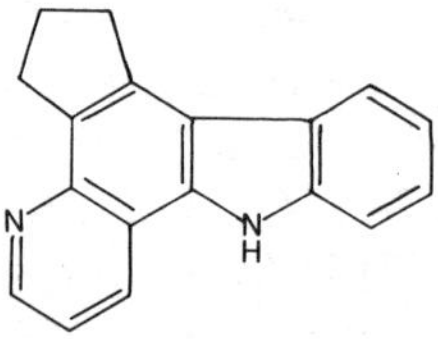 | 86 | L-Lysine pyrolysate (126) |

[a]M. Nagao, personal communication.
[b]Positive in SCE induction (120).

**Table 1** (continued)

| Name (abbreviation) | Structure | Mutagenic activity on *S. typhimurium* TA98 + S9 mix (revertants/μg) (109) | Original source |
|---|---|---|---|
| 9. 2-Amino-3-methyl-9*H*-pyrido[2,3,-*b*]-indole (MeAαC) | 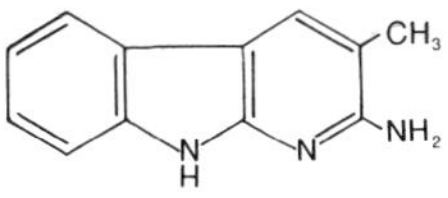 $CH_3$, $NH_2$, N, N, H | 200 | Soybean globulin pyrolysate (140) |
| 10. 2-Amino-3,4-dimethylimidazo-[4,5-*f*]quinoline (MeIQ) | 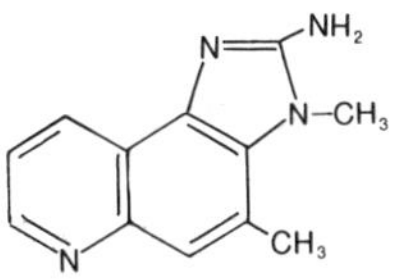 $NH_2$, N, N–$CH_3$, $CH_3$, N | 611,000 | Broiled sardine (58,59) |
| 11. 2-Amino-3,8-dimethylimidazo-[4,5-*f*]quinoxaline (MeIQx) | 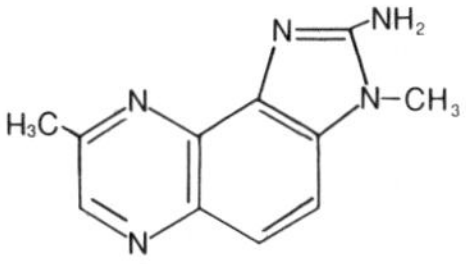 $NH_2$, N, N–$CH_3$, $H_3C$, N, N | 145,000 | Fried Beef (57) |
| 12. 9*H*-Pyrido[3,4-*b*]-indole (NorHar) | 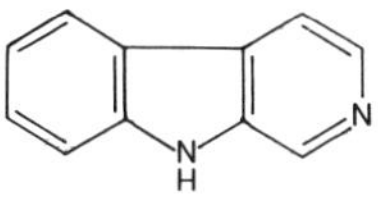 N, N, H | 0 (comutagenic) (87) | L-Tryptophan pyrolysate (61) |
| 13. 4-Amino-6-methyl-1*H*-2,5,10,10*b*-tetraaza-fluoranthene (Orn-P-1) | 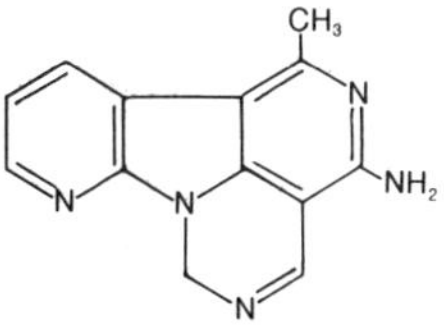 $CH_3$, N, $NH_2$, N, N, N | 56,800 | L-Ornithine pyrolysate (138) |
| 14. 2-Amino-5-phenyl-pyridine (Phe-P-l) | 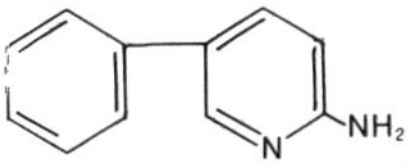 N, $NH_2$ | 41 | L-Phenyl-alanine pyrolysate (105) |
| 15. 3-Amino-1,4-dimethyl-5*H*-pyrido[4,3,-*b*]-indole (Trp-P-l) | 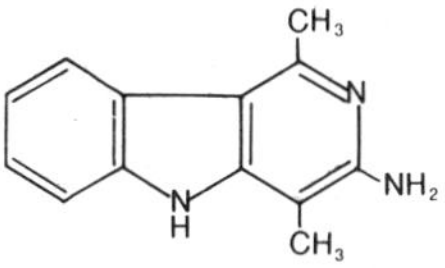 $CH_3$, N, $NH_2$, N, H, $CH_3$ | 39,000 | L-Tryptophan pyrolysate (105) |
| 16. 3-Amino-1-methyl-5*H*-pyrido[4,3-*b*]-indole (Trp-P-2) | 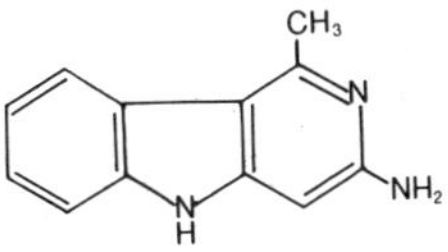 $CH_3$, N, $NH_2$, N, H | 104,000 | L-Tryptophan pyrolysate (105) |

**Table 2** Genotoxicity of pyrolysis products in mammalian cells in vitro

| Endpoint measured | Cells | Test compound | Exposure concentration | |
|---|---|---|---|---|
| 8-Azaguanine resistance (8AG$^{r}$) | Human embryonic diploid cells | Trp-P-1 | 0.3 | μg/ml |
| | | Trp-P-2 | 1.0 | μg/ml |
| | | Glu-P-2 | 0.3–30 | μg/ml |
| Diptheria toxin resistance (DT$^{r}$) | Chinese hamster lung cells (CHL) | AαC | 25–100 | μg/ml |
| | | Glu-P-1 | 250–750 | μg/ml |
| | | Glu-P-2 | 500–1500 | μg/ml |
| | | IQ | 5–40 | μg/ml |
| | | MeIQ | 10–50 | μg/ml |
| | | MeIQx | 10–100 | μg/ml |
| | | Trp-P-1 | 7–20 | μg/ml |
| | | Trp-P-2 | 1–5 | μg/ml |
| Ouabain resistance (Oub$^{r}$) | Chinese hamster V79 cells | Lys-P-1 | 10–50 | μg/ml |
| | | Trp-P-2 | 1–5 | μg/ml |
| Chromosomal aberration | PHA-stimulated human lymphocytes (HL) | Trp-P-1 | 0.2–0.5 | μg/ml |
| | | Trp-P-2 | 2–3 | μg/ml |
| | Chinese hamster cells (Don-6) | Trp-P-1 | 0.5–2.0 | μg/ml |
| | | Trp-P-2 | 5–7.5 | μg/ml |
| | Chinese hamster embryonic cells (B-131) | Trp-P-1 | 0.25–2.0 | μg/ml |
| | | Trp-P-2 | 2.5–10 | μg/ml |
| Sister Chromatid exchange | Human lymphoblastoid cells (NL3) | AαC | 1–100 | μM |
| | | 3AH | 100–500 | μM |
| | | 3AN | 100–1000 | μM |
| | | Glu-P-1 | 1–50 | μM |
| | | Trp-P-1 | 1–50 | μM |
| | | Trp-P-2 | 0.1–10 | μM |
| | Human embryonic fibroblasts (He 2144) | Trp-P-1 | 0.2–0.3 | μg/ml |
| | PHA-stimulated human lymphocytes (HL) | Trp-P-1 | 0.2–0.5 | μg/ml |
| | | Trp-P-2 | 1–3 | μg/ml |
| | Chinese hamster cells (Don-6) | Trp-P-1 | 0.1–1 | μg/ml |
| | | Trp-P-2 | 0.1–7.5 | μg/ml |
| | Chinese hamster embryonic cells (B-131) | Trp-P-1 | 0.25–1 | μg/ml |
| | | Trp-P-2 | 2.5–5 | μg/ml |
| Morphological transformation | Syrian Golden hamster embryo cells | Glu-P-1 | 10, 20 | μg/ml |
| | | Trp-P-1 | 0.1, 0.5 | μg/ml |
| | | Trp-P-2 | 0.1, 0.5 | μg/ml |
| | Golden hamster embryo cells | Trp-P-2 | 0.5 | μg/ml |
| | | Trp-P-2 | X ray 50 rad + | |
| | | Trp-P-2 | 0.5 | μg/ml |
| | | | X ray 100 rad + | |
| | | Trp-P-2 | 0.5 | μg/ml |

[a]t.c. = transformed colonies.

**Table 2** *(continued)*

| Exposure time | Results | References |
|---|---|---|
| 4 hr | 7.0 $8AG^r/10^5$ survivors | (64, 65) |
| 4 hr | 2.8 $8AG^r/10^5$ survivors | (66) |
| 4 hr | 0.9–2.7 $8AG^r/10^5$ survivors | (65) |
| 3 hr | 180–500 $DT^r/2.5\times10^5$ survivors | (88) |
| 3 hr | 100–170 $DT^r/2.5\times10^5$ survivors | |
| 3 hr | 50–120 $DT^r/2.5\times10^5$ survivors | |
| 3 hr | 75–120 $DT^r/2.5\times10^5$ survivors | |
| 3 hr | 80–150 $DT^r/2.5\times10^5$ survivors | |
| 3 hr | 80–150 $DT^r/2.5\times10^5$ survivors | |
| 3 hr | 70–130 $DT^r/2.5\times10^5$ survivors | |
| 3 hr | 50–260 $DT^r/2.5\times10^5$ survivors | |
| 2 days | 19.5–22.2 $Oub^r/10^6$ survivors | (117) |
| 2 days | 1.9–13.1 $Oub^r/10^6$ survivors | |
| 48 hr | 0.04–0.18 chromatid breaks/cell | (98) |
| 48 hr | 0.03–0.08 chromatid breaks/cell | |
| 26–30 hr | 0.07–1.17 chromatid breaks/cell | |
| 26–30 hr | 0.15–0.35 chromatid breaks/cell | |
| 25–27 hr | 0.10–0.31 chromatid breaks/cell | |
| 25–27 hr | 0.07–0.20 chromatid breaks/cell | |
| 2 hr | 1.6– 9.2 induced SCEs/cell | (119) |
| 2 hr | 1.1– 5.5 induced SCEs/cell | (120) |
| 2 hr | 3.5– 5.5 induced SCEs/cell | |
| 2 hr | 1.4– 9.0 induced SCEs/cell | (119) |
| 2 hr | 2.8–11.0 induced SCEs/cell | |
| 2 hr | 5.3–14.7 induced SCEs/cell | |
| 44 hr | 6.7– 7.9 induced SCEs/cell | (98) |
| 48 hr | 23.2–46.0 induced SCEs/cell | |
| 48 hr | 5.6–10.8 induced SCEs/cell | |
| 26–30 hr | 3.3–11.3 induced SCEs/cell | |
| 26–30 hr | 2.1– 9.3 induced SCEs/cell | |
| 25–27 hr | 28.8–33.1 induced SCEs/cell | |
| 25–27 hr | 3.8– 4.1 induced SCEs/cell | |
| 8 days | 2 t.c.[a]/ 730 or 811 survivors | (113) |
| 8 days | 2 t.c. / 412 and 3 t.c./223 survivors | (114) |
| 8 days | 3 t.c. / 505 and 7 t.c./459 survivors | |
| 10 days | 30 t.c. /2423 survivors | (7) |
| 10 days | 68 t.c. /4431 survivors | |
| 10 days | 95 t.c. /2220 survivors | |

**Table 3** Genotoxicity of pyrolysis products in vivo

| Endpoint measured | Species | Strain | Sex | Organ | Test compound | Exposure concentration | Exposure time | Results | References |
|---|---|---|---|---|---|---|---|---|---|
| Somatic eye-color mutation | *Drosophila melanogaster* | | M | Eye | Trp-P-1 | 200, 400 ppm | 24 hr | 19 red spots/7574 flies, 22 red spots/5059 flies | (16) |
| | | | | | Trp-P-2 | 400, 800 ppm | 24 hr | 11 red spots/6657 flies, 7 red spots/2304 flies | |
| Wing spot test | *Drosophila melanogaster* | | M,F | Wing | AαC | 400–1000 ppm | 1 day | 0.43–0.57 spot/wing | (139) |
| | | | | | Glu-P-1 | 100– 800 ppm | 1 day | 0.36–0.81 spot/wing | |
| | | | | | Glu-P-2 | 100– 800 ppm | 1 day | 0.50–0.67 spot/wing | |
| | | | | | IQ | 100–1000 ppm | 1 day | 0.42–0.59 spot/wing | |
| | | | | | MeAαC | 400 ppm | 1 day | 0.39 spot/wing | |
| | | | | | MeIQ | 100 ppm | 1 day | 0.53 spot/wing | |
| | | | | | MeIQx | 100– 200 ppm | 1 day | 0.44–0.51 spot/wing | |
| | | | | | Trp-P-1 | 200– 800 ppm | 1 day | 0.36–0.87 spot/wing | |
| | | | | | Trp-P-2 | 200– 800 ppm | 1 day | 0.55–0.89 spot/wing | |
| Spot test | Mouse | C57B1 /6J Han | F | Fur | Trp-P-1 | 4.2 mg/kg bw ip on days 8, 9, 10 of pregnancy | | 8 recessive spots/317 off spring | (54) |
| | | | | | Glu-P-1 | 18 mg/kg bw ip on days 8, 9, 10 of pregnancy | | 12 recessive spots/293 off spring | |
| ATPase-deficient foci | Rat | Sprague-Dawley | M | Liver | Trp-P-1 | 10 mg/kg bw/day × 6, ip + 0.05% phenobarbital diet 16 W | | 7.2 ATPase-deficient foci/10 $cm^2$ | (50) |
| | | | | | Trp-P-1 | 10 mg/kg bw/day × 6, ip + 5 mg/kg bw × 2/day × 3, ip + partial hepatectomy + 0.05% phenobarbital diet 16 W | | 11.4 ATPase-deficient foci/10 $cm^2$ | |

**Table 4** Carcinogenicity test of pyrolysis products on oral administration

| Pyrolysis Product | Species | Strain | Sex and number of animals | Percentage in diet | Duration[a] | Tumor site | References |
|---|---|---|---|---|---|---|---|
| AαC | Mouse | $CDF_1$ | M38 F34 | 0.08 | 685 d | Liver, interscapular brown-adipose tissue | (95) |
| Glu-P-1 | Rat | Fischer F344 | M42 F42 | 0.05 | 24 m | Liver, small intestine, colon, brain, zymbal gland, clitoral gland | (115) |
| | Mouse | $CDF_1$ | M34 F38 | 0.05 | 685 d | Liver, interscapular brown-adipose tissue | (95) |
| Glu-P-2 | Rat | Fischer F344 | M42 F42 | 0.05 | 24 m | Liver, small intestine, colon, brain, zymbal gland, clitoral gland | (115) |
| | Mouse | $CDF_1$ | M37 F36 | 0.05 | 685 d | Liver, interscapular brown-adipose tissue | (95) |
| IQ | Rat | Fischer F344 | M20 F4 | 0.03 | 300 d | Liver, small intestine, colon, skin, oral cavity, zymbal gland, clitoral gland | (116) |
| | Mouse | $CDF_1$ | M39 F36 | 0.03 | 675 d | Liver forestomach, lung | (94) |
| MeAαC | Mouse | $CDF_1$ | M37 F33 | 0.08 | 685 d | Liver, interscapular brown-adipose tissue | (95) |
| Trp-P-1 | Rat | Fischer F344 | M40 | 0.015 | 365 d | Liver | (116a) |
| | | | F40 | 0.02 | 365 d | Liver | |
| | Mouse | $CDF_1$ | M24 F26 | 0.02 | 621 d | Liver | (72) |
| Trp-P-2 | Rat | ACI | M10 F9 | 0.01 | 870 d | Liver | (27) |
| | Mouse | $CDF_1$ | M25 F24 | 0.02 | 621 d | Liver | (72) |

[a]Day = d, month = m.

chlorinated tap water (122). Trp-P-1, Trp-P-2, Glu-P-1, Glu-P-2, AαC, and MeAαC (but not IQ, MeIQ, and MeIQx) were converted to their hydroxy derivatives (Figure 3) when treated with nitrite under acidic conditions and thereby lost their mutagenic activities (121). These differences in inactivations by hypochlorite and nitrite can be used to distinguish 2-amino-pyridine-type mutagens (Trp-P-1/2, Glu-P-1/2, AαC, and MeAαC) from 2-amino-imidazole-type mutagens (IQ, MeIQ, and MeIQx) in cooked foods (109). Trp-P-1, Glu-P-1, and AαC are broken down by peroxidases (myeloperoxidase, lactoperoxidase, and horseradish peroxidase) with $H_2O_2$ (130).

Fresh juices from vegetables and fruits, such as cabbage, broccoli, green pepper, eggplant, apple, burdock (*Arctium Lappa* L.), stone-leek (*Allium fistulosum* L.), ginger, mint leaf, and pineapple can inactivate the mutagenicities of tryptophan pyrolysis products (80). The factor inactivating Trp-P-1 and Trp-P-2 in extracts of leaves of cabbage *(Brassica oleracea)* was identified as a peroxidase. Its molecular weight was 43,000 and it contained a sugar moiety (28). Inhibitors and activators of the mutagenic activities of these heterocyclic amines against *S. typhimurium* TA98 were found. Biological pyrrole pigments such as hemin, biliverdin, chlorophyllin, and protoporphyrin (4) and fatty acids such as oleic acid and linoleic acid (24) are inhibitors, while cysteine and cysteamine are activators (91).

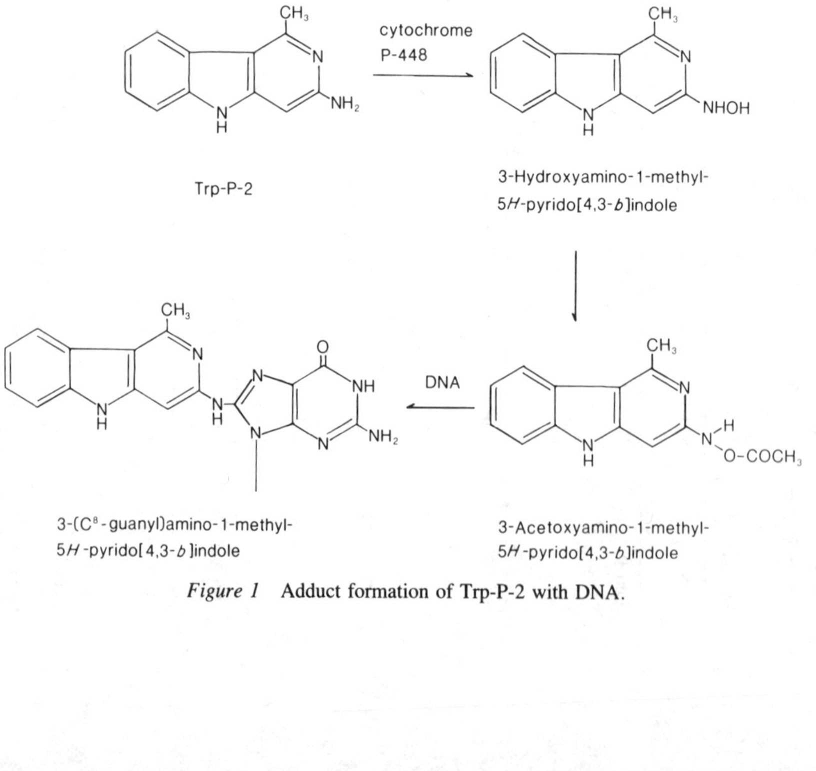

*Figure 1* Adduct formation of Trp-P-2 with DNA.

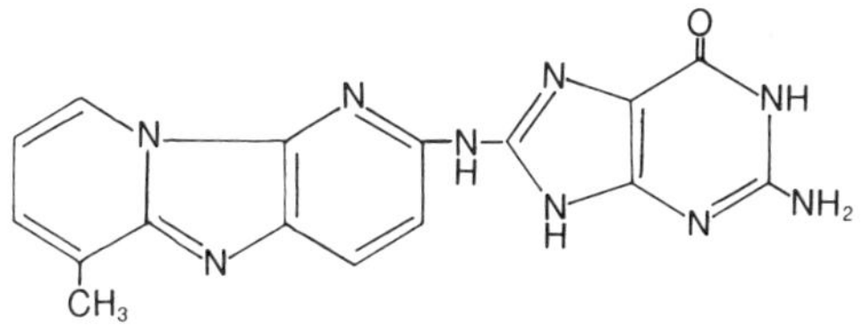

2-(C[8]-guanyl)amino-6-methyldipyrido[1,2-*a*:3',2'-*d*]imidazole

*Figure 2* Adduct of Glu-P-1 with guanine.

## *Amounts of Heterocyclic Amines in Cooked Foods*

There have been few quantitative determinations of heterocyclic amines in normal cooked foods. These chemicals were partially purified by extraction with methanol or 1-N HCl, partitioning between alkaline water and dichloromethane, silica gel column chromatography, Sephadex LH-20 column, thin-layer chromatography, and high-performance liquid chromatography (HPLC). Finally, gas chromatography/mass spectrography with multiple ion detection was used to quantify these mutagens. Reported data on the contents of these chemicals in cooked foods are listed in Table 5 (75, 107, 131–133).

## *Organic Syntheses of Heterocyclic Amines and Heterocyclic Imino Compounds*

Chemical syntheses of heterocyclic amines and heterocyclic imino compounds are shown in Figures 4*a* and 4*b*.

## *Formation of MeIQx and DiMeIQx from Creatinine, Amino Acids, and Saccharides*

Precursors of quinoline and quinoxaline derivatives in fish and meat are intriguing (51, 52, 78, 141). MeIQx was detected in a model system in which creatinine, glucose, and glycine were heated together (53), and 7,8-DiMeIQx was formed on heating this same mixture (89). The presence of DiMeIQx in

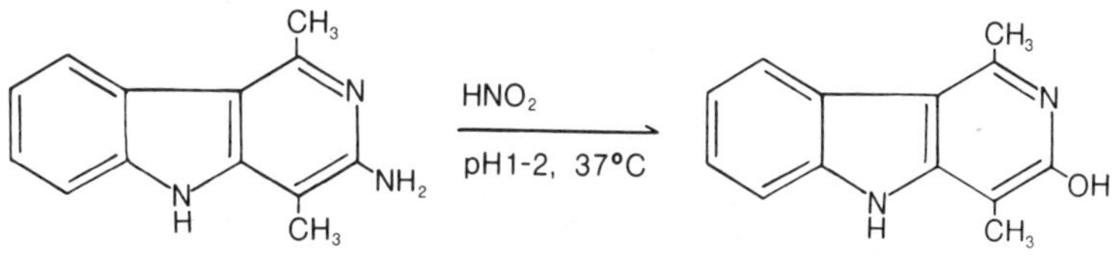

*Figure 3* Degradation of Trp-P-1 with nitrite.

**Table 5** Amounts of heterocyclic amines in cooked foods (μg/kg)[a]

| | AαC | Glu-P-2 | IQ | MeAαC | MeIQ | MeIQx | Trp-P-1 | Trp-P-2 |
|---|---|---|---|---|---|---|---|---|
| Broiled sun-dried sardine | | | 158 (107) | | 72 (107) | | 13.3 (133) | 13.1 (133) |
| Broiled or fried beef | 651 (75) | | 0.02–0.6 (107) | 63.5 (75) | | 1–2.4 (107) | 53 (132) | |
| Grilled chicken | 180 (75) | | | 15.1 (75) | | | | |
| Broiled sun-dried cuttle-fish | | 280 (131) | | | | | | |
| Grilled Chinese mush-room | 47.2 (75) | | | 5.4 (75) | | | | |
| Grilled onion | 1.5 (75) | | | ND[b] (75) | | | | |

[a]Numbers in parentheses are references.
[b]ND = not detected.

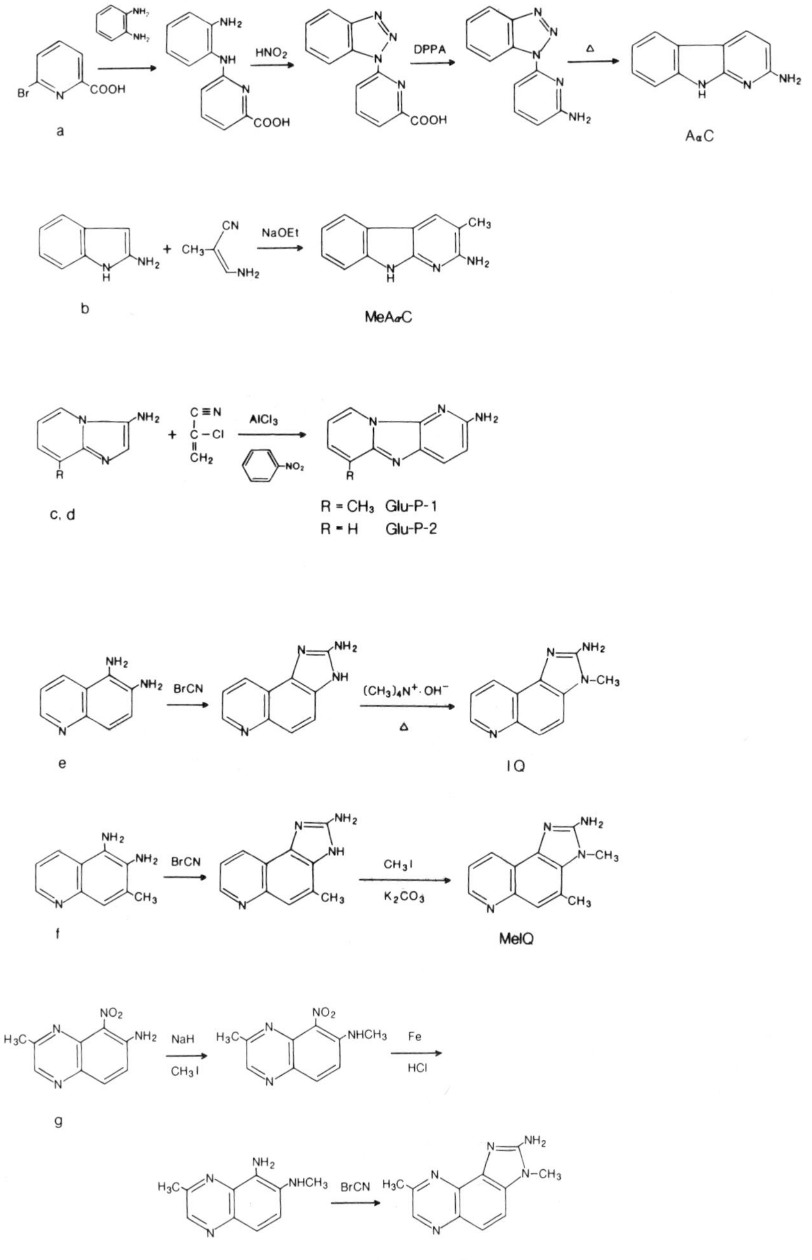

a

AαC

b

MeAαC

c, d

R = $CH_3$ Glu-P-1
R = H Glu-P-2

e

IQ

f

MeIQ

g

MeIQx

*Figure 4a* Organic syntheses of heterocyclic amines and heterocyclic imino compounds: (*a*) 6-Bromo-2-picolinic acid (77). (*b*) 2-Aminoindole (76). (*c*) 3-Amino-8-methylimidazo[1,2-α]pyridine (118). (*d*) 3-Aminoimidazo[1,2-α]pyridine (118). (*e*) 5,6-Diaminoquinoline (56). (*f*) 5,6-Diamino-7-methylquinoline (58). (*g*) 6-Amino-3-methyl-5-nitroquinoxaline (57).

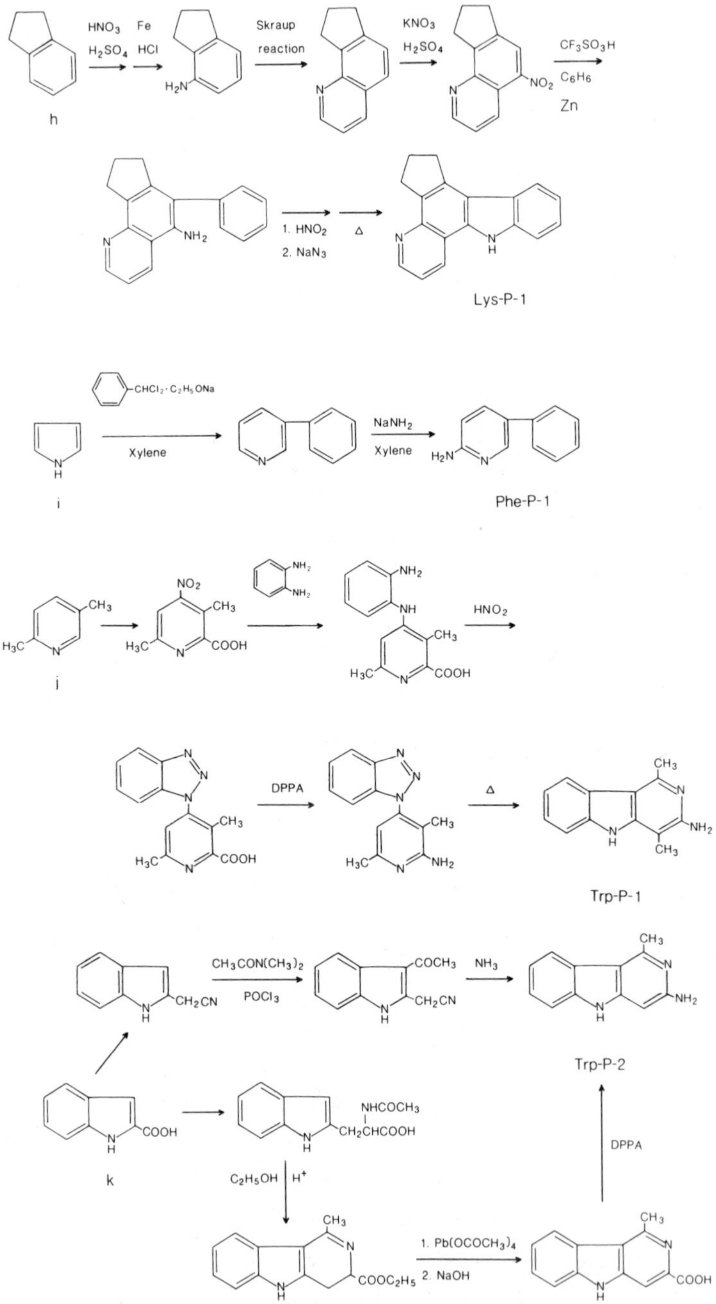

h

$HNO_3$ $H_2SO_4$ → Fe HCl → $H_2N$ → Skraup reaction → N → $KNO_3$ $H_2SO_4$ → $NO_2$ N → $CF_3SO_3H$ $C_6H_6$ Zn

$NH_2$ N → 1. $HNO_2$ 2. $NaN_3$ → Δ → N N H

Lys-P-1

$\text{C}_6\text{H}_5\text{-CHCl}_2\cdot\text{C}_2\text{H}_5\text{ONa}$

N H → Xylene → N → $NaNH_2$ Xylene → $H_2N$ N

i

Phe-P-1

$CH_3$ $H_3C$ N → $NO_2$ $CH_3$ $H_3C$ N COOH → ($NH_2$, $NH_2$) → $NH_2$ NH $CH_3$ $H_3C$ N COOH → $HNO_2$ →

j

N N N $CH_3$ $H_3C$ N COOH → DPPA → N N N $CH_3$ $H_3C$ N $NH_2$ → Δ → $CH_3$ N $NH_2$ N H $CH_3$

Trp-P-1

N H $CH_2CN$ → $CH_3CON(CH_3)_2$ $POCl_3$ → $COCH_3$ N H $CH_2CN$ → $NH_3$ → $CH_3$ N $NH_2$ N H

Trp-P-2

N H COOH → N H $NHCOCH_3$ $CH_2CHCOOH$

k

$C_2H_5OH$ $H^+$

$CH_3$ N N H $COOC_2H_5$ → 1. $Pb(OCOCH_3)_4$ 2. NaOH → $CH_3$ N N H COOH → DPPA → Trp-P-2

*Figure 4b* As in Figure 4*a*: (*h*) Indan (126). (*i*) Imidazole (123). (*j*) 2,5-Lutidine (1). (*k*) Indole-2-carboxylic acid (1).

cooked beef was suggested previously (15, 57). Formation of 4,8-DiMeIQx was demonstrated by heating a mixture of creatinine, glucose or ribose, and alanine or lysine (81) and a mixture of creatinine, glucose, and threonine (90). These mutagens were probably produced from creatinine, aldehydes, and Maillard reaction products. Formation of IQ in the heated product of a mixture of creatine and proline was also reported (142).

## POLYNUCLEAR AROMATIC HYDROCARBONS

### *Mutagens-Carcinogens in Cooked Foods*

That carcinogenic polycyclic aromatic hydrocarbons are present in cooked foods has been known since the late 1950s (5, 13, 20, 63, 69). At present, at least 18 mutagenic and/or carcinogenic polycyclic aromatic hydrocarbons (shown in Table 6) are known. These chemicals have also been found in uncooked vegetables, fruit, cereals, and vegetable oils. There are many reports on the amounts of polycyclic hydrocarbons in various foods (see Refs. 34, 47). The amount of polycyclic hydrocarbons present in cooked foods depends on the time of cooking, the distance of materials from the heat source, whether the melted fat is allowed to drop into the heat source, etc. In vegetables, fruits, and cereals, the amounts of these chemicals depend on the degrees of industrial and traffic pollutants in the areas in which they are grown. The amounts of carcinogenic polycyclic aromatic hydrocarbons in foods vary from 0 to 400 μg/kg, as shown in Table 6.

### *Mutagenicities*

The mutagenic activities of polycyclic aromatic hydrocarbons found in cooked foods are also shown in Table 6. The mutagenic activities against *S. typhimurium* TA98 or TA100 in the presence of S9 mix vary from 0.8 to 121 revertants per nmole, and these values are lower than those of heterocyclic amines found in cooked foods, as shown in Table 1.

### *Carcinogenicities*

Of the 18 polycyclic aromatic hydrocarbons that were detected in broiled meat (69) or smoked fish (71), at least 12 are known to be carcinogens, as shown in Table 6. Benz[*a*]anthracene, benzo[*a*]pyrene, benzo[*b*]fluoranthene, benzo[*j*]fluoranthene, dibenz[*a,h*]anthracene, 2-methylchrysene, and 3-methylchrysene are strong carcinogens; benzo[*e*]pyrene, chrysene, and indeno[1,2,3-*cd*]pyrene are moderate carcinogens; and anthanthrene and benzo[*b*]chrysene are weak carcinogens. Available data are inadequate to determine the carcinogenicities of benzo[*ghi*]perylene, coronene, perylene, and phenanthrene. The available data provide no evidence that fluoranthene and pyrene per se are carcinogenic to experimental animals.

**Table 6** Polynuclear aromatic hydrocarbons

| Name | Structure | Mutagenic activity on *S. typhimurium* + S9 mix (revertants/nmole) |
|---|---|---|
| 1. Anthanthrene | 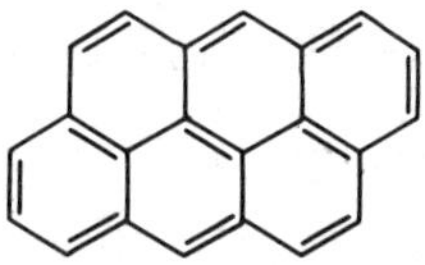 | 62 (TA98) (25) |
| 2. Benz[*a*]anthracene | 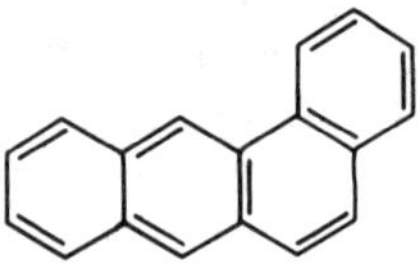 | 11 (TA100) (79) |
| 3. Benzo[*b*]chrysene | 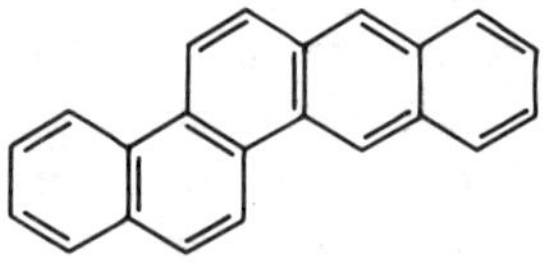 | — |
| 4. Benzo[*b*]fluoranthene | 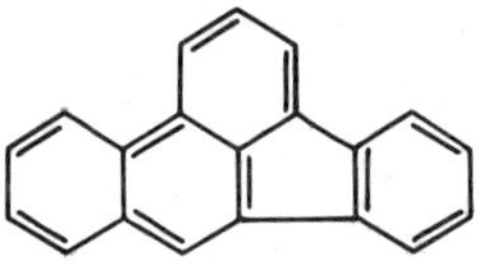 | 15 (TA98) (25) |
| 5. Benzo[*j*]fluoranthene | 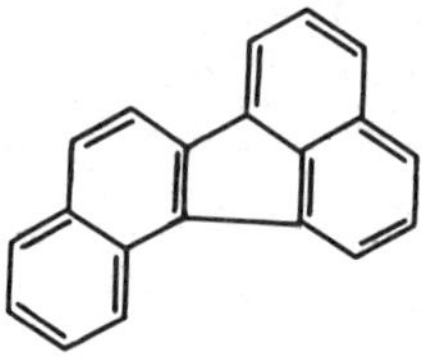 | 3 (TA98) (68) |
| 6. Benzo[*ghi*]perylene |  | 1.6 (TA100) (3) |
| 7. Benzo[*a*]pyrene | 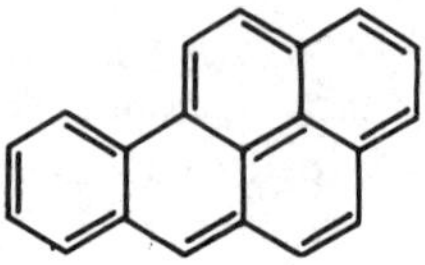 | 121 (TA100) (79) |

| Tumorigencity and carcinogenicity | Major source in foods (μg/kg) |
|---|---|
| skin, lung (37) | charcoal-broiled steak 2 (69) |
| lung adenoma, hepatoma, local sarcoma, skin papilloma, bladder carcinoma, forestomach papilloma, pulmonary adenocarcinoma (29) | broiled or smoked meat 0.2–31 (29, 69)<br>smoked fish 0.02–189 (71)<br>vegetables 0.3–230 (29)<br>vegetable oils 0.5–125 (29) |
| initiating activity (skin papilloma) (99) | broiled meat 0.5 (69) |
| skin (papilloma & carcinoma), local sarcoma (31) | broiled or smoked fish 0.1–37 (71)<br>smoked meat 0.4–15 (31) |
| skin (papilloma & carcinoma), lung carcinoma (39) | smoked fish 0.5–23 (71)<br>grilled sausages 0.2–15 (33)<br>margarine 2.3–10.5 (33) |
| inadequate experiments (38) | charcoal-broiled steak 4.5 (38, 69)<br>edible oils 0–18 (38) |
| forestomach (papilloma & carcinoma), skin (papilloma & carcinoma) local sarcomas, mammary carcinomas, leukemias, esophageal papilloma (30) | smoked meat 0.02–107 (5, 30)<br>vegetables 0.2–8 (30)<br>vegetable oils 0.9–62 (30) |

*(continued)*

**Table 6** *(continued)*

| Name | Structure | Mutagenic activity on *S. typhimurium* + S9 mix (revertants/nmole) |
|---|---|---|
| 8. Benzo[*e*]pyrene | 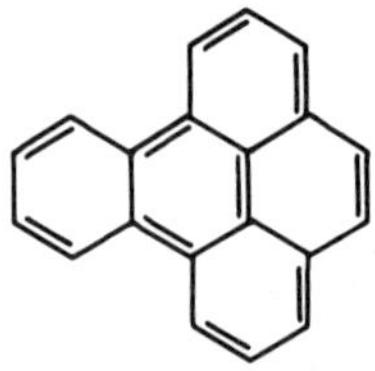 | 15 (TA98) (25) |
| 9. Chrysene | 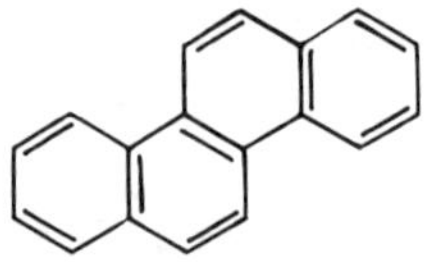 | 38 (TA100) (79) |
| 10. Coronene | 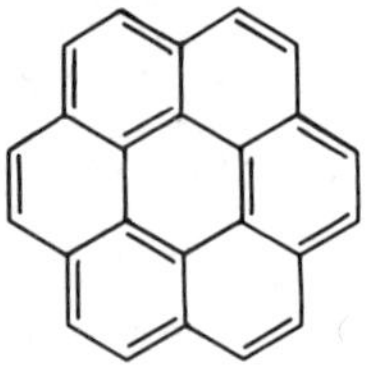 | 60 (TA98) (25) |
| 11. Dibenz[*a, h*]anthracene | 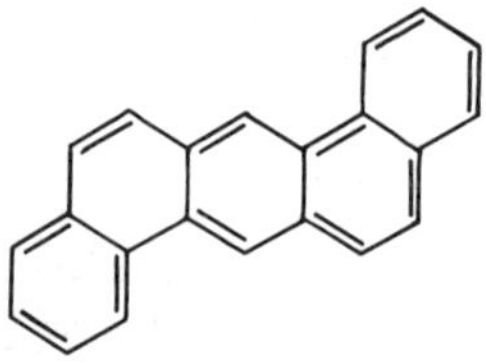 | 11(TA100) (79) |
| 12. Fluoranthene | 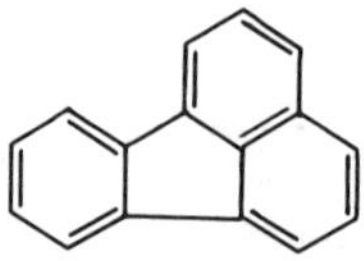 | 3 (TA98) (25) |
| 13. Indeno[1,2,3-*cd*]pyrene | 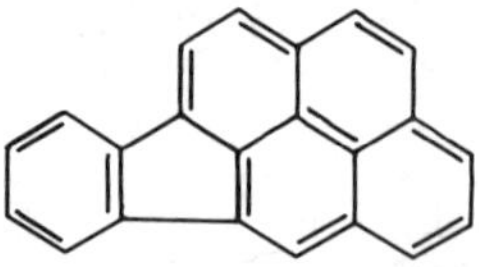 | 2.21 (TA98) (67) |
| 14. 2-Methylchrysene | 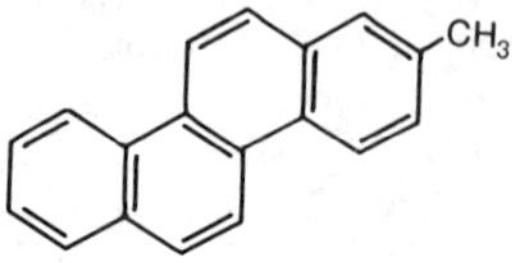 $CH_3$ | 3.7 (TA100) (11) |

| Tumorigenicity and carcinogenicity | Major source in foods (μg/kg) |
|---|---|
| skin (papilloma & carcinoma) (32) | smoked fish 1.9–29 (5, 71)<br>broiled or smoked meat 0.1–27 (32)<br>vegetable oils 0.6–32 (32) |
| skin (papilloma & carcinoma), local sarcoma, hepatic tumor (40) | broiled meat 0.6–25 (35)<br>smoked fish 0.3–173 (71)<br>vegetables 5.7–395 (35) |
| inadequate experiments (41) | charcoal-broiled steak 2.3 (41, 69)<br>edible oils 0–2.8 (41, 69) |
| forestomach (papilloma & carcinoma) (36) | broiled meat 0.2 (36, 69)<br>vegetable oils & fats 0–4 (36) |
| not carcinogenic (42) | charcoal-broiled steak 20 (69) |
| skin, local sarcoma (43) | broiled sausages 0.3–9 (43)<br>margarine 0.2–5.5 (43) |
| skin (44) | vegetables 0.9–6.2 (44) |

*(continued)*

**Table 6** *(continued)*

| Name | Structure | Mutagenic activity on *S. typhimurium* + S9 mix (revertants/nmole) |
|---|---|---|
| 15. 3-Methylchrysene | 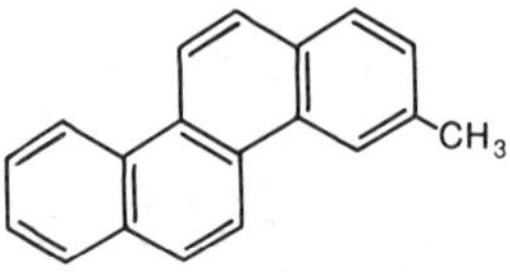 $CH_3$ | 4.1 (TA100) (11) |
| 16. Perylene | 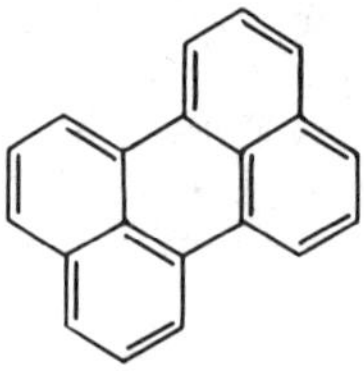 | 31 (TA98) (25) |
| 17. Phenanthrene | 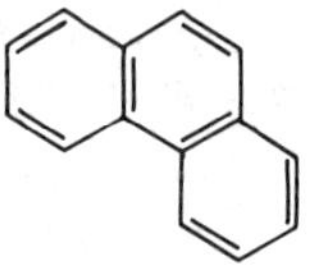 | 2 (TA100) (93) |
| 18. Pyrene | 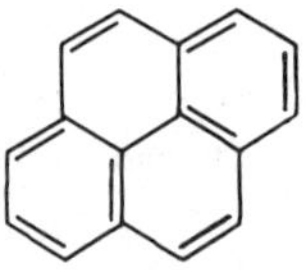 | 0.77 (TA 98) (85) |

# DICARBONYL COMPOUNDS

## *Methylglyoxal, Glyoxal, and Diacetyl*

Methylglyoxal (Figure 5), found in coffee and various heated foods, is a direct acting mutagen toward *S. typhimurium* TA 100 (100,000 revertants/mg) (55). Methylglyoxal (MG) forms an adduct with guanine base in nucleic acid in vitro (62, 100). However, this adduct is unstable after isolation by HPLC and easily reverts to guanine base (C. Furihata et al, unpublished data). Administration of MG by gastric tube to male F344 rats at doses of 100 to 600 mg per kg body weight induced a 100-fold increase in ornithine decarboxylase (ODC) activity within 7 hr, a 26-fold increase in DNA synthesis within 16 hr, a 16-fold increase in the labeling index of S-phase cells within 16 hr, and an apparent unscheduled DNA synthesis within 2 hr in the glandular stomach mucosa.

| Tumorigenicity and carcinogenicity | Major source in foods (μg/kg) |
|---|---|
| skin (44) | vegetables 1.7–20.2 (44) |
| inadequate experiment (45) | charcoal-broiled steak 2 (69) |
| inadequate experiment (46) | broiled meat 11 (69) |
| not carcinogenic (48) | broiled meat 18 (69) |

These results suggest that methylglyoxal has potential promoter activity and may also have initiating activity in glandular stomach carcinogenesis (18).

Repeated subcutaneous injections of methylglyoxal in saline at a concentration of 10 mg/ml into male and female F344 rats for 10 weeks induced subcutaneous tumors in 4 of 18 rats within 17 months (17). The mutagenicity of methylglyoxal was inactivated by bisulfite at a physiologically feasible concentration (110). Methylglyoxal (1 μg) induced four diphtheria-toxin-resistant mutants per $10^6$ CHL cells (108).

Glyoxal and diacetyl (Figure 5) were also found in coffee and were weakly mutagenic (6). The mutagenic activities of glyoxal and diacetyl against *S. typhimurium* TA100 without S9 mix are 9000 and 360 revertants/mg, respectively. Glyoxal at doses of 150 to 400 mg/kg body weight and diacetyl at doses of 300 to 1500 mg/kg body weight also induced ODC activity and DNA

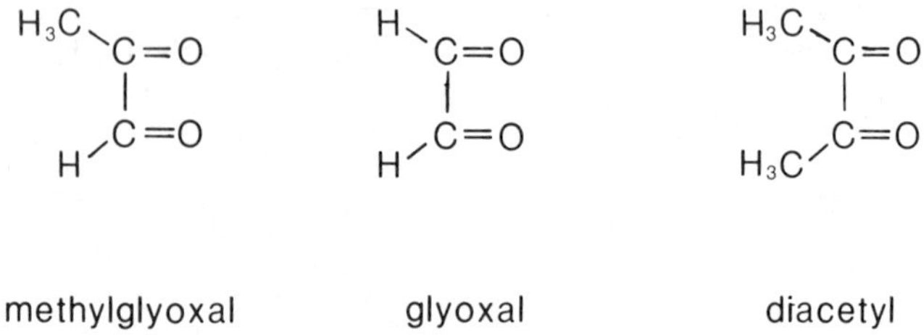

methylglyoxal glyoxal diacetyl

*Figure 5* Chemical structures of methylglyoxal, glyoxal, and diacetyl.

synthesis and apparent unscheduled DNA synthesis in rat stomach mucosa after a single administration via gastric tube (19).

ACKNOWLEDGMENTS

We wish to thank Dr. John Wassom and the staff at the Environmental Mutagen Information Center, Oak Ridge, Tennessee, for the literature survey.

## *Literature Cited*

1. Akimoto, H., Kawai, A., Nomura, H., Nagao, M., Kawachi, T., Sugimura, T. 1977. Syntheses of potent mutagens in tryptophan pyrolysates. *Chem. Lett.* 1977:1061–64
2. Ames, B. N. 1983. Dietary carcinogens and anticarcinogens. Oxygen radicals and degenerative diseases. *Science* 211: 1256–64
3. Andrews, A. W., Thibault, L. H., Lijinsky, W. 1978. The relationship between carcinogenicity and mutagenicity of some polynuclear hydrocarbons. *Mutat. Res.* 51:311–18
4. Arimoto, S., Ohara, Y., Namba, T., Negishi, T., Hayatsu, H. 1980. Inhibition of the mutagenicity of amino acid pyrolysis products by hemin and other biological pyrrole pigments. *Biochem. Biophys. Res. Commun.* 92:662–68
5. Baily, E. J., Dungal, N. 1958. Polycyclic hydrocarbons in Iceland smoked food. *Br. J. Cancer* 12:348–50
6. Bjeldanes, L. F., Chew, H. 1979. Mutagenicity of 1,2-dicarbonyl compounds: maltol, kojic acid, diacetyl and related substances. *Mutat. Res.* 67:367–71
7. Borek, C., Ong, A. 1981. The interaction of ionizing radiation and food pyrolysis products in producing oncogenic transformation in vitro. *Cancer Lett.* 12:61–66
8. Committee on Diet, Nutrition and Cancer. 1982. Additives and contaminants. In *Diet, Nutrition, and Cancer,* Chap. 14. Washington, DC: Natl. Acad. Press
9. Committee on Nitrite and Alternative Curing Agents in Food. 1981. *The Health Effects of Nitrate, Nitrite and N-Nitroso Compounds.* Washington, DC: Natl. Acad. Press
10. Commoner, B., Vitahyathil, A. J., Dolora, P., Nair, S., Madyastha, P., Cuca, G. C. 1978. Formation of mutagens in beef and beef extract during cooking. *Science* 201:913–16
11. Coombs, M. M., Dixon, C., Kissonerghis A.-M. 1976. Evaluation of the mutagenicity of compounds of known carcinogenicity, belonging to the benz[a]anthracene, chrysene, and cyclopenta[a]phenanthrene series, using Ames' test. *Cancer Res.* 36:4525–29
12. Doll, R., Peto, R. 1981. Quantitative estimates of avoidable risks of cancer in US today. *J. Natl. Cancer Inst.* 66:1191–1308
13. Dungal, N. 1959. Könen geräuchte Speisen krebserzeugend sein. *Krebsarzt* 14:22–24
14. Egan, H., Stoloff, L., Castegnara, M., Scott, P., O'Neil, I. K., Bartsch, H., Davis, W., eds. 1982. *Environmental Carcinogens: Selected Methods of Analysis,* Vol. 5—*Some Mycotoxins.* Lyon: Int. Agency for Res. on Cancer. 455 pp.
15. Felton, J. S., Knize, M. G., Wood, C., Wuebbles, B. J., Healy, S. K., et al. 1984. Isolation and characterization of

new mutagens from fried ground beef. *Carcinogenesis* 5:95–102

16. Fujikawa, K., Inagaki, E., Uchibori, M., Kondo, S. 1983. Comparative induction of somatic eye-color mutations and sex-linked recessive lethals in *Drosophila melanogaster* by tryptophan pyrolysates. *Mutat. Res.* 122:315–20
17. Fujita, Y., Wakabayashi, K., Kasai, H., Nagao, M., Sugimura, T., Kosuge, T. 1984. Carcinogenicity of methylglyoxal and its characteristic properties in mutagenicity. *Proc. Jpn. Cancer Assoc.* 43:34
18. Furihata, C., Sato, Y., Matsushima, T., Tatematsu, M. 1985. Induction of ornithine decarboxylase and DNA synthesis in rat stomach mucosa by methylglyoxal. *Carcinogenesis* 6:91–94
19. Furihata, C., Yoshida, S., Matsushima, T. 1985. Potential initiating and promoting activities of diacetyl and glyoxal in rat stomach mucosa. *Jpn. J. Cancer Res. (Gann)* 76:809–14
20. Gorelova, N. D., Dikun, P. P., Solinek, V. A., Emshanova, A. V. 1960. The content of 3,4-benzpyrene in fish smoked by different methods. *Vop. Onkol.* 6:33–37
21. Hashimoto, Y., Shudo, K., Okamoto, T. 1980. Metabolic activation of a mutagen, 2-amino-6-methyldipyrido[1,2-a,3',2'-d]imidazole. Identification of 2-hydroxyamino-6-methyldipyrido[1,2-a,3',2'-d]-imidazole and its reaction with DNA. *Biochem. Biophys. Res. Commun.* 92:971–76
22. Hashimoto, Y., Shudo, K., Okamoto, T. 1980. Activation of a mutagen, 3-amino-1-methyl-5H-pyrido[4,3-*b*]indole. Identification of 3-hydroxyamino-1-methyl-5H-pyrido[4,3-b]indole as its reaction with DNA. *Biochem. Biophys. Res. Commun.* 96:355–62
23. Hayashi, K., Hirono, I., MacGregor, J. T., Matsushima, T., Nagao, M., Sato, S. 1986. Mutagenicity of quercetin and related flavonoids: implications for genetic risk and carcinogenicity. *Mutat. Res.* In press
24. Hayatsu, H., Arimoto, S., Togawa, K., Makita, M. 1981. Inhibitory effect of the ether extract of human feces on activities of mutagens. Inhibition by oleic and linoleic acids. *Mutat. Res.* 81:287–93
25. Hermann, M. 1981. Synergistic effects of individual polycyclic aromatic hydrocarbons on the mutagenicity of their mixtures. *Mutat. Res.* 90:399–409
26. Higginson, J., Muir, C. S. 1979. Guest editorial: Environmental carcinogenesis: Misconceptions and limitations to cancer control. *J. Natl. Cancer Inst.* 63:1291–98
27. Hosaka, N., Matushima, T., Hirono, I., Sugimura, T. 1981. Carcinogenic activity of 3-amino-1-methyl-5*H*-pyrido[4,3-*b*]indole (Trp-P-2), a pyrolysis product of tryptophan. *Cancer Lett.* 13:23–28
28. Inoue, T., Morita, K., Kada, T. 1981. Purification and properties of a plant desmutagenic factor for the mutagenic principle of tryptophan pyrolysate. *Agric. Biol. Chem.* 45:345–53
29. International Agency for Research on Cancer. 1973. Benz[*a*]anthracene. *IARC Monogr.* 3:45–68
30. International Agency for Research on Cancer. 1973. Benzo[*a*]pyrene. *IARC Monogr.* 3:91–136
31. International Agency for Research on Cancer. 1973. Benzo[*b*]fluoranthene. *IARC Monogr.* 3:69–81
32. International Agency for Research on Cancer. 1973. Benzo[*e*]pyrene. *IARC Monogr.* 3:137–58
33. International Agency for Research on Cancer. 1973. Benzo[*j*]fluoranthene. *IARC Monogr.* 3:82–90
34. International Agency for Research on Cancer. 1973. *Certain Polynuclear Aromatic Hydrocarbons and Heterocyclic Compounds. IARC Monogr.*, Vol. 3. 237 pp.
35. International Agency for Research on Cancer. 1973. Chrysene. *IARC Monogr.* 3:159–77
36. International Agency for Research on Cancer. 1973. Dibenz[*a,h*]anthracene. *IARC Monogr.* 3:178–96
37. International Agency for Research on Cancer. 1983. Anthanthrene. *IARC Monogr.* 32:95–104
38. International Agency for Research on Cancer. 1983. Benzo[*ghi*]perylene. *IARC Monogr.* 32:195–204
39. International Agency for Research on Cancer. 1983. Benzo[*j*]fluoranthene. *IARC Monogr.* 32:155–61
40. International Agency for Research on Cancer. 1983. Chrysene. *IARC Monogr.* 32:247–61
41. International Agency for Research on Cancer. 1983. Coronene. *IARC Monogr.* 32:263–68
42. International Agency for Research on Cancer. 1983. Fluoranthene. *IARC Monogr.* 32:355–61
43. International Agency for Research on Cancer. 1973. Indeno[1,2,3-*cd*]pyrene. *IARC Monogr.* 3:229–37
44. International Agency for Research on Cancer. 1983. 1-, 2-, 3-, 4-, 5- and 6- methylchrysenes. *IARC Monogr.* 32:379–97
45. International Agency for Research on Cancer. 1983. Perylene. *IARC Monogr.* 32:411–18

46. International Agency for Research on Cancer. 1983. Phenanthrene. *IARC Monogr*. 32:419–30
47. International Agency for Research on Cancer. 1983. *Polynuclear Aromatic Compounds, Part 1, Chemical, Environmental and Experimental Data. IARC Monogr.*, Vol. 32. 477 pp.
48. International Agency for Research on Cancer. 1983. Pyrene. *IARC Monogr.* 32:431–46
49. Ishi, K., Ando, M., Kamataki, T., Kato, R., Nagao, M. 1980. Metabolic activation of mutagenic tryptophan pyrolysis products (Trp-P-1 and Trp-P-2) by a purified cytochrome P-450-dependent monooxygenase system. *Cancer Lett.* 9:271–76
50. Ishikawa, T., Takayama, S., Kitagawa, T., Kawachi, T., Sugimura, T. 1979. Induction of enzyme altered islands in rat liver by tryptophan pyrolysis products. *J. Cancer Res. Clin. Oncol.* 95:221–24
51. Jägerstad, M., Laser Reuterswärd, A., Olsson, R., Grivas, S., Nyhammar, T., et al. 1983. Creatin(in)e and Maillard reaction products as precursors of mutagenic compounds: Effects of various amino acids. *Food Chem.* 12:255–64
52. Jägerstad, M., Laser Reuterswärd, A., Öste, R., Dahlqvist, A. 1983. Creatinine and Maillard reaction products as precursors of mutagenic compounds formed in fried beef. See Ref. 127, pp. 507–19
53. Jägerstad, M., Olsson, K., Grivas, S., Negishi, C., Wakabayashi, K., et al. 1984. Formation of 2-amino-3,8-dimethylimidazo[4,5-*f*]quinoxaline in a model system by heating creatinine, glycine and glucose. *Mutat. Res.* 126:239–44
54. Jensen, N. J. 1983. Pyrolytic products from tryptophan and glutamic acid are positive in the mammalian spot test. *Cancer Lett.* 20:241–44
55. Kasai, H., Kumeno, K., Yamaizumi, Z., Nishimura, S., Nagao, M., et al. 1982. Mutagenicity of methylglyoxal in coffee. *Gann* 73:681–83
56. Kasai, H., Nishimura, S., Wakabayashi, K., Nagao, M., Sugimura, T. 1980. Chemical synthesis of 2-amino-3-methylimidazo[4,5-*f*]quinolin (IQ), a potent mutagen isolated from broiled fish. *Proc. Jpn. Acad. B* 56:382–84
57. Kasai, H., Yamaizumi, Z., Shiomi, T., Yokoyama, S., Miyazawa, T., et al. 1981. Structure of a potent mutagen isolated from fried beef. *Chem. Lett.* 1981:485–88
58. Kasai, H., Yamaizumi, Z., Wakabayashi, K., Nagao, M., Sugimura, T., et al. 1980. Structure and chemical synthesis of Me-IQ, a potent mutagen isolated from broiled fish. *Chem. Lett.* 1980:1391–94
59. Kasai, H., Yamaizumi, Z., Wakabayashi, K., Nagao, M., Sugimura, T., et al. 1980. Potent novel mutagens produced by broiling fish under normal conditions. *Proc. Jpn. Acad. B* 56:278–83
60. Kolonel, L. N., Hinds, M. W., Hankin, J. H. 1980. Cancer patterns among migrant and native-born Japanese in Hawaii in relation to smoking, drinking and dietary habits. In *Genetic Environmental Factors in Experimental and Human Cancer,* Princess Takamatsu Symp., ed. H. V. Gelboin, B. MacMahon, T. Matsushima, T. Sugimura, S. Takayama, H. Takebe, 10:327–40. Tokyo: Jpn. Sci. Soc. 369 pp.
61. Kosuge, T., Tsuji, K., Wakabayashi, K., Okamoto, T., Shudo, K., et al. 1978. Isolation and structure studies of mutagenic principles in amino acid pyrolysates. *Chem. Pharm. Bull.* 26:611–19
62. Krymkiewicz, N. 1973. Reactions of methylglyoxal with nucleic acids. *FEBS Lett.* 29:51–54
63. Kuratsune, M., Hueper, W. C. 1960. Polycyclic aromatic hydrocarbons in roasted coffee. *J. Natl. Cancer Inst.* 24:463–69
64. Kuroda, Y. 1980. Dose-rate effect of Trp-P-1 on survival and mutation induction in cultured human diploid cells. *Ann. Rep. Natl. Inst. Genet.* 30:47–48
65. Kuroda, Y. 1981. Mutagenic activity of Trp-P-2 and Glu-P-1 on embryonic human diploid cells in culture. *Ann. Rep. Natl. Inst. Genet.* 31:45–46
66. Kuroda, Y., Asakura, M. 1981. Metabolic activation of tryptophan pyrolysis products by S-9 Mix in induction of mutations in cultured Chinese hamster cells. *Ann. Rep. Natl. Inst. Genet.* 31:46–47
67. LaVoie, E., Bedenko, V., Hirota, N., Hecht, S. S., Hoffmann, D. 1979. A comparison of the mutagenicity, tumor-initiating activity and complete carcinogenicity of polynuclear aromatic hydrocarbons. In *Polynuclear Aromatic Hydrocarbons,* ed. P. W. Jones, P. Leber, pp. 705–21. Ann Arbor, Mich: Ann Arbor Sci.
68. LaVoie, E. J., Hecht, S. S., Amin, S., Bedenko, V., Hoffmann, D. 1980. Identification of mutagenic dihydrodiols as metabolites of benzo[j]fluoranthene and benzo[k]fluoranthene. *Cancer Res.* 40:4528–32
69. Lijinsky, W., Schubik, P. 1964. Benzo(a)pyrene and other polynuclear hydro-

carbons in charcoal-broiled meat. *Science* 145:53–55
70. Magee, P. N., ed. 1982. *Nitrosamines and Human Cancer,* Banbury Rep. 12. New York: Cold Spring Harbor Lab. 599 pp.
71. Masuda, Y., Mori, K., Kuratsune, M. 1966. Polycyclic aromatic hydrocarbons in common Japanese foods. I. Broiled fish, roasted barley, shoyu and caramel. *Gann* 57:133–42
72. Matsukura, N., Kawachi, T., Morino, K., Ohgaki, H., Sugimura, T., Takayama, S. 1981. Carcinogenicity in mice of mutagenic compounds from a tryptophan pyrolysate. *Science* 213:346–47
73. Matsumoto, T., Yoshida, D., Mizusaki, S. 1977. Enhancing effect of harman on mutagenicity in Salmonella. *Mutat. Res.* 56:85–88
74. Matsumoto, T., Yoshida, D., Mizusaki, S., Okamoto, H. 1978. Mutagenicities of the pyrolyzates of peptides and proteins. *Mutat. Res.* 56:281–88
75. Matsumoto, T., Yoshida, D., Tomita, H. 1981. Determination of mutagens, amino-α-carbolines in grilled foods and cigarette smoke condensate. *Cancer Lett.* 12:105–10
76. Matsumoto, T., Yoshida, D., Tomita, H. 1981. Synthesis and mutagenic activity of alkyl derivatives of 2-amino-9*H*-pyrido[2,3-*b*]indole. *Agric. Biol. Chem.* 45:2031–35
77. Matsumoto, T., Yoshida, D., Tomita, H., Matsushita, H. 1979. Synthesis of 2-amino-9H-pyrido[2,3-*b*]indole isolated as a mutagenic principle from pyrolytic products of protein. *Agric. Biol. Chem.* 43:675–77
78. Matsushima, T. 1982. Mechanisms of conversion of food components to mutagens and carcinogens. In *Molecular Interrelations of Nutrition and Cancer,* ed. M. S. Arnott, J. van Eys, Y.-M. Wang, pp. 35–42. New York: Raven. 474 pp.
79. McCann, J., Choi, E., Yamasaki, E., Ames, B. N. 1975. Detection of carcinogens as mutagens in the Salmonella/microsome mutagenicity test: Assay of 300 chemicals. *Proc. Natl. Acad. Sci. USA* 72:5135–39
80. Morita, K., Hara, M., Kada, T. 1978. Studies on natural desmutagens: Screening for vegetable and fruit factors active in inactivation of mutagenic pyrolysis products from amino acids. *Agric. Biol. Chem.* 42:1235–38
81. Muramatsu, M., Matsushima, T. 1984. Precursors of heated food mutagens (IQ, MeIQ, MeIQx). II. *Proc. Jpn. Cancer Assoc.* 43:29
82. Nagao, M., Fujita, Y., Wakabayashi, K., Sugimura, T. 1983. Ultimate forms of mutagenic and carcinogenic heterocyclic amines produced by pyrolysis. *Biochem. Biophys. Res. Commun.* 114:626–31
83. Nagao, M., Honda, M., Seino, Y., Yahagi, T., Kawachi, T., Sugimura, T. 1977. Mutagenicies of protein pyrolysates. *Cancer Lett.* 2:355–40
84. Nagao, M., Honda, M., Seino, Y., Yahagi, T., Sugimura, T. 1977. Mutagenicities of smoke condensates and the charred surface of fish and meat. *Cancer Lett.* 2:221–26
85. Nagao, M., Takahashi, Y. 1981. Mutagenic activity of 42 coded compounds in the Salmonella/microsome assay. *Progr. Mutat. Res.* 1:302–13
86. Nagao, M., Yahagi, T., Kawachi, T., Sugimura, T., Kosuge, T., et al. 1977. Comutagenic action of norharman and harman. *Proc. Jpn. Acad.* 53:95–98
87. Nagao, M., Yahagi, T., Sugimura, T. 1978. Differences in effects of norharman with various classes of chemical mutagens and amounts of S-9. *Biochem. Biophys. Res. Commun.* 83:373–78
88. Nakayasu, M., Nakazato, F., Sakamoto, H., Terada, M., Sugimura, T. 1983. Mutagenic activity of heterocyclic amines in Chinese hamster lung cells with diphtheria toxin resistance as a marker. *Mutat. Res.* 118:91–102
89. Negishi, C., Wakabayashi, K., Tsuda, M., Sato, S., Sugimura, T., et al. 1984. Formation of 2-amino-3,7,8-trimethylimidazo[4,5-*f*]quinoxaline, a new mutagen, by heating a mixture of creatinine, glucose and glycine. *Mutat. Res.* 140:55–59
90. Negishi, C., Wakabayashi, K., Yamaizumi, Z., Saito, H., Sato, S., et al. 1984. Identification of a new mutagen, 4,8-DiMeIQx. *Proc. Environ. Mutat. Soc. Jpn.* 13:27
91. Negishi, T., Hayatsu, H. 1979. The enhancing effect of cysteine and its derivatives on the mutagenic activities of the tryptophan-pyrolysis products, Trp-P-1 and Trp-P-2. *Biochem. Biophys. Res. Commun.* 88:97–102
92. Niwa, T., Yamazoe, Y., Kato, R. 1982. Metabolic activation of 2-amino-9*H*-pyrido[2,3-*b*]indole by rat-liver microsomes. *Mutat. Res.* 95:159–70
93. Oesch, F., Bücker, M., Glatt, H. R. 1981. Activation of phenanthrene to mutagenic metabolites and evidence for at least two different activation pathways. *Mutat. Res.* 81:1–10
94. Ohgaki, H., Kusama, K., Matsukura, N., Morino, K., Hasegawa, H., et al.

1984. Carcinogenicity in mice of a mutagenic compound, 2-amino-3-methylimidazo[4,5-*f*]quinoline, from broiled sardine, cooked beef and beef extract. *Carcinogenesis* 5:921–24
95. Ohgaki, H., Matsukura, N., Morino, K., Kawachi, T., Sugimura, T., Takayama, S. 1984. Carcinogenicity in mice of mutagenic compounds from glutamic acid and soybean globulin pyrolysates. *Carcinogenesis* 5:815–19
96. Okamoto, T., Shudo, K., Hashimoto, Y., Kosuge, T., Sugimura, T., Nishimura, S. 1981. Identification of a reactive metabolite of the mutagen, 2-amino-3-methylimdazolo[4,5-*f*]quinoline. *Chem. Pharm. Bull.* 29:590–93
97. Pariza, M. W., Ashoor, S. H., Chu, F. S., Lund, D. B. 1979. Effects of temperature and time on mutagen formation in pan-fried hamburger. *Cancer Lett.* 7:63–69
98. Sasaki, M., Sugimura, K., Yoshida, M. A., Kawachi, T. 1980. Chromosome aberrations and sister chromatid exchange induced by tryptophan pyrolysates, Trp-P-1 and Trp-P-2, in cultured human and Chinese hamster cells. *Proc. Jpn. Acad. B* 56:332–37
99. Scribner, J. D. 1973. Tumor initiation by apparently noncarcinogenic polycyclic aromatic hydrocarbons. *J. Natl. Cancer Inst.* 50:1717–19
100. Shapiro, R., Cohen, B. I., Shiuey, S.-J., Maurer, H. 1969. On the reaction of guanine with glyoxal, pyruvaldehyde, and kethoxal, and the structure of the acrylguanines. A new synthesis of $N^2$-alkylguanines. *Biochemistry* 8:238–45
101. Spingarn, N. E., Kasai, H., Vuolo, L. L., Nishimura, S., Yamaizumi, Z., et al. 1980. Formation of mutagens in cooked foods. III. Isolation of a potent mutagen from beef. *Cancer Lett.* 9:177–83
102. Spingarn, N. E., Slocu, L. A., Weisburger, J. H. 1980. Formation of mutagens in cooked foods. II. Foods with high starch content. *Cancer Lett.* 9:7–12
103. Spingarn, N. E., Weisburger, J. H. 1979. Formation of mutagens in cooked foods. *Cancer Lett.* 7:259–64
104. Sugimura, T. 1982. A view of cancer researcher on environmental mutagens. In *Environmental Mutagens and Carcinogens,* ed. T. Sugimura, S. Kondo, H. Takebe, pp. 3–20. Tokyo/New York: Univ. Tokyo Press. Liss. 775 pp.
105. Sugimura, T., Kawachi, T., Nagao, M., Yahagi, T., Seino, Y., et al. 1977. Mutagenic principle(s) in tryptophan and phenylalanine pyrolysis products. *Proc. Jpn. Acad.* 53:58–61
106. Sugimura, T., Nagao, M., Kawachi, T., Honda, M., Yahagi, T., et al. 1977. Mutagens-carcinogens in food with special reference to highly mutagenic pyrolytic products in broiled foods. In *Origins of Human Cancer,* Book C, ed. H. H. Hiatt, J. D. Watson, J. A. Winsten, pp. 1561–67. New York: Cold Spring Harbor Lab. 1889 pp.
107. Sugimura, T., Nagao, M., Wakabayashi, K. 1981. Mutagenic heterocyclic amine in cooked food. In *Environmental Carcinogens: Selected Methods of Analysis,* ed. H. Egan, L. Fishbein, M. Castegnaro, I. K. O'Neil, H. Bartsh, 4:251–67. Lyon: Int. Agency for Res. on Cancer. 347 pp.
108. Sugimura, T., Sato, S. 1983. Bacterial mutagenicity of natural materials, pyrolysis products and additives in foodstuffs and their association with genotoxic effects in mammals. In *Developments in the Science and Practice of Toxicology,* ed. A. H. Hayes, R. C. Schnell, T. S. Miya, pp. 115–33. Amsterdam/NY/Oxford: Elsevier Science. 614 pp.
109. Sugimura, T., Sato, S. 1983. Mutagens-carcinogens in foods. *Cancer Res.* 43: 2415s-21s (Suppl.)
110. Suwa, Y., Nagao, M., Kosugi, A., Sugimura, T. 1982. Sulfite suppresses the mutagenic property of coffee. *Mutat. Res.* 102:383–91
111. Tada, M., Saeki, H., Oikawa, A. 1983. The identification of 3-amino-9*H*-pyrido[3,4-*b*]indole derivatives in L-tryptophan pyrolysate. *Bull. Chem. Soc. Jpn.* 56:1450–54
112. Tada, M., Tada, M. 1975. Seryl-tRNA synthetase and activation of the carcinogen 4-nitroquinoline 1-oxide. *Nature* 255:510–12
113. Takayama, S., Hirakawa, T., Tanaka, M., Kawachi, T., Sugimura, T. 1979. In vitro transformation of hamster embryo cells with a glutamic acid pyrolysis product. *Toxicol. Lett.* 4:281–84
114. Takayama, S., Kato, Y., Tanaka, M., Nagao, M., Wakabayashi, K., Sugimura, T. 1977. In vitro transformation of hamster embryo cells with tryptophan pyrolysis products. *Proc. Jpn. Acad. B* 53:126–29
115. Takayama, S., Masuda, M., Mogami, M., Ohgaki, H., Sato, S., Sugimura, T. 1984. Induction of cancers in the intestine, liver, and various other organs of rats by feeding mutagens from glutamic acid pyrolysate. *Gann* 75:207–13
116. Takayama, S., Nakatsuru, Y., Masuda, M., Ohgaki, H., Sato, S., Sugimura, T. 1984. Demonstration of carcinogenicity in F344 rats of 2-amino-3-methylimida-

zo[4,5-*f*]quinoline from broiled sardine, fried beef and beef extract. *Gann* 75:467–70

116a. Takayama, S., Nakatsuru, Y., Ohgaki, H., Sato, S., Sugimura, T. 1985. Carcinogenicity in rats of a mutagenic compound, 3-amino-1,4-dimethyl-5*H*-pyrido[4,3-*b*]indole, from tryptophan pyrolysate. *Jpn. J. Cancer Res. (Gann)* 76: 815–17

117. Takayama, S., Tanaka, M. 1983. Mutagenesis of amino acid pyrolysis products in Chinese hamster V79 cells. *Toxicol. Lett.* 17:23–28

118. Takeda, K., Shudo, K., Okamoto, T., Kosuge, T. 1978. Synthesis of mutagenic principles isolated from L-glutamic acid pyrolysate. *Chem. Pharm. Bull.* 26: 2924–25

119. Tohda, H., Oikawa, A., Kawachi, T., Sugimura, T. 1980. Induction of sister-chromatid exchanges by mutagens from amino acid and protein pyrolysate. *Mutat. Res.* 77:65–69

120. Tohda, H., Tada, M., Sugawara, R., Oikawa, A. 1983. Actions of amino-β-carbolines on induction of sister-chromatid exchanges. *Mutat. Res.* 116:137–47

121. Tsuda, M., Takahashi, Y., Nagao, M., Hirayama, T., Sugimura, T. 1980. Inactivation of mutagens from pyrolysates of tryptophan and glutamic acid by nitrite in acidic solution. *Mutat. Res.* 78:331–39

122. Tsuda, M., Wakabayashi, K., Hirayama, T., Kawachi, T., Sugimura, T. 1983. Inactivation of potent pyrolysate mutagens by chlorinated tap water. *Mutat. Res. Lett.* 119:27–34

123. Tsuji, K., Yamamoto, T., Zenda, H., Kosuge, T. 1978. Studies on active principles of tar. VII. Production of biological active substances in pyrolysis of amino acids. (2) Antifungal constituents in pyrolysis products of phenylalanine. *Yakugaku Zasshi* 98:910–13

124. Umezawa, K., Shirai, A., Matsushima, T., Sugimura, T. 1978. Comutagenic effect of norharman and harman with 2-acetylaminofluorene derivatives. *Proc. Natl. Acad. Sci. USA* 75:928–30

125. Uyeta, M., Kanada, T., Masaki, M., Taue, S., Takahashi, S. 1979. Assaying mutagenicity of food pyrolysis products using the Ames Test. In *Naturally Occurring Carcinogens Mutagens and Modulators of Carcinogenesis,* Princess Takamatsu Symp., ed. E. C. Miller, J. A. Miller, I. Hirono, T. Sugimura, S. Takayama, 9:169–76. Tokyo/Baltimore: Japan Sci. Soc. Univ. Park Press. 399 pp.

126. Wakabayashi, K., Tsuji, K., Kosuge, T., Takada, K., Yamaguchi, K., et al. 1978. Isolation and structure determination of a mutagenic substance in L-lysine pyrolysate. *Proc. Jpn. Acad.* 54(B):569–71

127. Waller, G. R., Feather, M. S., eds. 1983. *The Maillard Reactions in Foods and Nutrition,* ACS Symp. Ser. 215. Washington, DC: Am. Chem. Soc. 585 pp.

128. Watanabe, J., Kawajiri, K., Yonekawa, H., Nagao, M., Tagashira, Y. 1982. Immunological analysis of the roles of two major types of cytochrome P-450 in mutagenesis of compounds isolated from pyrolysates. *Biochem. Biophys. Res. Commun.* 104:193–99

129. Wogan, G. N., ed. 1965. *Mycotoxins in Foodstuffs.* Cambridge, Mass: MIT Press. 291 pp.

130. Yamada, M., Tsuda, M., Nagao, M., Mori, M., Sugimura, T. 1979. Degradation of mutagens from pyrolysates of tryptophan, glutamic acid and globulin by myeloperoxidase. *Biochem. Biophys. Res. Commun.* 90:769–76

131. Yamaguchi, K., Shudo, K., Okamoto, T., Sugimura, T., Kosuge, T. 1980. Presence of 2-aminodipyrido[1,2-*a*:3',2'-*d*]imidazole in broiled cuttlefish. *Gann* 71:743–44

132. Yamaguchi, K., Shudo, K., Okamoto, T., Sugimura, T., Kosuge, T. 1980. Presence of 3-amino-1,4-dimethyl-5*H*-pyrido[4,3-*b*]indole in broiled beef. *Gann* 71:745–46

133. Yamaizumi, Z., Shiomi, T., Kasai, H., Nishimura, S., Takahashi, Y., et al. 1980. Detection of potent mutagens, Trp-P-1 and Trp-P-2, in broiled fish. *Cancer Lett.* 9:75–83

134. Yamamoto, T., Tsuji, K., Kosuge, T., Okamoto, T., Shudo, K., et al. 1978. Isolation and structure determination of mutagenic substances in L-glutamic acid pyrolysate. *Proc. Jpn. Acad. B* 54:248–50

135. Yamazoe, Y., Ishii, K., Kamataki, T., Kato, R., Sugimura, T. 1980. Isolation and characterization of active metabolites of tryptophan pyrolysate mutagen, Trp-P-2, formed by rat liver microsomes. *Chem. Biol. Interact.* 30:125–38

136. Yamazoe, Y., Shimada, M., Kamataki, T., Kato, R. 1982. Covalent binding of *N*-hydroxy-Trp-P-2 to DNA by cytosolic proline-dependent system. *Biochem. Biophys. Res. Commun.* 107:165–72

137. Yamazoe, Y., Tada, M., Kamataki, T., Kato, R. 1981. Enhancement of binding of *N*-hydroxy-Trp-P-2 to DNA by seryl-tRNA synthetase. *Biochem. Biophys. Res. Commun.* 102:432–39

138. Yokota, M., Narita, K., Kosuge, T.,

Wakabayashi, K., Nagao, M., et al. 1981. A potent mutagen isolated from a pyrolysate of L-ornithine. *Chem. Pharm. Bull.* 29:1473–75

139. Yoo, M. A., Ryo, H., Todo, T., Kondo, S. 1985. Mutagenic potency of heterocyclic amines in the *Drosophila* wing spot test and its correlation to carcinogenic potency. *Jpn. J. Cancer Res. (Gann)* 76:468–73
140. Yoshida, D., Matsumoto, T., Yoshimura, R., Matsuzaki, T. 1978. Mutagenicity of amino-α-carbolines in pyrolysis products of soybean globulin. *Biochem. Biophys. Res. Commun.* 83:915–20
141. Yoshida, D., Okamoto, H. 1980. Formation of mutagens by heating creatine and glucose. *Biochem. Biophys. Res. Commun.* 96:844–47
142. Yoshida, D., Saito, Y., Mizusaki, S. 1984. Isolation of 2-amino-3-methylimidazo[4,5-*f*]quinoline as mutagen from the heated product of a mixture of creatine and proline. *Agric. Biol. Chem.* 48:241–43

*Ann. Rev. Nutr. 1986. 6:95–112*


# SOMATIC NUTRIENT REQUIREMENTS OF RUMINANTS

*J. M. Asplund*

Department of Animal Science, University of Missouri-Columbia, Columbia, Missouri 65211

---

CONTENTS

INTRODUCTION .......... 95
ENERGY REQUIREMENTS .......... 96
AMINO ACID REQUIREMENTS .......... 99
*Methodology* .......... 100
*Indirect Studies* .......... 102
*Direct Studies* .......... 103
VITAMIN REQUIREMENTS .......... 106
*Fat-Soluble Vitamins* .......... 106
*Water-Soluble Vitamins* .......... 106
INORGANIC NUTRIENTS .......... 107
SUMMARY .......... 109

## INTRODUCTION

Ruminant species supply over half the meat and essentially all of the milk and animal fiber consumed by man, as well as being a significant source of draft power and fuel. The unique digestive and metabolic strategies of these animals make them particularly efficient in the conversion of food sources not suitable for human consumption. There are, however, some substantial inefficiencies in these strategies so that production per unit of available nutrient is usually lower for ruminants than for nonruminant domestic species. The correction or amelioration of these inefficiencies offers one of the most promising and attractive means of increasing food supplies from existing sources.



0199-9885/86/0715-0095$02.00

The salient feature of ruminant digestive function is the massive anaerobic pregastric fermentation with accompanying physiological mechanisms; these sort and reprocess food to achieve maximum exposure of ingested food to microbial action. Through this process, complex polysaccharides such as cellulose are degraded, large amounts of microbial protein are synthesized, and water-soluble vitamins are produced. Thus, the nutrients presented for absorption differ widely from those ingested. The host animal must therefore be metabolically adapted to the utilization of the nutrients absorbed, not those ingested. This review examines the metabolism of the host animal as distinct from the microbiological symbiota, describes the ways in which this metabolism is organized to accommodate the nutrient supply, and provides a basis for devising methods of improving the efficiency of nutrient retention in ruminants. The term "somatic" denotes the aggregate of all tissues in the animal except for the associated microorganisms in the digestive tract, while "whole-body" is meant to describe somatic plus microbial nutrition.

Since interest in somatic nutrition is very recent, and because experimental methods are only now being developed to study the subject, it will be necessary to discuss methodology. It may also be necessary to draw a number of inferences from the comparison of whole-body metabolism with estimates of the microbial contribution.

## ENERGY REQUIREMENTS

The principal energy source for functioning ruminants is volatile fatty acid (VFA) (59). Indeed, very little available carbohydrate ever reaches the small intestine. Mono- and oligosaccharide are rapidly and completely degraded by rumen microorganisms, and complex carbohydrates, if digested at all, will be degraded to VFA. A fraction of native starch from seeds may escape rumen alteration and arrive at the small intestine but this amount is small and rarely exceeds 10% of the total starch fed, even when all-grain diets are fed (32).

In contrast, VFAs are produced in both the rumen and the hindgut and are absorbed directly from the organs to supply in excess of 90% of all the nonprotein energy used by the animal (59). This basic VFA economy is reflected in fundamental differences in energy metabolism. Blood glucose levels are low and relatively constant (63). Glucose tolerance and renal threshold are also very low (72). Insulin is less responsive to glucose influx, and blood glucose levels (44) are less responsive to insulin increases as compared to nonruminants. On the other hand, insulin levels respond very rapidly to propionate influx (44). These differences indicate that, not only is the major metabolic energy substrate different in ruminants, but also the mechanisms for control of metabolism and transport are not those usually considered.

The change from a glucose to a VFA economy occurs during the first few weeks of life and is usually complete when the rumen begins to function. The rate at which the change to ruminant function is made can be altered somewhat by feeding and management, but blood glucose declines regardless of these changes and so appears to be independent of functioning rumination (56).

The glucose necessary for maintaining blood glucose levels, Krebs cycle intermediates, lactose synthesis, and other processes with obligatory glucose requirements is obtained by gluconeogenesis from propionate mostly (59), with some possibly obtained from glucogenic amino acids (9). There is very little fat in a ruminant diet, and producing ruminants deposit or secrete rather large amounts of fat, which is synthesized mainly from acetate. Hence, fat tissue, with its need for glycerol in fat synthesis, is probably a net user rather than a supplier of glucose to the economy (7).

There has been a great volume of work studying the relative efficiencies of utilization of individual VFAs (59). The current thinking is that, if there are adequate gluconeogenic precursors available, there is little difference in energetic efficiency of the three main VFAs. However, absorbed VFAs as a group tend to be utilized with only about 90% of the efficiency of glucose (43).

There are pathological conditions resulting from the relative scarcity of certain VFAs under certain physiological conditions. A lack of gluconeogenic precursors (i.e. propionate) during heavy lactation in dairy cows or late pregnancy in multiparous ewes can result in acetonemia with morbidity and even death. Conversely, a decreased proportion of acetate (which may result from high grain feeding) can cause low milk fat syndrome in dairy cows (38).

There appears to be little difference between ruminants and nonruminants in fasting heat production (FHP). Ruminant species were included in Brody's summary of FHP related to body weight and were not anomalous as a group (18). Indeed, sheep especially have, if anything, a lower FHP than the interspecies norm (77). However, the energy requirement for maintenance is usually considerably higher for ruminants than for nonruminants of similar size. For instance, the NRC digestible-energy (DE) recommendation for maintenance of an adult boar is 96 kcal/$BW^{0.75}$ kg/day (where BW stands for body weight) (52) while for an adult ram it is 192 kcal/$BW^{0.75}$ kg/day (53).

These comparisons suggest an unusually high heat increment of feeding (HIF). There are three main sources of this increased heat loss. The first, which is nonsomatic, is the heat of fermentation of the rumen and hindgut microorganisms, which, owing to their high metabolic activity, is considerable. The second component of HIF is associated with the physical act of eating and, to a lesser extent, rumination (76). This heat loss is in excess of what might be expected on the basis of the muscular work of prehension and digesta transport. It is accompanied, during eating, with some rather dramatic shifts in water compartmentation (23). The ruminant eats for a much longer time than most other species and, additionally, ruminates for an additional period of time (10).

It appears, then, that the heat loss associated with ingestion of food is a major source of energy inefficiency in the somatic ruminant.

The third component of HIF is the metabolic activity of gut tissue. Although gut tissue contains only 7% of the protein of the body, it accounts for 20% of the total heat production (76). Approximately half of this heat can be accounted for as the heat cost of protein synthesis. The fractional rate of protein synthesis is considerably higher for gut tissue than for any other major tissue in the body (76). The remainder is possibly due to substrate metabolism in gut tissue, which is a major site of substrate oxidation. Under most circumstances, even when animals are fed to achieve a significant amount of starch digestion in the small intestine, the gut is a net utilizer of glucose (34). There is also considerable conversion of propionate to lactate in gut tissue (35). Ruminants usually have a considerably greater weight of gut tissue in relationship to body size than nonruminant species. Thus, the high metabolic activity of gut tissue is a major contribution to the heat losses of ruminants.

As significant as these heat losses are, those associated with eating, ruminating, and gut metabolism, together with microbial fermentation heat, account for less than half of the total HIF (76). This suggests that the major loss of energy is associated with the basic metabolism in all tissues. While this is true of all species, the proportion of loss to total energy metabolized is higher for ruminants than for nonruminants. This has been ascribed to the lower efficiency of metabolism of VFA as compared to either glucose or long-chain fatty acid (17).

It has long been acknowledged that, even under the best environmental and dietary conditions, the efficiency of production of domestic ruminants is much less than that of nonruminants. Although some of these inefficiencies are related to the fibrous nature of ruminant feeds and the necessary fermentative losses in the rumen, a number of them are somatic in nature and may, perhaps, yield to dietary or environmental manipulations in order to improve the utilization of digested energy for productive purposes.

It is difficult to assign an energy requirement to somatic tissues as separate from the whole animal. Even HIF is composed of both microbial and somatic effects. Heat of fermentation is clearly microbial and heat production by gut tissues is clearly somatic, while the heat cost of eating is probably related to both. DE requirements, even when corrected for heat of fermentation, are higher for ruminants on an equal metabolic body size basis as compared to nonruminants (52, 53). Since the metabolizable energy requirements for maintenance vary greatly with energy level of intake and body composition (76), it is difficult to use this measure as an indication of somatic efficiency. As a consequence, the $K_m$ values presented by Blaxter (17) probably constitute the closest approximation of somatic energy use. It is suggested therefore, that the energy requirement for maintenance of somatic tissue is 10% higher for ruminant species than for nonruminants of comparable physiological age and size.

## AMINO ACID REQUIREMENTS

One of the most important influences of the pregastric fermentation of ingested food by ruminants is the very effective degradation of protein and the synthesis of microbiological protein from the degraded protein as well as from nonprotein nitrogen compounds such as urea. The process of microbial protein synthesis is so massive that the total protein requirement of producing animals can be met with microbial protein (74). Under practical situations, some dietary protein escapes degradation to be digested and absorbed post-ruminally, but microbial protein remains the major amino acid source for the host (46). In view of this, and considering the observation that the amino acid content of microbial protein is relatively unaltered by dietary conditions (14), it had long been considered a moot question to determine somatic amino acid requirements.

However, observations that post-ruminal infusions of methionine could increase wool growth and nitrogen balance (29) rekindled interest in this subject. It was seen that certain protein sources such as fish meal, blood meal, and corn gluten supported improved nitrogen retention and that these same properties could be bestowed upon other protein feeds by heat, aldehyde, or tannic acid treatment (25). These effects are associated with the ability of the feed protein to pass through the rumen fermentation process undegraded and yet be available for gastric and enteric digestion. This "undegraded" or "escape" protein has three possible advantageous properties. First, it may increase the total amount of amino acid nitrogen available for absorption since there is a limitation to the amount of protein that can be synthesized by rumen microorganisms. Second, even if all the nitrogen released by proteolysis in the rumen could be trapped by rumen microorganisms, the synthetic process diverts approximately 25% of the nitrogen into non-amino-acid compounds such as nucleic acids as well as into unusual amino acids that make no contribution to the protein metabolism. Third, the escape protein may alter the amino acid pattern of absorbed protein to improve its biological value.

Processes to protect individual amino acids from rumen degradation have been developed in order to manipulate the biological value of absorbed proteins (55). It has thus been demonstrated that the amino acid supply can, indeed, be manipulated in a variety of ways but results have so far been rather erratic. In making such manipulations, it is critical to know the somatic nutrient requirements for amino acids, since dietary alterations made in ignorance of the metabolic requirements are, at best, only speculative.

Clearly, the supply of essential amino acids available to somatic metabolism is that coming from the combination of microbial protein and undegraded food protein entering the post-ruminal digestive tract. The efficiency of utilization of this amino acid supply depends upon the digestibility of the individual amino acids and upon their relative proportions compared to the somatic requirements of the animal.

The amino acids that are metabolically essential (that is, not synthesized somatically) for the dairy cow, were shown by Black et al (15) to be fundamentally the same as for the rat. Arginine was synthesized in the animals but histidine was not. There were differences in the extent of incorporation of $^{14}C$ depending upon the energy substrate used for synthesis (16), but this gave no indication of the relative quantitative requirements for individual amino acids.

Ruminants respond to changes in amino acid patterns supplied post-ruminally (21, 42, 79). There is very little difference among protein sources fed orally unless they contain, or are treated to contain, large amounts of escape protein. However, nitrogen balance is improved when proteins of high quality for nonruminants, such as casein, are given directly into the post-rumen digestive tract. Conversely, poor quality proteins such as zein and gelatin given in this way generally depress nitrogen retention (42). The amino acid pattern found in sheep carcasses was much better utilized than a pattern similar to plasma free amino acids when these patterns were given intravenously (79).

## Methodology

It therefore appears that the somatic metabolism behaves much like the whole-body metabolism of a nonruminant and therefore could be studied using models similar to that used by Rose et al (62). However, the problem of ruminal amino acid synthesis must be resolved if reliable data are to be obtained. This has been approached in two ways. The pre-ruminant young has been used in studies of amino acid requirements (30, 78). Since the rumen in these animals is nonfunctional, the amino acids presented for absorption are essentially those ingested. Diets can therefore be altered to provide varying amino acid patterns to the animal. It is necessary, however, in the use of this model to assume that the somatic metabolism resembles that of the ruminating young. That is a very tenuous assumption in the light of the fundamental metabolic changes that accompany development of ruminating capacity. The changes in energy metabolism are well documented, but detection of alterations in amino acid utilization still awaits better methodology. If such changes are observed, the pre-ruminant model has little, if any, advantage over the use of nonruminant species such as swine. Additionally, the pre-ruminant is in a very transitory condition and occurs only during the milk-feeding period (40). Maintenance, gestation, or lactation requirements cannot be examined in pre-ruminant young.

The most promising technique in the investigation of somatic effects of amino acids is the use of post-ruminal administration of experimental regimens. Usual routes of administration have been abomasal, duodenal, or intravenous infusions. Using these infusions, nutrients can be supplied directly to absorption or utilization sites without undergoing microbial alteration. The infusions have been done in both the presence and absence of a functional rumen. If the rumen is discharging digesta into the abomasum, the rumen effluent must be considered as the diet and the infusate as a supplement. This method has been used extensively to attempt to determine the limiting amino acids in the nutrient supply to ruminating animals under a variety of conditions (60).

Researchers studying amino acid adequacy are faced with the problem of choosing an appropriate indicator of response to changes in amino acid patterns. Theoretically, biological value is the absolute measure of the correspondence of a specific amino acid pattern to somatic requirements. However, it is very difficult to measure and, in the ruminating animal, is actually not a function of dietary amino acid supply, but is influenced by a great variety of factors (1, 5). Under conditions where protein degradation by rumen microorganisms exceeds protein synthesis so that appreciable ammonia is lost, the errors can be significant (3, 5). When amino acids or proteins are administered post-ruminally either intragastrically or intravenously, biological value can be determined and gives a good indication of the adequacy of amino acid supply. This technique has been employed by Asplund et al (8) and Storm & Ørskov (70).

Although it is not an absolute measure, nitrogen balance is very useful in comparing and titrating animal response to different amino acid patterns. Nitrogen balance is perhaps the most reliable and responsive measure available at this time (3). It has been used by most of those engaged in amino acid studies for ruminants. Most of the variation in nitrogen balance in a given experiment occurs in the urinary losses, specifically, urea losses. Consequently, urinary urea excretion has been used as a measure of protein adequacy. However, even in animals receiving their amino acids intravenously it was less precise and responded to a lesser degree than did nitrogen balance (71). Similarly, plasma urea levels are closely correlated with nitrogen balance but actual measurements were less useful than was nitrogen balance (71).

It has been proposed that plasma levels of free amino acids can be a useful indicator of the relationship of a given amino acid supply to its requirement. This was extensively reviewed by Bergen (13). The two-phase curve, with its inflection at the requirement, has generally corresponded with nitrogen balance and other data for many amino acids. Plasma free methionine (58, 71), threonine (58), and valine (48) have all responded as expected to graded levels of ingestion of these amino acids. However, lysine failed to respond with an increase in plasma levels of the free amino acid at intakes beyond those that produced maximum nitrogen balance (8, 58, 75). When phenylalanine was administered in increasing amounts in the absence of tyrosine, plasma free phenylalanine did not respond in any way to increasing infusion, but plasma tyrosine levels increased dramatically at the levels at which nitrogen balance indicated adequate phenylalanine supply (9). It appears, therefore, that responses in plasma free amino acids can be used for some amino acids but not for others.

The rate of oxidation of lysine has been used to indicate an excess of lysine (19). The increased oxidation rate observed for the amino acid may also explain the failure to observe the expected increase in plasma free levels of lysine at above requirement intake.

## *Indirect Studies*

The identification of limiting amino acids provides some inferences concerning potentially valuable supplementation. The most consistently limiting amino acid is methionine. In almost every instance where post-ruminal supplementation has been effective, methionine was the first limiting amino acid (60). There have also been some responses to lysine, especially as a second limiting amino acid (20, 70). Other amino acids have occasionally improved nitrogen retention. Among these are threonine (57), histidine (22), and phenylalanine (22, 24). However, even if the response to added amino acids can be titrated, the resulting values reflect only the inadequacies of the amino acid supply under the dietary conditions of the trial and not the somatic requirements of the host. Requirements can be approximated if some measure of the amino acid content of rumen effluent or abomasal ingesta can be made. Although ingesta sampling can be done rather simply, quantitative inferences are meaningful only if rates of digesta flow are measured. This involves the use of markers or of re-entry cannulae, which increases the cost and difficulty and reduces the precision of the determinations. Additionally, these techniques can be useful only if the amino acid being supplemented is clearly limiting under the dietary conditions of the study.

Nimrick et al (57, 58) infused a number of amino acids into sheep receiving a diet in which all the nitrogen was from nonprotein sources. They reported amino acid requirements as "supplemental amino acid needs" with the assumption that these values indicated the deficiencies of microbial protein. The data did, indeed, indicate which amino acids were limiting and the general order in which limitation occurred but, in the absence of data regarding the available amino acid supply from the rumen, cannot be considered to be somatic requirements.

Similar work with a variety of diets was reported for methionine by Shelling et al (65). In the latter experiment, response to methionine varied with the diets used. Fenderson & Bergen (28) used estimates of abomasal contents and abomasal flow rates in connection with response to supplementation with methionine, lysine, threonine, and tryptophan. They estimated requirements for methionine in growing steers but observed that the animal responded only to methionine, so that the requirements for the other three amino acids did not exceed the abomasal flow.

This general approach was more precisely pursued by Storm & Ørskov (67–70). These workers used isolated microbial protein administered intragastrically so that "dietary" amino acid supply was controlled and known. The biological value of the dietary protein was determined and a mixed amino acid supplement given to bring the original diet to the value of 100%, based on the dietary intake. By serial deletion of individual amino acids, the order and extent of limitation for each was determined. This technique gave rational values for the appropriate requirement levels of the limiting amino acids, but values for those not limiting can be considered as simply not exceeding the levels in microbial protein.

## *Direct Studies*

Requirement estimates for all amino acids can be obtained by using chemically defined diets with crystalline amino acids. For ruminants, these must be administered post-ruminally and the rumen may not contribute measurable protein to the system. This state is achieved by a dual infusion method. Since the main energy substrate is VFA and the somatic tolerance for glucose is very low, a way must be derived to administer VFA. Intraruminal infusion of VFA accompanied by appropriate buffering has proven to be the most effective way of supplying energy in this form (59). This also has the advantage of keeping the rumen irrigated in the absence of any oral feeding with a resultant virtual cessation of protein synthetic activity.

In animals receiving energy by intraruminal infusion of VFA, intragastric or intravenous infusions of amino acids and other nutrients can be studied systematically with controlled and manipulatable dietary conditions. Using this model with intravenous amino acid infusions, data have been obtained for the somatic requirements of methionine (71), lysine and arginine (2, 8, 73) leucine (36), phenylalanine (9), valine (48), threonine (4), and tryptophan (unpublished data). In each study, the general design was the same. An amino acid mixture representing the most recent estimates of adequacy was used. This pattern began as the amino acid spectrum in sheep carcass (79) and was altered to incorporate the information from requirement trials as these were completed. The amino acid in question was deleted and added back at appropriate levels while the mixture remained isonitrogeneous with the addition or deletion of the required amounts of glycine. The level of amino acid that supported the highest nitrogen retention was taken to be the required level. Where appropriate, plasma free amino acid levels were also used to corroborate the nitrogen balance data. Trials were conducted at the energy level of 105 kcal per kg $BW^{0.75}$, which is an adequate maintenance allowance.

From these trials, a tentative requirement list for the essential amino acids for maintenance in the sheep was prepared (Table 1). The data, representing only a first estimation of these requirements, have been compared with figures for requirements of some amino acids obtained by other methods previously described and summarized by Lewis & Mitchell (39) (Table 1). It is observed that there is substantial agreement for both lysine and methionine but that the estimates of threonine requirement obtained directly by infusion are lower than previous estimates. However, the previous estimates were made in animals with intact functioning rumens, which seldom supply less threonine than the required amount. It has already been shown that the requirement of most amino acids does not exceed the gastric supply.

The spectrum of amino acids obtained by intravenous infusion was tested for biological value using intragastric administration of casein enriched with amino acids to match the pattern listed in Table 1 plus isoleucine at the levels in casein. The biological value of this mixture, calculated from the regression of urinary nitrogen on nitrogen intake, was 103 ± 8%; it very closely approximated the pattern of requirement for sheep at maintenance. Corresponding values for casein alone and gelatin infused intragastrically were 87 ± 4% and 7 ± 7% (6).

Although there appears to be very efficient retention of this pattern of amino acids for maintenance, several questions remain to be answered:

1. Maintenance as defined by the experimental design includes wool growth. This function involves the selective incorporation into a nonrecycling pool and thus differs from the exact definition of maintenance.
2. The influence of nonessential amino acids is not fully explained. It is possible that, if nonessential amino acids were limiting, the nitrogen available from the deamination of surplus essential amino acids could be used for nonessential amino acid synthesis and give false high estimates for biological value. However, the improvement over casein of the supplemented casein suggests that this was not the case. The role and importance of both level and composition of the nonessential amino acids remain subjects for further work.

**Table 1** Comparison of estimates of amino acid requirements for ruminants

| Amino acid | Intravenous model (6) (mg/kg $BW^{0.75}$) | Other estimates (39) (mg/kg $BW^{0.75}$) | Intravenous model (6) (% of essential) | Factorial estimate (66) (% of essential) |
|---|---|---|---|---|
| ARG | 219 | | 9.9 | |
| HIS | <62.5 | | 2.5 | 2 |
| LEU | 375 | | 16.8 | 15 |
| LYS | 437 | 408–<545 | 18 | 7 |
| MET | 225[a] | 105– 207 | 7.2 | 3[b] |
| PHE | 250 | | 11.4 | 9[c] |
| THR | 187 | 260– 340 | 7.6 | 13 |
| TRY | <62.5 | | 2.8 | 4 |
| VAL | 187 | | 9.6 | 11 |

[a]No other source of sulfur amino acids was available.
[b]Methionine only. Total sulfur amino acids were 14%.
[c]Phenylalanine only. Total aromatic amino acids were 22%.

3. The use of intravenous amino acid administration begs the question of absorptive efficiency and possible digestive tract degradation. However, the fact that intragastric infusion was used to test the adequacy of the pattern determined by intravenous administration suggests that absorption influences were slight.

There is considerable evidence that the qualitative as well as the quantitative requirements for growth, lactation, and active reproductive functions may be different from those for maintenance, especially when maintenance includes wool growth. Thus, the data presented can probably not represent optimum amino acid patterns in producing animals. This criticism is valid, and concerted effort is needed to ascertain the requirements for producing ruminants. However, the figures for maintenance provide a useful beginning. First of all, maintenance is the only productive function that does not involve the deposition of tissue and, therefore is the only function in which the amino acid accrual cannot be measured. Perhaps some factorial system incorporating maintenance estimates and tissue accumulation, adjusted for incorporation efficiency, might prove useful in describing the somatic requirements for all productive functions.

This factorial method has most recently been attempted by Smith (66). He considered the amino acid composition of body tissues and the relative growth of each and calculated amino acid requirements from these values. His results are in substantial agreement with the values obtained by direct infusion studies (Table 1), but differ from the values obtained from sheep carcass alone. The requirement values for both the factorial and infusion methods vary from the National Research Council recommended values for swine (52) in that they are relatively lower in methionine and phenylalanine.

It is not known if amino acid metabolism differs between ruminants and nonruminants. This is largely a result of the paucity of information on specific amino acid metabolic pathways in ruminants, since amino acid supply is so difficult to control. There are, however, some indications that the control mechanisms and, perhaps, at least quantitative differences may occur. For example, branched-chain amino acids are released intact from muscle tissue in ruminants and the activity of enzymes associated with their degradation is markedly lower in muscle tissue when compared with nonruminants (41). In contrast, adipose and mammary tissue are relatively more active in branched-chain amino acid degradation in ruminants (26).

There also appear to be some differences in sulfur amino acid metabolism. The methionine requirement for sheep appears to be lower than would be expected on the basis of the content of sulfur amino acids in wool. There was no increase in that value in the absence of microbial protein or of exogenous cysteine (71). Benevenga et al (11, 12) observed that less than 10% of methionine degradation occurred via transsulfuration in intact sheep. Thus the mechanisms and kinetics of cysteine biosynthesis in ruminants, especially sheep, would appear to be a very fruitful field for further studies. With experimental models now available, such studies should be undertaken.

## VITAMIN REQUIREMENTS

### *Fat-Soluble Vitamins*

There are no data to indicate specific needs, by microorganisms, for any fat-soluble vitamins and little reason to suppose that the ruminant differs from other mammals in its metabolism of these nutrients.

Vitamin K is synthesized by rumen microorganisms if natural feed supplies are otherwise deficient (47). Ruminants are fairly inefficient in the conversion of β-carotene to vitamin A (54) and there is some evidence to suggest that cattle have a specific β-carotene requirement as distinct from vitamin A (33). However, whole-body requirements would not appear to differ from the specific somatic requirements.

### *Water-Soluble Vitamins*

It has long been recognized that rumen microorganisms produce water-soluble vitamins (47). There have been no studies on the rate of destruction or incorporation of these nutrients. However, since in vivo studies always show a net increase in levels, it appears likely that supply will exceed demand under all normal conditions. The water-soluble vitamin requirements of pre-ruminant calves were studied some time ago. Deficiency symptoms for most of the B complex were demonstrated and optimum replacements determined (37). There were no substantial differences between calves and other nonruminant animals. However, it might be expected that the shift in the base of energy economy that occurs when the animal becomes ruminant might alter the requirements for at least those vitamins involved in carbohydrate metabolism.

There has been considerable recent interest in thiamin. Deficiency symptoms are observed when thiamin antimetabolites such as amprolium are fed or when natural sources of thiamin analogues such as bracken fern are eaten (27). More recently the condition of polioencephalomalacia or cerebrocortical necrosis was observed in animals fed high levels of rapidly degradable carbohydrates (64). This condition appears to be due to a thiamin analogue produced by an unusual rumen microflora rather than to a destruction and, hence, a simple deficiency of thiamin.

Using an infusion technique, Mueller & Asplund (51) were able to supply a thiamin-free diet to sheep. After a long period of time, blood lactate and pyruvate were elevated and erythrocyte transketolase responded dramatically to thiamin pyrophosphate in deficient sheep but no alterations in central nervous system tissue were detectable. Moreover, all of these indications of deficiency were eliminated by supplementation with 135 mg $kg^{-1}d^{-1}$ of thiamin hydrochloride, a level similar to that usually recommended for nonruminants. The slow development of biochemical lesions and the absence of specific physical pathologies would suggest that the thiamin requirement is considerably lower than the levels supplemented.

The only other water-soluble vitamin to be studied in ruminants is niacin. There is some suggestion that supplemental niacin might be beneficial in very high producing animals such as rapidly growing calves and lactating cows in peak production, but the results are quite erratic. It has been suggested that niacin reduces the risk of acetonemia in dairy cows (31) but there is not very much metabolic evidence of this. It appears, however, that if the effects are real, the site of action is in the rumen and not the somatic tissues.

There is little reason to expect that somatic requirements for water-soluble vitamins exceed those observed in nonruminant species. It may even be that some of the requirements are lower. In any event, rumen synthesis appears to be adequate under an extremely wide variety of dietary conditions.

## INORGANIC NUTRIENTS

In contrast to the organic nutrients, where microbial alteration of structure can change the ingested nutrients to increase or decrease supply, there is no basis to assume that mineral nutrients will be augmented or decreased by passage through the rumen. Only three conditions might obtain in which somatic requirements would vary from the whole-animal requirements. The first would be an increase or a decrease in availability attributable to the function of rumen microorganisms. The second condition would be a requirement by the microflora exceeding that of the somatic metabolism. The third would occur when the rumen microorganisms required an element in order to produce a specific organic compound for the somatic metabolism.

The influence of the first two conditions can be examined using phosphorus as an example, while the third is epitomized in the incorporation of cobalt into cobalamine.

Phosphorus availability varies widely between species and between dietary sources. Phytate phosphorus is used with varying efficiency by a number of species, but the ruminant appears to be able to use this form of phosphorus essentially completely, with the rumen being the primary site of phytase activity (61). However, Meredith & Asplund (unpublished data) demonstrated appreciable phytase activity in the small intestine of sheep. This activity increased during phosphorus deficiency, which indicates that the rumen is not the only source of phytate degradation. This results in an apparently lower whole-body dietary requirement for the element as compared with nonruminants, although this difference may only be due to the greater availability of dietary phosphorus. This destruction of phytate might in turn influence the availability of those trace elements that depend on phytate. It would appear, then, that recommended dietary allowances for phosphorus and trace elements, especially those that are traditionally inflated to compensate for lower availability, for the ruminant are certainly not greater and are perhaps less than those for nonruminant species.

The relationship between somatic and microbial requirements for phosphorus is more difficult to assess. There is considerable recycling of phosphorus to the rumen via the saliva and, although both salivary and rumen phosphorus levels are decreased in phosphorus deficiency, rumen levels are usually quite high. In a deficiency, one of the most striking symptoms is loss of appetite. It has long been debated whether this was due to decreased activity of rumen microorganisms or to somatic effects. Recent work by Milton & Ternouth (49) indicates that the lowered food intake is due to somatic influences. These researchers reduced recycling by exteriorizing the parotid salivary ducts and then feeding a phosphorus-deficient diet. Unsupplemented animals deprived of recycled phosphorus had only marginally reduced nutrient digestibilities but drastically impaired food intakes. Supplementation via the abomasum was just as effective in restoring food intake as was supplementation into the rumen. This supports the concept that food intake reduction is a somatic effect and that rumen microorganisms therefore do not have a higher phosphorus requirement than does the somatic metabolism. This is further supported by the observation that in vitro preparations perform optionally at phosphorus levels below those observed in the deficient state in this experiment (50).

Ruminants have an apparent whole-body requirement for cobalt. This is a result of microbial synthesis of cobalamine. The somatic system needs only cobalamine, and injections of cobalt are ineffective against a dietary cobalt deficiency. An absolute requirement of the microorganisms for cobalt has not been established. Growth and metabolite production by some species is influenced by cobalt supplementation (45), but there is no evidence that cobalt is involved in any reactions other than incorporation into cobalamine and numerous related analogues. Thus, we have a possible requirement of an element by the microorganisms but a requirement for the vitamin cobalamine specifically by the somatic tissue.

# SUMMARY

On the basis of existing information it is, perhaps, useful to propose tentative preliminary figures for somatic nutrient requirements (Table 2). Such a proposal may serve as a focus for research to clarify more precisely the somatic requirements for a given production function in a given species. The requirements, therefore, are presented as interspecies generalizations and are calculated per kilogram of metabolic body size for the maintenance of adult animals. Only those nutrients for which there are some experimental data are included, so the absence of a given nutrient is an indication that it has not been studied. The figure for energy was derived by subtracting from the metabolizable energy for maintenance those heat losses associated with bacterial action and with prehension and transport of food. The resulting value was then increased by an amount representing the relative inefficiency of VFA, as compared with glucose metabolism. Amino acid values are essentially those obtained by intravenous administration. Water-soluble vitamin values except for thiamin were not listed because they were not expected to differ from whole-body requirements. Thiamin data were based on the work of Mueller & Asplund (51).

The most obvious need is for definitive values for the amino acid requirements for productive functions and for water-soluble vitamin data. In the absence of such data, experiments with supplementation of these nutrients will continue to be haphazard and arbitrary.

**Table 2** Suggested somatic requirements for the maintenance of adult sheep

| Nutrient | Somatic requirement[a] |
|---|---|
| Metabolizable energy | 475 |
| ARG | 220 |
| HIS | 65 |
| ILE | 250 |
| LEU | 375 |
| LYS | 435 |
| MET | 225 |
| PHE | 250 |
| THR | 190 |
| TRY | 65 |
| VAL | 190 |
| Thiamin | 100 |
| Phosphorus | 140 |

[a]Metabolizable energy requirement measured in kcal/kg protein$^{0.75}$. All other nutrient requirements measured in mg/kg BW$^{0.75}$.

## Literature Cited

1. Asplund, J. M. 1968. Nitrogen balance, biological value and metabolic fecal nitrogen in mature sheep fed simplified rations. *Utah Acad. Sci. Arts and Lett.* 45(11):603–7
2. Asplund, J. M. 1975. A parenteral model to study amino acid requirements of functioning ruminants. *Proc. XI Int. Congr. Nutr.*, p. 239. (Abstr). Mexico City: Int. Union Nutr. Sci.
3. Asplund, J. M. 1975. The determination and significance of biological value of proteins for ruminants. In *Protein Nutritional Quality of Foods and Feeds,* ed. M. Friedman. New York: Dekker. 626 pp.
4. Asplund, J. M. 1976. Influence of threonine level for sheep totally nourished by infusions. *Fed. Proc.* 35:579
5. Asplund, J. M. 1979. The interpretation and significance of nutrient balance experiments. *J. Anim. Sci.* 49:826–31
6. Asplund, J. M. 1985. Metabolic amino acid requirements and biological value of single proteins for sheep. *Fed. Proc.* 44:750 (Abstr.)
7. Asplund, J. M., Ørskov, E. R., Hovell, F. D. DeB., Macleod, N. A. 1985. The effect of intragastric infusion of glucose, lipids or acetate on fasting nitrogen excretion and blood metabolites in sheep. *Br. J. Nutr.* 54:189–95
8. Asplund, J. M., Tao, R. C., Richter, B. G. 1977. Influence of lysine and arginine levels on nitrogen balance and free amino acids in sheep totally nourished by infusions. *Fed. Proc.* 36:1099 (Abstr.)
9. Asplund, J. M., Ward, C. 1982. The effects of levels of phenylalanine on nitrogen metabolism in infused sheep. *Fed. Proc.* 41:392 (Abstr.)
10. Balch, C. C. 1971. Proposal to use time spent chewing as an index of the extent to which diets for ruminants possess the physical properties of fibrousness characteristic of roughages. *Br. J. Nutr.* 26:383–92
11. Benevenga, N. J., Radcliffe, B. C., Eagen, A. R. 1983. Tissue metabolism of methionine in sheep. *Aust. J. Biol. Sci.* 36:475–85
12. Benevenga, N. J., Radcliffe, B. C., Eagen, A. R. 1984. Quantitative aspects of methionine metabolism in sheep. *Fed. Proc.* 42:542 (Abstr.)
13. Bergen, W. G. 1979. Free amino acids in blood of ruminants—physiological and nutritional regulation. *J. Anim. Sci.* 49:1577–89
14. Bergen, W. G., Purser, D. B., Cline, J. H. 1968. Effect of ration on the nutritive quality of rumen microbial protein. *J. Anim. Sci.* 27:1497–1508
15. Black, A. L., Kleiber, M., Smith, A. H. 1952. Carbonate and fatty acid as precursors of amino acids in casein. *J. Biol. Chem.* 197:365–70
16. Black, A. L., Kleiber, M., Smith, A. H., Stewart, D. N. 1957. Acetate as a precurser of amino acids of casein in the intact dairy cow. *Biochem. Biophys. Acta* 23:54–59
17. Blaxter, K. L. 1962. *The Energy Metabolism of Ruminants.* London: Hutchinson. 332 pp.
18. Brody, S. 1945. *Bioenergentics and Growth.* New York: Reinhold
19. Brookes, I. M., Owens, F. N., Brown, R. E., Garrigus, U. S. 1973. Amino acid oxidation and plasma amino acid levels in sheep with abomasal infusions of graded amounts of lysine. *J. Anim. Sci.* 36:965–70
20. Burris, W. R., Boling, J. A., Bradley, N. W., Young, A. W. 1976. Abomasal lysine infusions in steers fed a urea supplemented diet. *J. Anim. Sci.* 42:699–708
21. Chalmers, M. I., Cuthbertson, O. P., Synge, R. L. M. 1954. Ruminal ammonia formation in relation to the diet of sheep. I. Duodenal administration and heat processing as factors influencing fate of casein supplements. *J. Agric. Sci.* 44:254–62
22. Chalupa, W. 1975. Rumen bypass and protection of proteins and amino acids. *J. Dairy Sci.* 58:1198–1210
23. Christopherson, R. J., Webster, A. J. F. 1972. Changes during eating in oxygen consumption, cardiac function and body fluids in sheep. *J. Physiol.* 221:441–57
24. Clark, J. H. 1975. Lactational responses to postruminal administration of proteins and amino acids. *J. Dairy Sci.* 58:1178–97
25. Clark, J. H. 1975. Nitrogen metabolism in ruminants: protein solubility and rumen bypass of protein and amino acids. See Ref. 3, pp. 261–74
26. Clark, J. H., Spires, H. E., Davis, C. L. 1978. Uptake and metabolism of nitrogenous compounds by the lactating mammary gland. *Fed. Proc.* 37:1233–38
27. Edwin, E. E., Lewis, G. 1971. Thiamin deficiency with particular reference to cerebrocortical necrosis—a review and discussion. *J. Dairy Res.* 38:79–90
28. Fenderson, C. L., Bergen, W. G. 1975.

An assessment of the essential amino acid requirements of growing steers. *J. Anim. Sci.* 41:1759

29. Ferguson, K. A. 1975. The protection of dietary proteins and amino acids against microbial fermentation in the rumen. In *Digestion and Metabolism in the Ruminant,* ed. I. W. McDonald, A. C. I. Warner, pp. 448–64 Armidale, New South Wales: Univ. New England Publ. Unit
30. Foldager, J., Huber, J. T., Bergen, W. G. 1977. Methionine and sulfur amino acid requirement of the preruminant calf. *J. Dairy Sci.* 60:1095–1104
31. Fronk, T. J., Schultz, L. H. 1979. Oral nicotinic acid as a treatment for ketosis. *J. Dairy Sci.* 62:1804–7
32. Galyean, M. L., Wagner, D. G., Owens, F. N. 1979. Corn particle size and site of extent of digestion by steers. *J. Anim. Sci.* 49:203–10
33. Hemken, R. W., Bremel, D. H. 1982. Beta carotene in dairy cattle nutrition. *Proc. Cornell Nutr. Conf.,* pp. 13–15. Ithaca: Cornell Univ
34. Huntington, G. B. 1983. Net nutrient absorption in beef steers fed silage or high concentrate diets containing four levels of limestone. *J. Nutr.* 113:1157–64
35. Huntington, G. B., Prior, R. L. 1983. Digestion and absorption of nutrients by beef heifers fed a high concentrate diet. *J. Nutr.* 113:2280–88
36. Jensen, D. O., Asplund, J. M. 1979. The effect of leucine infusion on various nitrogen parameters in sheep. *Nutr. Rep. Int.* 20:115–23
37. Johnson, B. C., Pinkos, J. A., Burke, K. A. 1950. Pyridoxine deficiency in the calf. *J. Nutr.* 40:309–22
38. Kronfield, D. S. 1982. Major metabolic determinants of milk volume, mammary efficiency and spontaneous ketosis in dairy cows. *J. Dairy Sci.* 65:2204–12
39. Lewis, D., Mitchell, R. M. 1976. Amino acid requirements of ruminants. In *Protein Metabolism and Nutrition,* ed. D. J. A. Cole, K. N. Boorman, P. J. Buttery, D. Lewis, R. J. Neale, H. Swan, pp. 417–24. London: Butterworths
40. Liebholz, J. 1978. The development of ruminal digestion in the calf. II. The digestion of barley and urea. *Aust. J. Agric. Res.* 29:1293–99
41. Lindsay, D. B., Buttery, P. J. 1980. Metabolism in muscle. In *Protein Deposition in Animals,* ed. P. J. Buttery, D. B. Lindsay. London: Butterworths 305 pp.
42. Little, C. O., Mitchell, G. E. 1967. Abomasal vs oral administration of proteins to wethers. *J. Anim. Sci.* 26:411–20
43. MacRae, J. C., Lobley, G. E. 1982. Factors which influence energy losses of ruminants. *Livestock Prod. Sci.* 9:447–56
44. Manns, J. E., Boda, J. M. 1967. Insulin release by acetate, propionate, butyrate and glucose in lambs and adult sheep. *Am. J. Physiol.* 212:747–55
45. Martinez, A., Church, D. C. 1970. Effect of various mineral elements on in vitro rumen cellulose digestion. *J. Anim. Sci.* 31:982–90
46. McAllen, A. B., Smith, R. H. 1984. The efficiency of microbial protein synthesis in the rumen and the degradability of feed nitrogen between the mouth and abomasum in steers given different diets. *Br. J. Nutr.* 51:77–83
47. McElroy, L. W., Goss, H. 1940. A quantitative study of vitamins in the rumen contents of sheep and cows fed vitamin-low diets. I. Riboflavin and Vitamin K. *J. Nutr.* 20:527–40
48. Mesbah, M. M., Asplund, J. M. 1984. The influence of level of valine on nitrogen status and plasma free amino acid levels in infused sheep. *J. Nutr.* 114:1363–69
49. Milton, J. T. B., Ternouth, J. H. 1982. Site of the effect of phosphorus deficiency upon food intake. *Anim. Prod. Aust.* 13:630
50. Milton, J. T. B., Ternouth, J. H. 1984. The effects of phosphorus upon in vitro microbial digestion. *Anim. Prod. Aust.* 15:472–75
51. Mueller, R. E., Asplund, J. M. 1981. Evidence in the ovine that polioencephalomalacia is not a result of an uncomplicated thiamin deficiency. *Nutr. Rep. Int.* 24:95–104
52. National Research Council. 1973. *Nutrient Requirements of Domestic Animals, No. 2, Nutrient Requirements of Swine.* Washington, DC: Natl. Acad. Sci. 56 pp.
53. National Research Council. 1975. *Nutrient Requirements of Domestic Animals, No. 5, Nutrient Requirements of Sheep.* Washington, DC: Natl. Acad. Sci. 72 pp.
54. National Research Council. 1978. *Nutrient Requirements of Domestic Animals, No. 3, Nutrient Requirements of Dairy Cattle.* Washington, DC: Nat. Acad. Sci. 76 pp.
55. Neudoerffer, T. S., Duncan, D. B., Horney, F. D. 1971. The extent of release of encapsulated methionine in the intestine of cattle. *Br. J. Nutr.* 25:343–50
56. Nicolai, J. H., Stewart, W. E. 1965. Relationship between forestomach and glycemia in ruminants. *J. Dairy Sci.* 48:56–60
57. Nimrick, K., Hatfield, E. E., Kaminski, J., Owens, F. N. 1970. Qualitative as-

sessment of supplemental amino acid needs for growing lambs fed urea as the sole nitrogen source. *J. Nutr*. 100:1293–1300
58. Nimrick, K., Hatfield, E. E., Kaminski, J., Owens, F. N. 1970. Quantitative assessment of supplemental amino acid needs for growing lambs fed urea as the sole nitrogen source. *J. Nutr*. 100:1301–6
59. Ørskov, E. R., Grubb, D. A., Smith, J. S., Webster, A. J. F., Corrigal, W. 1979. Efficiency of utilization of volatile fatty acids for maintenance and energy retention in sheep. *Br. J. Nutr*. 41:L541–50
60. Owens, F. N., Bergen, W. G. 1983. Nitrogen metabolism of ruminant animals: Historical perspective, current understanding and future implications. *J. Anim. Sci*. 57(Suppl. 2):498–518
61. Reid, R. L. 1947. The utilization of phytate phosphorus by sheep. *Aust. Vet. J*. 23:136–40
62. Rose, W. C., Wixom, R. L., Lockhart, H. B., Lambert, G. F. 1955. The amino acid requirements of man. XV. The valine requirement, summary and final observations. *J. Biol. Chem*. 217:987–95
63. Ross, J. P., Kitts, W. D. 1973. Relationship between postprandial plasma volatile fatty acids, glucose and insulin levels in sheep fed different feeds. *J. Nutr*. 103:488–93
64. Sapienza, D. A., Brent, B. E. 1974. Ruminal thiaminase vs concentrate adaptation. *J. Anim. Sci*. 39:251 (Abstr.)
65. Schelling, G. T., Chandler, J. E., Scott, G. C. 1973. Post ruminal supplemental methionine infusion to sheep fed high quality diets. *J. Anim. Sci*. 37:1034–39
66. Smith, R. H. 1980. Comparative amino acid requirements. *Proc. Nutr. Soc*. 39:71–87
67. Storm, E., Ørskov, E. R. 1983. The nutritive value of rumen microorganisms in ruminants. I. Large-scale isolation and chemical composition of rumen microorganisms. *Br. J. Nutr*. 50:463–70
68. Storm, E., Ørskov, E. R., Smart, R. 1983. The nutritive value of rumen microorganisms in ruminants. 2. The apparent digestibility and net utilization of microbial N for growing lambs. *Br. J. Nutr*. 50:471–78
69. Storm, E., Brown, D. S., Ørskov, E. R. 1983. The nutritive value of rumen microorganisms in ruminants. 3. The digestion of microbial amino and nucleic acids in, and losses of endogenous nitrogen from the small intestine of sheep. *Br. J. Nutr*. 50:479–85
70. Storm, E., Ørskov, E. R. 1984. The nutritive value of rumen microorganisms in ruminants. 4. The limiting amino acids of microbial protein in growing sheep determined by a new approach. *Br. J. Nutr*. 52:613–20
71. Tao, R. C., Asplund, J. M., Kappel, L. C. 1974. Response of nitrogen metabolism, plasma amino acids and insulin levels to various levels of methionine infusion in sheep. *J. Nutr*. 104:1646–56
72. Tao, R. C., Asplund, J. M. 1975. Effect of energy sources on plasma insulin and nitrogen metabolism in sheep totally nourished by infusions. *J. Anim. Sci*. 41:1653–59
73. Tao, R. C., Wolfrom, G. W., Asplund, J. M. 1973. Total parenteral alimenation to study amino acid nutrition of sheep. *Nutr. Rep. Int*. 8:405–14
74. Virtanen, A. I. 1966. Milk production in cows on protein-free feed. *Science* 153:1603–13
75. Wakeling, A. E., Annison, E. F., Lewis, D. 1970. The amino acid requirements of ruminants. *Proc. Nutr. Soc*. 29:60 (Abstr.)
76. Webster, A. J. F. 1979. Energy costs of digestion and metabolism in the gut. In *Digestive Physiology and Metabolism in Ruminants,* ed. Y. Ruckenbusch, P. Thivend, pp. 469–84. Lancaster: MTP Press
77. Webster, A. J. F. 1984. Energetics of Maintenance and Growth. In *Mammalian Theriogenesis,* ed. L. Girardier, M. J. Stock, pp. 178–207. New York: Chapman & Hill
78. Williams, A. P., Hewitt, D. 1979. The amino acid requirements of the preruminant calf. *Br. J. Nutr*. 41:311–19
79. Wolfrom, G. W., Asplund, J. M. 1979. Effect of amino acid pattern and level in intravenously and intraruminally infused sheep. *J. Anim. Sci*. 49:752–63

Ann. Rev. Nutr. 1986. 6:113–30

# DIET AND HUMAN BEHAVIOR: HOW MUCH DO THEY AFFECT EACH OTHER?[1]

*Markus J. P. Kruesi and Judith L. Rapoport*

Child Psychiatry Branch, NIMH, Bethesda, Maryland 20892

CONTENTS

EVALUATION OF RESEARCH: GENERAL PRINCIPLES ........ 114
*Subjects and Sampling* ........ 114
*Nutrient Manipulation or Dosage* ........ 114
GROSS DIETARY DISRUPTION ........ 116
ACUTE MALNUTRITION: "FASTING" VERSUS "FED" STUDIES ........ 117
HYPERSENSITIVITY TO DIETARY SUBSTANCES ........ 119
BEHAVIORAL STUDIES WITH SPECIFIC DIETARY CONSTITUENTS ........ 121
*Caffeine* ........ 121
*Sweeteners* ........ 121
*Amino Acids* ........ 125
*Vitamins* ........ 126
CONCLUSION ........ 126

> "Popular interest in food-behavior questions in the 1980's is a special case of the spread and confluence of two more general ideas: that human behavior has controllable organic determinants, and that man's physical environment is a controllable determinant of well-being. What brings these two ideas together in the case of food and behavior is the widespread conviction that diet and nutrition are parts of the environment that most people can understand and control if they will."
>
> Thomas E. Cooney (12)

It is a prevalent idea among the public that diet affects behavior, and scientific investigators have also become interested in diet and behavior relationships, in

[1]The US Government has the right to retain a nonexclusive, royalty-free license in and to any copyright covering this paper.

part because of evidence that the brain is more sensitive to nutrient supply than previously thought (2).

This review of nutrition and behavior is focused on human studies, although animal studies are cited to illustrate particular points. The behavioral effects of diet in specific metabolic disorders such as phenylketonuria are not covered.

Three behavioral roles are most often postulated for nutrients: (*a*) nutrients as etiologic for a particular behavior, (*b*) nutrients as therapeutic agents, and (*c*) nutrients as correlates of behavior. The last possibility does not imply a cause-and-effect relationship.

## EVALUATION OF RESEARCH: GENERAL PRINCIPLES

The overall methodological level of most diet-behavior studies is extremely poor. For example, a review (32) of dietary factors alleged to influence delinquency criticized all studies on methodologic grounds, finding none adequate.

Research on diet and behavior consists of two general types: experimental and correlational or epidemiologic designs (2). Experimental designs involve manipulation of the variables (e.g. a dietary constituent such as caffeine) to examine their effect upon dependent measures (e.g. behavioral and/or cognitive factors such as continuous-performance test errors). Experimental designs permit causal relationships to be tested, whereas correlational studies do not. On the other hand, correlational studies have utility for hypothesis formation and experimental testing of relationships.

### *Subjects and Sampling*

Both experimental and correlational studies may be influenced by the sample selected. A standardized selection process for subjects (inclusion and exclusion criteria and methods used) should be clearly described. Strategies for decreasing error variance include crossover and single-case designs, in which the subject serves as his own control. While baseline periods are helpful in estimating variance and controlling for initial differences between subjects, they introduce problems of practice and order effects. Therefore, treatment order must be counterbalanced or, if precluded by large numbers of treatment conditions, randomized or otherwise equated through the use of Latin squares or lattice designs.

### *Nutrient Manipulation or Dosage*

Double-blind, controlled conditions are crucial in investigation of diet-behavior relationships. This is particularly true when the subject has strong beliefs about particular foods. In studies that involve challenges, subjects should be unable to discriminate between the placebo and the active substance on the basis of taste or appearance. As the magnitude of dietary alteration increases, blinding becomes progressively more difficult. Large dietary changes such as the salicylate-free and dye-free diet, once (21) believed to benefit childhood hyperactivity, are not easily tested (4).

Blinding is crucial and often very difficult in diet-behavior studies. The critical nature of double-blind conditions is seen in a study by Jewett (46). "Clinical ecologists" put forth in their practice the idea that behavioral symptoms could result from food sensitivity and that this sensitivity could be detected and treated. Jewett studied intradermal injections of food extracts using doses small enough (underdoses) to avoid wheal and flare reactions. Subjects were selected by practitioners of the technique as being reliably and repeatedly hypersensitive to such injections. This would include single-blind conditions: the physician would know the contents of a particular syringe but the patient would not. When 18 such patients were tested under double-blind conditions, where neither the tester nor the subject knew whether the injection was placebo or active, not a single one could significantly identify the contents or demonstrate a reaction.

The duration and timing of the manipulation are important. Chronic effects may arise that are not apparent in acute-dose studies. For example, aggression in rats increases after 14 days of low-protein, high-carbohydrate diet, but not after one day (48). The lack of knowledge regarding the pharmacokinetics of compounds such as food dyes raises the possibility that crossover studies may employ treatments of insufficient duration (79). Mood and performance are subtly affected by the time of day a nutrient is given (82). For example, caffeine was shown to benefit the performance of certain personality types on a task similar to the Graduate Record Exam when given in the morning but not in the evening (73).

The greater context of any dietary manipulation must be kept in mind when evaluating research. A dietary component is unlikely to exert its behavioral effects in isolation (1); diets in which the percentage of protein is changed result in altered fat and/or carbohydrate intake. Thus such a study may be viewed as the effect of an increased carbohydrate/protein (CHO/Pr) ratio because CHO was substituted for the missing Pr. A concomitant of implementing the Feingold diet was a decrease in sucrose (70).

Prior nutritional state is another potential source of variation in acute-challenge studies of nutrient influence upon behavior (1). The types and amounts of food eaten previously will influence the metabolism of subsequent meals (45) and neuroendocrine functions (44, 81). Standardizing dietary intake prior to the acute challenge can control this variation.

The particular state that an individual is in is a part of the context in which a dietary challenge is carried out. For example, the restorative effect of caffeine can be measured only in a fatigued and/or bored individual and not in an alert well-rested one (16). Cigarette smoking can almost double the rate of caffeine elimination via induction of metabolic enzymes (62).

One can attempt to monitor compliance by counting pills, weighing residual food, or keeping daily diaries. Ideally, assays are used for quantification of the biologically active and available substance (e.g. salivary caffeine concentration.)

## GROSS DIETARY DISRUPTION

Chronic protein-calorie malnutrition is a gross nutritional insult affecting the biological substrates of behavior. Patel (63) summarizes the effects of malnourishment on the biochemical and structural maturation of the brain as follows: (*a*) distortions in the generation cycle of replicating neuronal or glial cells, (*b*) permanent deficits in total cell number and a distortion of the cellular composition, (*c*) retardation in biochemical and structural development of the brain, and (*d*) distortions in the normal coordinated pattern of transmitter systems. General agreement exists that malnutrition is associated with cognitive and behavioral deficits, particularly for infants and children. Children surviving early malnutrition are profoundly impaired in acquiring language and motor skills, in developing interpersonal relationships, and in learning adaptive and motivational behavior. However, interpretation of these close relationships is complicated by the confounding variables of socioeconomic and environmental conditions, which can affect brain and mental developmental in experimental animals as well as in man (14, 55, 63).

Moreover, environmental deprivation and malnutrition may be synergistic. Galler and colleagues studied children 5 to 11 years old in Barbados who suffered protein-energy malnutrition during the first year of life. Their IQs were significantly lower than those of matched controls (26). The children's classroom behavior was significantly worse as well, displaying attention deficits, reduced social skills, and emotional instability; these deficits in classroom behavior were independent of IQ although not independent of academic achievement (27). Galler et al concluded that malnutrition in the first year of life is a potential factor in causing attention deficit disorder (the diagnostic nomenclature for what used to be termed the hyperactive child syndrome or minimal brain dysfunction) (27).

These results are impressive because unlike most other studies, the investigators could control somewhat for socioenvironmental variables. For example, health care delivery in Barbados was good and documented records of obstetric care and subsequent medical records of the children were available. In order to exclude common determinants of mental deficiency, the following exclusionary criteria were applied: (*a*) birth weight less than five pounds, (*b*) antecedent of prenatal complications, and (*c*) history of high fever, convulsions, head injury, or unconciousness. Moreover, multiple regression analyses using nutritional group and socioeconomic factors as independent variables indicated the relatively greater impact of nutrition in the first year of life compared to socioeconomic conditions.

However, in a more recent publication (28) the index of children's worse behavior at home appeared attributable to poor socioeconomic and home environment. Low maternal morale and adult involvement with the child, along with four other factors, significantly discriminated between the two groups. Thus even in this study some socioenviromental mediation is likely.

The choice of behavioral measures in older studies of malnutrition have been criticized (43) for relying on intelligence tests while running the risk of missing other effects. One example is a recent series of papers examining behavioral and cognitive sequelae of celiac disease, a lifelong malabsorption syndrome that starts in childhood (35–39). Adult patients, when first diagnosed, typically experienced a wide range of nutritional deficiencies. No consistent signs of cognitive impairment are found, but depressive symptoms severe enough to warrant disability pensions were seen.

Rumsey & Rapoport (75) point out that it may prove impossible to separate the effects of chronic malnutrition from the psychosocial concomitants by supplementation studies, where mother and/or infants at risk of malnutrition are given additional nutrition. Review of the past two decades of such studies concluded that nutrient supplementation of chronically and moderately malnourished infants in the prenatal and postnatal periods results in modest improvements in motor, language, and attentional skills (43). Only minor improvements in cognitive functioning were noted where the degree of malnutrition was marginal.

## ACUTE MALNUTRITION: "FASTING" VERSUS "FED" STUDIES

An acute short fast or skipping a meal seem very subtle examples of undernutrition when contrasted with the chronic studies above, but are certainly more common in an affluent society! The powerful effect of public belief in nutrition-behavior relationships as well as the interests of the food industry have fostered research in this area. The idea that children perform better in school if they have eaten a good breakfast appeared a reasonable idea to test, given that as many as one third of children in developed nations are thought to have inadequate caloric intake at breakfast. Public perception has already influenced US public policy in the Child Nutrition Act of 1966 (PL80-642) (65). A 1978 review of US long-term studies of the effect of feeding programs on school performance and behavior found all the studies to be methodologically weak and inconclusive (65). However, short-term studies indicate an acute benefit of eating breakfast compared to fasting. In 1983, two groups of investigators added support for an acute beneficial role of breakfast. When children skip breakfast, poorer performance and/or greater variability is seen on cognitive tests such as the matching familiar figures test (a skill having some correlation with educational achievement) (66), the continuous-performance test (an attentional task), and a task involving arithmetic problems (10).

Lunch effects have also received scrutiny; Craig (13) found evidence that lunch affects cognition more convincingly than does breakfast and in the opposite direction—impairment! A number of large epidemiologic studies have indicated a reduced work efficiency during the time period that follows lunch: error frequency in shift workers, the frequency of car drivers falling asleep, and the frequency of locomotive drivers compulsively braking all show increases following usual lunch times compared to preceeding or subsequent time periods. Specific effects of dietary constituents (alcohol, for example) and circadian effects may, of course, independently contribute to this pattern. Nonetheless, there is probably a more specific "meal effect" (13). Seven of the eleven studies reviewed found decrements in performance or perceptual sensitivity following the lunch condition (13).

Generally, fasting versus fed studies show the fed state to be better for mental performance, when the fast is of fairly long duration (e.g. overnight) (13). In addition to the breakfast studies in school children cited earlier, the only study (50) that found lunch to improve efficiency might more aptly be considered similar to the breakfast versus fast studies. Because breakfast was eaten between 4:30 and 5:30 in the morning in that study and the first test period was not until 1:30 in the afternoon, the test condition of "no lunch" represents at least an eight-hour fast. In this study of altitude tolerance, the time to complete a psychomotor task and the area of the visual blind spot were greater (worse) when lunch was skipped. However, obviously subjects could not be "blinded" to meal or fast conditions in these studies, and so the advantage of being fed might be psychological rather than nutrient based. In a study of food intake's effect upon reaction time during an eight-hour driving task, differences were seen in reaction time *prior* to the break in which food or no food was given (56). Poorer performance was seen on the no-food days. As this was a crossover design, anticipation or beliefs probably explain the finding.

Iron deficiency is believed to be the most common nutritional disorder. Three recent investigations have added support to earlier conclusions that iron deficiency results in behavioral impairment such as lassitude, decreased attention span, and irritability. Even in the absence of anemia, iron deficiency produced conditions that were ameliorated with parenteral iron (61). Developmental deficits occur in infants with iron-deficiency anemia even when socioeconomic level and general nutritional status are controlled (57). Additionally, reversible alterations in cognitive test performance were reported in mildly iron-deficient preschoolers (67). Studies of iron-deficient adolescents and adults before and after iron therapy would also be interesting.

Whether chronic or acute (fasts of eight or more hours), lack of nutrition has some negative effects. The magnitude of that decrement, although significant, appears small except in the case of massive chronic undernutrition. Even then, the psychosocial accompaniments probably account for a great measure of the cognitive impairment. It may be that some sequelae of chronic nutritional deprivation are as yet unappreciated. For example, the response to an induced brain lesion differed between animals malnourished earlier in life and normally fed controls, even though performance of the two groups was the same before the brain lesion (6). This important study suggests that there may be silent sequelae of malnutrition that can be unmasked by later insult. Thus "confounding" socioeconomic factors may in fact be synergistic and most relevant, not just experimental artifact.

## HYPERSENSITIVITY TO DIETARY SUBSTANCES

Dietary substances have been accused of being etiologic agents for many forms of behavioral distress and psychiatric illness. "Food allergy," a popular term often used in such claims, is a potential source of confusion in the recent literature. The term hypersensitivity is preferred here because it includes nonimmunologically mediated phenomena.

Sensitivity to gluten has been implicated in psychiatric illness. Dohan (17) postulated that peptides derived from gluten have a role in causing schizophrenia. Attempts have been made to add cereal-free diet regimens to standard pharmacologic treatments of schizophrenia. Two small studies with a combined total of 13 patients reported no worsening of symptoms with gluten challenges that followed periods of abstinence from milk, cereal grains, and gluten (60, 68). An earlier study did show a significant deterioration following double-blind gluten challenge (80). Two other approaches have been used to investigate this idea. A study of celiac patients found no cases of schizophrenia although it did find depression (37). Antibodies to food substances have been compared for psychiatric and control populations. Five of seven such studies (for references, see 74) found higher prevalences or higher titers of food antibodies in the psychiatric patients. While the data illustrating immunological differences between psychiatric patients and controls are intriguing, they do not constitute evidence for food allergy causing psychiatric illness; the findings may be results of the disorders or their treatment.

Of historical interest are the claims that food additives, particularly food dyes, caused hyperactivity in children. Meta-analysis (49) of the 23 controlled studies investigating this idea provides an emphatic negative conclusion: food dyes do not cause hyperactivity. There might be rare individual exceptions;

single-case studies have suggested that an occasional child may show behavioral sensitivity to food colors (58).

When properly "blinded," food-sensitivity studies have been negative. A double-blind study gave dried foods in capsules and bland foods disguised in a "milk shake" made from a soy-based milk substitute to 23 patients referred to a clinic because of suspected food allergy (64). Only four patients demonstrated actual food sensitivity. Sensitivity was assessed by (*a*) the skin test being positive and double-blinded sodium cromoglycate (which inhibits the release of histamine and other autocoids) blocking open provocation with the food, or (*b*) correctly identifying 5 out of 6 individual trials in a double-blind series. The four patients with actual food allergy had presenting symptoms associated with atopy: rhinitis, urticaria, asthma, or atopic eczema. Psychological symptoms were not among the presenting complaints of these four patients. In contrast, psychiatric symptom scores were much higher in the 14 patients who completed the allergy assessment and were not confirmed to have a food allergy.

Oligoantigenic diets are another rather complex approach to identification and treatment of behavioral reactions to foods. They go further than most exclusion diets because of the suspicion that multiple foods may provoke the same reaction(s). Recently, two trials of oligoantigenic treatment were carried out in London. Children with migraine and related symptoms (including behavior disorder in the first study and hyperactivity in the second) improved on a very limited diet (19, 20). Offending foods were later identified following their reintroduction into the diet. Subsequently this was confirmed by double-blind challenges. Indirect support comes from a double-blind, placebo-controlled trial in which oral sodium cromoglycate blocked the precipitation of migrane by food challenge (59).

Enthusiasm for these findings should be tempered. The improvement seen in hyperactive children was quite limited and other forms of management such as stimulant drug treatment continue to be required in those children. It is also not clear if all children went through all elimination maneuvers systematically. It appears that once something "worked" it was maintained. Most importantly, all food challenge studies have the problem of adequate blinding; for example, chocolate (to which over half of the hyperactive children in this study reacted) is so difficult to "blind" that results invite skepticism. Independent investigators need to reexamine this data, including examination of the success of the blind. Had a return to baseline occurred (no assessment was made), the trial would have been more convincing.

Even if these results were replicated, sensitization could still not be conclusively attributed to direct immunologic mechanisms. Learned histamine release has been demonstrated in animals using odors (76). Thus it is possible that behavioral reactions to foods, even if actually present, could also represent learned behaviors.

## BEHAVIORAL STUDIES WITH SPECIFIC DIETARY CONSTITUENTS

### *Caffeine*

In addition to its cognitive effects, caffeine has been well studied in relation to anxiety and childhood hyperactivity. "Caffeinism," a behavioral syndrome produced by high doses of caffeine, can produce symptoms indistinguishable from those of generalized anxiety disorder (30, 33). However, data are inconsistent as to whether caffeine intake in *moderate* doses potentiates anxiety.

Stimulant drugs are the medication of choice in treating children with attention deficit disorder with hyperactivity. In some settings, with high doses, these pharmacologic agents can also produce motor over-activity. Accordingly, studies have considered questions of behavioral toxicity of caffeine as well as the possibility of therapeutic benefit for pediatric populations. Interest and subsequent studies were spurred by an initial report that caffeine was as beneficial as Ritalin®, a frequently prescribed stimulant (78). Generally, the great majority of subsequent better-controlled studies found prescription drugs more beneficial (75). Furthermore, when caffeine was compared to placebo in hyperactive children, no significant benefit was seen (75). An exception to the apparent consensus is a recent study (77) that found very high doses of caffeine (600 mg/day) significantly ameliorated hyperactive behavior. While this trial compared varying doses of caffeine and/or amphetamine, it did not have a placebo comparison. The bothersome side effects seen with that dosage (stomach ache, nausea, insomnia) suggest that caffeine is unlikely to have clinical utility.

Other studies addressed whether caffeine might provoke childhood hyperactivity, and significant correlations were found between grade-school children's habitual caffeine consumption and teacher-rated classroom inattention and restlessness (71). Children reporting habitually high consumption (greater than 500 mg/day) had higher scores on the Conners teacher rating scale, higher scores on an anxiety questionnaire, and lower autonomic arousal than peers consuming low levels of caffeine, when both groups were assessed off caffeine. However, when challenged with caffeine (10 mg/kg/day), only children from the habitually *low*-intake group were more restless, while those with habitually high caffeine intake tended to be somewhat calmer. Similarly, only the low-intake children experienced side effects from caffeine. Thus caffeine was not shown to promote hyperactive behaviors and might possibly be self selected by children who tolerate or even benefit from it.

### *Sweeteners*

SUCROSE AND OTHER CARBOHYDRATES In the US, sweeteners (notably sucrose and aspartame) have received a great deal of public attention, and public concern that refined sugar may be linked to hyperactivity is widespread (15, 47, 83). Chiel & Wurtman (7) found that rats increased their motor activity as their dietary carbohydrate/protein ratio was raised, even though calories were held constant.

For scientists, particular impetus was given by human studies that found significant positive (70) correlations between dietary carbohydrate/protein ratios and directly observed restless and aggressive behaviors in a sample of 28 hyperactive children. Estimates of sugar intake based upon large categories of food correlated with the same behaviors of the hyperactives. Virkkunen (84) compared the insulin response to a glucose load seen in aggressive prisoners with that seen in nonaggressive men from the same institution and found greater insulin output among the more aggressive. As both of these studies are correlational, they do not address causality.

To date, eight double-blind, placebo-controlled challenge studies have been carried out examining the effects of sugar upon childrens' behavior and cognition. Four of the studies used versions of the Conners rating scale, which frequently demonstrates the effect of stimulant medication and differentiates hyperactives from normal children (3, 22, 52, 86). They did not find any significant behavioral difference between sucrose and the control conditions (5). Two of the studies, both negative, included parents as raters (34, 52). This is important because parents are most often the historians reporting a behavioral reaction to sugar. Seven of the studies used objective measures of activity to examine the possible motor effects of sugars. These are summarized in Table 1.

Behar et al noted a decrease in activity following sugar intake, but it only achieved statistical significance at one time point (two hours after challenge) when both sucrose and glucose were considered in comparison to saccharin (3). The two studies by Conners (10, 11) report opposite effects: the first found sugar increased activity and the second reported a decrease. Goldman et al (31) reported a sugar-induced increase in activity in eight preschool children. It is interesting to note that this study used a slightly higher dose than any of the others, which used body-weight-adjusted doses. On the other hand, three remaining studies (22, 52, 86) report no difference from placebo. These negative studies, the slight decrease observed by Behar (3), and Conners' conflicting results (10, 11) suggest that an acute challenge of sucrose or glucose, even in allegedly "sensitive" individuals, does not result in increased motor activity.

Cognitive effects of carbohydrates have received particular attention. Five of the challenge studies with children included cognitive measures. Three studies (3, 22, 86) found no difference in performance, one found improvements, and one found a decrement on the continuous performance testing (CPT) (31). (See Table 1). Similarly, a study in adults of meal composition and timing contrasted a high-carbohydrate meal with a high-protein one and found no difference on

**Table 1** Challenge studies of sugar's effect upon activity and attention in children

| Authors | Number of subjects | Sugars tested[a] | Dose(s) (g/kg) | Placebo/ Control[a] | Effect[b] of sugar on Activity | Effect[b] of sugar on Attention (CPT) |
|---|---|---|---|---|---|---|
| Behar et al (3) | 21 | S,G | 1.75 | X | −/= | = |
| Conners & Blouin (10) | 13 | F,G | 50[c] | OJ | + | |
| Conners et al (11) | 37(13)[d] | S,F | 1.25 | A | − | (+)[d] |
| Ferguson et al (22) | 8 | S | 1.5, 1.0, 0.5 | A | = | = |
| Goldman et al (31) | 8 | S | 2 | A+L | + | − |
| Kruesi et al (52) | 32 | S,G | 1.75 | A,X | = | |
| Woolraich et al (86) | 32 | S | 1.75 | A | = | = |

[a]The code for sugars and placebo/control is as follows: S, sucrose; G, glucose; F, fructose; L, lactose; X, saccharin; A, aspartame; OJ, orange juice.
[b]Symbols used: + increased, = no significant difference, − decreased.
[c]Measured in grams.
[d]The ( ) indicate the subsample.

the CPT (82). However, Prinz & Riddle did find a significant negative correlation between habitual sucrose intake and continuous-performance test scores (69).

Cognitive effects have been noted when blood glucose is lowered significantly and/or with tasks of longer duration requiring sustained effort. Holmes et al studied juvenile diabetics for whom blood glucose was held at constant levels by means of a pump supplying both insulin and glucose (42). Hyperglycemic (300 mg/dl), euglycemic (110 mg/dl), and comparatively hypoglycemic (60 mg/dl) conditions were studied. Attention and fine motor performance required during a reaction-time task were slowed at both high and low glucose levels. However, other psychometric tests in that study did not reveal differences between conditions. Craig, in reviewing the acute effects of meals on perceptual and cognitive efficiency, noted that lunch-induced deficits seem related at least in part to carbohydrate content, and that tasks of longer duration appear more sensitive to meal effects (13). Spring et al found lower overall accuracy and greater omission errors during a 20-minute dichotic listening task following a high-carbohydrate meal compared to a high-protein meal (82). As noted earlier, the CPT, which only required 2–3 minutes to complete, did not show this effect.

There have been popular claims of sugar-induced changes in behavior, but most studies of diet and criminal behavior are methodologically so flawed as to prevent interpretation. Although the studies of Virkkunen (84) are well done, they offer correlations, not cause-and-effect data. These correlations have not yet been replicated in an independent laboratory. The NIMH challenge study did not show an increase in aggressive or destructive behavior in disturbed children following acute sugar challenges.

ASPARTAME Aspartame is a dipeptide used as a nonsugar sweetener. Soft drinks are probably the most frequently consumed form of aspartame; thus questions of behavioral and cognitive effects secondary to its ingestion apply to a broad population of adults as well as children. Questions of potential behavioral toxicity were raised by Wurtman in 1983 (87) because aspartame causes brain phenyalanine and tyrosine to rise and it blocks glucose-induced change in 5-hydroxyindoles (89).

Behavioral studies of aspartame with humans are limited. In most studies, aspartame was used as a "control" for sugar in an equivalent sweetness dose. Consequently, when no other artificial sweetner is used as a control, the possibility exists of effects being due to caloric differences or to the sugar itself. When sugar or saccharin are the compared substances, a difference in one could be interpreted as the activity of the other.

Aspartame has demonstrated little or no behavioral effect in most studies to date. Woolraich et al (86) studied 32 children with a battery of behavioral and cognitive measures and found no significant differences between aspartame (6.26 mg/kg) and sucrose (1.75 g/kg). Conners et al (11) reported that activity seen following 1.25 mg/kg of sucrose or fructose was less than after aspartame. If the sugars serve as reference points, then aspartame might be claimed to increase activity. Similarily the reported improvement in attention with the sugars in that subsample of 13 children might be viewed as a decline due to aspartame. Ferguson et al (22) found nonsignificant differences between aspartame (8.33, 5.6, 2.78 mg/kg) and sucrose (1.5, 1.0, 0.5 mg/kg). Unfortunately the dose of aspartame was small in these studies.

In a study with 32 preschoolers at the NIMH (52), a challenge of 30 mg/kg of aspartame (a daily dose estimated to be in the 90th percentile) was compared to glucose, sucrose, and saccharin. Motor activity as measured by an acceleration-sensitive device was significantly less than that seen after sucrose or glucose ingestion, and there was a trend ($P<0.06$, Bonferroni-corrected *t* test) for preschoolers to be less active after aspartame than after saccharin ingestion. However, other behavioral measures, including the behavioral ratings of the in-room observer during the playroom sessions, did *not* show any significant differences. Thus behavioral effects of an acute aspartame challenge, if present, are subtle. The children who were comparatively slowed down on aspartame had significantly higher "internalizing" scores on the Achenbach Child Behavior Checklist (often a measure of anxiety or depression) than children who were not slowed down. The intriguing possibility exists that the effects of aspartame, if present, might more clearly be seen by targeting internalizing as opposed to externalizing children (such as those with hyperactivity).

Goldman et al (31) used a sweetener containing aspartame and lactose and 2 g/kg of sucrose and found less activity and improved attention following aspartame. This result can be interpreted as a sugar or an aspartame effect, although the low dose of aspartame make this unlikely.

In summary, acute sugar challenge does not cause hyperactivity and few or no cognitive effects are seen unless the magnitude of blood sugar change is sizable. Aspartame in high doses might have behavioral effects, although the NIMH study (with the exception of some equivocal findings) did not support the anecdotal reports of adverse behavioral reactions—usually increased activity and aggression.

## *Amino Acids*

Proteins and their constituent amino acids are the major source of precursors for neurotransmitter synthesis. Fernstrom & Wurtman (24, 25) presented scientific rationale for dietary and behavioral effects and thereby stimulated more rigorous research. Fernstrom et al (23) demonstrated that central nervous system serotonin can be altered by dietary manipulations that change the ratio of tryptophan (tryp) to other large neutral amino acids (LNAA). High-carbohydrate meals cause insulin release, an attendant increase in plasma tryp/LNAA ratio (which increases tryp crossing the blood-brain barrier), and ultimately an increase in central serotonin synthesis. In part because of this work, tryptophan is the most frequently studied amino acid in diet-behavior research.

Tryptophan's (modest) sleep-inducing effects have been demonstrated repeatedly during the past 10 years. Sleep latency, that is the time it takes to fall asleep, is decreased by tryp (41). Similarly, infants fed tryp and glucose entered both quiet and active phases of sleep sooner than those fed commercially available formula (88). Valine (which competes with tryp for brain entry and which would therefore lower the tryp/LNAA) had the opposite effect. Although one may consider manipulations of single amino acids pharmacologic rather than "dietary" in nature, the ready availability of amino acids as "dietary supplements" for purchase by the general public is blurring the boundries between pharmacology and nutrition.

Prompted by serotonergic theories of depression, researchers gave tryp as an antidepressant but no consensus exists as to its efficacy. Young and colleagues found that mixtures of amino acids that were free of tryp, those that were tryp supplemented, and those that were a balance of amino acids in a slurry (reminiscent of the so-called liquid protein diet drinks) had little effect, although tryp depletion caused an acute and mild dysphoria (91).

Aggression in animals can be influenced by alterations of central serotonergic systems. Normal subjects did not show alterations in aggression, as assessed by the Buss Durkee Paradigm, with either tryp supplementation or depletion (90). Preliminary data suggest (12) aggressive schizophrenics may benefit from tryp supplementation (90).

Lieberman et al found that an acute 100 mg/kg oral dose of tyrosine, also a precursor for catecholamine synthesis, had no significant effect on a variety of measures including reaction time, manipulative dexterity, mood, and pain perception (53). Because of noradrenergic theories of depression, chronic tyrosine administration has been tried as antidepressant treatment but the encouraging pilot work by Gelenberg et al (29) has not been confirmed.

Glutamate has at least putative status as a neurotransmitter. While most reports have addressed its toxicity, a study of five adults with learning disabilities and five controls suggested 300 mg of monosodium glutamate daily improved oral reading speed in the learning-disabled group (51).

### *Vitamins*

Vitamin deficiency is capable of producing behavioral change, which in some cases can appear as frank psychiatric symptoms such as depression and psychosis (55). The classical example, of course, is pellagra. A more subtle and less rare situation is vitamin insufficiency illness (5). Wernicke-Korsakoff syndrome, characterized by amnesia, disorientation, confabulation, ophthalmoplegia, and peripheral neuropathy, is an example. Although many alcoholics have poor nutritional intake, only a very few develop psychiatric illness. This may be explained by a variant of thiamine-dependent transketolase, in which the affinity of the apoenzyme for the cofactor was a tenth of the usual values (5). Thus, although these individuals may otherwise appear to have had unremarkable growth and development, their nutritional sensitivity may be unmasked by the stresses of chronic alcohol intake.

Vitamin supplements as treatment for behavioral problems in the absense of deficiency or demonstrated insufficiency seem less likely to be beneficial. As reviewed by Lipton & Golden, there is little well-controlled evidence to support the idea of vitamins as treatment for any psychiatric illness (54).

However, a recent rat study demonstrates that vitamin C enhances the antiamphetamine and cataleptogenic effects of haloperidol, an antipsychotic drug (72). Given the widespread availability of vitamins in large doses and the implication that vitamin C plays an important role in modulating the behavioral effects of antipsychotic drugs, further behavioral research would be interesting.

## CONCLUSION

In conclusion, chronic nutritional deficiency can result in behavioral change, but not in all cases. Furthermore, the context, particularly psychosocial variables, interacts with nutritional effects in complex ways. Nonetheless, behavioral or cognitive changes following acute manipulations add credence to the view that diet can influence behavior. These acute effects of foods are subtle at best, and not of clinical magnitude. Consequently, future research should focus on the much more difficult area of chronic exposure (or nonexposure in the case of depletion, hypersensitivity, or insufficiency) to nutritional factors.

*Literature Cited*


1. Anderson, G. H., Hrboticky, N. 1986. Approaches to assessing the dietary component of the diet-behavior connection. *Nutr. Rev.* Suppl.
2. Anderson, G. H., Johnston, J. L. 1983. Nutrient control of brain neurotransmitter synthesis and function. *Can. J. Physiol. Pharmacol.* 61:271–81
3. Behar, D., Rapoport, J. L., Adams, A. J., Berg, C. J., Cornblath, M. 1984. Sugar challenge testing with children considered behaviorally "sugar reactive." *Nutr. Behav.* 1:277–88
4. Bennett, F. C., McClelland, S., Kriegsmann, E. A., Andrus, L. B., Sells, C. J. 1983. Vitamin and mineral supplementation in Down's Syndrome. *Pediatrics* 72:707–13
5. Blass, J. P., Gibson, G. E. 1977. Abnormality of a thiamin-requiring enzyme in patients with Wernicke-Korsakoff syndrome. *N. Engl. J. Med.* 297:1367–70
6. Bouzrara, A., Silva, M., Waksman, D., Finger, S., Almi, C. R. 1985. Relation between the severity of early malnutrition and the effects of later frontal cortical lesions in rats. *Physiol. Psychol.* 13:1–6
7. Chiel, H. J., Wurtman, R. J. 1981. Short-term variations in diet composition change the pattern of spontaneous motor activity in rats. *Science* 213:676–78
8. Deleted in proof
9. Conners, C. K. 1981. Artificial colors in the diet and disruptive behavior: Current status of research. In *Nutrition and Behavior,* ed. S. A. Miller, pp. 137–43. Philadelphia: Franklin Inst. Press
10. Conners, C. K., Blouin, A. G. 1982/83. Nutritional effects on behavior of children. *J. Psychiatr. Res.* 17:193–202
11. Conners, C. K., Caldwell, J., Caldwell, L., Schuab, E., Kronsberg, S., et al. 1986. Experimental studies of sugar and aspartame on autonomic, cortical and behavioral responses of children. *Nutr. Rev.* Suppl.
12. Cooney, T. E. 1982/83. The socio-political context of food-behavior research. *J. Psychiatr. Res.* 2:227–30
13. Craig, A. 1986. Acute effects of meals on perceptual and cognitive efficiency. *Nutr. Rev.* 43:Suppl.
14. Crnic, L. S. 1984. Nutrition and mental development. *Am. J. Ment. Defic.* 88: 526–33
15. Crook, W. 1975. Food allergy—the great masquerader. *Pediatr. Clin. North Am.* 22:227–38
16. Dews, P. B. 1982/83. Comments on some major methodologic issues affecting analysis of the behavioral effects of foods and nutrients. *J. Psychiatr. Res.* 17:223–25
17. Dohan, F. C. 1966. Cereals and schizophrenia data and hypothesis. *Acta Psychiatr. Scand.* 42:125–52
18. Deleted in proof
19. Egger, J., Carter, C. M., Graham, P. J., Gumby, D., Soothill, J. F. 1985. Controlled trial of oligo antigenic treatment in the hyperkinetic syndrome. *Lancet* 1:540–44
20. Egger, J., Carter, C. M., Wilson, J., Turner, M. W., Soothill, J. F. 1983. Is migraine food allergy? *Lancet* 2:865–69
21. Feingold, B. F. 1975. *Why Your Child is Hyperactive*. New York: Random House
22. Ferguson, H. B., Stoddart, C., Simeon, J. G. 1986. Double-blind challenge studies of behavioral and cognitive effects of sucrose-aspartame ingestion in normal children. *Nutr. Rev.* 43:Suppl.
23. Fernstrom, J. D., Larin, R., Wurtman, R. J. 1973. Correlation between brain tryptophan and plasma neutral amino acid levels following food consumption in rats. *Life Sci.* 13:517–24
24. Fernstrom, J. D., Wurtman, R. J. 1971. Brain serotonin content: physiological dependence on plasma tryptophan levels. *Science* 178:414–16
25. Fernstrom, J. D., Wurtman, R. J. 1971. Brain serotonin content: increases following ingestion of carbohydrate diet. *Science* 174:1023–25
26. Galler, J. R., Ramsey, F., Solimano, G., Lowell, W. E., Mason, E. 1983. The influence of early malnutrition on subsequent behavioral development. I. Degree of impairment in intellectual performance. *J. Am. Acad. Child Psychiatry* 22:8–15
27. Galler, J. R., Ramsey, F., Solimano, G., Lowell, W. E. 1983. The influence of early nutrition on subsequent behavioral development. II. Classroom behavior, *J. Am. Acad. Child Psychiatry* 22:16–22
28. Galler, J. R., Ramsey, F., Solimano, G. 1985. Influence of early malnutrition on subsequent behavioral development. V.

Child's behavior at home. *J. Am. Acad. Child Psychiatry* 24:58–64
29. Gelenberg, A. J., Wojcik, J. D., Gibson, C. J., Wurtman, R. J. 1982/83. Tyrosine for depression. *J. Psychiatr. Res.* 17: 175–80
30. Gilbert, R. 1976. Caffeine as a drug of abuse. In *Research Advances in Alcohol and Drug Problems,* ed. R. J. Gibbine, pp. 49–176. New York: Wiley
31. Goldman, J. A., Lerman, R. H., Contois, J. H., Udall, J. N. 1984. The behavior of preschool children following ingestion of sucrose. Presented at the Ann. Meet. Am. Psychol. Assoc. Toronto, Canada, August
32. Gray, G. E., Gray, L. K. 1983. Diet and juvenile delinquency. *Nutr. Today* 18: 14–22
33. Greden, J. 1981. Caffeinism and caffein withdrawal. In *Substance Abuse,* ed. J. Lowinson, P. Ruiz, pp. 274–86. Baltimore: Williams & Wilkins
34. Gross, M. D. 1984. Effect of sucrose on hyperkinetic children. *Pediatrics* 74: 876–78
35. Hallert, C., Astrom, J. 1982. Psychic disturbances in adult coeliac disease. II. Psychological findings. *Scand. J. Gastroenterol.* 17:21–24
36. Hallert, C., Astrom, J., Sedvall, G. 1982. Psychic disturbances in adult coeliac disease. III. Reduced central monoamine metabolism and signs of depression. *Scand. J. Gastroenterol.* 17: 25–28
37. Hallert, C. 1982. Psychiatric illness, gluten and coeliac disease. *Biol. Psychiatry* 17:959–61
38. Hallert, C., Derefeldt, T. 1982. Psychic disturbances in adult coeliac disease. I. Clinical observations. *Scand. J. Gastroenterol.* 17:17–19
39. Hallert, C., Astrom, J. 1983. Intellectual ability of adults after lifelong intestinal malabsorption due to coeliac disease. *J. Neurol. Neurosurg. Psychiatry* 46:87–89
40. Deleted in proof
41. Hartmann, E., Greenwald, D. 1984. Tryptophan and human sleep: An analysis of 43 studies. In *Progress in Tryptophan and Serotonin Research,* ed. H. G. Schlossberger, W. Kochen, B. Linzen, H. Steinhart, pp. 297–304. New York: de Gruyter
42. Holmes, C. S., Hayford, J. T., Gonzalez, J. L., Weydart, J. A. 1983. A survey of cognitive functioning at different glucose levels in diabetic persons. *Diabetes Care* 6:180–85
43. Howard, R. B., Cronk, C. 1983. Nutrition and development. In *Developmental-Behavioral Pediatrics,* ed. M. D. Levine, W. B. Carey, A. C. Crocker, R. T. Gross, pp. 412–26. Philadelphia: Saunders
44. Ishizuka, B., Quigley, M. E., Yen, S. S. C. 1983. Pituitary hormone release in response to food ingestions: Evidence for neuroendocrine signals from gut to brain. *J. Clin. Endocrinol. Metab.* 57:1111–16
45. Jenkins, D. J. A., Wolever, T. M. S., Taylor, R. H., Griffiths, C., Krzeminski, K., et al. 1982. Slow release carbohydrate improves second meal tolerance. *Am. J. Clin. Nutr.* 35:1339–46
46. Jewett, D. L. 1984. Double-blind testing of symptom provocation by injections of diluted food extracts. Presented at Los Angeles Soc. Allergy and Clin. Immunol. and Am. Acad. Allergy and Immunol. Food Allergy: Update 1984, Beverly Hills, Calif. Sept. 29
47. Josephson, A. M., Yellin, A. M., Miner, R. A. 1984. The role and meaning of dietary manipulations in families with a hyperactive child. Presented at the Ann. Meet. Am. Acad. Child Psychiatry, Toronto, Canada, October 9–13
48. Kantak, K. M., Eichelman, B. 1982. Low dietary protein and the facilitation of defensive and predatory aggression in adult rats. *Nutr. Behav.* 1:47–54
49. Kavale, K. A., Forness, S. R. 1983. Hyperactivity and diet treatment: A meta analysis of the Feingold hypothesis. *J. Learn. Disabil.* 16:324–30
50. King, C. G., Bickerman, H. A., Bouvet, W., Harner, C. J., Oyler, J. R., Seitz, C. P. 1945. Effects of pre-flight and inflight meals of varying composition with respect to carbohydrate, protein or fat. *J. Aviat. Med.* 16:69–84
51. Kripke, B., Lynn, R., Madsen, J. A., Gay, P. E. 1982. Familial learning disability, easy fatigue and maladroitness: preliminary trial of monosodium glutamate in adults. *Dev. Med. Child Neurol.* 24:745–51
52. Kruesi, M. J. P., Rapoport, J. L., Cummings, M., Yarrow, M., Waxler, C., et al. 1985. Sugar and aspartame challenge study in "sugar reactive" preschool children. Presented at 4th World Congr. Biol. Psychiatry, Philadelphia, Pa.
53. Leiberman, H. R., Corkin, S., Spring, B. J., Growden, J. H., Wurtman, R. J. 1982/83. Mood, performance, and pain sensitivity: Change induced by food constituents. *J. Psychiatr. Res.* 17:135–46
54. Lipton, M. A., Golden, R. 1984. Nutritional therapies. In *The Psychiatric Therapies,* ed. T. B. Karasu, pp. 173–

210. Washington, DC: Am. Psychiatr. Assoc.

55. Lipton, M. A., Kane, F. J. 1983. Psychiatry. In *Nutritional Support of Medical Practice,* ed. H. A. Scheider, C. E. Anderson, D. Coursin, pp. 562–80. Philadelphia: Harper & Row. 2nd ed.
56. Lisper, H. O., Eriksson, B. 1980. Effects of the length of a rest break and food intake on subsidiary reaction-time performance in an 8-hour driving task. *J. Appl. Psychol.* 65:117–22
57. Lozoff, B., Brittenham, G. M., Viteri, F. E., Wolf, A. W., Urrutia, J. J. 1982. The effects of short-term oral iron therapy on developmental deficits in iron-deficient anemic infants. *J. Pediatr.* 100:351–57
58. Mattes, J. A., Gettelman-Klein, R. 1978. An intensive crossover study of the effects of artificial food colorings in a hyperactive child. *Am. J. Psychiatry* 135:987–88
59. Monro, J., Carini, C., Brostoff, J. 1984. Migraine is food-allergic disease. *Lancet* 2:719–21
60. Osborn, M., Crayton, J. W., Javaid, J. 1982. Lack of effect of a gluten-free diet on neuroleptic blood levels in schizophrenic patients. *Biol. Psychiatry* 17: 627–29
61. Oski, F. A., Honig, A. S., Helu, B., Howanitz, P. 1983. Effect of iron therapy on behavior performance in nonanemic, iron-deficient infants. *Pediatrics* 71: 877–80
62. Parsons, N. D., Neims, A. H. 1978. Effect of smoking on caffeine clearance. *Clin. Pharmacol. Ther.* 24:40–45
63. Patel, A. 1983. Undernutrition and brain development. *Trends Neurosci.* 6:151–54
64. Pearson, D. J., Rix, K. J. B. 1983. Food allergy: how much in the mind? *Lancet* 1:1259–61
65. Pollitt, E., Gersovitz, M., Gargiulo, M. 1978. Educational benefits of the United States School Feeding Program: A critical review of the literature. *Am. J. Public Health* 68:477–81
66. Pollitt, E., Lewis, N. S., Garza, C., Shulman, R. 1982/83. Fasting and cognitive function. *J. Psychiatr. Res.* 17:169–74
67. Pollitt, E., Leibel, R. L., Greenfield, D. B. 1983. Iron deficiency and cognitive test performance in preschool children. *Nutr. Behav.* 1:137–46
68. Potkin, S. G., Weinberger, D., Kleinman, J. 1981. Wheat gluten challenge in schizophrenia patients. *Am. J. Psychiatry* 138:1208–11
69. Prinz, R. J., Riddle, D. B. 1986. Associations between nutrition and behavior in five-year-old children. *Nutr. Rev.* 43:Suppl.
70. Prinz, R. J., Roberts, W. A., Hantman, E. 1980. Dietary correlates of hyperactive behavior in children. *J. Consult. Clin. Psychol.* 48:760–69
71. Rapoport, J. L., Berg, C. J., Ismond, D. R., Zahn, T. P., Neims, A. 1984. Behavioral effects of caffeine in children. *Arch. Gen. Psychiatry* 41:1073–79
72. Rebec, G. V., Centore, J. M., White, L. K., Alloway, K. D. 1985. Ascorbic acid and the behavioral response to haloperidol: implications for the action of antipsychotic drugs. *Science* 227:438–40
73. Revelle, W., Humphreyes, M., Simon, L., Gililand, K. 1980. The intersection effect of personality, time of day and caffeine: A test of the arousal model. *J. Exp. Psychol.* 109:1–31
74. Rix, K. J. B., Ditchfield, J., Freed, D. L. J., Goldberg, D. P., Hillier, V. F. 1985. Food antibodies in acute psychoses. *Psychol. Med.* 15:347–54
75. Rumsey, J. M., Rapoport, J. L. 1983. Assessing behavioral and cognitive effects of diet in pediatric populations. In *Nutrition and the Brain,* ed. R. J. Wurtman, J. J. Wurtman, 6:101–61. New York: Raven
76. Russell, M., Dark, K. A., Cummins, R. W., Ellman, G., Callaway, E., Peeke, H. V. S. 1984. Learned histamine-release. *Science* 225:733–34
77. Schecter, M. D., Timmons, G. D. 1985. Objectively measured hyperactivity. II. Caffeine and amphetamine effects. *J. Clin. Pharmacol.* 25:276–80
78. Schnackenberg, R. C. 1973. Caffeine as a substitute for schedule II. Simulants in hyperactive children. *Am. J. Psychiatry* 130:796–98
79. Silbergeld, E. K., Anderson, S. M. 1982. Artificial food colors and childhood behavior disorders. *Bull. NY Acad. Med.* 58:275–95
80. Singh, M. M., Kay, S. R. 1976. Wheat gluten as a pathologic factor in schizophrenia. *Science* 191:401–2
81. Slag, M. F., Ahmed, M., Gannon, M. C., Nuttall, F. Q. 1981. Meal stimulation of cortisol secretion: A protein-induced effect. *Metabolism* 30:1104–8
82. Spring, B., Maller, O., Wurtman, J., Digman, L., Cozolino, L. 1982/83. Effects of protein and carbohydrate meals on mood and performance: interactions with sex and age. *J. Psychiatr. Res.* 17:155–67
83. Varley, C. 1984. Diet and the behavior of

children with attention deficit disorder. *J. Am. Acad. Child Psychiatry* 223:182

84. Virkkunen, M. 1983. Insulin secretion during the glucose tolerance test in antisocial personality. *Br. J. Psychiatry* 142:598–604
85. Deleted in proof
86. Woolraich, M., Milich, R., Stumbo, P., Schultz, F. 1985. The effects of sucrose ingestion on the behavior of hyperactive boys. *J. Pediatr.* 106:575–682
87. Wurtman, R. J. 1983. Neurochemical changes following high dose aspartame with dietary carbohydrates. *N. Engl. J. Med.* 309:429–30
88. Yogman, M. W., Zeisel, S. H. 1983. Diet and sleep patterns in newborn infants. *N. Engl. J. Med.* 309:1147–49
89. Yokogoshi, H., Robert, C. H., Caballero, B., Wurtman, R. J. 1984. Effects of aspartame and glucose administration on brain and plasma levels of large neutral amino acids and brain 5-hydroxyindoles. *Am. J. Clin. Nutr.* 40:1–7
90. Young, S. N. 1986. The effect of altering tryptophan levels on aggression and mood. *Nutr. Rev.* 43:Suppl.
91. Young, S. N., Smith, S., Pihl, R. O., Ervin, F. R. 1986. Tryptophan depletion causes a rapid lowering of mood in normal males. *Psychopharmacology*. In press

*Ann. Rev. Nutr. 1986. 6:131–54*


# NUTRITION AND INFECTION

*Gerald T. Keusch*

Division of Geographic Medicine, Tufts–New England Medical Center, Boston, Massachusetts 02111, USA

*Michael J. G. Farthing*

Department of Gastroenterology, St. Bartholomew's Hospital, London EC1A 7BE, United Kingdom

CONTENTS

INTRODUCTION ........ 131
ENDOGENOUS MEDIATORS AND METABOLIC RESPONSE TO INFECTION ........ 133
*Metabolic Sequelae of Infection* ........ 133
*Macrophage Mediators of Metabolic Responses* ........ 135
IRON AND INFECTION ........ 143
*Evidence That Iron Deficiency Promotes Infection* ........ 144
*Evidence That Iron Deficiency Protects Against Infection* ........ 145
*The Current Status of the Paradox* ........ 148

## INTRODUCTION

The critical events by which infections lead to malnutrition and malnutrition interferes with host defense have been the subject of intense study during the past 20 years (7, 8, 55, 56, 101). Some of the important mechanisms by which infection not only increases nutritional requirements but also simultaneously reduces dietary intake are now being defined. Similarly the myriad of effects of macro- and micronutrients on immune and nonimmune host defense have been recognized and are gradually being unravelled. It is clear that suboptimal nutritional status resulting from recurrent infection with associated anorexia and reduced dietary intake may lead to impaired host defense (Figure 1). Many



0199-9885/86/0715-0131$02.00

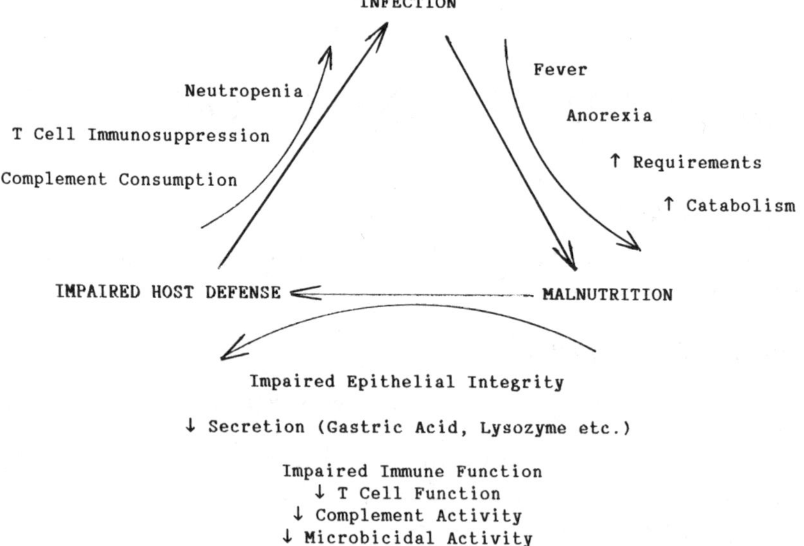


*Figure 1* The triangle of interaction between malnutrition, infection, and host defense. Malnutrition may be initiated by primary or secondary dietary deficiency (e.g. malabsorptive states), or by the metabolic effects of infection. The consequence of this is impairment in host defenses, which in turn leads to an increased burden of infection and further malnutrition.

questions remain to be answered, particularly with respect to determining those key, accessible links in the triangle depicted in the figure where intervention might be effective. With this in mind, we review new information on the role of endogenous peptide mediators produced by activated leukocytes in the regulation of host metabolism during infection.

Some still argue, however, that the interaction of malnutrition and infection may not be all bad. Relative undernutrition does appear to impede the expression of certain infections under restricted conditions. However, this is a highly controversial subject and as yet has not been applied in clinical practice, that is therapeutic (?selective) starvation. Observations of the major shifts in minerals and the importance of trace minerals for both the infectious agent and the infected host have stimulated studies of the impact of altered mineral status on infectious disease. We have therefore chosen to discuss some of the controversy surrounding iron deficiency and its possible detrimental and beneficial effects on host defenses.

## ENDOGENOUS MEDIATORS AND METABOLIC RESPONSE TO INFECTION

While the physiological reasons for the metabolic responses to infection have never been adequately understood, the phenomena have been clearly described by many investigators over six or more decades of work. When these events are reviewed in the context of modern physiology and clinical nutrition, however, a typical or stereotyped response to either infection or noninfectious inflammatory stress becomes obvious (8, 55). Dramatic changes in the pattern of utilization of carbohydrates, proteins, lipids, and minerals appear to anticipate inadequate food intake on the one hand, and a need to restrict the availability of some nutrients for invading microorganisms on the other hand (56). Recent studies have begun to define the mechanisms underlying these metabolic alterations, in particular the role of secreted macrophage products (endogenous mediators), which serve to link and coordinate the metabolic and the immune responses to infection.

### *Metabolic Sequelae of Infection*

The major metabolic changes during infection are listed in Table 1. It is important to note that both anabolic and catabolic processes occur at the same time, accentuating the magnitude of the metabolic alterations. Since these processes are generally accompanied by fever, which increases metabolic rate by about 13% per °C (31), energy requirements are much greater than usual at a time when the host is often anorexic. Since carbohydrate stores are inadequate to meet these needs (15), and lipid stores are not effectively used in the infected patient (9), another source of energy is required. In most infections, this turns out to be gluconeogenesis, the production of glucose by the liver from amino acid precursors released from contractile proteins of muscle (68–71).

There is an apparent coordination of protein and energy metabolism, as the branched-chain amino acids released by proteolysis of muscle are oxidized in situ for energy, while the amino acids reaching the blood stream are taken up by the liver and utilized for new protein synthesis of acute-phase protein reactants and other anabolic repair and stress responses (70, 93). These complex adaptations are aided by increases in circulating insulin, glucagon, and growth hormone levels, loss of diurnal variation and elevation in glucocorticoid levels, and functional insulin resistance in muscle (7, 97). Gluconeogenic activity is manifested by a pseudodiabetic state, with fasting hyperglycemia, abnormal glucose disappearance curves, and exaggerated insulin secretion following a glucose load, as well as an increased glucose pool size and oxidation rate (69).

Lipid metabolism can be grossly altered as well, depending in part on the nature of the infectious stress, the duration of infection, and its severity (13, 35,

**Table 1** Metabolic changes during infection that alter host nutritional status[a]

| | |
|---|---|
| Protein metabolism | Increased nitrogen loss (negative balance)<br>Catabolism of muscle protein<br>Conversion of amino acids to glucose<br>Decreased synthesis of albumin, transferrin<br>Increased synthesis of acute-phase proteins by liver, and proliferation of phagocytes and lymphoid cells |
| Carbohydrate metabolism | "Pseudodiabetes"<br>Increased glucose oxidation<br>Peripheral (muscle) insulin resistance<br>Augmented gluconeogenesis |
| Mineral metabolism | Removal of plasma iron to the liver<br>Reticuloendothelial system uptake of zinc<br>Increased plasma ceruloplasmin copper<br>Urine, stool, and sweat losses of Mg, P, K, and S |

[a]Adapted with permission from (56).

36). Plasma free fatty acid levels and triglycerides may be increased or decreased, depending on the activity of lipoprotein lipase and fatty acid synthetase and acetyl–coenzyme A carboxylase. Lipid changes are particularly evident during gram-negative bacillary infections, in which defective lipid clearance from serum results in extreme hypertriglyceridemia (51). Utilization of ketones is impaired, associated with decreased production of 3-hydroxybutyrate and acetoacetate, and the consequence of this failure to use lipid stores efficiently is a drain on endogenous protein stores (9).

Protein metabolism during infection is characterized by a dominance of catabolic over anabolic processes, manifested by absolute losses of nitrogen and wasting of lean body mass (55). Amino acids released from breakdown of muscle are taken up in the liver and deaminated during gluconeogenesis, with subsequent excretion of the nitrogen in the form of urea and other nitrogenous compounds in urine, sweat, and other body fluids (111). Since the carbon backbone of the amino acid is converted to glucose, which is oxidized to $CO_2$ and excreted by the lungs, the entire protein structure is ultimately lost from the body. This has been demonstrated in septic humans as an increased conversion rate of infused $^{14}C$-alanine to glucose along with an increase in urinary 3-methyl histidine excretion, a nonreutilizable amino acid marker of muscle protein breakdown (68, 71).

Tremendous changes also occur in a number of minerals during infection (8, 55). Best documented are the decreases in serum levels of iron and zinc due to uptake in liver cells and mononuclear phagocytes, and the elevation in serum copper as a consequence of increased synthesis of ceruloplasmin, the copper carrier protein. Iron uptake is mediated by unsaturated lactoferrin, the intracellular iron-binding protein from the specific granules of neutrophils (58). Released into the plasma from activated neutrophils, lactoferrin binds iron, and depending on the degree of saturation of the protein, the complex is subsequently cleared from the circulation, resulting in hypoferremia (108). This mechanism explains why serum iron does not decrease in infected neutropenic animals. Sequestered iron ultimately appears as hemosiderin and other nonutilizable iron storage compounds (7). Decreased serum zinc is also related to a metal-binding protein, metallothionine, which is an intracellular acute-phase protein reactant synthesized during infection or inflammation (8, 103).

The reasons for the shifts in these metals are not really known, but plausible benefits to the host can be postulated. For example, reduction in the availability of iron to microorganisms may impair their growth or production of virulence factors; uptake of zinc may prime the host to turn on cellular proliferation since many of the key enzymes involved are zinc metalloenzymes; and the presence in plasma of copper ceruloplasmin, a ferroxidase that oxidizes ferrous iron in the transfer to apotransferrin, may increase the efficiency of iron utilization for hemoglobin synthesis to compensate for the decrease in iron availability (8, 89).

## *Macrophage Mediators of Metabolic Responses*

It is now known that the metabolic alterations during infection can be initiated by peptide mediators produced by stimulated macrophages and not directly by microbial factors. Since the metabolic response is, in fact, not identical from infection to infection, it is possible that multiple distinct mediators could be involved, each with a range of metabolic effects. Moreover, as macrophage peptide mediators are known to affect the function of the immune system as well, they could be the means to coordinate the host protective response and the metabolic needs of the infected individual.

INTERLEUKIN-1 (IL-1) One of the more important mechanisms for regulation of the immune response is the peptide monokine, IL-1 (27). Although specialized cells such as keratinocytes, epithelial cells of gingiva and cornea, astrocytes from brain, and mesangial cells of the kidney can also produce physiologically similar peptides that may function in situ, systemic effects are due to macrophage IL-1 (26). The activities of IL-1 were originally defined by assessing biological activity of leukocyte-derived peptides, for example endogenous pyrogen (EP) activity causing fever or leukocyte endogenous mediator (LEM) resulting in hypoferremia and hypozincemia (27). A multiplicity of biological effects are now known, a number of which are illustrated in Figure 2. Since the various mediators defined in this way were all small (15,000–18,000 $M_r$) peptides, the concept gradually arose that either one

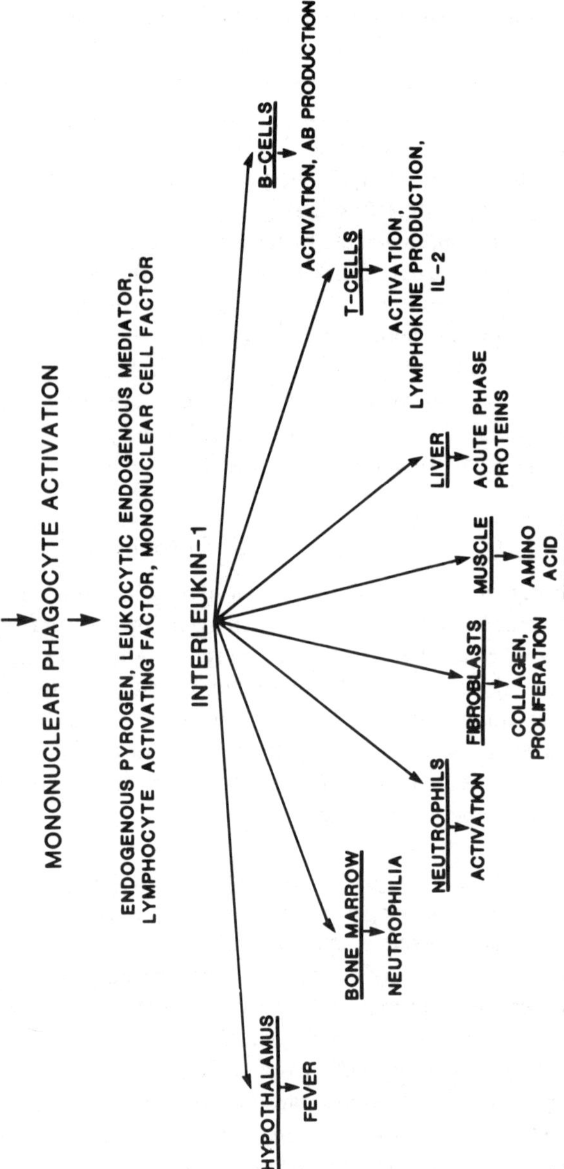


*Figure 2* Initiation of the acute-phase response and the diverse effects of interleukin-1 on host nutrition and immune responses. Reprinted with permission from (26).

molecule or a family of similar mediators was produced by activated cells. In 1979 the name IL-1 was proposed for macrophage-derived mediators that prime lymphocyte immune responses, and it is increasingly the accepted term to describe the peptides affecting metabolic responses as well (27).

It is most likely that IL-1 really does represent a family of similar but distinct molecules (28). Several forms of IL-1 differing in isoelectric point are produced by human blood monocytes. Poly A-mRNA to pI 5 and pI 7 forms of human IL-1 have been used to prepare c-DNA's distinguishable by restriction enzyme analysis. These also code for peptides that are only 26% homologous in amino acid sequence.

Recently, the nucleotide sequence of human monocyte IL-1 precursor cDNA has been determined (4). This gene codes for a 269-amino-acid polypeptide of molecular weight 30,747. The molecule is quite unique in that there is no signal sequence or cleavage peptide sequence, which explains why most of the IL-1 produced remains intracellular (or possibly on the macrophage cell surface) until secretion is activated (62, 63). IL-1-specific mRNA, isolated by in vitro hybridization to this oligonucleotide, has been both translated in a cell-free reticulocyte system to produce immunoreactive IL-1, and injected into *Xenopus laevis* oocytes in which it results in production of biologically active IL-1 (4).

It is not yet clear whether there is one gene with post-translational modifications resulting in the distinct forms of IL-1 or a family of genes coding for different IL-1's (26). Although human IL-1 has never been demonstrated in plasma, IL-1 activity can be recovered in lower molecular weight fragments in plasma, urine, or peritoneal fluid (16, 17, 29, 41, 57). A 4000-$M_r$ peptide has been found in the plasma of febrile humans that activates muscle proteolysis in vitro (21). Based on this effect, the peptide has been called "proteolysis-inducing factor," PIF, and it presumably represents a domain of IL-1. A similar biologically active peptide has been isolated as a breakdown product of IL-1 (29), further supporting the relationship of PIF and IL-1.

*Metabolic effects induced by IL-1 and peptide fragments* IL-1 can reproduce many of the cardinal metabolic alterations associated with infection (27). Fever was the first described effect of IL-1 and this is known to be secondary to its ability to release arachidonic acid and stimulate production of prostaglandin $E_2$ in the hypothalamus (30). Recent experiments in rats support the idea that fever-induced anorexia is due to the same mediator (77). In these studies, endotoxin administration resulted in both fever and reduced food intake. Antipyretics inhibited the fever response, but did not alter endotoxin effects on food intake. In contrast, animals made tolerant to endotoxin by repeated injection did not show a significant fever response nor diminish food intake. Since endotoxin-tolerant animals are also refractory to other IL-1 effects, such as hypoferremia and production of acute-phase proteins (50, 92), it is highly likely that the anorectogenic effects of endotoxin are due to IL-1 release.

The changes in carbohydrate metabolism in infection are conditioned by the endocrine responses, and it is significant that IL-1 releases both insulin and glucagon from the endocrine pancreas (39, 86). Muscle breakdown, releasing gluconeogenic precursor amino acids into the blood stream, occurs concomitantly (20, 98). IL-1 added to muscle in vitro results in proteolysis via induction of prostaglandin $E_2$ synthesis (4a). At the same time, a 33-amino-acid glycopeptide probably containing sialic acid with an estimated molecular weight of 4274, was isolated from plasma of patients with sepsis and shown to cause a 221% elevation in proteolysis in the in vitro system with no reduction, and perhaps a slight stimulation, of protein synthesis rates (21). In 10 septic patients, the in vivo proteolysis rate of muscle was estimated by comparing tyrosine plus phenylalanine concentrations in femoral vein and artery blood. This correlated well ($r = 0.64$, $p < 0.05$) with the release of tyrosine from muscle in vitro. The level of this proteolysis-inducing factor (PIF) also correlated with the fever response, an indication that PIF and IL-1 are related. Direct evidence for this has now been obtained. First, low-molecular-weight fragments can be derived from highly purified monocyte-derived IL-1 and these exhibit both PIF and the well-studied in vitro biological activity of IL-1, lymphocyte-activating factor (LAF) (29). Second, PIF has been purified from plasma of febrile patients and shown to be active in the LAF assay (29). Finally, $^{125}$I-labelled IL-1 also breaks down into smaller fragments that retain pyrogenicity and LAF activity (29). Thus, the evidence is consistent with the concept that PIF is a small-molecular-weight cleavage product of IL-1.

Release of amino acids into the blood of septic patients is not associated with increased plasma amino acid levels (111); rather reutilizable amino acids are taken up by the liver and used for new protein synthesis (20, 98). Both amino acid uptake by liver and synthesis of acute-phase proteins are stimulated by purified monocyte-derived IL-1 or PIF purified from septic humans (67). When IL-1 or PIF is injected into the peritoneal cavity of rats, hepatic protein synthesis is significantly elevated (70% increase in incorporation of $^{14}$C-tyrosine into structural and secreted proteins) and de novo synthesis of C3 and fibrinogen increases in parallel.

These experimental results are supported by observations in patients, in whom the central plasma clearance rate for amino acids (CPCR-AA) was determined as a surrogate for actual liver uptake data (67). This measures total amino acid uptake by the central tissues, including liver, splanchnic bed, bone marrow, lymph nodes, and other tissues using amino acids for protein synthesis or energy production. CPCR-AA correlated with in vitro protein synthesis by liver tissue obtained by biopsy at surgery in the same patients, which indicates that CPCR-AA is a reasonable measure of amino acid uptake for protein synthesis by central tissues. In addition, CPCR-AA correlated with PIF activity in patient plasma, and with the rate of incorporation of $^{14}C$-tyrosine into hepatic protein by the biopsy specimens in vitro. In vitro data also show the ability of IL-1 to induce synthesis of a number of acute-phase proteins typical of infection and inflammation (38, 96, 102, 104). Thus, IL-1 and PIF not only induce muscle proteolysis, but also can direct the hepatic uptake of amino acids and accelerate the synthesis of acute-phase proteins; they are central to the catabolic and anabolic responses in infection.

Another property of IL-1 is the induction of the acute shifts of divalent cations in infected hosts (91, 103, 107). Under the influence of IL-1, lactoferrin is released from neutrophil-specific granules and binds iron and facilitates its clearance from plasma (59), while synthesis of metallothionine is triggered (103), leading to zinc uptake. Since ceruloplasmin is an acute-phase protein stimulated by IL-1, elevation of serum copper during infection is a third manifestation of IL-1 effects on minerals (94).

Finally, it is worth noting that in addition to fever and anorexia, the other generalized manifestations of infection, such as myalgias and fatigue, are probably also related to IL-1 effects. Myalgia is undoubtedly due to PIF-induced proteolysis of muscle, since this effect is blocked by antipyretics that relieve myalgias (4a). Recently IL-1 was shown to induce slow wave sleep (61), measured by EEG recording, in a manner similar to a factor (S) derived from sleep-deprived humans, except for a rapid onset rather than a delay of about one hour. Thus, factor S may act by local release of IL-1 from astrocytes in brain. The resulting sleep could benefit the host by reducing energy demands at a time when IL-1 is mobilizing host metabolism for the defense responses required for survival. This is another example of the extraordinary coordination of the host responses mediated by IL-1 to function in the most economic and efficient fashion. IL-1 is a well-conserved protein, being found in reptiles, amphibians, bony fish, and birds, as well as in mammals. This suggests that it has evolutionary significance as a protective factor (60).

*Immunologic effects of IL-1* Interleukin-1 was first defined as a macrophage product (monokine) needed for the function of lymphocytes, and its ability to activate thymocytes exposed to submitogenic concentrations of PHA or ConA (LAF activity) was used as a bioassay for the peptide. The effects of IL-1 on the immune system were reviewed recently (27, 81), and only a brief summary need be presented here.

It is fair to state that IL-1 plays a critical role in immunoregulation, for it contributes to the initiation of both humoral and cell-mediated immune responses (32, 64, 81). Although the specific locus of action of IL-1 in B-cell activation remains uncertain, the molecule is one of several mediators apparently necessary for regulation of antibody production. It has become clear that the human monocyte-derived monokine called B-cell-activating factor (BAF), which increases the anti–sheep cell response of splenocytes from antigen-stimulated nude mice when directly added in vitro, is in fact IL-1. The effect of IL-1 actually may be twofold: first a direct effect in B-cell activation and proliferation, and second an indirect effect through activation of T helper and suppressor cells. It is certainly not a chance phenomenon that most adjuvants are IL-1 inducers and pyrogens as well (27). The effect on CMI is more clearly at the early stage of T-cell activation, as IL-1 signals the production of lymphokines, the most important of which is IL-2. IL-2 and the induction of IL-2 receptors on responsive T cells, leads to clonal expansion of functional subsets of helper, suppressor, and cytotoxic T cells (73). IL-1 also augments natural killer activity and synergizes with IL-2 or interferon in this effect (24).

IL-1 also exhibits the neutrophilia-inducing activity associated with the acute-phase response (48). Partially purified pyrogen induces peak neutrophilia in 60–90 minutes after i.v. injection, and repetitive injections result in sustained elevation in neutrophil counts with no evidence of tolerance or tachyphylaxis to daily injection, as well as an increase in plasma levels of neutrophil colony-stimulating factor (49). Although the preparations of IL-1 used in these studies were not pure, Dinarello (27) has concluded that the possible level of contamination with C3a could not account for the findings and that IL-1 causes direct release of neutrophils from bone marrow.

One of the dramatic effects of IL-1 is the induction of acute-phase protein synthesis in liver. The role of the acute-phase proteins in the host inflammatory response is not fully defined but may serve, at least in part, to dampen the destructive effects of unrestrained inflammation by anti-enzyme effects, for example the antitrypsin, elastase, collagenase, plasmin, thrombin, and kallikrein activity of $\alpha_1$-antitrypsin and/or $\alpha_2$-macroglobulin (95). In addition, some of the acute-phase proteins, such as serum amyloid A (SAA) and C-reactive protein (CRP), are also immunoregulatory in vitro, particularly affecting T-cell responses and complement activation, respectively (10, 109). The full significance of the acute-phase protein response for host defense and immunoregulation remains to be determined.

CACHECTIN Based on observations of debilitating cachexia in *Trypanosoma brucei* infection in cattle, Rouzer & Cerami (99) experimentally infected rabbits and found that they became moribund and extremely cachectic, even when there was minimal parasitemia, and they exhibited extreme elevation of very low density lipoprotein (VLDL). The hypertriglyceridemia was shown to be the consequence of a clearing defect due to depressed lipoprotein lipase (LPL) activity. Using another model known to result in hypertriglyceridemia, endotoxin administration, Kawakami & Cerami (53) observed that endotoxin-sensitive C3H/HeN mice demonstrated the same loss of LPL in adipose tissue and elevation of VLDL, while endotoxin-resistant C3H/HeJ mice were unaffected. However, resistance of C3H/HeJ mice was overcome by injecting serum from C3H/HeN mice treated two hours previously with endotoxin or by conditioned medium from elicited peritoneal exudate cells incubated in the presence of endotoxin (53, 90). This suggested that the endotoxin effect was due to activation of macrophages to produce a soluble mediator. Cerami and colleagues went on to prove this by demonstrating such a monokine in stimulated macrophages and macrophage cell lines (RAW 264.7) that suppressed the LPL activity of the adipocyte cell line, 3T3-L1 (11, 44, 75). This monokine was called cachectin.

Cachectin was then obtained from endotoxin-activated cultured RAW 264.7 macrophages, concentrated and desalted over an Amicon PM-10 filter, and then purified by successive isoelectric focusing in a glycerol gradient, Con A sepharose affinity chromatography, and preparative polyacrylamide gel electrophoresis (PAGE). The specific activity of the purified cachectin was increased by 80-fold, but with only a 2% yield, as assayed by ability to suppress heparin-releasable LPL activity of 3T3-L1 cells. One peak of bioactivity was obtained by isoelectric focusing at a pH of 4.7 and a single species was found by preparative PAGE under nondenaturing conditions. SDS-PAGE also demonstrated a single peptide of $M_r$ 17,000, which contained cachectin bioactivity when eluted from sliced unfixed gels.

When the purified cachectin was labeled by the iodogen method, 70% of the bioactivity was recovered in the $M_r$ 17,000 region on SDS-PAGE. This preparation bound specifically to 3T3-L1 cells, and $\sim 10^4$ high-affinity receptor sites were present by Scatchard analysis, with an association constant ($K_a$) of 3 x $10^9$ $M^{-1}$. A similar number of high-affinity binding sites could also be detected on $C_2$ muscle cells, and specific binding to mouse liver cell membranes but not to erythrocytes or lymphocytes was also detected.

Cachectin thus resembles IL-1 in several ways: it has a similar cell of origin (monocyte/macrophage), is endotoxin inducible, and has similar pI and molecular size. Other data indicate these are distinct molecules. RAW 264.7 cells produce little LAF activity under conditions resulting in cachectin release while purified cachectin does not exhibit LAF activity and highly purified recombinant mouse IL-1 fails to compete for binding of $^{125}$I-cachectin to 3T3-L1 cells (11).

The mechanism by which cachectin inhibits triglyceride clearance has been investigated using 3T3-L1 cells. This fibroblast line differentiates to adipocytes, which produce considerable quantities of three key lipid biosynthetic enzymes; lipoprotein lipase, needed for transport of exogenous lipid into the cell; and acetyl-CoA carboxylase and fatty acid synthetase, both essential for endogenous fatty acid synthesis. As already noted, adding cachectin to these cells results in a rapid decrease in LPL activity, serving as a bioassay for the monokine. LPL activity decreases in the medium, in the cell itself, and in the heparin-releasable membrane-associated enzyme. This is not due to enzyme inhibition, since addition of cachectin to LPL does not alter the decay curve of bioactivity (53). Instead, biosynthesis of LPL is selectively decreased. When $^{35}$S-methionine incorporation was measured in the presence of cachectin, there was no reduction in total protein synthesis. However, a 220,000-dalton peptide present in cultures without cachectin was missing in the cachectin-containing cultures. In addition, using antibodies to fatty acid synthetase or acetyl-CoA carboxylase for an immunoprecipitation assay, researchers observed that immunoreactive enzyme progressively decreased in the cachectin-treated cultures (90a).

Using a stable adipogenic line, TA1, derived from 3T3-L1 adipocytes, Torti et al showed that lipogenic enzymes are suppressed by a selective alteration in gene expression (105a). Under normal conditions, TA1 cells activate several genes within three days after reaching confluent growth. These genes are detectable by dot-blot hybridization of mRNA with nick-translated cDNA clones. Using clones specific for genes expressed in differentiated adipocytes but not in preadipocytes, Torti et al observed that cachectin prevented the transcriptional activation of adipose-inducible mRNA but had no effect on the noninducible actin gene (105a). No effect was found when endotoxin was added to conditioned medium from RAW 264.7 cells, which demonstrates that the role of endotoxin is to induce monokine production. Cachectin also resulted in an inhibition of oil-red–O-positive lipid accumulation in TA1 cells. All effects were reversed during incubation in cachectin-free medium.

Cachectin did not alter cell growth or viability (105a). However, because adipocytes do not proliferate in vivo, in vitro experiments were repeated with mature confluent nonmultiplying cultures. By 4–6 days in the presence of cachectin, the percentage of oil-red–O-positive cells decreased from 80% to 10%. The effect of cachectin on adipocyte specific genes was consistent with these results and even more impressive. Within 24 hours, cachectin resulted in a 90% decrease in RNA hybridizing with the cDNA's. The level of mRNA for glycerophosphate dehydrogenase also paralleled the bioactivity of the enzyme in the cell.

These results can explain the effects of certain acute infections, for example gram-negative sepsis, on lipid metabolism (51, 52). The cachectin-induced depression in LPL activity, which leads to hypertriglyceridemia in vivo, is not reversed in vitro by insulin in high concentration, although there is no alteration in either insulin receptor expression or the function of the receptor-coupled glucose transport unit in cachectin-treated adipocytes. In the septic patient, hyperglycemia due to gluconeogenesis and direct IL-1 effects on pancreatic islet β cells both lead to elevated insulin levels. Although this can result in glucose uptake by adipocytes, cachectin-affected cells cannot utilize this for fatty acid synthesis and the glucose diffuses out of the cell into plasma, contributing in circular fashion to hyperglycemia and hyperinsulinemia. Thus, the combination of IL-1 and cachectin can explain most of the alterations in energy metabolism in the septic patient. Chronic inhibition of lipid metabolism can also explain the cachexia associated with chronic infection or malignancy.

Cachectin has a high degree of sequence homology to another previously described macrophage secretory product called tumor necrosis factor (TNF) (11a). Indeed, recombinant human TNF appears to cause lipid mobilization from adipocytes and to inhibit synthesis of lipogenic enzymes (105a), and purified cachectin has TNF activity. Antibody to cachectin that has no demonstrable reactivity with the endotoxin used to elicit the monokine has been employed to passively immunize mice prior to administration of a lethal dose of endotoxin (11a). The significant protective effect observed suggested that lethal events in endotoxic shock may be due to cachectin-induced events. This antibody did not abrogate the pyrogenic effect of endotoxin, consistent with the evidence that IL-1 and cachectin are distinct monokines. The beneficial and potentially harmful effects of cachectin remain uncertain at this writing; however, we may anticipate considerable progress in the next few years.

## IRON AND INFECTION

Nutritional deficiency is usually considered to be deleterious and in particular to affect adversely the defense mechanisms against infectious diseases (55). This view has been challenged recently, especially with respect to micronutrient deficiency, notably that due to iron. Thus two extremes of opinions have now been established: (*a*) iron deficiency increases host susceptibility to infection, a situation that can be reversed by appropriate iron replacement therapy; and (*b*) since microbial pathogens require iron for survival, iron deficiency can actually reduce the likelihood of infection and correcting this deficiency may harm the host by promoting replication of the invading pathogens (45). These views present an apparently irreconcilable controversy between the possible benefit and detriment of iron for the infected human host. However, some of the data on which such views are based have not always been well controlled, and in some instances the apparent association of iron status with infection rates remains only an association without firm evidence of causality.

It is clear, however, that free iron is required by microorganisms and in vitro studies have shown that indeed the iron is necessary for microbial growth (113). In addition, iron deficiency has been shown to protect both birds and mammals from some experimental bacterial infections, while infection can be enhanced by iron administration (112). What relevance does this have for the human host and what is the evidence for and against a significant role of iron in the pathogenesis of human infectious disease?

## *Evidence That Iron Deficiency Promotes Infection*

In 1928, Mackay (74) reported the results of a survey of 541 nonhospitalized infants in London and observed that anemia was common in both breast-fed and artificially fed subjects. Oral supplementation with iron not only increased hemoglobin but reduced attack rates of respiratory and diarrheal disease by approximately 50% compared to untreated controls. However, the groups were not selected on a random basis and it is uncertain whether or not they were well matched for other important health-related variables. Yet Mackay concluded that iron treatment resulted in "a striking improvement in general health and resistance to infection." Therefore, "artificially-fed babies should be given iron before (they are) two months old" and "many breast-fed babies also require iron treatment."

Andelman & Sered (2) examined the effect of feeding an iron-containing milk formula for a period of 6–9 months to 603 infants of a low socioeconomic status and compared the results with a group of 445 control children. While growth was similar for children in both groups, anemia was prevented in the treated infants and there was a striking reduction in the incidence of respiratory infection. More recently Lovric (72) found that children with anemia, the majority of whom had iron-deficiency anemia, had a significantly higher prevalence of gastroenteritis than nonanemic controls. Another community-based study in Maori infants showed that administration of parenteral iron during the first few days of life reduced hospital admission rates during the subsequent two years, particularly for some respiratory infections and gastroenteritis, compared to untreated controls (18).

Other interventional community-based studies also suggest that iron deficiency predisposes to infection and its correction leads to an apparent reduction in infection rate. A study of children with malnutrition in Colombia showed a reduction in infections, notably gastroenteritis, after iron deficiency was corrected with iron supplements (3). Similarly, in an urban population in Chile, the diarrheal disease rate diminished after introduction of an iron-fortified milk formula, although in this instance comparisons were made with disease morbidity during the two-month period immediately prior to introduction of the new formula (89a). Additionally, a placebo-controlled trial of prophylactic parenteral iron in early infancy significantly reduced the death rate from infectious disease in Eskimo infants (89b). However, a more recent survey of normal infants in England showed first that hemoglobin concentration was generally higher than reported previously, and second that placebo-controlled iron administration, while increasing hemoglobin in some infants, failed to make any impact whatsoever on the incidence of infection (14).

An association between the prevalence of urinary infection and anemia in pregnancy was reported by Giles & Brown in 1962 (40); they found that urinary infection was more than twice as common in 463 anemic pregnant women compared to 447 nonanemic pregnant controls. Unfortunately, it cannot be determined from this study whether urinary infection and anemia are dependent or independent variables, and cause and effect are difficult to separate. Other studies have shown that urinary infection is associated with a marginal reduction in hemoglobin concentration (1, 100) although an extensive survey of 5000 pregnant women failed to confirm an association between urinary infection and iron deficiency (65).

Increased susceptibility to mucocutaneous candidiasis has also been reported in severe iron-deficiency anemia, which was reversed when iron stores were repleted (37, 43). At the same time, other studies have failed to show that iron status or iron repletion for iron deficiency had a significant impact on either oral or genital candidiasis (23, 110). More recently a retrospective analysis of anemic, iron-deficient, hospitalized infants in Papua New Guinea showed that meningitis and pneumonia were more common in the presence of iron deficiency (87).

Although many of these studies suggest that iron deficiency in infants and children predisposes to infection, particularly of the respiratory and gastrointestinal tracts, and that administration of iron in some circumstances can reduce infection rates, the majority of these studies have serious shortcomings. Many are uncontrolled or at best poorly controlled. Historical or retrospective controls are now unacceptable because epidemics and other seasonal factors in illness can distort data analysis and produce fallacious conclusions. Similarly, one can never be certain that an intervention such as the introduction of iron-fortified formula is the only change that occurred during that period. Few of these studies match patients for overall nutritional status, which may be a more important determinant of host susceptibility to infection for which iron deficiency is merely a surrogate measure. Finally, many of the children studied have had multiple health problems, making data analysis even more complex.

Thus none of these studies permit reliable conclusions about whether iron deficiency alone predisposes to infection and if iron supplementation and correction of iron deficiency as the sole intervention can reduce prevalence and morbidity from infection. We look forward to the results of prospective, randomized, double-blind, placebo-controlled trials of iron prophylaxis in infants (such as the study underway in Papua New Guinea), which should overcome many of the deficiencies of previous studies (88), finally ending a controversy that has remained unanswered for more than half a century.

### *Evidence That Iron Deficiency Protects Against Infection*

During the past decade an apparently heretical concept has evolved; it proposes that nutritional deficiency, both generalized and specific, may in some situations be protective against infectious diseases (101). There is evidence to suggest that relative or absolute iron deficiency may reduce susceptibility to certain infections and that treatment with iron exacerbates these processes. As previously discussed, it has been known for many years that serum iron falls during infection, largely because circulating iron is removed by the liver and to a lesser extent because iron absorption by the intestine is reduced (19, 42, 66). It has been proposed that this "iron shift" reduces the availability of free iron to infectious agents and therefore induces a degree of "nutritional immunity" (112, 113).

Over 100 years ago, Trousseau (106) observed that in patients with quiescent tuberculosis, iron supplementation often led to clinical recrudescence of the disease. McFarlane et al (78) suggested that in their study the rapid demise of children with kwashiorkor was related to refeeding, especially micronutrient supplementation with iron. They suggested that because of the low transferrin in these children, iron administration resulted in high levels of the free circulating iron, which was instrumental in promoting bacterial infection. Subsequently they showed that sera from children with kwashiorkor readily supported growth of *Staphylococcus aureus,* particularly when serum transferrin was low, whereas addition of purified transferrin to cultures inhibited bacterial growth (79).

Several studies followed supporting the view that repletion of iron deficiency actually enhances the prevalence of infection. Masawe et al (76) investigated infection rates in 110 anemic patients in Tanzania. Of 67 patients with iron-deficiency anemia, only 7% had bacterial infection compared with 65% of 43 patients with anemia of other etiologies. Malaria was more common in the patients with iron deficiency, but clinical malarial attacks frequently occurred after initiation of iron replacement therepy. Often cited data for the apparent protective effects of iron deficiency comes from the observational and interventional studies of Murray et al (82–84). Somali nomads are commonly iron deficient because of the limited iron available from their almost exlusively milk diet. In a survey of 90 Somali nomads, 26 were shown to be iron deficient, based on hemoglobin < 11 g/dl, serum iron < 25 μl/100 ml, transferrin saturation < 15%, and a hypochromic anemia (83). None of them, however, had clinical evidence of infection. Of the remaining 64 with normal iron status, 19 (30%) had laboratory evidence of infection, particularly malaria (positive blood smear), brucellosis (agglutination titer > 1:320), tuberculosis (positive acid fast stain), and urinary schistosomiasis (nonquantitative examination of urine for ova). Clinical status was not reported.

Following these pilot observations, a placebo-controlled study of iron supplementation was performed in 137 iron-deficient individuals (84). Treatment was continued for 30 days, during which active surveillance for infection was maintained. In the 71 subjects receiving iron replacement therapy, there were 36 "infectious" processes, including 29 febrile episodes in 27 (38%)

subjects, compared with only 7 episodes and 6 fevers occurring in 5 of 66 (7.6%) placebo-treated controls. The most common specific infection observed was malaria, accounting for 13 episodes in untreated subjects, but only 1 in control subjects. This excess of fevers in the treated group occurred during days 20–30 of observation. Brucellosis and tuberculosis were also diagnosed more frequently in the iron-treated patients on the basis of antibody titer and acid fast stain of drainage from infected tissue (lymph node in two patients and breast in one).

In an earlier study in Central Africa, Murray et al also observed that malaria attacks were most common during refeeding after famine, and were associated with hyperferremia (82). However, an alternative interpretation can be offered to explain some results of this study. It is possible that iron repletion improved T-cell function, thus leading to an improved *Brucella* antibody response in previously infected patients and an enhanced inflammatory response to pre-existing tuberculous infections, as well as increasing phagocytic cell function, manifested as purulent lesions with fever due to IL-1 release. It is somewhat strange that schistosome ova were found in 11 of 71 untreated individuals compared to only 2 of 66 placebo-treated subjects. Since it is biologically impossible for this to reflect new infection during the 30-day observation period, the findings raise the question of some hidden bias in sample selection. At the very least, these data are in need of independent confirmation and careful reinterpretation.

Iron deficiency in infancy has been recognized in many populations, particularly in infants from low socioeconomic groups. Iron deficiency in these infants has historically been regarded as damaging to health, which persuaded some clinicians to advise routine prophylaxis with parenteral iron during the first weeks of life (105). Several studies have shown, however, this may have detrimental effects. In 1970 the National Women's Hospital in Auckland, New Zealand, began routinely to administer iron-dextran complex during the first week of life as prophylaxis against iron-deficiency anemia. In the period 1971–1972, 21 cases of *E. coli* meningitis were reported, 18 of which followed within 5 days of administration of iron dextran (6, 33, 34). In the years preceding 1970 only one or two cases of *E. coli* meningitis were observed each year. During the same period in New Zealand at Hawke's Bay, Barry & Reeve (5) observed a similar phenomenon in Polynesian infants. During a period of iron prophylaxis, the neonatal sepsis rate was 17 per 1000 births, but this fell dramatically to 2.7 per 1000 on cessation of the iron supplementation program.

A major deficit in both of these studies is that concurrent controls were not available. However, Barry & Reeve reported that neonatal sepsis rates in European infants during the same periods remained steady throughout and were comparable with sepsis rates observed in Polynesian infants when iron supplementation was discontinued. Although the dangers of giving iron have been considered and debated for more than a century, there is as yet no satisfactory randomized, placebo-controlled, double-blind trial of iron supplementation for iron deficiency that assesses its impact on the prevalence of infection. The trial of Oppenheimer et al in Papua New Guinea should go a long way to answer these questions, certainly with respect to the effects of iron supplementation in infancy and early childhood (88).

The proposed detrimental effect of iron is also inferred from reports relating iron overload and other causes of increased serum iron concentration to the prevalence of infection. For example, hemochromatosis, an inherited disorder of iron metabolism resulting in elevated serum iron concentration and massive accumulation of iron in many organs of the body, has been associated with an increased risk of infection from *Yersinia enterocolitica* and *Entamoeba histolytica* (25, 80). Iron overload is also seen in South African native men as a result of excessive ingestion of iron in home-made beer brewed in iron vessels. Severe hepatic amebiasis is more common in these men compared with native women whose exposure to the same parasite would appear to be identical (25). In contrast the nomadic Masai who inhabit the Rift Valley are curiously free of amebiasis, which has been attributed to their custom of drinking milk, resulting in mild iron-deficiency anemia and low transferrin saturation. Iron supplementation of the Masai during a one-year period not only increased hemoglobin and transferrin saturation, but also resulted in a marked increase in prevalence of amebas in stool- and smear-positive malaria (85).

The dangers of the hyperferremic state are often considered to be exemplified by the enhanced risk of bacterial infection in conditions associated with decreased red cell survival, notably thalassemia and sickle cell anemia (113). Serum iron concentration is elevated during acute malaria attacks as a result of red cell destruction, and the increase in bacterial infection, particularly salmonellosis, has been attributed to this change in circulating iron levels (12). A similar increase in *Salmonella* and other bacterial infections has been observed during the severe hemolytic phase of bartonellosis (22); however, the mechanism is only indirectly related to iron, which is taken up by the mononuclear phagocyte system where it results in impaired clearance of circulating microorganisms (RES blockade) (54).

Although these data are used to support the hypothesis that high levels of free circulating iron are detrimental to the host and increase susceptibility to infection (112, 113), none of the above-cited studies clearly show causality. One must remain skeptical of such an association because the variables might easily be dependent.

## *The Current Status of the Paradox*

From the data discussed above, it is difficult to develop a unifying hypothesis that explains such apparently disparate views regarding the influence of iron status on susceptibility to infection. Accepting our reservations about the design and interpretation of data in many of the studies cited, we currently and cautiously entertain the possibility that indeed both points of view are partially true.

Iron deficiency in an otherwise well-nourished individual with normal serum transferrin may well be a risk factor for infection. Some studies supporting this point of view were performed in children in industrialized nations who did not have severe PEM and in whom serum transferrin levels would be normal or nearly normal. Therefore, iron supplementation, particularly when given orally, is unlikely to produce the very high levels of circulating free iron that have been observed in infants receiving parenteral iron-dextran. Thus, to the extent that iron deficiency impairs immune function it may result in enhanced infection, and yet iron administration is not harmful. In contrast, in children with overt PEM and very low serum transferrin levels, iron supplementation (whether oral or parenteral) can result in rapid increments in serum free iron, which may indeed be advantageous to invading pathogens. The "physiological" mild iron deficiency observed in early infancy can be considered to be an intermediate state in which the deficiency is not harmful at the same time that iron is less available to pathogens. It may be part of nature's protective design and need not and probably should not be aggressively treated. Whether or not this applies to oral iron supplementation to prevent or mitigate iron deficiency is not certain but seems unlikely.

Nonetheless, it would seem prudent to direct future studies to define iron-deficiency anemia clearly and to determine both its association with and the binding capacity of iron transport proteins to the prevalence of infection. In addition, the presence of other potentially confounding nutrient deficiencies must be ruled out and the effect of iron supplementation determined. The results of iron supplementation must also be related to changes in bound and free serum iron as well as the hematopoietic response. Only then will we be able to make reasonable judgments about the specific effects of iron nutriture on infection.

ACKNOWLEDGMENT

Supported in part by a grant in Geographic Medicine (GTK) from The Rockefeller Foundation, New York, and a lectureship in Tropical Medicine (MJGF) from the Wellcome Foundation, London.

## *Literature Cited*

1. Abramson, J. H., Sacks, J. C., Flug, D., Elishkorvsky, R., Cohen R. 1971. Bacteriuria and hemoglobin levels in pregnancy. *J. Am. Med. Assoc.* 2155:1631–37
2. Andelman, M. B., Sered, B. R. 1966. Utilization of dietary iron by term infants. *Am. J. Dis. Child.* 111:45–55
3. Arbeter, A., Echeverri, L., Franco, D., Munson, D., Velez, H., Vitale, J. 1971. Nutrition and infection. *Fed. Proc.* 30:1421–28
4. Auron, P. E., Webb, A. C., Rosenwasser, L. J., Mucci, S. F., Rich, A., et al. 1984. Nucleotide sequence of human monocyte interleukin 1 precursor cDNA. *Proc. Natl. Acad. Sci. USA* 81:7907–11

4a. Baracos, V., Rodemann, H. P., Di-

narello, C. A., Goldberg, A. L. 1983. Stimulation of muscle protein degradation and prostaglandin $E_2$ release by leukocytic pyrogen (interleukin-1). *N. Engl. J. Med.* 308:553–58
5. Barry, D. M. J., Reeve, A. W. 1977. Increased incidence of gram-negative neonatal sepsis with intramuscular iron administration. *Pediatrics* 60:908–12
6. Becroft, D. M. O., Dix, M. R., Farmer, K. 1977. Intramuscular iron-dextran and susceptibility of neonates to bacterial infections. *Arch. Dis. Child.* 52:778–81
7. Beisel, W. R. 1977. Magnitude of the host nutritional response to infection. *Am. J. Clin. Nutr.* 30:1236–47
8. Beisel, W. R. 1984. Metabolic effects of infection. *Prog. Food Nutr. Sci.* 8:43–75
9. Beisel, W. R., Wannemacher, R. W. 1980. Gluconeogenesis, ureagenesis, and ketogenesis during sepsis. *J. Parenter. Enteral Nutr.* 4:277–85
10. Benson, M. D., Aldo-Benson, M. A. 1982. SAA supression of *in vitro* antibody response. *Ann. NY Acad. Sci.* 389:121–25
11. Beutler, B., Mahoney, J., Le Trang, N., Pekala, P., Cerami, A. 1985. Purification of cachectin, a lipoprotein lipase-suppressing hormone secreted by endotoxin-induced RAW 264.7 cells. *J. Exp. Med.* 161:984–95
11a. Beutler, B., Milsark, I. W., Cerami, A. C. 1985. Passive immunization cachectin/tumor necrosis factor protects mice from lethal effect of endotoxin. *Science* 229:869–71
12. Black, P. H., Kunz, L. J., Swartz, M. N. 1960. Salmonellosis—a review of some unusual aspects. *N. Engl. J. Med.* 262:811–17, 864–70, 921–27
13. Blackburn, G. L. 1977. Lipid metabolism in infection. *Am. J. Clin. Nutr.* 30:1321–32
14. Burman, D. 1972. Haemoglobin levels in normal infants aged 3 to 24 months and the effect of iron. *Arch. Dis. Child.* 47:261–71
15. Cahill, G. F. Jr. 1970. Starvation in man. *N. Engl. J. Med.* 282:688–75
16. Cannon, J. G., Dinarello, C. A. 1985. Biological properties of putative interleukin-1 fragments in human plasma. *J. Leuk. Biol.* 37:689–90
17. Cannon, J. G., Dinarello, C. A. 1985. Increased plasma interleukin-1 activity in women after ovulation. *Science* 227:1247–49
18. Cantwell, R. J. 1972. Iron deficiency anaemia of infancy. *Clin. Pediatr.* 11:443–49
19. Cartwright, G. E., Lauritsen, M. A., Jones, P. J., Merrill, I. M., Wintrobe, M. M. 1946. The anemia of infection. I. Hypoferremia, hypercupremia and alterations in porphyrin metabolism in patients. *J. Clin. Invest.* 25:65–80
20. Clowes, G. H. A. Jr., Randall, H. T., Cha, C.-J. 1980. Amino acid and energy metabolism in septic and traumatized patients. *J. Parenter. Enteral Nutr.* 4:195–205
21. Clowes, G. H. A. Jr., George, B. C., Villee, C. A. Jr., Saravis, C. A. 1983. Muscle proteolysis induced by a circulating peptide in patients with sepsis or trauma. *N. Engl. J. Med.* 308:545–52
22. Cuadra, M. 1956. Salmonellosis complication in human bartonellosis. *Tex. Rep. Biol. Med.* 14:97–113
23. Davidson, F., Hayes, J. P., Hussein, S. 1977. Recurrent genital candidosis and iron metabolism. *Br. J. Vener. Dis.* 53:123–25
24. Dempsey, R. A., Dinarello, C. A., Mier, J. W., Rosenwasser, L. J., Allegretta, M., et al. 1982. The differential effects of human leukocytic pyrogen/lymphocyte activating factor, T cell growth factor, and interferon on human natural killer activity. *J. Immunol.* 129:2504–10
25. Diamond, L. S., Harlow, D. R., Phillips, B. P., Keister, D. B. 1978. *Entamoeba histolytica:* iron and nutritional immunity. *Arch. Invest. Med. Suppl.* 1:329–38
26. Dinarello, C. A. 1984. Interleukin-1 and the pathogenesis of the acute-phase response. *N. Engl. J. Med.* 311:1413–18
27. Dinarello, C. A. 1984. Interleukin-1. *Rev. Infect. Dis.* 6:51–95
28. Dinarello, C. A. 1985. An update on human interleukin-1: From molecular biology to clinical relevance. *J. Clin. Immunol.* 5:1–11
29. Dinarello, C. A., Clowes, G. H. A. Jr., Gordon, H. A., Saravis, C. A., Wolff, S. M. 1984. Cleavage of human interleukin-1: Isolation of a peptide fragment from the plasma of febrile pationts and from activated monocytes. *J. Immunol.* 133:1332–38
30. Dinarello, C. A., Wolff, S. M. 1982. Molecular basis of fever in humans. *Am. J. Med.* 72:799–819
31. DuBois, E. F. 1937. *The Mechanism of Heat Loss and Temperature Regulation.* Stanford Univ. Press, Calif.
32. Falkoff, R. J. M., Muraguchi, A., Hong, J-X., Butler, J. L., Dinarello, C. A., Fauci, A. S. 1983. The effects of interleukin 1 in human B cell activation and proliferation. *J. Immunol.* 131:801–5
33. Farmer, K. 1976. The disadvantages of

routine administration of intramuscular iron to neonates. *NZ Med. J.* 84:286–87
34. Farmer, K., Becroft, D. M. 1976. Administration of parenteral iron to newborn infants. *Arch. Dis. Child.* 51:486
35. Fiser, R. H., Denniston, J. C., Beisel, W. R. 1972. Infection with *Diplococcus pneumoniae* and *Salmonella typhimurium* in monkeys: changes in plasma lipids and lipoproteins. *J. Infect. Dis.* 125:54–60
36. Fiser, R. H., Denniston, J. C., Beisel, W. R. 1974. Endotoxemia in the rhesus monkey: alterations in host lipid and carbohydrate metabolism. *Pediatr. Res.* 8:13–17
37. Fletcher, J., Mather, J., Lewis, M. J., Whiting, G. 1975. Mouth lesion in iron-deficient anemia: relationship to *Candida albicans* in saliva and to impariment of lymphocyte transformation. *J. Infect. Dis.* 131:44–50
38. Gauldie, J., Sauder, D. N., McAdam, K. P. W. J., Dinarello, C. A. 1985. Purified human interleukin-1 stimulates secretion of multiple acute phase proteins *in vitro*. In *Physiologic, Metabolic and Immunologic Actions of Interleukin-1,* ed. M. J. Kluger, J. J. Oppenheim, M. C. Powanda, New York: Liss
39. George, D. T., Abeles, F. B., Mapes, C. A., Sobocinski, P. Z., Zenser, T. V., Powanda, M. C. 1977. Effect of leukocytic endogenous mediators on endocrine pancreas secretory responses. *Am. J. Physiol.* 233:E240–45
40. Giles, C., Brown, J. A. H. 1962. Urinary infection and anaemia in pregnancy. *Br. Med. J.* 2:10–13
41. Gordon, A. H., Parker, I. D. 1980. A pyrogen derived from human white cells which is active in mice. *Br. J. Exp. Pathol.* 61:534–39
42. Greenberg, G. R., Ashenbrucker, H., Lauritsen, M. A., Worth, W., Humphreys, S. R., Wintrobe, M. M. 1947. The anemia of infection. V. Fate of injected radioactive iron in the presence of inflammation. *J. Clin. Invest.* 26:121–25
43. Higgs, J. M., Wells, R. S. 1972. Chronic muco-cutaneous candidiasis: associated abnormalities of iron metabolism. *Br. J. Dermatol.* 86(Suppl. 8):88–102
44. Hotez, P. J., Le Trang, N., Fairlamb, A. H., Cerami, A. 1984. Lipoprotein lipase suppression in 3T3-L1 cells by a haematoprotozoan-induced mediator from peritoneal exudate cells. *Parasite Immunol.* 6:203–9
45. Humbert, J. R., Moore, L. L. 1983. Iron deficiency and infection: A dilemma. *J. Pediatr. Gastroenterol. Nutr.* 2:403–6
46. Deleted in proof
47. Deleted in proof
48. Kampschmidt, R. K., Upchurch, H. F. 1977. Possible involvement of leukocytic endogenous mediator in granulopoiesis. *Proc. Soc. Exp. Biol. Med.* 155:89–93
49. Kampschmidt, R. K., Upchurch, H. F. 1980. Neutrophil release after injections of endotoxin or leukocytic endogenous mediator into rats. *J. Reticulendothel. Soc.* 28:191–201
50. Kampschmidt, R. K., Upchurch, H. F., Eddington, C. L. 1969. Hypoferremia produced by plasma from endotoxin-treated rats. *Proc. Soc. Exp. Biol. Med.* 132:817–20
51. Kaufmann, R. L., Matson, C. F., Beisel, W. R. 1976. Hypertriglyceridemia produced by endotoxin: role of impaired triglyceride disposal mechanisms. *J. Infect. Dis.* 133:548–55
52. Kaufmann, R. L., Matson, C. F., Rawberg, A. H., Beisel, W. R. 1976. Defective lipid disposal mechanisms during bacterial infection in rhesus monkeys. *Metabolism* 25:615–24
53. Kawakami, M., Cerami, A. 1981. Studies of endotoxin-induced decrease in lipoprotein lipase activity. *J. Exp. Med.* 154:631–39
54. Kaye, D., Gill, F. A., Hook, E. W. 1967. Factors influencing host resistance to salmonella infections: The effects of hemolysis and erythrophagocytosis. *Am. J. Med. Sci.* 254:205–15
55. Keusch, G. T. 1979. Nutrition as a determinant of host response to infection and the metabolic sequelae of infectious disease. *Semin. Infect. Dis.* 2:265–303
56. Keusch, G. T. 1984. Nutrition and infection. In *Current Clinical Topics in Infectious Diseases,* ed. J. S. Remington, M. N. Swartz, pp. 106–23. New York: McGraw-Hill
57. Kimball, E. S., Pickeral, S. F., Oppenheim, J. J., Rossio, J. L. 1984. Interleukin-1 activity in normal human urine. *J. Immunol.* 122:256–61
58. Klempner, M. S., Gallin, J. I. 1978. Separation and functional characterization of human neutrophil subpopulations. *Blood* 51:659–69
59. Klempner, M. S., Dinarello, C. A., Gallin, J. I. 1978. Human leukocytic pyrogen induces release of specific granule contents from human neutrophils. *J. Clin. Invest.* 61:1330–36
60. Kluger, M. J., Ringler, D. H., Anver, M. R. 1975. Fever and survival. *Science* 188:166–68
61. Kreuger, J. M., Walter, J., Dinarello, C. A., Wolff, S. M., Chedid, L. 1984.

Sleep-promoting effects of endogenous pyrogen (interleukin-1). *Am. J. Physiol.* 246:R994–99

62. Kurt-Jones, E. A., Beller, D. I., Mizel, S. B., Unanue, E. R. 1985. Identification of a membrane-associated interleukin-1 in macrophages. *Proc. Natl. Acad. Sci. USA* 82:1204–8
63. Lepe-Zuniga, J. L., Gery, I. 1984. Production of intracellular and extracellular interleukin-1 (IL-1) by human monocytes. *Clin. Immunol. Immunopathol.* 31:222–30
64. Lipsky, P. E., Thompson, P. A., Rosenwasser, L. J., Dinarello, C. A. 1983. The role of interleukin 1 in human B cell activation: inhibition of B cell proliferation and the generation of immunoglobulin secreting cells by an antibody against human leukocytic pyrogen. *J. Immunol* 130:2708–14
65. Little, P. J. 1966. The incidence of urinary infection in 5000 pregnant women. *Lancet* 2:925–28
66. Locke, A., Main, E. R., Rosbach, D. O. 1932. The copper and non-hemoglobins iron contents of the blood serum in disease. *J. Clin. Invest.* 11:527–42
67. Loda, M., Clowes, G. H. A. Jr., Dinarello, C. A., George, B. C., Lane, B., Richardson, W. 1984. Induction of hepatic protein synthesis by a peptide in blood plasma of patients with sepsis and trauma. *Surgery* 96:204–13
68. Long, C. L., Kinney, J. M., Geiger, J. W. 1976. Non-suppressability of gluconeogenesis by glucose in septic patients. *Metabolism* 25:193–201
69. Long, C. L. 1977. Energy balance and carbohydrate metabolism in infection and sepsis. *Am. J. Clin. Nutr.* 30:1301–10
70. Long, C. L., Jeevanandum, M., Kim, B. M., Kinney, J. M. 1977. Whole-body protein synthesis and catabolism in septic man. *Am. J. Clin. Nutr.* 30:1340–44
71. Long, C. L., Schiller, W. R., Blakemore, W. S., Geiger, J. W., Odell, M., Henderson, K. 1977. Muscle protein catabolism in the septic patient as measured by 3-methylhistidine excretion. *Am. J. Clin. Nutr.* 30:1349–52
72. Lovric, V. A. 1970. Normal haematologic values in children aged 6 to 36 months and socio-medical implications. *Med. J. Aust.* 2:366–77
73. Luger, T. A., Smolen, J. S., Chused, T. M., Steinberg, A. D., Oppenheim, J. J. 1982. Human lymphocytes with either OKT4 or OKT8 phenotype produce interleukin 2 in culture. *J. Clin. Invest.* 70:470–73
74. Mackay, H. M. M. 1928. Anaemia in infancy: its prevalence and prevention. *Am. J. Dis. Child.* 111:45–55
75. Mahoney, J. R. Jr., Beutler, B. A., Le Trang, N., Vine, W., Ikeda, Y., Kawakami, M., Cerami, A. 1984. Lipopolysaccharide-treated RAW 264.7 cells produce a mediator that inhibits lipoprotein lipase in 3T3-L1 cells. *J. Immunol.* 134:1673–75
76. Masawe, A. E. J., Muindi, J. M., Swai, G. B. R. 1974. Infections in iron deficiency and other types of anaemia in the tropics. *Lancet* 2:314–17
77. McCarthy, D. O., Kluger, M. J., Vander, A. J. 1984. The role of fever in appetite suppression after endotoxin administration. *Am. J. Clin. Nutr.* 40:310–16
78. McFarlane, H., Reddy, S., Adcock, K. J., Adeshina, H., Cooke, A. R., Akene, J. 1970. Immunity, transferrin and survival in kwashiorkor. *Br. Med. J.* 4:268–70
79. McFarlane, H., Okubadejo, M., Reddy, S. 1972. Transferrin and *Staphylococcus aureus* in kwashiorkor. *Am. J. Clin. Pathol.* 57:587–91
80. Melby, K. L., Slordahl, S., Gutterberg, T. J., Nordbro, S. A. N. 1982. Septicemia due to *Yersinia enterocolitica* after oral overdose of iron. *Br. Med. J.* 285:467–68
81. Mizel, S. B. 1982. Interleukin-1 and T-cell activation. *Immunol. Rev.* 63:51–72
82. Murray, M. J., Murray, A. B., Murray, C. J., Murray, M. B. 1975. Refeeding—malaria and hyperferraemia. *Lancet* 1:653–54
83. Murray, M. J., Murray, A. B. 1977. Starvation suppression and refeeding activation of infection. An ecological necessity? *Lancet* 1:123–25
84. Murray, M. J., Murray, A. B., Murray, M. B., Murray, C. J. 1978. The adverse effect of iron repletion on the course of certain infections. *Br. Med. J.* 2:113–15
85. Murray, M. J., Murray, A. B., Murray, C. J. 1980. The salutory effect of milk on amoebiasis and its reversal by iron. *Br. Med. J.* 1:1351–52
86. Neufeld, H. A., Pace, J. G., Kaminski, M. V., George, D. T., Jahring, P. B., et al. 1977. A probable endocrine basis for the depression of ketone bodies during infectious or inflammatory states in rats. *Endocrinology* 107:596–601
87. Oppenheimer, S. J. 1980. Anaemia of infancy and bacterial infections in Papua, New Guinea. *Ann. Trop. Med. Parasitol.* 74:69–72
88. Oppenheimer, S. J., Hendrickse, R. G., MacFarlane, S. B. J., Moody, J. B., Har-

rison, C., et al. 1984. Iron and infection in infancy—report of field studies in Papua New Guinea: II Protocol and description of study cohort. *Ann. Trop. Pediatr.* 4:145–53

89. Osaki, S., Johnston, D. A., Frienden, E. 1966. The possible significance of the ferroxidase activity of ceruloplasmin in normal human serum. *J. Biol. Chem.* 241:2746–51

89a. Oski, F. A., Pearson, M. A., eds. 1981. Iron nutrition revisited—infancy, childhood, adolescence. In *Rep. 82nd Ross Conf. Pediatr. Nutr.,* p. 72. Columbus, Ohio: Ross Labs.

89b. See Ref. 89a, p. 73

90. Pekala, P. H., Lane, M. D., Cerami, A. 1982. Lipoprotein lipase suppression in 3T3-L1 cells by an endotoxin-induced mediator from exudate cells. *Proc. Natl. Acad. Sci. USA* 79:912–16

90a. Pekala, P. H., Kawakami, M., Angus, C. W., Lane, M. D., Cerami, A. 1983. Selective inhibition of synthesis of enzymes for de novo fatty acid biosynthesis by an endotoxin-induced mediator from exudate cells. *Proc. Natl. Acad. Sci. USA* 80:2743–47

91. Pekarek, R., Beisel, W. R. 1971. Characterization of the endogenous mediator(s) of serum zinc and iron depression during infection and other stresses. *Proc. Soc. Exp. Biol. Med.* 138: 728–32

92. Pekarek, R., Wannemacher, R., Powanda, M., Abeles, F., Mosher, D., Dinterman, R., Beisel, W. 1974. Further evidence that leukocytic endogenous mediator (LEM) is not endotoxin. *Life Sci.* 14:1765–76

93. Powanda, M. C. 1977. Changes in body balances of nitrogen and other key nutrients: description and underlying mechanisms. *Am. J. Clin. Nutr.* 30:1254–68

94. Powanda, M. C., Beisel, W. R. 1982. Hypothesis: leukocyte endogenous mediator/endogenous pyrogen/lymphocyte-activating factor modulates the development of nonspecific and specific immunity and affects nutritional status. *Am. J. Clin. Nutr.* 35:762–68

95. Powanda, M. C., Moyer, E. D. 1981. Plasma protein alterations during infection: Potential significance of these changes to host defense and repair systems. In *Infection: The Physiologic and Metabolic Response of the Host,* ed. M. C. Powanda, P. G. Canonico, pp. 271–98. Amsterdam: Elsevier/North Holland

96. Ramadori, G., Sipe, J. D., Dinarello, C. A., Mizel, S. B., Colten, H. R. 1985. Pretranslational modulation of acute phase hepatic protein synthesis by murine recombinant interleukin-1 (IL-1) and purified human IL-1. *J. Exp. Med.* 162:930–42

97. Rayfield, E. J., Curnow, R. T., George, D. T., Beisel, W. R. 1973. Impaired carbohydrate metabolism during a mild viral illness. *N. Engl. J. Med.* 298:618–21

98. Rosenblatt, S., Clowes, G. H. A. Jr., George, B. C., Hirsch, E., Lindberg, B. 1983. Exchange of amino acids by muscle and liver in sepsis. Comparative studies in vivo and in vitro. *Arch. Surg.* 118:167–75

99. Rouzer, C. A., Cerami, A. 1980. Hypertriglyceridemia associated with *Trypanosoma brucei brucei* infection in rabbits: role of defective triglyceride removal. *Mol. Biochem. Parasitol.* 2:31–38

100. Savage, W. E., Hajj, S. N., Kass, E. H. 1967. Demographic and prognostic characteristics of bacteriuria in pregnancy. *Medicine* 46:385–407

101. Scrimshaw, N. S., Taylor, C. E., Gordon, J. E. 1968. *Interactions of Nutrition and Infection.* WHO Monogr. Ser. 57. Geneva

102. Sipe, J. D., Vogel, S. N., Ryan, J. L., McAdam, K. P. W. J., Rosenstreich, D. L. 1979. Detection of a mediator derived from endotoxin-stimulated macrophages that induces the acute phase serum amyloid A response in mice. *J. Exp. Med.* 150:597–606

103. Sobocinski, P. Z., Canterbury, W. J. Jr., Mapes, C. A., Dinterman, R. E. 1978. Involvment of hepatic metallothioneins in hypozincemia associated with bacterial infection. *Am. J. Physiol.* 234:E399–E406

104. Sztein, M. B., Vogel, S. N., Sipe, J. D., Murphy, P. A., Mizel, S. B., Oppenheim, J. J. 1981. The role of macrophages in the acute-phase response: SAA inducer is closely related to lymphocyte activating factor and endogenous pyrogen. *Cell Immunol.* 63:164–76

105. Tonkin, S. 1970. Maori infant health: Trial of intramuscular iron to prevent anaemia in Maori babies. *NZ Med. J.* 71:129–35

105a. Torti, F. M., Dieckmann, B., Beutler, B., Cerami, A., Ringold, G. M. 1985. A macrophage factor inhibits adipocyte gene expression: an in vitro model of cachexia. *Science* 229:867–69

106. Trousseau, A. 1882. *Lectures on Clinical Medicine,* p. 96. London: New Sydenham Soc.

107. Van Miert, A. S. J. P. A. M., Van Duin, C. T. M., Verheijden, J. H. M., Schot-

man, A. J. H., Nieuwenhuis, J. 1984. Fever and changes in plasma zinc and iron concentrations in the goat: the role of leukocyte pyrogen. *J. Comp. Pathol.* 94:543–57

108. Van Snick, J. L., Masson, P. L., Heremans, J. F. 1974. The involvement of lactoferrin in the hyposideremia of acute inflammation. *J. Exp. Med.* 140:1068–84
109. Volanakis, J. E. 1982. Complement activation by C-reactive protein complexes. *Ann. NY Acad. Sci.* 389:235–49
110. Walker, D. M., Dolby, A. E., Joynson, D. H. M., Jacobs, A. 1973. *Candida* and the immune defects in iron deficiency. *J. Dent. Res.* 52:938–39
111. Wannemacher, R. W. Jr., Dinterman, R. E., Pekarek, R. S. 1975. Urinary amino acid excretion during experimentally induced sandfly fever in man. *Am. J. Clin. Nutr.* 28:110–18
112. Weinberg, E. D. 1978. Iron and Infection. *Microbiol. Rev.* 42:45–66
113. Weinberg, E. D. 1984. Iron withholding: A defense against infection and neoplasia. *Physiol. Rev.* 64:65–102

*Ann. Rev. Nutr. 1986. 6:155–78*


# GASTROINTESTINAL MICROFLORA IN MAMMALIAN NUTRITION

*Dwayne C. Savage*

Department of Microbiology, University of Illinois, Urbana, Illinois 61801

---

CONTENTS

INTRODUCTION ........ 155
*The Gastrointestinal Microflora* ........ 155
*Biochemical Activities of the Microflora* ........ 157
*Limitations and Goals* ........ 157
THE MICROFLORA AND MONOGASTRIC NUTRITION ........ 158
*Intestinal Absorption* ........ 158
*Nutrients Provided by the Microflora* ........ 160
*Competition for Nutrients* ........ 162
*Overall Impact of the Microflora on Host Nutrition* ........ 164
THE MICROFLORA AND HUMAN NUTRITION ........ 165
*The Microflora and Normalcy in Man* ........ 165
*Nutrition in Developed Countries* ........ 165
*Nutrition in Developing Countries* ........ 172
SUMMARY ........ 172

## INTRODUCTION

### *The Gastrointestinal Microflora*

Even though representatives of only a relatively few species have been studied in detail, no doubt now exists that birds (97), adult mammals of all species, including *Homo sapiens* (45), and animals of many other species (106) have microbial floras indigenous to their alimentary canals. These microfloras develop soon after birth, consist of prokaryotic and eukaryotic microorganisms of many genera and species, and are essential for the health and welfare of their animal hosts. Mammals of many species (e.g. ungulates) and insects of certain



0199-9885/86/0715-0155$02.00

species (e.g. termites) are known to derive as adults essential elements of their nutrition from products of their alimentary microfloras (12, 18, 128). Even when their essential nutrients need not be microbial products, animals of many and perhaps even all species interact physiologically in various ways with their microflora; indeed, their capacity to survive in nature depends upon the microbial cells comprising that flora (64, 65). Thus, mammals and animals of most if not all species can be regarded as creatures consisting of eukaryotic animal cells in symbiosis with eukaryotic and prokaryotic microbial cells (106). In other words, animals exist under natural conditions as complex interactive organic units consisting of both animal and microbial cells.

The microflora of the foreguts (rumens) of sheep, cattle, and ungulates of a few other species has been defined in taxonomic terms (12, 22, 128). Likewise, the microflora of the foregut (crop or stomach), midgut (small intestines), and hindgut (cecum, large intestine) is now understood in broad taxonomic terms for chickens, man, and mammals of a few other species (4, 34, 50, 77, 81, 92, 97, 106). The microbial communities in those floras are composed of many species of numerous genera of bacteria; most of the species are strictly anaerobic; some are present in the communities at population levels exceeding $1 \times 10^{10}$ bacterial cells per gram dry (or wet) weight of material. Indeed, in the rumen and the foreguts (stomachs) of mammals of certain species (ruminants and pseudoruminants), and in the large intestines of birds and mammals of all species examined, the bacterial populations in aggregate can exceed $1 \times 10^{11}$ cells per gram dry weight of material. Such enormous microbial populations composed of prokaryotic and eukaryotic cells of many taxonomic classes can perform biochemical reactions of a large variety of types (see next section).

Microbial communities in gastrointestinal tracts can be found in the lumen (often in association with particles of digesta), on epithelial surfaces, and even deep in the crypts of Lieberkuhn (106–108). Depending upon the animal species under study, such communities can be found in those sites in each major region of tract (stomach, small intestine, large intestine) and even in subareas of the major regions. In a given area or subarea, the community in the lumen, and especially on surfaces of particles of digesta, can differ from that on the epithelial surface in the relative proportions of the populations of the various species. Likewise, those communities can differ in composition from cryptal communities. Indigenous lumenal communities exist in major areas where the rate of passage of digesta does not exceed the rates at which microorganisms can multiply (e.g. the large intestine). Epithelial communities can exist in any area. Cryptal communities have been reported so far to be present only in the lower small intestine and cecums and colons of animals of certain species (107). The microbial populations in the various communities can be specialized in the biochemical functions they perform (4).

## Biochemical Activities of the Microflora

Biochemical reactions catalyzed by microbial enzymes in the gastrointestinal canal can be categorized generally into two groups, one including reactions essential to the survival of the microbial cell, and one including reactions not obviously essential for cellular survival (109). Reactions essential to survival are those involved in hydrolysis, binding, and transport into the cell of nutrients; energy transfer and macromolecular synthesis and function; and motility and chemotaxis (when appropriate). Nonessential reactions are those the products of which are not obviously needed in some way in the functions of the microbial cells, for example deconjugation and transformation of steroids (16, 56).

Gastrointestinal microorganisms can perform many reactions that can be classified into one or the other of those broad categories (86). In general, however, any reaction of which such microorganisms are capable is one that can take place in the environment of the tract, which is virtually free of oxygen and has a quite low oxidation-reduction potential (86, 106). For that reason, few (if any) of the essential and none of the nonessential metabolic reactions involve oxygen. Moreover, many of the microbial enzymes involved can function well in experimental systems only in reaction mixtures poised at low oxidation-reduction potentials (86). Thus, the biochemical functions of the microflora reflect, as does its microbial composition, the anaerobic environment of the tract.

The enzymes catalyzing some essential reactions and even a few nonessential ones may be constitutive. However, the enzymes catalyzing some reactions are proving to be inducible (37, 68, 69, 72, 98). The latter reactions may or may not take place depending upon whether an appropriate inducer is present in the local environment. As amplified below, these properties have important implications for the nutritional role of the microflora.

## Limitations and Goals

In this review, I assess the current knowledge about how the gastrointestinal microflora influences the nutrition of the animal tissues of adult mammals of certain species. The discussion is limited principally to findings made in studies with adult monogastric animals not regarded as pseudoruminants (animals not classified as ungulates but having a complex rumen-like fermentation in their foreguts). Information on the nutritional function of the complex microflora of the foregut in pseudoruminants and ruminants has frequently been the subject of reviews (12, 128). Therefore, any such information discussed is presented only for perspective. The overall goal of the analysis is to evaluate the potential for functions of the microflora in adult human nutrition.

## THE MICROFLORA AND MONOGASTRIC NUTRITION

### *Intestinal Absorption*

The indigenous microflora is well known to influence various physiological functions of the gastrointestinal tract. Evidence for such influences has come primarily from research with germfree animals, or with animals, including humans, suffering certain intestinal abnormalities resulting in disturbances of the microflora. Findings gained from experiments with germfree animals are described and analyzed in recently published books and reviews (23, 130). Likewise, intestinal diseases resulting from disturbances of the flora, especially those of man, have been a subject of intense research in recent years and, as a consequence, of numerous books and reviews (41, 61). Certain of the intestinal functions affected by the microflora, those that influence absorptive processes, are pertinent to the major goal of this review and are examined in the following paragraphs.

The indigenous microflora is known to influence transit time in the tracts of animals raised under ordinary conditions (conventional animals). Digesta passes more rapidly through the tracts of conventional animals than through those of germfree animals (90, 130). The mechanism by which this happens remains obscure, but may involve dietary components and microbial metabolic end-products acting synergistically on neurotransmittance to smooth muscles in the tract (133, 135). Rapid passage of lumenal content through the small intestine could be expected somewhat to limit digestion and absorption of nutrients.

The indigenous microflora also influences the turnover of and enzymatic activities in enterocytes (absorptive epithelial cells) in the small intestine. Enterocytes turn over in the gastrointestinal canal by migrating from their mitosis in the crypts of Lieberkuhn to their extrusion at the tips of the villi and destruction in the lumen (110). In the small bowels of conventional laboratory rodents, this process operates at an apparent rate almost twice that in the intestine of germfree animals (110). The apical (lumenal) membranes of enterocytes are organized into microvilli, and contain glycoprotein enzymes involved in digestive absorption (e.g. disaccharidases, peptidases). As assessed by methods involving the entire bowel mucosa (i.e. not isolated epithelial cells) the specific activities of those enzymes are two to five times higher in germfree rodents than in those with a flora (60, 125).

The activities of enzymes in the microvillous membranes are a function of the position of the enterocytes on the villi; cells nearest the extrusion zones at the villous tips have higher activities of disaccharidases, peptidases, and other microvillous enzymes than those nearest the crypts. The activities develop as the cells glide (migrate) along the villi from the crypt to the extrusion zone at the tip (111). Thus, they could be higher in the guts of germfree rodents because they have longer to develop in cells migrating on the villi at a slower rate than they do in animals with a flora. Alternatively, the synthesis of glycoproteins associated with the microvillous membranes may differ in some way, rendering the enzymes less active in conventional than in germfree animals (119, 120). Neither of these possibilities explains entirely, however, the differences detected in the enzymatic activities in germfree and conventional mice.

In procedures by which epithelial cells can be isolated from intestinal mucosa, germfree mice yield from their upper small intestines one and one-half to two times more enterocytes than animals with a flora (111). In other words, by comparison with conventional mice, germfree mice have more enterocytes populating the mucosal surface of their small bowels. When assayed in such cellular preparations, the total activities of the enzymes in the microvillous membranes (i.e. the activity per total mass of cells) reflect those detected in assays of whole mucosa; the activities are two to three times higher in the preparations from germfree mice than in those from conventional animals (111). When assessed in relationship to the total amount of protein in the cell mass, however (that is, when specific activity is determined), the activities are essentially identical for cells from both germfree and conventional animals, except for a small fraction of cells nearest the villous tip (111). Cells nearest the tip have highest activities in germfree mice.

Since the specific activity of the enzymes per enterocyte is about the same in most cells from the germfree and conventional animals, the specific activities in the whole mucosa must be higher in the former than the latter because more enterocytes are present in the former than the latter (111). Thus, in mice at least, the microflora in conventional animals acts to maintain the activities of digestive-absorptive enzymes in the microvillous membranes below those found in germfree animals primarily by maintaining the population of enterocytes at levels below those found in the latter animals. The mechanisms of this microbial activity remain obscure.

Whatever those mechanisms and the mechanisms involved in the microbial influences on the transit time in the tract, conventional rats and mice could be expected to absorb carbohydrates, peptides, and other such nutrients less efficiently than do germfree animals. Evidence is mixed on this point (130), but derives from studies accomplished a number of years ago. The work deserves repeating in light of recent findings that fluids secreted by enterocytes near the villous crypts are absorbed by such cells near the villous tips (112). Such a process could facilitate intestinal absorption, and may have been disturbed by the methods used in the reported research.

The indigenous microflora influences water and electrolyte absorption in the rodent cecum, and undoubtedly that in other species. The water content of the digesta in the lumen of the cecum and colon in conventional rodents is lower than that in the cecum of germfree animals, while the content of $Cl^-$ and

$HCO_3^-$ is higher (40). In conventional animals, strains of bacterial species produce enzymes that catalyze hydrolysis of macromolecules passing into the lumen of the large bowel (87). In germfree animals, such macromolecules are not hydrolyzed, and thus accumulate in the lumen of the tract, leading to the high osmotic pressure and the content of water, $Cl^-$, and $HCO_3^-$ (40, 87). This process could influence the absorption of bacterial metabolic products (see below) used as carbon and energy sources by the animal tissues. Such molecules undoubtedly absorb into the blood by processes coupled to electrolyte absorption (5).

Bile steroids may also influence absorption in the colon. Such compounds are known to be altered in structure by reactions catalyzed by microbial enzymes. The gastrointestinal microflora influences the blood levels, chemical classes, and function of bile steroids, including cholesterol (56, 130), bile acids, (56, 130), and certain hormones (127). The compounds can be deconjugated (56, 130), desulfurated (56), and transformed (16, 32, 48, 56) by enzymes produced by bacterial strains in such floras. The chemistry of these processes is well studied, and was recently reviewed (56). Suprisingly little is known, however, about the nutritional consequences for the normal animal of such microbial chemistry. One such consequence may be an influence on electrolyte absorption in the large intestine (49), and thus the absorption of bacterial metabolites in that area of the tract (40).

The macromolecules hydrolyzed by microbial enzymes in the large intestine of monogastric animals derive from exogenous and endogenous sources (86). The former derive from the animals' ingesta. These are mostly fibrous components of food that cannot be digested and absorbed by the enzymes produced by the host's animal cells (98). The latter derive from the host's animal cells themselves, and are materials such as intestinal mucus (51), the macromolecular components of sluffed epithelial cells (110), immunoglobulins secreted into the tract (106), and pancreatic and other enzymes (84, 87). The nutritional influences of such hydrolyses are the subject of the section following.

## *Nutrients Provided by the Microflora*

PRODUCTS OF MICROBIAL ENERGY-YIELDING METABOLISM Lactic acid and ethanol are produced as metabolic end-products by bacteria and yeasts, respectively, living in epithelial communities in the stomachs of monogastric mammals of some species (6, 12, 63, 126). Such compounds could be absorbed and utilized as carbon and energy sources by the animal tissues. The population levels of the bacteria and yeasts in the gastric communities are low, however, rarely exceeding $1 \times 10^9$ organisms per gram of whole stomach with content. Therefore, except under conditions where the diet contains large amounts of readily fermentable monosaccharides [e.g. glucose (126)], the bacterial products are undoubtedly produced normally in amounts too small to contribute in more than negligible ways to the carbon requirements of the animal cells. Whether the hosts derive any other "benefit" from having an ethanol "factory" in their stomachs remains at best a subject of speculation.

Short-chain volatile organic acids, principally acetic, propionic, and butyric acids, and the gases hydrogen, methane, and carbon dioxide are end-products of microbial fermentations in the foreguts of ruminants and pseudoruminants (12, 128). The volatile acids are well known to be important sources of carbon and energy for the animal tissues of such hosts (12, 128). Indeed, adult ruminants depend solely upon such microbial processes for their carbon and energy. The organic acids are also important sources of carbon and energy for monogastric mammals with extensive microbial fermentations in their hindguts (9, 31, 71, 88, 134). As mentioned above, the microbial populations in cecums and colons are enormous, resembling ruminant populations in their size and complexity. These microbial populations produce the short-chain acids as end-products of fermentations of carbon compounds such as monosaccharides and amino acids (86). Those compounds derive principally from hydrolyses catalyzed by microbial enzymes of macromolecules entering the large intestine (as mentioned above) from exogenous (dietary) and endogenous sources.

To be available to animal tissues, the organic acids produced in the lumen of the cecum and colon must be absorbed into the blood through the mucosas of those regions, or passed into the stomach and small intestine by coprophagy. The compounds undoubtedly absorb through the mucosa in all animals with a cecum (71, 88, 121). However, some such animals also practice coprophagy on a regular basis. This latter process is raised to its highest practice in lagomorphs (rabbits, hares) where special fecal pellets bound with a membrane and referred to as cecal pellets (or soft feces) are preferentially consumed (58). These animals can receive substantial proportions of their organic carbon as volatile acids from their cecal fermentations (71).

Monogastric animals of species lacking a blind cecum (e.g. man) may also derive nutritional benefit from the short-chain acids produced by microbial processes in their large bowels. The case is less clear, however, than it is for animals with a blind cecum, and is discussed in the section on microflora and human nutrition.

PRODUCTS FROM LYSIS OR DIGESTION OF MICROBIAL CELLS Bacterial cells can lyse in the gastrointestinal tracts of mammals, and thereby release into the lumen molecular substances from their cytoplasm, membranes, and walls. Some such lysis is undoubtedly due to enzymes endogenous to the bacterial cells; the enzymes lyse the cells from within as natural concomitants of cellular senescence. Most is due, however, to enzymes produced by the animal tissues of the host (e.g. pancreatic enzymes), including enzymes able to catalyze hydrolysis of peptidoglycan found in the cell walls of bacteria. These "mura-lytic" enzymes (e.g. lysozyme) are present in many secretions of mammalian tissues (7).

Nutrients from digested bacterial cells may be of greatest benefit to a mammalian host when they are made available in the stomach or small intestine. Much of the microbial population in the rumens of adult ungulate mammals is digested in a gastric pouch of the animals, yielding precursors of macromolecules that are absorbed and incorporated into the macromolecules of the animal tissues (12). Microbial communities in the stomachs of monogastric animals or microbial populations from the hindgut passed into the stomach by coprophagy may also be sources of such compounds for their mammalian hosts. An interesting case in point is the recent discovery that queuine (the base of queuosine found in the first or "wobble" position of the anticodons of certain tRNAs) derives in mammals from the diet and intestinal microflora (33, 89). Such findings reveal that microbe-mammal symbioses extend to functions at the molecular and genetic level.

In addition to products of hydrolysis of the macromolecular constituents of their cells, lysed microbial cells are also sources of vitamins and other cofactors (1, 130). Germfree rats are known to require vitamin K in their diets, while conventional rats do not (130). Likewise, germfree rats and animals of certain other species require in their diets certain B vitamins (e.g. $B_{12}$, biotin, folic acid, and pantothenate) in concentrations higher than those required by their conventional counterparts (130). In these cases, the substances may derive predominantly from organisms residing in the cecums and colons, but may come as well from microbial cells growing on epithelial surfaces in the fore- and midguts.

Monogastric mammals can derive through coprophagy much of the nutritional benefit from the microbial cells in the hindgut flora (71). Noncoprophagic animals, e.g. adult humans, may derive little benefit unless molecules produced by or released from lysing microbial cells are absorbed into the blood in the cecum and colon. Evidence for that possibility is discussed in the section on the microflora and human nutrition.

## *Competition for Nutrients*

IN NORMAL HOSTS As noted earlier, monogastric mammals without extensive foregut fermentations may still have microbial communities associated with epithelial surfaces in their stomachs and small intestines (106, 107). Those microbial layers are able to take advantage of nutrients in the host's diet, and thus to compete with the animal cells for those nutrients. The mass of animal cells far outweighs that of the microbial populations, of course, and thus, under normal circumstances, should have considerable advantage over the microbial cells in absorption processes. Still, the microbial cells thrive in their communities, and must therefore have mechanisms for competing with the animal cells. They must consequently deprive the latter of some share of the food ingested.

Also as noted earlier, the animal cells probably derive some of their nutrition from the macromolecular components of lysed microbial cells and the products of the energy-yielding metabolism of such cells. For the animal cells to benefit fully from nutrients consumed in the diet, however, all of the microbial macromolecules and products would have to be utilized by the animal cells. Such is not the case; bacteria and yeasts from gastric communities can be found in the feces of animals (106). Therefore, because of competitive activities of the microflora, not all of the nutrients ingested are available to the host's animal tissues. As emphasized earlier, however, the amounts of dietary constituents involved must be trivial; the microbial populations in epithelial communities in the fore- and midguts are less than 1% the size of the communities in the hindgut (106).

The extensive microbial communities in the hindguts (colons and cecums) of monogastric animals may normally compete little with the host's animal tissues for components of the ingesta. As discussed earlier, microorganisms in such communities thrive primarily by hydrolyzing and fermenting the substituents of endogenous polymers or exogenous ones in the diet that cannot be digested by enzymes made by the animals cells (86). Moreover, they obtain at least some of their nitrogen as ammonia by hydrolyzing urea, a waste product of the host's animal tissues passing into the bowel (36, 46, 78). Thus, the hindgut communities are principally contributors to the nutrition of the animal tissues.

IN HOSTS WITH ABNORMALITIES Anatomical abnormalities have been introduced into the gastrointestinal tracts of monogastric mammals in order to study the effects of microfloras developing in areas of the tract where they are not normally found. A typical case is a "blind loop" or pouch created in the small bowels of laboratory rodents or lagomorphs (118). Such abnormalities are introduced surgically, and involve isolating from the normal flow of digesta a loop or pouch in intestine. The loops or pouches usually fill with digesta and fluids that become stagnant in the region and allow for microfloras to develop in them. These floras can be quite complex in composition and biochemical activity and may resemble, at least superficially, the microfloras in the cecum and colon (118). A similar situation may develop especially on the epithelial surface in the small intestines of rats fed certain lectins (10, 11).

These microfloras can profoundly affect the physiology and even microanatomy of the areas in which they develop. For example, the mucosa may lose its villous architecture and most of the absorptive surface (41). The microorganisms can deconjugate and transform bile acids in the area leading to fat malabsorption; they can also compete with epithelial cells for vitamins (e.g.

$B_{12}$) and other essential nutrients (38, 41). Thus, abnormalities allowing complex floras to develop in the midgut can lead to generalized malabsorption and manifold nutritional deficiencies in the animal tissues of mammalian hosts.

Nutritional deficiencies may develop also when animals are given therapeutic amounts of antibacterial drugs. As is widely recognized, such drugs given at sub-therapeutic levels may potentiate growth and improve the efficiency at which food is utilized in animals of commercial value (24). Given at therapeutic levels, however, the drugs may disrupt the microflora, disturbing its normal functions (21, 44). Such disturbances may be subtle in terms of the microbial composition of the flora, but dramatic in terms of its biochemical activity and nutritional influences (21), and may have important implications for the long-term health and welfare of the host. Knowledge in this area is primitive and needs enriching with evidence from research.

Even when operating in their normal habitats, microbial floras may contribute to diseases in their hosts by producing harmful compounds from endogenous and exogenous chemicals. Bile acids and other compounds altered by bacterial enzymes in the gut are believed to be involved in inducing cancer in man (42, 47, 59, 79, 80, 93). Likewise, products of bacterial changes in drugs and xenobiotics (39) consumed by animals may damage certain of their tissues. Studies in these areas are in an early stage and should be given impetus. Likewise, studies should be encouraged of the biochemistry and genetics of the mechanisms by which intestinal organisms degrade toxic molecules such as dietary oxalate (2, 3), convert certain amino acids into toxic metabolites (117), and alter certain glycosides into mutagens (67, 116).

## *Overall Impact of the Microflora on Host Nutrition*

FORE- AND MIDGUT FLORAS Indigenous microorganisms, principally strains of lactic acid bacteria and yeasts of certain genera, form epithelial communities in the stomachs and small intestines of monogastric mammals of some species. Microorganisms in those communities may influence the nutrition of the animal tissues of their host. For example, they may provide small amounts of certain vitamins, carbon energy, and nitrogen in the form of metabolic end-products and macromolecular precursors. The microbial cells may also compete for available dietary nutrients with the host's animal cells. However, the microbial populations involved are small by comparison with populations in the hindgut. Therefore, for these microbial communities, the contributive and competitive nutritional activities are probably of little overall significance to the nutrition of the animal tissues.

HINDGUT FLORAS Indigenous microorganisms, principally strains of strictly anaerobic bacteria, also form communities on epithelial surfaces and in the lumens of the cecums and colons of monogastric mammals (107). By comparison with those in the fore- and midguts, however, these communities contain enormous cellular populations (over 100-fold larger) and thus form substantial amounts of vitamins, metabolic end-products, and other compounds; they constitute a significant microbial mass. The metabolic products can be absorbed by the hindgut mucosa and utilized as carbon and energy sources by the animal tissues. In addition, such products, vitamins, and the constituents of the macromolecules in the microbial cells themselves may be utilized by the host's animal tissues, especially in animals that regularly practice coprophagy. All of these processes function in balance with the normal processes of the animal tissues as long as the microbial communities are not disturbed or displaced in some way. When the communities are disturbed, however, as through the actions of antibacterial drugs, animal tissues can suffer nutritional deprivation.

## THE MICROFLORA AND HUMAN NUTRITION

### *The Microflora and Normalcy in Man*

The student of the indigenous gastrointestinal microflora can view normalcy in humans from two perspectives, normalcy in people in developed countries and normalcy in at least some individuals native to certain developing countries. In both developed and developing countries, virtually all adults and children within a year or so after birth have in their large intestines fully developed communities of mixed microbial species (19, 34, 66, 81, 95). Individuals may differ substantially from each other in whether they have a flora in the small intestine, however, depending upon whether they are natives of a developed or a developing country. Normal adults in developed countries probably have no stable communities of microorganisms colonizing the epithelial surfaces of their small intestines (108). By contrast, adults in certain developing countries, functioning according to the norms of their populations, may possess communities of mixed bacterial species colonizing at substantial population levels the epithelium of at least the mid- and distal portions of their small bowels (14, 15, 20).

So far, no obvious and accepted explanation for these differences has emerged. Moreover, the experiments yielding the data from which the conclusions were derived, especially those concerning the small bowel floras in developing countries, should be reproduced and expanded. Nevertheless, the findings are sufficiently well grounded to pose interesting issues for a discussion of the role of the microflora in the nutrition of humans.

### *Nutrition in Developed Countries*

The general points made above concerning the overall impact of the microflora on the nutrition of monogastric animals cannot be applied in their entirety to ostensibly normal humans living in developed countries. Animals such as man, lacking stable microfloras in their stomachs and small bowels and not practicing coprophagy, would presumably experience few or none of the nutritional influences described for monogastric mammals possessing such floras and practicing coprophagy. Thus, for humans living in developed countries, the influences of interest are largely those of the microflora of the large bowel (53, 55). The past 10 years or so have seen active interest in research on those influences. Findings from the work are summarized in numerous recently published reviews (26, 73, 85, 114) and books (43, 132).

The research has focused on four general issues. The first of these is the biochemistry involved in the processes by which particular strains of species of indigenous bacteria hydrolyze endogenous and exogenous molecular polymers and utilize the end-products of the hydrolysis in their energy-yielding metabolism. The second concerns the organic end-products of those metabolic processes and whether those products are absorbed and utilized as carbon and energy sources by the host's animal tissues. (A corollary of this issue concerns gases produced as end-products in the microbial metabolic processes, their absorption into the blood, and excretion in air expired from the lungs.) The third research area concerns compounds produced by the microflora from exogenous or endogenous materials that may induce cancer or other diseases in the host. The fourth concerns efforts to manipulate the microbial metabolism, presumably to the nutritional advantage and health of the animal tissues.

The first of these issues has been explored most intensively with strains of species of two genera of bacteria isolated from human feces, *Bacteroides* and *Bifidobacterium*. The microflora of the adult human large bowel is similar in many respects to that in the cecums and colons of monogastric mammals of other species (22). Indeed, it even bears similarities to that of the rumen (128). It is composed principally of strains of many species of numerous genera of anaerobic bacteria. Strains representing over 400 species of at least 40 genera have been isolated from human feces. The populations of most of the strains are quite large, exceeding 10 billion cells per gram dry weight of fecal material (34). The aggregate population is so large, it may constitute over 50% of the mass of feces (115) and exceed the level of the total population of animal cells in an adult human (106). The greatest mass of that enormous population, however, consists of cells of strains of species of *Bacteroides* (34). Because their populations predominate in the tract, those strains have become tools of choice in studies of the biochemistry of polymer hydrolysis and energy-yielding metabolism (98). *Bifidobacterium* strains are present at high but not predominating population levels in the adult colon (34). They are of great interest, however, because they predominate in the feces of infants fed at the breast (19, 95).

Strains of species of both *Bacteroides* and *Bifidobacterium* can hydrolyze and grow on the end-products of the hydrolysis of exogenous polymers of several chemical classes found in the human diet (Table 1). In addition, some strains can hydrolyze and grow on the end-products of the endogenous polymers gastric mucus, hyaluronic acid, and other tissue components (Table 1). The biochemistry of those processes was recently reviewed (98). Of interest to the purposes of this review is the discovery that enzymes involved in transport and hydrolysis of such polymeric carbon and energy sources are often not secreted by the cells and are invariably inducible (37, 72, 98, 102, 103). Under such circumstances, a particular compound or similar ones able to induce the enzymatic systems must be present in the colon for the enzymes to be synthesized by microbial cells with the genetic capacity to make them. Moreover, the systems may be strongly repressed by feedback inhibition when supplies of fermentable substrates (e.g. glucose) are adequate for microbial growth in the tract. Finally, because the hydrolytic enzymes are not secreted, the microbial cells must be in intimate contact with the target polymers in order to hydrolyze them. These discoveries have important implications for the design of experiments on all aspects of the role of the flora in nutrition.

Humans introduce into their gastrointestinal tracts dietary polymers of a large variety of chemical classes (98). Peptides, nucleic acids, and certain polysaccharides such as starch entering with the ingesta can be hydrolyzed by enzymes produced by animal tissues (132). Some such compounds in the diet undoubtedly make their way into the colon, the amounts depending upon how much is consumed and the materials with which they are associated in the food (17). Nevertheless, dietary polymers passing into the cecal portion of the large intestine and becoming available to the microflora are principally polysaccharides of chemical structures that cannot be hydrolyzed by enzymes produced by the animal tissues (Table 1). As noted earlier, endogenous macromolecular polymers, some of chemical classes other than polysaccharides, also enter the large bowel, principally intestinal mucus, digestive enzymes, secreted immunoglobulins, and the components of sluffing epithelial cells. Most research on the bacteria able to hydrolyze polymers has been accomplished, however, with complex dietary polysaccharides (98). Dietary polysaccharides are receiving most attention, in part because they predominate in the cecal content but also because of interest in dietary fiber and its impact on human nutrition (113).

The metabolic processes by which the human microflora gains carbon and energy from the components of the dietary and endogenous polymers produce end-products that are generally similar in chemical class to those produced in ruminant and cecal fermentations in mammals other than man (128). As discussed above, those products are principally short-chain organic acids and the gases $H_2$, $CH_4$, and $CO_2$. Acetic, propionic, and *n*-butyric acids predominate (19, 25, 50, 55). According to one study (55), the acids are present in feces at aggregate total concentrations ranging from 28 to 188 mM/kg (with an

**Table 1** Some dietary and endogenous macromolecular polymers that may be hydrolyzed and utilized as carbon and energy sources by members of the indigenous gastrointestinal microflora of man[a]

| Polymer | Microorganism | Reference |
|---|---|---|
| | ENDOGENOUS | |
| Chondroitin sulfate | *Bacteroides thetaiotaomicron* | 98, 102, 103, 105 |
| Mucin (gastric) | Microflora; *Bacteroides fragilis; Bifidobacterium* spp. | 13, 50, 51, 76, 91, 98, 105 |
| Glycoproteins | Microflora | 82 |
| Hyaluronate | *Bacteroides* spp. | 105 |
| | DIETARY | |
| Heparin | *Bacteroides* spp. | 98, 105 |
| Pectin | *Bacteroides* spp.; microflora | 13, 27, 57, 98, 105 |
| Ovomucoid | *Bacteroides* spp. | 105 |
| Amylose, amylopectin | *Bacteroides* spp. | 98, 105 |
| Dextran | *Bacteroides* spp. | 105 |
| Gum tragacanth | *Bacteroides* spp.; *Bifidobacterium* spp. | 105 |
| Gum guar | *Bacteroides* spp.; *Bifidobacterium* spp.; *Bacteroides ovatus* | 8, 13, 37, 98, 105 |
| Larch arabinoglactan | *Bacteroides* spp. *Bifidobacterium* spp. | 13, 98, 99, 105 |
| Alginate | *Bacteroides* spp. | 98, 105 |
| Laminarin | *Bacteroides* spp. | 98, 104, 105 |
| Psyllorium hydrocolloid | *Bacteroides* spp. | 98, 101 |
| Xylan | *Bacteroides* spp. | 13, 98, 100 |
| Polygalacturonate | *Bacteroides* spp.; *Bifidobacterium* spp.; *Bacteroides thetaiotaomicron* | 72 |
| Gum arabic | *Bifidobacterium* spp. | 98 |
| Cellulose | Microflora | 98, 129 |

[a]This listing is not a complete record of all of the polymers known to be used for growth of intestinal bacteria (see 98). It is intended to indicate the diversity of the capacities of the bacteria.

average of 77 mM/kg, Table 2) in individuals consuming an ordinary diet. The concentrations may vary up to ±50% when samples are taken at different times during the day or on different days in the same individual (55). According to some reports, when adult humans are consuming defined diets containing single polysaccharides, the acids may be detected in feces at concentrations that vary depending upon the polysaccharide present (Table 2). Because the values can vary so widely from individual to individual, however, and even from day to day and time to time during the day (55), such findings are difficult to evaluate. Nevertheless, they do suggest that different dietary polysaccharides can influence, at least to some extent, the amounts of the metabolic products produced by the microflora.

**Table 2** Short-chain volatile fatty acids (VFA) in human feces following consumption of diets containing defined polysaccharides[a]

| VFA | "Ordinary Norwegian" | Course bran | Fine bran | Cellulose | Cabbage | "Basal" | Low E | Cellulose | Xylan | Pectin | Corn bran |
|---|---|---|---|---|---|---|---|---|---|---|---|
| Acetate | 37[b] | 69[c] | 51[c] | 53[c] | 78[c] | 38[d] | 33[d] | 35[d] | 42[d] | 34[d] | 51[d] |
| Propionate | 13 | 29 | 22 | 22 | 28 | 26 | 23 | 27 | 29 | 27 | 18 |
| Isobutyrate | 2 | 6 | 7 | 5 | 12 | 5 | 6 | 5 | 4 | 5 | 4 |
| Butyrate | 12 | 27 | 25 | 16 | 25 | 16 | 22 | 18 | 14 | 19 | 14 |
| Isovalerate | 3 | 7 | 8 | 6 | 15 | 9 | 11 | 9 | 7 | 9 | 8 |
| Valerate | 2 | 6 | 4 | 4 | 8 | 5 | 6 | 6 | 6 | 7 | 5 |
| Caproic | 1 | — | — | — | — | — | — | — | — | — | — |
| Subjects (No.) | 20 | 12 | 12 | 12 | 12 | 5 | 5 | 5 | 5 | 5 | 5 |
| Reference | 55 | 30 | 30 | 30 | 30 | 35 | 35 | 35 | 35 | 35 | 35 |

[a]Data from three recent studies are given (30, 35, 55). Values are given as reported by authors, but are rounded to nearest whole number.
[b]mM/kg feces.
[c]mM/5 ml "fecal inoculum."
[d]Percentage of total amount of VFA excreted.

Materials excreted in the feces are lost to the body as potential energy sources. To serve as energy sources to the host, therefore, volatile fatty acids must be absorbed by the large bowel mucosa, and must be produced in the cecum and colon at concentrations above those detected in the feces. Estimates have been made of the amounts of the acids produced in the tract; such estimates are based upon the amounts of acids in feces and theoretical yields of the compounds from bacterial action on dietary polymers. They indicate that greater amounts of the acids are produced than are excreted (73, 128). As noted, however, estimates of the amounts of the organic acids in feces are subject to a substantial variation. Moreover, the methods for estimating theoretical yields cannot be accepted as inviolate. Therefore, any speculations about nutrition based upon such estimates should probably be made with caution.

The estimates are supported, however, by findings from experimental tests. The acids disappear from dialysis bags placed in rectums (73) and from fluids perfused into colons (96). In addition, they can be absorbed and utilized by colonic epithelial cells maintained in culture (94). Butyric acid may be used preferentially by such cells (94).

The estimates are also supported by findings from experiments involving assays of absorbed fermentation gases. As noted earlier, in addition to the volatile fatty acids, the gases hydrogen and methane are produced in the fermentation processes (128). Hydrogen is produced in all individuals, while methane is produced in about 50% of persons (128). Both gases can be detected in the expired air and flatus (54, 70, 83). Calculations based upon measurements of the amounts of such expired gases and some assumptions about the amounts of organic acids and gases produced by the bacteria per unit amount of polymer hydrolyzed indicate that some organic acids must be absorbed by the host (54). Thus, humans may well gain carbon and energy from the products of the energy-yielding metabolism of microorganisms of their indigenous flora. The amount gained has been estimated to be about 10% of daily energy needs for persons in developed countries (73). That estimate should be evaluated with care, however; as noted, the amounts of acids produced probably vary considerably among individuals (55).

In spite of weaknesses in baseline data due principally to that and other sources of variation, investigators have begun to attempt to manipulate fermentation processes in the colon by feeding to humans diets containing various macromolecular sources (30, 35, 122). Most such research is motivated primarily by views that dietary fiber alters conditions in the bowel that lead to chronic diseases such as colonic cancer (122) and other serious conditions (123, 124). Some such research may be motivated, however, by a desire to find diets that increase the amounts of short-chain organic acids produced by the flora, and thus the amount available for use as carbon and energy sources by the host's animal tissues. For example, experimental systems have been established in which individuals are fed diets differing in fiber source, and then their feces are assayed for volatile acids (30, 35) or their breath and flatus are assayed for hydrogen and methane (70).

The acids may vary in relative proportions and concentrations in the feces, depending upon the fiber source in the diets of the subjects (Table 2). Moreover, the amounts of fermentation gases may vary depending upon the dietary polysaccharide (70). The amounts of the short-chain acids in human feces vary so widely from sample to sample (55), however, that at this time such findings give little encouragement that the fermentations in situ can be manipulated in controlled ways.

Colonic fermentations are also being studied with fecal microflora cultured in continuous and discontinuous fermentation systems (68, 75). Such efforts also are fraught with problems. Fecal flora may differ in composition from that in the cecum and colon, and certainly differs in spatial organization; lumenal, epithelial, and cryptal communities cannot form in fermentation vessels (108). In addition, the nutritional and environmental milieu in the culture vessels may differ substantially from that in the cecum and colon; endogenous materials present in the colon are missing from the systems (68). Moreover, the amounts of acids produced vary over time (75), and with pH (29) in the fermentation vessels. Nevertheless, findings from such systems tend to confirm that the amounts of short-chain acids made per unit amount of content depend upon the polysaccharide present. They are not yet supportive of the hypothesis, however, that the biochemistry of the human colonic microflora is subject to controlled manipulation.

Viewed as an ecological system, the large bowel flora in situ is probably well buffered against changes induced by dietary manipulation. The flora is most complex in microbial composition and biochemical activity. It is not much affected in its species composition by dietary change (28). As has been noted, dietary polymers are not the only macromolecules available to the flora in a living host. Endogenous polymers may be significant proportions of the microbial diet in the large bowel (52), while urea may be an important nitrogen source as it is in the ceca of mammals of other species (131). Some such nondietary substrates support an anaerobic microflora containing methanogens in a sigmoid colon isolated from the normal fecal stream (74). The endogenous polymers may well buffer against change induced by exogenous materials not only the species composition of the flora but also its biochemical activity. During hydrolysis, those polymers may yield ample amounts of fermentable substrates that inhibit enzymatic systems involved in hydrolyzing exogenous polymers. Until evidence on these biochemical and genetic issues becomes stronger, efforts to manipulate the composition and chemistry of the flora by manipulating the diet might be considered premature.

### *Nutrition in Developing Countries*

The microfloras indigenous to the large bowels of individuals living in developing countries are similar in composition and biochemical activities to those in the cecums and colons of persons living in developed lands (34). Thus, all comments about humans made above probably apply in both general and specific ways to the human populations in developing countries. However, in some cases at least, ostensibly normal persons living in developing countries have microfloras associated intimately with the epithelium of their small intestines (14, 15, 20). Therefore, the nutrition of such individuals could be influenced by the flora in ways similar to those discussed earlier for monogastric mammals with fore- and midgut floras. On the one hand, some such influences could be viewed as favoring the hosts. For example, the persons may be gaining some vitamins, energy, and carbon sources and some macromolecular precursors from the microflora. On the other hand, such individuals could be said to be suffering chronic malabsorption syndrome (41), a disease seen in developed countries only in persons with a microflora in their small intestines similar in composition to that in their cecums (41).

As discussed earlier, in certain abnormal circumstances a complex microflora may develop in areas of the small bowel, and cause malabsorption by hindering nutrient absorption. Individuals in developed countries may develop such conditions because of diseases (usually chronic and often of unknown etiology) that relax the factors regulating small bowel colonization (41, 106). Such persons may become acutely malnourished (41).

In some cases, persons in certain developing countries do suffer malabsorption in a condition called "tropical sprue" (62). This disease is said to be induced by some proteins ("toxins") synthesized and excreted by bacteria of certain species closely associated with the small bowel epithelium (62). If so, then the malabsorption is due to changes in absorptive cells similar to those occurring in acute bacterial diarrheas in both developed and developing countries (109), and is the abnormal result of the activities of microorganisms not normally found on the small bowel epithelium. Not all individuals with floras associated with their small bowel epithelia suffer from tropical sprue. Indeed, most of them are functioning physiologically according to the norms of their populations (14, 15, 20). Thus, they may be experiencing no harm from their small bowel microflora and may even be gaining some nutritional benefit. However, no direct evidence supporting such a concept is yet available.

## SUMMARY

A mammal is a complex organism consisting of eukaryotic animal cells and eukaryotic and prokaryotic microbial cells. Most of the microorganisms reside in communities in the gastrointestinal tract. These gastrointestinal microfloras are known to serve nutritional functions in ruminants, pseudoruminants, and monogastric mammals with only modest or no foregut fermentations but with extensive hindgut fermentations in blind cecal pouches. In adult animals, the microflora hydrolyzes exogenous (dietary) and endogenous polymers, and provides the adult with all or at least a significant proportion of its carbon, energy, vitamins, and macromolecular building blocks. The flora also functions as a conservator of nitrogen that would otherwise be excreted as urea. In exchange, the flora competes directly with the host tissues for nutrients ingested in the diet, and also competes indirectly by somewhat repressing the absorptive capacities of the animal tissues. When the synergism is in balance, the animal tissues and the microflora operate in harmony for the health and nutritional welfare of the host as a whole. The system may be unbalanced by antibacterial drugs that destroy the microflora and by diseases of the animal tissues that destroy the controls regulating where indigenous communities localize in the tract, their microbial composition, and their biochemical activities. At such times, the nutrition of the animal tissues can be adversely affected to the extreme.

Humans living in developed and developing countries have extensive microfloras in their hindguts. Humans living in developing countries may also have extensive microfloras in their small bowels. Those floras may function in nutrition of the animal tissues of man much the same as do floras in similar locations in the gastrointestinal tracts of mammals other than man. However, animals of some species other than human gain much of the nutritional benefit from their microflora through the practice of coprophagy. Since adult humans do not normally practice coprophagy, any nutritional benefit from the microflora depends upon the capacity of the bowel mucosa, principally that of the large bowel, to absorb bacterial products, e.g. short-chain volatile fatty acids. Such absorption undoubtedly occurs, but is surely not a major source of carbon and energy for the animal tissues of man.

ACKNOWLEDGMENTS

My experimental work discussed herein has been supported by Public Health Service Grant No. AI 11858. I express much appreciation to Lori Nappe for preparing the manuscript by word processing.

## *Literature Cited*

1. Albert, M. J., Mathan, V. I., Baker, S. J. 1980. Vitamin $B_{12}$ synthesis by human small intestinal bacteria. *Nature* 283: 781–82
2. Allison, M. J., Cook, H. M. 1981. Oxalate degradation by microbes of the large bowel of herbivores: the effect of dietary oxalate. *Science* 212:675–76
3. Allison, M. J., Dawson, K. A., Mayberry, W. R., Foss, J. G. 1985. *Oxalobacter formigenes* gen. nov.: oxalate-degrading anaerobes that inhabit the gastrointestinal tract. *Arch. Microbiol.* 141:1–7
4. Allison, M. J., Robinson, I. M., Bucklin, J. A., Booth, G. D. 1979. Comparison of bacterial populations of the pig cecum and colon based upon enumeration with specific energy sources. *Appl. Environ. Microbiol.* 37:1142–51
5. Argenzio, R. A., Southworth, M., Lowe, J. E., Stevens, C. E. 1977. In-

terrelationship of Na, $HCO_3$, and volatile fatty acid transport by equine large intestine. *Am. J. Physiol.* 233:E469–78
6. Artwohl, J. E., Savage, D. C. 1979. Determinants in microbial colonization of the murine gastrointestinal tract: pH, temperature, and energy-yielding metabolism of *Torulopsis pintolopesii*. *Appl. Environ. Microbiol.* 37:697–703
7. Atlas, R. M. 1984. *Microbiology, Fundamentals and Applications,* p. 115. New York: MacMillan. 879 pp.
8. Balascio, J. R., Palmer, J. K., Salyers, A. A. 1981. Degradation of guar gum by enzymes produced by a bacterium from the human colon. *J. Food Biochem.* 5:271–82
9. Banta, C. A., Clemens, E. T., Krinsky, M. M., Sheffy, B. E. 1979. Sites of organic acid production and patterns of digesta movement in the gastrointestinal tract of dogs. *J. Nutr.* 109:1592–1600
10. Banwell, J. G., Boldt, D. H., Meyers, J., Weber, F. L. Jr., Miller, B., Howard, R. 1983. Phytohemagglutinin derived from red kidney bean *(Phaseolus vulgaris):* a cause for intestinal malabsorption associated with bacterial overgrowth in the rat. *Gastroenterology* 84:506–15
11. Banwell, J. G., Howard, R., Cooper, D., Costerton, J. W. 1985. Intestinal microbial flora after feeding phytohemagglutinin lectins *(Phaseolus vulgaris)* to rats. *Appl. Environ. Microbiol.* 50:68–80
12. Bauchop, T. 1977. Foregut fermentation. In *Microbial Ecology of the Gut,* ed. R. T. J. Clark, T. Bauchop, pp. 223–50. London/New York/San Francisco: Academic. 410 pp.
13. Bayliss, C. E., Houston, A. P. 1984. Characterization of plant polysaccharide and mucin-fermenting anaerobic bacteria from human feces. *Appl. Environ. Microbiol.* 48:626–32
14. Bhat, P., Albert, M. J., Rajan, D., Ponniah, J., Mathan, V. I., Baker, S. J. 1980. Bacterial flora of the jejunum: a comparison of luminal aspirate and mucosal biopsy. *J. Med. Microbiol.* 13:247–56
15. Bhat, P., Shantakumari, S., Rajan, D., Mathan, V. I., Kapadia, C. R., et al. 1972. Bacterial flora of the gastrointestinal tract in southern Indian control subjects and patients with tropical sprue. *Gastroenterology* 62:11–21
16. Bokkenheuser, V. D., Winter, J. 1983. Biotransformation of steroids. See Ref. 45, pp. 215–40
17. Bond, J. H., Currier, B. E., Buchwald, H., Levitt, M. D. 1980. Colonic conservation of malabsorbed carbohydrate. *Gastroenterology* 78:444–47
18. Breznak, J. A. 1975. Symbiotic relationships between termites and their intestinal microbiota. In *Symbiosis, Symposia of the Society for Experimental Biology,* No. 29:559–80. Cambridge: University Press
19. Bullen, C. L., Tearle, P. V., Stewart, M. G. 1977. The effect of "humanized" milks and supplemented breast feeding on the faecal flora of infants. *J. Med. Microbiol.* 10:403–13
20. Cain, J. R., Mayoral, L. G., Lotero, H., Bolaños, O., Duque, E. 1976. *Enterobacteriaceae* in the jejunal microflora: prevalence and relationship to the biochemical and histological evaluations in healthy Colombian men. *Am. J. Clin. Nutr.* 29:1397–1403
21. Carlstedt-Duke, B., Gustafsson, B. E., Midtvedt, T. 1985. Clindamycin-induced alterations in intestinal microflora-associated characteristics in rats. *Scand. J. Gastroenterol.* 20:92–98
22. Clarke, R. T. J. 1977. The gut and its microorganisms. See Ref. 12, pp. 36–72
23. Coates, M. E., Gustafsson, B. E., eds. 1984. *The Germ-free Animal in Biomedical Research.* London: Laboratory Animals. 442 pp.
24. Committee Report. 1980. *The Effects on Human Health of Subtherapeutic Use of Antimicrobials in Animals Feeds.* Washington, DC: Natl. Acad. Sci. 376 pp.
25. Cummings, J. H. 1981. Short-chain fatty acids in the colon. *Gut* 22:763–79
26. Cummings, J. H. 1983. Fermentation in the human large intestine: evidence and implications for health. *Lancet* 2:1206–8
27. Cummings, J. H., Southgate, D. A. T., Branch, W. J., Wiggins, H. S., Houston, H., et al. 1979. The digestion of pectin in the human gut and its effect on calcium absorption and large bowel function. *Br. J. Nutr.* 41:477–85
28. Drasar, B. S., Jenkins, D. J. A., Cummings, J. H. 1976. The influence of a diet rich in wheat fibre on the human faecal flora. *J. Med. Microbiol.* 9:423–31
29. Edwards, C. A., Duerden, B. I., Read, N. W. 1985. The effects of pH on colonic bacteria grown in continuous culture. *J. Med. Microbiol.* 19:169–80
30. Ehle, F. R., Robertson, J. B., Van Soest, P. J. 1982. Influence of dietary fibers on fermentation in the human large intestine. *J. Nutr.* 112:158–66
31. Elsden, S. R., Hitchcock, M. W. S., Marshall, R. A., Phillipson, A. T. 1946. Volatile acid in the digesta of ruminants

and other animals. *J. Exp. Biol.* 22:191–202
32. Eyssen, H., Verhulst, A. 1984. Biotransformation of linoleic acid and bile acids by *Eubacterium lentum. Appl. Environ. Microbiol.* 47:39–43
33. Farkas, W. R. 1980. Effect of diet on the queuosine family of tRNAs of germfree mice. *J. Biol. Chem.* 255:6832–35
34. Finegold, S. M., Sutter, V. L., Mathisen, G. E. 1983. Normal indigenous intestinal flora. See Ref. 45, pp. 3–32
35. Fleming, S. E., Rodriguez, M. A. 1983. Influence of dietary fiber on fecal excretion of volatile fatty acids by human adults. *J. Nutr.* 113:1613–25
36. Forsythe, S. J., Parker, D. S. 1985. Nitrogen metabolism by the microbial flora of the rabbit caecum. *J. Appl. Bacteriol.* 58:363–69
37. Gherardini, F., Babcock, M., Salyers, A. A. 1985. Purification and characterization of two α-galactosides associated with catabolism of guar gum and other galactosides by *Bacteroides ovatus. J. Bacteriol.* 161:500–6
38. Giannella, R. A., Broitman, S. A., Zamcheck, N. 1971. Vitamin $B_{12}$ uptake by intestinal microorganisms: mechanism and relevance to syndromes of intestinal bacterial overgrowth. *J. Clin. Invest.* 50:1100–7
39. Goldman, P. 1983. Biochemical pharmacology and toxicology involving the intestinal flora. See Ref. 45, pp. 241–64
40. Gordon, H. H., Bruckner, G. 1984. Anomalous lower bowel function and related phenomena in germ-free animals. See Ref. 23, pp. 193–214
41. Gracey, M. 1983. The contaminated small bowel syndrome. See Ref. 45, pp. 495–516
42. Gupta, I., Suzuki, K., Bruce, W. R., Krepinsky, J. J., Yates, P. 1984. A model study of fecapentaenes: mutagens of bacterial origin with alkylating properties. *Science* 225:521–23
43. Hallgren, B., ed. 1983. *Nutrition and the Intestinal Flora*. Stockholm: Almqvist & Wiksell Int. 141 pp.
44. Heimdahl, A., Nord, C. E. 1982. Effect of erythromycin and clindamycin on the indigenous human anaerobic flora and new colonization of the gastrointestinal tract. *Eur. J. Clin. Microbiol.* 1:38–48
45. Hentges, D. J., ed. 1983. *Human Intestinal Microflora in Health and Disease*. New York: Academic. 568 pp.
46. Hespell, R. B., Smith, C. J. 1983. Utilization of nitrogen sources by gastrointestinal tract bacteria. See Ref. 45, pp. 167–88
47. Hill, M. J. 1983. Bile, bacteria and bowel cancer. *Gut* 24:871–75
48. Hirano, S., Masuda, N. 1982. Characterization of NADP-dependent 7β-hydroxysteroid dehydrogenases from *Peptostreptococcus productus* and *Eubacterium aerofaciens. Appl. Environ. Microbiol.* 43:1057–63
49. Hofmann, A. F., Mekhjian, H. S. 1973. Bile acids and the intestinal absorption of fat and electrolytes in health and disease. In *The Bile Acids,* ed. P. P. Nair, D. Kritchevsky, 2:103–52. New York/London: Plenum. 329 pp.
50. Hoogkamp-Korstanje, J. A. A., Lindner, J. G. E. M., Marcelis, J. H., den Daas-Slagt, H., deVos, N. M. 1979. Composition and ecology of the human intestinal flora. *Antonie van Leeuwenhoek* 45:33–40
51. Hoskins, L. C., Boulding, E. T. 1981. Mucin degradation in human colon ecosystems. *J. Clin. Invest.* 67:163–72
52. Høverstad, T., Bjørneklett, A. 1984. Short-chain fatty acids and bowel functions in man. *Scand. J. Gastroenterol.* 19:1059–65
53. Høverstad, T., Bjørneklett, A., Midtvedt, T., Fausa, O., Bøhmer, T. 1984. Short-chain fatty acids in the proximal gastrointestinal tract of healthy subjects. *Scand. J. Gastroenterol.* 19:1053–58
54. Høverstad, T., Bøhmer, T., Fausa, O. 1982. Absorption of short-chain fatty acids from the human colon measured by the $^{14}CO_2$ breath test. *Scand. J. Gastroenterol.* 17:373–78
55. Høverstad, T., Fausa, O., Bjørneklett, A., Bøhmer, T. 1984. Short-chain fatty acids in the normal human feces. *Scand. J. Gastroenterol.* 19:375–81
56. Hylemon, P. B., Glass, T. L. 1983. Biotransformation of bile acids and cholesterol by the intestinal microflora. See Ref. 45, pp. 189–214
57. Jensen, N. S., Canale-Parola, E. 1985. Nutritionally limited pectinolytic bacteria from the human intestine. *Appl. Environ. Microbiol.* 50:172–73
58. Jilge, B., Meyer, H. 1975. Coprophagy-dependent changes of the anaerobic bacterial flora in stomach and small intestine of the rabbit. *Z. Versuchstierkd.* 17:308–14
59. Kawai, Y. 1980. Depression of intestinal lysosomal β-glucuronidase and acid phosphatase activities by gastrointestinal microorganisms. *Microbiol. Immunol.* 24:753–56
60. Kawai, Y., Morotomi, M. 1978. In-

testinal enzyme activities in germfree, conventional, and gnotobiotic rats associated with indigenous microorganisms. *Infect. Immun.* 19:771–78

61. Kirsner, J. B., Shorter, R. G. 1975. *Inflammatory Bowel Disease*. Philadelphia: Lea & Febriger. 465 pp.
62. Klipstein, F. A., Schenk, E. A. 1975. Enterotoxigenic intestinal bacterial in tropical sprue. II. Effect of the bacteria and their enterotoxins on intestinal structure. *Gastroenterology* 68:642–55
63. Kunstýr, I. 1974. Some quantitative and qualitative aspects of the stomach microflora of the conventional rat and hamster. *Zentralbl. Veterinaermed. Reihe A* 21:553–61
64. Luckey, T. D. 1974. Introduction: the villus in chemostat man. *Am. J. Clin. Nutr.* 27:1266–76
65. Luckey, T. D. 1977. Bicentennial overview of intestinal microecology. *Am. J. Clin. Nutr.* 30:1753–61
66. Mackowiak, P. A. 1982. The normal microbial flora. *N. Engl. J. Med.* 307:83–93
67. Mader, J. A., MacDonald, I. A. 1984. Potential mutagenic activity of some vitamin preparations in the human gut. *Appl. Environ. Microbiol.* 48:902–4
68. Mallett, A. K., Bearne, C. A., Rowland, I. R. 1983. Metabolic activity and enzyme induction in rat fecal microflora maintained in continuous culture. *Appl. Environ. Microbiol.* 46:591–95
69. Mallett, A. K., Rowland, I. R., Wise, A. 1983. Interaction between pectin and rat hindgut microflora. *Appl. Environ. Microbiol.* 45:116–21
70. Marthinsen, D., Fleming, S. E. 1982. Excretion of breath and flatus gases by humans consuming high-fiber diets. *J. Nutr.* 112:1133–43
71. McBee, R. H. 1977. Fermentation in the hindgut. See Ref. 12, pp. 185–222
72. McCarthy, R. E., Kotarski, S. F., Salyers, A. A. 1985. Location and characteristics of enzymes involved in the breakdown of polygalacturonic acid by *Bacteroides thetaiotaomicron*. *J. Bacteriol.* 161:493–99
73. McNeil, N. I. 1984. The contribution of the large intestine to energy supplies in man. *Am. J. Clin. Nutr.* 39:338–42
74. Miller, T. L., Weaver, G. A., Wolin, M. J. 1984. Methanogens and anaerobes in a colon segment isolated from the normal fecal stream. *Appl. Environ. Microbiol.* 48:449–50
75. Miller, T. L., Wolin, M. J. 1981. Fermentation by the human large intestine microbial community in an *in vitro* semicontinuous culture system. *Appl. Environ. Microbiol.* 42:400–7
76. Miller, R. S., Hoskins, L. C. 1981. Mucin degradation in human colon ecosystems. *Gastroenterology* 81:759–65
77. Mikel'Saar, M. E., Tjuri, M. E., Väljaots, M. E., Lencner, A. A. 1984. Anaerobe Inhalts- und Wandmikroflora des Magen-Darm-Kanals. *Die Nahrung* 28(6/7):727–33
78. Moreau, M.-C., Ducluzeau, R., Raibaud, P. 1976. Hydrolysis of urea in the gastrointestinal tract of "monoxenic" rats: effect of immunization with strains of ureolytic bacteria. *Infect. Immun.* 13:9–15
79. Morotomi, M., Nanno, M., Watanabe, T., Sakurai, T., Mutai, M. 1985. Mutagenic activation of biliary metabolites of 1-nitropyrene by intestinal microflora. *Mutat. Res.* 149:171–78
80. Mueller, R. L., Hagel, H.-J., Greim, G., Ruppin, H., Domschke, W. 1983. Die endogene Synthese Kanzerogener *N*-Nitrosoverbindungen: Bakterienflora und Nitritbildung im gesunden menschlichen Magen. *Zentralbl. Bakteriol. Parasitenkd. Infektion. Abt. Orig. B* 178:297–315
81. Norin, K. E., Gustafsson, B. E., Lindblad, B. S., Midtvedt, T. 1985. The establishment of some microflora associated biochemical characteristics in feces of children during the first years of life. *Acta Paediatr. Scand.* 74:207–12
82. Perman, J. A., Modler, S. 1982. Glycoproteins as substrates for production of hydrogen and methane by colonic bacterial flora. *Gastroenterology* 83:388–93
83. Perman, J. A., Modler, S., Olson, A. C. 1981. Role of pH in production of hydrogen from carbohydrates by colonic bacterial flora. *J. Clin. Invest.* 67:643–50
84. Philips, S. M., Fuller, R. 1983. The activities of amylase and a trypsin-like protease in the gut contents of germ-free and conventional chickens. *Br. Poult. Sci.* 24:115–21
85. Plaut, A. G. 1984. Gut bacterial metabolism and human nutrition. In *The Role of Gastrointestinal Tract in Nutrient Delivery*, ed. M. Green, H. L. Greene, pp. 199–208. Orlando, Fla: Academic. 290 pp.
86. Prins, R. A. 1977. Biochemical activities of gut micro-organisms. See Ref. 12, pp. 73–184
87. Reddy, B. S., Pleasant, J. R., Wostmann, B. S. 1969. Pancreatic enzymes in germfree and conventional rats fed chemically defined, water-soluble diet

free from natural substrates. *J. Nutr.* 97:327–34
88. Rérat, A. 1978. Digestion and absorption of carbohydrates and nitrogenous matters in the hindgut of the omnivorous nonruminant animal. *J. Anim. Sci.* 46:1808–37
89. Reyniers, J. P., Pleasant, J. R., Wostmann, B. S., Katze, J. R., Farkas, W. R. 1981. Administration of exogenous queuine is essential for the biosynthesis of the queuosine-containing transfer RNA in the mouse. *J. Biol. Chem.* 256:11159–94
90. Riottot, M., Sacquet, E., Vila, J. P., Leprince, C. 1980. Relationship between small intestine transit and bile acid metabolism in axenic and holoxenic rats fed different diets. *Reprod. Nutr. Dev.* 20:163–71
91. Roberton, A. M., Stanley, R. A. 1982. *In vitro* utilization of mucin by *Bacteroides fragilis*. *Appl. Environ. Microbiol.* 43:325–30
92. Robinson, I. M., Allison, M. J., Bucklin, J. A. 1981. Characterization of the cecal bacteria of normal pigs. *Appl. Environ. Microbiol.* 41:950–55
93. Rød, T. O., Midtvedt, T. 1977. Origin of intestinal β-glucuronidase in germfree, monocontaminated and conventional rats. *Acta Pathol. Microbiol. Scand. B* 85:271–76
94. Roediger, W. E. W. 1980. The role of anaerobic bacteria in the metabolic welfare of the colonic mucosa in man. *Gut* 21:793–98
95. Rotimi, V. O., Duerden, B. I. 1981. The development of the bacterial flora in normal neonates. *J. Med. Microbiol.* 14:51–62
96. Ruppin, H., Bar-Mein, S., Soergel, K. H., Wood, C. M., Schmitt, M. G. Jr. 1980. Absorption of short-chain fatty acids by the colon. *Gastroenterology* 78:1500–7
97. Salanitro, J. P., Blake, I. G., Muirhead, P. A., Maglio, M., Goodman, J. R. 1978. Bacteria isolated from the duodenum, ileum and cecum of young chicks. *Appl. Environ. Microbiol.* 35:782–90
98. Salyers, A. A., Leedle, J. A. Z. 1983. Carbohydrate metabolism in the human colon. See Ref. 45, pp. 129–46
99. Salyers, A. A., Arthur, R., Kuritza, A. 1981. Digestion of larch arabinogalactan by a strain of human colonic *Bacteroides* growing in continuous culture. *J. Agric. Food Chem.* 29:475–80
100. Salyers, A. A., Gherardini, F., O'Brien, M. 1981. Utilization of xylan by two species of human colonic *Bacteroides*. *Appl. Environ. Microbiol.* 41:1065–68
101. Salyers, A. A., Harris, C. J., Wilkins, T. D. 1978. Breakdown of psyllium hydrocolloid by strains of *Bacteroides ovatus* from the human intestinal tract. *Can. J. Microbiol.* 24:336–38
102. Salyers, A. A., Kotarski, S. F. 1980. Induction of chondroitin sulfate lyase activity in *Bacteroides thetaiotaomicron*. *J. Bacteriol.* 143:781–88
103. Salyers, A. A., O'Brien, M., Kotarski, S. F. 1982. Utilization of chondroitin sulfate by *Bacteroides thetaiotaomicron* growing in carbohydrate-limited continuous culture. *J. Bacteriol.* 150:1008–15
104. Salyers, A. A., Palmer, J. K., Wilkins, T. D. 1977. Laminarinase (β-glucanase) activity in *Bacteroides* from the human colon. *Appl. Environ. Microbiol.* 33: 1118–24
105. Salyers, A. A., Vercellotti, J. R., West, S. E. H., Wilkins, T. D. 1977. Fermentation of mucin and plant polysaccharides by strains of *Bacteroides* from the human colon. *Appl. Environ. Microbiol.* 33: 319–22
106. Savage, D. C. 1977. Microbial ecology of the gastrointestinal tract. *Ann. Rev. Microbiol.* 31:107–33
107. Savage, D. C. 1980. Adherence of normal flora to mucosal surfaces. In *Bacterial Adherence,* ed. E. H. Beachey, pp. 33–59. London: Chapman & Hall. 466 pp.
108. Savage, D. C. 1983. Associations of indigenous microorganisms with gastrointestinal epithelial surfaces. See Ref. 45, pp. 55–78
109. Savage, D. C. 1985. Effects on host animals of bacteria adhering to epithelial surfaces. In *Bacterial Adhesion,* ed. D. C. Savage, M. Fletcher, pp. 437–63. New York: Plenum. 476 pp.
110. Savage, D. C., Siegel, J. E., Snellen, J. E., Whitt, D. D. 1981. Transit time of epithelial cells in the small intestines of germfree mice and ex-germfree mice associated with indigenous microorganisms. *Appl. Environ. Microbiol.* 42:996–1001
111. Savage, D. C., Whitt, D. D. 1982. Influence of the indigenous microbiota on amounts of protein, DNA, and alkaline phosphatase activity extractable from epithelial cells of the small intestines of mice. *Infect. Immun.* 37:539–49
112. Schultz, S. G. 1984. Small intestinal absorption and secretion in health and disease. See Ref. 85, pp. 119–32
113. Spiller, G. A., Kay, R. M., eds. 1980.

*Medial Aspects of Dietary Fiber*. New York/London: Plenum. 299 pp.

114. Stephen, A. M., Cummings, J. H. 1980. Mechanism of action of dietary fibre in the human colon. *Nature* 284:283–84
115. Stephen, A. M., Cummings, J. H. 1980. The microbial contribution to human faecal mass. *J. Med. Microbiol.* 13:45–56
116. Tamura, G., Gold, C., Ferro-Luzzi, A., Ames, B. N. 1980. Fecalase: A model for activation of dietary glycosides to mutagens by intestinal flora. *Proc. Natl. Acad. Sci. USA* 77:4961–65
117. Tohyama, K., Kobayashi, Y., Kan, T., Yazawa, K., Terashima, T., Mutai, M. 1981. Effect of lactobacilli on urinary indican excretion in gnotobiotic rats and in man. *Microbiol. Immunol.* 25:101–12
118. Trippestad, A., Midtvedt, T. 1973. Chemotactic activity of intestinal strangulation obstruction fluid from germfree and conventional rats. *Acta Pathol. Microbiol. Scand. B* 81:227–32
119. Umesaki, Y., Sakata, T., Yajima, T. 1982. Abrupt induction of GDP-fucose asialo GMI fucosyl-transferase in the small intestine after conventionalization of germ-free mice. *Biochem. Biophys. Res. Commun.* 105:439–43
120. Umesaki, Y., Tohyama, K., Mutai, M. 1981. Appearance of fucolipid after conventionalization of germ-free mice. *J. Biochem.* 90:559–61
121. Umesaki, Y., Yajima, T., Tohyama, K., Mutai, M. 1980. Characterization of acetate uptake by the colonic epithelial cells of the rat. *Pflügers Arch.* 388:205–9
122. Van Dokkum, W., Pikaar, N. A., Thissen, J. T. N. M. 1983. Physiological effects of fibre-rich types of bread. 2. Dietary fibre from bread: digestibility by the intestinal microflora and water-holding capacity in the colon of human subjects. *Br. J. Nutr.* 47:451–60
123. Vince, A. J., Burridge, S. M. 1980. Ammonia production by intestinal bacteria: The effects of lactose, lactulose and glucose. *J. Med. Microbiol.* 13:177–91
124. Vince, A., Killingley, M., Wrong, O. M. 1978. Effect of lactulose on ammonia production in a fecal incubation system. *Gastroenterology* 74:544–49
125. Whitt, D. D., Savage, D. C. 1981. Influence of indigenous microbiota on amount of protein and activities of alkaline phosphatase and disaccharidases in extracts of intestinal mucosa in mice. *Appl. Environ. Microbiol.* 42:513–20
126. White, R. W., Lindsay, D. B., Ash, R. W. 1972. Ethanol production from glucose by *Torulopsis glabrata* occurring naturally in the stomachs of newborn animals. *J. Appl. Bacteriol.* 35:631–46
127. Winter, J., O'Rourke-Locasio, S., Bokkenheuser, V. D., Mosbach, E. H., Cohen, B. I. 1984. Reduction of 17-ketosteroids by anaerobic microorganisms isolated from human fecal flora. *Biochim. Biophys. Acta* 795:209–11
128. Wolin, M. J. 1981. Fermentation in the rumen and human large intestine. *Science* 213:1463–68
129. Wolin, M. J., Miller, T. L. 1983. Interactions of microbial populations in cellulose fermentations. *Fed. Proc.* 42:109–13
130. Wostmann, B. S. 1981. The germfree animal in nutritional studies. *Ann. Rev. Nutr.* 1:257–79
131. Wozny, M. A., Bryant, M. P., Holdeman, L. V., Moore, W. E. C. 1977. Urease assay and urease-producing species of anaerobes in the bovine rumen and human feces. *Appl. Environ. Microbiol.* 33:1097–1104
132. Wrong, O. M., Edmonds, C. J., Chadwick, V. S. 1981. *The Large Intestine: Its Role in Mammalian Nutrition and Homeostasis*. New York: Wiley. 217 pp.
133. Yajima, T., Kojima, K., Tohyama, K., Mutai, M. 1981. Effect of short-chain fatty acids on electrical activity of the small intestinal mucosa of rat. *Life Sci.* 28:983–89
134. Yang, M. G., Manoharan, K., Mickelson, O. 1970. Nutritional contribution of volatile fatty acids in the cecum of rats. *J. Nutr.* 100:545–50
135. Yokokura, T., Yajima, T., Hashimoto, S. 1977. Effect of organic acid on gastrointestinal motility of rat *in vitro*. *Life Sci.* 21:59–62

*Ann. Rev. Nutr. 1986. 6:179–209*


# METABOLISM OF SULFUR-CONTAINING AMINO ACIDS

*Martha H. Stipanuk*

Division of Nutritional Sciences, Cornell University, Ithaca, New York 14853

---

CONTENTS

INTRODUCTION .......... 179
METHIONINE METABOLISM .......... 180
*The Formation and Utilization of S-Adenosylmethionine* .......... 180
*The Transmethylation and Transsulfuration Pathway* .......... 183
*The Polyamine Pathway* .......... 190
*The Transamination Pathway of Methionine Metabolism* .......... 192
CYSTEINE (AND METHIONINE SULFUR) METABOLISM .......... 193
*The Cysteinesulfinate Pathway: Taurine Production* .......... 193
*Desulfuration Pathways of Cysteine Metabolism* .......... 196
SUMMARY AND CONCLUSIONS .......... 199

## INTRODUCTION

It has long been recognized that L-methionine (Met) is metabolized by transmethylation and transsulfuration, but recent studies have provided more information about the regulation of flux through these pathways and about the fate of the transferred methyl group and sulfur atom. The role of the polyamine pathway and the possible role of a transamination pathway in Met metabolism were demonstrated more recently. L-Cysteine (Cys) metabolism has received relatively little attention, but the interpretation of several recent studies in light of the older literature provides some new insights. The intent of this review is to provide an overview of current knowledge about pathways of sulfur-containing amino acid metabolism in mammalian tissues and the physiological regulation



0199-9885/86/0715-0179$02.00

of flux through these pathways. Most of the research on sulfur-containing amino acid metabolism has focused on the liver and, hence, so does this review. However, the relative roles of the liver and other tissues in the metabolism of Met and Cys in vivo have not been well established, so extrahepatic tissues may also play a significant role in Met and Cys metabolism.

## METHIONINE METABOLISM

### *The Formation and Utilization of S-Adenosylmethionine*

The first step in Met metabolism is the formation of the high-energy sulfonium compound, S-adenosyl-L-methionine (AdoMet). AdoMet is both the methyl donor for transmethylation reactions and the precursor of decarboxylated AdoMet [dAdoMet; S-adenosyl(5')-3-methylthiopropylamine], which is the aminopropyl donor for the synthesis of polyamines. Met adenosyltransferase (EC 2.5.1.6) catalyzes the formation of AdoMet by transfer of the adenosyl moiety of ATP to the sulfur atom of Met. Multiple isozymes of Met adenosyltransferase exist in mammalian tissues (112, 113, 116, 134, 138, 139, 206, 209, 216). Three isozymes (I, II, and III) have been identified in rat liver (206). Met adenosyltransferase-I ($\alpha$) shows Michaelis-Menten kinetics with a $K_m$ for Met of 41 $\mu$M, is slightly inhibited by AdoMet, and comprised about 15% of the total Met adenosyltransferase activity in rat liver preparations when activity was assayed at 25 $\mu$M Met. Met adenosyltransferase-II ($\gamma$), which also appears to be the isozyme found in normal rat kidney, has a Met concentration required for half-maximal velocity [$S_{0.5}$ (Met)] of 8 $\mu$M, is strongly inhibited by AdoMet, and comprised about 5% of the total activity in rat liver. The predominant isozyme in rat liver, Met adenosyltransferase-III ($\beta$), has a $S_{0.5}$ (Met) of 215 $\mu$M and demonstrates positive cooperative modulation by AdoMet at physiological metabolite concentrations (50–150 $\mu$M Met, 50–200 $\mu$M AdoMet). Thus, the velocity of AdoMet synthesis in extraheptic tissues would be expected to be nearly maximal, relatively unaffected by an increase in Met concentration, and sensitive to feedback/product inhibition by AdoMet. In contrast, the velocity of AdoMet synthesis by the high-$K_m$ hepatic isozyme should increase in response to elevated Met and AdoMet levels, permitting rapid clearance of excess Met by the liver.

The Met adenosyltransferase isozyme pattern is altered in fetal and neoplastic liver and in liver of patients with hereditary tyrosinemia, with a marked reduction in levels of the high-$K_m$ isozyme, MAT-III (112, 113, 116, 139, 216). Gaull et al (71) and Finkelstein et al (62) studied children with low levels of hepatic Met adenosyltransferase activity (8–18% of control values for adults) concomitant with the presence of normal amounts of enzyme in erythrocytes, cultured fibroblasts, and lymphoid cell lines. Despite persistent hypermethioninemia, these patients were free of adverse symptoms. Although hepatic Met adenosyltransferase activity in one child was 8% of the control level when activity was assayed at 1 mM Met, it was 39% of control levels when the assays were performed with 6–12 μM Met. It seems probable that these children lacked active Met adenosyltransferase-III, but had normal levels of the low-$K_m$ isozymes.

AdoMet serves as the methyl donor for essentially all known biological methylation reactions with the notable exception of those involved in methylation of L-homocysteine (Hcy). The co-product of transmethylation, S-adenosyl-L-homocysteine (AdoHcy), is hydrolyzed to yield Hcy, which can be remethylated to Met or condensed with serine to form cystathionine. Formation of cystathionine commits the Met molecule to catabolism by the transsulfuration pathway. These transmethylation reactions and the transsulfuration pathway are depicted in Figure 1.

A second fate of AdoMet involves its decarboxylation to form dAdoMet, which is the donor of aminopropyl groups for synthesis of spermidine and

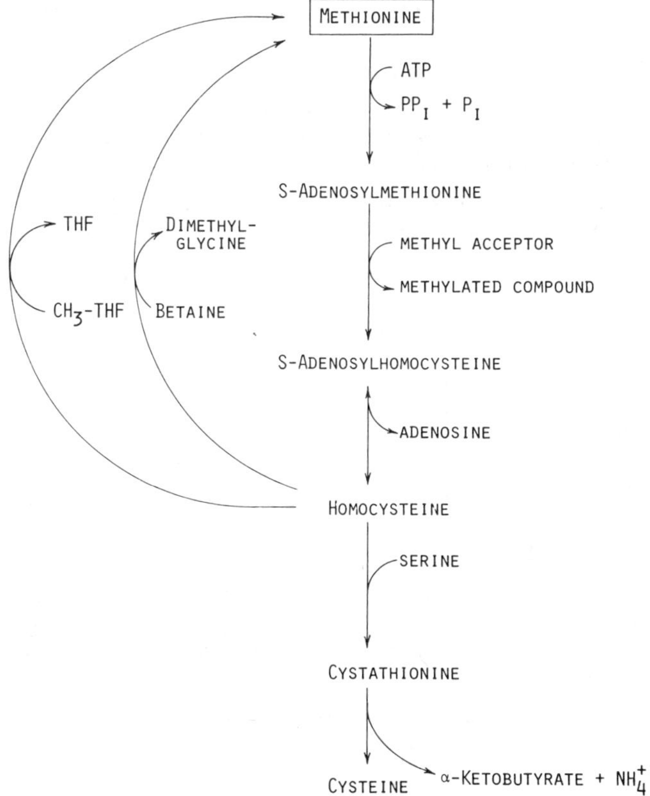


*Figure 1* The transmethylation-transsulfuration pathway.

spermine. Polyamine synthesis also results in the formation of 5'-methylthioadenosine (MTA) from dAdoMet. The sulfur and methyl group of MTA may be reincorporated into Met by the MTA salvage pathway, whereas the aminopropyl group does not appear to be recycled. The reactions involved in polyamine synthesis and MTA salvage are summarized in Figure 2.

Few estimates have been made of the relative flux of AdoMet through these two pathways. Recycling of Hcy and of MTA to Met can lead to underestimation of the magnitude of AdoMet flux through either transmethylation reactions or the polyamine pathway. Giulidori et al (72) measured the $^{14}CO_2$ produced by intact rats given intravenous S-adenosyl-[1-$^{14}$C]Met or S-adenosyl-[3,4-$^{14}$C]Met. They suggested that 30% of the irreversibly catabolized AdoMet was used for the aminopropylation pathway following decarboxylation. About 70% of the AdoMet apparently was catabolized by the transsulfuration pathway following transmethylation, as there was no evidence for nonenzymatic decomposition of AdoMet. These estimates are probably maximal for decarboxylation-aminopropylation and minimal for transmethylation because the authors made no corrections for Hcy recycling or for incomplete or differential recovery of the carbon atoms as $CO_2$. The recovery of the 1-carbon should have been substantially greater than that of the 3- and 4-carbons because of direct decarboxylation of AdoMet or of α-ketobutyrate compared to metabolism of the 3- and 4-carbons via the tricarboxylic acid cycle.

Iizasa & Carson (89) estimated the relative rates of polyamine synthesis and transmethylation from AdoMet in malignant human and murine cell lines deficient in MTA phosphorylase. These cells did not detectably cleave MTA

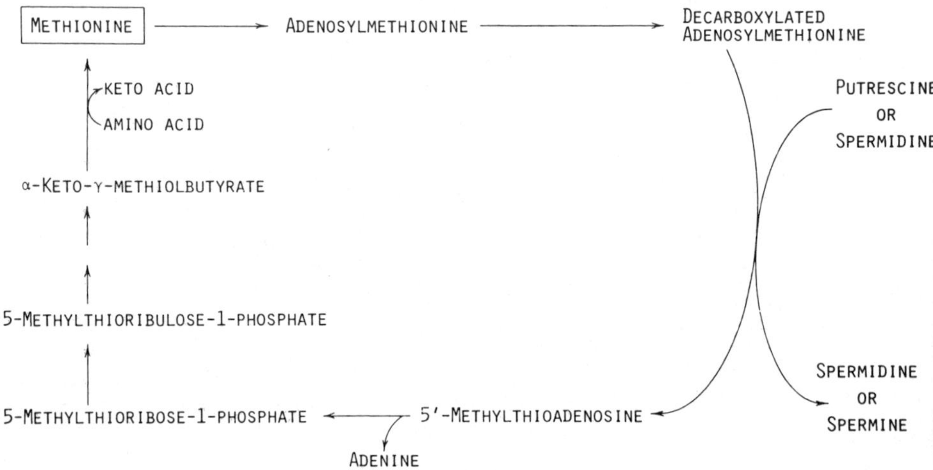


*Figure 2* The polyamine pathway.

and did not appreciably metabolize Hcy. Both MTA and Hcy were excreted into the growth medium. During exponential growth of lymphoblasts, the MTA excretion rate was 80–130 and the Hcy excretion rate was 210–290 $pmol \cdot h^{-1} \cdot 10^6$ $cells^{-1}$; thus, MTA excretion represented about 30% of the AdoMet consumption in these rapidly growing cells. Both the rates of MTA and Hcy production would be expected to be substantially lower in non- or slowly dividing cells.

## *The Transmethylation and Transsulfuration Pathway*

METHYLATION REACTIONS The methyl group of AdoMet is transferred to a nitrogen, oxygen, or sulfur atom of a wide range of compounds in reactions catalyzed by numerous methyltransferases. The major use of labile methyl groups appears to be for the formation of creatine from guanidinoacetate. Mudd & Poole (132) reported urinary excretions of creatinine that were approximately 15–16 $mmol \cdot day^{-1}$ in men and 10 $mmol \cdot day^{-1}$ in women, whereas other methylated compounds excreted in urine, including creatine, only accounted for 1.6–2.6 meq of labile methyl $groups \cdot day^{-1}$.

Loss of labile methyl groups via oxidation of the carbon to C-1 intermediates at oxidation levels of formaldehyde, formate, or $CO_2$ appears to occur primarily via formation and degradation of sarcosine, as shown in Figure 3 (129, 225a, 229). Based on sarcosine excretion by a female sarcosinuric patient, Mudd et al (129) estimated that about 1.5–3.0 mmol of labile methyl groups were oxidized via the sarcosine pathway each day when the subject was on a relatively normal dietary intake; total daily utilization of Met methyl groups in transmethylation reactions was estimated to be 13–14 meq. Intake of labile methyl groups (Met or choline) beyond the apparent requirement of approximately 14 meq per day resulted in nearly equimolar increases in sarcosine production beyond those accounted for by choline degradation; this sarcosine was presumably synthesized via the glycine methyltransferase reaction. De novo synthesis of methyl groups via the tetrahydrofolate (THF) system appeared to be minimal when labile methyl intake was sufficient or excessive. The labile methyl group intake beyond which additional methyl groups were used for sarcosine production was in agreement with the sum of methyl group utilization for various methylation reactions under basal conditions; this agreement suggests that Mudd and coworkers have accounted for most, if not all, of the major routes of Met methyl group utilization (129, 132). It seems clear that the major daily requirement for labile methyl groups is for creatine formation and that the major mechanism for removal of excess methyl groups is via sarcosine production and degradation.

Data from studies with intact rats are also consistent with metabolism of excess Met methyl carbon via the combined action of Met adenosyltransferase (probably isozyme-III), glycine methyltransferase (EC 2.1.1.20), and sarco-

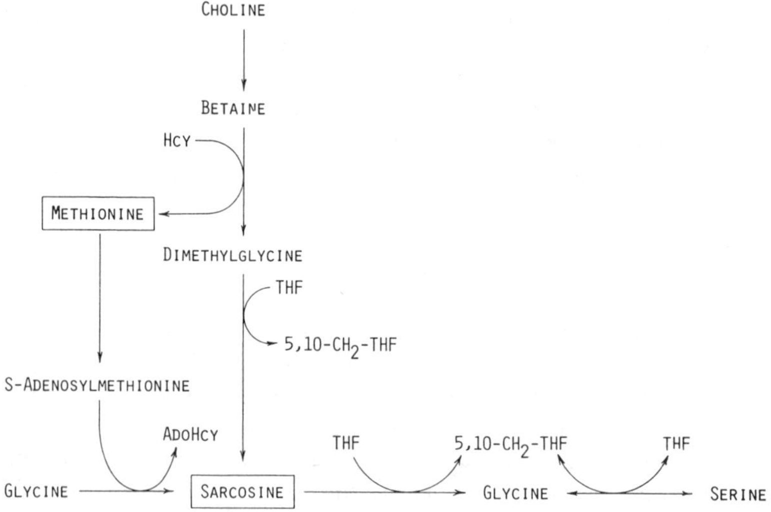


*Figure 3* Pathway for methyl group oxidation.

sine dehydrogenase (EC 1.5.99.1). In intact rats given intraperitoneal injections of [Me-$^{14}$C]Met, up to 40% of the label incorporated into hepatic proteins was recovered in serine and a smaller amount was found in Cys (2, 3). The labeling of serine presumably occurred via conversion of sarcosine to glycine and $N^{5,10}$ methylene-tetrahydrofolate (methylene-THF) (225a, 229)] in the reaction catalyzed by sarcosine dehydrogenase, followed by conversion of glycine and methylene-THF to serine in the reversible reaction catalyzed by serine hydroxymethyltransferase (EC 2.1.2.1). A small amount of label was presumably incorporated into Cys by utilization of the labeled serine in the transsulfuration pathway. As would be expected if production of sarcosine is dependent upon the availability of excess labile methyl groups, both the conversion of the Met methyl carbon to $CO_2$ and the incorporation of the methyl carbon into serine were decreased when the rats were fed choline-devoid or Met-deficient diets (2).

Recently, Wagner (225b) reported that glycine methyltransferase is allosterically inhibited by the polyglutamate form of $N^5$-methyltetrahydrofolate (methyl-THF), which accumulates in the cell during Met deficiency. Thus, regulation of glycine methyltransferase may play a role in conservation of labile methyl groups when Met intake is inadequate.

Oxidation of excess labile methyl groups via sarcosine production and degradation appears to be dependent upon the methylation of glycine rather than upon phosphatidylcholine turnover, both of which generate sarcosine from the methyl group of AdoMet. Case et al (26) showed that phosphatidylcholine turnover did not account for a significant amount of Met methyl group oxidation in the intact rat. Additionally, phosphatidylcholine biosynthesis by methylation of phosphatidylethanolamine or by incorporation of pre-formed choline appears to be regulated to maintain a relatively constant level of phosphatidylcholine in tissues (29, 159). As expected, increased incorporation of label from [Me-$^{14}$C]Met into tissue phosphatidylcholine was observed in rats fed choline-devoid diets, whereas decreased incorporation was observed in rats fed Met-deficient diets (2, 3). This is in marked contrast to the similar effects that changes in either Met or choline intake had on the conversion of the methyl carbon of Met to serine, sarcosine, or $CO_2$.

METABOLISM OF S-ADENOSYLHOMOCYSTEINE AdoHcy is hydrolyzed to adenosine (Ado) and Hcy by AdoHcy hydrolase (EC 3.3.1.1). This reaction is apparently the sole means of intracellular removal of AdoHcy in mammalian tissues (44, 46). The reaction is reversible with the equilibrium far in the direction of synthesis ($K_{eq}$ = 1 μM), but hydrolysis occurs in vivo when Ado is removed by Ado deaminase (EC 3.5.4.4) or Ado kinase (EC 2.7.1.20) and when Hcy is removed by cystathionine β-synthase (EC 4.2.1.22), betaine-Hcy methyltransferase (EC 2.1.1.5), or Met synthase (tetrahydropteroylglutamate methyltransferase, EC 2.1.1.13). AdoHcy hydrolase contains tightly bound $NAD^+$, which participates in the catalytic process (69). The $S_{0.5}$ of the rat or mouse liver enzyme for AdoHcy has been reported to range from 0.75 to 20 μM when measured with low concentrations of enzyme (41, 69, 95, 219) and to be 120 μM at cellular concentrations of enzyme (219); tissue concentrations of AdoHcy range from <0.8 to 56 nmol·g$^{-1}$ (43, 61, 83, 221, 226).

Hydrolysis of AdoHcy is inhibited by the presence of either product, Hcy or Ado, and inhibition is accompanied by the accumulation of AdoHcy and AdoMet (84, 168). Purine nucleoside toxicity (observed in children with Ado deaminase deficiency or purine nucleoside phosphorylase deficiency and in patients treated with 9-β-D-arabinofuranosyladenine) as well as the growth inhibitory properties of MTA may be mediated partially through inhibition of AdoHcy hydrolase (16, 21, 53, 68, 94, 106, 160). Inhibition of AdoHcy hydrolase may lead to decreased intracellular Met synthesis from Hcy and altered folate metabolism due to the methyl trap effect (16, 21), inhibition of intracellular transmethylation reactions (22, 106), and inhibition of Ado kinase (68).

The cellular concentration of AdoHcy itself or the ratio of AdoMet to AdoHcy may serve as a feedback regulator of biological methylation reactions. Most methyltransferases that utilize AdoMet as the methyl donor are inhibited by AdoHcy, and the inhibitory constants vary over a wide range ($K_i$ for AdoHcy = 1–35 μM; $K_m$ for AdoMet = 1–570 μM) (22, 23, 83, 84, 98). Whether or not regulation of methyltransferase reactions by AdoHcy occurs under physiological conditions is questionable, because the ratio of the concentration of AdoHcy to that of AdoMet is relatively low compared to that required for inhibition of methyltransferases, and the activity of AdoHcy hydrolase is higher than that of Met adenosyltransferase in most tissues (43, 45, 61, 83, 226). However, when AdoHcy levels in perfused rat liver or in intact rats or mice were increased as a result of inhibition of AdoHcy hydrolase by Ado, Hcy, or 9-β-D-arabinofuranosyladenine, a parallel increase in AdoMet levels was generally seen; the increased levels of AdoMet were probably the result of decreased utilization of AdoMet by methyltransferases that were inhibited by AdoHcy (46, 78, 84). However, when high amounts of both Ado and Hcy were added, a further increase in the concentration of AdoHcy without a parallel increase in the concentration of AdoMet was observed; this increase was presumably due to synthesis of AdoHcy by reversal of the hydrolase reaction (84).

Data from studies with rat hepatocytes and from in vitro experiments with nearly cellular levels of enzyme (10 μM) and of substrates (2 μM Ado, 50 μM AdoHcy) suggest that a substantial portion of cellular AdoHcy hydrolase exists as a stable complex with Ado (219, 220). This enzyme does not appear to participate in the metabolic hydrolysis of AdoHcy but functions instead as an Ado-binding protein in intact cells. The Ado sequestered by the enzyme was not available for synthesis of AdoHcy in the presence of Hcy or for deamination by Ado deaminase (219).

REMETHYLATION OF HOMOCYSTEINE TO SYNTHESIZE METHIONINE The transmethylation-transsulfuration pathway has a branch point at the level of Hcy, as shown in Figure 1. Hcy may be remethylated to Met in the reaction catalyzed by Met synthase or in that catalyzed by betaine-Hcy methyltransferase. It may also be used for resynthesis of AdoHcy by reversal of the hydrolysis catalyzed by AdoHcy hydrolase, as discussed above, or irreversibly converted to cystathionine via the reaction catalyzed by cystathionine β-synthase. This branch point is an important regulatory locus (64, 129, 132).

Met synthase is widely distributed in mammalian tissues (59, 97, 230). It is responsible for the de novo synthesis of Met methyl groups from one-carbon units in the THF coenzyme system. It utilizes methyl-THF as the methyl donor and methylcobalamin as a tightly bound coenzyme. A catalytic amount of AdoMet is required, which apparently is involved in generating the active form of the $B_{12}$-coenzyme or in stimulating methyltransferase activity (19, 20, 123, 124). The $K_m$ of rat liver Met synthase for Hcy is 60 μM (55).

Met synthase is clearly important in Hcy metabolism. This is evidenced by the elevated levels of homocyst(e)ine and normal or low concentrations of Met that are found in plasma of human patients with inborn errors of metabolism affecting the availability of methyl-THF or active $B_{12}$-coenzyme and, hence, the activity of Met synthase (77, 85, 131, 169, 177). The inactivation of Met synthase by exposure of intact animals to nitrous oxide decreased tissue concentrations of Met and AdoMet and impaired essential methylation reactions (119, 120, 223).

In Met deficiency and in vitamin $B_{12}$ deficiency (which presumably mimics a Met deficiency at the cellular level) methyl-THF accumulates in the cell at the expense of other forms of folate (170, 174, 225b). This decreased use of methyl-THF is caused by a lack of active Met synthase (vitamin $B_{12}$ deficiency) or by a lack of Hcy, the methyl group acceptor (Met deficiency). Addition of Met, by increasing the availability of Hcy or by increasing the concentration of AdoMet, results in demethylation of methyl-THF. AdoMet inhibits the conversion of methylene-THF to methyl-THF by methylene-THF reductase (EC 1.1.99.15), a reaction that is essentially irreversible under physiological conditions (36, 109, 225). Inhibition of the reductase occurred at concentrations of AdoMet that were somewhat greater than the normal range for tissue concentrations, and this inhibition was reversed by the presence of AdoHcy (15, 109). Activation of Met synthase by AdoMet is unlikely to play a role in the demethylation of methyl-THF, because Met synthase was fully stimulated at normal tissue concentrations of AdoMet and was unaffected by addition of AdoHcy (15).

Demethylation of methyl-THF causes a redistribution of THF derivatives to other coenzyme forms and allows flux of one-carbon units to other reactions; it also increases the hepatic concentration of total folate and causes a large increase in the hepatic levels of pteroylpolyglutamates (30, 42, 105). Methyl-THF is a poor substrate for rat liver pteroylpolyglutamate synthetase. Thus, methyl-THF taken up from the plasma must be converted to THF via the methyltransferase reaction before it can be converted to a pteroylpolyglutamate, the form of folate that is preferentially retained by tissue (30, 118, 225, 225b). A direct stimulatory effect of Met on the transport of folates in mammalian cells has also been suggested (91).

Unlike Met synthase, which is widely distributed in mammalian tissues, betaine-Hcy methyltransferase is generally found in high concentrations only in mammalian liver (59). Activity has been found in kidney and pancreas of some species (131, 230); substantial levels of activity have been reported for both liver and kidney of human infants and children (131). The enzyme is specific for Hcy, but certain analogs of betaine can also serve as the methyl donor (5, 182). The reported $K_m$ values of the human liver enzyme for Hcy and betaine are 120 and 100 $\mu$M, respectively, whereas those for the rat liver enzyme are 15–21 and 49–56 $\mu$M, respectively (57, 182).

Betaine-Hcy methyltransferase is inhibited in vitro by the presence of dimethylglycine and possibly by Met, both products of the reaction, and by preincubation with AdoMet (57, 65, 182). Substantial inhibition of the rat liver enzyme by 50 $\mu$M Met has been reported (57), but the human liver enzyme was unaffected by Met (182). A protective effect of AdoHcy on the inactivation of betaine-Hcy methyltransferase by AdoMet has been demonstrated (64, 65); higher levels of AdoHcy that are clearly unphysiological appear to inhibit (competitively with Hcy) the methyltransferase (60).

Hepatic betaine-Hcy methyltransferase activity was increased in rats fed diets that contained no Met and also in those fed diets with high levels of protein or Met (58, 59). Supplemental betaine or choline also induces the enzyme (66, 74). Thus, the enzyme appears to respond to the increased need for labile methyl group transfer or conservation of Hcy when Met intake is low, to the need to metabolize Hcy when Met intake is high, and also to the need to dispose of betaine when betaine or choline intake is high.

The availability of betaine appears to influence conservation or recycling of the Hcy moiety of Met. This suggests that, at least when dietary Met is limited or when Hcy removal by other reactions is blocked, both betaine-Hcy methyltransferase and Met synthase are essential for adequate methylation of Hcy to Met. Addition of betaine to liver slices increased the recycling of the Hcy moiety of Met (8, 230). Betaine supplementation of the diet of fruit bats that had been treated with nitrous oxide (which severely inhibits Met synthase) resulted in reduced weight loss and delayed onset of neurological impairment (224). Furthermore, betaine therapy has been effective in decreasing the Hcy concentration and increasing the Met and Cys concentrations in plasma of patients with homocystinuria (186, 228).

CATABOLISM OF HOMOCYSTEINE—THE TRANSSULFURATION PATHWAY Cystathionine synthase catalyzes the replacement of the β-OH group of L-serine with Hcy to form cystathionine. Cystathionine synthase contains tightly bound pyridoxal 5'-phosphate and also possesses serine sulfhydrase activity (102, 103). The translational product of the synthase gene appears to be a polypeptide of 63,000 kd, which is initially assembled into a tetramer. This product is subject to limited post-translational proteolysis, which reduces the $M_r$ of the original subunit to 48,000 and is associated with a change from a tetrameric to a dimeric structure, a 30-fold decrease in the $K_m$ for Hcy, and a 60-fold increase in specific activity (103, 104, 183, 184). This active form of the enzyme has a $K_m$ of 0.6–0.8 mM for Hcy and 0.1–0.4 mM for serine (103, 184). Proteolytic activation may be tissue specific; it has been observed in human and rat liver but not in human fibroblast extracts (103, 183, 184). Cystathionine synthase is also activated by AdoMet (63, 64), but the effects of proteolytic cleavage and activation by AdoMet are not additive (102). Activation by AdoMet does not appear to be related to the presence of a soluble effector and presumably involves some modification of the enzyme structure (63). Cystathionine synthase may also be activated in vitro by high levels of AdoHcy (60).

The AdoMet concentration may be an important physiological regulator of cystathionine synthase activity. Supplementation of a low Met diet with cyst(e)ine instead of Met results in less hepatic cystathionine synthase activity, which may occur as a result of less activation of the enzyme by AdoMet in vivo (67). The ability of Cys to replace a portion of the dietary Met may be due to this effect on cystathionine synthase activity, but a primary effect of Cys on utilization of Met for protein synthesis could also explain the reduced flux of Met to Cys (196). Patients with a genetic deficiency of Met adenosyltransferase activity have a concomitant decrease in cystathionine synthase activity, which is possibly due to the absence of activation by AdoMet. Although the hypothesis has not been tested, it is tempting to speculate that some of the beneficial effect of betaine therapy in patients with homocystinuria may be related to the resulting increase in Met and, hence, AdoMet levels, which could stimulate cystathionine synthase activity and increase the irreversible flux of Hcy through the transsulfuration pathway.

Finkelstein & Martin (64) studied the metabolism of Hcy using incubation systems reconstituted to contain enzymes (from tissue extracts) and reactants at concentrations that approximated those present in vivo. Systems were modeled on the liver of rats fed chow, 3.5% casein, or 55% casein. They measured flux of Hcy through the reactions catalyzed by Met synthase, betaine-Hcy methyltransferase, and cystathionine synthase by adding either 5-[Me-$^{14}$C]methyl-THF, [Me-$^{14}$C]betaine, or L-[3-$^{14}$C]serine to otherwise identical tubes and measuring the labeled product, Met or cystathionine. When the system was modeled on the liver of chow-fed rats, the activities of Met synthase, betaine-Hcy methyltransferase, and cystathionine synthase accounted for 27, 27, and 46%, respectively, of the Hcy consumed. Inhibition of Met synthase or betaine-Hcy methyltransferase shifted relative flux through the three pathways in a manner suggesting that Met synthase had the highest affinity for Hcy and that cystathionine synthase had the least. This suggestion is consistent with the reported $K_m$ values for these two enzymes (55). The finding that 54% of the Hcy consumed was converted to Met is also consistent with estimates of the extent of remethylation of Hcy to Met in human subjects (129, 132), in the perfused rat liver (55) and in the intact rat (189), all of which were about 50%. Changes in flux through the three pathways in the systems modeled on the livers of rats fed 3.5% casein or 55% casein could be largely explained by changes in enzyme, substrate, and effector concentrations.

Cystathionase (cystathionine γ-lyase, EC 4.4.1.1) catalyzes the γ-cleavage of cystathionine to form Cys and α-ketobutyrate, the final step of the transsulfuration pathway. This pyridoxal 5'-phosphate-dependent enzyme also catalyzes the deamination of homoserine and the desulfhydration of cyst(e)ine (142, 237). The $K_m$ for cystathionine of cystathionase purified from liver of several species has been reported to be in the range of 0.3 to 3.5 mM (14, 222, 237).

The importance of the transsulfuration pathway in Met metabolism is suggested by a number of observations. The ability of Cys to replace a substantial portion of dietary Met on a nearly equimolar basis (187, 200) and the incorporation of Met or Hcy sulfur into Cys and, thence, into cysteinyl residues of protein and glutathione (9, 202, 211, 212) suggest that transsulfuration is a major pathway for metabolism of Met sulfur. Reduced levels of cystathionine synthase or cystathionase activity in humans with inborn errors of metabolism or in animals fed vitamin $B_6$–deficient diets result in elevated levels of homocyst(e)-ine and cystathionine in plasma and urine (55, 130, 176, 185, 203). Inhibition of cystathionase with an irreversible inhibitor, propargylglycine, markedly reduced $^{35}SO_4$ excretion in rats given [$^{35}$S]Met or L-[$^{35}$S]cystathionine (but not in rats given [$^{35}$S]cysteine) and equally depressed the metabolism of L-[carboxy-*n*-propyl-1-$^{14}$C]cystathionine and [1-$^{14}$C]Met to $^{14}CO_2$ (47, 193, 195). Treatment of hepatocytes or intact rats with propargylglycine also resulted in the excretion or accumulation of labeled cystathionine formed from labeled Met (9, 193). The accumulation of homocyst(e)ine and cystathionine as well as the reduction in oxidation of Met to $SO_4^{-2}$ and $CO_2$ when flux through the transsulfuration pathway is reduced clearly demonstrates the importance of this pathway in normal Met metabolism.

## *The Polyamine Pathway*

FORMATION AND UTILIZATION OF DECARBOXYLATED S-ADENOSYLMETHIONINE The polyamine pathway is important for the synthesis of the polyamines, spermidine and spermine, and possibly for the synthesis of methylthio compounds. The importance of these compounds in cellular physiology is not yet well understood, but the present evidence suggests that they are essential for normal growth (208). As shown in Figure 2, polyamines are synthesized in mammalian cells from ornithine and AdoMet by the actions of ornithine decarboxylase and AdoMet decarboxylase, which provide putrescine and dAdoMet, and of spermidine synthase and spermine synthase, which catalyze the transfer of the aminopropyl group from dAdoMet to putrescine to form spermidine and to spermidine to form spermine (149, 166, 208). The MTA formed from dAdoMet during polyamine synthesis is salvaged by conversion of the methylthioribose moiety into Met and of adenine into adenine nucleotides (7, 96, 166). Polyamine degradation leads to formation of a number of derivatives, but there is no evidence for any reutilization of the aminopropyl group of polyamines (150, 172).

The activated aminopropyl group needed for polyamine synthesis is generated by decarboxylation of AdoMet in a reaction catalyzed by AdoMet decarboxylase (EC 4.1.1.50); this reaction commits the Met molecule to the polyamine pathway. AdoMet decarboxylase contains a covalently linked pyruvoyl group, which is essential for enzymatic activity, and does not contain pyridoxal 5'-phosphate (39, 143, 145). The activity of AdoMet decarboxylase is regulated by changes in the concentration of putrescine, an activator of the enzyme. AdoMet decarboxylase is activated over a physiological range of putrescine concentrations (0–50 μM), probably by a decrease in the apparent $K_m$ of the enzyme for AdoMet (157, 158, 163). Increased ornithine decarboxylase activity can indirectly increase the supply of dAdoMet by increasing the cellular concentration of putrescine, which, in turn, activates AdoMet decarboxylase (145, 149). This mechanism may ensure that a parallel supply of dAdoMet and putrescine is available and, therefore, that putrescine is efficiently converted to spermidine.

AdoMet decarboxylase activity is also regulated in mammalian tissues by changes in the amount of enzyme protein. The enzyme turns over rapidly with a $t_{1/2}$ of less than 2 h in most tissues (173). The amount of enzyme protein is increased in response to spermidine depletion and to a variety of physiological and nutritional treatments (86, 92, 122, 128, 144, 145, 148, 151, 152, 154, 178, 213). Some studies indicate that high levels of dAdoMet can inhibit AdoMet decarboxylase and limit its accumulation (144, 236), but physiological levels of dAdoMet are probably not high enough to have an effect.

It is likely that the supply of dAdoMet limits the rate of spermidine and spermine synthesis. Concentrations of dAdoMet in rat tissues have been reported to be 0.9–2.5 nmol per gram wet weight compared to AdoMet concentrations of 23–67 nmol per g wet wt (81, 147). The rapid utilization of dAdoMet (so that it does not accumulate in the cell) may be related to the coordinated regulation of putrescine and dAdoMet production (149), to the presence of spermidine synthase and spermine synthase activities at levels that are in substantial excess of that of AdoMet decarboxylase (161), and to the high affinities of the aminopropyltransferases for dAdoMet ($K_m$ = 0.6 and 1.1 μM for spermine synthase and spermidine synthase, respectively) (140, 164).

Polyamine synthesis appears to be the major, if not the only, route for the further metabolism of dAdoMet. Decarboxylated AdoMet accumulated to levels that were many-fold the control levels in cells cultured in vitro and in ventral prostate of intact rats when its utilization was blocked by inhibition of ornithine decarboxylase or of spermidine synthase (35, 121, 144, 151, 152). In incubations of soluble protein from rat liver with putrescine (as substrate for spermidine synthase) and adenine (to inhibit MTA degradation by MTA phosphorylase), inhibition of AdoMet decarboxylase by methylglyoxal bis-(guanylhydrazone) (MGBG) blocked formation of labeled MTA from S-[8-$^{14}$C]adenosyl-L-methionine and of labeled spermidine from S-adenosyl-L-[2-$^{14}$C]methionine; the decreased production of MTA and spermidine was accompanied by a nearly equimolar decrease in disappearance of AdoMet (44). A similar dose-dependent effect of MGBG on MTA synthesis was observed in studies with human lymphoblastoid cell lines (96).

SALVAGE OF METHYLTHIORIBOSE FOR RESYNTHESIS OF METHIONINE As indicated in Figure 2, the MTA formed from dAdoMet during polyamine synthesis is metabolized by MTA phosphorylase to adenine and 5-methylthioribose-1-phosphate (54, 70, 96). The primary fate of 5-methylthioribose-1-phosphate in cell-free homogenates of rat liver is the formation of Met (6, 7). Carbons from the ribose portion, the carbon and hydrogens of the methyl group, and the sulfur of MTA are all incorporated into Met. Thus, the pathway by which MTA is converted to Met involves modifications in the ribose portion of the molecule to form the α-aminobutyrate portion of Met rather than a transfer of the methylthio group to an acceptor molecule (7). The steps involved in the conversion of 5-methylthioribose-1-phosphate to Met have been partially elucidated (6, 214, 215). 5-Methylthioribose-1-phosphate undergoes isomerization to 5-methylthioribulose-1-phosphate (215), which is then converted to α-keto-γ-methiolbutyrate, the keto acid precursor of Met. The intermediates and reactions involved in this conversion have not been fully characterized; the pathway appears to include formation of a phosphate ester, removal of the phosphate to form an intermediate at the oxidation state of ribose, and subsequent stoichiometric consumption of $O_2$ and production of formate (215). The final step in the pathway for Met synthesis is the transamination of the keto acid, which may be catalyzed by glutamine aminotransferase (6).

This pathway for MTA metabolism is physiologically important for the removal of MTA as well as for the conservation of the adenine and methylthioribose moieties of AdoMet. MTA is a strong inhibitor of the aminopropyltransferases involved in polyamine production (80, 146), of AdoHcy hydrolase (53, 160), and of adenosine kinase (68). Inhibition is not seen in vivo because a low concentration of MTA (1–2 $nmol \cdot g^{-1}$ in most rat tissues) is normally maintained in mammalian tissues due to the action of MTA phosphorylase (147, 171).

## *The Transamination Pathway of Methionine Metabolism*

Benevenga and coworkers (11, 24, 191) proposed that Met is metabolized by an alternate pathway that involves transamination as the initial step. Met is transaminated to α-keto-γ-methiolbutyrate (perhaps by cytosolic glutamine aminotransferase) in the presence of α-keto-γ-methiolbutyrate, pyruvate, the keto acids of the branched-chain amino acids, or phenylpyruvate (12, 114, 115, 127, 191). Apparently, the keto acid of Met is transported into the mitochondria on the pyruvate carrier (115) where it is decarboxylated (perhaps by the branched-chain keto acid dehydrogenase complex) to give 3-methylthiopropionyl-CoA (40, 115, 191). 3-Methylthiopropionate (3-methylthiopropionyl-CoA) may be further metabolized to methanethiol, hydrogen sulfide, sulfate, carbon dioxide, and possibly formaldehyde and formate, but the details of these conversions have not been elucidated (12, 25, 31, 192).

The role of a pathway of Met metabolism that is independent of the formation of AdoMet is not well established in the intact cell or animal, but deserves further consideration. Metabolic studies with isolated rat hepatocytes support a role of the transamination pathway of Met metabolism (115), and continuous infusion tracer dilution studies in intact sheep support the existence of some alternate pathway of Met metabolism (12). Additional support for the transamination pathway comes from studies indicating that metabolites produced by the transamination pathway may be related to the marked toxicity of Met in the rat (190).

Evidence for an alternate pathway of Met metabolism must be considered in light of the many data indicating that only the transmethylation-transsulfuration pathway is quantitatively important in the oxidation of the sulfur atom and methyl group of Met. Many of the observations of increased oxidation of the methyl group of Met in rats fed diets with excess Met can be explained, at least partially, by increased flux of Met through the Met adenosyltransferase, glycine methyltransferase, and sarcosine dehydrogenase system (10, 25, 126, 136). Experiments with labeled AdoMet and labeled Met suggest that the sulfur atom and methyl and carboxyl carbons of these two compounds are similarly metabolized in the intact rat, which is consistent with the conversion of Met to AdoMet prior to its oxidation (72). "Abnormal" metabolites of Met that would be formed by the transamination pathway have not been observed in man and animals under conditions where "normal" metabolism is partially blocked and where plasma Met is elevated; in fact, intermediates of the transsulfuration pathway have been found in increased amounts under these conditions (56, 130, 155, 186).

## CYSTEINE (AND METHIONINE SULFUR) METABOLISM

### *The Cysteinesulfinate Pathway: Taurine Production*

Cys, whether from an exogenous source or formed from serine and the sulfur of Met by the transsulfuration pathway (or possibly by direct sulfhydration of serine), is metabolized by the animal to yield either taurine (2-aminoethanesulfonate) and $CO_2$ or sulfate, urea, and $CO_2$ (108, 111). Several pathways of Cys metabolism have been demonstrated, but the physiological roles of these are not well understood.

The cysteinesulfinate pathway of Cys metabolism is depicted in Figure 4.

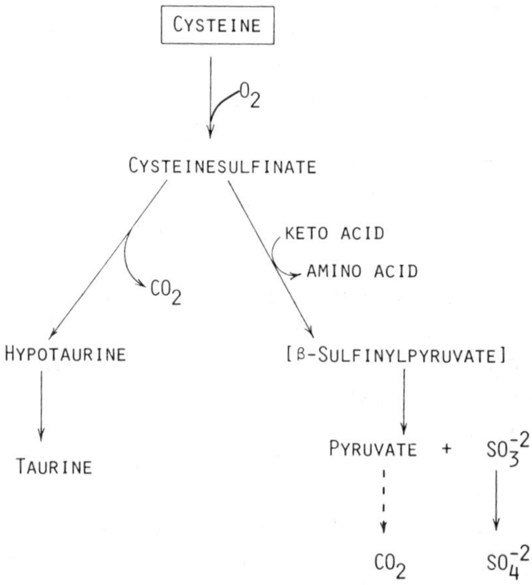


*Figure 4* The cysteinesulfinate pathway.

The oxidation of Cys to cysteinesulfinate is catalyzed by Cys dioxygenase (EC 1.13.11.20), an iron-containing enzyme that seems to be specific for Cys, with an apparent $K_m$ of 0.45 mM (232). Cysteinesulfinate may then be decarboxylated to hypotaurine (2-aminoethanesulfinate) by action of cysteinesulfinate decarboxylase (EC 4.1.1.29), a pyridoxal 5'-phosphate-dependent enzyme that has an apparent $K_m$ for cysteinesulfinate of 0.045–0.17 mM and that can also use cysteic acid (cysteinesulfonate) as a substrate (75, 135). Brain glutamate decarboxylase (EC 4.1.1.15) can also catalyze the decarboxylation of cysteinesulfinate (135). Alternatively, cysteinesulfinate may undergo transamination or oxidative deamination to form the putative intermediate, β-sulfinylpyruvate, which spontaneously decomposes to yield pyruvate and sulfite (180).

About 70–90% of the cysteinesulfinate oxidized by rat hepatocytes or by intact rats or mice was converted to hypotaurine plus taurine (37, 38, 73, 199); this indicates that, under normal conditions, the rat or mouse metabolizes cysteinesulfinate primarily to taurine rather than to pyruvate and sulfite. Apparent flux of cysteinesulfinate through the transamination pathway in the intact mouse was increased when cysteinesulfinate decarboxylase was inhibited by β-methylene-DL-aspartate (73); this conversion of cysteinesulfinate to pyruvate and sulfite was presumably catalyzed by aspartate aminotransferase, which has a $K_m$ for cysteinesulfinate of 3–25 mM (162, 231).

In mammals, hypotaurine is apparently oxidized to taurine via a poorly characterized enzymatic reaction that appears to require $NAD^+$, $Cu^{+2}$, and $O_2$ (101, 137). The apparent $K_m$ of the enzyme for hypotaurine is 0.20 mM (101, 137). The rates of hypotaurine oxidation catalyzed by rat or mouse tissues in vitro are too low to account for the rates observed in vivo (137, 153). Hypotaurine does not usually accumulate in mammalian tissues (82), but substantial levels have been found in rat liver after partial hepatectomy (204). Hypotaurine may also undergo transamination to sulfinylacetaldehyde, which presumably decomposes to sulfite and acetaldehyde, but this reaction appears to make a very minor contribution to hypotaurine metabolism in mammalian tissues (50, 51, 73).

The cysteinesulfinate pathway seems to be the major route of taurine formation in mammals. This conclusion is supported by the detection of labeled cysteinesulfinate and taurine in tissues of animals given labeled Cys (141), by the presence of the enzymes involved in the conversion of Cys to cysteinesulfinate and hypotaurine in most mammalian tissues (38, 233), and by the general association, both within and among species, of hepatic cysteinesulfinate decarboxylase activity with the capacity of the animal to synthesize taurine (38, 76, 234).

Hepatic Cys dioxygenase activity was elevated in rats fed diets with excess Met, Cys or protein (34, 99, 194, 199). These increases in Cys dioxygenase activity appeared to parallel an increase in the hepatic Cys concentration to 0.2–0.3 μmol per gram wet weight (control level, 0.1 $\mu mol \cdot g^{-1}$) and to precede an increase in hepatic taurine concentration to 6–8 μmol per gram wet tissue (control level, 3–4 $\mu mol \cdot g^{-1}$) (99).

In contrast to the increase in Cys dioxygenase activity, cysteinesulfinate decarboxylase activity in rat liver decreased to approximately 50% of control levels in rats fed excess protein or excess Cys (34, 117, 199). As expected, decreased cysteinesulfinate decarboxylase activity was associated with decreased oxidation of cysteinesulfinate in hepatocytes isolated from rats that had been fed a high-Cys diet (197). However, these hepatocytes oxidized Cys to $CO_2$ and to taurine as rapidly or more rapidly than did cells from control animals. Thus, the low cysteinesulfinate decarboxylase activity did not appear to be rate-limiting for Cys oxidation in hepatocytes from rats fed excess Cys.

Studies in animals have yielded conflicting results. Estimates of the oxidation of Cys or cysteinesulfinate to $CO_2$ in intact rats fed a high-Cys diet were the same as for control rats (199), whereas excess dietary Met or Cys generally led to an increase in the urinary excretion of Cys sulfur as taurine (34, 194). Rats fed excess protein had markedly reduced levels of hepatic cysteinesulfinate decarboxylase activity but elevated levels of urinary taurine (13). These observations seem to suggest that, in animals fed excess protein or sulfur-containing amino acids, either Cys is oxidized primarily by cysteinesulfinate-independent pathways or increased Cys dioxygenase activity compensates for the decrease in cysteinesulfinate decarboxylase activity.

Taurine is used in conjugation reactions (i.e. bile acids) but does not otherwise appear to be further metabolized by mammalian tissues (52). Taurine that is not reabsorbed by the kidney is excreted as such in the urine (205); renal clearance of taurine in the rat appears to adapt to alterations in the sulfur amino acid and taurine content of the diet (28). Taurine is also secreted as taurine-conjugated bile acids and then degraded to sulfate by intestinal microorganisms (79, 201, 205). The sulfate formed in the intestine is largely reabsorbed and excreted in the urine with little sulfur being excreted in the feces (79, 107, 188). Most [$^{35}$S]taurine administered orally or intravenously to rats was excreted as [$^{35}$S]taurine rather than as [$^{35}$S]sulfate (79).

Other possible pathways of taurine production from cysteine sulfur in mammalian tissues have been identified. One involves the reaction of 3'-phosphoadenosine-5'-phosphosulfate and serine to form cysteic acid, which may be decarboxylated to form taurine; this pathway appears to make a very minor, if any, contribution to taurine production in mammals (87, 125). Cysteinesulfinate may be oxidized nonenzymatically to cysteic acid, which may be decarboxylated by cysteinesulfinate decarboxylase to yield taurine; the rate of conversion of cysteinesulfinate to cysteic acid appears to be too slow for this route of taurine production to be significant (199, 210). Another pathway involves the production of cysteamine (2-mercaptoethylamine) followed by formation of hypotaurine via action of cysteamine dioxygenase (48, 88). Cysteamine production from Cys appears to be a branch of the coenzyme A synthetic pathway, with cysteamine being produced from pantetheine by action of pantetheinase; other possible routes of taurine production via cysteamine have also been proposed (27, 165). Further investigation of this potential route of taurine synthesis is needed.

The quantitative significance of taurine production in Cys metabolism in animals varies substantially among species. Indirect estimates based on the evolution of $^{14}CO_2$ by animals following intraperitoneal injections of [1-$^{14}$C]- or [3-$^{14}$C]-labeled cyst(e)ine indicate that about 70–80% of Cys is converted to taurine in the intact male rat (199, 233, 234), whereas only about 20% of the Cys that is oxidized is converted to taurine in the kitten (38). However, the rat, like other animals, excretes much more Cys sulfur as sulfate than as taurine (34, 108); this suggests that the estimate of 70–80% for Cys conversion to taurine in the rat may be high. Recent studies of Cys metabolism in hepatocytes suggest that only about 25% of Cys oxidation in rat liver involves production of hypotaurine and taurine (37).

### *Desulfuration Pathways of Cysteine Metabolism*

Production of pyruvate and inorganic sulfur from Cys may occur by several pathways that do not involve conversion of Cys to cysteinesulfinate (195). In contrast to the production of pyruvate and $SO_3^{-2}$ (which is readily oxidized to sulfate by sulfite oxidase) from cysteinesulfinate, these desulfuration pathways all involve the release of Cys sulfur in a reduced oxidation state. Data from studies with rat liver mitochondria (227), the perfused rat liver (179), and hepatocytes (37, 197) suggest that a substantial amount of Cys may be metabolized by cysteinesulfinate-independent pathway(s). Wainer (227) demonstrated production of $^{35}SO_4$ by rat liver mitochondria incubated with [$^{35}$S]Cys at a rate that was not substantially decreased by addition of cysteinesulfinate. In experiments with livers from 72-hour starved rats, Simpson & Freedland (179) found that perfusion with 10 mM cysteinesulfinate in addition to 10 mM [U-$^{14}$C]Cys decreased the recovery of radioactivity in glucose by only 30%. The pattern for accumulation of nitrogenous products was markedly different when cells were incubated with 25 mM Cys than when they were incubated with 25 mM cysteinesulfinate. Increased production of urea and ammonia accounted for the nitrogen from ~80% of the oxidized Cys, whereas hypotaurine plus taurine accounted for 80–90% of the oxidized cysteinesulfinate (M. H. Stipanuk, unpublished observations). In other studies with rat hepatocytes, 25 mM cysteinesulfinate reduced recovery of the 1-carbon of Cys in $CO_2$ by 30–40% when the Cys concentration in the incubation medium was 0.2–1.0 mM, but by only 10% when the Cys concentration was 25 mM (M. H. Stipanuk, unpublished observations). Thus, high Cys concentrations may favor Cys catabolism by desulfuration pathways.

Pyruvate and reduced inorganic sulfur can be produced by the cleavage of cystine to pyruvate, ammonia, and thiocysteine, which is catalyzed by cystathionase, followed by further enzymatic or nonenzymatic reaction of thiocysteine with the enzyme or another thiol to reform a disulfide accompanied by release of sulfide (195, 235). The apparent $K_m$ of rat liver cystathionase for L-cystine has been estimated to be about 0.03–0.07 mM compared with 0.8–3.5 mM for L-cystathionine and 15–20 mM for L-homoserine (222, 235, 237). Thus, cystine should compete favorably with other substrates for the enzyme. Pyruvate and sulfane sulfur can also be formed by transamination of Cys with α-ketoglutarate (or pyruvate) to form β-mercaptopyruvate, which may undergo desulfuration (or transsulfuration) catalyzed by β-mercaptopyruvate sulfurtransferase (4, 90, 218). The $K_m$ of purified Cys:α-ketoglutarate aminotransferase for Cys is about 22 mM, whereas its $K_m$ for aspartate is about 0.06–0.5 mM (4, 217). Thus, it is unlikely that Cys is a good substrate for transamination in vivo. Sulfide may also be formed from the substitution of the thiol group of Cys with a variety of thiol compounds to form the corresponding thioether in a reaction catalyzed by cystathionine synthase (18, 110, 156). However, cystathionine synthase apparently has a much higher $K_m$ for Cys (36 mM) than for L-serine (2–8 mM) or Hcy (0.1–9 mM) (17, 103, 133).

All three of these pathways appeared to play a role in the production of acid-labile sulfide from Cys by liver and kidney homogenate systems designed to approach physiological values for substrate concentrations and pH (195, 198), but the role of these pathways in the intact animal has not been assessed. Because of the existence of multiple pathways, blocking one pathway may have little effect on the overall ability of the animal to metabolize Cys. Patients with a genetic lack of β-mercaptopyruvate sulfurtransferase excrete low levels of the mixed disulfide of β-mercaptolactate and Cys, which suggests that at least a small amount of Cys is metabolized by transamination in vivo (32, 33). These patients excrete normal levels of urinary sulfate. Inhibition of cystathionase by propargylglycine had no effect on sulfate production from Cys (195), but metabolites potentially produced via action of cystathionase on Cys have been observed in urine of rats (49). Patients who have low levels of cystathionine synthase appear to convert Met and Cys to sulfate normally (155).

If sulfur were released from Cys as sulfane sulfur, the sulfide presumably would be oxidized to sulfate prior to its excretion. Inorganic sulfur metabolism has received little attention in recent years, but the elegant experiments of Koj et al (100), published in 1967, support a central role of thiosulfate in the oxidation of sulfide by animal tissues. Based on studies with $(^{35}S{\cdot}SO_3)^{-2}$ and $(S{\cdot}^{35}SO_3)^{-2}$, they proposed that thiosulfate is an intermediate in the formation of sulfate from sulfane sulfur. Their work clearly suggests that sulfide must be incorporated into thiosulfate (and that the outer S must become the inner S in $SSO_3{}^{-2}$) prior to its oxidation to sulfate and, also, that $SO_3{}^{-2}$ formed from $SSO_3{}^{-2}$ is not reincorporated into $SSO_3{}^{-2}$ to any extent:

$$2HS^- + 2O_2 \rightarrow (SSO_3)^{-2} + H_2O \qquad 1.$$

$$(SSO_3)^{-2} + 2GSH \rightarrow HS^- + HSO_3{}^- + GSSG \qquad 2.$$

$$SO_3{}^{-2} + \tfrac{1}{2}O_2 \rightarrow SO_4{}^{-2} \qquad 3.$$

The results obtained by Szczepkowski et al (207) in tracer experiments with intact rats suggest that thiosulfate is a normal intermediate in the production of sulfate from Cys in the animal. When a large excess of unlabeled thiosulfate was injected at the same time as $[^{35}S]$cystine, the excretion of radioactive sulfur as urinary thiosulfate was about 20-fold that of control rats who did not receive thiosulfate, and the excretion of radioactive sulfur as urinary sulfate was markedly reduced. The appearance of increased urinary levels of thiosulfate as well as of sulfite in individuals with sulfite oxidase deficiency due to inborn errors of metabolism (93, 175) or dietary molybdenum deficiency (1) also supports a central role of thiosulfate in sulfur metabolism. Because mammalian tissues do not have an enzymatic system for reducing sulfite or sulfate to sulfide, incorporation of $^{35}S$ from $[^{35}S]$Cys into thiosulfate also indicates that sulfur is released from Cys as sulfane sulfur.

Sulfane sulfur appears to be incorporated into some pool of reduced sulfur that has a relatively long half-life in the intact animal. In contrast to the rapid excretion of label from injected $(S \cdot {}^{35}SO_3)^{-2}$ or ${}^{35}SO_4{}^{-2}$, labeled sulfur from injected $({}^{35}S \cdot SO_3)^{-2}$ or from metabolized [$^{35}$S]Met or [$^{35}$S]Cys is slowly excreted in the urine (34, 107, 181, 193, 194). Schneider & Westley (167) demonstrated the existence of a slowly metabolized pool of sulfur that was formed from the outer but not the inner sulfur of thiosulfate. They suggested, based on studies in intact rats, that elemental sulfur associated with protein and polythionate sulfur $({}^{-}O_3SS_nSO_3{}^{-})$ are likely possibilities for the form of this retained intermediate that is subsequently slowly metabolized to provide reduced sulfur. Thus, it is conceivable that Cys is metabolized by pathways that involve release of sulfide followed by incorporation of the sulfur into some pool of reduced sulfur that has a relatively long half-life prior to its oxidation to sulfate.

## SUMMARY AND CONCLUSIONS

Met metabolism occurs primarily by activation of Met to AdoMet and further metabolism of AdoMet by either the transmethylation-transsulfuration pathway or the polyamine biosynthetic pathway. The catabolism of the methyl group and sulfur atom of Met ultimately appears to be dependent upon the transmethylation-transsulfuration pathway because the MTA formed as the co-product of polyamine synthesis is efficiently recycled to Met. On the other hand, the fate of the four-carbon chain of Met appears to depend upon the initial fate of the Met molecule. During transsulfuration, the carbon chain is released as α-ketobutyrate, which is further metabolized to $CO_2$. In the polyamine pathway, the carboxyl carbon of Met is lost in the formation of dAdoMet, whereas the other three carbons are ultimately excreted as polyamine derivatives and degradation products.

The role of the transamination pathway of Met metabolism is not firmly established. Cys (which may be formed from the sulfur of Met and the carbons of serine via the transsulfuration pathway) appears to be converted to taurine and $CO_2$ primarily by the cysteinesulfinate pathway, and to sulfate and pyruvate primarily by desulfuration pathways in which a reduced form of sulfur with a relatively long biological half-life appears to be an intermediate. With the exception of the nitrogen of Met that is incorporated into polyamines, the nitrogen of Met or Cys is incorporated into urea after it is released as ammonium [in the reactions catalyzed by cystathionase with either cystathionine (from Met) or cystine (from Cys) as substrate] or it is transferred to a keto acid (in Cys or Met transamination).

Many areas of sulfur-containing amino acid metabolism need further study. The magnitude of AdoMet flux through the polyamine pathway in the intact animal as well as details about the reactions involved in this pathway remain to be determined. Both the pathways and the possible physiological role of alternate (AdoMet-independent) Met metabolism, including the transamination pathway, must be elucidated. Despite the growing interest in taurine, investigation of Cys metabolism has been a relatively inactive area during the past two decades. Apparent discrepancies in the reported data on Cys metabolism need to be resolved. Future work should consider the role of extrahepatic tissues in amino acid metabolism as well as species differences in the relative roles of various pathways in the metabolism of Met and Cys.

*Literature Cited*


1. Abumrad, N. N., Schneider, A. J., Steel, D., Rogers, L. S. 1981. Amino acid intolerance during prolonged total parenteral nutrition reversed by molybdate therapy. *Am. J. Clin. Nutr.* 34: 2551–59
2. Aguilar, T. S. 1981. Importance of serine formation and choline supply in methionine methyl carbon oxidation in the rat. *Acta Cient. Venezolana* 32:314–23
3. Aguilar, T. S., Benevenga, N. J., Harper, A. E. 1974. Effect of dietary methionine level on its metabolism in rats. *J. Nutr.* 104:761–71
4. Akagi, R. 1982. Purification and characterization of cysteine aminotransferase from rat liver cytosol. *Acta Med. Okayama* 36:187–97
5. Awad, W. M. Jr., Whitney, P. L., Skiba, W. E., Mangum, J. H., Wells, M. S. 1983. Evidence for direct methyl transfer in betaine: homocysteine S-methyltransferase. *J. Biol. Chem.* 258:12790–92
6. Backlund, P. S. Jr., Chang, C. P., Smith, R. A. 1982. Identification of 2-keto-4-methylthiobutyrate as an intermediate compound in methionine synthesis from 5'-methylthioadenosine. *J. Biol. Chem.* 257:4196–4202
7. Backlund, P. S. Jr., Smith, R. A. 1981. Methionine synthesis from 5'-methylthioadenosine in rat liver. *J. Biol. Chem.* 256:1533–35
8. Barak, A. J., Beckenhauer, H. C., Tuma, D. J. 1982. Use of S-adenosylmethionine as an index of methionine recycling in rat liver slices. *Anal. Biochem.* 127:372–75
9. Beatty, P. W., Reed, D. J. 1980. Involvement of the cystathionine pathway in the biosynthesis of glutathione by isolated hepatocytes. *Arch. Biochem. Biophys.* 204:80–87
10. Benevenga, N. J. 1974. Toxicities of methionine and other amino acids. *J. Agric. Food Chem.* 22:2–9
11. Benevenga, N. J. 1984. Evidence for alternative pathways of methionine catabolism. *Adv. Nutr. Res.* 6:1–18
12. Benevenga, N. J., Eagen, A. R. 1983. Quantitative aspects of methionine metabolism. In *Sulfur Amino Acids, Biochemical and Clinical Aspects,* ed. K. Kuriyama, R. J. Huxtable, H. Iwata, pp. 327–41. New York: Liss
13. Benjamin, L. R., Steele, R. D. 1985. Hepatic cysteine sulfinate decarboxylase activity and urinary taurine excretion in rats fed varying levels of dietary protein. *Fed. Proc.* 44:1764 (Abstr.)
14. Bikel, I., Pavlatos, T. N., Livingston, D. M. 1978. Purification and subunit structure of mouse liver cystathionase. *Arch. Biochem. Biophys.* 186:168–74
15. Billings, R. E., Noker, P. E., Tephly, T. R. 1981. The role of methionine in regulating folate-dependent reactions in isolated rat hepatocytes. *Arch. Biochem. Biophys.* 208:108–20
16. Boss, G. R., Pilz, R. B. 1984. Decreased methionine synthesis in purine nucleoside-treated T and B lymphoblasts and reversal by homocysteine. *J. Clin. Invest.* 74:1262–68
17. Braunstein, A. E., Goryachenkova, E. V., Lac, N. D. 1969. Reactions catalyzed by serine sulfhydrase from chicken liver. *Biochim. Biophys. Acta* 171:366–68
18. Braunstein, A. E., Goryachenkova, E. V., Tolosa, E. A., Willhardt, I. H., Yefremova, L. L. 1971. Specificity and some other properties of liver serine sulfhydrase: Evidence for its identity with cystathionine β-synthase. *Biochim. Biophys. Acta* 242:247–60
19. Burke, G. T., Mangum, J. H., Brodie, J. D. 1970. Methylcobalamin as an intermediate in mammalian methionine biosynthesis. *Biochemistry* 9:4297–4302
20. Burke, G. T., Mangum, J. H., Brodie, J. D. 1971. Mechanism of mammalian cobalamin-dependent methionine biosynthesis. *Biochemistry* 10:3079–85
21. Cantoni, G. L., Aksamit, R. R., Kim, I.-K. 1982. Methionine biosynthesis and vidarabine therapy. *N. Engl. J. Med.* 307:1079
22. Cantoni, G. L., Chiang, P. K. 1980. The

role of S-adenosylhomocysteine and S-adenosylhomocysteine hydrolase in the control of biologic methylations. In *Natural Sulfur Compounds: Novel Biochemical and Structural Aspects,* ed. D. Cavallini, G. E. Gaull, V. Zappia, pp. 67–80. New York: Plenum
23. Cantoni, G. L., Richards, H. H., Chiang, P. K. 1979. Inhibitors of S-adenosylhomocysteine hydrolase and their role in the regulation of biological methylation. In *Transmethylation,* ed. E. Usdin, R. T. Borchardt, C. R. Creveling, pp. 155–64. New York: Elsevier/North Holland
24. Case, G. L., Benevenga, N. J. 1976. Evidence for S-adenosylmethionine-independent catabolism of methionine in the rat. *J. Nutr.* 106:1721–36
25. Case, G. L., Benevenga, N. J. 1977. Significance of formate as an intermediate in the oxidation of the methionine, S-methyl-L-cysteine and sarcosine methyl carbons to $CO_2$ in the rat. *J. Nutr.* 107:1665–76
26. Case, G. L., Mitchell, A. D., Harper, A. E., Benevenga, N. J. 1976. Significance of choline synthesis in the oxidation of the methionine methyl group in rats. *J. Nutr.* 106:735–46
27. Cavallini, D., Dupré, S., Federici, G., Solinas, S., Ricci, G., et al. 1978. Isethionic acid as a taurine co-metabolite. In *Taurine and Neurological Disorders,* ed. A. Barbeau, R. J. Huxtable, pp. 29–34. New York: Raven
28. Chesney, R. W., Gusowski, N., Dabbagh, S., Padilla, M. 1985. Renal cortex taurine concentration regulates renal adaptive response to altered dietary intake of sulfur amino acids. In *Taurine, Biological Actions and Clinical Perspectives,* ed. S. S. Oja, L. Ahtee, P. Kontro, M. K. Paasonen, pp. 33–42. New York: Liss
29. Chiang, P. K., Im, Y. S., Cantoni, G. L. 1980. Phospholipids biosynthesis by methylations and choline incorporation: Effect of 3-deazaadenosine. *Biochem. Biophys. Res. Commun.* 94:174–81
30. Chiao, F. F., Stokstad, E. L. R. 1977. Effect of methionine on hepatic folate metabolism in rats fed a vitamin $B_{12}$- and methionine-deficient diet. *Proc. Soc. Exp. Biol. Med.* 155:433–37
31. Cohen, L. M., Benevenga, N. J. 1985. Quantitation and identification of volatile sulfur evolved in the metabolism of 3-methylthiopropionate. *Fed. Proc.* 44: 800 (Abstr.)
32. Crawhall, J. C. 1978. β-Mercaptolactate-cysteine disulfiduria. In *The Metabolic Basis of Inherited Disease,* ed. J. B. Stanbury, J. B. Wyngaarden, D. S. Fredrickson, pp. 504–13. New York: McGraw-Hill. 4th ed.
33. Crawhall, J. C. 1985. A review of the clinical presentation and laboratory findings in two uncommon hereditary disorders of sulfur amino acid metabolism, β-mercaptolactate cysteine disulfideuria and sulfite oxidase deficiency. *Clin. Biochem.* 18:139–42
34. Daniels, K. M., Stipanuk, M. H. 1982. The effect of dietary cysteine level on cysteine metabolism in rats. *J. Nutr.* 112:2130–41
35. Danzin, C., Claverie, N., Wagner, J., Grove, J., Koch-Weser, J. 1982. Effect on prostatic growth of 2-difluoromethylornithine, an effective inhibitor of ornithine decarboxylase. *Biochem. J.* 202:175–81
36. Daubner, S. C., Matthews, R. G. 1982. Purification and properties of methylenetetrahydrofolate reductase from pig liver. *J. Biol. Chem.* 257:140–45
37. De La Rosa, J., Stipanuk, M. H. 1985. The oxidation of cysteine and cysteinesulfinate in rat and cat hepatocytes. *Fed. Proc.* 44:1591 (Abstr.)
38. De La Rosa, J., Stipanuk, M. H. 1985. Evidence for a rate-limiting role of cysteinesulfinate decarboxylase activity in taurine biosynthesis in vivo. *Comp. Biochem. Physiol.* 81B:565–71
39. Demetriou, A. A., Cohn, M. S., Tabor, C. W., Tabor, H. 1978. Identification of pyruvate in S-adenosylmethionine decarboxylase from rat liver. *J. Biol. Chem.* 253:1684–86
40. Dixon, J. L., Benevenga, N. J. 1980. The decarboxylation of α-keto-γ-methiolbutyrate in rat liver mitochondria. *Biochem. Biophys. Res. Commun.* 97: 939–46
41. Døskeland, S. O., Ueland, P. M. 1982. Comparison of some physicochemical and kinetic properties of S-adenosylhomocysteine hydrolase from bovine liver, bovine adrenal cortex and mouse liver. *Biochim. Biophys. Acta* 708:185–93
42. Eells, J. T., Black, K. A., Makar, A. B., Tedford, C. E., Tephly, T. R. 1982. The regulation of one-carbon oxidation in the rat by nitrous oxide and methionine. *Arch. Biochem. Biophys.* 219:316–26
43. Eloranta, T. O. 1977. Tissue distribution of S-adenosylmethionine and S-adenosylhomocysteine in the rat: Effect of age, sex and methionine administration on the metabolism of S-adenosylmethionine, S-adenosylhomocysteine and polyamines. *Biochem. J.* 166:521–29

44. Eloranta, T. O., Kajander, E. O. 1984. Catabolism and lability of S-adenosyl-L-methionine in rat liver extracts. *Biochem. J.* 224:137–44
45. Eloranta, T. O., Kajander, E. O., Raina, A. M. 1976. A new method for the assay of tissue S-adenosylhomocysteine and S-adenosylmethionine: Effect of pyridoxine deficiency on the metabolism of S-adenosylhomocysteine, S-adenosylmethionine and polyamines in rat liver. *Biochem. J.* 160:287–94
46. Eloranta, T. O., Kajander, E. O., Raina, A. M. 1982. Effect of 9-β-D-arabinofuranosyladenine and erythro-9-(2-hydoxy-3-nonyl)adenine on the metabolism of S-adenosylhomocysteine, S-adenosylmethionine, and adenosine in rat liver. *Med. Biol.* 60:272–77
47. Engstrom, M. A. 1981. *Quantitative importance of an alternative route for methionine catabolism*. PhD thesis. Univ. Wisconsin, Madison
48. Federici, G., Ricci, G., Santoro, L., Antonucci, A., Cavallini, D. 1980. Cysteamine pathway of taurine biosynthesis. See Ref. 22, pp. 195–200
49. Fellman, J. H., Avedovech, N. A. 1982. Cysteine thiosulfonate in cysteine metabolism. *Arch. Biochem. Biophys.* 218: 303–8
50. Fellman, J. H., Roth, E. S. 1981. Hypotaurine aminotransferase. *Adv. Exp. Med. Biol.* 139:99–113
51. Fellman, J. H., Roth, E. S., Avedovech, N. A., McCarthy, K. D. 1980. Mammalian hypotaurine aminotransferase, isethionate is not a product. *Life Sci.* 27:1999–2004
52. Fellman, J. H., Roth, E. S., Fujita, T. S. 1978. Taurine is not metabolized to isethionate in mammalian tissue. See Ref. 27, pp. 19–24
53. Ferro, A. J., Vanderbark, A. A., MacDonald, M. R. 1981. Inactivation of S-adenosylhomocysteine hydrolase by 5'-deoxy-5'-methylthioadenosine. *Biochem. Biophys. Res. Commun.* 100:523–31
54. Ferro, A. J., Wrobel, N. C., Nicolette, J. A. 1979. 5-Methylthioribose 1-phosphate: A product of partially purified, rat liver 5'-methylthioadenosine phosphorylase activity. *Biochim. Biophys. Acta* 570:65–73
55. Finkelstein, J. D. 1974. Methionine metabolism in mammals: The biochemical basis for homocystinuria. *Metabolism* 23:387–98
56. Finkelstein, J. D. 1979. Regulation of methionine metabolism in mammals. See Ref. 23, pp. 49–58
57. Finkelstein, J. D., Harris, B. J., Kyle, W. E. 1972. Methionine metabolism in mammals: Kinetic study of betaine-homocysteine methyltransferase. *Arch. Biochem. Biophys.* 153:320–24
58. Finkelstein, J. D., Harris, B. J., Martin, J. J., Kyle, W. E. 1982. Regulation of hepatic betaine-homocysteine methyltransferase by dietary methionine. *Biochem. Biophys. Res. Commun.* 108:344–48
59. Finkelstein, J. D., Kyle, W. E., Harris, B. J. 1971. Methionine metabolism in mammals: Regulation of homocysteine methyltransferases in rat tissue. *Arch. Biochem. Biophys.* 146:84–92
60. Finkelstein, J. D., Kyle, W. E., Harris, B. J. 1974. Methionine metabolism in mammals: Regulatory effects of S-adenosylhomocysteine. *Arch. Biochem. Biophys.* 165:774–79
61. Finkelstein, J. D., Kyle, W. E., Harris, B. J., Martin, J. J. 1982. Methionine metabolism in mammals: Concentration of metabolites in rat tissues. *J. Nutr.* 112:1011–18
62. Finkelstein, J. D., Kyle, W. E., Martin, J. J. 1975. Abnormal methionine adenosyltransferase in hypermethioninemia. *Biochem. Biophys. Res. Commun.* 66: 1491–97
63. Finkelstein, J. D., Kyle, W. E., Martin, J. J., Pick, A.-M. 1975. Activation of cystathionine synthase by adenosylmethionine and adenosylethionine. *Biochem. Biophys. Res. Commun.* 66:81–87
64. Finkelstein, J. D., Martin, J. J. 1984. Methionine metabolism in mammals: Distribution of homocysteine between competing pathways. *J. Biol. Chem.* 259:9508–13
65. Finkelstein, J. D., Martin, J. J. 1984. Inactivation of betaine-homocysteine methyltransferase by adenosylmethionine and adenosylethionine. *Biochem. Biophys. Res. Commun.* 118:14–19
66. Finkelstein, J. D., Martin, J. J., Harris, B. J., Kyle, W. E. 1983. Regulation of hepatic betaine-homocysteine methyltransferase by dietary betaine. *J. Nutr.* 113:519–21
67. Finkelstein, J. D., Mudd, S. H. 1967. Trans-sulfuration in mammals: The methionine-sparing effect of cystine. *J. Biol. Chem.* 242:873–80
68. Fox, I. H., Palella, T. D., Thompson, D., Herring, C. 1982. Adenosine metabolism: Modification by S-adenosylhomocysteine and 5'-methylthioadenosine. *Arch. Biochem. Biophys.* 215:302–8
69. Fujioka, M., Takata, Y. 1981. S-Adenosylhomocysteine hydrolase from

rat liver: Purification and some properties. *J. Biol. Chem.* 256:1631–35

70. Garbers, D. L. 1978. Demonstration of 5'-methylthioadenosine phosphorylase activity in various rat tissues. *Biochim. Biophys. Acta* 523:82–93
71. Gaull, G. E., Tallan, H. H., Lonsdale, D., Pyzyrembel, H., Schaffner, F., von Bassewitz, D. B. 1981. Hypermethioninemia associated with methionine adenosyltransferase deficiency: Clinical, morphologic, and biochemical observations on four patients. *J. Pediatr.* 98: 734–41
72. Giulidori, P., Galli-Kienle, M., Catto, E., Stramentinoli, G. 1984. Transmethylation, transsulfuration, and aminopropylation reactions of S-adenosyl-L-methionine in vivo. *J. Biol. Chem.* 259: 4205–11
73. Griffith, O. W. 1983. Cysteinesulfinate metabolism: Altered partitioning between transamination and decarboxylation following administration of β-methyleneaspartate. *J. Biol. Chem.* 258: 1591–98
74. Grzelakowska-Sztabert, B., Balińska, M. 1980. Induction of betaine: homocysteine methyltransferase in some murine cells cultured in vitro. *Biochim. Biophys. Acta* 632:164–72
75. Guion-Rain, M.-C., Portemer, C., Chatagner, F. 1975. Rat liver cysteine sulfinate decarboxylase: Purification, new appraisal of the molecular weight and determination of catalytic properties. *Biochim. Biophys. Acta* 384:265–76
76. Hardison, W. G. M., Wood, C. A., Proffitt, J. H. 1977. Quantitation of taurine synthesis in the intact rat and cat liver. *Proc. Soc. Exp. Biol. Med.* 155:55–58
77. Harpey, J.-P., Rosenblatt, D. S., Cooper, B. A., Moël, G. L., Roy, C., Lafourcade, J. 1981. Homocystinuria caused by 5,10-methylenetetrahydrofolate reductase deficiency: A case in an infant responding to methionine, folinic acid, pyridoxine, and vitamin $B_{12}$ therapy. *J. Pediatr.* 98:275–78
78. Helland, S., Ueland, P. M. 1983. S-Adenosylhomocysteine and S-adenosylhomocysteine hydrolase in various tissues of mice given injections of 9-β-D-arabinofuranosyladenine. *Cancer Res.* 43:1847–50
79. Hepner, G. W., Sturman, J. A., Hofmann, A. F., Thomas, P. J. 1973. Metabolism of steroid and amino acid moieties of conjugated bile acids in man. II. Cholytaurine (taurocholic acid). *J. Clin. Invest.* 52:433–40
80. Hibasami, H., Borchardt, R. T., Chen, S. Y., Coward, J. K., Pegg, A. E. 1980. Studies of inhibition of rat spermidine synthase and spermine synthase. *Biochem. J.* 187:419–28
81. Hibasami, H., Hoffman, J. L., Pegg, A. E. 1980. Decarboxylated S-adenosylmethionine in mammalian cells. *J. Biol. Chem.* 255:6675–78
82. Hirschberger, L. L., De La Rosa, J., Stipanuk, M. H. 1985. Determination of cysteinesulfinate, hypotaurine and taurine in physiological samples by reversed-phase liquid chromatography. *J. Chromatogr.* 343:303–13
83. Hoffman, D. R., Cornatzer, W. E., Duerre, J. A. 1979. Relationship between tissue levels of S-adenosylmethionine, S-adenosylhomocysteine, and transmethylation reactions. *Can. J. Biochem.* 57:56–65
84. Hoffman, D. R., Marion, D. W., Cornatzer, W. E., Duerre, J. A. 1980. S-Adenosylmethionine and S-adenosylhomocysteine metabolism in isolated rat liver: Effects of L-methionine, L-homocysteine, and adenosine. *J. Biol. Chem.* 255:10822–27
85. Hollowell, J. G. Jr., Hall, W. K., Coryell, M. E., McPherson, J. Jr., Hahn, D. A. 1969. Homocystinuria and organic aciduria in a patient with vitamin-$B_{12}$ deficiency. *Lancet* 2:1428
86. Hopkins, D., Manchester, K. L. 1980. Control of activity of S-adenosylmethionine decarboxylase in muscle by spermidine. *FEBS Lett.* 109:299–302
87. Huovinen, J. A., Gustafsson, B. E. 1967. Inorganic sulphate, sulphite and sulphide as sulphur donors in the biosynthesis of sulphur amino acids in germ-free and conventional rats. *Biochim. Biophys. Acta* 136:441–47
88. Huxtable, R., Bressler, R. 1976. The metabolism of cysteamine to taurine. In *Taurine,* ed. R. Huxtable, A. Barbeau, pp. 45–57. New York: Raven
89. Iizasa, T., Carson, D. A. 1985. Differential regulation of polyamine synthesis and transmethylation reactions in methylthioadenosine phosphorylase deficient mammalian cells. *Biochim. Biophys. Acta* 844:280–87
90. Ishimoto, Y. 1979. Transaminative pathway of cysteine metabolism in rat tissues. *Physiol. Chem. Phys.* 11:189–91
91. Jägerstad, M., Åkesson, B., Fehling, C. 1980. Effect of methionine on the metabolic fate of liver folates in vitamin $B_{12}$-deficient rats. *Br. J. Nutr.* 44:361–69
92. Jänne, J., Pösö, H., Raina, A. 1978. Polyamines in rapid growth and cancer. *Biochim. Biophys. Acta* 473:241–93

93. Johnson, J. L., Waud, W. R., Rajagopalan, K. V., Duran, M., Beemer, F. A. 1980. Inborn errors of molybdenum metabolism: Combined deficiencies of sulfite oxidase and xanthine dehydrogenase in a patient lacking the molybdenum cofactor. *Proc. Natl. Acad. Sci. USA* 77:3715–19
94. Kajander, E. O. 1982. Inactivation of liver S-adenosylhomocysteine hydrolase in vitro of rats treated with erythro-9-(2-hydroxynon-3-yl)-adenine. *Biochem. J.* 205:585–92
95. Kajander, E. O., Raina, A. M. 1981. Affinity-chromatographic purification of S-adenosyl-L-homocysteine hydrolase: Some properties of the enzyme from rat liver. *Biochem. J.* 193:503–12
96. Kamatani, N., Carson, D. A. 1981. Dependence of adenine production upon polyamine synthesis in cultured human lymphoblasts. *Biochim. Biophys. Acta* 675:344–50
97. Keating, J. N., Weir, D. G., Scott, J. M. 1985. Demonstration of methionine synthetase in the intestinal mucosal cells of the rat. *Fed. Proc.* 44:1396 (Abstr.)
98. Kerr, S. J. 1972. Competing methyltransferase systems. *J. Biol. Chem.* 247: 4248–52
99. Kohashi, N., Yamaguchi, K., Hosokawa, Y., Kori, Y., Fujii, O., Ueda, I. 1978. Dietary control of cysteine dioxygenase in rat liver. *J. Biochem.* 84:159–68
100. Koj, A., Frendo, J., Janik, Z. 1967. [$^{35}$S]Thiosulphate oxidation by rat liver mitochondria in the presence of glutathione. *Biochem. J.* 103:791–95
101. Kontro, P., Oja, S. S. 1980. Hypotaurine oxidation by mouse tissues. See Ref. 22, pp. 201–12
102. Koraćević, D., Djordjević, V. 1977. Effect of trypsin, S-adenosylmethionine and ethionine on L-serine sulfhydrase activity. *Experientia* 33:1010–11
103. Kraus, J., Packman, S., Fowler, B., Rosenberg, L. E. 1978. Purification and properties of cystathionine β-synthase from human liver: Evidence for identical subunits. *J. Biol. Chem.* 253:6523–28
104. Kraus, J. P., Rosenberg, L. E. 1983. Cystathionine β-synthase from human liver: Improved purification scheme and additional characterization of the enzyme in crude and pure form. *Arch. Biochem. Biophys.* 222:44–52
105. Krebs, H. A., Hems, R., Tyler, B. 1976. The regulation of folate and methionine metabolism. *Biochem. J.* 158:341–53
106. Kredich, N. M., Hershfield, M. S., Johnston, J. M. 1979. Role of adenosine metabolism in transmethylation. See Ref. 23, pp. 225–30
107. Krijgsheld, K. R., Frankena, H., Scholtens, E., Zweens, J., Mulder, G. J. 1979. Absorption, serum levels and urinary excretion of inorganic sulfate after oral administration of sodium sulfate in the conscious rat. *Biochim. Biophys. Acta* 586:492–500
108. Krijgsheld, K. R., Glazenburg, E. J., Scholtens, E., Mulder, G. J. 1981. The oxidation of L- and D-cysteine to inorganic sulfate and taurine in the rat. *Biochim. Biophys. Acta* 677:7–12
109. Kutzbach, C., Stokstad, E. L. R. 1971. Mammalian methylenetetrahydrofolate reductase: Partial purification, properties, and inhibition by S-adenosylmethionine. *Biochim. Biophys. Acta* 250:459–77
110. Lak, N. D., Goryachenkova, E. V., Braunstein, A. E. 1970. Investigation of substrate specificity of serine sulfhydrase from the hen liver and its relation to some inhibitors. *Biokhimia* 35:270–77
111. Laster, L., Mudd, S. H., Finkelstein, J. D., Irreverre, F. 1965. Homocystinuria due to cystathionine synthase deficiency: The metabolism of L-methionine. *J. Clin. Invest.* 44:1708–19
112. Liau, M. C., Chang, C. F., Belanger, L., Grenier, A. 1979. Correlation of isozyme patterns of S-adenosylmethionine synthetase with fetal stages and pathological states of the liver. *Cancer Res.* 39:162–69
113. Liau, M. C., Chang, C. F., Giovanella, B. C. 1980. Demonstration of an altered S-adenosylmethionine synthetase in human malignant tumors xenografted into athymic nude mice. *J. Natl. Cancer Inst.* 64:1071–75
114. Livesey, G. 1984. Methionine degradation: "anabolic and catabolic." *Trends Biochem. Sci.* 9:27–29
115. Livesey, G., Lund, P. 1980. Methionine metabolism via the transamination pathway in rat liver. *Biochem. Soc. Trans.* 8:540–41
116. Lombardini, J. B., Sufrin, J. R. 1983. Chemotherapeutic potential of methionine analogue inhibitors of tumor-derived methionine adenosyltransferases. *Biochem. Pharmacol.* 32:489–95
117. Loriette, C., Pasantes-Morales, H., Portemer, C., Chatagner, F. 1979. Dietary casein levels and taurine supplementation: Effects on cysteine dioxygenase and cysteine sulfinate decarboxylase activities and taurine concentration in brain, liver and kidney of the rat. *Nutr. Metab.* 23:467–75

118. Lumb, M., Deacon, R., Perry, J., Chanarin, I., Minty, B., et al. 1980. The effect of nitrous oxide inactivation of vitamin $B_{12}$ on rat hepatic folate: Implications for the methylfolate-trap hypothesis. *Biochem. J.* 186:933–36
119. Lumb, M., Sharer, N., Deacon, R., Jennings, P., Purkiss, P., et al. 1983. Effects of nitrous oxide–induced inactivation of cobalamin on methionine and S-adenosylmethionine metabolism in the rat. *Biochim. Biophys. Acta* 756:354–59
120. Makar, A. B., Tephly, T. R. 1983. Effect of nitrous oxide and methionine treatments on hepatic S-adenosylmethionine and methylation reactions in the rat. *Mol. Pharmacol.* 24:124–28
121. Mamont, P. S., Danzin, C., Wagner, J., Siat, M., Joder-Ohlenbusch, A.-M., Claverie, N. 1982. Accumulation of decarboxylated adenosyl-L-methionine in mammalian cells as a consequence of the inhibition of putrescine biosynthesis. *Eur. J. Biochem.* 123:499–504
122. Mamont, P. S., Joder-Ohlenbusch, A.-M., Nussli, M., Grove, J. 1981. Indirect evidence for a strict negative control of S-adenosyl-L-methionine decarboxylase by spermidine in rat hepatoma cells. *Biochem. J.* 196:411–22
123. Mangum, J. H., North, J. A. 1971. Isolation of a cobalamin containing 5-methyltetrahydrofolate-homocysteine transmethylase from mammalian kidney. *Biochemistry* 10:3765–69
124. Mangum, J. H., Smith, M. R., Awad, W. M. Jr. 1985. Methionine biosynthesis: The purification and characterization of methionine synthetase. *Fed. Proc.* 44:1214 (Abstr.)
125. Martin, W. G., Sass, N. L., Hill, L., Tarka, S., Truex, R. 1972. The synthesis of taurine from sulfate. IV. An alternate pathway for taurine synthesis by the rat. *Proc. Soc. Exp. Biol. Med.* 141:632–33
126. Mitchell, A. D., Benevenga, N. J. 1976. Importance of sarcosine formation in methionine methyl carbon oxidation in the rat. *J. Nutr.* 106:1702–13
127. Mitchell, A. D., Benevenga, N. J. 1976. The role of transamination in methionine oxidation in the rat. *J. Nutr.* 108:67–78
128. Moore, P., Swendseid, M. E. 1983. Dietary regulation of the activities of ornithine decarboxylase and S-adenosylmethionine decarboxylase in rats. *J. Nutr.* 113:1927–35
129. Mudd, S. H., Ebert, M. H., Scriver, C. R. 1980. Labile methyl group balances in the human: The role of sarcosine. *Metabolism* 29:707–20
130. Mudd, S. H., Levy, H. L. 1978. Disorders of transsulfuration. See Ref. 32, pp. 458–503
131. Mudd, S. H., Levy, H. L., Morrow, G. III. 1970. Deranged $B_{12}$ metabolism: Effects on sulfur amino acid metabolism. *Biochem. Med.* 4:193–214
132. Mudd, S. H., Poole, J. R. 1975. Labile methyl balances for normal humans on various dietary regimens. *Metabolism* 24:721–35
133. Nakagawa, H., Kimura, H. 1968. Purification and properties of cystathionine synthetase from rat liver: Separation of cystathionine synthetase from serine dehydratase. *Biochem. Biophys. Res. Commun.* 32:208–14
134. Oden, K. L., Clarke, S. 1983. S-Adenosyl-L-methionine synthetase from human erythrocytes: Role in the regulation of cellular S-adenosylmethionine levels. *Biochemistry* 22:2978–86
135. Oertel, W. H., Schmechel, D. E., Weise, V. K., Ransom, D. H., Tappaz, M. L., et al. 1981. Comparison of cysteine sulphinic acid decarboxylase isoenzymes and glutamic acid decarboxylase in rat liver and brain. *Neuroscience* 6:2701–14
136. Ogawa, H., Fujioka, M. 1982. Induction of rat liver glycine methyltransferase by high methionine diet. *Biochem. Biophys. Res. Commun.* 108:227–32
137. Oja, S. S., Kontro, P. 1981. Oxidation of hypotaurine in vitro by mouse liver and brain tissues. *Biochim. Biophys. Acta* 677:350–57
138. Okada, G., Teraoka, H., Tsukada, K. 1981. Multiple species of mammalian S-adenosylmethionine synthetase: Partial purification and characterization. *Biochemistry* 20:934–40
139. Okada, G., Watanabe, Y., Tsukada, K. 1980. Changes in patterns of S-adenosylmethionine synthetases in fetal and postnatal rat liver. *Cancer Res.* 40:2895–97
140. Pajula, R.-L., Raina, A., Eloranta, T. 1979. Polyamine synthesis in mammalian tissues: Isolation and characterization of spermine synthase from bovine brain. *Eur. J. Biochem.* 101:619–26
141. Pasantes-Morales, H., Chatagner, F., Mandel, P. 1980. Synthesis of taurine in rat liver and brain in vivo. *Neurochem. Res.* 5:441–51
142. Pascal, T. A., Tallan, H. H., Gillam, B. M. 1972. Hepatic cystathionase: Immunochemical and electrophoretic studies of the human and rat forms. *Biochim. Biophys. Acta* 285:48–59

143. Pegg, A. E. 1977. Evidence for the presence of pyruvate in rat liver S-adenosylmethionine decarboxylase. *FEBS Lett.* 84:33–36
144. Pegg, A. E. 1984. The role of polyamine depletion and accumulation of decarboxylated S-adenosylmethionine in the inhibition of growth of SV-3T3 cells treated with α-difluoromethylornithine. *Biochem. J.* 224:29–38
145. Pegg, A. E. 1984. S-Adenosylmethionine decarboxylase: a brief review. *Cell Biochem. Funct.* 2:11–15
146. Pegg, A. E., Borchardt, R. T., Coward, J. K. 1981. Effects of inhibitors of spermidine and spermine synthesis on polyamine concentrations and growth of transformed mouse fibroblasts. *Biochem. J.* 194:79–89
147. Pegg, A. E., Coward, J. K. 1981. Inhibition of aminopropyltransferases. *Adv. Polyamine Res.* 3:153–61
148. Pegg, A. E., Hibasami, H. 1980. Polyamine metabolism during cardiac hypertrophy. *Am. J. Physiol.* 233:E372–78
149. Pegg, A. E., Hibasami, H., Matsui, I., Bethell, D. 1981. Formation and interconversion of putrescine and spermidine in mammalian cells. *Adv. Enzyme Regul.* 19:427–51
150. Pegg, A. E., McCann, P. P. 1982. Polyamine metabolism and function. *Am. J. Physiol.* 243:C212–21
151. Pegg, A. E., Pösö, H., Shuttleworth, K., Bennett, R. A. 1982. Effect of inhibition of polyamine synthesis on the content of decarboxylated S-adenosylmethionine. *Biochem. J.* 202:519–26
152. Pegg, A. E., Tang, K.-C., Coward, J. K. 1982. Effects of S-adenosyl-1,8-deamino-3-thiooctane on polyamine metabolism. *Biochemistry* 21:5082–89
153. Pierre, Y., Loriette, C., Chatagner, F. 1980. Metabolism of hypotaurine in some organs of the rat. See Ref. 22, pp. 195–200
154. Piik, K., Rajamäki, P., Guha, S. K., Jänne, J. 1977. Regulation of L-ornithine decarboxylase and S-adenosyl-L-methionine decarboxylase in rat ventral prostate and seminal vesicle. *Biochem. J.* 168: 379–85
155. Poole, J. R., Mudd, S. H., Conerly, E. B., Edwards, W. A. 1975. Homocystinuria due to cystathionine synthase deficiency: Studies of nitrogen balance and sulfur excretion. *J. Clin. Invest.* 55: 1033–48
156. Porter, P. N., Grishaver, M. S., Jones, O. W. 1974. Characterization of human cystathionine β-synthase: Evidence for the identity of human L-serine dehydratase and cystathionine β-synthase. *Biochim. Biophys. Acta* 364:128–39
157. Pösö, H., Hannonen, P., Himberg, J.-J., Jänne, J. 1976. Adenosylmethionine decarboxylase from various organisms: Relation of the putrescine activation of the enzyme to the ability of the organism to synthesize spermine. *Biochem. Biophys. Res. Commun.* 68:227–34
158. Pösö, H., Pegg, A. E. 1981. Differences between tissues in response of S-adenosylmethionine decarboxylase to administration of polyamines. *Biochem. J.* 200:629–37
159. Pritchard, P. H., Vance, D. E. 1981. Choline metabolism and phosphatidylcholine biosynthesis in cultured rat hepatocytes. *Biochem. J.* 196:261–67
160. Ragione, F. D., Pegg, A. E. 1983. Effect of analogues of 5'-methylthioadenosine on cellular metabolism: Inactivation of S-adenosylhomocysteine hydrolase by 5'-isobutylthioadenosine. *Biochem. J.* 210:429–35
161. Raina, A., Pajula, R.-L., Eloranta, T. 1976. A rapid assay method for spermidine and spermine synthases: Distribution of polyamine-synthesizing enzymes and methionine adenosyltransferase in rat tissues. *FEBS Lett.* 67:252–55
162. Recasens, M., Benezra, R., Basset, P., Mandel, P. 1980. Cysteine sulfinate aminotransferase and aspartate aminotransferase isoenzymes of rat brain: Purification, characterization, and further evidence for identity. *Biochemistry* 19: 4583–89
163. Sakai, T., Hori, C., Kano, K., Oka, T. 1979. Purification and characterization of S-adenosyl-L-methionine decarboxylase from mouse mammary gland and liver. *Biochemistry* 18:5541–48
164. Samejima, K., Yamanoha, B. 1982. Purification of spermidine synthase from rat ventral prostate by affinity chromatography on immobilized S-adenosyl (5')-3-thiopropylamine. *Arch. Biochem. Biophys.* 216:213–22
165. Scandurra, R., Federici, G., Dupré, S., Cavallini, D. 1978. Taurine and isethionic acid production in mammals. *Bull. Mol. Biol. Med.* 3:141–47
166. Schlenk, F. 1983. Methylthioadenosine. *Adv. Enzymol.* 54:195–265
167. Schneider, J. F., Westley, J. 1969. Metabolic interrelations of sulfur in proteins, thiosulfate, and cystine. *J. Biol. Chem.* 244:5735–44
168. Schrader, J., Schütz, W., Bardenheuer, H. 1981. Role of S-adenosylhomocysteine hydrolase in adenosine metabolism in mammalian heart. *Biochem. J.* 196: 65–70

169. Schuh, S., Rosenblatt, D. S., Cooper, B. A., Schroeder, M.-L., Bishop, A. J., et al. 1984. Homocystinuria and megaloblastic anemia responsive to vitamin $B_{12}$ therapy: An inborn error of metabolism due to a defect in cobalamin metabolism. *N. Engl. J. Med.* 310:686–90
170. Scott, J. M., Weir, D. G. 1981. The methyl folate trap. *Lancet* 2:337–40
171. Seidenfeld, J., Wilson, J., Williams-Ashman, H. G. 1980. Androgenic regulation of 5'-deoxy-5'-methylthioadenosine concentrations and methylthioadenosine phosphorylase activity in relation to polyamine metabolism of rat prostate. *Biochem. Biophys. Res. Commun.* 95:1861–68
172. Seiler, N., Bolkenius, F. N., Knödgen, B. 1985. The influence of catabolic reactions on polyamine excretion. *Biochem. J.* 225:219–26
173. Seyfried, C. E., Oleinik, O. E., Degen, J. L., Resing, K., Morris, D. R. 1982. Purification, properties and regulation of the level of bovine S-adenosylmethionine decarboxylase during lymphocyte mitogenesis. *Biochim. Biophys. Acta* 716: 169–77
174. Shane, B., Stokstad, E. L. R. 1985. Vitamin $B_{12}$–folate interrelationships. *Ann. Rev. Nutr.* 5:115–41
175. Shih, V. E., Abroms, I. F., Johnson, J. L., Carney, M., Mandell, R., et al. 1977. Sulfite oxidase deficiency: Biochemical and clinical investigations of a hereditary metabolic disorder in sulfur metabolism. *N. Engl. J. Med.* 297:1022–28
176. Shin, H. K., Linkswiler, H. M. 1974. Tryptophan and methionine metabolism of adult females as affected by vitamin B-6 deficiency. *J. Nutr.* 104:1348–55
177. Shinnar, S., Singer, H. S. 1984. Cobalamin C mutation (methylmalonic aciduria and homocystinuria) in adolescence: A treatable cause of dementia and myelopathy. *N. Engl. J. Med.* 311:451–54
178. Shirahata, A., Pegg, A. E. 1985. Regulation of S-adenosylmethionine decarboxylase activity in rat liver and prostate. *J. Biol. Chem.* 260:9583–88
179. Simpson, R. C., Freedland, R. A. 1975. Relative importance of the two major pathways for the conversion of cysteine to glucose in the perfused rat liver. *J. Nutr.* 105:1440–46
180. Singer, T. P., Kearney, E. B. 1956. Intermediary metabolism of L-cysteinesulfinic acid in animal tissues. *Arch. Biochem. Biophys.* 61:397–409
181. Skarżyński, B., Szczepkowski, T. W., Weber, M. 1959. Thiosulphate metabolism in the animal organism. *Nature* 184:994–95
182. Skiba, W. E., Taylor, M. P., Wells, M. S., Mangum, J. H., Awad, W. M. Jr. 1982. Human hepatic methionine biosynthesis: Purification and characterization of betaine:homocysteine S-methyltransferase. *J. Biol. Chem.* 257:14944–48
183. Skovby, F., Kraus, J. P., Rosenberg, L. E. 1984. Biosynthesis of human cystathionine β-synthase in cultured fibroblasts. *J. Biol. Chem.* 259:583–87
184. Skovby, F., Kraus, J. P., Rosenberg, L. E. 1984. Biosynthesis and proteolytic activation of cystathionine β-synthase in rat liver. *J. Biol. Chem.* 259: 588–93
185. Smolin, L. A., Benevenga, N. J. 1982. Accumulation of homocyst(e)ine in vitamin B-6 deficiency: A model for the study of cystathionine β-synthase deficiency. *J. Nutr.* 112:1264–72
186. Smolin, L. A., Benevenga, N. J., Berlow, S. 1981. The use of betaine for the treatment of homocystinuria. *J. Pediatr.* 99:467–72
187. Sowers, J. E., Stockland, W. L., Meade, R. J. 1972. L-Methionine and L-cystine requirements of the growing rat. *J. Anim. Sci.* 35:782–88
188. Spaeth, D. G., Schneider, D. L. 1976. Turnover of taurine in rat tissues. *J. Nutr.* 104:179–86
189. Spector, R., Coakley, G., Blakely, R. 1980. Methionine recycling in brain: A role for folates and vitamin $B_{12}$. *J. Neurochem.* 34:132–37
190. Steele, R. D., Barber, T. A., Lalich, J., Benevenga, N. J. 1979. Effects of dietary 3-methylthiopropionate on metabolism, growth and hematopoiesis in the rat. *J. Nutr.* 109:1739–51
191. Steele, R. D., Benevenga, N. J. 1978. Identification of 3-methylthiopropionic acid as an intermediate in mammalian methionine metabolism in vitro. *J. Biol. Chem.* 253:7844–50
192. Steele, R. D., Benevenga, N. J. 1979. The metabolism of 3-methylthiopropionate in rat liver homogenates. *J. Biol. Chem.* 254:8885–90
193. Stipanuk, M. H. 1977. *Interrelationships of methionine and cyst(e)ine metabolism.* PhD thesis. Univ. Wisconsin, Madison
194. Stipanuk, M. H. 1979. Effect of excess dietry methionine on the catabolism of cysteine in rats. *J. Nutr.* 109:2126–39
195. Stipanuk, M. H., Beck, P. W. 1982. Characterization of the enzymic capacity for cysteine desulphydration in liver and kidney of the rat. *Biochem. J.* 206:267–77

196. Stipanuk, M. H., Benevenga, N. J. 1977. Effect of cystine on the metabolism of methionine in rats. *J. Nutr.* 107:1455–67
197. Stipanuk, M. H., Drake, M. R., De La Rosa, J. 1985. Pathways of cysteine catabolism in rat hepatocytes. *Fed. Proc.* 44:1591 (Abstr.)
198. Stipanuk, M. H., King, K. M. 1982. Characteristics of the enzymatic capacity for cysteine desulfhydration in cat tissues. *Comp. Biochem. Physiol.* 73B: 595–601
199. Stipanuk, M. H., Rotter, M. A. 1984. Metabolism of cysteine, cysteinesulfinate and cysteinesulfonate in rats fed adequate and excess levels of sulfur-containing amino acids. *J. Nutr.* 114: 1426–37
200. Stockland, W. L., Meade, R. J., Wass, D. F., Sowers, J. E. 1973. Influence of levels of methionine and cystine on the total sulfur amino acids requirements of the growing rat. *J. Anim. Sci.* 36:526–30
201. Sturman, J. A. 1973. Taurine pool sizes in the rat: Effects of vitamin-$B_6$ deficiency and high taurine diet. *J. Nutr.* 103:1566–80
202. Sturman, J. A., Beratis, N. G., Guarini, L., Gaull, G. E. 1980. Transsulfuration by human long-term lymphoid lines: Normal and cystathionase-deficient cells. *J. Biol. Chem.* 255:4763–65
203. Sturman, J. A., Cohen, P. A., Gaull, G. E. 1970. Metabolism of L-$^{35}$S-methionine in vitamin $B_6$ deficiency: Observations on cystathioninuria. *Biochem. Med.* 3:510–23
204. Sturman, J. A., Fellman, J. H. 1983. Methionine metabolism in the rat: Accumulation of hypotaurine after partial hepatectomy. See Ref. 12, pp. 435–47
205. Sturman, J. A., Hepner, G. W., Hofmann, A. F., Thomas, P. J. 1975. Metabolism of [$^{35}$S]taurine in man. *J. Nutr.* 105:1206–14
206. Sullivan, D. M., Hoffman, J. L. 1983. Fractionation and kinetic properties of rat liver and kidney methionine adenosyltransferase isozymes. *Biochemistry* 22: 1641–45
207. Szczepkowski, T. W., Skarżyński, B., Weber, M. 1961. The metabolic state of thiosulphate. *Nature* 189:1007–8
208. Tabor, C. W., Tabor, H. 1984. Polyamines. *Ann. Rev. Biochem.* 53: 749–90
209. Tallan, H. H. 1979. Methionine adenosyltransferase in man: Evidence for multiple forms. *Biochem. Med.* 21:129–40
210. Tamura, J., Ohkuma, S., Ida, S., Zuo, P. P., Kuriyama, K. 1984. Cysteine uptake and taurine biosynthesis in freshly isolated and primary cultured rat hepatocytes. *Cell Biochem. Funct.* 2:195–200
211. Tateishi, N., Higashi, T., Naruse, A., Hikita, K., Sakamoto, Y. 1981. Relative contributions of sulfur atoms of dietary cysteine and methionine to rat liver glutathione and proteins. *J. Biochem.* 90: 1603–10
212. Tateishi, N., Hirasawa, M., Higashi, T., Sakamoto, Y. 1982. The L-methionine-sparing effect of dietary glutathione in rats. *J. Nutr.* 112:2217–26
213. Tisdale, M. J. 1981. Effect of methionine deprivation on S-adenosylmethionine decarboxylase of tumour cells. *Biochim. Biophys. Acta* 675:366–72
214. Trackman, P. C., Abeles, R. H. 1981. The metabolism of 1-phospho-5-methylthioribose. *Biochem. Biophys. Res. Commun.* 103:1238–44
215. Trackman, P. C., Abeles, R. H. 1983. Methionine synthesis from 5'-S-methylthioadenosine: Resolution of enzyme activities and identification of 1-phospho-5-S-methylthioribulose. *J. Biol. Chem.* 258:6717–20
216. Tsukada, K., Okada, G. 1980. S-adenosylmethionine synthetase isozyme patterns from rat hepatoma induced by *N*-2-fluorenylacetamide. *Biochem. Biophys. Res. Commun.* 94:1078–82
217. Ubuka, T., Umemura, S., Yuasa, S., Kinuta, M., Watanabe, K. 1978. Purification and characterization of mitochondrial cysteine aminotransferase from rat liver. *Physiol. Chem. Phys.* 10:483–500
218. Ubuka, T., Yuasa, S., Ishimoto, Y., Shimomura, M. 1977. Desulfuration of L-cysteine through transamination and transsulfuration in rat liver. *Physiol. Chem. Phys.* 9:241–46
219. Ueland, P. M., Helland, S. 1980. S-Adenosylhomocysteinase from mouse liver: Catalytic properties at cellular enzyme level. *J. Biol. Chem.* 255:7722–27
220. Ueland, P. M., Helland, S. 1983. Binding of adenosine to intracellular S-adenosylhomocysteine hydrolase in isolated rat hepatocytes. *J. Biol. Chem.* 258:747–52
221. Ueland, P. M., Helland, S., Broch, O. J., Schanche, J.-S. 1984. Homocysteine in tissues of the mouse and rat. *J. Biol. Chem.* 259:2360–64
222. Uren, J. R., Ragin, R., Chaykovsky, M. 1978. Modulation of cysteine metabolism in mice: Effects of propargylglycine and L-cyst(e)ine-degrading enzymes. *Biochem. Pharmacol.* 27:2807–14
223. van der Westhuyzen, J., Fernandes-Costa, F., Metz, J. 1982. Cobalamin in-

activation by nitrous oxide produces severe neurological impairment in fruit bats: Protection by methionine and aggravation by folates. *Life Sci.* 31: 2001–10
224. van der Westhuyzen, J., Metz, J. 1984. Betaine delays the onset of neurological impairment in nitrous oxide–induced vitamin B-12 deficiency in fruit bats. *J. Nutr.* 114:1106–11
225. Vidal, A. J., Stokstad, E. L. R. 1974. Urinary excretion of 5-methyltetrahydrofolate and liver S-adenosylmethionine levels of rats fed a vitamin $B_{12}$–deficient diet. *Biochim. Biophys. Acta* 362:245–57
225a. Wagner, C. 1982. Cellular folate binding proteins; function and significance. *Ann. Rev. Nutr.* 2:229–48
225b. Wagner, C. 1985. Folate-binding proteins. *Nutr. Rev.* 43:293–99
226. Wagner, J., Claverie, N., Danzin, C. 1984. A rapid high-performance liquid chromatographic procedure for the simultaneous determination of methionine, ethionine, S-adenosylmethionine, S-adenosylethionine, and the natural polyamines in rat tissues. *Anal. Biochem.* 140:108–16
227. Wainer, A. 1964. The production of sulfate from cysteine without the formation of free cysteinesulfinic acid. *Biochem. Biophys. Res. Commun.* 16:141–44
228. Wilcken, D. E. L., Wilcken, B., Dudman, N. P. B., Tyrrell, P. A. 1983. Homocystinuria: The effects of betaine in the treatment of patients not responsive to pyridoxine. *N. Engl. J. Med.* 309:448–53
229. Wittwer, A. J., Wagner, C. 1981. Identification of the folate-binding proteins of rat liver mitochondria as dimethylglycine dehydrogenase and sarcosine dehydrogenase: Flavoprotein nature and enzymatic properties of the purified proteins. *J. Biol. Chem.* 256:4109–15
230. Xue, G.-P., Snoswell, A. M. 1985. Comparative studies on the methionine synthesis in sheep and rat tissues. *Comp. Biochem. Physiol.* 80B:489–94
231. Yagi, T., Kagamiyama, H., Nozaki, M. 1979. Cysteine sulfinate transamination activity of aspartate aminotransferases. *Biochem. Biophys. Res. Commun.* 90: 447–52
232. Yamaguchi, K., Hosokawa, Y., Kohashi, N., Kori, Y., Sakakibara, S., Ueda, I. 1978. Rat liver cysteine dioxygenase (cysteine oxidase): Further purification, characterization, and analysis of the activation and inactivation. *J. Biochem.* 83:479–91
233. Yamaguchi, K., Sakakibara, S., Asamizu, J., Ueda, I. 1973. Induction and activation of cysteine oxidase of rat liver. II. The measurement of cysteine metabolism in vivo and the activation of in vivo activity of cysteine oxidase. *Biochim. Biophys. Acta* 297:48–59
234. Yamaguchi, K., Shigehisa, S., Sakakibara, S., Hosokawa, Y., Ueda, I. 1975. Cysteine metabolism in vivo of vitamin $B_6$–deficient rats. *Biochim. Biophys. Acta* 381:1–8
235. Yamanishi, T., Tuboi, S. 1981. The mechanism of the L-cystine cleavage reaction catalyzed by rat liver γ-cystathionase. *J. Biochem.* 89:1913–21
236. Yamanoha, B., Samejima, K. 1980. Inhibition of S-adenosylmethionine decarboxylase from rat liver by synthetic decarboxylated S-adenosylmethionine and its analogs. *Chem. Pharm. Bull.* 28:2232–34
237. Yao, K., Kinuta, M., Akagi, R. 1979. Cat liver cystathionase. *Physiol. Chem. Phys.* 11:257–60

*Ann. Rev. Nutr. 1986. 6:211–24*


# MONOSACCHARIDES IN HEALTH AND DISEASE

*Rachmiel Levine*

City of Hope National Medical Center, Duarte, California 91010

CONTENTS

GLUCOSE HOMEOSTASIS .......... 212
INSULIN-INDEPENDENT PATHWAYS OF GLUCOSE METABOLISM .......... 212
*The Polyol Pathway* .......... 213
EFFECT OF COMPLEX CARBOHYDRATES ON GLUCOSE TOLERANCE .......... 215
METABOLIC EFFECTS OF SPECIFIC SUGARS AND SUGAR ALCOHOLS .......... 217
*Sucrose* .......... 217
*Xylitol* .......... 218
SUMMARY .......... 219

It is difficult to conceive that a normal, important, everyday nutrient such as glucose could be the cause of chronic functional changes and permanent structural damage in many bodily tissues of man and animals. We have, over the years, accepted the atherogenic consequences of high levels of plasma cholesterol and triglycerides, particularly when they are carried as LDL. We have taken note of the damage done to nephrons by very high protein intakes. Yet, somehow, many of us have resisted the notion that an abnormally high blood glucose level could be responsible, in whole or in part, for the severe and often fatal complications of diabetes: loss of vision (retinopathy); painful damage to peripheral nerves (neuropathy); irreversible renal failure (nephropathy); and to a certain degree the increased frequency and severity of cardiac and peripheral atherosclerosis (2, 5, 51, 68, 71, 96, 115).

Experimental and clinical observations over the past 20–30 years, supported by plausible biochemical data, have brought convincing evidence that those



0199-9885/86/0715-0211$02.00

who advocated "strict" control of the blood sugar in the treatment of diabetes will be shown to have been right in this long controversy.

## GLUCOSE HOMEOSTASIS

In man and other homeothermic animals, the level of fasting blood glucose (as well as the range of its excursions when perturbed by meals, by fasting, by exercise, etc) are kept well controlled by a variety of enzymatic and hormonal factors. The diurnal curve of blood glucose in man lies between a low of about 70–80 mg% and a high of 120–130 mg% attained for a short period after a sizeable meal. These lower values of the range serve, of course, to maintain the supply of the obligatory fuel for the central nervous system. Hypoglycemia (<40 mg%) inflicts severe functional and anatomical damage on brain tissue.

But are there any damaging functional and morphological consequences of hyperglycemia? Above a level of 200 mg% in the blood, glucosuria supervenes with the consequent loss of fuel from the body. But that does not wholly explain the biological origin and survival value of all the mechanisms operating to keep the circulating glucose below 120–130 mg% at all times.

Diabetes mellitus in all of its clinical and experimental forms, whatever be the etiology of a particular case, is characterized by a persistent chronic state of hyperglycemia. This is, of course, rather easily influenced by the quantity and kinds of foods ingested. Dietary and hormonal treatments that markedly reduce or abolish the urinary excretion of sugar completely relieve the classical metabolic symptomatology of diabetes. How important is it then to reduce the patient's blood sugar to within the normal ranges? The older clinicians advocated "strict" blood sugar control because (*a*) the ideal was to change any abnormal values to "normal" and (*b*) in their experience adherence to strict criteria of control seemed to decrease the incidence and extent of the "complications" of the disease: retinopathy, neuropathy, nephropathy, and atherosclerosis.

For years this viewpoint was challenged mainly on the basis that in many instances there was no consistent correlation between blood sugar "control" and severity of complications; and also because it was difficult to believe that glucose (as a substance), could be involved in damaging small and large blood vessels throughout the body and in peripheral nerve degeneration.

## INSULIN-INDEPENDENT PATHWAYS OF GLUCOSE METABOLISM

During the past 20–25 years, however, a growing body of evidence has been developed implicating certain metabolic pathways of glucose and galactose in the production of changes in various tissues that may lead to many of the diabetic complications (14, 31–34, 44, 66, 77, 80, 102, 108). Hence, the nutritional details of the diet for diabetics have become very important for the patient and the physician. The goal is to structure caloric and carbohydrate intake together with appropriate medication and muscular exercise, so as to approach as closely as possible to the diurnal blood sugar curves of the nondiabetic individual.

We review here our present state of knowledge of two chemical pathways glucose may take in the body that are thought to have chronic injurious effects. One is the so-called polyol pathway; and the other is the nonenzymatic glycosylation of proteins.

## *The Polyol Pathway*

Muscle tissue, the fat cells, and the cells of connective tissue all require insulin for the transmembrane entry of glucose. Insulin is also necessary for the efficient autoregulation of liver sugar output by the blood glucose level. Neurons, as well as all epithelial and endothelial cells, do not depend upon insulin for glucose entry. Their carbohydrate metabolism depends primarily upon the level of circulating glucose. The overwhelming bulk of glucose is processed by initial phosphorylation to G-6-phosphate for storage and/or oxidative breakdown. At high blood sugar levels in those tissues that possess the particular enzyme (aldose reductase), glucose and other aldoses are reduced to the corresponding sugar alcohols; glucose forms glucitol (better known as sorbitol) (14, 31, 33, 34, 44, 66, 72, 80, 102, 108), and galactose gives rise to galactitol or dulcitol. A second enzyme, iditol dehydrogenase, catalyzes the transformation of sorbitol to fructose. In states of hyperglycemia the polyols (sugar alcohols) tend to accumulate within those cells and tissues that are not insulin sensitive (1).

It was thought at first that the polyols are retained within cells and then damage tissues by the osmotic imbibition of water. This osmotic damage theory could not be wholly substantiated (44). Yet, in some way the activity of the polyol pathway is involved because substances that inhibit the action of aldose reductase may prevent or reverse the functional and/or morphologic changes (1, 6, 7, 24, 39, 43, 71, 72, 87, 95, 104, 111).

Coincident with the rise of tissue levels of sorbitol there generally occurs a fall in another of the normal sugar alcohols, myoinositol (14, 15, 41, 44, 45, 79). The full role of inositol in cellular functions is not yet clear, but it is most probably related to the functions of the membrane-bound phosphoinositides, which are involved in signal transmission for the regulation of ion fluxes, propagation of the nerve impulse, and synaptic transmission.

When the first enzyme of the polyol pathway (aldose reductase) is inhibited, myoinositol levels return toward normal values. The relationship between the polyol pathway and myoinositol levels may be indirect in that hyperglycemia may enhance polyol formation and also inhibit myoinositol uptake (41, 42, 44, 119).

Until very recently the aldose reductase system had been implicated to some degree in cataract formation and in the neuropathic changes of diabetes. Now, however, work has appeared linking diabetic vascular disease to the aldose reductase pathway. Induction of diabetes in rats increases capillary permeability to albumin in newly formed vessels. This phenomenon is increased markedly by galactose feeding (79) and is prevented by the use of an orally active aldose reductase inhibitor (39, 65, 87, 95, 111).

Of interest is the recent finding that castration of the diabetic animal has the same ameliorative effect on the increased vascular permeability as does the use of the aldose reductase inhibitor. This seems to be due to the fact that reductase is a sex-steroid-dependent enzyme.

The obvious therapeutic deduction from all of these studies is the need for regimens of treatment, nutritional and hormonal, that result in nearly normal levels of blood glucose. When needed, this could be supplemented by safe, orally effective aldose reductase inhibitors.

GLYCOSYLATION In 1968 Rahbar, a hematologist then working in Iran, screened a large number of patients and found that diabetics had an increased concentration of an "abnormal" Hb component, previously described by Allen & Schroeder (see 49). This was designated as $HbA1_c$ (91). Further studies by Holmquist & Schroeder (49), Bookchin & Gallop (9), and H. F. Bunn and colleagues (10–12) established that this form of Hb was created by the attachment of a molecule of glucose to the *N* terminus of the β-chain. This occurs chemically without the intervention of an enzyme by the formation of a Schiff base that is converted to a ketoamine linkage by an Amadori rearrangement.

The content of $HbA1_c$ in terms of percentage of total Hb seems to depend on the mean blood glucose level and the survival time of the red blood cells. In the nondiabetic population the hemolysate contains, on the average, 4–5% of the $A1_c$ variant; among diabetics the percentage varies between 8 and 15% depending upon the degree of chronic hyperglycemia (8, 29, 38, 40, 67, 74, 75, 106).

These findings have led to the use of $HbA1_c$ determinations to assess the average degree of metabolic control in individuals and groups during several weeks preceding the assay. This has, of course, the advantage of not depending upon the peaks and valleys of the diurnal curve of blood glucose, nor upon the acute administration of insulin or an oral hypoglycemic agent. These assays are used widely in outpatient diabetes clinics for routine follow-up and for evaluating the chronic effects of dietetic and drug therapy (20, 21, 28, 35, 86).

Interest in protein glycosylation goes beyond using the $HbA1_c$ test. It has been established that most proteins will condense with sugars even at the physiological concentrations of glucose found in the body. Those known to form glucose adducts include collagen, the crystallins of the lens (98, 103), serum proteins (25, 62, 118), nerve myelin, all membrane proteins (70, 93), transferrin (83), fibronectin (105), etc. Those diabetics tested incorporate more glucose in albumin (70, 93), red cell membrane proteins, collagen, and basement membranes (16, 19, 69, 73, 82).

In the case of lens crystallin, it has been argued that glycosylation may predispose to cataract formation by rendering the proteins more susceptible to formation of aggregates of high molecular weight. Glycosylated circulating plasma proteins may be transported across capillary walls at rates different from the non-sugar-containing molecules. It is tempting to speculate that glycosylation of certain degree may change some functional properties of certain circulating and cellular proteins, and thus induce those structural changes in the tissues that form the basis for the vascular and renal complications.

While the evidence for the role of the polyol pathway in the genesis of diabetic complications is stronger than that for protein glycosylation, neither one has as yet been clearly defined as to mechanism. In the practice of medicine, however, ethical considerations demand that we adopt a therapeutic regime fashioned by pragmatism even if, as yet, the demands of scientific proof have not been wholly met.

The conditions of the polyol pathway and of glycosylation dictate that a desirable treatment of a diabetic be based upon maintaining a diurnal blood sugar curve oscillating between about 80 and 130 mg%. This therapeutic need is the basis for (*a*) administering insulin by multiple small injections per day, or by means of computer-driven pumps; (*b*) glucose level monitoring by patients; and (*c*) other devices aiming at strict control. Among these other devices are the purely nutritional methods of slowing the rate of appearance, and the subsequent rise of blood glucose related to food intake. Hence, the search for techniques to slow the rates of digestion and absorption of carbohydrates.

## EFFECTS OF COMPLEX CARBOHYDRATES ON GLUCOSE TOLERANCE

Plant "fiber," which is a mixture of many polysaccharides and lectins (e.g. guar, tragaranth, pectins, and the celluloses), has been ingested for ages as a preventative of chronic constipation. It seems to lower postprandial glycemia, perhaps by inhibiting the rate of polysaccharide digestion and/or sugar absorption in the small intestine. Hence, it is being advocated as an important adjuvant in the dietary regimen for diabetics in general (both Types I and II) (3, 30, 52, 58, 64, 76, 78, 92, 94).

Acarbose, an oligosaccharide obtained from certain strains of actinomycetes, is a competitive inhibitor of the brush-border glucosidases, especially sucrase, and it also inhibits glucoamylase and pancreatic α-amylase. It is therefore able to lower the postprandial blood glucose rise (27, 53, 89, 90, 104, 107). The combination of acarbose with the guar fiber is especially favorable since it seems to decrease markedly any side reactions.

Until very recently the dietary formulae devised for diabetics concerned themselves only with the total amount per meal and per day, and with the ratio of simple sugars to complex carbohydrates present in foods. The concept of carbohydrate "exchange" was based on quantitative chemical analysis of foods rather than on actual testing in vivo (59–61) since it was assumed that these parameters predicted more or less the extent of the postprandial rise in blood glucose. However, it seems that the degree of rise in blood sugar and the shape of the rise in the blood sugar curve after ingestion of test meals containing equal amounts and ratios of simple and complex carbohydrates differ over a wide range. The glycemic response after meals compared to the pure glucose test meal is about 30% for legumes, 35% for dairy products, 50% for fruit, and 60% for cereals (55, 56, 113). The judicious choice of foods with small glycemic responses and the addition of fiber to the meals, can significantly affect the blood sugar excursions of diabetics whether of the Type I or Type II variety. These dietary maneuvers aid in achieving diurnal glucose curves approaching the normal range (55, 56, 113).

Factors responsible for the variation in the glycemic indices of various meals are not precisely understood. It has been speculated that a variety of conditions might be responsible, such as (*a*) differential susceptibility of particular starches to hydrolytic enzymes (61, 84); (*b*) chain length of the amyloses (113); (*c*) amount and kind of proteins in the foods being tested; and (*d*) the amount and nature of the nondigestible polysaccharides or "fiber" in the food mixture (4, 58, 78, 100).

Jenkins, who with his colleagues has contributed greatly to this field (52, 54, 60), argues that the use of purified fiber preparations and enzyme inhibitors (of amylases and glucosidases) is creating a new and useful nutritional pharmacology by modifying the rates of gastrointestinal events. This allows the achievement of "carbohydrate lente," i.e. meals that consist of sustained-release carbohydrate, which in turn facilitates a dietary management of diabetes aimed at achieving a normal diurnal blood sugar curve (3, 37, 57, 100).

The special nutritional features and properties exhibited by sugars other than glucose have been reviewed in the biochemical and clinical literature quite frequently and need not be explained here (63, 85, 101, 114). However, particular aspects of some importance that have been recently observed deserve mention.

## METABOLIC EFFECTS OF SPECIFIC SUGARS AND SUGAR ALCOHOLS

### *Sucrose*

Diabetogenic effects of a high sucrose intake have been asserted and denied over the years. Sucrose consumption seems to cause a degree of insulin resistance as shown by elevations of both glucose and insulin levels. Fructose is the responsible component of sucrose for these effects, both in rodents (13, 46, 47, 85, 110) and in normal and diabetic humans (18, 22, 23, 117, 120). Fructose does not elicit an *acute* insulin response, but the chronic feeding of fructose or sucrose leads to hyperinsulinemia and high triglyceride levels in rodents (47) as well as to a very significant loss of insulin sensitivity (110, 112, 116). These findings are reminiscent of the observations made years earlier that a high sucrose intake could be diabetogenic in certain selected populations in man and among rodents (18, 99, 109).

Fructose appears attractive in constructing diets for diabetics since it is sweeter to the taste than glucose, and because in normal humans and mild diabetics fructose ingestion produces a milder excursion in the blood sugar curve than does glucose (50). However, the situation changes under chronic conditions and also depends upon the metabolic severity present in the tested patient. Over time, moderate insulin resistance develops and the mean blood sugar rises, as does the blood insulin and the blood fats—a situation resembling mild Type II diabetes.

While the development of obesity is related chiefly to high caloric intake, there is increasing evidence that under certain conditions foods may be oxidized with less or more efficiency of production of useful metabolic energy. Thus, it has been argued that the degree of thermogenesis after meals may vary widely. This may depend on many factors, including the type of carbohydrate ingested (48, 81, 97).

High sucrose diets tend to induce obesity in rats as compared to the equicaloric intake of glucose. A glucose meal is followed by significant rises in oxidation rates of brown adipose tissue, while fructose is not. Fructose is used more "efficiently". Hence, it can, over time, result in greater deposition of fat than glucose (17).

We have previously referred to the diabetogenic potential of high sucrose and/or fructose intakes, as seen in certain ethnic groups and selected rodent strains. Among other observations it was noted that sucrose and fructose induced retinal vascular damage resembling diabetic retinopathy or renal glomerulosclerosis. The precise mechanisms responsible for such lesions have not been demonstrated. Speculation and indirect evidence have centered on a secondary vitamin A deficiency, increased lactate production, selenium and/or chromium deficiencies. The latter suggestion is of great interest, since chromium deficiency leads to the loss of glucose tolerance factor and increasing glucose intolerance (88).

## *Xylitol*

For over 100 years attempts have been made to influence the metabolic state of diabetes by providing carbohydrates of equal sweetness and caloric value that would not raise the patient's blood glucose levels significantly, and that would not require insulin for their entry and prompt metabolism by cells. More recently nonglucose monosaccharides, especially fructose and the sugar alcohols sorbitol and xylitol, have been advocated for use by parenteral infusion for the nutritional support of patients after the trauma of surgery, during severe infections, etc (36). (The paper by Georgieff et al is a thorough review of the literature on this sugar alcohol in relation to its nutritional use.) Since under such conditions of physical stress the hormonal setting favors insulin resistance, it was thought advantageous to supply the carbohydrate calories in a form not requiring the extra secretion of insulin in the process of utilization.

In actual practice, the use of fructose and some of the sugar alcohols did not meet with more than temporary success or acceptability for a variety of reasons, as described in many reviews. As our knowledge of intermediary metabolism developed, it became obvious what the difficulties were that gave rise to years of controversy.

In the first place, fructose and the sugar alcohols are not utilized significantly by extrahepatic tissues. In the liver they are fairly rapidly metabolized to trioses, which are then catabolized further to $CO_2$ or synthesized into the hexosephosphates and glycogen. Thus, any portion not immediately "oxidized" ultimately becomes blood glucose by the gluconeogenetic pathway. This is immediately evident when such sugars or polyols are given to a severe diabetic; hyperglycemia and glucosuria follow rapidly. This undoubted fact has deterred many from using these "substitute" carbohydrates, since it seemed to be a waste of effort of providing "glucose" in a circuitous manner.

It would be of advantage, however, if one could provide fructose or xylitol in amounts that would inhibit proteolysis and lipolysis yet would not raise blood glucose values significantly. At infusion levels of about 0.2 g/kg/hr, xylitol apparently produces no rise in blood glucose. The oxidative rates of its metabolism are raised independently of glucose and of insulin. There is also no tendency to deposit liver fat when xylitol is infused compared to lipogenesis stimulated by glucose and insulin.

Felber has shown that when insulin secretion is suppressed by pharmacologic means, carbohydrate utilization from the infusion of fructose, sorbitol, and xylitol is significantly increased. The rise in carbohydrate oxidation rates and the decrease in lipid oxidation when using the nonglucose sugar alcohols or fructose were the same whether or not insulin secretion was kept suppressed. This was true when the infusion rates were kept at about 20–25 g of substrate per hour (26).

## SUMMARY

In healthy persons, glucose homeostasis maintains blood glucose levels between 70 and 130 mg/dl despite perturbations by meals, fasting, and exercise. Long-term follow-up of diabetic patients has suggested that "good control" of blood sugar levels minimizes the long-term complications of diabetes, such as retinopathy, nephropathy, and atherosclerosis.

It now seems likely the products of insulin-independent metabolic pathways in epithelial and endothelial cells leading to polyol formation and protein glycosylation may be factors in the genesis of retinopathy, neuropathy, nephropathy, and premature atherosclerosis of diabetic patients.

Dietary complex carbohydrates of various type, including those rich in dietary fiber, which are the cell walls of fruits, vegetables, and cereals, may slow the rate of absorption of glucose from those diets and contribute to a lowering of the postprandial glucose peak. Glycemic responses to various foods compared to glucose have been studied and show a large variation, which is dependent upon gastric emptying, overall effects on rate of hydrolysis and absorption of glucose from food mixtures.

Dietary sucrose seems to cause a degree of insulin resistance. The active part of the disaccharide is fructose, which does not elicit an acute insulin response, but appears indirectly to increase insulin levels in both animals and man. Sucrose in animals appears to promote obesity more than glucose because of its lack of stimulation of thermogenesis. Xylitol has been used as a sweetener and as a sugar substitute in total parenteral nutrition.

It is a paradox that the most physiological of sugars (glucose) can be a menace at high concentrations. The use of nonphysiological sugars or their derivatives in diabetics and patients with special needs, such as TPN, requires much more investigation to develop a sound rationale in nutrition management.

### *Literature Cited*

1. Akagi, Y., Yayima, Y., Kador, P. F., Kuwabara, T., Kinoshita, J. H. 1984. Localization of aldose reductase in the human eye. *Diabetes* 33:562–66
2. Alberti, K. G. M. M., Hockaday, T. D. R. 1975. The biochemistry of the complications of diabetes mellitus. In *Complications of Diabetes,* ed. H. Keen, J. Jarrett, pp. 221–64. Chicago: Yearbook Med.
3. Anderson, J. W., Ward, K. 1978. Long-term effects of high fiber diets on glucose and lipid metabolism: a preliminary report on patients with diabetes. *Diabetes Care* 1:77–82
4. Aro, A., Uusitupa, M., Voutilainen, E., Hersio, K., Korhonen, T., Seitonen, O. 1981. Improved diabetic control of hypocholesterolemic effect induced by long-term dietary supplementation with guar gum in Type 2 (insulin-independent) diabetes. *Diabetologia* 21:29–33

5. Barbosa, J. 1980. Nature and nurture: The genetics of diabetic microangiopathy. In *Secondary Diabetes,* ed. S. Podolsky, M. Viswanathan, pp. 67–76. New York: Raven
6. Beyer-Mears, A., Cruz, E. 1985. Reversal of diabetic cataract by sorbinil, and aldose reductase inhibitor. *Diabetes* 34:15–21
7. Beyer-Mears, A., Ku, L., Cohen, M. P. 1984. Glomerular polyol accumulation in diabetes and its prevention by oral sorbinil. *Diabetes* 33:604–7
8. Boden, G., Master, R. W., Gordon, S. S., Shuman, C. R., Owen, O. E. 1980. Monitoring metabolic control in diabetic outpatients with glycosylated hemoglobins. *Ann. Intern. Med.* 92:357–60
9. Bookchin, R. M., Gallop, P. M. 1968. Structure of hemaglobin $A1_c$: nature of the *N*-terminal beta chain blocking group. *Biochem. Biophys. Res. Commun.* 32:86–93
10. Bunn, H. F., Gabbay, K. H., Gallop, P. M. 1978. The glycoslation of hemoglobin: relevance to diabetes mellitus. *Science* 200:21–27
11. Bunn, H. F., Haney, D. N., Gabbay, K. H., Gallop, P. M. 1975. Further identification of the nature and linkage of carbohydrate in hemoglobin $A1_c$. *Biochem. Biophys. Res. Commun.* 67:103–9
12. Bunn, H. F., Haney, D. N., Kamin, S., Gabbay, K. H., Gallop, P. M. 1976. The biosynthesis of human hemoglobin $A1_c$: Slow glycoslation of hemoglobin in vivo. *J. Clin. Invest.* 57:1652–59
13. Christenson, H. N. 1984. The regulation of amino acid and sugar absorption by diet. *Nutr. Rev.* 42:237–42
14. Clements, R. S. Jr. 1979. Diabetic neuropathy—new concepts of its etiology. *Diabetes* 28:604–11
15. Clements, R. S. Jr., Stockard, C. P. 1980. Effect of insulin treatment. *Diabetes* 29:227–35
16. Cohen, A. M., Rosemann, E. 1985. Effect of the estrogen antagonist, tamoxifen, on development of glomerulosclerosis in the Cohen diabetic rat. *Diabetes* 34:634–38
17. Cohen, A. M., Teitelbaum, A. 1964. Effect of different levels of sucrose and starch on oral glucose tolerance and insulin-like activity. *Am. J. Physiol.* 206:105–11
18. Cohen, A. M., Teitelbaum, A., Saliternik, R. 1972. Genetics and diet as factors in development of diabetes mellitus. *Metabolism* 21:235–40
19. Cohen, M. P., Urdanivia, E., Surma, M., Ciborowski, C. J. 1981. Nonenzymatic glycosylation of basement membranes. *Diabetes* 30:367–71
20. Cole, R. A. 1978. The significance of hemoglobin $A1_c$ in diabetes mellitus. In *Current Concepts*. Kalamozoo, Mich: Upjohn
21. Compagnucci, P., Cartechini, M. G., Bolli, G., De Feo, P., Santeusanio, F., Brunetti, P. 1981. The importance of determining irreversibly glycosylated hemoglobin in diabetes. *Diabetes* 30:607–12
22. Crapo, P. A. 1984. The metabolic effects of 2 weeks fructose feeding in normal subjects. *Am. J. Clin. Nutr.* 39:525–34
23. Crapo, P. A., Kolterman, O. G., Olefsky, J. M. 1980. Effect of oral fructose in normal, diabetic, and impaired glucose tolerance subjects. *Diabetes Care* 3:575–81
24. Datiles, M., Fuki, H., Kuwabara, T., Kinoshita, J. H. 1982. Galactose cataract prevention with sorbinin, an aldose reductase inhibitor: a light microscopic study. *Invest. Ophthalmol. Vis. Sci.* 22:174–79
25. Day, J. F., Thorpe, S. R., Baynes, J. W. 1979. Nonenzymatically glucosylated albumin. *J. Biol. Chem.* 254:595–97
26. de Kalbermatten, N., Ravussin, E., Maeder, E., Geser, C., Jequier, E., Felber, J. P. 1980. Comparison of glucose, fructose, sorbitol, and xylitol utilization in humans during insulin suppression. *Metabolism* 29:62–67
27. Dimitriadis, G. D., Tessari, P., Go, V. L. W., Gerich, J. E. 1985. α-Glucosidase inhibition improves postprandial hyperglycemia and decreases insulin requirements in insulin-dependent diabetes mellitus. *Metabolism* 34:261–65
28. Ditzel, J., Dyerberg, J. 1977. Hyperlipoproteinemia, diabetes and oxygen affinity of hemoglobin. *Metabolism* 26: 141–50
29. Dunn, P. J., Cole, R. A., Soeldner, J. S., Glenson, R. E. 1979. Reproductibility of hemoglobin $A1_c$ and sensivity to various degrees of glucose tolerance. *Ann. Intern. Med.* 91:390–96
30. Ellis, P. R., Apling, E. C. 1981. Guar bread: acceptability and efficacy combined. Studies on blood glucose, serum insulin and satiety in normal subjects. *Br. J. Nutr.* 46:267–76
31. Engerman, R. L., Kern, T. S. 1983. Experimental galactosemia produces diabetic-like retinopathy. *Diabetes* 33:97–100
32. Fagius, J., Jameson, S. 1981. Effects of aldose reductase inhibitor treatment in diabetic polyneuropathy: a clinical and

neurophysiologic study. *J. Neurol. Neurosurg. Psychiatry* 44:991–1001
33. Gabbay, K. H. 1973. The sorbitol pathway and the complications of diabetes. *N. Engl. J. Med.* 288:881–86
34. Gabbay, K. H. 1975. Hyperglycemia, polyol metabolism and complications of diabetes mellitus. *Ann. Rev. Med.* 26: 521–26
35. Gabbay, K. H., Hasty, K., Breslow, J. L., Ellison, R. C., Bunn, H. F., Gallop, P. M. 1977. Glycosylated hemoglobins and long-term blood glucose in diabetes mellitus. *J. Clin. Endocrinol. Metab.* 44:859–64
36. Georgieff, M., Moldawer, L. L., Bistrian, B. R., Blackburn, G. L. 1985. Xylitol, an energy source for intravenous nutrition after trauma. *J. Parent. Enteral Nutr.* 9:199–209
37. Gerard, J., Luyck, A. S., Lefebvre, P. J. 1982. Long-term improvement of metabolic control in insulin-treated diabetes by the α-glucoside inhibitor acarbose. *Diabetologia* 21:446–51
38. Gonen, B., Rubenstein, A. H., Rochman, H., Tanega, S., Horwitz, D. L. 1977. Haemoglobin A1: An indicator of the metabolic control of diabetic patients. *Lancet* 2:734–36
39. Gonzalez, A. M., Sochor, M., McLean, P. 1983. The effect of an aldose reductase inhibitor (sorbinil) on the level of metabolites in lenses of diabetic rats. *Diabetes* 32:482–85
40. Graf, R. J., Porte, D. 1977. Glycosylated hemaglobin (GHB) as an index of glycemia independent of plasma insulin (IRI) in normal (N) and diabetic (D) subjects. *Diabetes* (Suppl. 1) 26:368
41. Greene, D. A. 1983. Metabolic abnormalities in diabetic peripheral nerve: relation to impaired function. *Metabolism* 32:118–23
42. Greene, D. A., Lattimer, S. A. 1983. Impaired rat sciatic nerve sodium-potassium adenosine triphosphatase in acute streptozocin diabetes and its correction by dietary myoinositol supplementation. *J. Clin. Invest.* 72:1058–63
43. Greene, D. A., Lattimer, S. A. 1984. Action of sobinil in diabetic peripheral nerve. *Diabetes* 33:712–16
44. Greene, D. A., Lattimer, S., Ulbrecht, J., Carroll, P. 1985. Glucose-induced alterations in nerve metabolism. *Diabetes Care* 8:290–99
45. Greene, D. A., Yagihashi, S., Lattimer, S. A., Sima, A. A. F. 1984. Nerve $Na^+$-$K^+$-ATPase, conduction and myoinositol in the insulin deficient BB rat. *Am. J. Physiol.* 247:E534–39
46. Hallfrisch, J., Ellwood, K. C., Michaelis, O. E. IV. 1983. Effects of dietary fructose on plasma glucose and hormone responses in normal and hyperinsulinemic men. *J. Nutr.* 113:1819–26
47. Hallfrisch, J., Reiser, S., Prather, E. S. 1983. Blood lipid distribution of hyperinsulinemic men consuming three levels of fructose. *Am. J. Clin. Nutr.* 37:740–48
48. Himms-Hagen, J. 1976. Cellular thermogenesis *Ann. Rev. Physiol.* 38:315–51
49. Holmquist, W. R., Schroeder, W. A. 1966. A new *N*-terminal blocking group involving a Schiff base in hemoglobin $A1_c$. *Biochemistry* 5:2489–2503
50. Ionescu-Tirgoviste, C., Popa, E., Sintu, E., Mihalache, N., Cheta, D., Mincu, I. 1983. Blood glucose and plasma insulin responses to various carbohydrates in Type II (non-insulin-dependent) diabetes. *Diabetologia* 24:80–84
51. Jarrett, R. J. 1971. Diabetes, hyperglycaemia and arterial disease. In *Blood Vessel Disease in Diabetes Mellitus,* ed. K. Lundbaek, H. Keen. *Acta Diabetol. Lat.* 8(Suppl. 1): p. 7. Milano: Casa Editrice Il Ponte SRL
52. Jenkins, D. J. A. 1982. Lente carbohydrate: A newer approach to the dietary management of diabetes. *Diabetes Care* 5:634–41
53. Jenkins, D. J. A., Barker, H. M., Taylor, R. H., Fielden, H. 1982. Low dose acarbose without symptoms of malabsorption in the dumping syndrome. *Lancet* 1:109–14
54. Jenkins, D. J. A., Ghafari, H., Wolever, T. M. S., Taylor, R. H., Barker, H. M., et al. 1982. Relationship between the rate of digestion of foods and postprandial glycaemia. *Diabetologia* 22:450–55
55. Jenkins, D. J. A., Leeds, A. R., Gassull, M. A., Wolever, T. M. S., Goff, D. V., et al. 1976. Unabsorbable carbohydrates and diabetes: decreased postprandial hyperglycaemia. *Lancet* 2:172–74
56. Jenkins, D. J. A., Leeds, A. R., Gassull, M. A., Cockett, B., Alberti, K. G. M. 1977. Decrease in postprandial insulin and glucose concentrations by guar and pectin. *Ann. Intern. Med.* 86:20–23
57. Jenkins, D. J. A., Taylor, R. H., Goff, D. V., Fielden, H., Misiewicz, J. J., et al. 1981. Scope and specificity of acarbose on slowing carbohydrate absorption in man. *Diabetes* 30:951–54
58. Jenkins, D. J. A., Wolever, T. M. S., Bacon, S., Nineham, R., Lees, R., et al. 1980. Diabetic diets: high carbohydrate combined with high fiber. *Am. J. Clin. Nutr.* 33:1729–33
59. Jenkins, D. J. A., Wolever, T. M. S.,

Taylor, R. H., Barker, H. M., Fielden, H. 1980. Exceptionally low blood glucose response to dried beans: comparison with other carbohydrate foods. *Br. Med. J.* 281:578–80
60. Jenkins, D. J. A., Wolever, T. M. S., Taylor, R. H., Barker, H. M., Fielden, H., et al. 1981. Glycemic index of foods: a physiological basis for carbohydrate exchange. *Am. J. Clin. Nutr.* 34:362–66
61. Jenkins, D. J. A., Wolever, T. M. S., Taylor, R. H., Ghafari, H., Jenkins, A. L., et al. 1980. Rate of digestion of foods and postprandial glycaemia in normal and diabetic subjects. *Br. Med. J.* 281: 14–17
62. Jones, I. R., Owens, D. R., Williams, S., Ryder, R. E. J., Birtwell, A. J., et al. 1983. Glycosylated serum albumin: An intermediate index of diabetic control. *Diabetes Care* 6:501–3
63. Keller, U., Froesch, E. R. 1972. Vergleichende Untersuchungen uber den Stoffwechsel von Xylit, sorbit and fruktose beim menschen. *Schweiz. Med. Wochenschr.* 102:1017–22
64. Kiehm, T. G., Anderson, J. W., Ward, K. 1976. Beneficial effects of a high carbohydrate high fiber diet in hyperglycemic men. *Am. J. Clin. Nutr.* 29:895–99
65. Kilzer, P., Chang, K., Marvel, J., Rowold, E., Jaudes, P., et al. 1985. Albumin permeation of new vessels is increased in diabetic rats. *Diabetes*. In press
66. Kinoshita, J. H., Fukushi, S., Kadar, P., Merola, L. O. 1979. Aldose reductase in diabetic complications of the eye. *Metabolism* 28:462–69
67. Koenig, R. J., Peterson, C. M., Jones, R. L., Saudek, C., Lehrman, M., Cerami, A. 1976. Correlation of glucose regulation and hemoglobin $A1_c$ in diabetes mellitus. *N. Engl. J. Med.* 295:417–20
68. Kohner, E. M. 1981. Abnormal physiological processes in the retina. In *Handbook of Diabetes Mellitus,* ed. M. Brownlee, 4:1–21. New York: Garland
69. Lorenzi, M., Cagliero, E., Toledo, S. 1985. Glucose toxicity for human endothelial cells in culture: delayed replication, disturbed cell cycle, and accelerated death. *Diabetes* 34:621–27
70. Lubec, G., Legenstein, E., Pollak, A., Meznik, E. 1980. Glomerular basement membrane changes. Hb $A1_c$ and urinary excretion of acid glycosaminoglycans in children with diabetes mellitus. *Clin. Chim. Acta* 103:45–49
71. Malone, J. I., Leavengood, H., Peterson, M. J., O'Brien, M. M., Page, M. G., Aldinger, C. E. 1984. Inhibition by sorbinil in insulin-dependent diabetic subjects. *Diabetes* 33:45–49
72. Malone, J. I., Knox, G., Benford, S., Tedesco, T. A. 1980. Red cell sorbitol: an indicator of diabetic control. *Diabetes* 29:861–64
73. Mayer, T. K., Freedman, Z. R. 1983. Protein glycosylation in diabetes mellitus: a review of laboratory measurements and of their clinical utility. *Clin. Chim. Acta* 127:147–84
74. McDonald, J. M., Davis, J. E. 1979. Glycosylated hemoglobins and diabetes mellitus. *Hum. Pathol.* 10:279–91
75. Miller, J. M., Crenshaw, M. C., Welt, S. I. 1979. Hemoglobin $A1_c$ in normal and diabetic pregnancy. *J. Am. Med. Assoc.* 242:2785–87
76. Miranda, P. M., Horwitz, D. L. 1978. High fiber diets in the treatment of diabetes mellitus. *Ann. Intern. Med.* 88: 482–86
77. Mogensen, C. E. 1981. Abnormal physiological processes in the kidney. See Ref. 68, pp. 23–85
78. Monnier, L. H., Blotman, M. J., Colette, C., Monnier, M. P., Mirouze, J. 1981. Effects of dietary fibre supplementation in stable and labile insulin-independent diabetics. *Diabetologia* 20: 12–17
79. Morrison, A. D. 1985. Linkage of polyol pathway activity and myoinositol in aortic smooth muscle. *Diabetes* 34:12A
80. Morrison, A. D., Clements, R. S., Winegrad, A. I. 1972. Effects of elevated glucose concentrations on the metabolism of the aortic wall. *J. Clin. Invest.* 51:3114–23
81. Moss, D., Ma, A., Cameron, D. P. 1985. Defective thermoregulatory thermogenesis in monosodium glutamate–induced obesity in mice. *Metabolism* 34:626–30
82. Nathan, D. M., Singer, D. E., Hurxthal, K., Goodson, J. D. 1984. The clinical information value of the glycosylated hemoglobin assay. *N. Engl. J. Med.* 310:341–46
83. Ney, K. A., Pasqua, J. J., Colley, K. J., Guthrow, C. E., Pizzo, S. V. 1985. In vitro preparation of nonenzymatically glucosylated human transferrin, $\alpha_2$-macroglobulin, and fibrinogen with preservation of function. *Diabetes* 34:462–70
84. O'Dea, K., Snow, P., Nestel, P. 1981. Rate of starch hydrolysis in vitro as a predictor of metabolic responses to complex carbohydrate in vivo. *Am. J. Clin. Nutr.* 34:1991–93
85. Olefsky, J. M., Crapo, P. 1980. Fructose, xylitol and sorbitol. *Diabetes Care* 3:390–93

86. Peterson, C. M., Koenig, R. J., Jones, R. L., Saudek, C. D., Cerami, A. 1977. Correlation of serum triglyceride levels and hemoglobin $A1_c$ concentrations in diabetes mellitus. *Diabetes* 26:507–9
87. Peterson, M. J., Sages, R., Aldinger, C. E., McDonald, D. P. 1979. A novel aldose reductase inhibitor that inhibits polyol pathway activity in diabetic and galactosemic rats. *Metabolism* 28 (Suppl. 1):456–61
88. Potter, J. F., Levin, P., Anderson, R. A., Freiberg, J. M., Andres, R., Elahi, D. 1985. Glucose metabolism in glucose-intolerant people during chromium supplementation. *Metabolism* 34:199–204
89. Puls, W., Keup, V., Krause, H. P., Thomas, G., Hoffmeister, F. 1977. Glucosidase inhibition: a new approach to the treatment of diabetes, obesity and hyperlipoproteinaemia. *Naturwissenschaften* 64:536–58
90. Radziuk, J., Kemmer, F., Morishima, T., Berchtold, P., Vranic, M. 1984. The effects of an alpha-glucoside hydrolase inhibitor on glycemia and the absorption of sucrose in man determined using a tracer methods. *Diabetes* 33:207–13
91. Rahbar, S. 1980–1981. Glycosylated hemoglobins. *Tex. Rep. Biol. Med.* 40: 373–85
92. Rainbird, A. L., Low, A. G., Zebrowski, T. 1984. Effect of guar gum on glucose and water absorption from isolated loops of jejunum in conscious growing pips. *Br. J. Nutr.* 52:489–98
93. Reddi, A. L. 1978. Diabetic microangiopathy I. Current state of the chemistry and metabolism of the glomerular basement membrane. *Metabolism* 27:107–24
94. Rivellese, A., Riccardi, G., Giacco, A., Pacioni, D., Genovese, S., et al. 1980. Effect of dietary fibre on glucose control and serum lipoproteins in diabetic patients. *Lancet* 2:447–50
95. Robey, C., Dasmahaptra, A., Cohen, M. P., Suarez, S. 1985. Sorbinil prevents decreased erythrocyte (RBC) deformability in diabetes mellitus. *Diabetes* 34:41A
96. Ross, H., Bernstein, G., Rifkin, H. 1983. Relationship of metabolic control of diabetes to long-term complications. In *Diabetes Mellitus: Theory and Practice,* ed. Ellenberg, Rifkin, pp. 907–25. New York: Med. Exam. Publ. 3rd ed.
97. Rothwell, N. J., Stock, M. J. 1979. A role for brown adipose tissue in diet-induced thermogensis. *Nature* 28:31–35
98. Service, F. J., Molnar, G. D., Taylor, W. F. 1972. Urine glucose analysis during continuous blood glucose monitoring. *J. Am. Med. Assoc.* 222:294–98
99. Shafrir, E. 1984. Sucrose diet induced enzymatic and hormonal responses affecting carbohydrate lipid and energy metabolism in two species. *Int. J. Biochem.* 16:375–82
100. Simpson, H. C. R., Simpson, R. W., Lousley, S., Carter, R. D., Hockaday, T. D. R., Mann, J. I. 1981. A high carbohydrate leguminous fibre diet improves all aspects of diabetic control. *Lancet* 1:1–5
101. Sipple, H. L., McNutt, K. W. 1974. *Sugars in Nutrition.* New York: Academic
102. Skyler, J. 1979. Complications of diabetes mellitus. *Diabetes Care* 2:499–509
103. Stevens, V. J., Rouzer, C. A., Monnier, V. M., Cerami, A. 1978. A diabetic cataract formation: Potential role of glycosylation of lens crystalline. *Proc. Natl. Acad. Sci. USA* 75:2918–22
104. Stribling, D., Mirrlees, D. J., Harrison, H. E., Earl, D. C. N. 1985. Properties of ICI 128, 436, a novel aldose reductase inhibitor, and its effect on diabetic complications in the rat. *Metabolism,* 34: 336–44
105. Tarsio, J. F., Wigness, B., Rhode, T. D., Rupp, W. M., Buchwald, H., Furcht, L. T. 1985. Nonenzymatic glycation of fibronectin and alterations in the molecular components in diabetes mellitus. *Diabetes* 34:477–84
106. Tattersall, R. B., Pike, D. A., Ranney, H. M., Bruckheimer, S. M. 1975. Hemoglobin components in diabetes mellitus: Studies in identical twins. *N. Engl. J. Med.* 293:1171–73
107. Taylor, R. H., Jenkins, D. J. A., Barker, H. M., Fielden, H., Goff, D. V., et al. 1982. Effect of acarbase on the 24-hr blood glucose profile and pattern of carbohydrate absorption. *Diabetes Care* 5:92–96
108. Tchobroutsky, G. 1978. Relation of diabetic control to development of microvascular complications. *Diabetologia* 15:143–52
109. Thornber, J. M., Eckbert, C. D. 1984. Protection against sucrose-induced retinal capillary damage in the Wistar rat. *J. Nutr.* 114:1070–75
110. Tobey, T. A., Mondon, C. E., Zavaroni, I., Reaven, G. M. 1982. Mechanism of insulin resistance in fructose-fed rats. *Metabolism* 31:608–12
111. Tomlinson, D. R., Moriarty, R. J., Mayer, J. H. 1984. Prevention and reversal of defective axonal transport and motor nerve conduction velocity in rats with

experimental diabetes by treatment with the aldose reductase inhibitor sorbinil. *Diabetes* 33:470–76

112. Vrana, A., Fabry, P. 1983. Metabolic effects of high sucrose of fructose intake. *World Rev. Nutr. Diet.* 42:56–101
113. Wahlquist, M. L., Wilmshurst, E. G., Murton, C. R., Richardson, E. N. 1978. The effect of chain length on glucose absorption and the related metabolic response. *Am. J. Clin. Nutr.* 31:1998–2001
114. Wang, Y. M., van Eys, J. 1981. Nutritional significance of fructose and sugar alcohols. *Am. Rev. Nutr.* 1:437–76
115. Ward, J. D. 1981. Abnormal processes in the nerve. See Ref. 68, pp. 87–113
116. Wright, D. W. 1983. Sucrose-induced insulin resistance in the rat. *Am. J. Clin. Nutr.* 38:879–83
117. Wright, D. W., Hansen, R. I., Mondon, C. E., Reaven, G. M. 1983. Sucrose-induced insulin resistance in the rat: modulation by exercise and diet. *Am. J. Clin. Nutr.* 38:879–83
118. Yue, D. K., Morris, K., McLennan, S., Turtle, J. R. 1980. Glycosylation of plasma protein and its relation to glycosylated hemoglobins in diabetes. *Diabetes* 29: 296–301
119. Yue, D. K., Hanwell, M. A., Satchell, P. M., Handelsman, D. J., Turtle, J. R. 1984. The effects of aldose reductase inhibition on nerve sorbitol and myoinositol concentrations in diabetic and galactosemic rats. *Metabolism* 33:1119–22
120. Zavaroni, I., Sander, S., Scott, S., Reaven, G. M. 1980. Effect of fructose feeding on insulin secretion and insulin action in the rat. *Metabolism* 29:970–73

*Ann. Rev. Nutr. 1986. 6:225–44*


# PROTEIN AND AMINO ACID REQUIREMENTS OF FISHES

*Robert P. Wilson*

Department of Biochemistry, Mississippi State University, Mississippi State, Mississippi 39762

*John E. Halver*

School of Fisheries WH-10, University of Washington, Seattle, Washington 98195

---

CONTENTS

INTRODUCTION ........ 226
GROSS PROTEIN REQUIREMENTS ........ 226
FACTORS AFFECTING REQUIREMENTS ........ 228
MAINTENANCE REQUIREMENTS ........ 229
QUALITATIVE AMINO ACID REQUIREMENTS ........ 229
QUANTITATIVE AMINO ACID REQUIREMENTS ........ 230
*Arginine* ........ 233
*Histidine* ........ 233
*Isoleucine* ........ 233
*Leucine* ........ 235
*Valine* ........ 235
*Isoleucine-Leucine-Valine Interactions* ........ 235
*Lysine* ........ 236
*Arginine-Lysine Interactions* ........ 236
*Phenylalanine* ........ 236
*Methionine* ........ 238
*Threonine* ........ 239
*Tryptophan* ........ 239
SUMMARY ........ 239



0199-9885/86/0715-0225$02.00

## INTRODUCTION

Fish are poikilothermic animals with metabolic rate determined by water temperature. They also require almost half their diet to be protein. Fish can be carnivores, omnivores, or herbivores. All hatchlings are carnivorous and this review concentrates on the apparent protein and amino acid requirements of the major carnivorous and omnivorous fishes on which nutritional requirement studies have been done.

Proteins are the major organic material in fish tissue, making up about 65–75% of the total on a dry-weight basis. Fish consume protein to obtain amino acids and use excess amino acids as an energy source. The protein is digested to release free amino acids, which are absorbed from the intestinal tract and used by various tissues to synthesize new protein. A consistent intake of amino acids is required because these are used continually by the fish to build new proteins. Inadequate protein in the diet results in a reduction of growth and loss of weight. When excess protein is supplied in the diet, only part is used for protein synthesis; the remainder is converted into energy.

The first definitive studies on the protein and amino acid nutrition of fish were made in the late 1950s and early 1960s with chinook salmon, *Oncorhynchus tshawytscha*. The initial amino acid test diets were formulated on the amino acid content of chicken whole-egg protein, chinook salmon egg protein, and chinook yolk-sac fry protein (23). The diet with an amino acid profile of chicken whole-egg protein gave the best growth and feed efficiency, and was therefore adopted. It was used to determine the qualitative amino acid requirements of the chinook salmon (26). The gross protein requirement was determined by feeding test diets containing a mixture of casein, gelatin, and crystalline amino acids to simulate the amino acid content of whole-egg protein (17). Subsequent experiments utilized test diets containing a mixture of casein, gelatin, and crystalline amino acids to form an amino acid pattern of 40% whole-egg protein to determine the quantitative amino acid requirements of the 10 indispensable amino acids for the chinook salmon (9, 18, 24, 27).

## GROSS PROTEIN REQUIREMENTS

Fish do not have a true protein requirement, but need a well-balanced mixture of indispensable and dispensable amino acids. Many investigators have used semipurified and purified diets to estimate the protein requirement of fish (Table 1). Most of these values have been estimated from dose response curves yielding the minimum of dietary protein necessary for maximal growth. Some of these requirement values may have been overestimated.

The dietary protein requirement for fish is influenced by the dietary protein-to-energy balance, the amino acid composition and the digestibility of the test

**Table 1** Estimated protein requirements of juvenile fish

| Species | Protein source(s) | Estimated requirements (%) | References |
|---|---|---|---|
| Channel catfish (*Ictalurus punctatus*) | Whole-egg protein | 32–36 | 21 |
| Chinook salmon (*Oncorhynchus tshawytscha*) | Casein, gelatin, and amino acids | 40 | 17 |
| Coho salmon (*Oncorhynchus kisutch*) | Casein | 40 | 108 |
| Common carp (*Cyprinus carpio*) | Casein | 38 | 64 |
| | | 31 | 89 |
| Estuary grouper (*Epinephelus salmoides*) | Tuna muscle meal | 40–50 | 91 |
| Gilthead bream (*Chrysophrys aurata*) | Casein, FPC[a], and amino acids | 40 | 79 |
| Grass carp (*Ctenopharyngodon idella*) | Casein | 41–43 | 15 |
| Japanese eel (*Anguilla japonica*) | Casein and amino acids | 44–145 | 60 |
| Largemouth bass (*Micropterus salmoides*) | Casein and FPC | 40 | 3 |
| Milkfish (fry) (*Chanos chanos*) | Casein | 40 | 46 |
| Plaice (*Pleuronectes platessa*) | Cod muscle | 50 | 13 |
| Puffer fish (*Fugu rubripes*) | Casein | 50 | 35 |
| Rainbow trout (*Salmo gairdneri*) | Fish meal | 40 | 80 |
| | Casein and gelatin | 40 | 107 |
| | Casein, gelatin, and amino acids | 45 | 25 |
| Red sea bream (*Chrysophrys major*) | Casein | 55 | 104 |
| Smallmouth bass (*Micropterus dolomieui*) | Casein and FPC | 45 | 3 |
| Snakehead (*Channa micropeltes*) | Fish meal | 52 | 98 |
| Sockeye salmon (*Oncorhynchus nerka*) | Casein, gelatin, and amino acids | 45 | 25 |
| Striped bass (*Morone saxatilis*) | Fish meal and soy proteinate | 47 | 55 |
| Tilapia | | | |
| (*Tilapia aurea*) | Casein and egg albumin | 34 | 103 |
| (*T. mossambica*) | White fish meal | 40 | 34 |
| (*T. nilotica*) | Casein | 30 | 97 |
| (*T. zillii*) | Casein | 35 | 50 |
| Yellowtail (*Seriola quinqueradiata*) | Sand eel and fish meal | 55 | 87 |

[a] Fish protein concentrate.

protein(s), and the amount of nonprotein energy sources in the test diet. Excess energy in the test diet may limit consumption, since fish, like other animals, eat to meet their energy requirement (45, 65). Most investigators state they used isoenergetic diets to determine the protein requirements; however, the metabolizable energy of the various ingredients have not been determined for most fishes and various physiological fuel values have been used. Values of 4, 8, and 1.6 kcal/g of protein, fat, and carbohydrate have been used for salmonids (67). Other values are used for different fish, for example 3.5, 8.1, 2.5 (57) and 4, 9, 4 (21) for channel catfish, *Ictalurus punctatus;* 4, 8, 2 (63) and 4, 9, 4 (107) for rainbow trout, *Salmo gairdneri;* 4.5, 9.0, 4.0 (50) and 4.5, 8.5, 3.5 (34) for *Tilapia zillii* and *T. mossambica,* respectively; 5, 9, 2 (98) for snakehead, *Channa micropeltes;* and 5.7, 9.5, 4 (13) for plaice, *Pleuronectes platessa*. The influence of changes in dietary protein-to-energy ratios on growth and protein utilization has been demonstrated in several species of fish: rainbow trout (45, 90); yellowtail, *Seriola quinqueradiata* (83, 87); common carp, *Cyprinus carpio* (89); channel catfish (21, 65); brook trout, *Salvelinus fontinalis* (72); *Tilapia aurea, T. mossambica* (34, 103); and the estuary grouper, *Epinephelus salmoides* (91).

Many investigators have demonstrated the important sparing effect of nonprotein energy sources on the utilization of dietary protein. The utilization of dietary carbohydrate is known to vary among species, and it has been shown to spare protein in salmonids (7, 8, 45, 68, 72); plaice (11); turbot, *Scophtalmus maximus* (1); channel catfish (21, 22); sea bass, *Dicentrarchus labrax* (2); common carp (63, 81, 89); and red sea bream, *Chrysophrys major* (20). Lipids have also been shown to spare protein and enhance protein utilization in salmonids (45, 71, 72, 88, 90, 93, 105, 106); common carp (84, 85, 93); channel catfish (21, 22, 56, 65, 86); turbot (1); striped bass, *Morone saxatilis* (55); and *Tilapia aurea* (103). The quality of the dietary protein used in the test diets to determine the protein requirements also affects the estimated requirement value.

## FACTORS AFFECTING REQUIREMENTS

Generally, the protein requirements of fish decrease with increasing size and age. For example, the optimal dietary protein level for very young salmonids is 45–50% of the diet, while juveniles require 40% and yearlings require about 35% dietary protein (31, 58). Similarly, channel catfish fry require about 40% protein, whereas fingerlings require 30–35% protein, and larger fish require 25–35% protein (57, 65). Dietary protein levels have also been recommended (57) for common carp of various sizes: 43–47% for fry, 37–42% for fingerlings and subadults, and 28–32% for adult and brood fish. Balarin & Haller (6) have reviewed various studies on tilapia and concluded that fish of less than 1 g require 35–50% protein, 1–5-g fish require 30–40% protein, 5–25-g fish require 25–30% protein; tilapia weighing more than 25 g require 20–25% protein.

Changes in water temperature have been shown to alter the protein requirement in some fish. Chinook salmon require 40% protein at 8°C and 55% protein at 15°C (17). Similarly, striped bass were found to require 47% protein at 20°C and about 55% at 24°C (54, 55). Rainbow trout were fed practical diets containing 35, 40, and 45% crude protein at temperatures ranging from 9 to 18°C and no apparent differences in protein requirement were reported (58).

## MAINTENANCE REQUIREMENTS

The methodology used to evaluate the excretion of endogenous nitrogen by fish was recently reviewed by Luquet & Kaushik (48). Two types of methods have generally been used: direct methods that involve measuring the combined fecal, urinary, and branchial losses; and an indirect method based on carcass analysis. The fish are maintained without food, fed on protein-free diets, or fed diets containing low levels of protein.

Carcass analysis is the most convenient method to use for fish. Nitrogen retention is revealed by the difference between nitrogen consumed and nitrogen retained by the fish at the end of the experimental period. These data can also be combined with growth data obtained by feeding increasing ration size and obtaining the nitrogen or protein intake that results in zero growth.

Luquet & Kaushik (48) summarized the various estimated endogenous nitrogen excretion values for several fish species. These workers also discussed several factors that appear to influence these measurements. The protein requirement for maintenance can be calculated from the endogenous nitrogen excretion data by taking into account the digestibility and biological value of the test protein. Ogino & Chen (62) obtained a maintenance requirement of 0.95 g protein/kg body weight/day for carp fed casein as the sole protein source. Kaushik et al (38) estimated the maintenance requirement for rainbow trout to be 1.6 g protein/kg body weight/day based on data obtained by feeding fish meal as the sole protein source. The maintenance requirement for channel catfish was found to be 1.3 g protein/kg body weight/day based on growth rates of fish fed at 0 to 5% of body weight/day of diets containing either 25 or 35% crude protein diets made from a casein-gelatin mixture (R. P. Wilson, unpublished data). The requirement was found to be about 1.0 g protein/kg body weight/day based on protein retention data from the above growth studies.

## QUALITATIVE AMINO ACID REQUIREMENTS

The first successful amino acid test diet for fish was reported in 1957 (23). It was based on previous amino acid test diets used by Rose and co-workers in determining the amino acid requirements of the young albino rat (52). Halver

(23) compared test diets containing 70% crystalline L-amino acids formulated on the amino acid patterns of whole chicken egg protein, chinook salmon egg protein, and chinook yolk-sac fry protein. The test diet based on whole chicken egg protein gave the best growth and feed efficiency for chinook salmon over a 12-week period. Therefore, this test diet was used to determine the qualitative amino acid needs of chinook salmon (26). These workers determined the essentiality of the 18 common protein amino acids by comparing the relative growth rates of fish fed the basal and specific amino acid–deficient diet over a 10-week period. For each of the 10 indispensable amino acids, groups of the deficient fish were split at 6 weeks, with one lot being continued on the deficient diet and the other lot fed the basal diet. In each of the lots shifted to the basal diet, the fish showed an immediate and substantial growth response to the complete diet.

Several other workers have utilized amino acid test diets similar to those developed by Halver (23) to study the essentiality of various amino acids in other species. Such studies in common carp were initially unsuccessful. The young carp would consume the test diets but a marked reduction in growth rate was observed corresponding to the relative amount of free amino acids in the test diets (4). Dupree & Halver (19) and Nose et al (61) found that the amino acid test diets must be neutralized before they can be utilized by channel catfish and common carp, respectively.

Cowey et al (10) used radioactive labelled glucose to determine the qualitative amino acid requirements of the plaice and sole, *Solea solea*. Small (2–3 g) fish were injected intraperitoneally with [U-$^{14}$C] glucose and fed a natural diet for 6 days. The fish were then killed, homogenized, and the protein isolated. A sample of the protein was hydrolyzed and the constituent amino acids were separated by chromatography and counted for radioactivity. Significant radioactivity was incorporated into the dispensable amino acids and not into the indispensable amino acids. Similar studies have been done with the sea bass, *Dicentrarchus labrax* (53). All finfish studied to date have required the same 10 amino acids considered indispensable for most animals (Table 2). These are arginine, histidine, isoleucine, leucine, lysine, methionine, phenylalanine, threonine, tryptophan, and valine.

## QUANTITATIVE AMINO ACID REQUIREMENTS

Most investigators have used the basic method developed by Halver and co-workers (52) to determine the quantitative amino acid requirements for fish. This procedure involves feeding graded levels of one amino acid at a time in a test diet containing either all crystalline amino acids or a mixture of casein, gelatin, and crystalline amino acids formulated so that the amino acid profile is identical to whole chicken egg protein (except, of course, for the amino acid

**Table 2** Finfish known to require the same 10 indispensable amino acids

| Species | Kind of studies | Reference |
|---|---|---|
| Channel catfish *(Ictalurus punctatus)* | Growth | 19 |
| Chinook salmon *(Oncorhynchus tshawytscha)* | Growth | 26 |
| Common carp *(Cyprinus carpio)* | Growth | 61 |
| European eel *(Anguilla anguilla)* | Growth | 5 |
| Japanese eel *(Anguilla japonica)* | Growth | 5 |
| Plaice *(Pleuronectes platessa)* | $^{14}$C-labeling | 10 |
| Rainbow trout *(Salmo gairdneri)* | Growth | 82 |
| Red sea bream *(Chrysophrys major)* | Growth | 104 |
| Sea bass *(Dicentrarchus labrax)* | $^{14}$C-labeling | 53 |
| Sockeye salmon *(Oncorhynchus nerka)* | Growth | 29 |
| Sole *(Solea solea)* | $^{14}$C-labeling | 10 |
| Tilapia *(Tilapia zillii)* | Growth | 51 |

being tested). Diets are designed to contain protein levels at or slightly below the optimal protein requirement for that species to assure maximal utilization of the limiting amino acid. This procedure has been used successfully in chinook, coho, and sockeye salmon, Japanese eel, and rainbow trout. However, the amino acid test diets must be neutralized with a base before they can be utilized by common carp (61), and channel catfish (101).

Other investigators have used semipurified and practical-type test diets to estimate amino acid requirements in fish. The semipurified diet includes an imbalanced protein as the major source of dietary amino acids, for example zein (16, 36) or corn gluten (27, 39), which are deficient in certain amino acids. The practical-type diet involves normal feedstuffs to furnish the bulk of the amino acids in the test diets. These may be formulated with a fixed amount of the desired protein level and the remaining amount of the protein equivalent is made up of crystalline amino acids (32, 33, 49, 92, 94, 96). Wilson (99) has pointed out some of the possible problems inherent in using these types of diets in assessing the amino acid requirements of fish.

Most of the reported amino acid requirement values are estimates based on the conventional growth response curves or Almquist plots. Replicate groups of fish are fed diets containing graded levels of the test amino acid until measurable differences appear in their growth. A linear increase in growth rate is normally observed with increasing amino acid intake up to a plateau corresponding to the requirement for the specific amino acid.

Cowey & Tacon (14) and Cowey & Luquet (12) have reviewed the various problems involved in the accurate determination of the amino acid requirements of fish based on growth studies. Some of these problems are (*a*) imprecise interpretation of the growth response curves, i.e. the breakpoint of the curve is often determined subjectively; (*b*) the growth rates commonly observed with amino acid test diets being generally lower than those observed with intact protein diets; and (*c*) some of the crystalline amino acids in the test diets being leached during the feeding studies.

Some investigators have found a high degree of correlation of either serum or blood and muscle free amino acid levels to dietary amino acid intake in fish. The basic hypothesis suggests serum or tissue content of the amino acid will remain low until the requirement for that amino acid is met, and then increase to high levels when excessive amino acid is consumed. This technique has been useful in determining the amino acid requirement in only a few cases. The studies in the channel catfish of the 10 indispensable amino acids showed that serum lysine (101), threonine (100), histidine (102), and methionine (30) were required.

Amino acid oxidation studies have been used to estimate amino acid requirements for fish. Rainbow trout were fed test diets containing increasing levels of dietary lysine for 12 weeks. Three fish from each dietary treatment were injected intraperitoneally with a tracer dose of [U-$^{14}$C] lysine and the respired carbon dioxide was collected over a 20-hr period. The level of $^{14}C\text{-}CO_2$ produced was used as a direct measurement of the rate of oxidation of lysine in the fish. The level of oxidation observed was very low in those fish fed low dietary levels of lysine, somewhat higher for the intermediate dietary levels, and much higher for the higher levels of dietary lysine (96). The break-point of the dose response curve indicated a dietary requirement of 20 g lysine/kg diet, which was in close agreement with a value of 19 g lysine/kg diet obtained from growth data.

These same investigators have also used this method to assess the tryptophan requirement of rainbow trout (94). In this case, the requirement value was lower, 2.0 vs 2.5 g/kg diet, when determined by tryptophan oxidation than by growth data. Using one or more of the above techniques, researchers determined the indispensable amino acid requirements for several species of fish.

## *Arginine*

The arginine requirement values are summarized in Table 3. Salmon have the highest requirement at about 6% of dietary protein; the other species require about 4–5%. The arginine requirement in rainbow trout has been reported to be influenced by salinity (36). Kaushik found the requirement to be 3.3% of protein in freshwater and to decrease to 2.8% in 20 ppt salinity and to 2.2% of protein in full-strength seawater. These data indicate that the protein requirement should decrease as salinity increases. However, Zeitoun et al (107) reported that rainbow trout fingerlings require 40% protein for optimum growth at 10 ppt salinity and 45% protein at 20 ppt salinity. Additional studies are needed to confirm these observations before final conclusions can be drawn.

## *Histidine*

The histidine requirements of fish exhibit excellent agreement among the species studied, with a range of 1.5–2.1% of protein. Wilson et al (102) found that the serum free-histidine levels in channel catfish responded positively to graded dietary histidine intake. In serum, free histidine concentration increased significantly up to the dietary requirement (as determined by growth data) and then remained constant at higher dietary intake.

Muscle carnosine concentration has been shown to be altered by dietary histidine in the chinook salmon (47). It was depleted when a histidine-deficient diet was fed. Carnosine could not be detected in muscle tissue of the channel catfish regardless of the dietary level of histidine (102). This may, however, serve as another potential indicator of histidine status in other fishes.

## *Isoleucine*

The isoleucine requirements of fish appear to be about 2.0–2.6% of protein for those species studied except for the Japanese eel, which has a much higher value. The value originally reported for lake trout, *Salvelinus namaycush,* was lower (1.54–2.06% of protein) than those observed in other fishes (32). Hughes et al (32) state that the test diets were formulated to meet the required levels of amino acids for a 35% protein diet; however, when the total protein level is calculated based on the apparent nitrogen content of the test diets, a much lower dietary protein level is obtained. When the requirement value is recalculated based on the calculated nitrogen content of the diet, the requirement value is within the range reported for other species. Wilson et al (102) determined the effects of dietary isoleucine on serum free-isoleucine, leucine, and valine in the channel catfish. Even though the serum isoleucine increased somewhat with increasing isoleucine intake, these data did not confirm the requirement determined by growth data. The serum free-leucine and valine concentrations

**Table 3** Indispensable amino acid requirements[a]

| Fish | Arginine | Histidine | Isoleucine | Leucine | Valine |
|---|---|---|---|---|---|
| Chinook salmon | 6.0(2.4/40)(43) | 1.8(0.7/40)(43) | 2.2(0.9/41)(9) | 3.9(1.6/41)(9) | 3.2(1.3/40)(9) |
| Coho salmon | 5.8(2.3/40)(43) | 1.8(0.7/40)(43) | | | |
| Common carp | 4.3(1.6/38.5)(59) | 2.1(0.8/38.5)(59) | 2.5(0.9/38.5)(59) | 3.3(1.3/38.5)(59) | 3.6(1.4/38.5)(59) |
| Japanese eel | 4.5(1.7/37.7)(59) | 2.1(0.8/37.7)(59) | 4.0(1.5/37.7)(59) | 5.3(2.0/37.7)(59) | 4.0(1.5/37.7)(59) |
| Channel catfish | 4.3(1.03/24)(77) | 1.5(0.37/24)(102) | 2.6(0.62/24)(102) | 3.5(0.84/24)(102) | 3.0(0.71/24)(102) |
| Lake trout | | | 2.6(0.72/27.6)(32) | 3.5(0.96/27.6)(32) | 3.3(0.78/23.7)(32) |
| Rainbow trout | 3.3(1.2/36)(36) | | | | |
| | 4.0(1.4/35)(41) | | | | |
| | 5.9(2.8/47)(39) | | | | |
| Gilthead bream | 5.0(1.7/34)(49) | | | | |
| Tilapia | 4.01(1.59/40)(33) | | | | |

[a]Requirements are expressed as percentage of protein. In parentheses, the numerators are requirements as percentage of diet and the denominators are percentage of total protein in diet. References, in parentheses, follow each notation.

appeared to parallel the serum free-isoleucine concentrations. These workers also observed a much higher than expected mortality in their isoleucine-deficient fish.

### *Leucine*

The leucine requirements of fish are between 3.3 and 4.0% of protein for those species studied except for the eel, which has a much higher requirement. The value reported for lake trout (32) was lower (2.74–3.66% of protein); however, after the data were recalculated, they appear to agree with those previously reported for the other species.

Wilson et al (102) reported that the serum free-leucine level in channel catfish remained constant regardless of dietary leucine intake. There was, however, a marked effect of dietary leucine on the serum free-isoleucine and valine levels: about a six-fold increase in both concentrations at the 0.7% dietary leucine level, as compared to the 0.6% leucine level. These elevated levels of isoleucine and valine did not return to the base-line values until a dietary level of 1.2% or above was fed. This observation was interpreted to indicate that leucine may facilitate the tissue uptake of branched-chain amino acids and/or their intracellular metabolism.

### *Valine*

Reasonable agreement exists among the valine requirements reported for the species studied. The requirement ranges from about 3 to 4% of protein. A much lower value (1.77–2.23% of protein) was originally reported for lake trout (32); however, upon recalculation of the data the revised value fits within the range of those reported for other species.

The effect of valine intake on serum valine levels in the channel catfish was similar to that described for isoleucine (102).

### *Isoleucine-Leucine-Valine Interactions*

There are differences in the apparent isoleucine-leucine-valine interactions among different fishes. Chance et al (9) reported that the isoleucine requirement in chinook salmon was increased slightly with increasing levels of dietary leucine. This effect was not observed in either the common carp (59) or channel catfish (74). Nose (59) did, however, observe reduced growth rates in carp fed high dietary isoleucine levels during his study of leucine requirement. This reduced growth was not observed when the study was repeated at lower isoleucine levels. Hughes et al (32) observed a different pattern in plasma free branched-chain amino acids in lake trout fed increasing levels of valine than was previously observed in the channel catfish (102). No significant change in the plasma free-valine concentrations was observed until after the dietary requirement was met and then it increased about 2.5-fold. Plasma free-isoleucine and leucine were both elevated in the valine-deficient fish, and then decreased as dietary valine increased.

Robinson et al (74) concluded that a nutritional interrelationship does exist among the branched-chain amino acids in the channel catfish, but the interaction does not appear to be as severe as has been observed in certain other animals. These workers also suggest from their data that leucine may control either the tissue uptake or catabolism of valine and isoleucine in the channel catfish.

## *Lysine*

The lysine requirement values are listed in Table 4. Similar values have been reported for the chinook salmon, Japanese eel, channel catfish, and gilthead bream. A slightly higher value was found for common carp. The lower value for tilapia may be due to low growth rates observed and/or the type of test diet used. The requirement for rainbow trout appears to be lower than that observed for other species. Walton et al (96) observed excellent agreement between requirement values determined by growth studies and amino acid oxidation studies in rainbow trout. The much higher value reported by Ketola (39) appears to be out of line with the other values. Ketola (39) observed very high mortality and incidence of caudal fin erosion in fish fed the lysine-deficient diets. Since the caudal fin erosion was not observed in fish fed diets deficient in arginine, the author attributed the fin erosion specifically to the lysine deficiency. A recent report from the same laboratory has also indicated a high incidence of caudal fin erosion in tryptophan-deficient rainbow trout (70).

## *Arginine-Lysine Interactions*

A dietary interrelationship between arginine and lysine has been well documented in certain animals and is commonly known as the lysine-arginine antagonism. Robinson et al (77) could not demonstrate this antagonism in channel catfish when either excess lysine was fed in diets adequate or marginal in arginine, or when excess arginine was fed in diets adequate or marginal in lysine. Feeding excess lysine did not affect growth rates of rainbow trout fed low levels of arginine (41). Kaushik & Fauconneau (37) reported some biochemical evidence indicating that metabolic antagonism may exist between lysine and arginine in the rainbow trout. Increasing dietary lysine intake affected plasma arginine and urea levels and ammonia excretion. These changes were due to a decrease in the relative rate of arginine degradation as the level of dietary lysine increased (37).

## *Phenylalanine*

Phenylalanine and tyrosine are classified as aromatic amino acids, and adequate amounts of both are needed for proper protein synthesis and other physiological

**Table 4** Indispensable amino acid requirements[a]

| Fish | Lysine | Phenylalanine | Methionine | Threonine | Tryptophan |
|---|---|---|---|---|---|
| Chinook salmon | 5.0(2.0/40)(27) | 5.1(2.1/41)(9) | 4.0(1.6/40)(28) | 2.2(0.9/40)(18) | 0.5(0.2/40)(24) |
| | | Tyr = 0.4% | Cys = 1% | | |
| Coho salmon | | | | | 0.5(0.2/40)(24) |
| Sockeye salmon | | | | | 0.5(0.2/40)(24) |
| Common carp | 5.7(2.2/38.5)(59) | 6.5(2.5/38.5)(59) | 3.1(1.2/38.5)(59) | 3.9(1.5/38.5)(59) | 0.8(0.3/38.5)(59) |
| | | Tyr = 0% | Cys = 0% | | |
| | | | | | 0.3(0.13/42.5)(16) |
| Japanese eel | 5.3(2.0/37.7(59) | 5.8(2.2/37.7)(59) | 3.2(1.2/37.7)(59) | 4.0(1.5/37.7)(59) | 1.1(0.4/37.7)(59) |
| | | Tyr = 0% | Cys = 0% | | |
| Channel catfish | 5.1(1.23/24)(101) | 5.0(1.20/24)(75) | 2.3(0.56/24)(30) | 2.0(0.53/24)(100) | 0.5(0.12/24)(100) |
| | | Tyr = 0.3% | Cys = 0% | | |
| | 5.0(1.5/30)(76) | | | | |
| Rainbow trout | 3.7(1.3/35)(40) | | 2.2(1.0/46.4)(95) | | 0.5(0.25/55)(94) |
| | | | Cys = 0% | | |
| | 4.2(1.9/45)(96) | | | | 1.4(0.58/42)(70) |
| | 6.1(2.9/47)(39) | | 3.0(1.1/35)(78) | | |
| | | | Cys = 0.3% | | |
| | | | 2.9(1.0/35)(42) | | |
| | | | Cys = 0.5% | | |
| Gilthead bream | 5.0(1.7/34)(49) | | 4.0(1.4/34)(49) | | 0.6(0.2/34)(49) |
| | | | Cys = not stated | | |
| Tilapia | 4.1(1.62/40)(33) | | 3.2(1.27/40)(33) | | |
| | | | Cys = 0.7% | | |
| Sea bass | | | 2.0(1.0/50)(92) | | |
| | | | Cys = not stated | | |

[a]Requirements are expressed as percentage of protein. In parentheses, the numerators are requirements as percentage of diet and the denominators are percentage of total protein in diet. References, in parentheses, follow each notation. Cys and Tyr = percentage in the diet.

functions in fish. Fish can readily convert phenylalanine to tyrosine or utilize dietary tyrosine to meet their metabolic needs for this amino acid. Therefore, in order to determine the total aromatic amino acid requirement (phenylalanine plus tyrosine), the dietary requirement for phenylalanine is determined either in the absence of tyrosine or with test diets containing very low levels of tyrosine.

The phenylalanine or total aromatic amino acid requirements are listed in Table 4. Similar values have been reported for chinook salmon and channel catfish, with slightly higher values being required by the Japanese eel and common carp.

### *Methionine*

A relationship similar to phenylalanine and tyrosine exists for methionine and cystine. Cystine is considered dispensable because it can be synthesized by the fish from the indispensable amino acid methionine. When methionine is fed without cystine, a portion of the methionine is used for protein synthesis, and a portion is converted to cysteine for incorporation into protein. If cystine is included in the diet, it reduces the amount of dietary methionine needed. Fish have a total sulfur amino acid requirement rather than a specific methionine requirement.

The methionine or total sulfur amino acid requirement values (Table 4) reveal some differences among species. Chinook salmon and gilthead bream require the highest level at about 4% of protein, channel catfish require the least at 2.3% of protein, and the other species studied require about 3.0% of protein.

Rainbow trout appear to be unique in that methionine deficiency results in bilateral cataracts (69). Poston et al (69) observed cataracts in rainbow trout fed diets containing isolated soybean protein. The cataracts were prevented by supplementing the diet with methionine. Cataracts have also been observed in methionine-deficient rainbow trout by Walton et al (95) and Rumsey et al (78). This deficiency sign has not been reported in any other species of fish.

Several studies have shown that the presence of dietary cystine reduces the amount of dietary methionine necessary for maximum growth. The cystine replacement value for methionine on a sulfur basis has been determined to be about 60% for channel catfish (30) and 40% for rainbow trout (42).

Robinson et al (73) studied the utilization of several dietary sulfur compounds in channel catfish. Growth and feed efficiency data indicated that DL-methionine was utilized as effectively as L-methionine. Methionine hydroxy analogue was only about 25% as effective in promoting growth as L-methionine. No significant growth response was observed when taurine or inorganic sulfate was added to the basal diet. Page et al (66) were also unable to detect the utilization of taurine and inorganic sulfate as sulfur sources in rainbow trout. D-methionine has been shown to replace L-methionine on an equal basis in rainbow trout (42).

### *Threonine*

The Japanese eel and common carp appear to have a higher threonine requirement than the chinook salmon and channel catfish. DeLong et al (18) found the threonine requirement of young chinook salmon to be the same when determined at rearing temperatures of 8° and 15°C. These findings were not expected, since these workers have previously reported the protein requirement to increase from 40% at 8° to 55% at 15°C (17). The data on the threonine requirement would tend to indicate that the actual protein requirement for optimal protein synthesis does not change with increasing temperature.

### *Tryptophan*

A tryptophan level of 0.5% of protein appears to be adequate for most fishes, with the exception of the Japanese eel and possibly the common carp. The value of 0.3% of protein reported by Dabrowski (16) for common carp appears to be low, and may have resulted from the experimental conditions. The value obtained by Poston & Rumsey (70) for rainbow trout appears to be too high when compared to the other data reported for this species.

Tryptophan deficiency results in several anatomical deformities in certain salmonid species, but not in other fishes. Halver & Shanks (29) observed scoliosis and lordosis in sockeye salmon, but not in chinook salmon fed tryptophan-deficient diets. Scoliosis and lordosis has also been observed in tryptophan-deficient rainbow trout (82). These deformities were found to be reversible when the fish were fed adequate dietary tryptophan (44, 82). Other tryptophan deficiency signs in rainbow trout include renal calcinosis (44), caudal fin erosion, cataracts, and short gill opercula (70), and increased liver and kidney levels of calcium, magnesium, sodium, and potassium (94).

## SUMMARY

Tentative qualitative and quantitative amino acid requirements have been reported for the major species of fish reared for market or as replacement stocks for natural waters. Most work has concentrated upon juvenile fish or upon rapidly growing young market fish; these have high protein dietary requirements (30–50%) that are in direct contrast to the homothermic terrestial animals. Net protein utilization from the diet is similar or slightly better than that found in avian species, but energy needs are much lower in fish and as a result the body protein deposition in fish is larger (about 5 g protein/MJ for the chick versus about 10 g protein/MJ for young fish).

Qualitative amino acid requirements appear identical for all fish species examined; arginine, histidine, isoleucine, leucine, lysine, methionine, phenylalanine, threonine, tryptophan, and valine are all required for normal growth and metabolism. Quantitative requirements differ only slightly among species that have been tested. Salmon have higher arginine requirements than other fish examined (33, 36, 43, 59, 77). Catfish appear to have a lower requirement for histidine and threonine (100, 102), and the Japanese eel seems to need more tryptophan in the diet (59). However, when the quantitative requirements for indispensable amino acids are expressed as a percentage of the protein fed, then a remarkable harmony appears between values needed for maximal growth for most species examined. A review of Tables 3 and 4 will disclose the paucity of information available considering the large number of fish species reared commercially over the world. Most commercial diet formulations have relied upon the work done on salmon, catfish, and carp, and their amino acid and protein requirement values have been used. Remarkably, these diets have produced other species of fish economically.

Sparing effects of one amino acid on another have only been studied with cystine-methionine and tyrosine-phenylalanine. Arginine and analogues of methionine have been used as good nitrogen sources for salmon. Isoleucine-leucine ratios have been measured and experiments indicate some growth inhibition when the isoleucine-leucine ratio was greater than 2/1 (9). Valine at abnormally high levels also inhibited growth (9). Much more work needs to be done on the effects of subtle differences in amino acid ratios in the diet, and major emphasis should be placed on the important role of the dispensable amino acids in fish nutrition.

Fish production is expanding rapidly in northern Europe, in the southern US, and in the developing nations of the world. Protein and indispensable amino acid dietary intake are growth determinants, and the dietary requirement is higher for fish than for terrestrial animals. In the future, more emphasis can be expected on quantitative amino acid requirements and economical sources for protein for many new fish species reared under a variety of environmental conditions.

## *Literature Cited*


1. Adron, J. W., Blair, A., Cowey, C. B., Shanks, A. M. 1976. Effects of dietary energy level and dietary energy source on growth, feed conversion and body composition of turbot (*Scophthalmus maximus* L.). *Aquaculture* 7:125–32
2. Alliot, E., Pastoureaud, A., Nedelec, J. 1979. Etude de l'apport calorique et du rapport et la composition corporelle. In *Finfish Nutrition and Fishfeed Technology*, ed. J. E. Halver, K. Tiews, 1:241–52. Berlin: Heenemann
3. Anderson, R. J., Kienholz, E. W., Flickinger, S. A. 1981. Protein requirements of smallmouth bass and largemouth bass. *J. Nutr.* 111:1085–97
4. Aoe, H., Masuda, I., Abe, I., Saito, T., Toyoda, T., Kitamura, S. 1970. Nutrition of protein in young carp. I. Nutritive value of free amino acids. *Bull. Jpn. Soc. Sci. Fish.* 36:407–13
5. Arai, S., Nose, T., Hashimoto, Y. 1972. Amino acids essential for the growth of eels, *Anguilla anguilla* and *A. japonica*. *Bull. Jpn. Soc. Sci. Fish.* 38:753–59
6. Balarin, J. D., Haller, R. D. 1982. The intensive culture of tilapia in tanks, raceways and cages. In *Recent Advances in Aquaculture,* ed. J. F. Muir, R. J. Roberts, pp. 265–356. London: Croom Helm Ltd.
7. Bergot, F. 1979. Carbohydrate in rain-

bow trout diets: effects of the level and source of carbohydrate and the number of meals on growth and body composition. *Aquaculture* 18:157–67

8. Buhler, D. R., Halver, J. E. 1961. Nutrition of salmonoid fishes. IX. Carbohydrate requirement of chinook salmon. *J. Nutr.* 74:307–18
9. Chance, R. E., Mertz, E. T., Halver, J. E. 1964. Nutrition of salmonoid fishes. XII. Isoleucine, leucine, valine and phenylalanine requirements of chinook salmon and interrelations between isoleucine and leucine for growth. *J. Nutr.* 83:177–85
10. Cowey, C. B., Adron, J. W., Blair, A. 1970. Studies on the nutrition of marine flatfish. The essential amino acid requirements of plaice and sole. *J. Mar. Biol. Assoc. UK* 50:87–95
11. Cowey, C. B., Adron, J. W., Brown, D. A. 1975. Studies on the nutrition of marine flatfish. The metabolism of glucose by plaice *(Pleuronectes platessa)* and the effect of dietary energy source on protein utilization in plaice. *Br. J. Nutr.* 33:219–31
12. Cowey, C. B., Luquet, P. 1983. Physiological basis of protein requirements of fishes. Critical analysis of allowances. In *Protein Metabolism and Nutrition,* ed. R. Pion, M. Arnal, D. Bonin, 1:364–84. Paris: INRA
13. Cowey, C. B., Pope, J. A., Adron, J. W., Blair, A. 1972. Studies on the nutrition of marine flatfish. The protein requirement of plaice *(Pleuronectes platessa). Br. J. Nutr.* 28:447–56
14. Cowey, C. B., Tacon, A. G. J. 1983. Fish nutrition—relevance to invertebrates. In *Proc. 2nd Int. Conf. Aquaculture Nutrition: Biochemical and Physiological Approaches to Shellfish Nutrition,* ed. G. D. Pruder, C. J. Langdon, D. E. Conklin, pp. 13–30. Baton Rouge: Louisiana State Univ., Div. Continuing Educ.
15. Dabrowski, K. 1977. Protein requirements of grass carp fry (*Ctenopharyngodon idella* Val). *Aquaculture* 12:63–73
16. Dabrowski, K. R. 1981. Tryptophan requirement of common carp (*Cyprinus carpio* L.) fry. *Z. Tierphysiol. Tierernährg. Futtermittelkd.* 46:64–71
17. DeLong, D. C., Halver, J. E., Mertz, E. T. 1958. Nutrition of salmonoid fishes. VI. Protein requirements of chinook salmon at two water temperatures. *J. Nutr.* 65:589–99
18. DeLong, D. C., Halver, J. E., Mertz, E. T. 1962. Nutrition of salmonoid fishes. X. Quantitative threonine requirements of chinook salmon at two water temperatures. *J. Nutr.* 76:174–78
19. Dupree, H. K., Halver, J. E. 1970. Amino acids essential for the growth of channel catfish, *Ictalurus punctatus. Trans. Am. Fish. Soc.* 99:90–92
20. Furuichi, M., Yone, Y. 1971. Studies on nutrition of red sea bream. IV. Nutritive value of dietary carbohydrate. *Rep. Fish. Res. Lab. Kyushu Univ.* 1:75–81
21. Garling, D. L. Jr., Wilson, R. P. 1976. Optimum dietary protein to energy ratio for channel catfish fingerlings, *Ictalurus punctatus. J. Nutr.* 106:1368–75
22. Garling, D. L. Jr., Wilson, R. P. 1977. Effects of dietary carbohydrate-to-lipid ratios on growth and body composition of fingerling channel catfish. *Prog. Fish-Cult.* 39:43–47
23. Halver, J. E. 1957. Nutrition of salmonoid fishes. IV. An amino acid test diet for chinook salmon. *J. Nutr.* 62:245–54
24. Halver, J. E. 1965. Tryptophan requirement of chinook, sockeye and silver salmon. *Fed. Proc.* 24:229(Abstr.)
25. Halver, J. E., Bates, L. S., Mertz, E. T. 1964. Protein requirements for sockeye salmon and rainbow trout. *Fed. Proc.* 23:1778(Abstr.)
26. Halver, J. E., DeLong, D. C., Mertz, E. T. 1957. Nutrition of salmonoid fishes. V. Classification of essential amino acids for chinook salmon. *J. Nutr.* 63:95–105
27. Halver, J. E., DeLong, D. C., Mertz, E. T. 1958. Threonine and lysine requirements of chinook salmon. *Fed. Proc.* 17:1873(Abstr.)
28. Halver, J. E., DeLong, D. C., Mertz, E. T. 1959. Methionine and cystine requirements of chinook salmon. *Fed. Proc.* 18:2076(Abstr.)
29. Halver, J. E., Shanks, W. E. 1960. Nutrition of salmonoid fishes. VIII. Indispensable amino acids for sockeye salmon. *J. Nutr.* 72:340–46
30. Harding, D. E., Allen, O. W. Jr., Wilson, R. P. 1977. Sulfur amino acid requirement of channel catfish: L-methionine and L-cystine. *J. Nutr.* 107:2031–35
31. Hilton, J. W., Slinger, S. J. 1981. Nutrition and feeding of rainbow trout. *Can. Spec. Publ. Fish. Aquat. Sci.,* Vol. 55. 15 pp.
32. Hughes, S. G., Rumsey, G. L., Nesheim, M. C. 1983. Dietary requirements for essential branched-chain amino acids by lake trout. *Trans. Am. Fish. Soc.* 112:812–17
33. Jackson, A. J., Capper, B. S. 1982. Investigations into the requirements of the tilapia *Sarotherodon mossambicus* for dietary methionine, lysine and arginine in semisynthetic diets. *Aquaculture* 29: 289–97
34. Jauncey, K. 1982. The effects of varying

dietary protein level on the growth, food conversion, protein utilization, and body composition of juvenile tilapias *(Sarotherodon mossambicus). Aquaculture* 27:43–54

35. Kanazawa, A., Teshima, S., Sakamoto, M., Shinomiya, A. 1980. Nutritional requirements of the puffer fish: purified test diet and the optimum protein level. *Bull. Jpn. Soc. Sci. Fish.* 46:1357–61
36. Kaushik, S. 1979. Application of a biochemical method for the estimation of amino acid needs in fish: Quantitative arginine requirements of rainbow trout in different salinities. See Ref. 2, pp. 197–207
37. Kaushik, S. J., Fauconneau, B. 1984. Effects of lysine administration on plasma arginine and on some nitrogenous catabolites in rainbow trout. *Comp. Biochem. Physiol.* 79A:459–62
38. Kaushik, S. J., Luquet, P., Blanc, D. 1981. Usefulness of feeding protein and non-protein calories apart in studies on energy-protein interrelationships in rainbow trout. *Ann. Zootech.* 30:3–11
39. Ketola, H. G. 1983. Requirement for dietary lysine and arginine by fry of rainbow trout. *J. Anim. Sci.* 56:101–7
40. Kim, K. I., Kayes, T. B. 1982. Test diet development and lysine requirement of rainbow trout. *Fed. Proc.* 41:716 (Abstr.)
41. Kim, K. I., Kayes, T. B., Amundson, C. H. 1983. Protein and arginine requirements of rainbow trout. *Fed. Proc.* 42:2198 (Abstr.)
42. Kim, K. I., Kayes, T. B., Amundson, C. H. 1984. Requirements for sulfur-containing amino acids and utilization of D-methionine by rainbow trout. *Fed. Proc.* 43:3338 (Abstr.)
43. Klein, R. G., Halver, J. E. 1970. Nutrition of salmonoid fishes: Arginine and histidine requirements of chinook and coho salmon. *J. Nutr.* 100:1105–9
44. Kloppel, T. M., Post, G. 1975. Histological alterations in tryptophan-deficient rainbow trout. *J. Nutr.* 105:861–66
45. Lee, D. J., Putnam, G. B. 1973. The response of rainbow trout to varying protein/energy ratios in a test diet. *J. Nutr.* 103:916–22
46. Lim, C., Sukhawongs, S., Pascual, F. P. 1979. A preliminary study on the protein requirement of *Chanos chanos* (Forskal) fry in a controlled environment. *Aquaculture* 17:195–201
47. Lukton, A. 1958. Effect of diet on imidazole compounds and creatine in chinook salmon. *Nature* 182:1019–20
48. Luquet, P., Kaushik, S. J. 1981. Besoins en proteines et en acides amines. In *Nutrition des Poissons*, ed. M. Fontaine, pp. 171–83. Paris: CNRS
49. Luquet, P., Sabaut, J. J. 1974. Nutrition azotee et croissance chez la daurade et la truite. *Actes de colloques, Colloques Sur L'Aquaculture, Brest.* 1:243–53
50. Mazid, M. A., Tanaka, Y., Katayama, T., Rahman, M. A., Simpson, K. L., Chichester, C. O. 1979. Growth response of *Tilapia zillii* fingerlings fed isocaloric diets with variable protein levels. *Aquaculture* 18:115–22
51. Mazid, M. A., Tanaka, Y., Katayama, T., Simpson, K. L., Chichester, C. O. 1978. Metabolism of amino acids in aquatic animals. III. Indispensable amino acids for *Tilapia zillii. Bull. Jpn. Soc. Sci. Fish.* 44:739–42
52. Mertz, E. T. 1972. The protein and amino acid needs. In *Fish Nutrition,* ed. J. E. Halver, pp. 105–43. New York: Academic
53. Metailler, R., Febvre, A., Alliot, E. 1973. Preliminary note on the essential amino acids of the sea bass *Dicentrarchus labrax* (Linne). *Stud. Rev. GFCM* 52:91–96
54. Millikin, M. R. 1982. Effects of dietary protein concentration on growth, feed efficiency and body composition of age-0 striped bass. *Trans. Am. Fish. Soc.* 111:373–78
55. Millikin, M. R. 1983. Interactive effects of dietary protein and lipid on growth and protein utilization of age-0 striped bass. *Trans. Am. Fish. Soc.* 112:185–93
56. Murray, M. W., Andrews, J. W., DeLoach, H. L. 1977. Effects of dietary lipids, dietary protein and environmental temperatures on growth, feed conversion and body composition of channel catfish. *J. Nutr.* 107:272–80
57. National Research Council. 1977. *Nutrient Requirements of Warmwater Fishes.* Washington, DC: Natl. Acad. Sci. 78 pp.
58. National Research Council. 1981. *Nutrient Requirements of Coldwater Fishes.* Washington, DC: Natl. Acad. Sci. 63 pp.
59. Nose, T. 1979. Summary report on the requirements of essential amino acids for carp. See Ref. 2, pp. 145–56
60. Nose, T., Arai, S. 1972. Optimum level of protein in purified test diet for eel, *Anguilla japonica. Bull. Freshw. Fish Res. Lab. Tokyo* 22:145–55
61. Nose, T., Arai, S., Lee, D. L., Hashimoto, Y. 1974. A note on amino acids essential for growth of young carp. *Bull. Jpn. Soc. Sci. Fish.* 40:903–8
62. Ogino, C., Chen, M. S. 1973. Protein nutrition in fish. V. Relation between biological value of dietary proteins and

their utilization in carp. *Bull. Jpn. Soc. Sci. Fish.* 39:955–59
63. Ogino, C., Chiou, J. Y., Takeuchi, T. 1976. Protein nutrition in fish. VI. Effects of dietary energy sources on the utilization of proteins by rainbow trout and carp. *Bull. Jpn. Soc. Sci. Fish.* 42:213–18
64. Ogino, C., Saito, K. 1970. Protein nutrition in fish. I. The utilization of dietary protein by young carp. *Bull. Jpn. Soc. Sci. Fish.* 36:250–54
65. Page, J. W., Andrews, J. W. 1973. Interactions of dietary levels of protein and energy on channel catfish *(Ictalurus punctatus). J. Nutr.* 103:1339–46
66. Page, J. W., Rumsey, G. L., Riis, R. C., Scott, M. L. 1978. Dietary sulfur requirements of fish: nutritional and pathological criteria. *Fed. Proc.* 37:1189 (Abstr.)
67. Phillips, A. M. Jr. 1969. Nutrition, digestion, and energy utilization. In *Fish Physiology,* ed. W. S. Hoar, D. J. Randall, 1:351–432. New York/London: Academic
68. Pieper, A., Pfeffer, E. 1979. Carbohydrates as possible sources of dietary energy for rainbow trout (*Salmo gairdneri,* Richardson). See Ref. 2, pp. 209–19
69. Poston, H. A., Riis, R. C., Rumsey, G. L., Ketola, H. G. 1977. The effect of supplemental dietary amino acids, minerals and vitamins on salmonids fed cataractogenic diets. *Cornell Vet.* 67: 472–509
70. Poston, H. A., Rumsey, G. L. 1983. Factors affecting dietary requirement and deficiency signs of L-tryptophan in rainbow trout. *J. Nutr.* 113:2568–77
71. Reinitz, G. L., Orme, L. E., Lemm, C. A., Hitzel, F. N. 1978. Influence of varying lipid concentrations with two protein concentrations in diets for rainbow trout *(Salmo gairdneri). Trans. Am. Fish. Soc.* 107:751–54
72. Ringrose, R. C. 1971. Calorie-to-protein ratio for brook trout *(Salvelinus fontinalis). J. Fish. Res. Board Can.* 28:1113–17
73. Robinson, E. H., Allen, O. W. Jr., Poe, W. E., Wilson, R. P. 1978. Utilization of dietary sulfur compounds by fingerling channel catfish: L-methionine, DL-methionine, methionine hydroxy analogue, taurine and inorganic sulfate. *J. Nutr.* 108:1932–36
74. Robinson, E. H., Poe, W. E., Wilson, R. P. 1974. Effects of feeding diets containing an imbalance of branched-chain amino acids on fingerling channel catfish. *Aquaculture* 37:51–62
75. Robinson, E. H., Wilson, R. P., Poe, W. E. 1980. Total aromatic amino acid requirement, phenylalanine requirement and tyrosine replacement value for fingerling channel catfish. *J. Nutr.* 110:1805–12
76. Robinson, E. H., Wilson, R. P., Poe, W. E. 1980. Reevaluation of the lysine requirement and lysine utilization by fingerling channel catfish. *J. Nutr.* 110:2313–16
77. Robinson, E. H., Wilson, R. P., Poe, W. E. 1981. Arginine requirement and apparent absence of a lysine-arginine antagonist in fingerling channel catfish. *J. Nutr.* 111:46–52
78. Rumsey, G. L., Page, J. W., Scott, M. L. 1983. Methionine and cystine requirements of rainbow trout. *Prog. Fish-Cult.* 45:139–43
79. Sabaut, J. J., Luquet, P. 1973. Nutritional requirements of the gilthead bream *(Chrysophrys aurata),* quantitative protein requirements. *Mar. Biol. (Berlin)* 18:50–54
80. Satia, B. P. 1974. Quantitative protein requirements of rainbow trout. *Prog. Fish-Cult.* 36:80–85
81. Sen, P. R., Rao, N. G. S., Ghosh, S. R., Rout, M. 1978. Observations on the protein and carbohydrate requirements of carps. *Aquaculture* 13:245–55
82. Shanks, W. E., Gahimer, G. D., Halver, J. E. 1962. The indispensable amino acids for rainbow trout. *Prog. Fish-Cult.* 24:68–73
83. Shimeno, S., Hosokawa, H., Takeda, M., Kajiyama, H. 1980. Effects of calorie to protein ratios in formulated diet on the growth, feed conversion and body composition of young yellowtail. *Bull. Jpn. Soc. Sci. Fish.* 46:1083–87
84. Sin, A. W. 1973. The dietary protein requirements for growth of young carp *(Cyprinus carpio). Hong Kong Fish. Bull.* 3:77–81
85. Sin, A. W. 1973. The utilization of dietary protein for growth of young carp *(Cyprinus carpio)* in relation to variations in fat intake. *Hong Kong Fish. Bull.* 3:83–88
86. Stickney, R. R., Andrews, J. W. 1972. Effects of dietary lipids on growth, food conversion, lipid and fatty acid composition of channel catfish. *J. Nutr.* 102:249–58
87. Takeda, M., Shimeno, S., Hosokawa, H., Kajiyama, H., Kaisyo, T. 1975. The effect of dietary calorie-to-protein ratio on the growth, feed conversion and body composition of young yellowtail. *Bull. Jpn. Soc. Sci. Fish.* 41:443–47
88. Takeuchi, T., Watanabe, T., Ogino, C.

1978. Supplementary effects of lipids in high protein diets of rainbow trout. *Bull. Jpn. Soc. Sci. Fish.* 44:677–81

89. Takeuchi, T., Watanabe, T., Ogino, C. 1979. Optimum ratio of dietary energy to protein for carp. *Bull. Jpn. Soc. Sci. Fish.* 45:983–87
90. Takeuchi, T., Yokoyama, M., Watanabe, T., Ogino, C. 1978. Optimum ratio of dietary energy to protein for rainbow trout. *Bull. Jpn. Soc. Sci. Fish.* 44:729–32
91. Teng, S., Chua, T., Lim, P. 1978. Preliminary observations on the dietary protein requirement of estuary grouper, *Epinephelus salmoides* Maxwell, cultured in floating net-cages. *Aquaculture* 15:257–71
92. Thebault, H. 1983. *Etude du besoin en methionine chez le loup, Dicentrarchus labrax, en milieu controle.* These de Doctorat, Univ. D'Aix-Marseille, France
93. Viola, S., Rappaport, U. 1979. The "extra-caloric" effect of oil in the nutrition of carp. *Bamidgeh* 31:51–68
94. Walton, M. J., Coloso, R. M., Cowey, C. B., Adron, J. W., Knox, D. 1984. The effects of dietary tryptophan levels on growth and metabolism of rainbow trout *(Salmo gairdneri). Br. J. Nutr.* 51:279–87
95. Walton, M. J., Cowey, C. B., Adron, J. W. 1982. Methionine metabolism in rainbow trout fed diets of differing methionine and cystine content. *J. Nutr.* 112:1525–35
96. Walton, M. J., Cowey, C. B., Adron, J. W. 1984. The effect of dietary lysine levels on growth and metabolism of rainbow trout *(Salmo gairdneri). Br. J. Nutr.* 52:115–22
97. Wang, K. W., Takeuchi, T., Watanabe, T. 1985. Effect of dietary protein levels on growth of *Tilapia nilotica. Bull. Jpn. Soc. Sci. Fish.* 51:133–40
98. Wee, K. L., Tacon, A. G. J. 1982. A preliminary study on the dietary protein requirement of juvenile snakehead. *Bull. Jpn. Soc. Sci. Fish.* 48:1463–68
99. Wilson, R. P. 1986. Amino acid and protein requirements of fish. In *Nutrition and Feeding in Fish,* ed. C. B. Cowey, A. M. Mackie, J. G. Bell. London: Academic. In press
100. Wilson, R. P., Allen, O. W. Jr., Robinson, E. H., Poe, W. E. 1978. Tryptophan and threonine requirements of fingerling channel catfish. *J. Nutr.* 108:1595–99
101. Wilson, R. P., Harding, D. E., Garling, D. L. Jr. 1977. Effect of dietary pH on amino acid utilization and the lysine requirement of fingerling channel catfish. *J. Nutr.* 107:166–70
102. Wilson, R. P., Poe, W. E., Robinson, E. H. 1980. Leucine, isoleucine, valine and histidine requirements of fingerling channel catfish. *J. Nutr.* 110:627–33
103. Winfree, R. A., Stickney, R. R. 1981. Effects of dietary protein and energy on growth, feed conversion efficiency and body composition of *Tilapia aurea. J. Nutr.* 111:1001–12
104. Yone, Y. 1976. Nutritional studies of red sea bream. In *Proc. 1st Int. Conf. Aquaculture,* ed. K. S. Price, W. N. Shaw, K. S. Danberg, pp. 39–64. Lewes: Univ. Delaware
105. Yu, T. C., Sinnhuber, R. O. 1981. Use of beef tallow as an energy source in coho salmon *(Oncorhynchus kisutch)* rations. *Can. J. Fish. Aquat. Sci.* 38:367–70
106. Yu, T. C., Sinnhuber, R. O., Putnam, G. B. 1977. Use of swine fat as an energy source in trout rations. *Prog. Fish-Cult.* 39:95–97
107. Zeitoun, I. H., Tack, P. I., Halver, J. E., Ullrey, D. E. 1973. Influence of salinity on protein requirements of rainbow trout *(Salmo gairdneri)* fingerlings. *J. Fish. Res. Board Can.* 30:1867–73
108. Zeitoun, I. H., Ullrey, D. E., Halver, J. E., Tack, P. I., Magee, W. T. 1974. Influence of salinity on protein requirements of coho salmon *(Oncorhynchus kisutch)* smolts. *J. Fish. Res. Board Can.* 31:1145–48

*Ann. Rev. Nutr. 1986. 6:245–72*


# REGULATION OF CHOLESTEROL BIOSYNTHESIS

*Harry Rudney and Russell C. Sexton*

Department of Biochemistry and Molecular Biology, College of Medicine, University of Cincinnati, Cincinnati, Ohio 45267-0522

CONTENTS

THE CHOLESTEROL BIOSYNTHETIC PATHWAY .......... 245
*Introduction* .......... 245
*Overview of Polyisoprenoid Synthesis and the Role of HMG-CoA Reductase* .......... 246
*Endogenous and Exogenous Factors Regulating HMG-CoA Reductase Activity* .......... 248
*Post-mevalonate Regulation of Polyisoprenoid and Cholesterol Synthesis* .......... 251
*Oxysterols as Regulators of Cholesterol Synthesis* .......... 254
DIETARY FACTORS .......... 258
*Rates of Cholesterogenesis in Various Tissues* .......... 258
*Effects of Dietary Fats on Hepatic Cholesterogenesis* .......... 259
*Effects of Vitamin A Active Substances* .......... 260
*Effects of Vitamin D Active Substances* .......... 261
*Role of Cholesterogenesis in Hepatic VLDL Production* .......... 263
*Diurnal Variations in Hepatic Cholesterogenesis* .......... 264
CONCLUSION .......... 265

## THE CHOLESTEROL BIOSYNTHETIC PATHWAY

### *Introduction*[1]

Regulation of endogenous biosynthesis of cholesterol is a topic that has engaged the interest of a wide spectrum of researchers over the past 30 years. This process in all its ramifications bears on many essential aspects of cell

[1]Abbreviations:

HMG-CoA 3-Hydroxy-3-methylglutaryl Coenzyme A
IPP Isopentenyl pyrophosphate
FPP Farnesyl pyrophosphate
LDL Low-density lipoproteins
MVA Mevalonic acid
SO Squalene 2,3-oxide
SDO Squalene 2,3:22,23-dioxide
OSC Oxidosqualene cyclase.



0199-9885/86/0715-0245$02.00

function and thus new advances in cell and molecular biology are being applied to the problem. Because of considerable variation in methodology among workers, the results often supply answers that vary among different groups. In addition, there is difficulty in applying data obtained in animals to man. We indicate in this review those areas where further work is required to resolve controversies. Despite these problems, remarkable advances have been made, culminating in the sequencing of the genes for HMG-CoA reductase and the LDL receptor, two key elements in determining the level of cholesterol in the organism (62). This accomplishment will provide a firm foundation for many advances in the future. Because of constraints of space, we focus on a limited number of topics, and we offer our apologies to those colleagues whose important work we were unable to include in this review.

## *Overview of Polyisoprenoid Synthesis and the Role of HMG-CoA Reductase*

The three major constituents of cells that are of polyisoprenoid origin are the sterols, dolichols, and ubiquinones. The synthesis of these substances is closely related to growth, development, and differentiation of all cells. It is to be expected that the regulatory sites in the biosynthetic pathway common to each would be subject to several regulatory feedback loops, and these would be greatly influenced by the level of each product. In this review we focus primarily on the regulation of cholesterol biosynthesis. The other polyisoprenoid products are discussed insofar as they influence cholesterol synthesis.

There is general agreement that many factors that regulate cholesterol biosynthesis modulate the activity of the enzyme 3-hydroxy-3-methylglutaryl Coenzyme A reductase (HMG-CoA reductase), which reduces HMG-CoA to mevalonic acid. The subsequent biosynthesis of polyisoprenoids from mevalonic acid and the role that HMG-CoA reductase plays in determining the flux of isopentenyl pyrophosphate units throughout the pathway are shown in Figure 1.

Note that in addition to the three major products (the sterols, dolichols, and the polyisoprenoid side-chain of ubiquinone) there are some components minor in amount but not in importance, e.g. isopentenyl tRNA. The regulation of such a multibranched pathway is extraordinarily complex and, as might be expected, a multiplicity of factors are brought to bear on the regulation of the key regulatory enzyme, HMG-CoA reductase. Regulation at this particular step might be thought of as a coarse control, and other steps in different branches of the pathway might be tuned for finer control. The chart in Figure 1 is used as a reference to point out some of the new factors that have recently been elucidated; as they are discussed, we indicate areas in which further work is required.

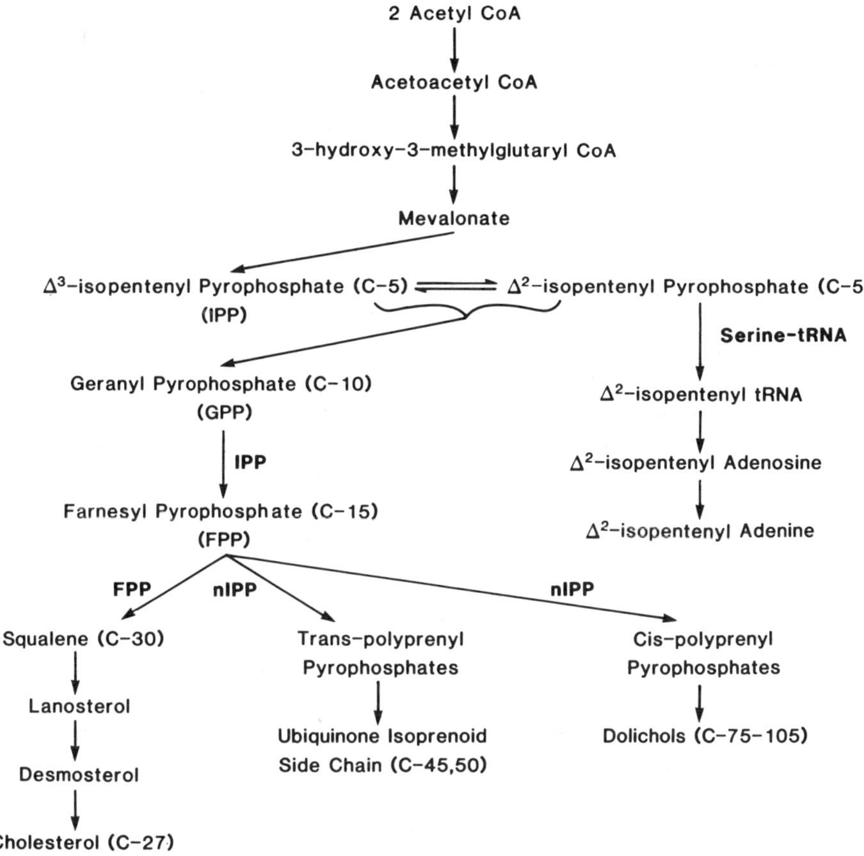


*Figure 1* Pathway of isoprenoid biosynthesis. The numbers in parentheses refer to the number of carbon atoms in the molecule. From (106) with permission of the publishers.

With respect to the overall polyisoprenoid pathway, it should be noted that after mevalonic acid has formed, a series of phosphorylations and decarboxylations, not shown in detail, forms the basic 5-carbon isoprenoid building block, isopentenyl pyrophospate (IPP). This latter compound polymerizes to form a 10-carbon intermediate, geranyl pyrophosphate (GPP), and a 15-carbon derivative, farnesyl pyrophosphate (FPP). FPP also represents a major branch point in the pathway: two moles may condense to form squalene with subsequent conversion to the sterols. On the other hand, IPP can continue in a sequential series of condensations with a molecule of FPP to form a longer all-*trans* polyprenyl derivative that becomes a side-chain of ubiquinone. The FPP can also be extended by sequential IPP addition in another direction to form the dolichols. The latter differ from the all-*trans* polyprenyl pyrophosphate in that they contain isoprenoid units with *cis* double bonds instead of *trans*, the molecules are larger, and they generally contain sixteen 5-carbon isoprenoid units. In addition to an initial all-*trans* farnesyl unit, the remaining double bonds are *cis* and generally one of the terminal double bonds is saturated. FPP serves as the base on which IPP is added to lead to the formation of ubiquinones (101) and dolichols (106) as well as the synthesis of squalene; this shows that FPP is an important branch point in the synthesis of all the major products of the polyisoprenoid pathway. Figure 1 also includes isopentenyl tRNA as a product because recent work has shown that it or another product of the mevalonic pathway, i.e. isopentenyl adenosine or isopentenyl adenine, is implicated in an as yet unknown manner with the initiation of DNA synthesis in the S phase of the cell growth cycle (140).

In summary the IPP unit can be directed to at least four products, and controlling the flow of the IPP units to these important cellular materials is now a major area of research. In addition to the FPP branch point, HMG-CoA reductase represents one of the first major, committed steps; consequently it has been the object of a great deal of research (for review, see 115, 125).

In recent landmark work from the Brown and Goldstein laboratory, the gene of HMG-CoA reductase from a Chinese hamster ovary cell line was isolated and sequenced. This work, as well as detailing the amino acid sequence, revealed many features of the structure of HMG-CoA reductase (88, 119). The molecule consists of a polypeptide of 887 amino acids. Of particular interest are the amino acid sequence encompassing the membrane-spanning region and the role that anchorage in the endoplasmic reticulum membrane plays in regulation (53). Recently the complete amino acid sequence of the human enzyme has been deduced from full-length cDNA clones (90). It is 888 amino acids long and displays a high degree of conserved sequences with the hamster enzyme. The conserved domains are in the membrane-spanning region and the catalytic site.

### *Endogenous and Exogenous Factors Regulating HMG-CoA Reductase Activity*

In cholesterol synthesis, it seems clear that cholesterol, introduced to the cell as cholesterol esters transported on low-density lipoproteins (LDL), modulates sterol synthesis by exerting a feedback regulation on the concentration of LDL membrane receptors and on the level of HMG-CoA reductase. There is also evidence that the enzymes HMG-CoA synthase (26) and acetoacetyl CoA synthase are coordinately linked to the modulation of sterol synthesis. Also, under certain conditions HMG-CoA and/or acetoacetyl CoA synthase activity can take over the rate-limiting function (5, 152). These aspects are omitted from the discussion because of space restraints. For an excellent review of this area the reader is referred to the discussion by Bergstrom et al (5). Our focus is primarily on HMG-CoA reductase.

The nature of the down regulation of reductase by LDL has been much studied (12, 61, 62). Studies of tissue cultures have demonstrated lipoprotein receptors on the surface membranes of hepatic and extrahepatic cells including fibroblasts, smooth muscle cells, and lymphocytes (61). Once LDL is bound to the receptor, it is internalized by endocytosis. As a result of lysosomal fusion with the endocytotic vesicle, the LDL protein component is degraded to amino acids and cholesterol esters are hydrolyzed. The free cholesterol is available for transfer into the cytosolic compartment possibly on one of several identified sterol carrier proteins (8, 51). The presence of increased amounts of free cholesterol within the cell results in the down regulation of HMG-CoA reductase activity by a mechanism as yet not completely understood.

Studies of cultured Chinese hamster ovary (CHO) cells (18), UT-1 cells (48), avian myleoblasts (145), and rat hepatocytes (41) indicate that cholesterol derived from LDL causes a decrease in the amount of HMG-CoA reductase enzyme by accelerating its degradation, as well as by reducing its rate of synthesis. Recently, Chin et al (23) reported the successful transfection of UT-2 cells, a mutant CHO cell line that lacks HMG-CoA reductase, with a pRed-227 plasmid that contains a cDNA for hamster HMG-CoA reductase. In these transfected cells, cholesterol derived from LDL did not repress the synthesis of HMG-CoA reductase but did cause a 50–60% decrease in enzyme activity. These results clearly demonstrated the significant effect of cholesterol on enzyme degradation independent of its effect on enzyme synthesis.

The mechanism by which cholesterol stimulates the degradation of HMG-CoA reductase protein has not been established. One controversial mechanism that has been proposed involves phosphorylation of the enzyme (83). Another possible mechanism involves an indirect effect of cholesterol on the physical properties of the membrane in which HMG-CoA reductase is embedded. By changing the fluidity of the membrane surrounding the enzyme, the reductase protein may be more susceptible to degradation by a cytosolic protease. Alternatively, Chin et al (22) suggested that cholesterol binding in the membranous domain of the reductase may cause the enzyme to cluster and eventually bud off into the cytosol where it is eventually degraded within lysosomes.

The Brown and Goldstein group has shown that, in a cell line induced to produce large amounts of HMG-CoA reductase by continually growing CHO cells in the presence of the competitive inhibitor compactin, LDL decreases reductase activity primarily by reducing the level of mRNA for the reductase, although increased degradation of the enzyme is also an important factor (22). Brown and Goldstein presented evidence that the signal for this increased degradation is mediated via localization of cholesterol in the membrane domain of the reductase (53). More recent work from this group (103) has shown that sequences responsible for both promotion and inhibition of transcription are distributed over 500 base pairs extending 300 base pairs upstream of the reductase transcription initiation sites. This portion of the 5′ end of the reductase gene contains sequences responsible for cholesterol-mediated inhibition of transcription. Kandutsch and collaborators (14, 15, 21, 52, 78) have provided definitive evidence that an oxysterol derivative of cholesterol may be the active inhibitor rather than cholesterol. 25-Hydroxycholesterol has been used as a typical inhibitory oxysterol to study the effect of these derivatives on cholesterogenesis. Recently, Saucier et al (125a) demonstrated its presence in cultured cells.

Kandutsch's group (14) presented evidence, based on enucleated cells, that 25-hydroxycholesterol affects reductase by attaching to a protein (79) that interacts with the genetic machinery either at the transcription or translational level. The nature of the interaction is not known but the result is that the synthesis of the enzyme can be inhibited (48, 139). In addition, there is evidence that the degradation of the reductase is also increased. Edwards and colleagues (145) have shown that this is the major effect in avian myeloblasts. In a CHO cell line (UT-1) 25-OH cholesterol affects both processes but the major effect is a suppression of synthesis (48). Recently, Chang et al (17, 18) showed that 25-hydroxycholesterol or LDL inactivated the reductase in CHO cells by accelerating the reductase degradation rate. It is interesting to note that this acceleration required the synthesis of mediator proteins with a rapid turnover rate. Other studies have investigated the enhanced level of reductase resulting from the combined effects of feeding mevinolin (an inhibitor analogous to compactin) and cholestyramine to rats. The data show an increase in the mRNA level that is lowered when the animals are fed cholesterol (40, 89).

It has been observed that large amounts of mevalonolactone given to rats greatly reduce reductase levels. Edwards and collaborators reported (41) that mevalonolactone inhibits the rate of synthesis and enhances the rate of degradation of the reductase in rat hepatocytes. The level of mRNA was also reduced by the mevalonolactone treatment (24). These observations were recently extended by Popjak et al (114), who showed that mevalonate gives rise to a product that decreases the level of reductase-specific mRNA. On the other hand, Peffley & Sinensky (110) reported evidence that mevalonate inhibits the reductase in a mutant cell Mev-1 auxotrophic for mevalonate via a mechanism that strongly suggests translational control rather than reduction in transcription. Mevalonate also plays a role in the initiation of DNA synthesis in the cell cycle. This effect may be exerted via isopentenyl adenine. This topic has been reviewed by Siperstein (140) and indicates that a nonsterol product of mevalonate metabolism may also be involved in regulation of sterol biosynthesis.

A large number of cytosolic protein factors have also been shown to affect the activity of the reductase. These are the sterol carrier proteins ($SCP_1$ and $SCP_2$), fatty-acid-binding protein, and Z protein (146). These proteins may be a related family that can influence the effect of lipids on the activity of HMG-CoA reductase and other enzymes in the polyisoprenoid pathway. They could act by influencing the binding of the hydroxysterol metabolites of cholesterol or they might bind lipid inhibitors, e.g. fatty acyl CoA's, which our group found to be powerful inhibitors of the reductase (86). The same considerations apply to the hydroxylated methyl sterols, intermediates between lanosterol and cholesterol. The reader is referred to the excellent reviews of Schroepfer (127, 128) for an extensive analysis of these effects.

There are several cascade-type reactions that bear directly upon the formation of an active and an inactive form of the HMG-CoA reductase enyzme. The control mechanism involves regulation by a cycle of phosphorylation and dephosphorylation via protein kinases, which in turn are also regulated by kinases and phosphatases. The cycle, as finally worked out by Gibson, Beg, and Rodwell and coworkers (4, 68, 73, 80, 81), closely resembles the amplification cascade of phosphorylation and dephosphorylation that regulates glycogen synthesis and breakdown. Gibson and coworkers (108) recently showed a connection between phosphorylation of the enzyme and its increased susceptibility to degradation. This observation has great potential significance in explaining the role of phosphorylation and dephosphorylation in regulating overall enzyme activity and the relatively short half-life of the enzyme. However, the regulatory importance of this phosphorylation-dephosphorylation cycle is still a major research area. The pro and con arguments were objectively discussed in a recent review by Kennelly & Rodwell (83).

### *Post-mevalonate Regulation of Polyisoprenoid and Cholesterol Synthesis*

This area has seen much activity within the last few years because the production and metabolism of mevalonic acid must be carefully regulated in order to provide the isopentenyl pyrophosphate and farnesyl pyrophosphate needed for the synthesis of sterols, dolichols, and ubiquinones. Furthermore, the rate of sterol synthesis is several hundred-fold greater in most instances than the rate of synthesis of the other components. Additionally, the requirement for these other isoprenoid products will vary as the cell goes through its growth and developmental cycles. One may then anticipate that some of the pathways will be shut down and others will be accelerated as the cell adjusts pathways to maximize the production of the isoprenoid products most in need. In addition to regulation at the HMG-CoA reductase step, in the cholesterol pathway regulation also occurs beyond mevalonic acid. The early studies of Gould & Swyryd (63), and more recently Faust et al (47) and Nambudiri et al (98), showed that when HMG-CoA reductase is bypassed by the addition of mevalonic acid (MVA), cholesterol added in the form of LDL suppressed the incorporation of MVA into sterols. Gould & Swyryd showed that this inhibitory step was beyond the farnesyl pyrophosphate (FPP) step; Faust et al (46) indicated that the squalene synthetase reaction was a site at which the LDL exerts an inhibitory effect.

The other two major products of the isoprenoid pathway, the dolichols and the ubiquinones, share the same biosynthetic steps until the FPP branch point is reached. Attempts have been made to study whether procedures that inhibit sterol biosynthesis have the same effect on the dolichol and ubiquinone pathways. Mills & Adamany (96) showed that 25-hydroxycholesterol, a powerful inhibitor of reductase, inhibited dolichol synthesis in smooth muscle cells. James & Kandutsch (74), working with L-cells in tissue culture, observed that dolichol synthesis was closely related to the level of HMG-CoA reductase, but in some situations, large fluctuations in sterol synthesis occurred with little change in dolichol synthesis. Keller et al (82) claimed that they could not observe a correlation between the activity of reductase and dolichol synthesis in liver. James & Kandutsch (75) showed that dolichol synthesis was affected by treatments known to alter reductase activity and, furthermore, dolichol synthesis was decreased by dietary cholesterol and by fasting, and was increased by feeding cholestyramine. A plot of the rates of dolichol vs cholesterol synthesis suggested that, after the formation of the isoprenoid units, the dolichol pathways were saturated at a lower concentration of isoprene units than is required for cholesterol synthesis. A similar observation was made by Gold & Olson (57) in an early study with respect to ubiquinone synthesis in liver.

Kandutsch extended these studies with a thorough analysis of what occurs in differentiating tissues (for review, see 76). In developing brain, the situation appears to be quite different in that dolichol synthesis is independent of sterol synthesis. A similar situation pertains to other differentiating processes, i.e. spermatogenesis and erythroid cell development. Other studies by Carson & Lennarz (13), using compactin to inhibit HMG-CoA reductase activity, showed that development in sea urchin embryos could be restored by the addition of dolichol. They also showed that there was a period during development when the embryos were sensitive to compactin, i.e. when the synthesis of large amounts of dolichol were needed. These results generally support those of Kandutsch and his colleagues showing that when dolichols are needed specifically for development, then the synthesis of dolichol synthesis can be quite sensitive to inhibitors of HMG-CoA reductase.

The foregoing results indicate that under some conditions, specific inhibition of reductase activity affects both sterol and dolichol synthesis in a parallel manner. On the other hand, there is evidence to indicate that differentiating cells produce differential inhibitions of isoprenoid compound synthesis. Some products of the polyisoprenoid pathway are synthesized relatively normally while sterol synthesis is inhibited (76).

A consensus seems to be forming that HMG-CoA reductase will be subject to inhibitory signals by LDL cholesterol and other nonsteroid products of the polyisoprenoid pathway, either acting singly or in concert, depending upon the needs of the cell. The latter are in general closely related to the stages of cell development. Brown & Goldstein (12), in a review, outlined these possibilities and present the hypothesis that HMG-CoA reductase is never completely suppressed unless cholesterol and one or more nonsterol products are present. This feedback regulation hypothesis for reductase is analogous to those that have been worked out in bacterial systems and termed "multivalent" feedback regulation.

Several investigations have attempted to determine which factors regulate the flow of isopentenyl pyrophosphate to the three major polyisoprenoid entities: sterols, dolichols, and ubiquinone. Faust et al (47) carried out studies with human fibroblasts on the effect of inhibitors of HMG-CoA reductase, e.g. LDL and compactin, on sterol and ubiquinone biosynthesis. They found that adding these substances to the medium of a confluent cell culture inhibited the incorporation of mevalonic acid into cholesterol while the incorporation to ubiquinone was greatly stimulated. They reasoned that in the presence of LDL or compactin, MVA incorporation to cholesterol was inhibited because LDL cholesterol was inhibiting some post-MVA step. They reasoned further that the inhibition was probably at the FPP-to-squalene step, and this allowed IPP to be shunted to ubiquinone synthesis. This was supported by the observation of Faust et al (46) indicating that LDL inhibited mevalonate incorporation into cholesterol at the squalene synthetase level.

Studies by Nambudiri et al (98) showed that the same data could be interpreted in another way. Under the conditions in which MVA incorporation into ubiquinone increased in the presence of compactin or LDL, the incorporation of 4-hydroxybenzoic acid (the aromatic precursor of ubiquinone) was actually inhibited, and the inhibition could only be restored by increasing the concentration of MVA. This showed that the increase of MVA incorporation into ubiquinone in the presence of compactin was apparently due to an increased specific activity of the precursor, and not an increase in flux. Nambudiri et al (98) offered the explanation that when inhibitors of HMG-CoA reductase were present, the synthesis of MVA was inhibited and consequently the pool of endogenous MVA was very small. Thus, an exogenous labeled MVA molecule would not be appreciably diluted, and the specific activity of the pool would be increased. The consequent rise in MVA incorporation into ubiquinone would reflect enhanced specific radioactivity but not increased synthesis. This explanation was supported by similar results when acetate was the tracer (118). The final conclusion was that in confluent fibroblasts, both ubiquinone and cholesterol synthesis are regulated at the same step, i.e. HMG-CoA reductase, and that the diversion of isoprenoid units to ubiquinone synthesis when sterol synthesis is inhibited was not the cause of the apparent increase in ubiquinone synthesis (124). Studies by Wilton (153) of the effect of cholesterol on the synthesis of both ubiquinone and tetrahymenol in *Tetrahymena pyriformis* confirmed the interpretations of Nambudiri et al (98).

Volpe & Obert (149) added an inhibitor of cholesterol biosynthesis, 3β(2-diethylaminoethoxy)androst-5-ene-17-one hydrochloride (U-18666A) (113), to cultured glial and neuroblastoma cell lines. They observed that nanomolar quantities of U-18666A caused a marked inhibition of total sterol synthesis from acetate or mevalonate within three hours. There was no effect on fatty acid synthesis. They located the site of inhibition as the reduction of desmosterol to cholesterol, confirming earlier observations by Cenedella and collaborators (7, 16) on the site of U-18666A inhibition. Volpe & Obert (149) also noted that exposure of C-6 glial cells to the drug caused a marked stimulation of the incorporation of [$^{14}$C]acetate and of [$^{3}$H]mevalonate into ubiquinone, yet caused no inhibition of HMG-CoA reductase. These results supported the interpretation of the data of Faust et al (47), who postulated that the flow of isopentenyl pyrophosphate units was directed toward ubiquinone when the pathway to cholesterol was blocked. These data seemed to contradict the hypothesis of Nambudiri et al (98); however, further work on this point has confirmed the hypothesis of Nambudiri et al (98) and is discussed in the following section.

## *Oxysterols as Regulators of Cholesterol Synthesis*

Sexton et al (131) re-examined the effect of U-18666A in a line of intestinal epithelial cells (IEC-6) and in human skin fibroblasts (GM 0043). They confirmed the observations of Volpe & Obert (149) that cholesterol synthesis from mevalonic acid was inhibited and reductase activity was unaffected. However, the increased incorporation of mevalonic acid into ubiquinone was artifactual and was due to the generation of a contaminant by the drug. Sexton et al identified the substance as squalene 2,3:22,23-dioxide (SDO) (131). Previous work (19, 27, 49, 50, 99, 102) had shown that squalene 2,3-oxide (SO) and SDO accumulate in the presence of inhibitors of oxidosqualene cyclase (OSC). It became clear that U-18666A was a powerful inhibitor of OSC in the cell lines used by Sexton et al. Nelson et al (99) studied the conversion of SDO to polar sterols, extending the previous studies of Corey et al (27) and Shishibori et al (138). The latter authors observed that SDO was converted to 24,25-oxidolanosterol by preparations of OSC from liver. Nelson et al (99) found SDO conversion to 24,25-oxidolanosterol only under anaerobic conditions. Under aerobic conditions, the rat liver homogenate converted SDO to a new product, 24,25-epoxycholesterol. No evidence of 25-hydroxycholesterol could be found, although 25-hydroxylanosterol could be converted to 25-hydroxycholesterol. This work has been extended by Spencer et al (141a), who showed that 24(S),25-epoxycholesterol repressed HMG-CoA reductase activity in cultured cells.

Sexton et al found that SDO accumulated in the presence of U-18666A was metabolized to compounds more polar than cholesterol when the drug was removed from the culture medium (131). The relationship of these changes to regulation of HMG-CoA reductase was investigated further by the same laboratory (105). It was noted that U-18666A caused a small inhibition of reductase activity, which was greatly enhanced when the drug was withdrawn. The assumption was that the SDO accumulated in the presence of the drug was converted to inhibitory oxysterols when the drug was removed. A further surprising observation was the fact that U-18666A exerted a biphasic effect on reductase activity, i.e. it was inhibitory at low concentrations of U-18666A and noninhibitory or stimulatory at higher concentrations. SDO was also shown to be a potent inhibitor of reductase activity and this inhibition could be abolished by U-18666A. These observations could be rationalized by the assumption that SDO, because it was converted to an inhibitory oxysterol by the action of oxidosqualene cyclase, was a powerful inhibitor of reductase. This would be the situation at low concentrations of U-18666A where partial inhibition of OSC would allow SDO to be formed. At high concentrations, OSC activity was completely shut down; thus no cyclized derivatives of SDO could be formed and the inhibition was abolished. These observations emphasized the existence of an alternate pathway for formation of oxysterols which branched off from the normal pathway at the level of squalene 2,3-oxide via squalene oxidocyclase. This is shown in Figure 2.

According to this scheme, addition of a preformed oxysterol beyond the OSC step should inhibit reductase and not be affected by U-18666A. This was observed with oxysterol inhibitors such as 25-hydroxycholesterol (105) and epoxylanosterol (24,25-epoxy-5α-lanost-8-ene-3β-ol) and 25-hydroxylanosterol (5α-lanost-8-ene-3β,25-diol) (104). These compounds did not affect general metabolism of cells, as evidenced by the maintenance of normal fatty acid metabolism and overall protein synthesis. Recent observations by Rachal et al (116), Watson & Scallen (126, 150) and Spencer et al (141a) confirm the role of SDO derivatives described above (150). In addition to oxygenated lanosterol analogs derived from SDO, it should be noted that

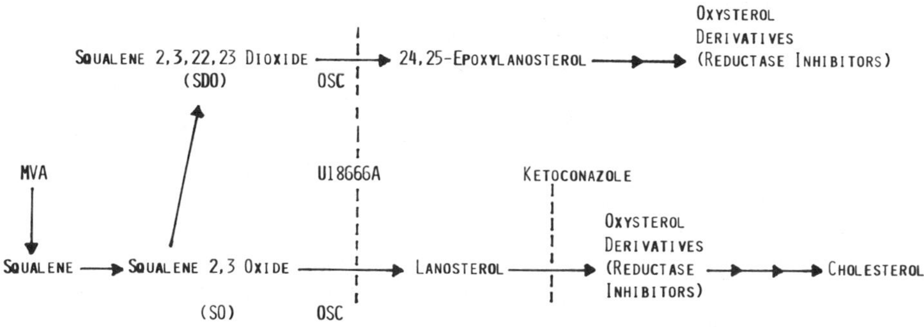


*Figure 2* Alternate pathway for oxysterol formation.

lanosterol derivatives bearing an additional oxygen function at carbon 32 have been shown to inhibit reductase activity in cell cultures (52, 78). These compounds are normal intermediates in the conversion of lanosterol to cholesterol. However, situations where these oxysterols might accumulate endogenously have not been established. Possible pathways of formation and proposed regulatory roles of oxysterols in sterol biogenesis are extensively reviewed by Schroepfer (127, 128).

Our laboratory has also investigated the role of lanosterol and its oxygenated metabolites with the drug ketoconazole. This drug is an orally active imidazole derivative and is used clinically as an antifungal agent (10). It inhibits the conversion of lanosterol to ergosterol in fungi in nanomolar concentrations, whereas micromolar concentrations are required in mammalian tissues (69, 148). This action is exerted by inhibition of a cytochrome P-450 system involved in lanosterol demethylation (134). Gupta et al (67) worked with an extrahepatic nonsteroidogenic cell line in order to minimize the presence of alternate pathways related to bile acid and/or steroid hormone synthesis because these could influence the levels of oxysterols. They observed that incubation of intestinal mucosal cells with 0.15–1.5 μM ketoconazole resulted in a concentration-dependent inhibition of reductase activity. However, as the drug concentration approached 15 μM, the reductase activity paradoxically returned to control values; at 30 μM ketoconazole, a stimulation of enzyme activity was observed. The drug had no effect on reductase activity in homogenates of IEC-6 cells. Ketoconazole (0.15–30 μM) caused a concentration-dependent inhibition of the incorporation of [$^3$H]mevalonolactone into cholesterol with a concomitant accumulation of radioactivity in lanosterol (methyl sterols) and 24,25-epoxylanosterol. Treatment of cells with ketoconazole (60 μM) and [$^3$H]mevalonolactone followed by removal of the drug and radio label resulted in an inhibition of reductase activity and a redistribution of radioactivity from methyl sterols and epoxylanosterol to cholesterol and polar sterols. When 24,25-epoxylanosterol was added directly to the cells, an inhibition of reductase activity was observed, but the inhibition could be attenuated by ketoconazole. This observation suggested that 24,25-epoxylanosterol per se was not an inhibitory oxysterol but an intermediate that could be metabolized to a suppressor via a ketoconazole-sensitive pathway. In this connection, the observations of Imai et al are of interest (72). They showed that intravenous injection of SDO and 24,25-epoxylanosterol caused cell death, inflammation, and repair in rabbit aortas and pulmonary arteries within 10 days of administration. They suggested that oxygenated sterols may play the primary role in arterial cell wall injury and lesion development.

From the above discussion, it is evident that a large body of data is accumulating to support the hypothesis of Kandutsch et al (78) that oxysterols generated endogenously can play a major role in the regulation of cholesterol synthesis via modulation of HMG-CoA reductase activity. Furthermore, the evidence indicates that these oxysterols can arise from two pathways, as shown in Figure 2: (*a*) from diversion of squalene 2,3-oxide to SDO and subsequent cyclization to oxylanosterol derivatives, and (*b*) directly from intermediates arising in the conversion of lanosterol to cholesterol. U-18666A is an inhibitor of pathway (*a*) while ketoconazole is an inhibitor of pathway (*b*). These drugs should be useful in detailing the role of these pathways in the generation of regulatory oxysterols. Further work in this area will be focused on the identity of the regulatory oxysterols and their mechanism of action.

Until recently there was no direct evidence to show that 25-hydroxycholesterol is formed in the cell. Saucier et al (125a) have now identified 24(S),25-epoxycholesterol and 25-hydroxycholesterol in cultured fibroblasts. The endogenous concentration of these oxysterols appears to be within the range required for regulation of HMG-CoA reductase. Other cholesterol derivatives with a hydroxyl group in the side-chain have been detected in extrahepatic tissues. L. L. Smith and collaborators found that 24-hydroxycholesterol [(24S)-cholest-s-en-3β-24-diol] can be synthesized from cholesterol in bovine and rat brain (31, 87). 26-Hydroxycholesterol, which is a primary intermediate in bile acid metabolism, has been detected in various lipoprotein fractions in serum (77). However, there is some question whether the concentrations present in serum would be sufficient to influence sterol synthesis (17). Since the major portion of cholesterol coming to a cell is in the form of cholesterol ester carried on low-density lipoproteins (LDL), the question arose whether the down regulation of HMG-CoA by LDL cholesterol might involve formation of an oxysterol. Panini et al (105) observed that U-18666A abolished the effect of LDL in down regulating HMG-CoA reductase, and they raised the possibility that the effect of LDL might involve the formation of a regulatory oxysterol derived from the SDO pathway.

Suppression of reductase activity resulting from the receptor-mediated internalization of LDL involves several steps (2): binding of LDL to specific cell membrane receptors, internalization and lysomal degradation of the protein, and hydrolysis of the cholesterol esters. Ketoconazole and U-18666A do not affect any of these steps (105, 132). Furthermore, although these drugs are inhibitors of acyl CoA cholesterol: acyl transferase (ACAT), the decreased cholesterol ester formation was found to be unrelated to the phenomenon of LDL-induced suppression of HMG-CoA reductase activity since other ACAT inhibitors do not prevent LDL suppression of reductase (132). The foregoing studies with ketoconazole suggest that hydroxylation involving cytochrome P-450–linked oxidases may play a role in the endogenous generation of regulatory oxysterols directly from the cholesterol molecule, which in turn regulate cholesterol formation. In support of this assumption, Sexton et al found in preliminary experiments that substances preventing LDL action in down regulating reductase are also cytochrome P-450 inhibitors (130). More intensive investigation is required into the potential importance of this class of oxidases in regulating cholesterol synthesis.

## DIETARY FACTORS

### *Rates of Cholesterogenesis in Various Tissues*

Cholesterol levels in all cells represent a balance between synthesis (or uptake of preformed cholesterol) and degradation. The same factors are involved in an assessment of the pool of cholesterol in the whole animal. These were discussed in an excellent review by Turley & Dietschy (147). Large variations are observed in the ability of animals to absorb dietary cholesterol and accomplish endogenous synthesis. Each stage in the absorption process is beset with difficulties in rate measurement (because of variations in enzyme activity of the key enzymes in the absorptive process) as well as controversy about the actual measurement of the biosynthesis of the cholesterol molecule as a whole. Thus, it is not surprising that some of the measurements reported in the literature are still subject to controversy. Nonetheless, the data obtained by Dietschy illustrates the remarkable differences in the absorption rate in animals and man. It appears that man can absorb two to four milligrams of cholesterol per day per kilogram of body weight, whereas other species (e.g. canines and rodents) can absorb 35 to 50 times this amount. Thus, the limited absorptive capacity of man may be a major protective factor in minimizing the pathological effects of excessive dietary cholesterol.

There are also wide species variations in the synthetic rate of cholesterol in whole animals. This can vary from 118 milligrams per day per kilogram of body weight in the rat to nine milligrams per day per kilogram of body weight in man. The data on synthesis and uptake suggest that endogenous synthesis in man plays a major role in the adjustment of the body pool of cholesterol. Hence, its regulation may be a very significant factor in the formation of the body pool of cholesterol in man.

The extent of feedback repression of cholesterol biosynthesis by dietary cholesterol in human liver is open. The variation in the effects of dietary cholesterol on plasma cholesterol (147) in man suggests that variable feedback control occurs in liver. The question requires further extensive investigation. There is evidence from studies with rats (34), squirrel monkey (35), and man (6, 32) that cholesterol feeding markedly inhibits hepatic cholesterogenesis. In rats, the degree of inhibition of cholesterogenesis is directly proportional to the chylomicron remnants and LDL concentration in the blood (85, 151).

Dietschy and collaborators (33, 147) have used [$^3$H]water to great advantage to compare in vivo and in vitro overall rates of cholesterol synthesis in a variety of tissues in different species. Rat liver shows the highest rate of cholesterol synthesis in vitro, while in man the rate is one sixth that of the rat. The rates in guinea pig and hamster are lower than in man. Measurements in vivo of rates of cholesterol synthesis with [$^3$H]water in different tissues of the rat and squirrel monkey again show that the liver accounted for a large percentage of the cholesterol synthesis by the body. However, in some species, extrahepatic tissues also play a major role. In the rat and the squirrel monkey, the liver accounted for 51% and 41% of the rate of cholesterol synthesis in the whole body. Among the extrahepatic tissues, skin muscle and the small intestine accounted for the majority of the remainder.

## *Effects of Dietary Fats on Hepatic Cholesterogenesis*

Although a large number of studies have been performed on this topic, no clear-cut explanation has been put forward to rationalize the disagreement in results. In an early study, Avigan & Steinberg (2) found that feeding of polyunsaturated fats to rats significantly stimulated the rate of hepatic cholesterol synthesis. Subsequent work by Serdarevich & Carroll (129) confirmed these observations by showing that rats fed corn oil showed higher hepatic cholesterogenesis than a comparable group fed butter. Goldfarb & Pitot (60) showed that the stimulatory effect of dietary corn oil on cholesterogenesis was due to an increase in the activity of HMG-CoA reductase. A number of workers (28, 71, 71a, 109) have reported on the general stimulatory effects of dietary lipids on cholesterogenesis in rats, especially in animals that have been fasted and refed. Ide and coworkers (71, 71a, 71b) performed a detailed study on the effect of dietary fats of various degrees of unsaturation on HMG-CoA reductase activity and cholesterogenesis in normal and fasted-refed rats. In normal rats fed the experimental diet for a 2-week period, they observed that HMG-CoA reductase activity rose with chain length of the fat but declined with the degree of unsaturation (71). In rats fasted for 2 days and refed for 3 days, safflower oil (105) decreased reductase and cholesterogenic activities more than saturated fat. Mitropoulos et al (96a) also observed that unsaturated fat (safflower oil) fed to rats for 12 hours reduced the activity of reductase in liver microsomes compared to saturated fat (tristearin). Concomitantly there was a rise in acyl CoA: cholesterol acyl transferase activity in the animals fed unsaturated fats.

There have been several explanations offered for each type of result. For example, the stimulation in hepatic cholesterogenesis observed with unsaturated fats is explained on the basis of the observation that diets rich in unsaturated fats increased bile acid synthesis (91) and thus cholesterol catabolism leading to increased activity of HMG-CoA reductase. Another explanation, suggested by Paul et al (109), is that the microscopic fluidity of high-density lipoproteins responsible for cholesterol efflux from cells is increased following dietary uptake of unsaturated fats (137). This increased fluidity may allow more cholesterol to be solubilized by the high-density lipoprotein molecules, thus allowing greater cellular efflux of cholesterol and reducing end-product inhibition effects on HMG-CoA reductase. A similar explanation based on the removal of cholesterol from the cell being incorporated into a lipoprotein has been proposed by Goh & Heimberg (54, 55). These investigators showed that the perfusion of rat livers with oleic acid increased the efflux of cholesterol from the cells, increased cholesterol synthesis, and markedly stimulated the activity of HMG-CoA reductase. The authors suggested that the uptake of oleic acid led to an increase in very low-density lipoprotein (VLDL) synthesis, which required the incorporation of cholesterol before secretion into the blood. As a result of enhanced lipoprotein synthesis and secretion, hepatic cholesterol stores would be decreased, thus releasing the end-product inhibition of HMG-CoA reductase activity (56), and thus increasing endogenous cholesterol synthesis.

On the other hand, the observations of Mitropoulos et al (96a) are consistent with the presence of higher concentrations of free cholesterol in the endoplasmic reticular membrane in the environment of reductase and of acyl transferase after feeding unsaturated fats compared with saturated fat. However, Ide et al (71a,b) could not observe this correlation. The work of Van Zuiden et al (148a) provides the best simple unifying explanation of these discrepancies and suggests parameters for future investigations in this field. These workers studied the effect of removing chylomicron remnants of different composition on hepatic HMG-CoA reductase activity and hepatic VLDL secretion in perfused rat liver and in vivo. They observed that the ratio of cholesterol to triglycerides in the remnant's lipoprotein played an important role in determining the level of hepatic HMG-CoA reductase activity. Consequently a remnant lipoprotein can have two opposing effects on reductase activity. The first due to cholesterol content is inhibitory, the second due to triglyceride content is stimulatory. The net effect on regulation of reductase activity and cholesterogenesis would depend on the relative amounts of cholesterol and triglyceride in the particles. They suggested that further permutations of these effects could also be induced by the degree of unsaturation of the triglycerides and phospholipids of a lipoprotein remnant that could be manipulated by dietary means. Much more work along those lines is required to sort out these factors. For a much more comprehensive discussion of the effect of dietary manipulation of saturated and unsaturated fats administered to animals and humans on the composition and metabolism of lipoproteins, see the review by Goldberg & Schonfeld (58) in Volume 5 of the *Annual Review of Nutrition*.

### *Effects of Vitamin A Active Substances*

There is a large body of literature on the biological roles of vitamin A active substances in a variety of cellular functions, and the subject was recently reviewed (142, 154). Vitamin A derivatives administered to man (84, 123) and animals (1, 9, 11, 44, 155) appear to lower serum cholesterol levels. On the other hand, recent studies (5a, 156) on isoretinoin (13-*cis*-retinoic acid) administration to humans showed significant increases in mean plasma levels of cholesterol. However, many of these studies may need to be reexamined. Ott & LaChance (103a) critically analyzed factors that could influence the results of experimentation in animals. They reviewed the effect of vitamin A on cholesterol biosynthesis in the rat animal model, and cited many inconsistent and complex actions of this vitamin on cholesterol synthesis, ranging from depression to no effect to enhancement. Ott & LaChance point out that the action of this nutrient is affected by the following factors: vitamin A status of the animal, form of vitamin A used, vitamin A metabolites, animal feeding regimen, substrate flux, and supernatant protein factors.

Some studies at the cellular level with tissue extracts and cell cultures show that the direct addition of vitamin A derivatives to these preparations inhibit acetate incorporation into cholesterol. Thus Eskelson et al (45) and Erdman et al (42, 43) showed that vitamin A and its derivatives inhibited cholesterol biosynthesis from acetate/mevalonate in post-mitochondrial supernatants of perfused rat liver. These authors (43) suggested that the inhibition was localized at the 2,3-oxidosqualene cyclase step. Recently Ringler et al (120) reported that retinoic acid caused a significant decrease in the incorporation of acetate into cholesterol in hamster embryo fibroblasts.

Gupta et al (66) treated fibroblast cultures with retinoid derivatives (e.g. retinol, retinyl acetate, and retinoic acid). They observed that $5 \times 10^{-6}$ M retinol and retinyl acetate caused a 50% inhibition of HMG-CoA reductase activity. Retinoic acid was less effective. These derivatives also caused an inhibition in the conversion of squalene to cholesterol, with concomitant formation of polar sterols. Thus these observations support the earlier suggestions of Erdman et al (43). Further studies should help to delineate the role that polar sterol formation may play in the expression of vitamin A effects on sterol synthesis.

### *Effects of Vitamin D Active Substances*

A vast literature has arisen about the structure and function of vitamin D and its hydroxylated derivatives in relation to calcium and phosphorus metabolism. For recent reviews see (30, 70, 100). The model for the mechanism of action of the fat-soluble vitamin D derivatives is similar to the classic steroid hormones. Vitamin D is the steroid hormone involved in calcium homeostasis and it exerts its effects by virtue of its further metabolism to more polar metabolites that bind to receptor proteins. This complex then produces the response by interaction with the genome leading to the induction of specific proteins. The elements of the vitamin D endocrine system involve conversion of 7-dehydro-cholesterol to vitamin $D_3$ by UV light or dietary ingestion of vitamin $D_3$. Then vitamin $D_3$ metabolizes to 25-hydroxy vitamin $D_3$ [25(OH)$D_3$], the principal form of vitamin D present in blood. This conversion takes place primarily in the liver via a cytochrome P-450 reaction. This is followed by conversion in the kidney to the two principal dihydroxylated metabolites 1,25-dihydroxy-$D_3$ [1,25$(OH)_2D_3$] and 24,25-dihydroxy-$D_3$ [24,25$(OH)_2D_3$], which are then transported to a variety of target organs. The principal targets are bone, intestine, and kidney, where major effects on calcium and phosphorus metabolism are exerted. In addition to these, a new set of targets has been discovered (30, 100).

A large number of studies have been performed to determine the biological role of 24,25-$(OH)_2D_3$ and these are discussed in the reviews noted above. There is little doubt that 24,25$(OH)_2D_3$ is a product of 25(OH)$D_3$ metabolism as well as 1,25$(OH)_2D_3$ in the kidney. In fact, it appears that 1,25$(OH)_2D_3$ is the inducer of the 24-hydroxylase. Thus under normal conditions both dihydroxylated metabolites are being produced. While there is no question of the role of 1,25$(OH)_2D_3$ in mediating the $D_3$ responses, some controversy is centered on the role of 24,25$(OH)_2D_3$. DeLuca & Schnoes (30) have advanced the thesis that the 24,25$(OH)_2D_3$ derivatives are not important and they are primarily precursors of a catabolic pathway for vitamin $D_3$ derivatives. Norman and coworkers, on the other hand, claim that both 1,25$(OH)_2D_3$ and 24,25$(OH)_2D_3$ must be present to express several biological functions (70).

That the derivatives of Vitamin $D_3$ metabolism are related to sterol biosynthesis is suspected because the metabolic conversion of $D_3$ involves insertion of a hydroxyl function into a side-chain that is essentially similar to that of cholesterol. This raises the possibility that hydroxylated vitamin $D_3$ derivatives because of their sterol nature may affect sterol synthesis in a manner analogous to other oxysterols. These considerations were further supported by the observations of Phillipot et al (112) that 25(OH)$D_3$ and 1,25$(OH)_2D_3$ at $10^{-7}$ M are potent inhibitors of the incorporation of acetate into cholesterol. The cell lines they used were normal and leukemic guinea pig lymphocytes. They found that 1,25$(OH)_2D_3$ was even more effective than 25-hydroxycholesterol as an inhibitor of cholesterol synthesis.

Because Philippot et al (112) did not determine whether the effect was on HMG-CoA reductase, our laboratory has initiated some studies on the role of vitamin D derivatives in the regulation of cholesterol synthesis. Our preliminary observations show that HMG-CoA reductase is inhibited by vitamin $D_3$. Further studies on the mechanism of this effect are in progress. The role of vitamin $D_3$ in sterol biosynthetic processes is worthy of study in view of the fact that hydroxylated vitamin $D_3$ derivatives provide another model of an inhibitory sterol. In addition Peng & Taylor (111) have surveyed a large body of evidence suggesting that moderately excessive amounts of vitamin $D_3$ derivatives exert a pathological effect on arterial tissues and thus may greatly increase the risk factor in the induction of arteriosclerosis in man and animals.

## *Role of Cholesterogenesis in Hepatic VLDL Production*

A major unresolved question is the relation of cholesterol synthesis in the liver to the production of VLDL. VLDL is the chief lipoprotein secreted by the liver and its metabolism in the blood leads to the production of intermediate-density lipoprotein (IDL) and LDL (Apo-B-100–containing lipoproteins). The major organ for clearance of these modified plasma lipoproteins is the liver via receptors for Apo-B-100 and Apo-E. Dietschy and colleagues (141), studying the rates of cholesterol synthesis and LDL uptake in livers of rats and hamsters, found these rates were independently regulated. Furthermore it appeared that the primary response of the liver to changes in cholesterol availability was the regulation of sterol synthesis. Alterations in LDL uptake occur only when the endogenous synthetic mechanisms cannot satisfy the needs of the liver for cellular cholesterol.

Dietschy and colleagues (143) also studied the origin of cholesterol in the mesenteric lymph of the rat. Under normal conditions, it appears that approximately 60% of the cholesterol in the lymph is derived from the absorption of luminal sterol that is primarily of biliary origin. This implies that the liver was the primary site of formation of this cholesterol. Concomitant fat absorption plays a major role in determining the fate or disposition of the cholesterol synthesized in mucosal cells. In the absence of fat absorption, endogenously synthesized cholesterol was incorporated into cell membranes of the endothelium and very little appeared in the intestinal lymph. However, when fat absorption occurred, a fraction of the endogenously synthesized cholesterol was incorporated into lipoproteins and delivered by the lymph to the body pools of cholesterol.

Various situations may occur in which the output of VLDL is greatly increased. These increases can be of primary or secondary origin. Grundy (65) points out that the causes of primary overproduction of VLDL are unknown. There are a variety of reasons for secondary overproduction of VLDL, discussed in detail by Grundy in several theoretical models, that are based on defects in VLDL metabolism. These can account for the variation in observations of VLDL and LDL levels. However, as Grundy points out this is an area in which much more work is needed.

Finally, with respect to humans, a key question deals with the role that increased absorption of cholesterol plays in affecting the amounts of cholesterol secreted in VLDL and secondarily in LDL. There seems little doubt that the ingestion of large amounts of dietary cholesterol can raise the levels of plasma lipoprotein cholesterol. But this can occur in many different ways that have not been clearly delineated in man. Consequently, answers to this basic question are very complex. Some of the factors that must be considered in the interpretation of data obtained in this area are analyzed in two recent volumes of the *Annual Review of Nutrition* (58, 64). These reviews point out the need for further specific investigation, particularly in the areas in which reported data leads to opposite conclusions.

## *Diurnal Variations in Hepatic Cholesterogenesis*

A diurnal cycle in hepatic cholesterol synthesis has been demonstrated in rodents (38, 93, 135, 136), swine (122), and chickens (117). Similar fluctuations in cholesterol synthesis have also been demonstrated in small intestine (135) and transplantable hepatomes (59). In man, although a diurnal cycle has not been directly studied, recent analysis of plasma cholesterol precursors, mevalonic acid (107), squalene, and methyl sterols (95) showed an increase in their concentrations at night, which suggests an increase in the overall cholesterol synthetic pathway with a release of some of the pathway intermediates into the blood (94). In almost all cases, the diurnal cycle of cholesterol synthesis has been traced to a change in the activity of HMG-CoA reductase (121). Cholesterol 7$\alpha$-hydroxylase (29, 97), which is involved in bile acid synthesis, and lysosomal acid cholesteryl ester hydrolase (144), involved in the hydrolysis of cholesteryl esters derived from lipoproteins, have been shown to have a circadian rhythm. More extensive studies are needed before their roles in controlling the circadian rhythm of cholesterol synthesis can be established.

McGuire et al (92) recently demonstrated that sterol carrier protein ($SCP_1$), a major regulatory protein of lipid metabolism and transport with rat liver, undergoes a diurnal cycle with a 7- to 10-fold increase at its peak in the dark period. Direct quantitation of SCP mRNA sequences with a cDNA probe showed that the total SCP mRNA level or its polysomal distribution did not account for the diurnal variation in SCP synthesis. Again, more studies are required to determine the significance of these observations related to the control of cholesterol synthesis through the diurnal cycle.

The diurnal cycle of cholesterol synthesis correlated with HMG-CoA reductase activity has been well documented in hepatic (3, 36) and intestinal (38, 135) tissue of the rat. Several investigators have shown that cycloheximide (37, 133) or actinomycin D (39) can abolish the cycle, which suggests that reductase mRNA production and enzyme synthesis were required for expression of the diurnal cycle. Clarke et al (25) recently used a reticulocyte lysate translation system and a reductase cDNA probe to demonstrate that during the diurnal cycle the amounts of both functional and total reductase mRNA played a major role in controlling the synthesis of HMG-CoA reductase. The mechanisms responsible for changing levels of reductase mRNA during the diurnal cycle are not well understood. Withdrawal of food, addition of cholesterol to the diet, and fluctuations in hormones occur during a normal cyclic period; each has a significant effect on cholesterol synthesis and expression of reductase activity (121). At present, the effect of these variables on reductase mRNA transcription and translation are yet to be clearly delineated.

# CONCLUSION

We have attempted to highlight some of the active areas of research in the regulation of cholesterol biosynthesis. Obviously there are more questions than there are answers at the present time, particularly when attempts are made to extrapolate the observations in tissue culture and animal systems to man. Nonetheless, spurred on by new techniques in molecular and cell biology, remarkable progress has been made. Cholesterol synthesis is closely related to many metabolic pathways and the cholesterol molecule is central to cell membrane structure and function. Thus many complex relationships remain to be understood before its role can be accurately assessed in normal and pathological cellular processes, e.g. atherosclerosis. The level of research activity in this field will remain high for many years to come.

ACKNOWLEDGMENT

Work carried out in our laboratory described in this review was supported by the National Institute of Health NIADDK AM-12402 and the National Science Foundation PCM 8204817.

## *Literature Cited*

1. Amen, R. J., LaChance, P. A. 1974. The effect of β-carotene and canthaxanthin on serum cholesterol levels in the rat. *Nutr. Rep. Int.* 10:269–76
2. Avigan, J., Steinberg, D. 1958. Effects of saturated and unsaturated fat on cholesterol metabolism in the rat. *Proc. Soc. Exp. Biol. Med.* 97:814–16
3. Bach, B., Hamprecht, B., Lynen, F. 1969. Regulation of cholesterol biosynthesis in rat liver: diurnal changes of activity and influence of bile acids. *Arch. Biochem. Biophys.* 133:11–21
4. Beg, Z. H., Brewer, H. B. 1981. Regulation of HMG-CoA reductase. *Curr. Top. Cell Regulat.* 20:139–84
5. Bergstrom, J. D., Wong, C. A., Edwards, P. A., Edmond, J. 1984. The regulation of acetoacetyl CoA synthase activity by modulators of cholesterol synthesis in vivo and utilization of acetoacetate for cholesterogenis. *J. Biol. Chem.* 259:14548–53

5a. Bershad, S., Rubinstein, A., Paternita, J. R. Jr., Le, N., Poliak, S. C., et al. 1985. Changes in plasma lipids and lipoproteins during isoretinoin therapy for acne. *N. Engl. J. Med.* 313:981–85

6. Bhattathiry, E. P. M., Siperstein, M. D. 1963. Feedback control of cholesterol synthesis in man. *J. Clin. Invest.* 42: 1613–18
7. Bierkamper, G. G., Cenedella, R. J. 1978. Induction of chronic epileptiform activity in the rat by an inhibitor of cholesterol synthesis, U18666A. *Brain Res.* 150:343–51
8. Billheimer, J. T., Gaylor, J. L. 1980. Cytosolic modulators of activities of microsomal enzymes of cholesterol biosynthesis. *J. Biol. Chem.* 255:8128–36
9. Bonner, M. J., Miller, B. F., Kothari, H. R. 1973. Influence of vitamin A on experimental atherosclerosis in rabbits. *Experientia* 29:187–88
10. Borgers, M. 1980. Mechanism of action of antifungal drugs with special reference

to the imidazole derivatives. *Rev. Infect. Dis.* 2:520–34

11. Bring, V. W., Ricard, C. A., Zehringer, N. V. 1965. Relationship between cholesterol and vitamin A metabolism in rats fed at different levels of vitamin A. *J. Nutr.* 80:400–6
12. Brown, M. S., Goldstein, J. L. 1980. Multivalent feedback regulation of HMG-CoA reductase, a control mechanism coordinating isoprenoid synthesis and cell growth. *J. Lipid Res.* 21:505–17
13. Carson, D. D., Lennarz, W. J. 1979. Inhibition of polyisoprenoid and glycoprotein biosynthesis causes abnormal embryonic development. *Proc. Natl. Acad. Sci. USA* 76:5709–13
14. Cavenee, W. K., Chen, H. W., Kandutsch, A. A. 1981. Regulation of cholesterol biosynthesis in enucleated cells. *J. Biol. Chem.* 256:2675–81
15. Cavenee, W. K., Gibbons, G. F., Chen, H. W., Kandutsch, A. A. 1979. Effects of various oxygenated sterols on cellular sterol biosynthesis in Chinese hamster lung cells resistant to 25-hydroxycholesterol. *Biochim. Biophys. Acta* 575:255–65
16. Cenedella, R. J. 1980. Concentration-dependent effects of AY9944 and U18666A on sterol synthesis in brain. *Biochem. Pharmacol.* 29:2751–54
17. Chang, T.-Y. 1983. Mammalian HMG-CoA reductase and its regulation. *Enzymes* 16:491–521
18. Chang, T.-Y., Limanek, J. S., Chang, C. C. Y. 1981. Evidence indicating that inactivation of HMG-CoA reductase by low density lipoprotein or by 25-hydroxycholesterol requires mediator protein(s) with rapid turnover rate. *J. Biol. Chem.* 256:6174–80
19. Chang, T.-Y., Schiavoni, E. S. Jr., McRae, K. R., Nelson, J. A., Spencer, J. A. 1979. Inhibition of cholesterol biosynthesis in Chinese hamster ovary cells by 4,4,10β,Trimethyl-trans-decal-3β-ol: A specific 2,3 oxidosqualene cyclase inhibitor. *J. Biol. Chem.* 254:11258–63
20. Deleted in proof
21. Chen, H. W., Cavenee, W. K., Kandutsch, A. A. 1979. Sterol synthesis in variant Chinese hamster lung cells selected for resistance to 25-hydroxycholesterol. *J. Biol. Chem.* 254:715–20
22. Chin, D. J., Luskey, K. L., Faust, J. R., MacDonald, R. J., Brown, M. S., Goldstein, J. L. 1982. Molecular cloning of 3-hydroxy-3-methylglutaryl CoA reductase and evidence for regulation of its mRNA. *Proc. Natl. Acad. Sci. USA* 79:7704–8
23. Chin, D. J., Gil, G., Faust, J. R., Goldstein, J. L., Brown, M. S., Luskey, K. L. 1985. Sterols accelerate degradation of hamster 3-hydroxy-3-methylglutaryl coenzyme A reductase encoded by a constitutively expressed cDNA. *Mol. Cell. Biol.* 5:634–41
24. Clarke, C. F., Edwards, P. A., Lan, S.-F., Tanaka, R. D., Fogelman, A. M. 1983. Regulation of HMG-CoA reductase mRNA levels in rat liver. *Proc. Natl. Acad. Sci. USA* 80:3305–8
25. Clarke, C. F., Fogelman, A. M., Edwards, P. A. 1984. Diurnal rhythm of rat liver mRNAs encoding 3-hydroxy-3-methylglutaryl coenzyme A reductase. *J. Biol. Chem.* 259:10439–47
26. Clinkenbeard, K. D., Sugiyama, T., Reed, W. D., Lane, D. M. 1975. Cytoplasmic 3-hydroxy-3-methylglutaryl CoA synthase from liver. *J. Biol. Chem.* 250:3124–35
27. Corey, E. J., Ortiz de Montellano, P. R., Lin K., Dean, P. D. G. 1967. 2,3-Iminosqualene, a potent inhibitor of the enzymic cyclization of 2,3-oxidosqualene to sterols. *J. Am. Chem. Soc.* 89:2797–98
28. Craig, M. C., Dugan, R. E., Mursgin, R. A., Slakey, L. L., Porter, J. W. 1972. Comparative effects of dietary regimens on the levels of enzyme regulating the synthesis of fatty acids and cholesterol in rat liver. *Arch. Biochem. Biophys.* 151: 128–36
29. Danielson, H. 1972. Relationship between diurnal variations in biosynthesis of cholesterol and bile acids. *Sterols* 20:63–72
30. DeLuca, H. F., Schnoes, H. K. 1983. Vitamin D: recent advances. *Ann. Rev. Biochem.* 52:411–39
31. Dhar, A. K., Teng, J. I., Smith, L. L. 1973. Biosynthesis of cholest-5-ene-3β-24-diol (cerebrosterol) by bovine cerebral cortical microsomes. *J. Neurochem.* 21:51–60
32. Dietschy, J. M., Gamel, W. G. 1971. Cholesterol synthesis in the intestine of man: regional differences and control mechanisms. *J. Clin. Invest.* 50:872–80
33. Dietschy, J. M., Spady, D. K. 1984. Measurement of rates of cholesterol synthesis using tritiated water. *J. Lipid Res.* 25:1469–76
34. Dietschy, J. M., Siperstein, M. D. 1967. Effect of cholesterol feeding and fasting on sterol synthesis in seventeen tissues of the rat. *J. Lipid Res.* 8:97
35. Dietschy, J. M., Wilson, J. D. 1968. Cholesterol synthesis in the squirrel monkey: relative rates of synthesis in var-

ious tissues and mechanism of control. *J. Clin. Invest.* 47:166–74

36. Dugan, R. E., Slakey, L. L., Briedis, A. V., Porter, J. W. 1972. Factors affecting the diurnal variation in the level of β-hydroxy-β-methylglutaryl coenzyme A reductase and cholesterol-synthesizing activity in rat liver. *Arch. Biochem. Biophys.* 152:21–27
37. Edwards, P. A., Gould, R. G. 1972. Turnover rate of hepatic 3-hydroxy-3-methylglutaryl coenzyme A reductase as determined by use of cyclohexamide. *J. Biol. Chem.* 247:1520–24
38. Edwards, P. A., Muroya, H., Gould, R. G. 1972. *In vivo* demonstration of the circadian rhythm of cholesterol biosynthesis in the liver and intestine of the rat. *J. Lipid Res.* 13:396–401
39. Edwards, P. A., Gould, R. G. 1974. Dependence of the circadian rhythm of hepatic β-hydroxy-β-methylglutaryl coenzyme A on ribonucleic acid synthesis. *J. Biol. Chem.* 249:2891–96
40. Edwards, P. A., Lan, S.-F., Fogelman, A. M. 1983. Alterations in the rates of synthesis and degradation of rat liver HMG-CoA reductase produced by cholestyramine and mevinolin. *J. Biol. Chem.* 258:10219–22
41. Edwards, P. A., Lan, S.-F., Tanaka, R. D., Fogelman, A. M. 1983. Mevalonolactone inhibits the rate of synthesis and enhances the rate of degradation of HMG-CoA reductase in rat hepatocytes. *J. Biol. Chem.* 258:7272–75
42. Erdman, J. W. Jr., Elliott, J. G., LaChance P. A. 1977. The effect of retinoic acid upon mevalonic acid-2-$^{14}$C incorporation into lipids in an isolated rat liver fraction. *Nutr. Rep. Int.* 16:37–46
43. Erdman, J. W. Jr., Elliott, J. G., LaChance, P. A. 1977. The effect of three forms of vitamin A upon *in vitro* lipogenesis from three cholesterol precursors. *Nutr. Rep. Int.* 16:47–57
44. Erdman, J. W. Jr., LaChance, P. A. 1974. Failure of non–vitamin A active carotenoid lycopine to act as an anti-hypercholesterolemic agent in rats. *Nutr. Rep. Int.* 10:277–84
45. Eskelson, C. D., Jacobi, H. P., Cazee, C. R. 1970. Some effects of the fat soluble vitamins on in vitro cholesterologenesis. *Physiol. Chem. Phys.* 2:135–50
46. Faust, J. R., Goldstein, J. L., Brown, M. S. 1979. Squalene synthetase activity in human fibroblasts: regulation via the low density lipoprotein receptor. *Proc. Natl. Acad. Sci. USA* 76:5018–22
47. Faust, J. R., Goldstein, J. L., Brown, M. S. 1979. Synthesis of ubiquinone and cholesterol in human fibroblasts: regulation of a branched pathway. *Arch. Biochem. Biophys.* 192:86–89
48. Faust, J. R., Luskey, K. L., Chin, D. J., Goldstein, J. L., Brown, M. S. 1982. Regulation of synthesis and degradation of HMG-CoA reductase by low density lipoprotein and 25-hydroxycholesterol in UT-1 cells. *Proc. Natl. Acad. Sci. USA* 79:5205–9
49. Field, R. B., Holmlund, C. E. 1977. Isolation of 2,3:22,23 dioxidosqualene and 24,25-oxidolanosterol from yeast. *Arch. Biochem. Biophys.* 180:465–71
50. Fung, B., Holmlund, C. E. 1976. Effect of triparanol and $^{3}$β-(β-dimethylamino ethoxy)-androst-5-en-17-one on growth and non-saponifiable lipids of saccharomyces cerevisiae. *Biochem. Pharmacol.* 25:1249–54
51. Gavey, K. L., Noland, B. J., Scallen, T. J. 1981. The participation of sterol carrier protein in the conversion of cholesterol to cholesterol ester by rat liver microsomes. *J. Biol. Chem.* 256:2993–99
52. Gibbons, G. F., Pullinger, C. R., Chen, H. W., Cavenee, W. K., Kandutsch, A. A. 1980. Regulation of cholesterol biosynthesis in cultured cells by probable natural precursor sterols. *J. Biol. Chem.* 255:395–400
53. Gil, G., Faust, J. R., Chin, D. J., Goldstein, J. L., Brown, M. S. 1985. Membrane-bound domain of HMG-CoA reductase is required for sterol-enhanced degradation of the enzyme. *Cell* 41:249–58
54. Goh, E. H., Heimberg, M. 1973. Stimulation of hepatic cholesterol biosynthesis by oleic acid. *Biochem. Biophys. Res. Commun.* 55:382–88
55. Goh, E. H., Heimberg, M. 1976. Effect of oleic acid and cholesterol on the activity of hepatic hydroxymethylglutaryl coenzyme A reductase. *FEBS Lett.* 63:209–10
56. Goh, E. H., Heimberg, M. 1977. Effects of free fatty acids on activity of hepatic microsomal 3-hydroxy-3-methylglutaryl coenzyme A reductase and on secretion of triglycerides and cholesterol by liver. *J. Biol. Chem.* 252:2822–26
57. Gold, P. H., Olson, R. E. 1966. Studies on coenzyme Q. The biosynthesis of coenzyme $Q_9$ in rat tissue slices. *J. Biol. Chem.* 241:3507–16
58. Goldberg, A. C., Schonfeld, G. 1985. Effects of diet on lipoprotein metabolism. *Ann. Rev. Nutr.* 5:195–212
59. Goldfarb, S., Pitot, H. C. 1971. The regulation of β-hydroxy-β-methylglutaryl coenzyme A reductase in Morris hepatomas 5123C, 7800, and 9618A. *Cancer Res.* 31:1879–82

60. Goldfarb, S., Pitot, H. C. 1972. Stimulatory effects of dietary lipid and cholestyramine on hepatic HMG-CoA reductase. *J. Lipid Res.* 13:797–801
61. Goldstein, J. L., Brown, M. S. 1977. The low-density lipoprotein pathway and its relation to atherosclerosis. *Ann. Rev. Biochem.* 46:897–930
62. Goldstein, J. L., Brown, M. S. 1984. Progress in understanding the LDL receptor and HMG-CoA reductase, two membrane proteins that regulate the plasma cholesterol. *J. Lipid Res.* 25:1450–68
63. Gould, R. G., Swyryd, E. A. 1966. Sites of control of hepatic cholesterol biosynthesis. *J. Lipid Res.* 7:698–707
64. Grundy, S. M. 1983. Absorption and metabolism of dietary cholesterol. *Ann. Rev. Nutr.* 3:71–96
65. Grundy, S. M. 1985. Pathogenesis of hyperlipoproteinemia. *J. Lipid Res.* 25: 1611–18
66. Gupta, A., Sexton, R. C., Rudney, H. 1985. Inhibition of HMG-CoA reductase by vitamin A compounds in cultured human fibroblasts. *Fed. Proc.* 44:1786
67. Gupta, A., Sexton, R. C., Rudney, H. 1985. Endogenous formation of oxysterols in the regulation of 3-hydroxy-3-methylglutaryl Coenzyme A reductase in rat intestinal epithelial cells. *J. Lipid Res. Abstr.* In press
68. Harwood, H. J., Rodwell, V. W. 1982. HMG-CoA reductase kinase: measurement of activity by methods that preclude interference by inhibitors of HMG-CoA reductase activity or by mevalonate kinase. *J. Lipid Res.* 23:754–61
69. Henry, M. J., Sisler, H. D. 1979. Effects of miconazole and dodecylimidazole on sterol biosynthesis in *Ustilago maydis*. *Antimicrob. Agents Chemother.* 15:603–7
70. Henry, H. L., Norman, A. W. 1984. Vitamin D: metabolism and biological actions. *Ann. Rev. Nutr.* 4:493–520
70a. Hillmar, I., Henze, K. R., Barth, C. A. 1983. Influence of fatty acids on cholesterol synthesis of hepatocytes in monolayer culture. *J. Nutr.* 113:2239–44
71. Ide, T., Okamatsu, H., Sugano, M. 1978. Regulation by dietary fats of 3-hydroxy-3-methylglutaryl coenzyme A reductase in rat liver. *J. Nutr.* 108:601–12
71a. Ide, T., Tanaka, T., Sugano, M. 1979. Dietary fat-dependent changes in hepatic cholesterogenesis and the activity of 3-hydroxy-3-methylglutaryl CoA reductase in fasted-refed rats. *J. Nutr.* 109:807–18
71b. Ide, T., Gotoh, Y., Sugano, M. 1980. Dietary regulation of hepatic 3-hydroxy-3-methylglutaryl-CoA reductase and cholesterol synthetic activities in fasted-refed rats. *J. Nutr.* 110:158–68
72. Imai, H., Werthessen, N. T., Subramanyam, V., LeQuesne, P. W., Soloway, A. H., Kanisawa, M. 1980. Angiotoxicity of oxygenated sterols and possible precursors. *Science* 207:651–53
73. Ingebritsen, T. S. 1983. Molecular control of HMG-CoA reductase: regulation by phosphorylation/dephosphorylation. See Ref. 125, pp. 129–52
74. James, M. J., Kandutsch, A. A. 1979. Interrelationships between dolichol and sterol synthesis in mammalian cell cultures. *J. Biol. Chem.* 254:8442–46
75. James, M. J., Kandutsch, A. A. 1980. Regulation of hepatic-dolichol synthesis by HMG-CoA reductase. *J. Biol. Chem.* 255:8618–22
76. James, M. J., Potter, J. E. R., Kandutsch, A. A. 1983. HMG-CoA reductase and the synthesis of ubiquinone and dolichol. See Ref. 125, pp. 11–18
77. Javitt, N. B., Kok, E., Burstein, S., Cohen, B., Kutscher, J. 1981. 26-Hydroxycholesterol. Identification and quantitation in human serum. *J. Biol. Chem.* 256:12644–46
78. Kandutsch, A. A., Chen, H. W., Heininger, H. J. 1978. Biological activity of some oxygenated sterols. *Science* 201: 498–501
79. Kandutsch, A. A., Shown, E. P. 1981. Assay of oxysterol binding protein in a mouse fibroblast cell free system: Dissociation constant and other properties of the system. *J. Biol. Chem.* 256:13068–73
80. Keith, M. L., Rodwell, V. W., Rogers, D. H., Rudney, H. 1979. In vitro phosphorylation of HMG-CoA reductase: analysis of $^{32}$P-labelled inactivated enzyme. *Biochem. Biophys. Res. Commun.* 90:969–75
81. Keith, M. L., Kennelly, P. J., Rodwell, V. W. 1983. Evidence for multiple phosphorylation sites in rat liver HMG-CoA reductase. *J. Protein Chem.* 2:209–20
82. Keller, R. K., Adair, W. T. Jr., Ness, G. C. 1979. Studies on the regulation of glycoprotein biosynthesis. An investigation of the rate-limiting steps of dolichyl phosphate biosynthesis. *J. Biol. Chem.* 254:9966–69
83. Kennelly, P. J., Rodwell, V. W. 1985. Regulation of 3-hydroxy-3-methylglutaryl coenzyme A reductase by reversible phosphorylation-dephosphorylation. *J. Lipid Res.* 26:903–14
84. Kinley, L. J., Krause, R. F. 1959. Influence of vitamin A on cholesterol blood

levels. *Proc. Soc. Exp. Biol. Med.* 102:353

85. Lasser, N. L., Roheim, P. S., Edelstein, D., Eder, H. A. 1973. Serum lipoproteins of normal and cholesterol fed rats. *J. Lipid Res.* 14:1–8
86. Lehrer, G. M., Panini, S. R., Rogers, D. H., Rudney, H. 1981. Modulation of rat liver HMG-CoA reductase by lipid inhibitors, substrates and cytosolic factors. *J. Biol. Chem.* 256:5612–19
87. Lin, Y. Y., Smith, L. L. 1974. Biosynthesis and accumulation of cholest-5-ene-3β,24-diol (cerebrosterol) in developing rat brain. *Biochem. Biophys. Acta* 348: 189–96
88. Liscum, L., Finer-Moore, J., Stroud, R. M., Luskey, K. L., Brown, M. S., Goldstein, J. D. 1985. Domain structure of HMG-CoA reductase, a glycoprotein of the endoplasmic reticulum. *J. Biol. Chem.* 260:522–30
89. Liscum, L., Luskey, K. L., Chin, D. J., Ho, Y. K., Goldstein, J. L., Brown, M. S. 1983. Regulation of HMG-CoA reductase and its mRNA in rat liver as studied with a monoclonal antibody and a cDNA probe. *J. Biol. Chem.* 259:8450–55
90. Luskey, K. L., Stevens, B. 1985. Human 3-hydroxy-3-methylglutaryl coenzyme A reductase: Conservation domains responsible for catalytic activity and sterol-regulated degradation. *J. Biol. Chem.* 260:10271–77
91. McGovern, R. F., Quackenbush, F. W. 1973. Influence of dietary fat on bile acid secretion of rats after portal injection of $^{3}$H-cholesterol and [4-$^{14}$C] cholesterol esters. *Lipids* 8:473
92. McGuire, D. M., Chan, L., Smith, L. C., Towle, H. C., Dempsey, M. E. 1985. Translational control of the circadian rhythm of liver sterol carrier protein. *J. Biol. Chem.* 260:5435–39
93. Mercer, N. J. H., Holub, B. J. 1981. Measurement of hepatic sterol synthesis in the Mongolian gerbil *in vivo* using [$^{3}$H] water: diurnal variation and effects of type of dietary fat. *J. Lipid Res.* 22:792–99
94. Miettinen, T. A. 1969. Serum squalene and methyl sterols as indicators of cholesterol synthesis *in vivo*. *Life Sci.* 8:713–21
95. Miettinen, T. A. 1982. Diurnal variation of cholesterol precursors squalene and methyl sterols in human plasma lipoproteins. *J. Lipid Res.* 23:466–73
96. Mills, J. T., Adamany, A. M. 1978. Impairment of dolichyl saccharide synthesis and dolichol-mediated glycoprotein assembly in the aortic smooth muscle cell in culture by inhibitors of cholesterol biosynthesis. *J. Biol. Chem.* 253:5270–73

96a. Mitropoulos, K. A., Venkatesan, S., Balasubramanian, S. 1980. On the mechanism of regulation of hepatic 3-hydroxy-3-methylglutaryl CoA reductase and of acyl coenzyme A : cholesteryl acyl transferase by dietary fat. *Biochem. Biophys. Acta* 619:247–57

97. Myant, N. B., Mitropoulos, K. A. 1977. Cholesterol 7α-hydroxylase. *J. Lipid Res.* 18:135–53
98. Nambudiri, A. M. D., Ranganathan, S., Rudney, H. 1980. The role of HMG-CoA reductase activity in the regulation of ubiquinone synthesis in human fibroblasts. *J. Biol. Chem.* 255:5894–99
99. Nelson, J. A., Steckbeck, S. R., Spencer, T. A. 1981. Biosynthesis of 24,25-epoxycholesterol from squalene 2,3:22,23 dioxide. *J. Biol. Chem.* 256:1067–68
100. Norman, A., Roth, J., Onci, L. 1982. The vitamin D endocrine system: steroid metabolism, hormone receptors, and biological response (calcium binding proteins). *Endocr. Rev.* 3:331–66
101. Olson, R. E., Rudney, H. 1983. Biosynthesis of ubiquinone. *Vitamins Hormones* 40:1–43
102. Ono, T., Bloch, K. 1975. Solubilization and partial characterization of rat liver squalene epoxidase. *J. Biol. Chem.* 250: 1571–79
103. Osborne, T. F., Goldstein, J. L., Brown, M. S. 1985. 5' end of HMG-CoA reductase gene contains sequences responsible for cholesterol-mediated inhibition of transcription. *Cell* 42:203–12

103a. Ott, D. B., LaChance, P. A. 1984. Vitamin A action on hepatic cholesterol biosynthesis. *Nutr. Res.* 4:137–44

104. Panini, S. R., Sexton, R.C., Parish, E. J., Rudney, H. 1985. Inhibition of HMG-CoA reductase activity in rat intestinal epithelial cells (IEC-6) by oxysterols derived from squalene dioxide. *Fed. Proc.* 44:1787
105. Panini, S. R., Sexton, R. C., Rudney, H. 1984. Regulation of HMG-CoA reductase by oxysterol by-products of cholesterol biosynthesis. Possible mediators of low density lipoprotein action. *J. Biol. Chem.* 259:7767–71
106. Panini, S. R., Rogers, D. H., Rudney, H. 1985. Regulation of HMG-CoA reductase and the biosynthesis of non-sterol prenyl derivatives. In *Regulation of HMG-CoA Reductase,* ed. B. Preiss. New York: Academic
107. Parker, T. S., McNamara, D. J., Brown, C., Garrigan, O., Kolb, R., et al. 1982.

Mevalonic acid in human plasma: relationship of concentration and circadian rhythm to cholesterol synthesis rates in man. *Proc. Natl. Acad. Sci. USA* 79: 3037–41
108. Parker, R. A., Miller, S. J., Gibson, D. M. 1984. Phosphorylation of microsomal HMG-CoA reductase increases susceptibility to proteolytic degradation *in vitro*. *Biochem. Biophys. Res. Commun.* 125:629–35
109. Paul, R., Ramesha, C. S., Ganguly, J. 1980. On the mechanism of hypocholesterolemic effects of polyunsaturated lipids. *Adv. Lipid Res.* 17:155–71
110. Peffley, D., Sinensky, M. 1985. Regulation of 3-hydroxy-3-methylglutaryl coenzyme A reductase synthesis by a nonsterol mevalonate-derived product in MEV-1 cells: Apparent translational control. *J. Biol. Chem.* 260:9949–52
111. Peng, S. K., Taylor, C. B. 1980. Probable role of excesses of vitamin D in genesis of arteriosclerosis. *Arterial Wall* 6:63–68
112. Philippot, J. R., Cooper, A. G., Wallach, D. F. H. 1976. 25-Hydroxycholecalciferol and 1,25-dihydroxycholecalciferol are potent inhibitors of cholesterol biosynthesis by normal and leukemic ($L_2C$) guinea-pig lymphocytes. *Biochem. Biophys. Res. Commun.* 72: 1035–41
113. Phillips, W. A., Avigan, J. 1963. Inhibition of cholesterol biosynthesis in the rat by 3β-(2-diethylaminoethoxy)androst-5-en-17-one hydrochloride. *Proc. Soc. Exp. Biol. Med.* 112:233–36
114. Popjak, G., Clarke, C. F., Hadley, C., Meenan, A. 1985. Role of mevalonate in regulation of cholesterol synthesis and 3-hydroxy-3-methylglutaryl coenzyme A reductase in cultured cells and their cytoplasts. *J. Lipid Res.* 26:831–41
115. Preiss, B., ed. 1985. *Regulation of HMG-CoA Reductase*. New York: Academic
116. Rachal, E., Harval, C. M., Scallen, T. J., Watson, J. A. 1985. Lipoprotein mediated synthesis of Lanosterol-1-24, 25-epoxide. *Fed. Proc.* 44:656
117. Ramirez, H., Alejandre, M. J., Garcia-Peregrin, E. 1982. Development of the diurnal rhythm of chick 3-hydroxy-3-methylglutaryl-CoA reductase. *Lipids* 17:434–36
118. Ranganathan, S., Nambudiri, A. M. D., Rudney, H. 1981. The regulation of ubiquinone synthesis in fibroblasts: the effect of modulators of β-hydroxy-β-methylglutaryl CoA reductase activity. *Arch. Biochem. Biophys.* 210:592–97
119. Reynolds, G. A., Basu, S. K., Osborne, T. F., Chin, D. J., Gil, G., et al. 1984. HMG-CoA reductase: a negatively regulated gene with unusual promoter and 5' untranslated regions. *Cell* 38:275–85
120. Ringler, M. B., Erbland, J. F., Singh, B. B., Schuster, G. S. 1984. The effects of retinoic acid on [$^{14}$C]acetate incorporation into lipids of normal and transformed hamster fibroblasts. *Exp. Cell Res.* 154: 171–80
121. Rodwell, V. W., Nordstrom, J. L., Mitschellen, J. J. 1976. Regulation of HMG-CoA reductase. *Adv. Lipid Res.* 14:1–74
122. Rogers, D. H., Kim, D. N., Lee, K. T., Reiner, J. M., Thomas, W. A. 1981. Circadian variations of 3-hydroxy-3-methylglutaryl coenzyme A reductase activity in swine liver and ileum. *J. Lipid Res.* 22:811–19
123. Ross, F. C., Campbell, A. H. 1961. The effect of vitamin A and vitamin D capsules upon the incidence of coronary heart disease and blood cholesterol. *Med. J. Aust.* 48:307–11
124. Rudney, H., Nambudiri, A. M. D., Ranganathan, S. 1981. The regulation of the synthesis of coenzyme Q in fibroblasts and in heart muscle. In *Biomedical and Clinical Aspects of Coenzyme Q,* ed. K. Folkers, Y. Yamamura, 3:279–90. Amsterdam: Elsevier
125. Sabine, E. J. R., ed. 1983. 3-Hydroxy-3-methylglutaryl. In *Coenzyme A Reductase*. Boca Raton, Fla: CRC
125a. Saucier, S. E., Kandutsch, A. A., Taylor, F. R., Spencer, T. A., Phirwa, S., et al. 1985. Identification of regulatory oxysterols 24(S),25-epoxycholesterol and 25-hydroxycholesterol in cultured fibroblasts. *J. Biol. Chem.* 260:14571–79
126. Scallen, T. J., Watson, J. A., Morrow, C. J., Arebalo, R. E., Montano, R. M. 1985. Regulatory signal steroids: Endogenous formation of lanosterol-24,25-epoxide following a single cholesterol meal. *Fed. Proc.* 44:656
127. Schroepfer, G. J. Jr. 1981. Sterol biosynthesis. *Ann. Rev. Biochem.* 50: 585–621
128. Schroepfer, G. J. Jr. 1982. Sterol biosynthesis. *Ann. Rev. Biochem.* 51:555–85
129. Serdarevich, B., Carroll, K. K. 1972. *In vivo* incorporation of labeled acetate into liver and serum lipids of rats on different dietary regimens. *Can. J. Biochem.* 50:557–62
130. Sexton, R., Gupta, A., Shertzer, H., Rudney, H. 1985. Involvement of cytochrome P-450 in the down regulation of HMG-CoA reductase activity by low

density lipoproteins in cultured human skin fibroblasts and rat epithelial cells. *J. Lipid Res.* (Abstr.) In press

131. Sexton, R. C., Panini, S. R., Azran, F., Rudney, H. 1983. Effects of 3-β[2-(diethylamino)ethoxy]androst-5-en-17-one on the biosynthesis of cholesterol and ubiquinone in rat intestinal epithelial cell cultures. *Biochemistry* 22:5687–92
132. Sexton, R. C., Panini, S. R., Gupta, A., Rudney, H. 1985. Prevention of low density lipoproteins (LDL) effects on HMG-CoA reductase (HMGR) activity and acyl CoA cholesterol acyl transferase (ACAT) activity in rat IEC-6 cells by U18666A. *Fed. Proc.* 44:1786
133. Shapiro, J. J., Rodwell, V. W. 1969. Diurnal variation and cholesterol regulation of hepatic HMG-CoA reductase activity. *Biochem. Biophys. Res. Commun.* 37:867–72
134. Sheets, J. J., Mason, J. I. 1984. Ketoconazole: a potent inhibitor of cytochrome P-450 dependent drug metabolism in rat liver. *Drug Metab. Dispos.* 12:603–6
135. Shefer, S., Hauser, S., Lapar, V., Mosbach, E. H. 1972. Diurnal variation of HMG-CoA reductase activity in rat intestine. *J. Lipid Res.* 13:571–73
136. Shefer, S., Hauser, S., Lapar, V., Mosbach, E. H. 1972. HMG-CoA reductase of intestinal mucosa and liver of the rat. *J. Lipid Res.* 13:402–12
137. Shepherd, J., Packard, C. J., Patsch, J. R., Gotto, A. M. Jr., Taunton, O. D. 1978. Effects of dietary polyunsaturated and saturated fat on the properties of high density lipoproteins and the metabolism of apolipoprotein A-I. *J. Clin. Invest.* 61:1582–92
138. Shishibori, T., Fukui, T., Suga, T. 1973. Steroid biosynthesis: Relative efficiencies of the enzymatic transformation of terminally modified squalene 2,3-oxide analogs into lanosterol analogs by 2,3-oxidosqualene cyclase. *Chem. Lett.* 12: 1289–92
139. Sinensky, M., Torget, R., Edwards, P. A. 1981. Radioimmune precipitation of HMG-CoA reductase from Chinese hamster fibroblasts. Effect of 25-hydroxycholesterol. *J. Biol. Chem.* 256: 11774–79
140. Siperstein, M. D. 1985. Role of cholesterogenesis and isoprenoid synthesis in DNA replication and cell growth. *J. Lipid Res.* 24:1462–68
141. Spady, D. K., Turley, S. D., Dietschy, J. M. 1985. Rates of low density lipoprotein uptake and cholesterol synthesis are regulated independently in the liver. *J. Lipid Res.* 26:465–73

141a. Spencer, T. A., Gayen, A. K., Phirwa, S., Nelson, J. A., Taylor, F. R., et al. 1985. 24(S),25-Epoxycholesterol: evidence consistent with a role in the regulation of hepatic cholesterogenesis. *J. Biol. Chem.* 260:13391–94

142. Sporn, M. B., Roberts, A. B., Goodman, D. S., eds. 1984. *The Retinoids*, Vols. I, II. New York: Academic
143. Stange, E. F., Dietschy, J. M. 1985. The origin of cholesterol in the mesenteric lymph of the rat. *J. Lipid Res.* 26:175–84
144. Tanaka, M., Yonekura, R., Iio, T., Tabata, T. 1985. A diurnal variation of hepatic acid cholesteryl ester hydrolase activity in the rat. *Lipids* 20:46–48
145. Tanaka, R. D., Edwards, P. A., Lan, S.-F., Fogelman, A. M. 1983. Regulation of HMG-CoA reductase in avian myeloblasts. *J. Biol. Chem.* 258:13331–39
146. Trzaskos, J. M., Gaylor, J. L. 1983. Molecular control of HMG-CoA reductase: The role of cytosolic proteins. See Ref. 125, pp. 469–187
147. Turley, S. D., Dietschy, J. M. 1982. Cholesterol metabolism and excretion. In *The Liver; Biology and Pathobiology*, ed. I. Arias, H. Popper, D. Schacter, D. A. Shatritz, pp. 467–92. New York: Raven
148. Van den Bossche, H., Willemsen, G., Cools, W., Cornelissen, F., Lauwers, W. F., van Cutsem, J. M. 1980. In vitro and in vivo effects of the antimycotic drug ketoconazole on sterol synthesis. *Antimicrob. Agents Chemother.* 17:922–28

148a. VanZuiden, P. E., Erickson, S. K., Cooper, A. D. 1983. Effect of removal of lipoproteins of different composition on hepatic 3-hydroxy-3-methylglutaryl coenzyme A reductase activity and hepatic very low density lipoprotein secretion. *J. Lipid. Res.* 24:418–28

149. Volpe, J. J., Obert, K. A. 1982. Interrelationships of ubiquinone and sterol synthesis in cultured cells of neural origin. *J. Neurochem.* 38:931–38
150. Watson, J. A., Scallen, T. J. 1985. Cholesterol regulates HMG-CoA reductase through the mediation of endogenously produced lanosterol-24,25-epoxide. *Fed. Proc.* 44:1600
151. Weis, H. J., Dietschy, J. M. 1969. Failure of bile salts to control hepatic cholesterogenesis: Evidence for endogenous cholesterol feedback. *J. Clin. Invest.* 48:2398–2408
152. White, L. W., Rudney, H. 1970. Regulation of 3-hydroxy-3-methylglutarate and

mevalonate biosynthesis by rat liver homogenates. Effects of fasting, cholesterol feeding, and triton administration. *Biochemistry* 9:2725–31

153. Wilton, D. C. 1983. The effect of cholesterol on ubiquinone and tetrahymenol biosynthesis in *Tetrahymena pyriformis*. *Biochem. J.* 216:203–6

154. Wolf, G. 1984. Multiple functions of vitamin A. *Physiol. Rev.* 64:873–937

155. Wood, J. D. 1960. Dietary marine fish oils and cholesterol metabolism. 2. The effect of vitamin A and lingcod liver oil components on serum cholesterol levels in chicks. *Can. J. Biochem. Physiol.* 38:879–87

156. Zech, L. A., Gross, E. G., Peck, G. L., Brewer, H. B. 1983. Changes in plasma cholesterol and triglyceride levels after treatment with oral isoretinoin. *Arch. Dermatol.* 119:987–93

*Ann. Rev. Nutr. 1986. 6:273–97*


# METABOLISM, NUTRITION, AND FUNCTION OF CAROTENOIDS

*T. W. Goodwin*

Department of Biochemistry, University of Liverpool, Liverpool L69 3BX, England

---

CONTENTS

INTRODUCTION .......... 273
METABOLISM IN FISH .......... 276
*Nature of Pigments* .......... 276
*Astaxanthin Formation* .......... 277
*Xanthophyll Formation in Marine Fish* .......... 280
*Reductive Metabolism of Xanthophylls in Fish* .......... 280
*Carotenoids as Vitamin A Precursors* .......... 281
*Regulation of Vitamin A Synthesis* .......... 283
*Coloration in Artificially Reared Fish* .......... 283
METABOLISM IN BIRDS .......... 284
*Absorption, Storage, and Metabolism—General* .......... 284
*Metabolism in Retina and Embryo* .......... 285
*Nutrition* .......... 286
METABOLISM IN INSECTS .......... 286
*Formation of Hydrocarbons* .......... 287
DE NOVO SYNTHESIS IN ANIMALS .......... 287
FUNCTIONS OTHER THAN AS VITAMIN A PRECURSORS .......... 288
*Invertebrates* .......... 288
*Vertebrates* .......... 288
*Protection Against Photosensitization* .......... 289
*Mechanism of Photoprotection* .......... 290
CAROTENOIDS AS ANTITUMOR AGENTS .......... 291
CONCLUSIONS .......... 292

## INTRODUCTION

Carotenoids represent one of the most widespread groups of natural pigments. They are synthesized de novo by all plants and some microorganisms but they are also found throughout the animal kingdom, where they accumulate either



0199-9885/86/0715-0273$02.00

unchanged from the diet or are metabolically modified. Modification is most apparent in the lower animals (39). Over 500 carotenoids are now known to occur in nature but only a small number concern us in this review. They are all based on the hydrocarbons α-carotene (β,ε-carotene) (I), β-carotene (β,β-carotene) (II), and ε-carotene (ε,ε-carotene) (III). The numbering of the carotenoid molecule is given in Formula I, where it will be noticed that a chiral center exists; the structure indicated is (6'*R*)β,ε-carotene, while that of Formula III is (6*R*,6'*R*)ε,ε-carotene. All these are the structures of the plant carotenes.

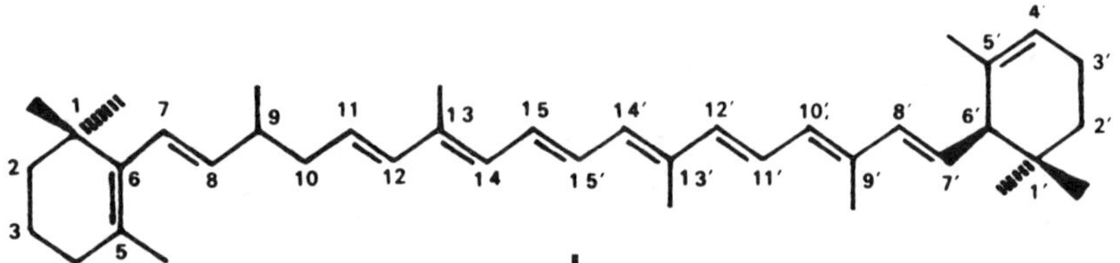

I

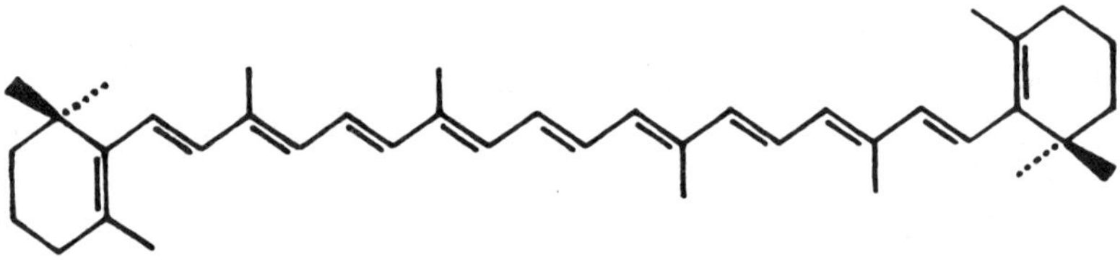

II

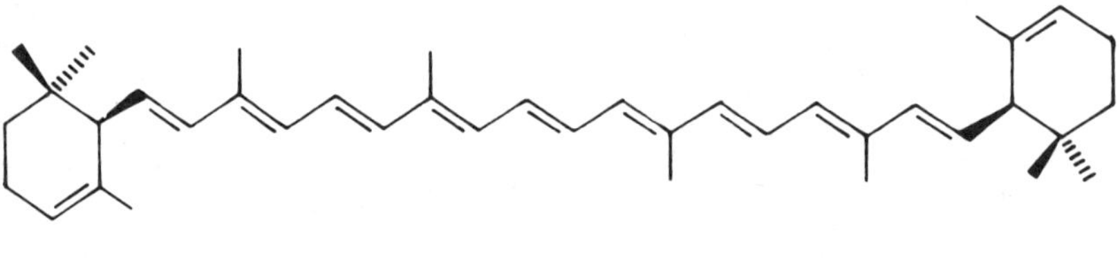

III

Carotenoids that contain oxygen functions are termed xanthophylls and the main components considered here are (3*R*,3'*R*)-zeaxanthin (IV), (3*R*,3'*R*,6'*R*)lutein (V), and (3*S*,3'*S*)astaxanthin (VI)[1]. As with the carotenes mentioned, these are the chiral species found in plants. It was previously

[1]The *R*, *S* convention is the internationally accepted way of denoting chirality. It depends on "priorities" of the groups attached to the chiral center. This can make for confusion, for example the *absolute configuration* at C-3' of lutein (V) is opposite to that at C-3 although application of the priority rules leads to both being designated *R*. Similarly 3*R*,3*R*' zeaxanthin (IV) has the same absolute configuration as 3*S*,3'*S*-astaxanthin (VI). When ambiguity might arise the structures are given in full. See (40) for a simplified explanation of the application of the *R*, *S* convention.

thought that when these pigments were found in animals they had the same chirality as those from the ultimate dietary source, plants (39). It is now clear that sometimes they have and sometimes they have not the same chirality, in fact almost all possible epimers have been found somewhere in the animal kingdom.

The recent penetrating studies, discussed in detail later, on carotenoid metabolism in lower animals have revealed many new aspects and destroyed some cherished dogmas about carotenoid nutrition. The scientific aspects of using carotenoids to treat diseases involving photosensitization is also considered here, together with the evidence suggesting that carotenoids can delay the onset of some tumors. Many other aspects of carotenoid chemistry and biochemistry are not considered because of shortage of space, but the reader is referred to recently published monographs (5, 38, 39) and to the published proceedings of the last three triennial Symposia on Carotenoids, held in Maidson, Liverpool, and Munich, respectively (11, 24, 37).

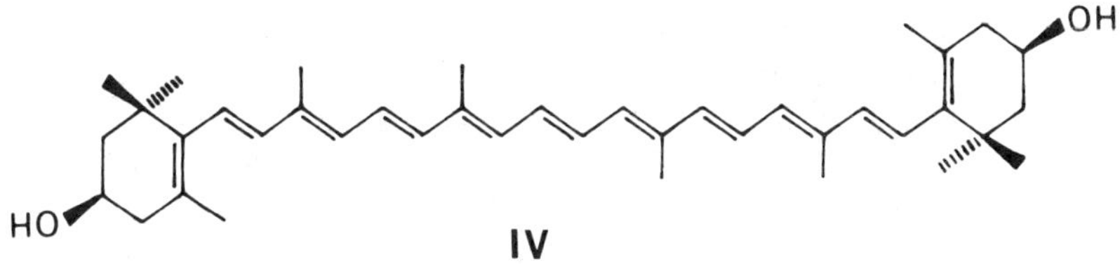

HO OH

IV

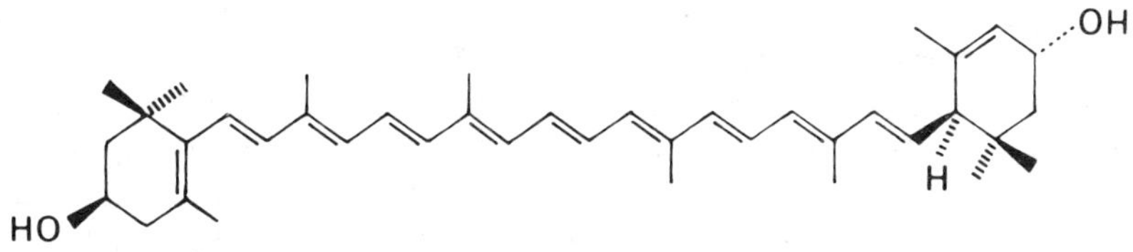

HO OH H

V

HO O O OH

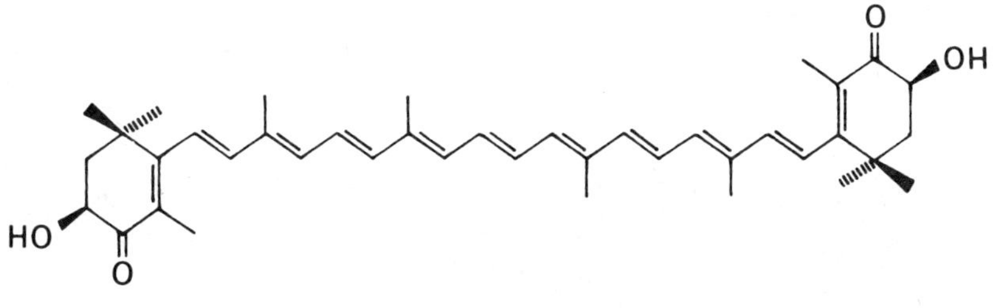

VI

## METABOLISM IN FISH

### *Nature of Pigments*

The bulk of the yellow and red colors in fish skin are xanthophylls that are generally esterified (39). According to early investigators, the main pigments were astaxanthin, lutein, and taraxanthin, a pigment of unknown structure that has gradually disappeared from current literature (39). The generalization concerning astaxanthin and lutein is still true but stereochemically imprecise. The separation by high performance liquid chromatography (HPLC) of diastereomeric camphanates of xanthophylls (103, 112, 127) has made possible chiral analysis of carotenoids. Thus it emerged that lutein from goldfish, trout, and salmon is not "plant" lutein (V) but the 3'-epimer (3*R*,3'*S*,6'*R*)-epilutein (structure illustrated in Figure 2) (17, 93). It is significant that so far epilutein has been reported only once in plants, in the petals of *Caltha palustris* (16). The reported widespread occurrence of lutein in fish (see 39) needs now to be reassessed. In marine fish, C-6' lutein epimers, i.e. (6'*S*)-lutein, are reported with configurations 3*R*,3'*S*,6'*S*-, 3*R*,3'*R*,6'*S*-, and 3*S*,3'*R*,6'*S* (88). It is of considerable evolutionary significance to discover whether in general 6'*R*-luteins are confined to freshwater fish and 6'*S*-luteins to marine fish.

The "astaxanthin" from the flesh of Atlantic and Pacific salmon consists of three isomers with 3*S*,3'*S*-(VI),3*R*,3'*R*- and 3*R*,3'*S*- configurations; the relative amounts in both species were 8:1.5:0.5, respectively (115). In contrast, samples of plant astaxanthin so far examined contain essentially only the 3*S*,3'*S*-isomer (108, 109).

Tunaxanthin, first isolated from *Thunnus orientalis* (53) and shown to be an ε,ε-carotene-3,3'-diol (21), has now been found in a number of Japanese fish in three chiral forms: tunaxanthin A (3*S*,6*S*,3'*S*,6'*S*) (IX), tunaxanthin B (3*R*, 6*S*, 3'*S*, 6'*S*) (VIII) and tunaxanthin C (3*R*,6*S*,3'*R*,6'*S*) (VII) (91, 92, 111). These pigments are identical with oxyxanthin 45, oxyxanthin 51, and oxyxanthin 58, respectively (92), pigments isolated from the Southern Californian *Oxiulis californica* (8). There is also one report of the presence of (3*S*,6*R*,3'*S*,6'*R*)-chiriquixanthin B (X), a C-6, C-6'-epimer of tunaxanthin A, in the fish *Sebastes flavidus* (8). The chiriquixanthins, which have the *R* configuration at C-6 and C-6', are so called because they were first isolated from the frog *Atelopus chiriquiensis* (7).

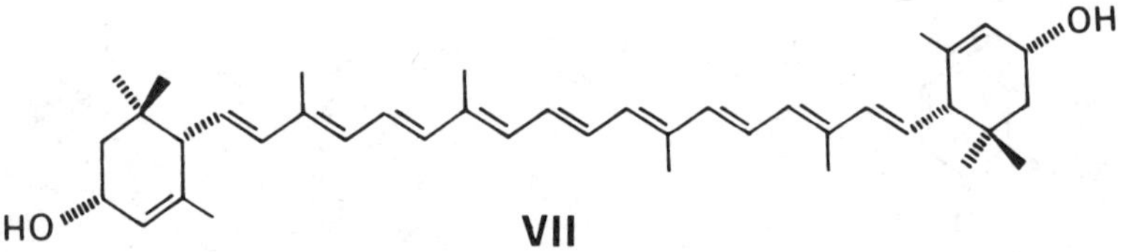

HO OH

VII

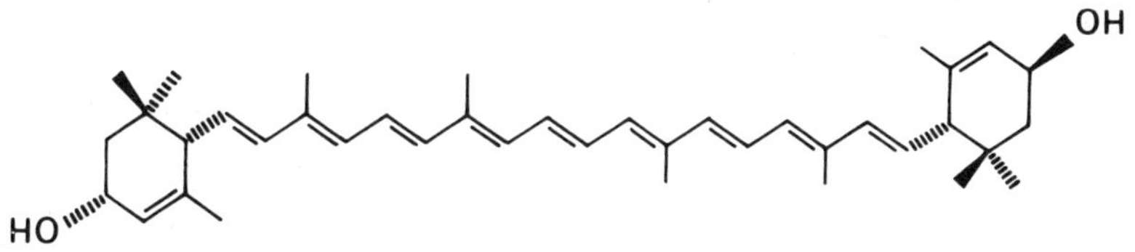

VIII

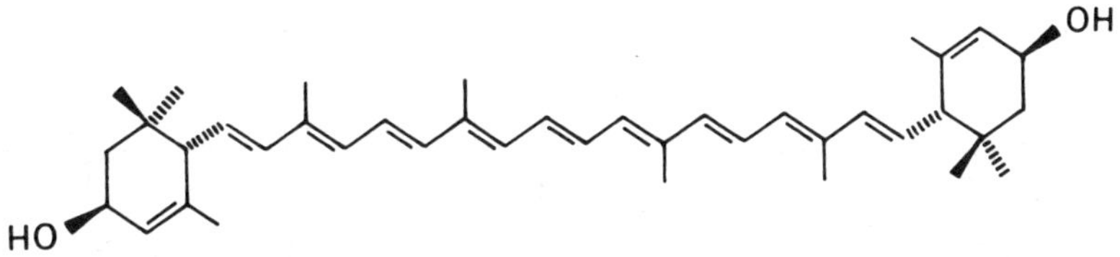

IX

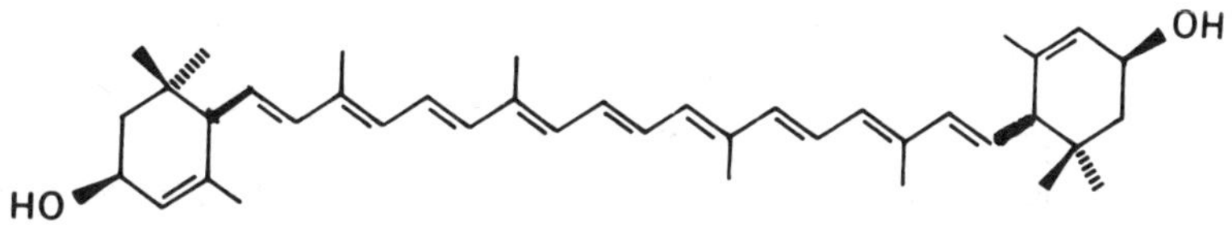

X

## *Astaxanthin Formation*

FRESHWATER FISH β-Carotene can be converted into 3*S*,3'*S*-astaxanthin in goldfish and the probable steps in the conversion are indicated in Figure 1. The proposed intermediates isocryptoxanthin, echinenone, and canthaxanthin all yield astaxanthin when fed to pigment-depleted fish (110); 4'-hydroxyechinenone (Figure 1) is the only proposed intermediate that has not been detected in the fish (110). Other workers suggest that this is only a minor pathway and that zeaxanthin (IV) is a key intermediate (47). However, in the fish *Tilapia nilotica* zeaxanthin is oxidized to rhodoxanthin (4',5'-didehydro-4,5'-retro-β,β-carotene-dione) (XI) (89). Incidentally, the pathway followed in prawns (59) and lobsters (60) is that outlined in Figure 1.

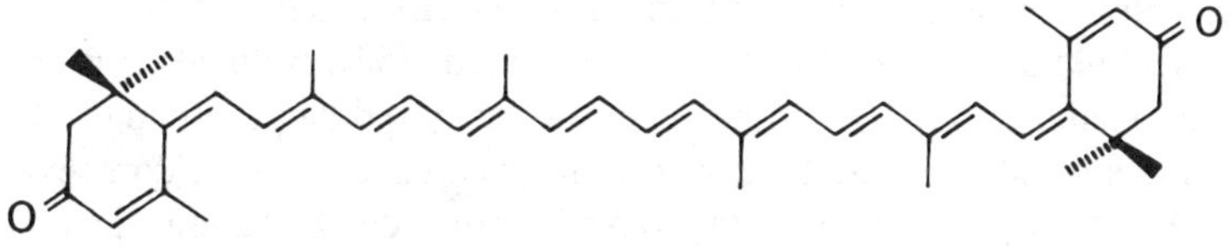

XI

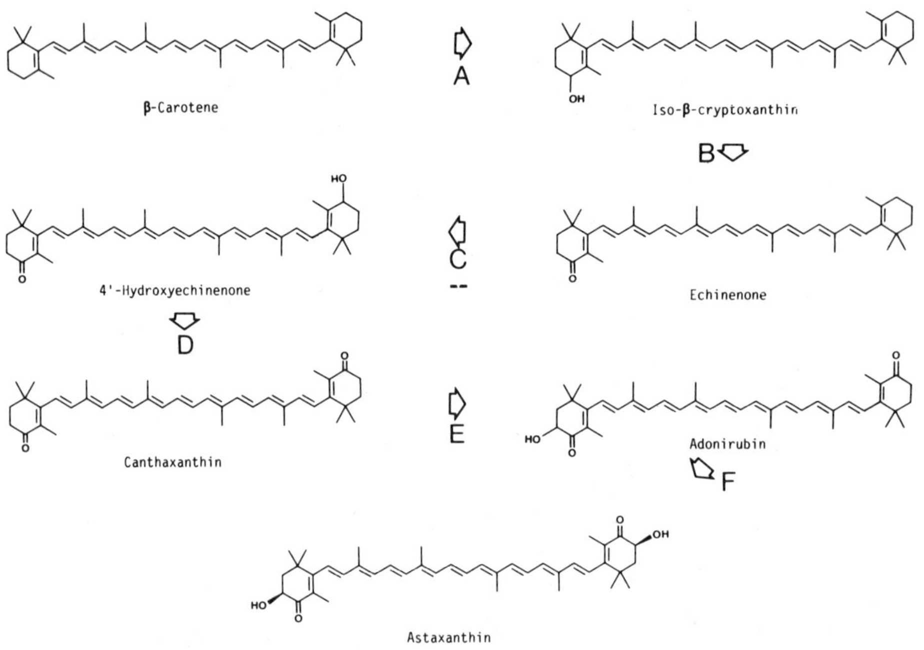

β-Carotene → A → Iso-β-cryptoxanthin → B → Echinenone → C → 4'-Hydroxyechinenone → D → Canthaxanthin → E → Adonirubin → F → Astaxanthin

*Figure 1* Possible pathway of conversion of β-carotene into astaxanthin in goldfish (adapted from 15). Reproduced with permission.

Rather unexpected is the clear demonstration over the past few years of the conversion of (3*R*,3'*R*)-lutein (V) into (3*S*,3'*S*)astaxanthin (VI) in goldfish and fancy red carp (see 121). The difference of chirality at C-3' in lutein and astaxanthin first put this result in question (15) but the discovery that "lutein" in skin is in fact 3'-epilutein (16) removed this difficulty and so it is reasonable to assume that as a first step in the formation of astaxanthin in goldfish (3*R*,3'*R*)-lutein is inverted to 3'-epilutein via 3'-O-didehydrolutein (*A, B* in Figure 2). 3'-O-Didehydrolutein has been otherwise observed only in the petals of *Caltha palustris* and egg yolk (16) and probably in some moths, particularly *Philosamia cynthia* under the name philosamiaxanthin, although the chirality of this pigment is not known (see 61). Lability of this compound to alkali suggests that it may be more widespread than so far reported because alkali treatment is frequently an essential early step in purifying carotenoid extracts.

[$^{14}$C] Lutein is converted into α-doradexanthin (54), β-doradexanthin (54), and astaxanthin (54, 105) in goldfish and fancy red carp, although in other experiments with goldfish the conversion appeared to stop at α-doradexanthin (*C* in Figure 2) (47). However, the conversion of β-doradexanthin into astaxanthin (*E* in Figure 2) is well documented (47, 49). The only doubtful step is *D*, which involves the isomerization of a β-ring into an ϵ-ring. This is much more

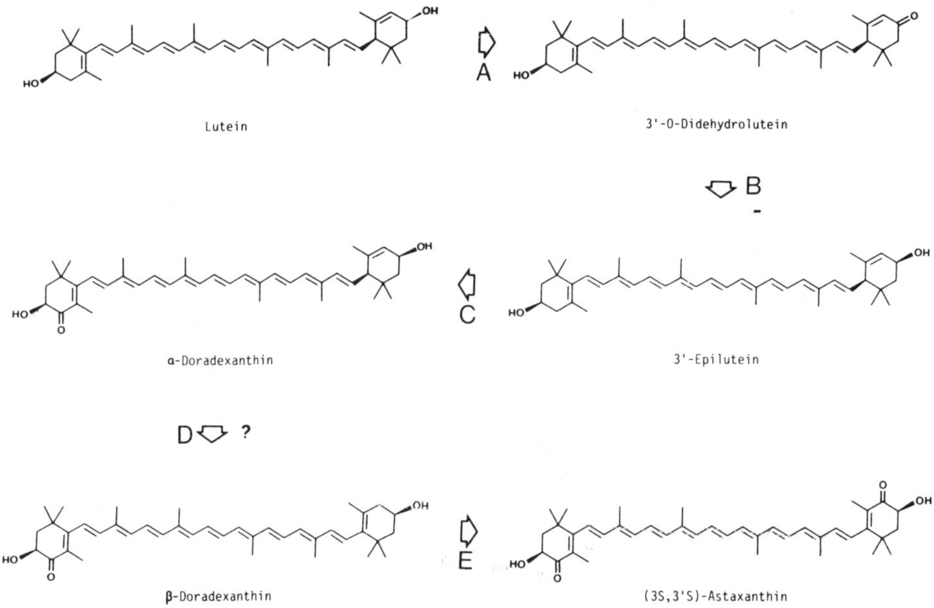

A

Lutein

3'-O-Didehydrolutein

B

C

α-Doradexanthin

3'-Epilutein

D ?

E

β-Doradexanthin

(3S,3'S)-Astaxanthin

*Figure 2* Possible pathway of conversion of 3*R*,3'*R*-lutein into astaxanthin in goldfish (adapted from 15). Reproduced with permission

likely than was thought a few years ago and has been established in chicken retinas (see next section); it does not occur in plants (38). Support for α-doradexanthin as an intermediate comes from the demonstration that its configuration at C-3 and C-3' is the same as that in the major astaxanthin epimer present (15).

(3*R*,3'*R*)-Zeaxanthin (IV) is also converted into (3*S*,3'*S*)-astaxanthin (49, 50) and a possible intermediate, idoxanthin (105), has recently been shown to have the appropriate absolute configuration [(3*S*,3'*S*,4'*R*)-trihydroxy β,β-carotene-4-one] (96). The exact pathway is not known but it will be recalled (Figure 1) that zeaxanthin is not involved in the conversion of β-carotene into astaxanthin.

The explanation of the existence of small amounts of (*3R*,3'*R*)-astaxanthin and (3*R*,3'*S*)-astaxanthin in fish is not yet apparent. In some cases they may be supplied preformed in the small crustacea in the diet of *Salvelinus alpinus* and, possibly, *Salmo trutta* (125). This, of course, only pushes the problem one step further back and the question whether or not algal chiral carotenoids are stereochemically pure needs to be addressed.

SALMON AND RAINBOW TROUT Salmon and rainbow trout differ from goldfish for they cannot oxidize 3,3'-dihydroxy carotenoids (e.g. zeaxanthin) to astaxanthin (48). Because the absorption of dietary β-carotene is almost zero (116), this pigment also cannot be a precursor and one must conclude that astaxanthin in these fish is essentially of dietary origin.

## *Xanthophyll Formation in Marine Fish*

Two biosynthetic problems are posed by the existence of the widely distributed tunaxanthins: (*a*) how are pigments with two ε,ε-rings formed, and (*b*) how is the 6*S*' chirality achieved? A pathway from β-carotene has been suggested (15) but as yet there is no accompanying experimental evidence. On the other hand astaxanthin is converted into the tunaxanthins in the yellowtail *(Seriola quinqueradiata)* (32, 99, 100), and the red Sea Bream (33). A thorough study, including the determination of chirality, of the carotenoids found in the eggs of the dolphin *(Coryptiaena hippurus)* and flying fish *(Prognichthys agoo)* (90) led to the proposal of a putative pathway for the formation of tunaxanthin A, B, C from (3S,3'*S*)-astaxanthin via (3*R*,3'*R*)-zeaxanthin, (3*R*,6'*S*)-3-hydroxy-β,ε-caroten-3'-one, and (6*S*,6'*S*)-ε,ε-carotene-3,3'-dione.

Direct biochemical evidence still remains to be reported but it should be emphasized that the proposals involve a *reductive* pathway of metabolism for astaxanthin; other such pathways of astaxanthin are considered in the next section.

## *Reductive Metabolism of Xanthophylls in Fish*

A number of reports of reductive pathways of metabolism of fish carotenoids have recently appeared. The formation of tunaxanthins, just discussed, is a case in point. Reductive reactions in freshwater fish are of the utmost importance leading as they do to a new source of vitamin A in the food chain. Thorough investigations with labelled (3*S*,3'*S*)-astaxanthin revealed a number of metabolites in the skin of rainbow trout *(Salmo gairdneri)* (Figure 3); the skin is the main site of accumulation in the trout (116).

The pathway of reduction involves the stepwise removal of the keto groups at C-4 and C-4' to form zeaxanthin, which then appears to undergo more conventional degradative processes beginning with epoxidation. Adonixanthin and (3*R*,3'*R*)-zeaxanthin, which are normally present in trout skin, are thus probable metabolites of dietary astaxanthin obtained from small crustacea (117). Feeding of adonirubin and canthaxanthin (Figure 3) confirmed the elimination of the keto groups at C-4,4' but again, in the case of adonirubin, there was no elimination of the C-3 hydroxyl group. This means that only canthaxanthin, not normally a dietary carotenoid, can give rise in the skin to β-carotene, the vitamin A precursor.

In Atlantic salmon *(Salmo salar)* dietary astaxanthin and trout are deposited more efficiently in the flesh than in the skin, in contrast to the rainbow trout (116). The reductive metabolic pathway of the two pigments is the same in both

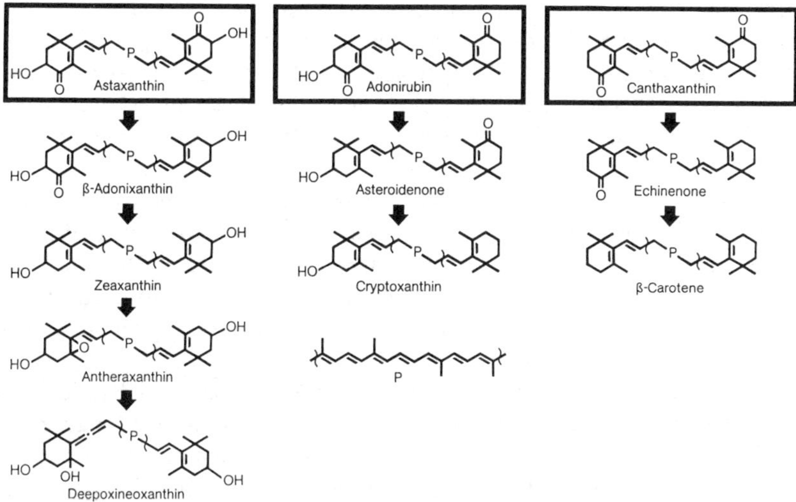


*Figure 3* The metabolism of astaxanthin, adonirubin, and canthaxanthin in skin of rainbow trout (116). Reproduced with permission.

species although idoxanthin, a putative intermediate between astaxanthin and adonixanthin, was found in salmon (116). Similar results have been reported in *Oncorhynchus keta* (63), and in the freshwater fish *Heteropneustes fossilis* astaxanthin is converted into β-carotene and crustaxanthin (β,β-carotene, 3,4,3',4'-tetraol) (41). (3*S*,3'*S*)-Astaxanthin is also reduced to (3*R*,3'*R*)-zeaxanthin in eggs of mackerel *(Pneumatophorus japonicus)* and yellowtail *(Seriola quinqueradiata)* (90). (3*R*,3'*R*)-Zeaxanthin is the isomer present in plants (38) but recently the (3*S*,3'*S*) diastereomer was obtained from trout skins (116). As dietary astaxanthin is not epimerized at C-3,3' during absorption and metabolism in the trout (30, 116), the conclusion must be that (3*R*,3'*R*)-astaxanthin, present in small amounts in the crustacean food, is the direct precursor of (3*S*,3'*S*)-zeaxanthin (116).

Parasiloxanthin, 7',8'-dihydrozeaxanthin, and 7,8-dihydroparasiloxanthin are xanthophylls with reduced in-chain double bonds. They are reported in the Japanese catfish *Parasilurus asotus* (95) and are said to arise in vivo by reduction of zeaxanthin; similarly lutein is reduced to 7,8-dihydrolutein (94).

## *Carotenoids as Vitamin A Precursors*

Nutritionists first became aware of the importance of carotenoids as the ultimate source of vitamin A when Moore (101) showed conclusively that β-carotene is a precursor of vitamin A (retinol) in mammals. The essential structural requirement in the carotenoid molecule is one unsubstituted β-ring attached to an intact conjugated polyene structure from C-7 to C-15 (see Formula I); thus β-carotene

(II), with two essential structural units, is the most potent pro–vitamin A. The main site of conversion is the intestinal mucosa and two enzymes are involved: the first is β-carotene-15,15'-oxygenase, which splits the molecule at the central (C-15,15') double bond to yield vitamin A aldehyde, retinal; the second is retinal reductase, an NADPH-dependent enzyme that converts retinal into retinol (see 39).

It has been known for some time that animals, particularly those of the lower orders, can oxidize dietary carotenoids to hydroxy and keto carotenoids. The latest work in this area was discussed in previous sections. However, the reductive pathways recently discovered (see previous section) open up the possibility that xanthophylls can be precursors of vitamin A by virtue of their conversion into β-carotene.

Claims in the older literature (see 39) that astaxanthin is a precursor of vitamin A, particularly in crustacea, were not seriously pursued for 25 years until feeding experiments strongly indicated that astaxanthin, canthaxanthin, and isozeaxanthin (β,β-carotene-4,4'-diol) were all converted into both vitamins A and $A_2$ (3,4-didehydroretinol—which generally accompanies retinol in freshwater fish) in guppies and platies (45). However, $^{3}$H-crustaxanthin, a suggested intermediate from astaxanthin, was not active in carp (9). Definitive isotope experiments have now unequivocally demonstrated in rainbow trout the conversion of astaxanthin, canthaxanthin, and zeaxanthin into vitamins A and $A_2$ as they cross the intestinal wall (116). Similarly [$^{14}$C]-β-carotene, -zeaxanthin, -lutein, and -canthaxanthin are all converted into both vitamins in goldfish.[2]

In trout the conclusion must be that, because carotenoids with or without oxygen functions at C-3 and C-4 are active, the common intermediate in the formation of retinol is β-carotene. As already indicated (Figure 3), canthaxanthin, which is not a usual dietary constituent in trout, is metabolized in the skin to β-carotene, but this is not so with astaxanthin, so specific enzymes must exist in the intestinal mucosa to reduce astaxanthin to β-carotene (116). This investigation emphasizes that the basic structural requirement for vitamin A activity in carotenoids in trout remains the same as in mammals. The key difference between the two groups is that mammals do not possess a reductive pathway for xanthophyll metabolism. Furthermore the major site of conversion of β-carotene into vitamin A is the same in both groups—the intestinal mucosa—and presumably the key enzyme that splits the chain is a 15,15'-oxygenase in both cases. Eventually the determination of the degree of homology between the various oxygenases will be important for students of biochemical evolution.

In the experiments on trout the specific activity of the isolated retinol (A) was always greater than that of dehydroretinol ($A_2$) which demonstrates that vitamin

[2]B. H. Davies, B. W. Davies, Univ. Coll. Wales, Aberystwyth, personal communication.

A is the precursor of vitamin $A_2$ and confirms the pioneering feeding experiments in 1939 (102) and similar later investigations (51, 67). The same relationship was found in the A and $A_2$ in the liver and intestine of goldfish fed labelled carotenoid precursors, the ratio of specific activity of A/$A_2$ being 4:1 (however, the ratio in the eye is 1:1).[2] No explanation is yet forthcoming for this observation.

A series of feeding experiments on an Indian freshwater fish *(Heteropneustes fossilis)* indicates the lutein may be the specific precursor of vitamin $A_2$ (3, 4, 41, 42), with anhydrolutein (3',4'-didehydro-β-β-carotene-3-ol) as an intermediate that is cleaved at the center of the molecule to give 3,4-didehydroretinol ($A_2$) and 3-hydroxyretinol. β-Carotene apparently does not give rise to $A_2$ in this fish (4). In the goldfish experiments just cited, lutein behaved similarly to other carotenoids in apparently making vitamin $A_2$ from $A_1$. β-Cryptoxanthin is converted into retinol in freshwater Indian fish that normally accumulate retinol, and into 3,4-didehydroretinol and 3-hydroxyretinol in fish that normally accumulate dehydroretinol (42, 43).

## *Regulation of Vitamin A Synthesis*

In the trout experiments discussed above (116), almost no vitamin A could be detected in the liver of very young fish (50 g) raised on a diet containing the vitamin, but the amount increased rapidly in fish weighing 200 g or more. Carotenoids, poorly absorbed in young fish, are rapidly taken up by vitamin A–depleted fish nearing sexual maturity and are converted into vitamin A. After administering labelled astaxanthin, as much as 17% of the radioactivity in the liver was in the vitamin A fraction. The purified vitamin furthermore had almost the same specific activity as the precursor, that is the molecular specific activity was approximately one half that of the administered astaxanthin. However, when fish saturated with vitamin A were used in a similar experiment, no significant conversion of astaxanthin into retinol was observed. Similar results were obtained with labelled canthaxanthin: 7.4% of the label was recovered in the vitamin A from fish already on a diet containing it, in contrast to 54% in fish that were vitamin A–depleted. On the other hand, accumulation of vitamin A itself (fed as retinyl acetate) was not significantly influenced by the vitamin A status of the fish. Clearly an important negative feedback control is operating on the activity of the 15,15'-oxygenase.

## *Coloration in Artificially Reared Fish*

The great commercial expansion in aquaculture in recent years has stimulated considerable interest in the cosmetic aspect of carotenoid biochemistry. The aquaculturist must produce trout and salmon the appearance of which approximates to that of wild fish in order to meet customer expectation and acceptance. The considerable technical literature on this subject has been most thoroughly reviewed (121); suffice it to say here that natural canthaxanthin either in shrimp meal (18–20) or added to diets in the form of pure synthetic material stabilized in beadlets (118) is currently the pigment of choice (122). The low level of the pigment in natural shrimp meal, which itself has a low digestibility because of its high chitin and calcium carbonate content, has led to industrial extraction of the pigment with hot soybean oil. The colored extract, containing some 155 mg pigment/100 g oil, is well utilized by trout when it is fed either alone or incorporated into a solid diet at a level of 6–9 mg/100 g feed (123). The stabilized beadlets fed at a level of 190 mg/kg feed produced after 31 weeks rainbow trout with a flesh color similar to that of red salmon (118).

## METABOLISM IN BIRDS

The characteristic carotenoid pattern in birds is the accumulation of xanthophylls to the almost complete exclusion of carotenes in all tissues except the retina (14, 39). Most nutritional and metabolic studies have been carried out on poultry and a comprehensive review on carotenoids in poultry feeds has recently appeared (72). Here we concentrate on recent investigations in chickens, particularly of their eggs and retinas.

### *Absorption, Storage, and Metabolism—General*

On a maize (corn)-based feed lutein and zeaxanthin are equally well absorbed by chickens and stored in the egg yolk, whereas only traces of β-carotene reach the yolk (114). Canthaxanthin and astaxanthin are also well absorbed from shrimp meal (72) but zeaxanthin is three times better absorbed than astaxanthin (114).

Experiments with [$^3$H](3*R*,3'*R*)-zeaxanthin and [$^3$H](3*S*,3'*S*)-astaxanthin showed that both appear in blood, muscle, liver, fat, skin, and feathers of young birds; the stores in the muscle and skin are transferred to the ovaries with the onset of sexual maturity. In the laying hen, 50% of the total body zeaxanthin is localized in the ovaries and 20% of the ingested pigment is eliminated in the egg yolk (116). (3*R*,3'*R*)-Zeaxanthin is metabolized in the yolk by oxidation, first at C-3 and then at C-3' accompanied by allylic rearrangement that yields (3*R*,6'*S*)β,ε-caroten-3'-one and 6*S*,6*S*'-ε,ε-carotene-3,3'-one (114). Thus we have the first clear demonstration of the formation of an ε-ring from a β-ring. Lutein, on the other hand, is converted into (3*R*,6'*R*)-3-hydroxy-β,ε-caroten-3-one and (6*S*,6*R*)-ε,ε-carotene-3,3'-dione (114); thus the β-ring is metabolized as in zeaxanthin whereas the preformed 3'-hydroxy-ε-ring is simply oxidized to the corresponding 3'-one. (3*R*,3'*R*)-Zeaxanthin is slightly better absorbed by chickens than is the (3*S*,3'*S*)-diastereoisomer, but the absorption of the meso (3*R*,3'*S*) form is only 40% of that of the chiral forms (114); this suggests the involvement of an active transport process in zeaxanthin absorption.

The metabolism of astaxanthin in chickens contrasts with that of zeaxanthin in a number of ways: (*a*) as indicated above it is considerably less well absorbed; (*b*) it is not esterified in the body whereas most of the zeaxanthin is esterified and stored in the liver; and (*c*) it is not oxidatively metabolized but reduced to idoxanthin and crustaxanthin, which are rather quickly eliminated from the liver (114).

## *Metabolism in Retina and Embryo*

The colored oil droplets of the cones of birds' retinas yield a mixture of conventional carotenoids, including lutein, zeaxanthin, and astaxanthin (39, 97, 98). In addition there are also unequivocally present in hen and turkey retinas a carotene, 6*S*,6*S*'-ε,ε-carotene, (22) galloxanthin, (3*R*-10'-apo-β-carotene-3,10-diol (XII), and ε-galloxanthin (3*R*,6*S*,10'-apo-ε-carotene-3,10-diol) (22[3]).

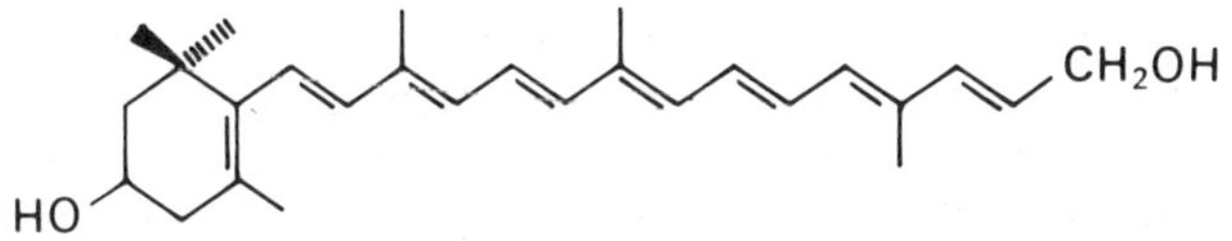

HO ... $CH_2OH$

**XII**

Recent analysis by the most sophisticated methods of turkey retina extracts yielded a complex mixture of carotenoids, with many components exhibiting unexpected chirality.[4] Full assessment of this detailed investigation is not yet available but there is no doubt that the situation is less simple than previously thought. A compound present in the retinas was originally reported to be 14'-apo-β-caroten-14'-ol (22, 106), but was eventually revealed as an artefact formed by the reaction of retinal with acetone during the extraction procedure (23). The concentration of carotenoids in the retinal droplets is high (56) and particularly in the droplets from turtle retinas, which have cones similar to those in birds, where it can reach molar levels (71). The precursor of ε,ε-carotene, galloxanthin, and astaxanthin, which are not normal constituents of birds' diet, has not been fully settled but preliminary experiments with [$^{14}$C]zeaxanthin, a putative precursor, injected into the sub-blastodermic fluid of fertile chicken eggs showed that mobilization of radioactivity into the retinal lipid coincided with the appearance of the characteristic oil droplet carotenoids (25). Recently that activity has been associated with galloxanthin, ε-galloxanthin, and astaxanthin.[5]

[3]See also B. H. Davies, S. Pollard, R.-J. Lewis-Jones, A. Akers, A. Lachenmeir, H. Pfander, Univ. Coll. Wales, Aberystwyth, personal communication.

[4]B. H. Davies, B. W. Davies, A. Akers, K. Schiedt, Univ. Coll. Wales, Aberystwyth, personal communication.

[5]B. H. Davies, Univ. Coll. Wales, Aberystwyth, personal communication.

### *Nutrition*

Most of the many papers on carotenoids in poultry feeds are concerned with providing broilers whose appearance is attractive to the public and providing eggs with an acceptable depth and shade (72). Important as these investigations are to the food industry they have little fundamental nutritional content. Perhaps of more importance have been the efforts to provide satisfactory diets to improve and maintain the plumage color of birds kept in captivity. Space is available only to mention the classical work of the late D. L. Fox on carotenoid metabolism in flamingoes (31), the spin-off from which is the world-wide improvement in plumage color of captive flamingoes. Canthaxanthin appears to be the carotenoid of choice to be added to the diet of many birds to obtain optimum coloration (72).

## METABOLISM IN INSECTS

As is the case with fish and birds, many insects accumulate carotenoids that are absent from their food (39, 61). Most important insect carotenoids are astaxanthin (Locusta), various carotenoids uniquely substituted at C-2 with both *R* and *S* configurations (stick insects—Phasmida), and hydrocarbons such as lycopene (ψ,ψ-carotene) (XIII), torulene (XIV), and γ,γ-carotene (XV).

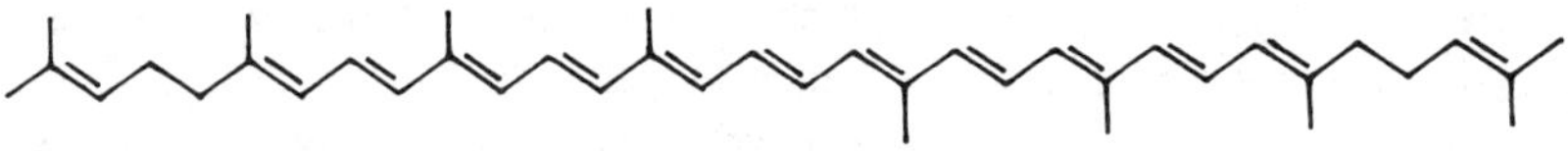

XIII

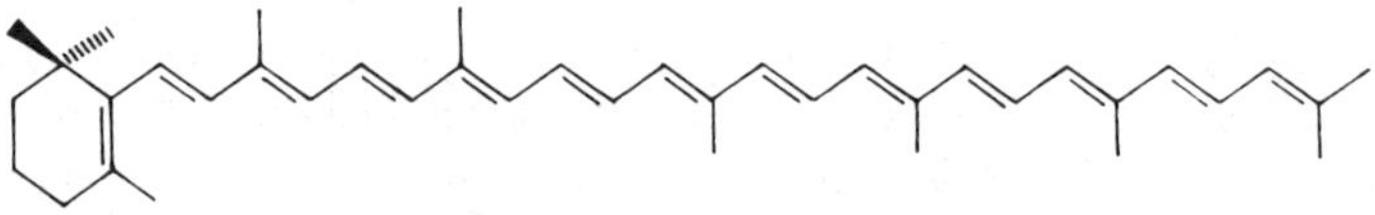

XIV

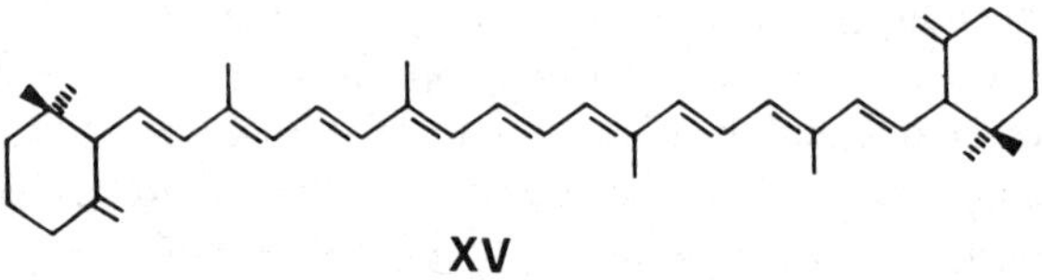

XV

Although no experiments with labelled substrates have been reported, the conversion of β-carotene into canthaxanthin and astaxanthin appears well established (46, 70, 104), thus confirming very early work in developing locust eggs, where β-carotene the major pigment in newly laid eggs gradually disappears and is replaced by astaxanthin (36). Lutein may be converted into astaxanthin via a route similar to that observed in fish. However, the chirality of presumed intermediates has yet to be determined. In particular the following questions remain: (*a*) Is endogenous insect "lutein" really lutein or is it 3'-epilutein? (*b*) Has philosamiaxanthin the same absolute configuration as 3'-O-didehydrolutein? (*c*) Is the configuration of papilioerythrin from *Papilio xuthus* (61) the same as that of α-doradexanthin, as claimed (46)?

The new 2-hydroxy and 2-oxy carotenoids found in stick insects are derived from β-carotene as shown by isotope experiments in *Carausius* (61), but these experiments and kinetic studies during embryonic development of *Ectatosoma tiaratum* (61) did not settle unequivocally the sequence of reactions involved. In particular it is not known whether the first step is hydroxylation or the formation of a ketone. The question of how *R* and *S* isomers arise is also not solved. Different insects metabolize the 2-substituted carotenoids in various ways (62).

### *Formation of Hydrocarbons*

A new aspect of carotenoid metabolism has arisen from detailed studies on the aphid *Microsiphum liriodendri* (Hemiptera) (1, 128) and the ladybird beetle (ladybug) *(Coccinella septempunctata)* (Coleoptera) (12, 13). *M. liriodendri* exists in two dimorphic forms, one green and one pink; the pink form is characterized by carotenoids prominent in red yeasts, namely torulene, γ-carotene (β,ψ-carotene), lycopene, and 3,4-dehydrolycopene. As these carotenoids are not present in the aphids' food and as aphids are obligatorily associated with endosymbiotic microorganisms, it was concluded that these microorganisms, presumably fungi, are the source of the carotenoids that contribute the pink color to the aphids. Far less pigment is present in the green strains of the aphid but the components are still characteristically fungal; presumably the greens contain different and fewer colored symbionts.

The presence of lycopene in the elytra (wing cases) of ladybirds was reported nearly 50 years ago (see 39). Although this was recently confirmed, lycopene was by no means the only or the major hydrocarbon present (12, 13). The complex mixture was again characteristic of the carotenoids of red yeasts and contained partly saturated polyenes, such as phytoene (7,8,11,12,7',8',11',12'-octahydrolycopene), which are well established precursors in the de novo synthesis of colored carotenoids. The conclusion from these observations is that the ladybird pigments arise from the biosynthetic activities of symbiotic red yeasts and not to any great extent from the aphids they eat. Thus the food chain in insects can be more complex than appears at first sight.

## DE NOVO SYNTHESIS IN ANIMALS

Although overwhelming evidence exists for the view that animals cannot synthesize carotenoids de novo, there has been a report that such a total biosynthesis occurs in bovine corpora lutea (2), where the β-carotene levels reach very high values (see 39). Recently in a reinvestigation of this claim an enzyme preparation from bovine corpora lutea was obtained that will incorporate 65% of added [2-$^{14}$C]mevalonic acid (the specific precursor of sterols and carotenoids) into the unsaponifiable fraction of the preparation. The β-carotene isolated from this fraction after purification by HPLC, however, contained no radioactivity. Furthermore, no biosynthetic intermediates, such as phytoene, were detected.[6] A possible explanation of earlier positive results is that crystallization yields a less radiochemically pure product than does HPLC. Corpora lutea can synthesize retinol from β-carotene (35).

## FUNCTIONS OTHER THAN AS VITAMIN A PRECURSORS

### *Invertebrates*

The important contribution of carotenoids to the color pattern in invertebrates is well known and was touched on earlier in this review. They occur either as the free pigments or as carotenoproteins, which open up a much wider spectral range of light absorption than that achieved by free pigments. For example, the green of lobster eggs and the deep purple of their carapace are due to the presence of astaxanthin (orange in free state) attached to different proteins (10, 39). A clear metabolic function for carotenoids per se remains elusive—if one exists at all. It has been reported that only mussels with high concentrations of carotenoids in their nervous tissue can withstand extended period of anoxia. The absorbance at 450 nm in the nerves is increased in anoxia, twofold in 10–15 h, and decreased when the animals are allowed access to oxygen. The decrease in absorbance was attributed to the formation of in-chain epoxides, which would shift the absorption maximum to much lower wavelengths. The epoxides were considered to represent an oxygen reserve that could be utilized for ATP production in the anoxic condition, with the concomitant regeneration of the fully conjugated pigments (58, 129). This claim was reinvestigated using *Mytilus edulis* and sensitive analytical procedures, but no significant changes were noted in carotenoid pattern in mussels subjected to 116 hours of anoxia. Furthermore there was no indication of the presence of in-chain epoxides (107).

### *Vertebrates*

FISH The important work discussed previously clearly establishes for the first time the pro–vitamin A activity of xanthophylls but it must be emphasized that in fish carotenoids do have a function per se. Many fish owe their bright yellow,

[6]B. H. Davies, A. Akers, Univ. Coll. Wales, Aberystwyth, personal communication.

orange, and red color patterns to the carotenoids concentrated in the integumentary chromatophores (39). The characteristic cryptic coloration for protection and the sexual dichroism that attracts females at spawning time are carotenoid based. In the Salmonidae, carotenoids are mobilized from the flesh and possibly the liver into the eggs at spawning time. Their function in eggs is primarily to provide the developing embryos with a source of pigments with which to produce the characteristic color pattern in the skin. There have been claims that high levels of carotenoids in salmonid eggs improve their viability; however, a thorough assessment of published data (20a) indicates no simple relationship between carotenoid content and viability although it appears that with eggs containing about 1–3 μg/g 80% hatchability can be expected. Below these levels the expectation drops below 50%. The evidence is not, however, conclusive (20a). Any other suggested biochemical functions for carotenoids per se (39) are all tenuously based and require critical assessment.

MAMMALS There is no well-established basic biological function for carotenoids per se in mammals, but they have become of medical value as drugs to treat diseases involving photosensitization and they may become increasingly important anticancer agents. Both aspects are discussed below but, in addition, effects of β-carotene on immunological responses have been reported; it is said to increase T-cell response generally (69) and particularly that to concanavalin A (6).

## *Protection Against Photosenitization*

The development of carotenoids as drugs in treatment of photosensitization is an excellent example of the imaginative application of the results of basic research to treat a human disorder (77–79). It is well established that carotenoids can protect against photosensitization in photosynthetic organisms (see 38) and in nonphotosynthetic bacteria (74). Laboratory mice photosensitized by administration of hematoporphyrin were protected by injection of very large doses of β-carotene (3 mg per mouse) 18–24 h before administration of the hematoporphyrin (73). Because of the known lack of toxicity of β-carotene, large doses were tested on patients with erythropoietic protoporphyria and it was revealed to be an effective therapeutic measure in most patients; at least 180 mg/day is necessary for a positive response (79). The US Food and Drug Administration have approved the use of β-carotene in this treatment. It should be emphasized that carotenoids do not cure the disease. Full clinical information can be found in the work of Mathews-Roth (75–78).

Decrease in the number of lesions in Günther's disease (congenital porphyria) has been reported after carotenoid medication; similarly, patients with polymorphous light eruption also responded to carotenoid therapy (see 79). Carotenoids have, however, so far been ineffective in treating actinic reticuloid, porphyria cutanea tarda, solar urticaria, and hydroa aestivale (see 78–80). They do ameliorate skin lesions associated with feline solar dermatitis (55).

The possible toxicity of the high doses of carotenoids used has often been considered but no significant side effects, other than innocuous carotenodermia, have been reported (75, 77, 78). Large intakes of carrots are said to cause leucopenia but this is almost certainly due to constituents of the carrots other than β-carotene (see 78). Although carotenodermia has been known since 1917, the actual isolation of the pigment from the skin was only recently reported (68, 126); previously it had only been obtained from the horny layers scraped from the soles and knees of a patient (44). The carotenodermia is usually not a significant problem, the only likely effect is slight cosmetic worry. The excessive conversion of β-carotene into vitamin A could theoretically lead to the accumulation of toxic amounts of vitamin A in the liver, but early reports indicated no hypervitaminosis A in subjects on high carotene diets (77). A recent examination of biopsy and autopsy material from patients on a high β-carotene regime furthermore revealed no β-carotene in the liver and only traces in the brain. Hepatic vitamin A levels were also normal. Furthermore, no patients on carotene therapy showed enhanced blood levels of vitamin A (85). Obviously an effective feed-back mechanism is in operation. At the molecular biology level there are reports that β-carotene has no ill effects on the genome (52, 57).

## *Mechanism of Photoprotection*

In plants and protista, carotenoids function as scavengers for the highly active singlet oxygen ($^1O_2$) produced mainly during photosynthesis. In the reaction, triplet (ground-state) oxygen is generated together with triplet carotene, which dissipates its energy to its surroundings and returns to its ground state. It is then ready to continue the reaction in cyclic fashion (38, 64):

$$^1O_2 + \text{car} \longrightarrow {}^3O_2 + {}^3\text{car}$$

$$^3\,\text{car} \longrightarrow \text{car} + h\nu.$$

Singlet oxygen was detected when human epidermis samples were illuminated (hematoporphyrin, a photosensitizer, had been added to the samples) (28). Similar results were obtained in vivo with hairless mice made porphyric with collidine (83). In this experiment production of $^1O_2$ in mice treated with either β-carotene or canthaxanthin was reduced compared with untreated controls. Inhibition of succinate oxidation in preparations from photosensitized mice was also reduced in carotene-treated animals (83). Although $^1O_2$ is strongly implicated in this type of photosensitization, the $^1O_2$ probe (1,3-diphenylisobenzofuran) used is not completely specific for this species, so the possibility of other mechanisms such as the formation of free radicals, which are know to be intercepted by carotenoids (64, 65), cannot be excluded. Reactive oxygen species are, however, involved in lipid peroxidation observed in rat epidermal microsomes; this peroxidation is inhibited in the presence of β-carotene (26). β-Carotene also protects against in vivo lipid peroxidation (66).

## CAROTENOIDS AS ANTITUMOR AGENTS

Many reports have appeared over the past 20–30 years on the antitumor activity of vitamin A (80, 124) and it was not unexpected that β-carotene would be tested for similar activity (see 84). A summary of the findings of the major investigations is given in Table 1. A general conclusion is that carotenoids slow down growth of tumors induced by UV-A, UV-B, BP, BP/UV-A, and 8-methoxypsoralen irrespective of their inherent ability or otherwise to act as precursors of vitamin A. However, the lack of effect of canthaxanthin compared with β-carotene on DMB-induced tumors suggests that in this case conversion into vitamin A is essential for activity (82). With UV-B-induced tumors, pigment administration after the appearancc of the first tumors slows down the manifestation of later tumors (82).

Quantitative results show some variance; β-carotene when added to the diet in an alcoholic solution to give a concentration of 90 mg/kg diet decreased the incidence of DMBA tumors in rats (119) whereas the same amount in the form of stabilized beadlets was ineffective (82). When the beadlet dose was increased to 700 mg/kg however, protection was observed (82). These very high levels can only be obtained with commercial beadlet preparations. There is one report that topically applied β-carotene increased DMBA/croton oil or resin-induced tumors in hairless mice (120). This unexpected result might be due to the action of some product of β-carotene oxidation because on application to the skin the pigment rapidly bleaches (86).

**Table 1** Activity of carotenoid in delaying development of skin tumors in mice

| Carcinogen | Activity[a] β-carotene | canthaxanthin | phytoene | Reference |
|---|---|---|---|---|
| DMBA[b] | + | | | 27 |
| UV-B | + | + | + | 76, 80 |
| UV-B | + | | | 29 |
| DMBA/croton oil | + | − | − | 82 |
| DMBA/UV-B | + | + | − | 80 |
| DBP[c] | + | + | | 113 |
| BP/UV-A | + | + | | 113 |
| *S*-Methoxypsoralen | + | + | | 113 |
| UV-A | + | + | | 113 |

[a] +, positive effect: −, no effect: no symbol, not tested.
[b] 9,10-Dimethyl-1,2-benzanthracene.
[c] Benzpyrene

Because carotenoids quench singlet oxygen or free radical formation, they are clearly important in treating photosensitization. There are also indications that the pigments are functioning in a similar way in protecting against tumors induced by agents other than UV-B alone. Phytoene is much less effective than β-carotene or canthaxanthin in protecting against tumors induced by DMBA/croton oil or DMBA/UV-B, which correlates with the fact that β-carotene and canthaxanthin are much more effective quenchers of $^1O_2$ than is phytoene (87).

The water-soluble colored carotenoid crocetin (XVI) in the form of the unsaponifiable extract of saffron is reported to delay the onset of skin tumors induced by DMBA (croton oil) in Swiss Webster mice (34). However, pure crocetin was much less effective than β-carotene in DMBA (croton oil)-induced tumors in hairless mice and also had no discernible effect on UV-B-induced tumors (81).

A long-term investigation on the anticancer effect of β-carotene in humans is under way (84).

## CONCLUSIONS

Two of the major recent developments in animal carotenoid metabolism are (*a*) the discovery of many chiral epimers of well-known plant carotenoids in fish, birds, and insects, and (*b*) the partial elucidation of the pathways by which the epimers are formed from dietary carotenoids. Xanthophylls, which are not vitamin A precursors in mammals, were found to be active in lower animals by reason of these animals' ability to metabolize them reductively to β-carotene, which is then converted into vitamin A. This discovery reveals the missing link in the vitamin A food chain of lower animals and is nutritionally the most important recent development in carotenoid biochemistry. The enzymes that carry out the conversion of β-carotene into Vitamin A are apparently very similar throughout the animal kingdom. The most significant development in mammals has little to do with basic carotenoid biochemistry but with the use of massive doses of β-carotene in ameliorating the distressing photosensitization associated with a number of diseases—a development that stemmed from the extrapolation of observations on the basic function of carotenoids in plants and bacteria. The antitumor action of carotene therapy appears to be well established in skin tumors in mice. Investigations in human beings are under way.

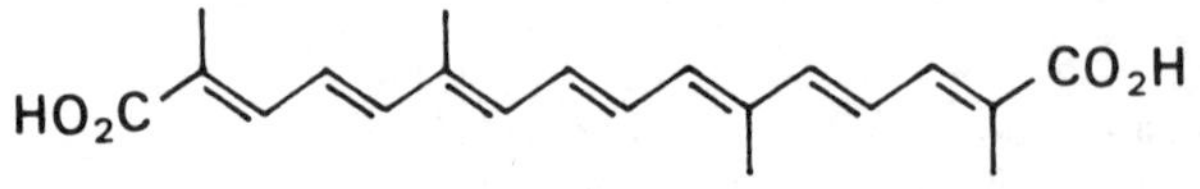

$HO_2C$ … $CO_2H$

**XVI**

The future certainly holds more surprises as further details of chiral studies on the lower animals are brought to light. Furthermore, the techniques now available have the potential to allow investigators to study in detail the degradation of carotenoids in plants and stored foods; in particular, the exact fate of ingested carotenoids in mammals can now be investigated.

## *Literature Cited*


1. Andrewes, A. G., Kjösen, H., Liaaen-Jensen, S., Weisgraber, K. H., Lousberg, R. J. J. C., Weiss, U. 1971. Animal carotenoids of two colour variants of the aphid *Macrosiphum liriodendri*—identification of natural γ,γ-carotene. *Acta Chem. Scand.* 25:3878–80
2. Austern, B. M., Gawienowski, A. M. 1969. *In vitro* biosynthesis of β-carotene by bovine corpus luteum. *Lipids* 4:227–29
3. Barua, A. B., Goswami, U. C. 1977. Formation of vitamin A in a fresh-water fish. *Biochem. J.* 166:133–36
4. Barua, A. B., Singh, H. T., Das, R. C. 1978. Conversion of lutein into dehydroretinol by the freshwater fish *Saccobranchus fossilis*. *Br. J. Nutr.* 30:1–12
5. Bauernfeind, J. C., ed. 1981. *Carotenoids as Colorants and Vitamin A Precursors*. New York: Academic. 938 pp.
6. Bendich, A., Shapiro, S. 1984 Effect of dietary β-carotene on lymphocyte response to mutagens *Fed. Proc.* 43:787
7. Bingham, A., Mosher, H. S., Andrewes, A. G. 1977. Epimeric 3,3'-dihydroxy-ε,ε-carotene from the skin of the yellow frog *Atelopus chiriquiensis*. *Chem. Commun.* 1977:96–97
8. Bingham, A., Wilkie, D. W., Mosher, H. S. 1979. Tunaxanthin: occurrence and absolute stereochemistry. *Comp. Biochem. Physiol.* 62B:489–95
9. Boonjawat, J., Olson, J. A. 1975. The metabolism of radioactive crustaxanthin (3,3',4,4'-tetrahydroxy-β-carotene). *Comp. Biochem. Physiol.* 50B:363–68
10. Britton, G., Armitt, G. M., Lau, S. Y. M., Patel, A. K., Shone, C. C. 1982. Carotenoproteins. See Ref. 11, pp. 237–51
11. Britton, G., Goodwin, T. W., eds. 1982. *Carotenoid Chemistry and Biochemistry*. Oxford: Pergamon. 399 pp.
12. Britton, G., Goodwin, T. W., Harriman, G. A., Lockley, W. J. S. 1977. Carotenoids of the ladybird beetle, *Coccinella septempunctata*. *Insect Biochem.* 7:337–45
13. Britton, G., Lockley, W. J. S., Harriman, G. A., Goodwin, T. W. 1977. Pigmentation of the ladybird beetle *Coccinella septempuntata* by carotenoids that are not of plant origin. *Nature* 266:49–50
14. Brush, A. H. 1981. Carotenoids in wild and captive birds. See Ref. 5, pp. 539–62
15. Buchecker, R. 1981. A chemist's view of animal carotenoids. See Ref. 11, pp. 175–93
16. Buchecker, R., Eugster, C. H. 1979. Eine Suche nach 3'-epilutein (= 3*R*,3'*S*,6'*R*-β,ε-carotin-3,3'-diol) und 3'-*O*-didehydrolutein (= 3*R*,6'*R*-3-hydroxy-β,ε-carotin-3'-on) in Eigelb, in Bluten von *Caltha palustris* und in Herbstblättern. *Helv. Chim. Acta* 62:2817–24
17. Buchecker, R., Eugster, C. H., Weber, A. 1978. Absolute konfiguration von α-doradexanthin, einem neuen Carotinoid aus *Fritschiella tuberosa* Iyeng. *Helv. Chem. Acta* 61:1962–68
18. Choubert, G. 1982. Methods for colour assessment of canthaxanthin-pigmented rainbow trout (*Salmo gairdneri* Rich). *Sci. Aliments*. 2:451–63
19. Choubert, G. 1983. Effects d'un pigment carotenoide, la canthaxanthin, sur la pigmentation de la truite arc-en-ciel *Salmo gairdneri* Rich. *Bull. Fr. Piscic.* 289:112–27
20. Choubert, G., Luquet, P. 1983. Utilization of shrimp meal for rainbow trout (*Salmo gairdneri,* Rich.) pigmentation. Influence of fat content of the diet. *Aquaculture* 32:19–26

20a. Craik, J. C. A. 1985. Egg quality and egg pigment content in salmonid fishes. *Aquaculture* 47:61–88

21. Crozier, G. F., Wilkie, D. W. 1966. Occurrence of a dihydroxy-ε,ε-carotene in a fish. *Comp. Biochem. Physiol.* 18:801–4
22. Davies B. H. 1979. Solved and unsolved problems of carotenoid formation. *Pure Appl. Chem.* 51:623–30
23. Davies, B. H. 1985. Carotenoid metabolism in animals: a biochemists view *Pure Appl. Chem.* 57:679–84
24. Davies, B. H., Rau, W., eds. 1985. Proc. 7th Int. Symp. Carotenoids. *Pure Appl. Chem.* 57:639–821

25. Davies, B. W., Akers, A., Davies, B. H. 1985. Carotenoid of avian retina: mobilization of zeaxanthin from yolk to retina during development of the chick embryo. *Abstr. 7th Int. Carotenoid Symp. Munich,* p. 14
26. Dixit, R., Mukhtar, H., Bickers, D. R. 1983. Studies on the role of reactive oxygen species in mediating lipid peroxide formation in epidermal microsomes of rat skin. *J. Invest. Dermatol.* 81:369–75
27. Dorogokupla, A. C., Troitzkaia, E. G., Adilgireieva, L. K., Postolnikov, S. F., Chekrygina, Z. P. 1973. Effect of carotene on the development of induced tumours. *Zdravookhr. Kaz.* 10:32–34
28. Dubertret, L., Santus, R., Bazin, M., de Sak Melo, T. 1982. Phytochemistry of human epidermis. A quantitative approach. *Photochem. Photobiol.* 35:103–7
29. Epstein, J. H. 1970. Ultraviolet carcinogenesis. In *Photophysiology,* ed. A. C. Giese, 5:235–73 New York: Academic
30. Foss, P., Storebakken, T., Schiedt, K., Liaaen-Jensen, S., Austreng, E., Streiff, K. 1984. Carotenoids in diets for salmonids. I. Pigmentation of rainbow trout with the individual optical isomers of astaxanthin in comparison with canthaxanthin. *Aquaculture* 41:213–26
31. Fox, D. L. 1976. *Animal Biochromes and Structural Colours.* Berkeley: Univ. Calif. 433 pp. 2nd ed.
32. Fujita, T., Sakate, M., Hikichi, S., Takeda, M., Shimeno, S., et al. 1983. Pigmentation of cultured yellow tail with krill oil. *Bull. Jpn. Soc. Sci. Fish.* 495:1595–1600
33. Fujita, T., Sakate, M., Watanabe, T., Kitajima, C. G., Miki, W., et al. 1983. Pigmentation of cultured red sea bream, with astaxanthin diesters purified from krill oil. *Bull. Jpn. Soc. Sci. Fish.* 49: 1855–61
34. Gainer, J. L., Wallis, D. A., Jones, J. R. 1976. The effect of crocetin on skin papillomas and Rous sarcoma. *Oncology* 33:222–24
35. Gawienowski, A. M., Stacewicz-Sapuncakis, M., Longley, R. 1974. Biosynthesis of retinol in bovine corpus luteum. *J. Lipid Res.* 15:375–78
36. Goodwin, T. W. 1949. The biochemistry of locusts. 2. Carotenoid distribution in solitary and gregarious phases of the African migratory locust (*Locsuta migratoria migratorioides* R. & F.) and the desert locust (*Schisterocera gregaria* Forst). *Biochem. J.* 45:472
37. Goodwin, T. W., ed. 1979. Carotenoids. *Pure Appl. Chem.* 51:435–886
38. Goodwin, T. W. 1981. *Biochemistry of Carotenoids,* Vol. 1, *Plants.* London: Chapman & Hall. 377 pp. 2nd ed.
39. Goodwin, T. W. 1984. *Biochemistry of the Carotenoids,* Vol. 2, *Animals.* London: Chapman & Hall. 224 pp. 2nd ed.
40. Goodwin, T. W., Mercer, E. I. 1983. *Introduction to Plant Biochemistry.* Oxford: Pergamon. 677 pp. 2nd ed.
41. Goswami, B. C., Barua, A. B. 1984. Studies in the metabolism of astaxanthin in the freshwater fish *Heteropneustes fossilis.* See Ref. 25, p. 31
42. Goswami, U. C. 1984. Metabolism of carotenoids in freshwater fish. See Ref. 25, p. 19
43. Goswami, U. C. 1984. Metabolism of cryptoxanthin in freshwater fish. *Br. J. Nutr.* 52:575–81
44. Grof, P., Bodzay, J., Kovaks, A. 1967. Carotenodermia. *Acta Med. Acad. Sci. Hung.* 24:129–39
45. Gross, J., Budowski, P. 1966. Conversion of carotenoids into vitamin $A_1$ and $A_2$ in two species of freshwater fish. *Biochem. J.* 101:747–54
46. Harashima, K., Ohno, T., Sawachika, T., Hidaka, T., Ohnishi, E. 1972. Carotenoids in orange pupae of swallowtail *Papilio xuthus. Insect Biochem.* 2: 29–48
47. Hata, M., Hata, M. 1972. Carotenoid pigments in goldfish. IV Carotenoid metabolism. *Bull. Jpn. Soc. Sci. Fish.* 38:331–38
48. Hata, M., Hata, M. 1973. Studies in astaxanthin formation in some freshwater fishes. *Tohoku J. Agric. Res.* 24:192–96
49. Hata, M., Hata, M. 1975. Carotenoid metabolism in fancy Red Carp. 1. Administration of carotenoids. *Bull. Jpn. Soc. Sci. Fish.* 41:653–55
50. Hata, M., Hata, M. 1976. Carotenoid metabolism in fancy Red Carp, *Cyprinus carpio.* II. Metabolism of [$^{14}$C]zeaxanthin. *Bull. Jpn. Soc. Sci. Fish.* 42:203–5
51. Hata, M., Hata, M., Onishi, T. 1973. Conversion of β-carotene and $retinol_1$ to $retinol_2$ in freshwater fish. *Tohoku J. Agric. Res.* 24:197–204
52. Haveland-Smith, R. B. 1981. Evaluation of genotoxicity of some natural food colours using bacterial assays. *Mutat. Res.* 91:285–90
53. Hirao, S., Yamada, J., Kikuchi, R. 1957. Pigments in fish. Distribution and differences of yellow carotenoids in freshwater and marine fish. *Bull. Tokai Reg. Fish. Res. Lab.* 16:53–58
54. Hsu, W.-J., Rodriguez, D. B., Chiches-

ter, C. O. 1972. Biosynthesis of astaxanthin VI. Conversion of [$^{14}$C]lutein and [$^{14}$C]β-carotene in goldfish. *Int. J. Biochem.* 3:333–38

55. Irving, R. A. 1982. Porphyrin values and treatment of feline solar dermatitis *Am. J. Vet. Med.* 43:2067–69
56. Johnston, D., Hudson, R. A. 1976. Isolation and composition of the carotenoid-containing oil droplets from cone photoreceptors. *Biochim. Biophys. Acta* 424:235–45
57. Kada, T., Tutikawa, T., Sudaie, Y. 1972. *In vitro* and host mediated "rec-Assay" procedure for screening chemical mutagens. *Mutat. Res.* 16:165–74
58. Karnaukhov, V. N. 1979. The role of filtrator molluscs rich in carotenoids in the self cleaning of fresh waters. *Symp. Biol. Hung.* 19:152–67
59. Katayama, T., Kamata, T., Shimaya, M., Deshimaru, O., Chichester, C. O. 1972. The biosynthesis of astaxanthin VIII. The conversion of labelled β-carotene-15,15'-$^3H_2$ into astaxanthin in the prawn *Penaeus japonicus*. *Bull. Jpn. Soc. Sci. Fish.* 38:1171–75
60. Katayama, T., Shimaya, M., Saeshima, M., Chichester, C. O. 1973. The Biosynthesis of astaxanthin XII. The conversion of labelled β-carotene-15,15'-$^3H_2$ into body astaxanthin in the lobster *Panulirus japonicus*. *Int. J. Biochem.* 4:223–25
61. Kayser, H. 1981. Carotenoid in insects. See Ref. 11, pp. 195–210
62. Kayser, H. 1982. Cartenoids in stick insects (Phasmids). A quantitative comparison of six species at major developmental stages. *Comp. Biochem. Physiol.* 72B:427–32
63. Kitahara, T. 1983: Behaviour of carotenoids in chum salmon *(O. keta)* during anadromous migration. *Comp. Biochem. Physiol.* 78B:97–101
64. Krinsky, N. 1979. Carotenoid protection against oxidation. *Pure Appl. Chem.* 51:649–60
65. Krinsky, N., Deneke, S. M. 1982. Interaction of oxygen and oxyradicals with carotenoids. *J. Natl. Cancer Inst.* 69: 205–9
66. Kunert, K. J., Tappel, A. L. 1983. The effect of vitamin C on *in vivo* lipid peroxidation in guinea pigs as measured by pentane and ethane production. *Lipids* 18:271–74
67. Lambertsen, G., Braekken, O. R. 1969. *In vivo* conversion of vitamin $A_1$ to vitamin $A_2$. *Acta Chem. Sand.* 23:1063–64
68. Lee, R., Mathews-Roth, M. M., Pathak, M. A. 1974. The detection of carotenoid pigments in human skin. *J. Invest. Dermatol.* 64:175–77
69. Leslie, C. A., Dube, D. P. 1982. Carotene and natural killer cell activity. *Fed. Proc.* 41:381
70. Leuenberger, F., Thommen, H. 1970. Keto-carotenoids in the Colorado beetle *Leptinotarsa decemlineata*. *J. Insect Physiol.* 16:1855–58
71. Liebman, P. A., Granda, A. M. 1975. Super dense carotenoid spectra resolved in single cone oil droplets. *Nature* 253:370–72
72. Marusich, W. L., Bauernfeind, J. C. 1981. Oxycarotenoids in poultry feeds See Ref. 5, pp. 319–462
73. Mathews-Roth, M. M. 1964. Protective effect of β-carotene against lethal photosenitization by haematoporphyrin. *Nature* 203:1092
74. Mathews, M. M., Sistrom, W. R. 1960. The function of carotenoid pigments of *Sarcina lutea*. *Arch. Mikrobiol.* 35:139–46
75. Mathews-Roth, M. M. 1978. Carotenoid pigments and the treatment of erythropoietic protoporphyria *J. Infect. Dis.* 138:924–27
76. Mathews-Roth, M. M. 1980. Carotenoid pigments as anti-tumour agents. In *Current Chemotherapy and Infectious Diseases,* ed. J. D. Nelson, C. Grassi, pp. 1053–55. Washington, DC: Am. Soc. Microbiol.
77. Mathews-Roth, M. M. 1981. Carotenoids in medical applications. See Ref. 5, pp. 755–85
78. Mathews-Roth, M. M. 1982. Medical applications and use of carotenoids. See Ref. 11, pp. 297–307
79. Mathews-Roth, M. M. 1982. Photosensitization by porphyrins and prevention of photosensitization by carotenoids. *J. Natl. Cancer Inst.* 69:279–83
80. Mathews-Roth, M. M. 1982. Antitumour activity of β-carotene, canthaxanthin and phytoene. *Oncology* 39:33–37
81. Mathews-Roth, M. M. 1982. Effect of crocetin on experimental skin tumours in hairless mice. *Oncology* 39:362–64
82. Mathews-Roth, M. M. 1983. Carotenoid pigment administration and delay in development of UV-B induced tumours. *Photochem. Photobiol.* 37:509–11
83. Mathews-Roth, M. M. 1984. Porphyrin photosensitization and carotenoid protection in mice: *in vitro* and *in vivo* studies. *Phytochem. Phytobiol.* 40:63–67
84. Mathews-Roth, M. M. 1985. Carotenoids and cancer prevention-experimental and epidemiological studies. *Pure Appl. Chem.* 57:717–22

85. Mathews-Roth, M. M., Abraham, A., Gabuzda, T. 1976. β-Carotene content of certain organs from two patients receiving high doses of β-carotene. *Clin. Chem. NY* 32:922–23
86. Mathews-Roth, M. M., Pathak, M. A., Fitzpatrick, T. B., Harber, L. C., Kass, E. H. 1974. β-Carotene as an oral protective agent in erthyropoietic protoporphyria. *J. Am. Med. Assoc.* 228: 1004–8
87. Mathews-Roth, M. M., Wilson, T., Fujimori, E., Krinsky, N. I. 1974. Carotenoid chromophore length and protection against photosensitization. *Photochem. Photobiol.* 19:217–22
88. Matsuno, T. 1985. New structures of carotenoids in marine animals. *Pure Appl. Chem.* 57:659–66
89. Matsuno, T., Katsuyama, M. 1982. Metabolism of zeaxanthin to rhodoxanthin in tilapia, *Tilapia nilotica*. *Bull. Jpn. Soc. Sci. Fish.* 48:1491–93
90. Matsuno, T., Katsuyama, M., Maoka, T., Hirmo, T., Komoi, T. 1985. Reductive metabolic pathway of carotenoids in fish (3*S*,3'*S*)-astaxanthin to tunaxanthins, A, B, and C. *Comp. Biochem. Physiol.* 80B:779–89
91. Matsuno, T., Maoka, T. 1983. Identity of tunaxanthin A with oxyxanthin 45. *Bull. Japan Soc. Sci. Fish.* 49:1299
92. Matsuno, T., Maoka, T., Katsuyama, M. 1984. The identity of tunaxanthin C and (3*R*,6*S*,3'*R*,6'*S*)-ϵ,ϵ-carotene-3,3'-diol (Oxyxanthin 58). *Bull. Jpn. Soc. Sci. Fish.* 50:1445
93. Matsuno, T., Matsutaka, H., Katsuyama, M., Nagata, S. 1980. Occurrence of 3'-epimer of lutein (calthaxanthin, 3'-epilutein) from fishes. *Bull. Jpn. Soc. Sci. Fish.* 46:337–40
94. Matsuno, T., Nagata, S. 1980. Biosynthesis of characteristic principal carotenoids of the Japanese Common catfish, parasiloxanthin (7',8'-dihydrozeaxanthin) and 7,8-dihydroparasiloxanthin. *Bull. Jpn. Soc. Sci. Fish.* 46:1363–67
95. Matsuno, T., Nagata, S., Kitamura, K. 1976. New carotenoids; parasiloxanthin and 7,8-dihydroparasiloxanthin. *Tetrahedron Lett.* 1976:4601–4
96. Matsuno, T., Sakaguchi, S. 1983. Absolute configuration of idoxanthin. *Bull. Jpn. Soc. Sci. Fish.* 49:1475
97. Meyer, D. B. 1977. The avian eye and its adaptions. In *The Visual System in Invertebrates,* ed. F. Crescitelli, pp. 549–611. Berlin: Springer Verlag. 814 pp.
98. Meyer, D. B., Stuckey, S. R., Hudson, R. A. 1971. Oil droplet carotenoids of avian cones 1. Dietary exclusion: models for biochemical and physiological studies. *Comp. Biochem. Physiol.* 40B:61–70
99. Miki, W., Yamaguchi, K., Konosu, S., Maoka, T., Katsuyama, M., Matsuno, T. 1984. Origin of tunaxanthin in integument of a marine fish, yellow tail. See Ref. 25, p. 66
100. Miki, W., Yamaguchi, K., Konosu, S., Takane, T., Satake, M., et al. 1985. Origin of tunaxanthins in the integument of yellow tail *(Seriola quinqueradiata)*. *Comp. Biochem. Physiol.* 80B:195–201
101. Moore, T. 1957. *Vitamin A*. London: Elsevier. 645 pp.
102. Morton, R. A., Creed, R. H. 1939. Conversion of carotene to vitamin $A_2$ by some freshwater fishes. *Biochem. J.* 33:318–24
103. Müller, R. K., Bernhard, K., Vecchi, M. 1981. Recent advances in the synthesis and analysis of 3,4-oxygenated xanthophylls. See Ref. 11, pp. 27–54
104. Mummery, R., Valadon, L. R. G. 1974. Carotenoids of the lily beetle *(Lilioceris lilii)* and of its food plant *(Lilium hansonii)*. *J. Insect Physiol.* 20:429–33
105. Nagata, S., Matsuno, T. 1979. The occurrence of idoxanthin in fancy red carp, *Cyprinus carpio*. *Bull. Jpn. Soc. Sci. Fish.* 45:537
106. Pollard, S. 1980. PhD thesis. Univ. Wales
107. Raines, P. S., Davies, B. H. 1984. Carotenoids of the common mussel *Mytilus edulis:* their hypothetical role of ATP production during anoxia. See Ref. 25, p. 15
108. Renström, B., Borch, G., Skulberg, O., Liaaen-Jensen, S. 1981. Optical purity of (3*S*,3'*S*)-astaxanthin from *Haematococcus pluvialis*. *Phytochemistry* 20:2561–64
109. Renström, B., Berger, H., Liaaen-Jensen, S. 1981. Esterified optically pure (3*S*,3'*S*)-astaxanthin from flowers of *Adonis annua*. *Biochem. Syst. Ecol.* 9:249–50
110. Rodriguez, D. B., Simpson, K. L., Chichester, C. O. 1973. The biosynthesis of astaxanthin XVIII. Intermediates in the conversion of β-carotene. *Int. J. Biochem.* 4:213–22
111. Rönneberg, H., Borch, G., Liaaen-Jensen, S., Matsutaka, H., Matsuno, T. 1978. Animal carotenoids 16. Tunaxanthin. *Acta Chem. Scand. B*32:621–23
112. Rüttimann, A., Schiedt, K., Vecchi, M. 1983. Separation of (3*R*,3'*R*)-, (3*R*,3'*S*-meso), (3*S*,3'*S*)-zeaxanthin, (3*R*,3'*R*,6'*S*)-, (3*R*,3'*S*,6'*S*)- and (3*S*,3'*S*,6'*S*)-lutein via the dicarbamates of *(S)-(+)*-α-(1-naphthyl)-ethyl isocyanide. *J. High Resolut. Chromatogr. Commun.* 6:612–16

113. Santamaria, L., Bianchi, A., Arnabaldi, A., Andreoni, L., Bermond, P. 1983. Dietary carotenoids block photocarcinogenic enhancement by benzo-(α)-pyrene and inhibit its carcinogenesis in the dark. *Experientia* 39:1043–45
114. Schiedt, K., Englert, G., Noack, K., Vecchi, M., Leuenberger, F. J. 1981. *Abstr. 6th Int. Carotenoid Symp., Liverpool*
115. Schiedt, K., Leuenberger, F. J., Vecchi, M. 1981. Natural occurrence of enantiomeric and *meso*-astaxanthin 5. Ex wild salmon (*Salmo salar* and *Oncorhynchus*). *Helv. Chim. Acta* 64:449–59
116. Schiedt, K., Leuenberger, F. J., Vecchi, M., Glinz, E. 1985. Absorption, retention and metabolic transformation of carotenoids in rainbow trout, salmon and chicken. *Pure Appl. Chem.* 57:685–92
117. Schiedt, K., Vecchi, M., Glinz, E. 1986. Astaxanthin and its metabolites in wild rainbow trout. *Comp. Physiol. Biochem.* 83B:9–12
118. Schmidt, P. J., Baker, E. G. 1969. The indirect pigmentation of salmon and trout flesh with astaxanthin. *J. Fish Res. Board Can.* 26:357–60
119. Seifter, E., Rettura, G., Levinson, S. M. 1984. Supplemental β-carotene (BC): prophylactic action against 7,12-dimethyl benz(α) anthracene carcinogenesis. *Fed. Proc.* 43:662
120. Shamberger, R. J. 1971. Inhibitory effect of vitamin A on carcinogenesis. *J. Natl. Cancer Res. Inst.* 47:667–72
121. Simpson, K. L., Chichester, C. O. 1981. Metabolism and nutritional significance of carotenoids. *Ann. Rev. Nutr.* 1:351–74
122. Simpson, K. L., Katayama, T., Chichester, C. O. 1981. Carotenoids in fish feeds. See Ref. 5, pp. 463–538
123. Spinelli, J., Mahnken, C. 1978. Carotenoid deposition in pen-reared salmonids fed diets containing oil extracts of red crab *(Pleuroncodes planipes)*. *Aquaculture* 13:213–23
124. Sporn, M. B., Roberts, A. B., Goodman, D. S., eds. 1984. *The Retinoids*, Vol. II. New York: Academic
125. Storebakken, T., Foss, P., Asgärd, T., Austreng, E., Liaaen-Jensen, S. 1984. Carotenoids in food chain studies—optical isomer composition of astaxanthin in crustaceans and fish from two subalpine lakes. See Ref. 25, p. 31
126. Vahlquist, A., Lee, J. B., Michaelsson, G., Rollman, O. 1982. Vitamin A in human skin. II. Concentrations of carotene, retinol and dehydroretinol in various components of normal skin. *J. Invest. Dermatol.* 79:94–97
127. Vecchi, M., Müller, R. K. 1979. Separation of (3*S*, 3'*S*)-, (3*R*, 3'*R*)- and (3*S*, 3'*R*)-astaxanthin via (−) camphanic acid esters. *J. High Resolut. Chromatogr. Commun.* 2:195
128. Weisgraber, K. H., Lousberg, R. J. J. C., Weiss, U. 1971. Chemical basis of the colour dimorphism of an aphid *Macrosiphum liriodendri* and a locust *Amblycorypha* species: Novel carotenoids. *Experientia* 27:1017–18
129. Zs-Nagy, I. 1977. Cytosomes (yellow pigment granules) of molluscs as cell organelles of anoxic energy production. *Int. Rev. Cytol.* 49:331–77

*Ann. Rev. Nutr. 1986. 6:299–316*


# THE PATHOPHYSIOLOGY OF ANOREXIA NERVOSA AND BULIMIA NERVOSA

*Regina C. Casper*

Eating Disorders Research & Treatment Program, Michael Reese Hospital; and Department of Psychiatry, University of Chicago, Chicago, Illinois 60637

---

CONTENTS

DIAGNOSTIC CRITERIA AND DIFFERENTIAL DIAGNOSIS .......... 300
ANOREXIA NERVOSA .......... 300
*Nutritional Intake* .......... 301
*The Consequences of Starvation* .......... 302
*Physiologic and Metabolic Abnormalities* .......... 303
*Endocrine Changes* .......... 306
*Treatment* .......... 307
BULIMIA NERVOSA .......... 309
*Eating Pattern and Abnormalities* .......... 311
*Medical Complications* .......... 311
*Treatment* .......... 313

Anorexia nervosa has been recognized as a distinct nosological syndrome for well over a century (23, 34), whereas bulimia has only recently been defined as a clinical entity (3). Descriptions of the phenomenology of both disorders date back to the Middle Ages and earlier (5). The onset of anorexia nervosa tends to be in early or middle adolescence, a time of accelerated physical and psychological growth and development. Bulimia occurs more commonly in late adolescence and young adulthood; females are predominantly affected in both disorders (14, 58). In mild cases, single episodes of anorexia nervosa and bulimia are common. More severely affected patients tend, without therapeutic



0199-9885/86/0715-0299$02.00

intervention, to have a chronic deteriorating course that, in the case of anorexia nervosa, can result in death.

## DIAGNOSTIC CRITERIA AND DIFFERENTIAL DIAGNOSIS

Other illnesses leading to food refusal and weight loss must be distinguished from anorexia nervosa. The loss of appetite and the aversion to food in organic illness, depression, hysterical disorders, and schizophrenia lack the drive for thinness, the fear of weight gain, and the pleasure in losing weight, all of which are typical features of anorexia nervosa. It is also important to note that even though the term anorexia nervosa connotes loss of appetite, hunger awareness and appetite are intact in anorexia nervosa unless the patient has reached a moribund state. Both Crohn's disease and ulcerative colitis have been reported in anorexia nervosa but are rare occurrences.

The morbid hunger and polyphagia of bulimia are not difficult to differentiate from the Klein-Levine syndrome, Froehlich's syndrome, and the Prader-Willi syndrome, all of which have their onset at a young age and are associated with multiple other symptoms, such as periodic somnolence, hypogonadism, and mental deficiency. In psychogenic vomiting (26) the regurgitation process reveals a symbolic meaning and, if present at all, the preoccupation with body weight or shape are not intense.

The attempt to outline concise diagnostic criteria in the DSM-III (3) has not been entirely successful. As a result most research centers retain a modification of the operational criteria originally proposed by Feighner et al (21).

1. Active refusal by the patient to eat enough or to maintain a normal body weight for age and height and/or sustained efforts to prevent food from being absorbed.
2. Intense fear of becoming obese, fear that does not diminish as weight loss progresses.
3. Loss of at least 25% of original body weight, or in children of 15% of weight- and height-adjusted body weight.
4. Body image disturbances (e.g. failure of the body image to adjust to the progressive emaciation).
5. Primary amenorrhea of at least three months duration.
6. No known physical illness that could account for the weight loss.

## ANOREXIA NERVOSA

The prevalence of anorexia nervosa has been estimated to be slightly less than 1% in teenage girls (age 12–18 years) and seems to be on the rise (14). The condition is rare in boys, the female-to-male ratio being about 20:1. Boys are typically affected during prepuberty or early puberty. Anorexia nervosa shows a familial and genetic pattern. Holland and associates (27) found nine of sixteen monozygotic twins concordant for anorexia nervosa as opposed to one of fourteen dizygotic twins. In the discordant pair the affected twin was more likely to reach menarche second and to be the less dominant one. An advanced maternal age at the patient's birth has been described (59) and relatives of patients seem to be more often affected than the general population.

The cause of anorexia nervosa is unknown. It seems to be a multifactorial disease. In a society with excess food, a high value is placed on thinness, which becomes representative of beauty, health, and self-control and hence efforts at weight control are culturally supported. The initial weight loss in anorexia nervosa is not always the result of a deliberate decision to diet. Physical illness, a gastrointestinal disorder, mononucleosis, or influenza can result in accidental weight loss that is then deliberately carried further. Individual personality traits that stand out include a drive for perfection and an excessive need for achievement; they are used to compensate for personal shortcomings and a low self-esteem. Bruch (8) has postulated perceptual disturbances in the recognition of hunger, satiety, or fatigue, and a sense of inadequacy. From a developmental viewpoint, anorexia nervosa can be conceived as avoidance of the adult female body, in particular avoidance of the sexual changes associated with puberty. Familial factors include excessive performance expectations and a tendency toward overweight among family members. A common denominator necessary to trigger the full syndrome is a starvation state with body weight dropping below the constitutional weight.

## *Nutritional Intake*

Regardless of what stimulated the initial weight loss, a feature invariably found in anorexia nervosa is the patient's pleasure in the low weight for personal and emotional reasons. This promotes the deliberate decision to sustain and further the weight loss. The decision is also supported by a phobic attitude that the patient develops toward weight and food. Any weight gain generates severe anxiety; weight loss reduces this anxiety.

Weight loss maintenance and its promotion then become the overriding goal in the patient's life. To this end, thoughts about how to restrict calories are constantly on the patient's mind and determine her meals.

The type of food eaten depends largely on the patient's knowledge about the nutritional value of food. Initially, deleting carbohydrates from meals is considered the fastest way to lose weight, thus dessert and sweets are banned. Instead, low-calorie vegetables, fruit, and green salads are consumed in larger amounts. Next, fatty foods are eliminated. There is a taboo on gravy, butter, salad dressing, and whole milk. The food reduction occurs gradually but occasionally can be as drastic as a fast with no meals eaten; in either case it is done surreptitiously.

The low-calorie foods eaten may vary considerably and reflect individual preference. One patient may find it easier to prepare a concoction of 2% milk, cauliflower, and eggs and eat small amounts throughout the day, another lives exclusively on apricot juice, a third likes fish and eats swordfish steak each day, in addition to salads without dressing, cantaloupe, and plums.

Supplemental vitamin intake has been shown to be highly variable (12). Urged by concerned parents, many patients agree to take one or another kind of vitamin supplement. In our study (12) about half the patients regularly took vitamin preparations with or without mineral supplements. Given the general catabolic state of an anorectic patient the amount of vitamins taken may well exceed the need. Another half of the patients did not take any vitamins, either because they were not provided at home or patients believed that the fruit and vegetables supplied sufficient vitamins. Classical vitamin and trace mineral deficiency states are rare; if they occur, they are more often found in the chronic restricting or debilitated patient. For example, we found plasma zinc levels within the low normal range, but there are exceptions in which zinc levels drop to 50% of normal values (12, 19). The slow tissue catabolism associated with the reduced metabolic rate and the supplemental vitamins added to foodstuffs protect against full-blown deficiency states. However, minor signs indicative of a combined lack of vitamin and nutrient are not infrequently observed. Scalp hair loss is common, fine lanugo-like hair grows on the face and the trunk. The skin becomes rough and scaly and petechial, and ekchymoses may appear. Silverman (55) described hypovitaminosis A in 62% of teenage patients and hypercarotenemia in 52%.

Another factor that introduces considerable variation in the nutritional status is the preferred or practiced dieting pattern. Two types of dieting prevail: the fasting, abstaining, or restricting type and the so-called bulimic type (10).

In the bulimic type of diet, patients are unable to fast consistently and fall into a pattern of periodic overeating in binges. Binge eating initially occurs in spurts but gradually becomes a habit. A few patients compensate for the binge eating through prolonged abstinence but most seize upon self-induced vomiting either alone or in combination with laxative and/or diuretic abuse as a means to get rid of excess calories. There is good evidence that the two dieting types reflect different personality styles and constitute psychopathological subtypes of anorexia nervosa. Since many studies on medical complications in anorexia nervosa conducted before 1980 did not take note of these differences in the eating pattern, some of the findings need to be reconsidered in light of this new information.

## *The Consequences of Starvation*

Each patient's body tolerates malnutrition in different ways, depending on such variables as (*a*) weight at onset, (*b*) speed of weight loss, (*c*) duration of illness, (*d*) self-induced vomiting, and (*e*) use of diuretics or laxatives.

The starvation effects observed in acute anorexia nervosa tend to be similar to but not altogether like those observed in famine, largely because protein deprivation is not predominant. Yet it must be realized that the caloric restriction generally is severe enough to lower body weight levels pathologically and to override the physiologic adjustments that normally result from the low caloric intake, for example lowering of the metabolic rate, decreased heat loss, lowered blood pressure, and hypothermia. The patient with acute anorexia nervosa presents a picture of both undernutrition and malnutrition to varying degrees for prolonged periods of time. Nevertheless, outright growth retardation leading to short stature is unusual, perhaps because most cases of restricted caloric intake start after age 13, when most girls have already had their first growth spurt.

Younger patients are at risk for growth retardation. Pugliese et al (48) recently described a group of children who fit a pattern of growth failure due to malnutrition. Because of their fear of becoming obese, these children had imposed chronic moderate dieting upon themselves, but they did not otherwise fit criteria for anorexia nervosa.

The starvation state of anorexia nervosa can perhaps best be compared to the semistarvation experiments conducted by Keys and Brozek (30) in Minnesota in the late forties. A group of 32 healthy young men, conscientious objectors, were subjected to semistarvation for 24 weeks, with normal physical activity being maintained despite a reduction in intake to an average of 1570 calories/day. Subsequently, the men were studied during 12 weeks of nutritional rehabilitation. A large amount of data was collected not only on the physiological but also on the intellectual and emotional effects of starvation. Table 1 contrasts the behavioral and psychological observations in these normal volunteers on a semistarvation diet with observations in anorexia nervosa patients.

## *Physiologic and Metabolic Abnormalities*

The physiologic and metabolic changes in anorexia nervosa are a function of the duration and severity of the reduced intake and the degree to which body weight has been lost. Figure 1 illustrates how this can vary in patients. The 12-year-old was treated early on and recovered in a brief time, whereas the 14-year-old suffered a relapse and rebound excessive weight gain after refeeding before she settled to a lower weight. With body weight losses of 25% or more (calculated for height and age) or a body mass index [weight/(height)$^2$] under 16, the emaciation is obvious although the patient does her best to conceal the signs. The skin is cold and pale with acrocyanosis, the bony structure is prominent, and the patient looks old beyond her age.

CARDIAC STATUS The most common and frequent electrocardiographic (ECG) change is sinus bradycardia with a pulse below 60 beats per minute (31,

**Table 1** Comparison of psychological and behavioral changes in semi-starvation and anorexia nervosa

| Change | Starvation | Anorexia nervosa |
|---|---|---|
| Mood or feeling state | Lack of initiative; labile mood, quarrelsomeness; indecisiveness; deterioration of personal appearance; continuous hunger. | Initiative high; labile mood, alternating with feeling good; "strong-willed"; pride in personal appearance, occasional exhibitionistic tendencies; hunger present, but easily suppressed. |
| Mental content | Thinking and dreaming about food; concentration of interest on food with narrowing of unrelated interests; daydreaming, reading, and conversing about food. | Same as in starvation, but preoccupation with thoughts of food continues after weight gain. |
| Eating behavior | Bizarre tastes; preference for bulky foods and hot meals; dwelling a long time over meals; picking up crumbs; bulimia. | Same as in starvation, but low-calorie foods and fluids are preferred, and carbohydrates are avoided. |
| Activity level | Fatigue; avoidance of physical exertion; restlessness and periodic quickening effect. | Seemingly inexhaustible energy; physical exercise sought; overactivity; restlessness with periodic quickening. |
| Sexual activity | Decrease in sexual fantasies, feelings, and interests; impotence; amenorrhea. | Same as in starvation; amenorrhea can precede weight loss. |

44, 60). We have observed heart rates as low as 34 beats per minute. S-T segment depression and T-wave morphological changes can be observed, mostly in those patients who use vomiting to lose weight. The blood pressure is usually low, below 100/50 mm Hg. Kalager and associates (29) found left ventricular functional impairment using systolic ejection time and cardiac output.

A systematic study of the effects of anorexia nervosa on body composition and body function in a fairly uniform population of thirty-one teenage patients (19 girls and 12 boys) was reported by Fohlin (22). The average weight loss in this group was 26% for the girls and 25% for the boys. Only four patients had heart rates faster than 60 beats per minute, with a mean heart rate of 53 beats per minute. Heart volume was significantly correlated to blood volume. Blood volume in turn and total body potassium correlated significantly with body weight. Glomerular filtration rate and renal plasma flow were reduced. Patients did not normalize their concentrating capacity following vasopressin adminis-

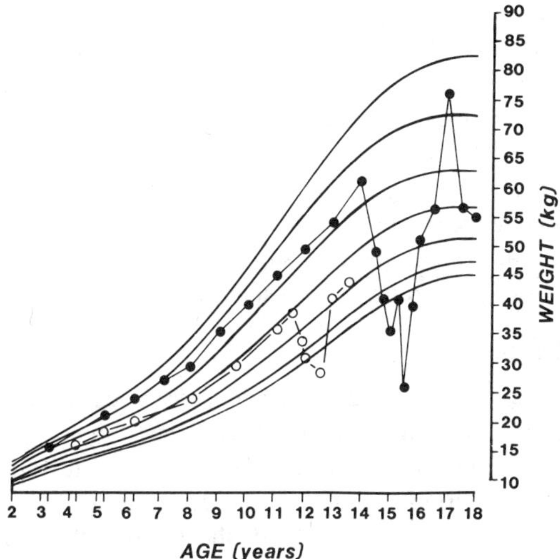


*Figure 1* Body weight curves illustrating normal growth, weight loss during anorexia nervosa, and weight gain during and following nutritional rehabilitation and treatment.

tration, which suggests a concentrating defect of renal origin, reversible after rehabilitation. ECG abnormalities, such as low voltage, bradycardia, and T-wave inversion, were common. The maximal heart rate and maximal oxygen uptake in response to exercise were markedly decreased. Fohlin (22) concluded that all pathophysiological findings indicated a functional adaptation to the decreased caloric supply.

Other functional changes may include increased overall motility, which is surprising because, given the emaciation, a conservation of energy and fatigue would be expected. The continued high activity level probably plays a role in maintaining bone structure, because fractures are rarely observed (1% in our sample). Nevertheless, sophisticated methodology has revealed osteopenia (4) and osteoporosis (51). Changes in sleep structure occur (15), with early morning awakening and nocturia being common. Taste recognition and acuity are reduced; the taste for salty and sweet substances is preserved the longest (12, 33).

Gastric motility is significantly reduced with delayed gastric emptying (18, 54). Patients are at risk of superior mesenteric artery syndrome (57). The syndrome involves vascular compression of the distal portion of the duodenum (45), which leads to vomiting and abdominal pain. The compression can be alleviated through positional changes and is probably the result of weight loss.

Hematologic changes include mild anemia with anisocytosis, leukopenia (sometimes pronounced) with relative lymphocytosis, and on occasion thrombocytopenia resulting in ecchymoses. In young patients bone marrow hypoplasia is not uncommon. The 16-year-old patient in Figure 1, for example, had the following findings: red blood cells were reduced to $2.5 \times 10^6$ per μl, with a hemoglobin to 8.6 g% and a hematocrit to 25.3%. Morphologically there was anisocytosis and poikilocytosis. The white cell count was 3000 per μl of which 22% were granulocytes and 78% were lymphocytes, with 1 myelocyte. The fasting blood sugar was 47 mg%. Most of the time, blood glucose levels remain in the low normal range. Liver enzymes are often elevated. The BUN tends to be on the low side, unless there is superimposed fluid restriction. Plasma cholesterol and plasma carotene levels tend to be increased.

## *Endocrine Changes*

Ever since Simmonds' publication on hypophyseal cachexia (56), anorexia nervosa had been considered a pituitary deficiency disease; but recently it became clear that virtually all endocrine changes were starvation induced. A full review of the endocrinology of anorexia nervosa is beyond the scope of this paper, and the reader is referred to the publications on this topic (6, 7, 62).

Once body weight drops below 60% of normal weight in the course of anorexia nervosa, virtually every endocrine system is affected.

THE HYPOTHALAMIC-PITUITARY-GONADAL AXIS (HPG) The hypothalamic-pituitary-gonadal system is usually involved the earliest. Originally it was believed that amenorrhea signalled a hypothalamic defect because in about a third of the cases menstruation ceases before a substantial weight loss has occurred. There is currently no evidence to support this hypothesis of a primary hypothalamic dysfunction (6). A more likely assumption is that initial dietary alterations in combination with emotional stress disrupt the HPG axis in patients vulnerable to such influences. For most patients the onset of amenorrhea occurs as body weight drops below the normal range. Subsequently, the luteinizing hormone (LH) secretion pattern regresses to continuously low LH plasma levels resulting in reduced ovarian stimulation, low estradiol levels, and nonmeasurable progesterone levels. In acute anorexia nervosa, LHRH stimulation fails to trigger a LH-follicle-stimulating (FSH) response.

HYPOTHALAMIC-PITUITARY-THYROID AXIS Clinically, anorexia nervosa patients display several signs of hypothyroidism, hypothermia, cold intolerance, bradycardia, constipation, a diminished basal metabolic rate, and raised levels of cholesterol and carotene. Nonetheless, TSH plasma levels remain in the normal range. Similarly, the TRH-induced TSH rise is normal in magnitude, albeit slightly delayed in occurrence (11) compared to normals.

The hypothyroidism in anorexia nervosa differs from true hypothyroidism since normal or low normal thyroxine ($T_4$) concentrations along with normal serum levels of protein-bound iodine are found along with depressed triiodothyronine ($T_3$) levels. Moshang and coworkers (41) have demonstrated that in anorexia nervosa, as in conditions of starvation, there is reduced $T_3$ formation from $T_4$ and preferential deiodination to 3,3-5-triidothyronine (reverse $T_3$), a metabolically less active isomer of $T_3$. This combination of lowered $T_3$ and the rise in reverse $T_3$ probably accounts for the hypothyroid status in anorexia nervosa.

HYPOTHALAMIC-PITUITARY-ADRENAL AXIS (HPA) In anorexia nervosa, plasma cortisol levels tend to be increased with raised or normal urinary "free" cortisol levels (9). Weiner (62) has reviewed the reasons for the increased mean plasma cortisol concentrations. There is evidence that the low-$T_3$ syndrome (41) prolongs the half-life of cortisol in plasma by delaying its metabolic clearance. There also seems to be an activation of the HPA in anorexia nervosa. Calculated for body mass and body surface area, the cortisol production rate (CPR) is significantly elevated in anorexia nervosa and the number of secretory episodes of cortisol are increased. Thus when dexamethasone is administered to patients with anorexia nervosa, their plasma cortisol levels are not suppressed.

What accounts for the HPA activation is not known. Among the possibilities would be an increased release of corticotropin-releasing hormone (CRH) or hypersensitivity of adrenal cortical cells to CRH stimulation. Weight gain to the normal premorbid weight reverses these changes, as well as all other endocrine changes in anorexia nervosa.

## *Treatment*

Because of the complexity of the disorder, anorexia nervosa requires a multivantage treatment approach: a supervised refeeding program supports body weight normalization; personality problems are explored in individual psychotherapy, which also assists the patient in becoming aware of the reasons for her exclusive attention to food and weight; and family therapy examines the kind of interaction and the relationships between family members that permitted the syndrome to develop.

In this section I focus on the nutritional rehabilitation programs. For obvious reasons, adequate nutrition is of utmost importance in the acutely ill, severely underweight patient. Moreover, without correcting the starvation state and the starvation-induced emotional and cognitive changes, the patient will physiologically and emotionally not be able to benefit from psychological treatment. Nevertheless, weight restoration and refeeding requires the patient's tacit or explict cooperation if it is to succeed, regardless of whether it is accomplished on an outpatient basis or, as is more often the case, in hospital. Even tube feeding or hyperalimentation cannot be performed unless the patient consents and complies, in principle.

The approach we have found useful is to discuss and negotiate a detailed treatment contract with the patient and her parents before treatment begins or before hospitalization. This procedure allows the patients to express what is emotionally tolerable, it engages their active collaboration by leaving some control in their hands, and it presumes progress will be consistent and predictable.

Restoration of normal body weight is accomplished in two steps. The first is to correct the malnutrition until most physical signs of the acute starvation state, including sleep difficulties, restlessness, and morbid dwelling on food, have subsided. To this end, weight needs to be brought to about 80% of normal. This part is considered the medically necessary treatment. During the second phase, the patient is given more leeway to gain weight at her own pace. Both a short-term and long-term treatment outline are negotiated. The short-term plan is periodically revised and the long-term plan details the desirable weight and psychologic changes necessary for discharge and reducing the risk of relapse. It is expected that by virture of their pathology patients will at times undermine or challenge the treatment plan. However, if the reasons for their manuevering can be explored and understood patients usually abide by the arrangement.

For adolescents the desirable body weight is extrapolated from the Iowa Growth Charts. Parents are asked to obtain the pediatric weights; these are then plotted on the Iowa Growth Charts, and the respective growth curves form the basis for predicting optimal weight. We tend to prescribe a low rather than a high normal weight. In our sample only two of 85 patients had become pathologically overweight six years later.

For implementing the refeeding program, intense nursing care is mandatory, administered by trained, experienced, emotionally mature and infinitely patient nurses. The procedure itself is simple: Initially only a liquid nutrient (Meritene®, Ensure®, or Sustacal®) is offered at regular intervals in six divided meals.

Depending upon the patient's age, height, and physical condition, from 1400 to 1800 calories (250–300 calories per meal) are offered for the first three days. This calculation is based on the Boothby and Berkson Food Nomogram (17). Confronted with this liquid diet regime most patients will, despite having been informed beforehand, protest and claim they would prefer pizza or milk shakes. If offered these foods, however, they will refuse them. Eliminating food initially relieves the patient from agonizing over what and what not to order and then what and what not to eat. Between 30 and 45 minutes are allowed to finish each meal. Unless there is excessive dehydration with oliguria or excessive fluid loss through sweating, no extra fluids are permitted. A record of fluid and caloric intake and output is kept for at least two weeks. Subsequently, only the caloric input will be recorded until the patient has reached a normal weight. The patient is weighed every morning (or sometimes less often for therapeutic reasons) in a gown on the same scale after voiding and the weight is recorded.

Every aspect of the program is explained in detail to invite the patient's cooperation. If the patient ignores her meals or refuses to drink the nutrient, the treating physician is called and the reasons for her refusal are explored and the patient is encouraged to drink. The nursing staff praises the patient's efforts and meets attempts at subterfuge and sabotage with good-humored firmness. Much time is spent talking with the patient during the first week, persuading her to eat again. By the second week the patient usually has a good appetite and follows the schedule on her own. The emotional reactions to eating and weight gain are explored in individual psychotherapy and family therapy. Care is taken to monitor the patient's reactions in order to avoid overstressing her, which can trigger acute disintegration and self-destructiveness.

This broad outline is followed with some flexibility. Adjustments for individual patients or young patients may be necessary; however, the patients themselves will be the first to challenge individual special adjustments, arguing that equal treatment is fair and unequal treatment is unfair. If patients are known to have vomited after meals, they remain under supervision in the common area for 45 minutes after each meal or they go to school supervised. If this arrangement does not provide sufficient control, the bathroom doors are locked. Depending upon the patient's readiness, food is introduced as one meal at a time under dietary guidance. Patients are expected before discharge to eat three meals and not to skip meals. Deliberate attempts are made to involve the patient in hobbies, homework, or activities unrelated to eating. It is important that the dietary and nursing staff be knowledgeable about anorexia nervosa so that they answer patients' questions and be helpful. For example, the distorted sense for bodily proportions extends to meal size. Patients generally overestimate and complain about the size of meals. On the other hand, in order to gain weight at a reasonable rate, 3000 calories and often more eventually need to be consumed. Unless meals are offered frequently, this carries the risk of binge eating. For this reason we retain dietary supplements as snacks. Agras et al (2) observed a positive correlation between meal size and amount of food eaten by the patient. As a result, some hospitals offer double meals from the beginning. Such a policy can induce cardiac decompensation (47) and risks teaching the patient to overeat.

## BULIMIA NERVOSA

Put in simplest terms, bulimia nervosa starts as an attempt at weight control and ends as a loss of self-control. The term *bulimia* denotes a ravenous appetite or literally "ox hunger" associated with powerlessness. *Kynorexia* ("fames canina," known to Xenophon about 400 BC) or "dog hunger" historically has been in use for a syndrome that closely resembles bulimia nervosa and in which large quantities of food were devoured without any feeling of satiation, ultimately leading to fullness, abdominal pains, and vomiting.

The critical behavior in bulimia nervosa is binge-eating episodes and the experience of a distressing sense of loss of control during overeating. There is agreement that dieting is a precondition for the development of binge eating, i.e. there is an attempt to replace normal physiological controls with cognitive rules. Thus, the disorder starts with dieting attempts in which hunger feelings become ravenous and lead to binge eating as a result of prolonged abstinence. Once patients discover that they can undo the consequences of binge eating by vomiting out the ingested food, they tend to restrain their binge eating less and begin to resort to binge eating not only when they feel hungry, but also when they feel tense, anxious, or are experiencing other distressing emotions.

Bulimia is described in the Diagnostic and Statistical Manual (3) as an eating disorder separate from anorexia nervosa.

A. Recurrent episodes of binge eating (rapid consumption of a large amount of food in a discrete period of time, usually less than two hours).
B. At least three of the following:
   1. consumption of high-caloric, easily ingested food during a binge;
   2. inconspicuous eating during a binge;
   3. termination of such eating episodes by abdominal pain, sleep, social interruption, or self-induced vomiting;
   4. repeated attempts to lose weight by severely restrictive diets, self-induced vomiting, or use of cathartics and/or diuretics;
   5. frequent weight fluctuations of greater than ten pounds due to alternating binges and fasts.
C. Awareness that the eating pattern is abnormal and fear of not being able to stop eating voluntarily.
D. Depressed moods and self-deprecating thoughts following eating binges.
E. The bulimic episodes are not due to anorexia nervosa or any known physical disorder.

Strictly applied, the criteria tend to be overinclusive because severity parameters such as frequency of binge eating or vomiting are lacking, and binge eating alone suffices for the diagnosis. Furthermore, bulimia as a syndrome is not uncommonly associated with anorexia nervosa (10). Typically, however, it occurs in young college-age women of normal weight or slightly overweight women.

Epidemiological surveys (13, 25) using these criteria have found a high incidence of binge-eating behavior in college populations (between 46 and 79% in females and from 41 to 60% in males). If more restrictive criteria are applied, such as a daily occurrence and vomiting or laxative abuse, the rates drop to 2–13% for women and 1.4–6.1% for males (42, 49).

## *Eating Pattern and Abnormalities*

Bulimic patients rarely eat normal meals. Forced by parents or by circumstances (for instance, by social occasions), most patients either consume very little or do not retain the ingested food. In the fully developed syndrome, binge eating is precipitated by a variety of conditions. Anxiety and tension (1), frustration (40), and depression in association with hunger (10) or simply the sight or smell of food or eating may trigger binge-eating episodes. During these episodes patients tend to consume "forbidden" food, high in carbohydrate and fat content such as ice cream, doughnuts, or bread and butter; others may eat leftovers or half-frozen unpalatable food. The food is consumed rapidly, without dwelling on the taste, and in secrecy. Patients are aware that the bulimic behavior pattern escapes voluntary control and takes on a life of its own; they describe it as an addiction to food.

The size of a binge varies considerably, with a range from 1,000 to 20,000 calories (38). Some patients begin to binge eat in the morning but the majority omit eating in the morning and begin to binge at midday. Most of the binge eating is done in the evening and at night when there is less of a chance of being interrupted. Following the binge, patients tend to feel uncomfortably full and become anxious and worried about any weight gain; they feel guilty and humiliated by the knowledge of having lost control and hence seek to undo the overeating, most commonly by regurgitating the ingested food. Vomiting eventually becomes coupled to binge eating; it can become a habit. Most patients overeat with the forethought of vomiting afterwards.

Impulse dyscontrol in bulimic patients is not limited to eating but is more generalized: shoplifting, particularly of food, is not infrequent, alcohol may be consumed to excess, and patients may be self-destructive. In severe cases the chaotic eating pattern tends to be a reflection of a severe personality dysfunction expressed in serious family problems and difficulties in personal relationships.

The weight of most bulimic patients varies considerably: weekly fluctuations of 5–25 lb are not unusual. Patients are extremely sensitive to such weight swings and react to the slightest weight gain with despair, a reaction that then sets off another bulimic cycle.

## *Medical Complications*

The physiologic effects and the medical complications of bulimia are less well known than those of anorexia nervosa because until recently the incidence of bulimia was very low. Overeating alone causes weight gain. It leads to gastric dilatation (28, 52) and on rare occasions to gastric rupture. Most medical complications are the result of excessive vomiting; patients may vomit up to twenty times daily and can vomit between 2 and 3 liters of fluid during one episode (38). The excessive use of laxatives or diuretics also causes medical complications (See Table 2) (43).

**Table 2** Medical complications of bulimia nervosa

| | |
|---|---|
| Mouth | Gum disease, teeth decalcification, caries; swelling of salivary glands; pharyngitis—hoarseness |
| Gastrointestinal tract | Rumination |
| | Esophagitis |
| | Gastric dilation and rupture; elevated serum amylase |
| Liver | Abnormalities in liver function |
| Blood | Dehydration; hypokalemia; hypochloremia; alkalosis |
| Cardiac | S-T changes; arrhythmia; cardiac arrest |
| Renal | Polydipsia; polyuria; elevated BUN; kidney (tubular) damage |
| Skin | Ekchymoses on face and neck; dehydration—edema; bruises and lacerations over knuckles |
| CNS | EEG abnormalities |

ELECTROLYTE AND FLUID DISTURBANCES The excess body fluid lost through vomiting results in fluctuations in the serum potassium levels, with hypokalemia, hypochloremia, and metabolic alkalosis (39). If vomiting episodes exceed five times daily, serum potassium concentrations can drop to dangerously low levels, usually around 2.5 meq/liter and rarely as low as 1.8 meq/liter. In such cases potassium supplements are indicated. Patients themselves rarely notice or mention cardiac symptoms such as irregular heart beats or palpitations because they seem to develop a high tolerance for feeling physically unwell. Thus potassium level monitoring becomes important and potentially life-saving.

With prolonged bulimia nervosa, esophageal reflex and herniation invariably occur. Rumination may occur with bulimia and persist after cessation of vomiting. To date little is known about the long-term effects of chronic induced vomiting upon the gastrointestinal tract. Dental enamel erosion and gingivitis occur. Swelling of the submaxillary salivary glands is common and may be diagnostic (16, 35) as might be a hoarse voice.

The irregular food intake results in constipation, which is cited as a reason for using laxatives. Laxative and diuretic use can become addictive behaviors, with patients developing tolerance to their effects and using ever-increasing amounts. Such patients are difficult to treat and generally require hospital supervision for withdrawal. Prolonged vomiting without diuretic abuse can result in kidney damage. In our follow-up investigation of 85 anorexia nervosa patients eight years after illness onset, two patients (whose vomiting started at age 12 and 16 years, respectively) had severe kidney damage with one patient requiring a kidney transplant.

Menstrual abnormalities in the form of oligomenorrhea, dysmenorrhea, and irregular menstruation are common. The endocrine investigations published so far, however (24), suffer from poor experimental control. Abnormal dexamethasone suppression tests have been reported, but in these studies the overeating-vomiting pattern was not fully controlled. Initial reports of EEG abnormalities (a 14- and 6-per-second spike pattern) in compulsive eaters (50) were not confirmed in a recent study (37). Only four of 25 EEG tracings of bulimic patients were considered abnormal. Since bulimia has only recently come to clinical attention, little is known about its long-term course.

## *Treatment*

The most immediate and manifest goal of treatment is to normalize the eating pattern. A variety of approaches have been used to assist the patient in regaining control over her eating.

PURELY PSYCHOLOGICAL STRATEGIES Most psychological approaches encourage the patient to make an explicit commitment to change. A combination of nutritional, educational, and self-monitoring techniques (63) are employed to increase awareness of the maladaptive behavior. An intervention program then seeks to change the eating behavior, to influence its antecedents and consequences, and to teach adaptive skills. A cognitive behavioral paradigm has been described by Fairburn (20), and recently the results of a behavioral self-monitoring approach combined with supportive psychotherapy were published by Lacey (32). Both approaches solicit the patient's active participation in the treatment program and seem to work well, provided that the patient is highly motivated and only moderately disturbed.

PHARMACOLOGICAL TREATMENTS The hypothesis that bulimia represented a depressive illness variant provided the rationale for the pharmacotherapy of bulimia. It was assumed that if the depressive-dysphoric states, anxiety, and tension that triggered bulimia would improve with antidepressant drugs, then patients would be less apt to use overeating to relieve these emotions. The following paragraph briefly summarizes the controlled drug trials.

Sabine et al (53) treated 50 bulimic patients with mianserine in a double-blind placebo-controlled trial over eight weeks. No differences in binge frequency, vomiting, or depression ratings were noted between drug and placebo groups. Imipramine given to 19 bulimic patients in a controlled study by Pope et al (46) markedly reduced the intensity of binge eating and decreased depressive symptoms. Mitchell & Groat (36) treated 32 bulimic outpatients with a behavioral program and amitriptyline (150 mg at night). The authors found a marked antidepressant effect in drug-treated patients and equal improvement in eating behavior for both groups. Walsh et al (61) recently published the results of a controlled 10-week treatment study with the monoaminoxidase inhibitor (MAOI) phenelzine sulfate (from 60 to 90 mg maximum) in 20 bulimic patients. Drug-treated patients dramatically reduced binge frequency from a mean of 12 per week to 2 per week as opposed to placebo-treated patients who showed no change. Although eating attitude scores dropped significantly, Hamilton depression ratings, which were low initially (<17), showed little change. One third of the patients entered into this study were unable to tolerate the side effects such as orthostatic hypotension, diarrhea, and sleep problems or they could not observe the dietary restrictions.

These studies suggest that antidepressants have a place in the treatment of bulimia, but further studies are required to identify the patient who will benefit from medication.

With a combination then of nutritional counselling, psychologic family and social therapy, and pharmacotherapy most patients can improve; however, most bulimic patients have great difficulty following through with any treatment plan.

## *Literature Cited*


1. Abraham, S. F., Beumont, P. J. V. 1982. How patients describe bulimia or binge eating. *Psychol. Med.* 12:625–35
2. Agras, W. S., Barlow, D. H., Chapin, H. N., Abel, G. G., Leitenberg, H. 1974. Behavior modification of anorexia nervosa. *Arch. Gen. Psychiatry* 30:249–86
3. American Psychiatric Association. 1980. *Diagnostic and Statistical Manual of Mental Disorders*. Washington, DC: Am. Psychiatr. Assoc. 3rd ed.
4. Ayers, J. W., Gidwani, G. P., Schmidt, I. M., Gross, M. 1984. Osteopenia in hypoestrogenic young women with anorexia nervosa. *Fertil. Steril.* 41:224–28
5. Bell, R. M. 1985. *Holy Anorexia*. Univ. Chicago Press
6. Beumont, P. J. V. 1979. The endocrinology of anorexia nervosa. *Med. J. Austr.* 1:611–13
7. Brown, G. M. 1983. *Endocrine alterations in anorexia nervosa*. In *Anorexia Nervosa: Recent Developments in Research,* ed. P. L. Darby, P. E. Garfinkel, D. M. Garner, D. V. Coscina, pp. 231–34. New York: Liss. 455 pp.
8. Bruch, H. 1973. *Eating Disorders*. New York: Basic Books. 396 pp.
9. Casper, R. C., Chatterton, R. T., Davis, J. M. 1979. Alterations in serum cortisol and its binding characteristics in anorexia nervosa. *J. Clin. Endocrinol. Metab.* 49:406–11
10. Casper, R. C., Eckert, E. D., Halmi, K. A., Goldberg, S. C., Davis, J. M. 1980. Bulimia—its incidence and clinical importance in patients with anorexia nervosa. *Arch. Gen. Psychiatry* 37:1030–40
11. Casper, R. C., Frohman, L. A. 1982. Delayed TSH release in anorexia nervosa following injection of thyroptropin-releasing hormone (TRH) *Psychoneuroendocrinology* 7:59–68
12. Casper, R. C., Kirschner, B., Sandstead, H., Jacob, R. A., Davis, J. M. 1980. An evaluation of trace metals, vitamins, and taste function in anorexia nervosa. *Am. J. Clin. Nutr.* 33:1801–8
13. Cooper, P. J., Fairburn, C. G. 1983. Binge-eating and self-induced vomiting in the community—a preliminary study. *Br. J. Psychiatry* 142:139–44
14. Crisp, A. H., Palmer, R. L., Kalucy, R. S. 1976. How common is anorexia nervosa? A prevalence study. *Br. J. Psychiatry* 128:549–54
15. Crisp, A. H., Stonehill, E. 1976. *Sleep, Nutrition and Mood,* pp. 21–24. London/New York/Sydney/Toronto: Wiley. 173 pp.
16. Dawson, J., Jones, C. 1977. Vomiting-induced hypokalemic alkalosis and parotid swelling. *Practitioner* 218:267–68
17. Division of Biometry and Medical Statistics. 1933. *The Boothby and Berkson Food Nomogram*. Rochester, Ohio: Mayo Clinic
18. Dubois, A., Gross, H. A., Ebert, M. H., Castell, D. O. 1979. Altered gastric emptying and secretion in primary anorexia nervosa. *Gastroenterology* 77: 319–23
19. Esca, S. A., Brenner, W., Mach, K., Gschnait, F. 1979. Kwashiorkor-like zinc deficiency syndrome in anorexia nervosa. *Acta Dermatol. Venereol.* 59: 361–64
20. Fairburn, C. G. 1984. Bulimia nervosa. In *Epidemiology and Management in Eating Disorders,* ed. A. J. Stunkard, E.

Stellar, pp. 235–58. New York: Raven. 280 pp.

21. Feighner, J. P., Robins, E., Guze, S. B., Woodruff, R. A., Winokur, G., Munoz, R. 1972. Diagnostic criteria for use in psychiatric research. *Arch. Gen. Psychiatry* 26:57–63
22. Fohlin, L. 1977. Body composition, cardiovascular and renal-function in adolescent patients with anorexia nervosa. *Acta Paediatr. Scand.* 1977 (Suppl. 268):7–20
23. Gull, W. W. 1873. Anorexia hysterica (apepsia hysterica). *Br. Med. J.* 2:527–32
24. Gwirtsman, H. E., Roy-Byrne, P., Yager, J., Gerner, R. H. 1983. Neuroendocrine abnormalities in bulimia. *Am. J. Psychiatry* 140:559–63
25. Halmi, K. A., Falk, J. R., Schwartz, E. 1981. Binge-eating and vomiting: A survey of a college population. *Psychol. Med.* 11:697–706
26. Hill, O. W. 1968. Psychogenic vomiting. *Gut* 9:348–52
27. Holland, A. J., Hall, A., Murray, R. M., Russell, G. F. M., Crisp, A. H. 1984. Anorexia nervosa: a study of 34 twin pairs and one set of triplets. *Br. J. Psychiatry* 145:414–19
28. Jennings, K. P., Klidjian, A. M. 1974. Acute gastric dilatation in anorexia nervosa. *Br. Med. J.* 1:477–78
29. Kalager, T., Brubakk, O., Bassoe, H. H. 1978. Cardiac performance in patients with anorexia nervosa. *Cardiology* 63:1–4
30. Keys, A., Brozek, J., Henschel, A., Mickelson, O., Taylor, H. L. 1950. *The Biology of Human Starvation.* Minneapolis: Univ. Minn. Press. 1385 pp.
31. Kjellberg, J., Reizenstein, P. 1970. Effect of starvation on body composition in obesity. *Acta Med. Scand.* 188:171–77
32. Lacey, J. H. 1983. Bulimia nervosa, binge eating and psychogenic vomiting: a controlled treatment study and long-term outcome. *Br. Med. J.* 286:1609–13
33. Lacey, J. H., Stanley, P. A., Crutchfield, M., Crisp, A. H. 1977. Sucrose sensitivity in anorexia nervosa. *J. Psychosomat. Res.* 21:17–20
34. Lasègue, D. 1964. De l'anorexie hystèrique. *Archives Générales de Medicine.* Reprinted in: Kaufman, R. M., Heiman, M., eds. 1964. *Evolution of Psychomatic Concepts. Anorexia Nervosa: A Paradigm,* pp. 141–55. Int. Univ. Press
35. Levin, P. A., Falko, J. M., Dixon, K., Gallup, E. M., Saunders, W. 1980. Benign parotid enlargement in bulimia. *Ann. Intern. Med.* 93:827–29
36. Mitchell, J. E., Groat, R. 1984. A placebo-controlled, double-blind trial of amitriptyline in bulimia. *J. Clin. Psychopharmacol.* 4:186–93
37. Mitchell, J. E., Hosfield, W., Pyle, R. L. 1983. EEG findings in patients with the bulimia syndrome. *Int. J. Eating Disorders* 2:17–23
38. Mitchell, J. E., Pyle, R. L., Eckert, E. D. 1981. Frequency and duration of binge-eating episodes in patients with bulimia. *Am. J. Psychiatry* 138:835–36
39. Mitchell, J. E., Pyle, R. L., Eckert, E. D., Hatsukami, D., Lentz, R. 1983. Electrolyte and other physiological abnormalities in patients with bulimia. *Psychol. Med.* 13:273–78
40. Morley, J. E., Levine, A. S. 1981. Stress-induced eating is mediated through endogenous opiates. *Science* 209:1259–62
41. Moshang, T., Parks, J. S., Baker, L., Vaidya, V., Utiger, R. D., et al. 1975. Low serum triidothyronine in patients with anorexia nervosa. *J. Clin. Endocrinol. Metab.* 40:470–73
42. Nogami, Y., Yabana, F. 1977. On kibarashi-gui (binge-eating). *Folia Psychiatr. Neurol. Jpn.* 31:159–66
43. Oster, J. R., Masterson, B. J., Rogers, A. I. 1980. Laxative abuse syndrome. *Am. J. Gastroenterol.* 74:451–58
44. Palossy, B., Oo, M. 1977. ECG alterations in anorexia nervosa. *Adv. Cardiol.* 19:280–82
45. Pentlow, B. D., Dent, R. G. 1981. Acute vascular compression of the duodenum in anorexia nervosa. *Br. J. Surg.* 68:665–66
46. Pope, H. G., Hudson, J. I., Jonas, J. M., Yurgelun-Todd, D. 1983. Bulimia treated with imipramine: A placebo-controlled double-blind study. *Am. J. Psychiatry* 140:554–58
47. Powers, P. S. 1982. Heart failure during treatment of anorexia nervosa. *Am. J. Psychiatry* 139:1167–70
48. Pugliese, M. T., Lifshitz, F., Grad, G., Fort, P., Marks-Katz, M. 1983. Fear of obesity: A cause of short stature and delayed puberty. *N. Engl. Med.* 309:513–18
49. Pyle, R. L., Mitchell, J. E., Eckert, E. D., Halvorson, P. A., Neuman, P. A., Goff, G. M. 1983. The incidence of bulimia in freshman college students. *Int. J. Eating Disorders* 2:75–85
50. Rau, J. H., Green, R. S. 1975. Compulsive eating. A neuropsychologic approach to certain eating disorders. *Compr. Psychiatry* 16:223–31
51. Rigotti, N. A., Nussbaum, S. R., Herzog, D. B., Neer, R. M. 1984. Osteoporosis in women with anorexia nervosa. *N. Engl. J. Med.* 311:1601–6

52. Russell, G. F. M. 1966. Acute dilation of the stomach in a patient with anorexia nervosa. *Br. J. Psychiatry* 112:203–7
53. Sabine, E. J., Yonace, A., Farrington, A. J., Barratt, K. H., Wakeling, A. 1983. Bulimia nervosa: A placebo-controlled double-blind therapeutic trial of mianserin. *Br. J. Clin. Pharmacol.* 15 (Suppl. 2):195S–202S
54. Saleh, J. W., Lebwohl, P. 1980. Metoclopramide-induced gastric emptying in patients with anorexia nervosa. *Am. J. Gastroenterol.* 74:127–32
55. Silverman, J. A. 1983. Medical consequences of starvation. See Ref. 7, pp. 293–99
56. Simmonds, M. 1916. Ueber Kachexie Hypophysaeren Ursprungs. *Dtsch. Med. Wochenschr.* 42:190–91
57. Sours, J. A., Vorhaus, L. J. 1981. Superior mesenteric artery syndrome in anorexia nervosa: A case report. *Am. J. Psychiatry* 138:519–20
58. Stangler, R. S., Printz, A. M. 1980. DSM-III: Psychiatric diagnosis in a university population. *Am. J. Psychiatry* 137:937–40
59. Theander, S. 1983. Research on outcome and prognosis of anorexia nervosa and some results from a Swedish long-term study. *Int. J. Eating Disorders* 2:167–74
60. Thurston, J., Marks, P. 1974. Electrocardiographic abnormalities in patients with anorexia nervosa. *Br. Heart J.* 36:719–23
61. Walsh, B. T., Stewart, J. T., Roose, S. P., Gladis, M., Glassman, A. H. 1984. Treatment of bulimia with phenelzine. *Arch. Gen. Psychiatry* 41:1105–9
62. Weiner, H. 1983. Abiding problems in the pychoendocrinology of anorexia nervosa. In *Understanding Anorexia Nervosa and Bulimia. Rep. 4th Ross Conf. on Med. Res.*, pp. 47–53. Columbus, Ohio: Ross Labs.
63. Willard, S. G., Anding, R. H., Winstead, D. K. 1983. Nutritional counseling as an adjunct to psychotherapy in bulimic treatment. *Psychosomatics* 24: 545–51

*Ann. Rev. Nutr. 1986. 6:317–43*


# INHERITABLE BIOTIN-TREATABLE DISORDERS AND ASSOCIATED PHENOMENA

*Lawrence Sweetman and William L. Nyhan*

Department of Pediatrics, University of California, San Diego, La Jolla, California 92093

---

CONTENTS

INTRODUCTION ........ 317
*History of Biotin* ........ 318
*Metabolic Role of Biotin and its Metabolism* ........ 319
*Dietary Requirement for Biotin* ........ 321
BIOTIN-RESPONSIVE MULTIPLE CARBOXYLASE DEFICIENCY ........ 323
*Isolated Deficiencies of Individual Carboxylases* ........ 323
*Abnormal Holocarboxylase Synthetase* ........ 324
*Biotinidase Deficiency* ........ 329
DIETARY DEFICIENCY OF BIOTIN ........ 332
CONCLUSION ........ 335

## INTRODUCTION

Although the vitamin biotin was discovered some sixty years ago, there was until recently relatively little emphasis on the study of biotin in man. This was because of the extremely rare occurrence of human clinical deficiency of biotin and the lack of knowledge of the associated biochemical abnormalities. The rarity of biotin deficiency is a consequence of the small daily requirement for this water-soluble vitamin, the broad distribution of biotin in foods, and the synthesis of biotin by intestinal flora. The recent increased interest in the metabolism of biotin was stimulated by the discovery in the last fifteen years of infants and children with inherited defects in the metabolism of biotin and by



0199-9885/86/0715-0317$02.00

the fact that they can be successfully treated with pharmacological doses of biotin. Two forms of "biotin-responsive multiple carboxylase deficiency" have greatly increased our knowledge about the clinical and biochemical consequences of abnormalities of biotin metabolism and of the deficiency of biotin. An excellent symposium on biotin was published recently (38).

## *History of Biotin*

In the 1920s and 1930s it was discovered that a diet high in raw egg white caused dermatitis, hair loss (alopecia), and neurologic abnormalities in rats (23, 24, 117, 118). These could be prevented by a "protective factor X" present in potato starch, yeast, egg yolk, and milk (24) as well as liver (117). A similar dermatitis in chicks fed a diet rich in egg white was corrected by liver extract (91). A factor protective against egg white injury was found in liver and yeast and named vitamin H (62, 63). A yeast growth factor initially isolated from yeast and then egg yolk was named biotin (83) and later noted to have vitamin H activity (44, 66). The structure of biotin was determined in 1942 (43, 97) and vitamin H and biotin were shown to be identical in microbiological assays (89). A legume nodule respiration factor, coenzyme R, was also shown to be identical to biotin (159). Biotin was first synthesized in 1943 (69), the crystal structure determined in 1956 (155), and the stereospecific total synthesis of the natural isomer *d*-(+)-biotin was accomplished in 1975 (35, 109).

The structure of the natural isomer, *d*-biotin, shown in Figure 1, contains a ureido group in a five-membered ring fused with a tetrahydrothiophene ring with a five-carbon side chain terminating in a carboxyl group. Biotin is synthesized biochemically from pimelic acid, a seven-carbon dicarboxylic acid, L-alanine, and L-cysteine by a variety of microorganisms (75). The biochemistry and genetics of the synthesis of biotin have been particularly well studied in *E. coli* (46).

The agent in raw egg white causing the toxic manifestations that are reversed or prevented by biotin is the protein avidin (45). Avidin binds biotin with a very

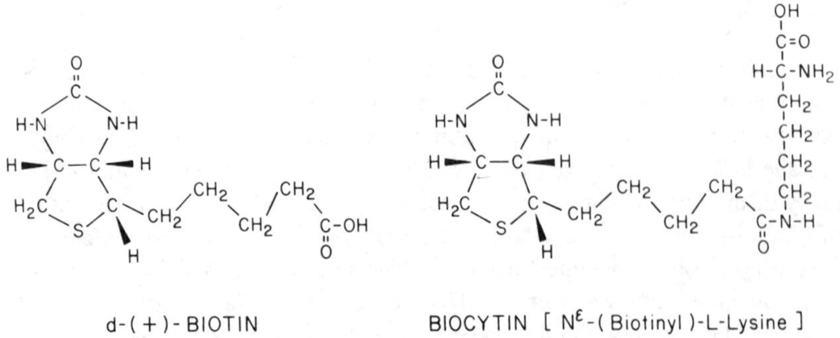

d-(+)-BIOTIN

BIOCYTIN [ $N^{\epsilon}$-(Biotinyl)-L-Lysine ]

*Figure 1* Structures of biotin and biocytin.

high affinity, the dissociation constant is $10^{-15}$ molar (60). Thus ingestion of large amounts of avidin leads to the formation of biotin-avidin complexes and prevents the absorption of biotin; this creates a deficiency of biotin and the resulting symptoms (64, 65).

## *Metabolic Role of Biotin and its Metabolism*

In mammals and birds, biotin is a covalently bound cofactor in four enzymes, all carboxylases involved in the fixation of carbon dioxide and requiring adenosine triphosphate (ATP) (102). Acetyl-CoA carboxylase catalyzes the formation of malonyl-CoA from acetyl-CoA, bicarbonate, and ATP. Malonyl-CoA is then utilized in fatty acid synthesis and fatty acid chain elongation. Thus biotin is essential for lipogenesis.

Pyruvate carboxylase catalyzes the synthesis of the tricarboxylic acid cycle intermediate, oxaloacetic acid from pyruvate, bicarbonate, and ATP. This provides an intermediate to prime the cycle as well as providing a source of carbon skeletons for the amino acids aspartate and glutamate derived from the cycle. In the gluconeogenic tissues liver and kidney, the oxaloacetic acid is utilized for the synthesis of glucose. Thus biotin plays a critical role in energy metabolism and in synthesis of amino acids and glucose.

Propionyl-CoA carboxylase catalyzes the carboxylation of propionyl-CoA to methylmalonyl-CoA, which is then isomerized to succinyl-CoA and enters the tricarboxylic acid cycle. Thus biotin is essential for the catabolism of propionic acid, which is derived from intestinal flora, from the catabolism of the amino acids isoleucine, valine, methionine, and threonine, the side chain of cholesterol, and from the oxidation of odd-numbered fatty acids.

3-Methylcrotonyl-CoA carboxylase forms 3-methylglutaconyl-CoA from 3-methylcrotonyl-CoA in the catabolic path of the amino acid leucine. Acetyl-CoA carboxylase is localized in the cytosol: the other three carboxylases are localized in the mitochondria. The function of biotin in the carboxylases is to carry the carbon dioxide. Carboxybiotin is formed with energy provided by ATP and the carboxyl group transferred to the organic acid substrate.

The carboxylases are synthesized as enzymatically inactive apocarboxylases lacking biotin. Enzymatically active holocarboxylases are formed by the covalent attachment of biotin to the apocarboxylases, catalyzed by the enzyme holocarboxylase synthetase (1). Holocarboxylase synthetase catalyzes two sequential reactions. The first is the activation of biotin with ATP to form biotinyl-adenylate. This then is reacted with the epsilon amino group of a lysine in the active site of the apocarboxylase, forming a covalent amide bond of *d*(+)biotinyl-ε-*N*-L-lysine. This biotinylated lysine is named biocytin.

Holocarboxylase synthetase is present in both the cytosol and mitochondria but it is not yet known whether biotin is attached to the mitochondrial carboxylases before or after their incorporation into the mitochondria. As discussed below, the properties of human mutant holocarboxylase synthetase indicate that both the mitochondrial and cytoplasmic forms are encoded by one gene and that the same holocarboxylase synthetase attaches biotin to all four apocarboxylases. Holocarboxylase synthetase from species as disparate as rabbit, yeast, and bacteria can attach biotin to apocarboxylases from the different species (95). In all of the carboxylases for which the amino acid sequences around the biocytin are known, the lysine is flanked by methione residues (174).

In the normal turnover of the holocarboxylases in cells, they are degraded by proteolysis to small biotin-containing peptides or biocytin. The biotin-lysine amide bond is not hydrolyzed by proteolytic enzymes or peptidases. A specific hydrolyase, biotinidase, catalyzes the cleavage of biocytin to biotin and lysine and of short biotinyl-peptides to biotin and peptides (82, 84, 153). This enzyme is found in the serum as well as in many tissues (175). One metabolic role for biotinidase is to release biotin from biocytin derived from proteolysis of holocarboxylases, permitting the reutilization of biotin. Most of the biotin in foods such as meat and cereals is protein-bound (63, 154) and biotinidase is the only known enzyme that catalyzes its release (170). Biotinidase is present in pancreatic juice and intestinal mucosa but is not enriched in intestinal brush-border membranes (168, 170). Thus it is likely that biotinidase plays an important role in the utilization of protein bound dietary biotin (170).

Very little is known about the mechanisms of absorption of biotin from the intestine. Everted sacs of rat intestine showed no concentrative uptake of biotin and a linear increase in movement across the intestine from 1–10 μM, which suggests diffusion (156). The concentration of biotin in rat intestinal contents was estimated to be 80–700 nM, and assuming rat plasma content of biotin to be comparable to the 0.8–3.0-nM biotin in human plasma, the concentration gradient would permit adequate uptake by diffusion. Another study of intestinal transport of biotin confirmed the lack of concentrative transport in the rat, rabbit, and guinea pig, but found concentrative transport in the mouse and hamster (137). Further study of the transport of biotin in the hamster small intestine showed it to be activated by sodium and to have a $K_t$ for biotin of 1 mM (20). There is some question about whether this is the physiological mechanism for biotin transport since the $K_t$ was so high and lipoic acid (thioctic acid) was a competitive inhibitor with a $K_i$ one third the $K_t$ for biotin. It has been shown in vivo in humans that, at high concentration, biotin can be absorbed in the large intestine as well as the small intestine (136). Even less is known about the absorption of biocytin, although it is a competitive inhibitor of biotin absorption in the small intestine of the hamster (137).

Some of the biotin in plasma is free but considerable amounts are bound (139). Biotin binds to crude fractions of human albumin and alpha- and beta-globulins (51). There is a biotin-binding glycoprotein in human plasma (54, 157). Whether this protein has a functional role in biotin transport is not known. The clearance of biotin by the kidneys is 41–44% of that of the clearance of creatinine at normal concentrations of biotin in plasma (17). This may be due to incomplete glomerular filtration as a consequence of the binding of biotin to plasma proteins or to tubular reabsorption. Rat renal brush border vesicles show facilitated diffusion of biotin (17).

The cellular uptake of biotin by fully differentiated mouse 3T3-L1 cells (adipocyte-like) is temperature dependent, saturable at concentrations less than 50 μM, and relatively specific (34). However the $K_m$ of 22 μM appears rather unphysiological since human plasma levels of biotin are about 10,000 times lower than this $K_m$. Above 50-μM biotin, the uptake was linear and nonsaturable, which suggests diffusion. Biotin uptake by HeLa cells in 20–400-μM biotin was temperature dependent but nonsaturable (39). In contrast, uptake of biotin in an avidin complex was temperature dependent, saturable, and greater than the uptake of free biotin. Similar results were found for human fibroblasts (30). It was suggested that the biotin-avidin complex was bound to the cells and taken up by pinocytosis. Since avidin is not a mammalian protein, they suggested that it mimics an as yet unknown biotin-binding plasma protein. There is considerable question about the physiological relevance of these studies since the lowest concentration of free biotin used was 0.8 μM, which is about 300 times the concentration of biotin in human plasma.

### *Dietary Requirement for Biotin*

The dietary requirement for biotin in man is not known with certainty. This is partially a result of uncertainty in the analysis of available biotin in foods and of uncertainty in the magnitude of biotin production by intestinal flora. The methods for analyzing biotin and its nutritional importance have been reviewed (25, 163). Most analyses for biotin have been done with microbiological assays (163). Some microorganisms can utilize only biotin, whereas others can utilize biotin and biocytin. More recent radioisotope dilution assays with avidin measure any ureido-containing metabolite as well as biotin (40). Another variable in the analysis is that of the techniques used to digest the foods to release biotin. There is some uncertainty about how much of the microbiologically assayed biotin in different foods is actually available for mammalian nutrition.

The approximate biotin contents of foods have been tabulated (68, 163). Note that the concentrations in (163) should be in μg/100 g rather than mg/100 g. Liver, egg yolks, and cooked cereals are highest in biotin, containing 20–100 μg/100 g. The calculated biotin in a composite Canadian diet was 62 μg per day and actual analysis of the diet gave 60 μg per day (73). A similar calculation of the British diet revealed an intake of 33 μg of biotin per day (27). When daily dietary intakes were 33, 37, and 54 μg of biotin, the daily urinary excretions of biotin were 30, 51, and 42 μg respectively, and daily fecal excretions of biotin were 79, 191, and 241 respectively (41, 52, 110). Thus urinary excretions of biotin were approximately equal to dietary input while fecal excretions were 2.5 to 5 times higher. This indicates considerable synthesis of biotin by the intestinal flora, but the amounts that are absorbed are unknown.

The extent of synthesis of biotin by the intestinal flora and the amount absorbed from the intestine have not been conclusively measured by attempts to sterilize the gut with antibiotics. Although fecal excretion of biotin decreased with oral administration of sulfonamides in one study (61), in another there was no decrease when avidin was not included in the diet (111). There was no decrease in the urinary excretion of biotin in these studies, nor was there a decrease when neomycin was given (93). In contrast, a very high dose of streptomycin caused a marked decrease in urinary biotin (130). It is possible that most of the biotin synthesized by intestinal flora is retained intracellularly as protein-bound biotin and that relatively little is available for human nutrition.

Typical dietary intakes of biotin are 30–60 μg per day (27, 73). The lack of any clinical indications of biotin deficiency at this level suggests that this is an adequate daily intake. European countries do not have a recommended intake of biotin, but in Canada 40 μg per day is the suggested intake (27) and in the United States intakes of 35 μg per day for infants, increasing with age to 200 μg per day, have been recommended (107). Human breast milk contains 0.7–1.3 μg of biotin per 100 ml or 0.17 μg per g of dry matter, similar to formulas based on whole cow's milk (0.21 μg per g dry matter); formulas based on skim milk or demineralized milk contains less biotin, a mean of 0.095 (72). Infants in the US who are breast fed or given formulas containing minimal biotin typically consume 6–10 μg of biotin per day (169). During mature milk production, 2–14% (1–11 μg per day) of the maternal intake of biotin (81 μg per day) was found in breast milk (36).

The human neonate begins extrauterine life with higher levels of biotin in the blood than those of adults. The concentration of biotin in cord blood is 35–50% higher than in maternal blood (3, 4). Oral or intramuscular administration of 200 μg of biotin to the mother 1–7 hours before birth significantly elevated biotin levels in both maternal and cord blood and increased the concentration in cord blood 100% above that in maternal blood (3). These studies indicate that placental transport of biotin occurs. In these studies, maternal blood levels of biotin were normal at the time of delivery. In another study maternal blood levels of biotin were about 50% of normal between 3 and 9 months of pregnancy (21). The intake of biotin from breast milk and the urinary output of biotin has been studied over the first week of life (67). Urinary biotin levels were higher from one to three days, then decreased five-fold by days six and seven. The intake of biotin was almost zero on days one and two then rose to a plateau by day six. Urinary excretion greatly exceeded intake from breast milk for the first four days, and at days six and seven intake was about double the excretion.

# BIOTIN-RESPONSIVE MULTIPLE CARBOXYLASE DEFICIENCY

## *Isolated Deficiencies of Individual Carboxylases*

Inherited deficiencies of each of the three mitochondrial biotin-containing carboxylases are known in humans. These isolated deficiencies are due to abnormal apoenzyme structures and do not respond to pharmacological doses of biotin.

Propionic acidemia is due to a deficiency of propionyl-CoA carboxylase. Patients with this disorder typically have episodic vomiting, severe ketosis, and metabolic acidosis, progressing to coma. If the disorder is not fatal in early infancy, many patients have failure to thrive and mental retardation (172). The characteristic biochemical abnormalities are elevated concentrations of propionic acid in blood and elevated levels of secondary metabolites in urine, including 3-hydroxypropionic acid, an oxidation product, and 2-methylcitric acid, which is formed by the condensation of propionyl-CoA and oxaloacetic acid in a reaction catalyzed by citrate synthetase. When patients are acutely ill, propionylglycine, tiglylglycine, 3-hydroxy-*n*-valeric acid, and other abnormal metabolites are found in the urine. In very young infants concentrations of ammonia are elevated in blood, as are concentrations of glycine in plasma and urine. Patients have been reported with biotin-responsive propionic acidemia (6, 71). In one, the concentrations of propionic acid in blood achieved after an isoleucine load appeared to be less after treatment with biotin (6), but the clinical course was not appreciably altered by treatment (J. V. Leonard, personal communication) and the activity of propionyl-CoA carboxylase in fibroblasts remained very low in the presence of high concentrations of biotin (L. Sweetman, unpublished). In the other (71), studies of peripheral lymphocyte carboxylases after a long period without biotin were completely normal and the patient was well (J. C. Williams and L. Sweetman, unpublished).

Isolated deficiency of 3-methylcrotonyl-CoA carboxylase has been reported in three patients. Two siblings were asymptomatic while receiving a low-protein diet (19). Increased dietary protein caused vomiting, acidosis, and hypoglycemia in one patient. There was some hair loss but no rash. Another patient presented with severe hypoglycemia, mild metabolic acidosis, hypotonia, and coma (8). All of the patients excreted large amounts of the metabolites of 3-methylcrotonyl-CoA: 3-hydroxyisovaleric acid (which is formed by hydration) and 3-methylcrotonylglycine (which is formed in a reaction catalyzed by glycine *N*-acylase) as well as variable amounts of 3-methylcrotonic acid. None of the patients responded to biotin with a decrease in the excretion of metabolites, but all were clinically well after treatment with diets restricted to 1.8–2.0 g of protein/kg body weight per day. A patient reported earlier with neurological symptoms similar to Werdnig-Hoffmann disease in whom 3-

methylcrotonylglycinuria and 3-hydroxyisovaleric aciduria were unresponsive to small doses of biotin may have had the same disorder, but multiple carboxylase deficiency was not totally excluded (138). This is true for another patient who excreted large amounts of 3-hydroxyisovaleric acid and was deficient in 3-methylcrotonyl-CoA carboxylase (49). In two additional patients with biotin-responsive excretion of 3-methylcrotonylglycine and 3-hydroxyisovaleric acid, multiple carboxylase deficiency was not excluded (32, 56, 80).

Isolated deficiency of pyruvate carboxylase causes an elevation of lactic acid, pyruvic acid, and alanine levels in blood (42). There are two forms of this disorder, a more severe form that does not produce the pyruvate carboxylase protein and a less severe form that produces an enzymatically defective pyruvate carboxylase (123). These patients usually have severe neurological problems and early death. None of the patients have responded to biotin therapy.

A patient with an isolated deficiency of acetyl-CoA carboxylase has been reported (22) but there was not a consistent deficiency of the enzyme in cultured fibroblasts (H. R. Scholte, personal communication).

## *Abnormal Holocarboxylase Synthetase*

The literature on biotin-responsive multiple carboxylase is confusing because of the evolution of terminology and knowledge. Most of the early studies by a variety of investigators were of a single patient, variously referred to as J.R. and J.Ri. Therefore it is useful to review the historical progression of the many studies on this patient that culminated in the characterization of an abnormal holocarboxylase synthetase.

J.R. was initially described in 1971 under the heading of biotin-responsive β-methylcrotonylglycinuria (58). He had tended to vomit since birth, and an erythematous skin rash began at six weeks of age. At five months he developed rapid respiration, persistent vomiting, and unresponsiveness, and was found to have ketosis and metabolic acidosis. Analysis of urine by gas chromatography–mass spectrometry showed a large elevation of 3-methylcrotonic acid and 3-methylcrotonylglycine, with lesser elevations of 3-hydroxyisovaleric acid and tiglylglycine (57, 58). The pattern of excretion of metabolites was largely consistent with a deficiency of 3-methylcrotonyl-CoA carboxylase. Reasoning that this was a biotin-requiring enzyme and that biotin might be therapeutic, an empirical dose of 10 mg of biotin per day was given orally. The clinical and biochemical response was dramatic. Vomiting, ketosis, and acidosis resolved in one day, the elevated levels of urinary metabolites became normal in 2–4 days. The skin rash cleared, and he developed normally with continued treatment with biotin. At two years of age, the dose of biotin was reduced until he began to excrete 3-methylcrotonylglycine and 3-hydroxyisovaleric acid. At that time the activity of 3-methylcrotonyl-CoA carboxylase in leucocytes was shown to be low, 12% of an age-matched control or 20% of the normal adult level of activity (59).

Two facts suggested that an abnormal 3-methylcrotonyl-CoA carboxylase was not the complete story. First, a deficiency of this enzyme did not account for the excretion of tiglylglycine since tiglyl-CoA is not a normal substrate for the enzyme. A year after the initial report, tiglylglycine levels were shown to be elevated in urine of patients acutely ill with propionic acidemia in whom there is a deficiency of another biotin-containing enzyme, propionyl-CoA carboxylase (121). Second, free biotin is not a substrate or cofactor for 3-methylcrotonyl-CoA carboxylase itself, but rather a substrate for holocarboxylase synthetase, which attaches biotin covalently to apo-3-methylcrotonyl-CoA carboxylase.

Although the specificity of holocarboxylase synthetase for apocarboxylase was not known, it was thought likely that it acted on more than one apocarboxylase. Consequently, studies on the possibility of a biotin-responsive deficiency of propionyl-CoA carboxylase were undertaken. At two years of age, while J.R. was clinically well but receiving only 0.5 mg of biotin per day, he had a large excretion of 3-hydroxyisovaleric acid of about 7 μmol per mg creatinine, and about 30% as much 3-methylcrotonylglycine (143). There were very significant elevations in the excretion of 3-hydroxypropionic and 2-methylcitric acids, which are the characteristic urinary metabolites of patients with propionic acidemia. Reanalysis of the urines obtained at the time of the initial diagnosis also showed elevated concentrations of 3-hydroxypropionic acid and 2-methylcitric acid (31). The activity of propionyl-CoA carboxylase was assayed in fibroblasts derived from J.R., which were cultivated in Eagle's Minimal Essential Medium with 10% fetal calf serum. They showed only 4% of normal activity, a level similar to the 2% of normal activity obtained in patients with propionic acidemia (143). It was fortunate that the fibroblasts were grown in this medium in which the only biotin was that from the fetal calf serum (about 6 nM). In a subsequent study the activity of propionyl-CoA carboxylase and 3-methylcrotonyl-CoA carboxylase was markedly deficient in this medium, but when the cells were cultivated in Hamm's F-10 medium, which contains about 100-nM biotin, the activities of both enzymes were in the normal range (160). Normal fibroblasts had the same activities of the carboxylases in both media.

When the patient's cells were cultivated in different concentrations of biotin, the activities of the two enzymes gave Michaelis-Menton curves with apparent $K_m$'s for biotin of 60–90 nM (10). When protein synthesis was inhibited in the patient's fibroblasts that had been cultivated without added biotin, there was a large increase in carboxylase activity within three hours of the addition of biotin, which indicates that biotin was being attached to preexisting apocarboxylases (11). The biotin-responsiveness of the two carboxylases suggested that the primary defect was in holocarboxylase synthetase. The third mitochondrial carboxylase, pyruvate carboxylase, was also shown to be deficient and biotin responsive in the fibroblasts of J.R. (132). These observations suggested that a single holocarboxylase synthetase attaches biotin to all three mitochondrial apocarboxylases. That the same holocarboxylase synthetase also attaches biotin to the cytoplasmic apoacetyl-CoA carboxylase was indicated by the demonstration of biotin-responsive deficiencies of acetyl-CoA carboxylase in fibroblasts of J.R. and other patients (48, 113).

Holocarboxylase synthetase was assayed in cultured fibroblasts by using as substrate apopropionyl-CoA carboxylase purified 200-fold from rats made biotin deficient by a high-avidin (raw egg white) diet (28). Fibroblast extracts were incubated with excess rat apopropionyl-CoA carboxylase, ATP, and various concentrations of biotin, and the holopropionyl-CoA carboxylase formed was assayed by fixation of radioactive bicarbonate and propionyl-CoA to the acid nonvolatile radioactive product methylmalonyl-CoA. In contrast to the $K_m$ for biotin of about 8 nM for normal fibroblasts, the patient's $K_m$ for biotin was about 60-fold higher and the maximum velocity was 30–40% of normal. These kinetic properties of the mutant holocarboxylase synthetase were consistent with the response of the carboxylases in fibroblasts to various concentrations of biotin in the culture media. They were also consistent with the in vivo response of the patient to biotin.

Normal levels of biotin in plasma are 0.8–3.0 nanomolar, which may be similar to intracellular levels. These values are only slightly below the $K_m$ of normal holocarboxylase synthetase and are sufficient for converting apocarboxylases to holocarboxylases. On the other hand, in the patient J.R. normal plasma levels of biotin would be about 1/170 of the $K_m$ of his holocarboxylase synthetase, effectively preventing the conversion of apocarboxylases to holocarboxylases. Treatment with 10 mg of biotin per day, about 200 times the normal intake, elevates the plasma concentration of biotin above the $K_m$ for his holocarboxylase synthetase, allowing conversion of apocarboxylases to holocarboxylases even though there is a somewhat decreased maximum velocity of holocarboxylase synthetase.

Many other patients with biotin-responsive multiple carboxylase deficiency have now been reported and a wide range of clinical symptoms have been observed. Some, such as an infant who died with 3-methylcrotonic aciduria and lactic acidemia (126), have been shown to have the same genetic defect as J.R. by lack of genetic complementation in fibroblast heterokaryons produced by cell fusion (132). Others have been shown to have an abnormal holocarboxylase synthetase by using endogenous lymphoblast or fibroblast apocarboxylases as substrates (9, 55, 131).

Fibroblasts from seven patients have been shown to have abnormal holocarboxylase synthetase activity using rat apopropionyl-CoA carboxylase as substrate and their clinical features are summarized (29).

The age of onset of clinical symptoms varied from the first day of life to eight months of age, but most patients presented before six weeks of age. Initially it had been thought that two forms of biotin-responsive multiple carboxylase deficiency could be differentiated by the age of onset. Those with holocarboxylase synthetase abnormalities generally presented within the first six weeks of life and were called the early-onset or neonatal multiple carboxylase deficiency (142). The form that generally presented after six months of age, now known to be due to a deficiency of biotinidase, was referred to as late-onset, late-infantile, or juvenile multiple carboxylase deficiency. It is now known that patients with an abnormal holocarboxylase synthetase can present at any age from one day to 15 months (135).

There may be some correlation of the age of onset with the degree of elevation of the $K_m$ for biotin of holocarboxylase synthetase (29). The patient with the highest $K_m$ for biotin (70 times normal) presented in the first few hours of life (171) and a previous sibling had died at three days of age (144). Patients in whom the $K_m$ values for biotin of holocarboxylase synthetase were 20 to 45 times normal presented between one day of life and seven weeks. The patient with a $K_m$ for biotin only three times normal presented at eight months of age (113). That holocarboxylase synthetase deficiency is a serious life-threatening disorder is indicated by the occurrence of death in the neonatal period in three patients (126, 144). In two of those the diagnosis was based on the presence of the characteristic organic aciduria in samples studied postmortem (144). The brother of one of these patients was documented to have the enzyme defect (29, 171).

Both males and females are affected with holocarboxylase synthetase abnormality, and the inheritance appears to be autosomal recessive. One patient was asymptomatic in whom treatment with biotin had been undertaken pre- and postnatally (114), but a previous sibling had presented with the typical clinical and biochemical features on the second day of life (115). Common clinical features were hypotonia, developmental delay or regression, rash, and alopecia. Typical biochemical features were hyperammonemia, metabolic acidosis, lactic acidemia, and the presence of the characteristic urinary metabolites. The pattern of the organic aciduria includes a large elevation of the level of 3-hydroxyisovaleric acid, a smaller and variable elevation of the amount of 3-methylcrotonylglycine, and lesser amounts of 3-hydroxypropionic acid and 2-methylcitric acid. All of the patients showed marked clinical and biochemical improvement after treatment with biotin. Most of the patients became clinically normal after receiving 10 mg of biotin per day and had no elevation of the urinary levels of metabolites.

Systematic studies to determine whether lower doses of biotin would be sufficient have not been done. The original patient J.R. had no elevation in the levels of urinary metabolites while he was receiving 10 mg of biotin per day

(58) but he did have significant amounts when the dose was 0.5 mg per day (143). Some patients, although clinically well when given 10 mg of biotin per day, had small amounts of urinary metabolites that became normal when the dose was 40 mg of biotin per day (114, 115). Another less responsive patient was clinically well when receiving 1 to 20 mg of biotin per day, but had elevated excretions of metabolites of leucine and activities of the carboxylases in leucocytes that were only 4 to 16% of normal when receiving 20 mg of biotin per day (106). The patient with the highest known $K_m$ for biotin (29) continued to have a skin rash, large excretions of metabolites, and subnormal activities of carboxylases in lymphocytes when receiving doses of biotin as high as 60 mg per day (29, 171). When provided with adequate biotin therapy, none of the patients have required dietary restriction of protein, although moderate restriction in the less-responsive patients could well decrease the excretion of metabolites as it does for patients with isolated biotin-unresponsive propionic acidemia (172) and 3-methylcrotonyl-glycinuria (8, 19).

Patients with biotin-responsive multiple carboxylase deficiency due to an abnormal holocarboxylase synthetase share a basic distinguishing biochemical feature: carboxylases have low activity in fibroblasts cultivated in medium containing biotin only in the amounts provided by the fetal calf serum, and they increase in activity when the medium is supplemented with high concentrations of biotin (29). In contrast, fibroblasts from patients with biotin-responsive multiple carboxylase deficiency that is due to a deficiency of biotinidase have normal activities of the carboxylases in both types of media (29). These criteria can be used to identify the patients in the literature with an abnormal holocarboxylase synthetase even if the synthetase enzyme has not been assayed directly (13, 14, 92, 112). Heterozygotes cannot be distinguished by this means but neither can they be detected by current assays of holocarboxylase synthetase. A rapid diagnostic method for distinguishing holocarboxylase synthetase abnormalities from biotinidase deficiency is the assay of the activity of carboxylases in lymphocytes isolated from blood that has or has not been preincubated with biotin (140). Assay of levels of biotin may be helpful, and of course assay of biotinidase is now a simple way of detecting that defect (140, 164).

An abnormal holocarboxylase synthetase can be diagnosed prenatally by demonstrating biotin-responsive deficiencies of carboxylases in cultured amniocytes obtained by amniocentesis (114). The prenatal diagnosis in this pregnancy was also based on the demonstration of a small but significant amount of 2-methylcitric acid in the amniotic fluid, as measured by stable isotope dilution. A much more significantly elevated concentration of 3-hydroxyisovaleric in the amniotic fluid was later shown by stable isotope dilution gas chromatography–mass spectrometry, while normal levels were found in a subsequent unaffected pregnancy (76). This appears to be the best method for the rapid prenatal diagnosis of this disorder.

Prenatal therapy was begun at 23.5 weeks of pregnancy by giving the mother 10 mg of oral biotin per day. This greatly increased her serum level of biotin and there were no ill effects (114). At birth the infant was clinically well and levels of urinary organic acids were normal. The prenatal diagnosis was confirmed by assay of holocarboxylase synthetase in cultured skin fibroblasts (29). The baby has remained asymptomatic while receiving 40 mg of biotin per day (114).

Prenatal therapy was also carried out without prior diagnosis at 34 weeks in a pregnancy at risk for an abnormal holocarboxylase synthetase (127). Clinically well fraternal twins were born with concentrations of biotin in cord blood 4–7 times normal and with normal urinary organic acids. Postnatal therapy with biotin was not given while fibroblasts were being cultured to establish a diagnosis; the twin who was affected presented at three months of age moribund, hypothermic, and in shock (128). He was severely acidotic and ketotic and had elevated levels of lactic and pyruvic acids in blood and large elevations in the concentrations of urinary metabolites. Treatment with 10 mg of biotin per day was effective and resulted in rapid clinical and biochemical improvement (125, 128).

## *Biotinidase Deficiency*

The patients who were initially designated as having "late-onset" biotin-responsive multiple carboxylase deficiency were shown by Wolf and colleagues in 1983 to have a deficiency of biotinidase in serum (164, 167). This clarified many of the problems in the earlier literature about the biochemistry of this disorder. Typically, patients with a deficiency of biotinidase have presented after three months of age with symptoms like those of patients with an abnormal holocarboxylase synthetase. These include hypotonia, developmental delay or regression, skin rash, and alopecia. They may present with life-threatening episodes of metabolic acidosis and this may be complicated by hyperammonemia. More specific abnormalities include lactic acidemia and the characteristic organic aciduria consisting of 3-methylcrotonylglycine, 3-hydroxyisovaleric acid, 3-hydroxypropionic acid and 2-methylcitric acid (29, 165). In addition many of the patients have had seizures, ataxia, candidiasis, and conjunctivitis. One patient had the cutaneous and neurological symptoms but an organic aciduria was not detected (146). This can be a fatal disorder. Two previous siblings who had had clinical symptoms similar to a diagnosed patient had died at 8 and 39 months of age (37, 161). The three infants in this family had defects in T-cell and B-cell immunity (37). The diagnosed patient had pretreatment levels of biotin in plasma that were somewhat below normal (116) as did other patients without abnormal T and B cells (104, 150). Another patient had fatty acid and biotin-responsive impairment of lymphocyte suppressive activity in vitro (50). Biotin deficiency in guinea pigs has been shown to decrease the numbers of B and T lymphocytes (120).

Some patients with biotinidase deficiency have had optic atrophy (124, 165) or neurosensory hearing loss (165, 166). A patient diagnosed at 10 months of age and treated with 10 mg of biotin per day (33) was subsequently shown to have a deficiency of biotinidase (12) and developed a sensorineural hearing loss and severe myopia suggestive of a progressive retinal epithelial dysplasia (149). None of the patients with an abnormal holocarboxylase synthetase have developed these neurosensory abnormalities, ruling out long-term treatment with biotin as a cause in the patients with biotinidase deficiency. The alopecia and skin rash in one patient with biotinidase deficiency responded to oral and cutaneous administration of unsaturated fatty acids (105). This suggests that a deficiency of acetyl-CoA carboxylase required for fatty acid synthesis may be involved in the pathogenesis of these symptoms.

Patients deficient in biotinidase usually respond to 10 mg of oral biotin per day, with reversion to normal of all of the biochemical and clinical features of the disease except for hearing loss and optic atrophy (33, 37, 104, 116, 150, 164, 165). Fibroblasts cultured from patients with biotinidase deficiency have normal activities of the carboxylases (13, 92, 94, 112, 116, 150). This is because there is sufficient biotin in fetal calf serum so that recycling of biocytin by biotinidase in the cells is unnecessary; in addition, fetal calf serum has biotinidase activity. Holocarboxylase synthetase exhibits normal kinetics in these cells (29).

Before the identification of biotinidase deficiency as the defect in "late-onset" biotin-responsive multiple carboxylase deficiency, there was speculation about a defect in the intestinal absorption of biotin since pretreatment levels of biotin in plasma and urine were often low (104, 116, 150). This was studied by administering small oral doses of biotin to patients with below normal plasma levels of biotin, and measuring the rise in plasma biotin compared to normals (103, 151). The less than normal rise in plasma biotin in the patients was attributed to defective intestinal absorption. With the discovery that biotinidase was deficient, a similar study was repeated after first treating the patient with enough biotin to raise the levels in plasma to somewhat above normal (152). Under these conditions, the rise in plasma biotin following a small oral load was normal, which indicates normal intestinal absorption. Apparently, in the previous studies the tissues were so depleted of biotin that absorbed biotin was rapidly removed from the plasma, preventing a normal rise in plasma levels.

In the biotin-deficient state, an increase in renal clearance of biotin was observed (151), but this became normal upon repletion with biotin (152). In another study, a normal rise in plasma biotin was found in a biotin-deficient patient (18). When plasma levels of biotin were normal, renal clearance of biotin was elevated in this patient. A more extensive study of five patients with biotinidase deficiency confirmed a renal clearance of biotin increased 2–3 times above normal when plasma biotin levels were normal (16, 17). Upon cessation of treatment with 10 mg of biotin per day, the patients had a more rapid fall in plasma biotin and a greater renal loss of biotin than did controls.

Biocytin was detected in the urine of six patients with biotinidase deficiency but not in normal urine (26). The levels of biocytin were considerably higher than the levels of biotin when the patients were not receiving biotin. The normal renal clearance of biotin is half that of creatinine, and if this reflects renal reabsorption, the increased clearance of biotin in biotinidase deficiency might be due to an inhibition of biotin reabsorption by the elevated amounts of biocytin. The clinical and biochemical features of biotinidase deficiency appear to be related to deficiencies of the carboxylases secondary to the functional deficiency of biotin. Some patients have deficient levels of biotin plasma while others have normal levels. Biocytin may compete with biotin as a substrate for holocarboxylase synthetase, thus increasing the concentration of biotin needed for effective holocarboxylase synthesis. It is possible that elevated levels of biocytin are toxic but this has not been studied experimentally.

Biotinidase deficiency is readily demonstrable by assay of the enzyme in serum (164, 167). Parents of affected infants have about 50% of normal activity, consistent with heterozygosity and autosomal recessive inheritance. The enzyme has also been shown to be deficient in the liver of a deceased patient (53). Biotinidase can be measured in a colorimetric assay using the artificial substrate, biotinyl-*p*-aminobenzoic acid (164). A more sensitive assay employs radioactively labeled biotinyl-$^{14}$C-*p*-aminobenzoic acid (173). A small amount of biotinidase activity was detectable in normal fibroblasts while none was found in patient fibroblasts. This assay also detected biotinidase activity in normal amniocytes, which suggests that prenatal diagnosis of biotinidase deficiency may be possible (134). A fluorometric assay with an artificial substrate for biotinidase has been described (158). A radiochemical assay with the natural substrate $^{14}$C-*d*-biotinyl-$\epsilon$-*N*-L-lysine has also been described (90).

The colorimetric assay for biotinidase activity has been adapted in a low-cost screening method for newborns, utilizing the dried blood samples spotted on filter papers for newborn screening for phenylketonuria (70). This was recently used to screen 81,243 newborns in Virginia, among whom two unrelated patients were diagnosed as having biotinidase deficiency (169). Two older, previously undiagnosed siblings with severe neurological abnormalities, developmental delay, and cutaneous symptoms were found by assay of the families of the two infants positive on the screening assay. From this study the incidence of biotinidase deficiency was estimated to be 1 in 40,000, but the ultimate incidence may be between 1 in 12,000 and 1 in 240,000 births. Biotinidase deficiency fits the accepted criteria for inclusion in mass newborn screening programs: it has a significant incidence, it is not easily recognized clinically before serious symptoms occur, it is life-threatening, treatment with biotin is very effective, and a low-cost screening method is available. It would be very worthwhile to make screening for biotinidase deficiency widely available.

## DIETARY DEFICIENCY OF BIOTIN

The literature on the dietary deficiency of biotin in man is small. Dietary deficiency appears to be rare as a result of the general availability of biotin in the diet and the small requirement for biotin. The synthesis of biotin by intestinal bacteria may be a factor. The early instances of biotin deficiency were all a consequence of diets containing large amounts of raw egg white in which avidin prevented intestinal absorption of biotin. In an experimental study, biotin deficiency was induced in four adult volunteers by using a diet in which raw egg white made up 30% of the caloric intake (147, 148). The subjects developed glossitis, anorexia, nausea, and an active distaste for the diet. Behavioral manifestations included depression, hallucinations, somnolence, and a panic state. A desquamating dermatosis developed. All of the symptoms were reversed by daily injection of 150 μg of biotin. Since this study was done before the biochemical role of biotin in metabolism was understood, no biochemical data were obtained other than levels of biotin, which decreased markedly in the urine while on the diet.

In contrast to this study patients with malignancies given equally large amounts of egg white and/or avidin in two studies did not develop clinical symptoms (79, 122). When urinary biotin was measured it did not decrease while the patients were receiving the diet (122).

Several patients have been reported in whom biotin deficiency developed as a consequence of unusual dietary habits that included ingestion of raw egg white. The first patient, a 66-year-old male, had for the previous six years consumed 3–10 raw eggs and 1–4 quarts of wine per day as well as very limited quantities of food (162). He had an erythematous exfoliative dermatitis for several years and conjunctivitis for several months. Histology of the skin showed an absence of sebaceous glands and atrophic hair follicles. Serum concentration of biotin was below normal but urinary biotin was normal. When placed on a normal hospital diet, even supplemented with his usual six raw eggs and a quart of wine per day, the skin rash resolved although the serum biotin remained below normal. Treatment with 500 μg of biotin injected on alternate days brought his serum levels of biotin to normal.

A 62-year-old female with cirrhosis was prescribed a regimen of six raw eggs daily for 18 months (15). She developed anorexia, nausea, vomiting, pallor, depression, lassitude, substernal pain, and a scaly dermatitis and desquamation of the lips. All of her symptoms were markedly improved by 2–5 days of the parenteral administration of 200 μg of biotin per day while continuing the raw egg diet. Prior to treatment, blood levels of biotin were low (250 ng/l; normal 820–2700) but urinary biotin was normal.

A 5-year-old boy requiring tube-feeding received six raw eggs daily as well as antibiotics (133). He developed a fine scaly dermatitis and severe alopecia after 18 months. Laboratory findings were normal except for hypercholesterolemia. On substituting egg yolks without egg whites and administering 2–4 mg of biotin parenterally and by mouth, the rash disappeared, the hair grew, and the serum cholesterol dropped. On further treatment without biotin but with cooked eggs, there were no clinical symptoms but cholesterol rose. In a similar situation an 11-year-old boy was given a diet of infant formula containing oil and two raw eggs per day (145). He developed a severe erythematous exfoliative dermatosis and total alopecia. Blood cholesterol was not elevated. Plasma concentration of biotin was low (156 ng/l; normal 330–722) as was urinary biotin (0.85–1.31 ng/mg creatinine; normal 11–95). He had the typical organic aciduria seen in biotin-responsive multiple carboxylase deficiency in which there are elevated quantities of 3-methylcrotonylglycine, 3-hydroxyisovaleric acid, 3-hydroxypropionic acid, and 2-methylcitric acid. In addition he had intermittent ketosis. The activities of propionyl-CoA carboxylase and 3-methylcrotonyl-CoA carboxylase in leucocytes were low (2% and 10% of normal, respectively). All of the biochemical and clinical manifestations resolved on substituting cooked eggs and providing 1 mg of intravenous and later oral biotin.

It is interesting that biotin deficiency occurred in these patients who received whole raw eggs. Egg yolks contain large amounts of biotin, slightly more than one would think would be bound by the avidin in the egg whites. Whole raw eggs do not cause symptomatic biotin deficiency in experimental animals. Factors that may have rendered these humans more susceptible to biotin deficiency include cirrhosis and age in the adults and chronic oral antibiotics in the children.

Milder forms of biotin deficiency may occur, manifested by apparent seborrheic dermatitis or Leiner's disease in infants (108). A number of studies have reported rapid clearing of the dermatitis with biotin treatment (98, 108, 141), but in one double-blind study biotin was ineffective (47). It is possible that different types of patients were studied in the different studies. Understanding of the possible role of biotin in seborrheic dermatitis is hampered by the lack of measurement of biotin levels in most of the studies and the total lack of other biochemical measurements such as leucocyte carboxylase activities or urinary organic acids (7).

Of clinical relevance are reports of frank biotin deficiency in patients receiving total parenteral nutrition (TPN). Many intravenous preparations do not contain biotin, and it had also been overlooked in regimens of TPN. An infant with short-gut syndrome receiving continuous antibiotics developed an erythematous rash after three months of TPN (101). After five months, total alopecia occurred with pallor, irritability, lethargy, and mild hypotonia. Essential fatty acids were not deficient and zinc supplementation was ineffective. The concentration of lactic acid was elevated in blood, and analysis of urinary organic acids showed the characteristic organic aciduria of biotin deficiency. Plasma and urinary concentrations of biotin were deficient. On treatment with 10 mg of biotin per day in the parenteral fluid, the biochemical and clinical manifestations reverted to normal. When the patient was given a maintenance dose of 100 μg of biotin per day for nine months, the manifestations did not reappear.

Two siblings with congenital secretory diarrhea and seizures developed similar clinical and biochemical abnormalities on total parenteral nutrition (81). Urinary biotin levels were low but serum biotin was normal. One child died with metabolic acidosis. In the other sibling 200 μg of intravenous biotin per day brought to normal the organic aciduria but not the skin lesions, which required 10 mg of biotin per day for resolution. An adult patient receiving home parenteral nutrition developed skin lesions, alopecia, acidosis, and neurological findings that resolved on the administration of 60 μg per day of intravenous biotin (96). Two adults receiving long-term parenteral nutrition developed severe alopecia that was reversed by 200 μg per day of biotin (74). Extensive study of three children with biochemical and clinical symptoms of biotin deficiency as a result of total parenteral nutrition revealed that all three had markedly depressed excretion of biotin but that only one had a low plasma level of biotin (99, 100). In the two infants treated with 100 μg of intravenous biotin per day, there was gradual clinical and biochemical improvement, but in one, urinary organic acids were still elevated after ten weeks of therapy. The response of these infants suggests that 100 μg of biotin per day is adequate for maintenance, but is inadequate to replenish rapidly the depleted levels of biotin. Thus the recommendation of the Nutritional Advisory Group of the American Medical Association for 20 μg of biotin per day for children on parenteral alimentation (2) should be increased.

Biotin deficiency may also occur as a result of chronic hemodialysis. Three patients with encephalopathy and peripheral neuropathy and one with peripheral neuropathy all showed marked improvement within three months of the daily administration of 10 mg of biotin per day (176). Although biotin levels were not reported, it is likely that biotin deficiency can occur in chronic hemodialysis because of the loss of free biotin in the dialysate.

Another potential cause of biotin deficiency is the long-term administration of anticonvulsant medications. Patients receiving phenytoin, pyrimidone, phenobarbital, or carbamazepine (but not those receiving sodium valproate) had significantly lower plasma concentrations of biotin ($227 \pm 80$ vs $448 \pm 201$ ng/l) (85, 86). In addition small elevations of the urinary levels of organic acids characteristic of biotin deficiency were found (87, 88). The mechanism by which the anticonvulsant medications lower levels of biotin is unknown, but it may be related to effects on the intestinal absorption or renal loss of biotin. The drugs all contain a carbamide group, as does biotin.

A syndrome in young poultry, known as fatty liver and kidney syndrome, causes sudden unexpected death from hypoglycemia after stress. It may be due to moderate deficiency of biotin although it occurs without other symptoms of biotin deficiency (5, 119). This observation led to the investigation of a possible similar etiology in the sudden infant death syndrome (SIDS) in humans. The median level of free biotin in 35 infants who died of SIDS was 336 ng/g of autopsy liver, significantly lower than the mean of 419 ng/g for 57 infants with explainable deaths (77, 78). Although this observation suggests that a marginal deficiency of biotin (together with stress, by analogy to the syndrome in poultry) may be related to sudden infant death syndrome, more direct biochemical evidence such as assay of pyruvate carboxylase activity in autopsy liver or organic acids in urine or tissues is needed.

## CONCLUSION

Considerable knowledge has been gained about the metabolism of biotin and its important role in humans through the elucidation of the biochemical abnormalities in the inherited human disorders that lead to biotin-responsive multiple carboxylase deficiency. Abnormalities have been studied in the two known enzymes of biotin metabolism, holocarboxylase synthetase and biotinidase. The biochemical abnormalities can be readily understood as the result of deficient activity of the biotin-containing carboxylases. In the presence of an abnormal holocarboxylase synthetase, in which there is an elevated $K_m$ for biotin, the biochemical response to large doses of biotin reflects the elevation of cellular biotin levels to the range of the elevated $K_m$'s. In biotinidase deficiency the carboxylase activities are low as a result of biotin deficiency and the response to biotin results from correcting this deficiency. The variable age of onset and clinical features of biotinidase deficiency probably reflect differences in the development of the biotin deficiency as a consequence of variations in the intakc of free biotin.

The clinical abnormalities seen in these disorders are not all so clearly understood. The hair loss and skin rash may be related to a deficiency of acetyl-CoA carboxylase, required for fatty acid synthesis, because isolated deficiencies of the other three carboxylases have not been shown to result in these manifestations. The cause of the neurological abnormalities is even less obvious, but may be related to a deficiency of pyruvate carboxylase in brain (129). It is not known whether the probable elevation of biocytin in biotinidase deficiency has any biochemical or clinical effects. If biocytin does compete with biotin as the substrate for holocarboxylase synthetase or for transport of biotin, treatment with doses of biotin much larger than needed to correct the biotin deficiency should minimize competition from biocytin.

The optimal dose of biotin for treatment has not been determined. In biotinidase deficiency, the same dose should be effective for all patients, and all would be expected to respond to biotin. With abnormalities of holocarboxylase synthetase, the required dose of biotin should be determined for each patient and will differ because there are differences in the degree of elevation of the $K_m$ for biotin and in the maximum velocity. It is probable that non-$K_m$ variants with deficient holocarboxylase synthetase activity exist that would not be responsive to biotin. These are likely to have considerable residual activity, as a complete deficiency would cause a complete deficiency of all four carboxylases and this would probably be incompatible with uterine development and life. No patients have been identified with biotin-responsive defects in the intestinal absorption of biotin, defects in plasma biotin-binding protein, defects of transport into cells, or defects in the renal handling of biotin. However, it is likely that these exist and will be encountered in the future.

The possibility of subclinical deficiencies of biotin exists in larger populations and may manifest only in susceptible or stressed individuals. Biotin deficiency in total parenteral nutrition should not be a problem now that adequate amounts of biotin are routinely added. Possible deficiency of biotin in patients receiving long-term hemodialysis should be determined. Marginal deficiencies of biotin in formula-fed infants should be eliminated by the fortification of formulas with larger amounts of biotin. The existence of lower levels of biotin in patients receiving long-term treatment with anticonvulsant medications is of concern, and other drugs should be investigated for possible similar effects. Treatment with moderate amounts of biotin would seem appropriate in long-term anticonvulsant therapy. The role of a marginal biotin deficiency as one possible cause of sudden infant death syndrome deserves further investigation.

*Literature Cited*


1. Achuta Murthy, P. N., Mistry, S. P. 1972. Synthesis of biotin-dependent carboxylases from their apoproteins and biotin. *J. Sci. Ind. Res.* 31:554–63
2. American Medical Association. 1979. Multivitamin preparations for parenteral use. A statement by the nutrition advisory board. *J. Parenter. Enteral Nutr.* 3:258–62
3. Baker, H., Frank, O., DeAngelis, B., Feingold, S., Kaminetzky, H. A. 1981. Role of placenta in maternal-fetal vitamin transfer in humans. *Am. J. Obstet. Gynecol.* 141:792–96
4. Baker, H., Thind, I. S., Frank, O., DeAngelis, B., Caterini, H., Louria, D. B. 1977. Vitamin levels in low-birth-weight newborn infants and their mothers. *Am. J. Obstet. Gynecol.* 129:521–24
5. Bannister, D. W. 1979. Recent advances in avian biochemistry: The fatty liver and kidney syndrome. *Int. J. Biochem.* 10: 193–99
6. Barnes, N. D., Hull, D., Balgobin, L., Gompertz, D. 1970. Biotin-responsive propionicacidaemia. *Lancet* 2:244–45
7. Barness, L. A. 1972. Letter: Treatment of seborrheic dermatitis with biotin

and vitamin B complex. *J. Pediatr.* 81: 631

8. Bartlett, K., Bennett, M. J., Hill, R. P., Lashford, L. S., Pollitt, R. J., Worth, H. G. J. 1984. Isolated biotin-resistant 3-methylcrotonyl CoA carboxylase deficiency presenting with life-threatening hypoglycaemia. *J. Inherit. Metab. Dis.* 7:182
9. Bartlett, K., Ghneim, H. K., Stirk, H.-J., Wastell, H. 1985. Enzyme studies in biotin-responsive disorders. *J. Inherit. Metab. Dis.* 8(Suppl. 1):46–52
10. Bartlett, K., Gompertz, D. 1976. Combined carboxylases defect: Biotin-responsiveness in cultured fibroblasts. *Lancet* 2:804
11. Bartlett, K., Gompertz, D. 1978. Biotin activation of carboxylase activity in cultured fibroblasts from a child with a combined carboxylase defect. *Clin. Chim. Acta* 84:399–401
12. Bartlett, K., Leonard, J. V. 1984. Letter: Phenotypic variability in biotinidase deficiency. *J. Pediatr.* 104:965
13. Bartlett, K., Ng, H., Dale, G., Green, A., Leonard, J. V. 1981. Studies on cultured fibroblasts from patients with defects of biotin-dependent carboxylation. *J. Inherit. Metab. Dis.* 4:183–89
14. Bartlett, K., Ng, H., Leonard, J. V. 1980. A combined defect of three mitochondrial carboxylases presenting as biotin-responsive 3-methylcrotonylglycinuria and 3-hydroxyisovaleric aciduria. *Clin. Chim. Acta* 100:183–86
15. Baugh, C. M., Malone, J. H., Butterworth, C. E. 1968. Human biotin deficiency. A case history of biotin deficiency induced by raw egg consumption in a cirrhotic patient. *Am. J. Clin. Nutr.* 21:173–82
16. Baumgartner, E. R., Suormala, T., Wick, H., Bausch, J., Bonjour, J.-P. 1985. Biotinidase deficiency: Factors responsible for the increased biotin requirement. *J. Inherit. Metab. Dis.* 8(Suppl. 1):59–64
17. Baumgartner, E. R., Suormala, T., Wick, H., Bausch, J., Bonjour, J.-P. 1985. Biotinidase deficiency associated with renal loss of biocytin and biotin. See Ref. 38, pp. 272–87
18. Baumgartner, E. R., Suormala, T., Wick, H., Geisert, J., Lehnert, W. 1982. Infantile multiple carboxylase deficiency: evidence of normal intestinal absorption but renal loss of biotin. *Helv. Paediatr. Acta* 37:499–502
19. Beemer, F. A., Bartlett, K., Duran, M., Ghneim, H. K., Wadman, S. K., et al. 1982. Isolated biotin-resistant 3-methylcrotonyl-CoA carboxylase in two sibs. *Eur. J. Pediatr.* 138:351–54
20. Berger, E., Long, E., Semenza, G. 1972. The sodium activation of biotin absorption in hamster small intestine *in vitro. Biochim. Biophys. Acta* 255:873–87
21. Bhagavan, H. N. 1969. Biotin content of blood during gestation. *Int. J. Vitam. Res.* 39:235–37
22. Blom, W., Scholte, H. R. 1981. Acetyl-CoA carboxylase deficiency: An inborn error of de novo fatty acid synthesis. *N. Engl. J. Med.* 305:465–66
23. Boas, M. A. 1924. LVIII. An observation on the value of egg-white as the sole source of nitrogen for young growing rats. *J. Biol. Chem.* 18:422–24
24. Boas, M. A. 1927. XCV. The effect of desiccation upon the nutritive properties of egg-white. *Biochem. J.* 21:712–24
25. Bonjour, J.-P. 1977. Biotin in man's nutrition and therapy—a review. *Int. J. Vitam. Nutr. Res.* 47:107–18
26. Bonjour, J.-P., Bausch, J., Suormala, T., Baumgartner, E. R. 1984. Detection of biocytin in urine of children with congenital biotinidase deficiency. *Int. J. Vitam. Nutr. Res.* 54:223–31
27. Bull, N. L., Buss, D. H. 1982. Biotin, pantothenic acid and vitamin E in the British household food supply. *Hum. Nutr. Appl. Nutr.* 36A:190–96
28. Burri, B. J., Sweetman, L., Nyhan, W. L. 1981. Mutant holocarboxylase synthetase: Evidence for the enzyme defect in early infantile biotin-responsive multiple carboxylase deficiency. *J. Clin. Invest.* 68:1491–95
29. Burri, B. J., Sweetman, L., Nyhan, W. L. 1985. Heterogeneity of holocarboxylase synthetase in patients with biotin-responsive multiple carboxylase deficiency. *Am. J. Hum. Genet.* 37:326–37
30. Chalifour, L. E., Dakshinamurti, K. 1982. The biotin requirement of human fibroblasts in culture. *Biochem. Biophys. Res. Commun.* 104:1047–53
31. Chalmers, R. A., Lawson, A. M., Watts, R. W. E. 1974. Studies on the urinary acidic metabolites excreted by patients with β-methylcrotonylglycinuria, propionic acidaemia and methylmalonic acidaemia, using gas-liquid chromatography and mass spectrometry. *Clin. Chim. Acta* 52:43–51
32. Chalmers, R. A., Spellacy, E. 1980. Biotin responsive 3-methylcrotonylglycinuria with normal carboxylase activities *in vitro:* Demonstration of a metabolic defect in the metabolism of isovalerate with a new assay. *Clin. Sci.* 58:18P–19P

33. Charles, B. M., Hosking, G., Green, A., Pollitt, R., Bartlett, K., Taitz, L. S. 1979. Biotin-responsive alopecia and developmental regression. *Lancet* 2:118–20
34. Cohen, N. D., Thomas, M. 1982. Biotin transport into fully differentiated 3T3-L1 cells. *Biochem. Biophys. Res. Commun.* 108:1508–16
35. Confalone, P. N., Pizzolato, G., Baggiolini, E. G., Lollar, D., Uskoković, M. R. 1975. A stereospecific total synthesis of *d*-biotin from L-(+)-cysteine. *J. Am. Chem. Soc.* 97:5936–38
36. Coryell, M. N., Harris, M. E., Miller, S., Rutledge, M. M., Williams, H. H., Macy, I. G. 1947. Metabolism of women during the reproductive cycle. XV. The utilizatin of biotin during lactation. *J. Lab. Clin. Med.* 32:1462–68
37. Cowan, M. J., Wara, D. W., Packman, S., Ammann, A. J., Yoshino, M., et al. 1979. Multiple biotin-dependent carboxylase deficiencies associated with defects in T-cell and B-cell immunity. *Lancet* 2:115–18
38. Dakshinamurti, K., Bhagavan, H. N., eds. 1985. *Biotin*. New York: NY Acad. Sci. 435 pp.
39. Dakshinamurti, K., Chalifour, L. E. 1981. The biotin requirement of HeLa cells. *J. Cell. Physiol.* 107:427–38
40. Dakshinamurti, K., Landman, A. D., Ramamurti, L., Constable, R. J. 1974. Isotope dilutin assay for biotin. *Anal. Biochem.* 61:225–31
41. Denko, C. W., Grundy, W. E., Porter, J. W., Berryman, G. H. 1946. The excretion of B-complex vitamins in the urine and feces of seven normal adults. *Arch. Biochem.* 10:33–40
42. DeVivo, D. C., Haymond, M. W., Leckie, M. P., Bussmann, Y. L., McDougal, D. B., Pagliara, A. S. 1977. The clinical and biochemical implications of pyruvate carboxylase deficiency. *J. Clin. Endocrinol. Metab.* 45:1281–96
43. DU Vigneaud, V., Melville, D. B., Folkers, K., Wolf, D. E., Mozingo, R., et al. 1942. The structure of biotin: A study of desthiobiotin. *J. Biol. Chem.* 146:475–85
44. DU Vigneaud, V., Melville, D. B., György, P., Rose, C. S. 1940. On the identity of vitamin H with biotin. *Science* 92:62–63
45. Eakin, R. E., Snell, E. E., Williams, R. J. 1940. A constituent of raw egg white capable of inactivating biotin in vitro. *J. Biol. Chem.* 136:801–2
46. Eisenberg, M. A. 1972. Biotin: biogenesis, transport, and their regulation. *Adv. Enzymol.* 36:317–72
47. Erlichman, M., Goldstein, R., Levi, E., Greenberg, A., Freier, S. 1981. Infantile flexural seborrhoeic dermatitis. Neither biotin nor essential fatty acid deficiency. *Arch. Dis. Child.* 56:560–62
48. Feldman, G. L., Wolf, B. 1981. Deficient acetyl CoA carboxylase activity in multiple carboxylase deficiency. *Clin. Chim. Acta* 111:147–51
49. Finnie, M. D. A., Cottrall, K., Seakins, J. W. T., Snedden, W. 1976. Massive excretion of 2-oxoglutaric acid and 3-hydroxyisovaleric acid in a patient with a deficiency of 3-methylcrotonyl-CoA carboxylase. *Clin. Chim. Acta* 73:513–19
50. Fischer, A., Munnich, A., Saudubray, J. M., Mamas, S., Coudé, F. X., et al. 1982. Biotin-responsive immunoregulatory dysfunction in multiple carboxylase deficiency. *J. Clin. Immun.* 2:35–38
51. Frank, O., Luisada-Opper, A. V., Feingold, S., Baker, H. 1970. Vitamin binding by humans and some animal plasma proteins. *Nutr. Rep. Int.* 1:161–68
52. Gardner, J., Parsons, H. T., Peterson, W. H. 1945. Human biotin metabolism on various levels of biotin intake. *Arch. Biochem.* 8:339–48
53. Gaudry, M., Munnich, A., Ogier, H., Marsac, C., Marquet, A., et al. 1983. Deficient liver biotinidase activity in multiple carboxylase deficiency. *Lancet* 2:397
54. Gehrig, D., Leuthardt, F. 1976. A biotin-binding glycoprotein from human plasma: isolation and characterization. *10th Int. Congr. Biochem., Hamburg,* p. 209. Frankfurt: Brönners Druckerei Breidenstein
55. Ghneim, H. K., Bartlett, K. 1982. Mechanism of biotin-responsive combined carboxylase deficiency. Lancet 1:1187–88
56. Gompertz, D., Bartlett, K., Blair, D., Stern, C. M. M. 1973. Child with a defect in leucine metabolism associated with β-hydroxyisovaleric aciduria and β-methylcrotonylglycinuria. *Arch. Dis. Child.* 48:975–77
57. Gompertz, D., Draffan, G. H. 1972. The identification of tiglylglycine in the urine of a child with β-methylcrotonylglycinuria. *Clin. Chim. Acta* 37:405–10
58. Gompertz, D., Draffan, G. H., Watts, J. L., Hull, D. 1971. Biotin-responsive β-methylcrotonylglycinuria. *Lancet* 2: 22–23
59. Gompertz, D., Goodey, P. A., Bartlett, K. 1973. Evidence for the enzymatic defect in β-methylcrotonylglycinuria. *FEBS Lett.* 32:13–14
60. Green, N. M. 1963. Avidin. The use of

[14C]biotin for kinetic studies and for assay. *Biochem. J.* 89:585–91
61. Grundy, W. E., Freed, M., Johnson, H. C., Henderson, C. R., Berryman, G. H. 1947. The effect of phthalylsulfathiazole (Sulfathalidine) on the excretion of B-vitamins by normal adults. *Arch. Biochem.* 15:187–94
62. György, P. 1937. Attempts to isolate the anti-egg injury factor (Vitamin H). *J. Biol. Chem.* 119:xliii-xliv
63. György, P. 1939. The curative factor (Vitamin H) for egg white injury, with particular reference to its presence in different foodstuffs and in yeast. *J. Biol. Chem.* 131:733–44
64. György, P., Rose, C. S. 1943. The liberation of biotin from the avidin-biotin complex (AB). *Soc. Exp. Biol. Med. Proc.* 53:55–57
65. György, P., Rose, C. S., Eakin, R. E., Snell, E. E., Williams, R. J. 1941. Egg-white injury as the result of nonabsorption or inactivation of biotin. *Science* 93:477–78
66. György, P., Rose, C. S., Hofmann, K., Melville, D. B., DU Vigneaud, V. 1940. A further note on the identity of vitamin H with biotin. *Science* 92:609
67. Hamil, B. M., Coryell, M., Roderuck, C., Kaucher, M., Moyer, E. Z., et al. 1947. Thiamine, riboflavin, nicotinic acid, pathothenic acid and biotin in the urine of newborn infants. *Am. J. Dis. Child.* 74:434–46
68. Hardinge, M. G., Crooks, H. 1961. Lesser known vitamins in foods. *J. Am. Diet. Assoc.* 38:240–45
69. Harris, S. A., Wolf, D. E., Mozingo, R., Folkers, K. 1943. Synthetic biotin. *Science* 97:447–48
70. Heard, G. S., McVoy, J. R. S., Wolf, B. 1984. A screening method for biotinidase deficiency in newborns. *Clin. Chem.* 30:125–27
71. Hillman, R. E., Keating, J. P., Williams, J. C. 1978. Biotin-responsive propionic acidemia presenting as the rumination syndrome. *J. Pediatr.* 92:439–41
72. Hood, R. L., Johnson, A. R. 1980. Supplementation of infant forumlations with biotin. *Nutr. Rep. Int.* 21:727–31
73. Hoppner, K., Lampi, B., Smith, D. C. 1978. An appraisal of the daily intakes of vitamin B12, pantothenic acid and biotin from a composite Canadian diet. *Can. Inst. Food Sci. Technol. J.* 11:71
74. Innis, S. M., Allardyce, D. B. 1983. Possible biotin deficiency in adults receiving long-term total parenteral nutrition. *Am. J. Clin. Nutr.* 37:185–87
75. Izumi, Y., Ogata, K. 1977. Some aspects of the microbial production of biotin. *Adv. Appl. Microbiol.* 22:145–76
76. Jakobs, C., Sweetman, L., Nyhan, W. L., Packman, S. 1984. Stable isotope dilution analysis of 3-hydroxyisovaleric acid in amniotic fluid: Contribution to the prenatal diagnosis of inherited disorders of leucine catabolism. *J. Inherit. Metab. Dis.* 7:15–20
77. Johnson, A. R., Hood, R. L., Cullen, J. A., Emery, J. L. 1978. Biotin and the sudden infant death syndrome (cot death). *Proc. Nutr. Soc. Aust.* 3:101
78. Johnson, A. R., Hood, R. L., Emery, J. L. 1980. Biotin and the sudden infant death syndrome. *Nature* 285:159–60
79. Kaplan, I. I. 1944. One-year observations of the treatment of cancer with avidin (egg white). *Am. J. Med. Sci.* 207: 733–43
80. Keeton, B. R., Moosa, A. 1976. Organic aciduria. Treatable cause of floppy infant syndrome. *Arch. Dis. Child.* 51:636–38
81. Kien, C. L., Kohler, E., Goodman, S. I., Berlow, S., Hong, R., et al. 1981. Biotin-responsive in vivo carboxylase deficiency in two siblings with secretory diarrhea receiving total parenteral nutrition. *J. Pediatr.* 99:546–50
82. Knappe, J., Brümmer, W., Biederbick, K. 1963. Reinigung und Eigenschaften der Biotinidase aus Schweinenieren und Lactobacillus Casei. *Biochem. Z.* 338: 599–613
83. Kögl, F., Tönnis, B. 1936. Über das Bios-Problem. Darstellung von krystallisiertem Biotin aus Eigelb. *Z. Physiol. Chem.* 242:43–73
84. Koivusalo, M., Pispa, J. 1963. Biotinidase activity in animal tissues. *Acta Physiol. Scand.* 58:13–19
85. Krause, K.-H., Berlit, P., Bonjour, J.-P. 1982. Erniedrigung des Biotins als möglicher Faktor im Wirkmechanismus von Antiepileptika. *Arch. Psychiatr. Nervenkr.* 231:141–48
86. Krause, K.-H., Berlit, P., Bonjour, J.-P. 1982. Impaired biotin status in anticonvulsant therapy. *Ann. Neurol.* 12: 485–86
87. Krause, K.-H., Bonjour, J.-P., Berlit, P., Kochen, W. 1985. Biotin status of epileptics. 1985. See Ref. 38, pp. 297–313
88. Krause, K.-H., Kochen, W., Berlit, P., Bonjour, J.-P. 1984. Excretion of organic acids associated with biotin deficiency in chronic anticonvulsant therapy. *Int. J. Vitam. Nutr. Res.* 54:217–22
89. Krueger, K. K., Peterson, W. H. 1948. Microbiological evidence for the identity of α and β-biotin. *J. Biol. Chem.* 173: 497–501

90. Le, P. T., Zielinska, B., Sweetman, L., Nyhan, W. L. 1985. Determination of biotinidase activity in human plasma using [$^{14}$C]biocytin as substrate. See Ref. 38, p. 434
91. Lease, J. G., Parsons, H. T. 1934. CCLXXVIII. The relationship of dermatitis in chicks to lack of vitamin B2 and to dietary egg-white. *Biochem. J.* 28:2109–15
92. Leonard, J. V., Seakins, J. W. T., Bartlett, K., Hyde, J., Wilson, J., Clayton, B. 1981. Inherited disorders of 3-methylcrotonyl-CoA carboxylation. *Arch. Dis. Child.* 56:53–59
93. Markkanen, T. 1960. Studies on the urinary excretion of thiamine, riboflavin, nicotinic acid, pantothenic acid and biotin in achlorhydria and after partial gastrectomy. *Acta Med. Scand.* 169 (Suppl. 360):1–52
94. Marsac, C., Gaudry, M., Augereau, C., Moncion, A., Saudubray, J.-M., et al. 1983. Biotin-dependent carboxylase activities in normal human and multicarboxylase deficient patient fibroblasts: relationship to the biotin content of the culture medium. *Clin. Chim. Acta* 129: 119–28
95. McAllister, H. C., Coon, M. J. 1966. Further studies on the properties of liver propionyl coenzyme A holocarboxylase synthetase and the specificity of holocarboxylase formation. *J. Biol. Chem.* 241:2855–61
96. McClain, C. J., Baker, H., Onstad, G. R. 1982. Biotin deficiency in an adult during home parenteral nutrition. *J. Am. Med. Assoc.* 247:3116–17
97. Melville, D. B., Moyer, A. W., Hofmann, K., du Vigneaud, V. 1942. The structure of biotin: The formation of thiophenevaleric acid from biotin. *J. Biol. Chem.* 146:487–92
98. Messaritakis, J., Kattamis, C., Karabula, C., Matsaniotis, N. 1975. Generalized seborrhoeic dermatitis. Clinical and therapeutic data of 25 patients. *Arch. Dis. Child.* 50:871–74
99. Mock, D. M., Baswell, D. L., Baker, H., Holman, R. T., Sweetman, L. 1985. Biotin deficiency complicating parenteral alimentation: Diagnosis, metabolic repercussions, and treatment. See Ref. 38, pp. 314–34
100. Mock, D. M., Baswell, D. L., Baker, H., Holman, R. T., Sweetman, L. 1985. Biotin deficiency complicating parenteral alimentation: Diagnosis, metabolic repercussions, and treatment. *J. Pediatr.* 106:762–69
101. Mock, D. M., DeLorimer, A. A., Liebman, W. M., Sweetman, L., Baker, H. 1981. Biotin deficiency. An unusual complication of parenteral alimentation. *N. Engl. J. Med.* 304:820–23
102. Moss, J., Lane, M. D. 1971. The biotin-dependent enzymes. *Adv. Enzymol.* 35: 321–442
103. Munnich, A., Saudubray, J.-M., Carré, G., Coudé, F. X., Ogier, H., et al. 1981. Defective biotin absorption in multiple carboxylase deficiency. *Lancet* 2:263
104. Munnich, A., Saudubray, J.-M., Cotisson, A., Coudé, F. X., Ogier, H., et al. 1981. Biotin-dependent multiple carboxylase deficiency presenting as a congenital lactic acidosis. *Eur. J. Pediatr.* 137:203–6
105. Munnich, A., Saudubray, J.-M., Coudé, F. X., Charpentier, C., Saurat, J. H., Frezal, J. 1980. Fatty-acid-responsive alopecia in multiple carboxylase deficiency. *Lancet* 1:1080–81
106. Narisawa, K., Arai, N., Igarashi, Y., Satoh, T., Tada, K. 1982. Clinical and biochemical findings on a child with multiple biotin-responsive carboxylase deficiencies. *J. Inherit. Metab. Dis.* 5:67–68
107. National Academy of Sciences. 1980. Biotin. In *Recommended Dietary Allowances,* pp. 120–22. Washington, DC
108. Nisenson, A. 1957. Seborrheic dermatitis of infants and Leiner's disease: A biotin deficiency. *J. Pediatr.* 51:537–48
109. Ohrui, H., Emoto, S. 1975. Stereospecific synthesis of (+)-biotin. *Tetrahedron Lett.* 32:2765–66
110. Oppel, T. W. 1942. Studies of biotin metabolism in man. Part I. The excretion of biotin in human urine. *Am. J. Med. Sci.* 204:856–75
111. Oppel, T. W. 1948. Studies of biotin metabolism in man. IV. Studies of the mechanism of absorption of biotin and the effect of biotin administration on a few cases of seborrhea and other conditions. *Am. J. Med. Sci.* 215:76–83
112. Packman, S., Caswell, N. M., Baker, H. 1982. Biochemical evidence for diverse etiologies in biotin-responsive multiple carboxylase deficiency. *Biochem. Genet.* 20:17–28
113. Packman, S., Caswell, N. M., Gonzalez-Rios, M. D. C., Kadlecek, T., Cann, H., et al. 1984. Acetyl CoA carboxylase in cultured fibroblasts: Differential biotin dependence in the two types of biotin-responsive multiple carboxylase deficiency. *Am. J. Hum. Genet.* 36:80–92
114. Packman, S., Cowan, M. J., Golbus, M. S., Caswell, N. M., Sweetman, L., et al. 1982. Prenatal treatment of biotin-responsive multiple carboxylase deficiency. Lancet 1:1435–40

115. Packman, S., Sweetman, L., Baker, H., Wall, S. 1981. The neonatal form of biotin-responsive multiple carboxylase deficiency. *J. Pediatr.* 99:418–20
116. Packman, S., Sweetman, L., Yoshino, M., Baker, H., Cowan, M. 1981. Biotin-responsive multiple carboxylase deficiency of infantile onset. *J. Pediatr.* 99:421–23
117. Parsons, H. T. 1931. The physiological effects of diets rich in egg white. *J. Biol. Chem.* 90:351–67
118. Parsons, H. T., Kelly, E. 1933. The effect of heating egg white on certain characteristic pellagra-like manifestations produced in rats by its dietary use. *Am. J. Physiol.* 104:150–64
119. Pearce, J., Balnave, D. 1978. A review of biotin deficiency and the fatty liver and kidney syndrome in poultry. *Br. Vet. J.* 134:598–609
120. Petrelli, F., Moretti, P., Campanati, G. 1981. Studies on the relationships between biotin and the behaviour of B and T lymphocytes in the guinea-pig. *Experientia* 37:1204–6
121. Rasmussen, K., Ando, T., Nyhan, W. L., Hull, D., Cottom, D., et al. 1972. Excretion of tiglylglycine in propionic acidemia. *J. Pediatr.* 81:970–72
122. Rhoads, C. P., Abels, J. C. 1943. The administration of egg white and avidin concentrates to patients with cancer. *J. Am. Med. Assoc.* 121:1261–63
123. Robinson, B. H., Oei, J., Saunders, M., Gravel, R. 1983. [$^3$H]Biotin-labeled proteins in cultured human skin fibroblasts from patients with pyruvate carboxylase deficiency. *J. Biol. Chem.* 258:6660–64
124. Rocco, M. D., Superti-Furga, A., Caprino, D., Oddino, N. 1984. Letter: Phenotypic variability in biotinidase deficiency. *J. Pediatr.* 104:964–65
125. Roth, K. S., Allan, L., Yang, W., Foreman, J. W., Dakshinamurti, K. 1981. Serum and urinary biotin levels during treatment of holocarboxylase synthetase deficiency. *Clin. Chim. Acta* 109:337–40
126. Roth, K., Cohn, R., Yandrasitz, J., Preti, G., Dodd, P., Segal, S. 1976. Beta-methylcrotonic aciduria associated with lactic acidosis. *J. Pediatr.* 88:229–35
127. Roth, K. S., Yang, W., Allan, L., Saunders, M., Gravel, R. A., Dakshinamurti, K. 1982. Prenatal administration of biotin in biotin responsive multiple carboxylase deficiency. *Pediatr. Res.* 16:126–29
128. Roth, K. S., Yang, W., Foreman, J. W., Rothman, R., Segal, S. 1980. Holocarboxylase synthetase deficiency: A biotin-responsive organic acidemia. *J. Pediatr.* 96:845–49
129. Sander, J. E., Packman, S., Townsend, J. J. 1982. Brain pyruvate carboxylase and the pathophysiology of biotin-dependent diseases. *Neurology* 32:878–80
130. Sarett, H. P. 1952. Effect of oral administration of streptomycin on urinary excretion of B vitamins in man. *J. Nutr.* 47:275–87
131. Saunders, M. E., Sherwood, W. G., Duthie, M., Surh, L., Gravel, R. A. 1982. Evidence for a defect of holocarboxylase synthetase activity in cultured lymphoblasts from a patient with biotin-responsive multiple carboxylase deficiency. *Am. J. Hum. Genet.* 34:590–601
132. Saunders, M., Sweetman, L., Robinson, B., Roth, K., Cohn, R., Gravel, R. A. 1979. Biotin-responsive organicaciduria. Multiple carboxylase defects and complementation studies with propionic acidemia in cultured fibroblasts. *J. Clin. Invest.* 64:1695–1702
133. Scott, D. 1958. Clinical biotin deficiency (egg white injury). *Acta Med. Scand.* 162:69–70
134. Secor McVoy, J. R., Heard, G. S., Wolf, B. 1984. Potential for prenatal diagnosis of biotinidase deficiency. *Prenatal Diagn.* 4:317–18
135. Sherwood, W. G., Saunders, M., Robinson, B. H., Brewster, T., Gravel, R. A. 1982. Lactic acidosis in biotin-responsive multiple carboxylase deficiency caused by holocarboxylase synthetase deficiency of early and late onset. *J. Pediatr.* 101:546–50
136. Sorrell, M. F., Frank, O., Thomson, A. D., Aquino, H., Baker, H. 1971. Absorption of vitamins from the large intestine *in vivo Nutr. Rep. Int.* 3:143–48
137. Spencer, R. P., Brody, K. R. 1964. Biotin transport by small intestine of rat, hamster, and other species. *Am. J. Physiol.* 206:653–57
138. Stokke, O., Eldjarn, L., Jellum, E., Pande, H., Waaler, P. E. 1972. Beta-methylcrotonyl-CoA carboxylase deficiency: A new metabolic error in leucine degradation. *Pediatrics* 49:726–35
139. Suchy, S. F., Wolf, B. 1982. Protein-bound biotin: A consideration in multiple carboxylase deficiency. *Lancet* 1: 108
140. Suormala, T., Wick, H., Bonjour, J.-P., Baumgartner, E. R. 1985. Rapid differential diagnosis of carboxylase deficiencies and evaluation for biotin-responsiveness in a single blood sample. *Clin. Chim. Acta* 145:151–62
141. Švejcar, J., Homolka, J. 1950. Ex-

perimental experiences with biotin in babies. *Ann. Paediatr.* 174:175–93

142. Sweetman, L. 1981. Two forms of biotin-responsive multiple carboxylase deficiency. *J. Inherit. Metab. Dis.* 4:53–54
143. Sweetman, L., Bates, S. P., Hull, D., Nyhan, W. L. 1977. Propionyl-CoA carboxylase deficiency in a patient with biotin-responsive 3-methylcrotonylglycinuria. *Pediatr. Res.* 11:1144–47
144. Sweetman, L., Nyhan, W. L., Sakati, N. A., Ohlsson, A., Mange, M. S., et al. 1982. Organic aciduria in neonatal multiple carboxylase deficiency. *J. Inherit. Metab. Dis.* 5:49–53
145. Sweetman, L., Surh, L., Baker, H., Peterson, R. M., Nyhan, W. L. 1981. Clinical and metabolic abnormalities in a boy with dietary deficiency of biotin. *Pediatrics* 68:553–58
146. Swick, H. M., Kien, C. L. 1983. Biotin deficiency with neurologic and cutaneous manifestations but without organic aciduria. *J. Pediatr.* 103:265–67
147. Sydenstricker, V. P., Singal, S. A., Briggs, A. P., DeVaughn, N. M., Isbell, H. 1942. Observations on the "egg white injury" in man. *J. Am. Med. Assoc.* 118:1199–1200
148. Sydenstricker, V. P., Singal, S. A., Briggs, A. P., DeVaughn, N. M., Isbell, H. 1942. Preliminary observations on "egg white injury" in man and its cure with a biotin concentrate. *Science* 95: 176–77
149. Taitz, L. S., Green, A., Strachan, I., Bartlett, K., Bennet, M. 1983. Biotinidase deficiency and the eye and ear. *Lancet* 2:918
150. Thoene, J., Baker, H., Yoshino, M., Sweetman, L. 1981. Biotin-responsive carboxylase deficiency associated with subnormal plasma and urinary biotin. *N. Engl. J. Med.* 304:817–20
151. Thoene, J. G., Lemons, R., Baker, H. 1983. Impaired intestinal absorption of biotin in juvenile multiple carboxylase deficiency. *N. Engl. J. Med.* 308:639–42
152. Thoene, J., Wolf, B. 1983. Biotinidase deficiency in juvenile multiple carboxylase deficiency. *Lancet* 2:398
153. Thoma, R. W., Peterson, W. H. 1954. The enzymatic degradation of soluble bound biotin. *J. Biol. Chem.* 210:569–79
154. Thompson, R. C., Eakin, R. E., Willams, R. J. 1941. The extraction of biotin from tissues. *Science* 94:589–90
155. Traub, W. 1956. Crystal structure of biotin. *Nature* 178:649–50
156. Turner, J. B., Hughes, D. E. 1962. The absorption of some B-group vitamins by surviving rat intestine preparations. *Q. J. Exp. Physiol.* 47:107–23
157. Vallotton, M., Hess-Sander, U., Leuthardt, F. 1965. Fixation spontanée de la biotine à une protéine dans le sérum humain. *Helv. Chim. Acta* 48:126–33
158. Wastell, H., Dale, G., Bartlett, K. 1984. A sensitive fluorimetric rate assay for biotinidase using a new derivative of biotin, biotinyl-6-aminoquinoline. *Anal. Biochem.* 140:69–73
159. West, P. M., Wilson, P. W. 1939. The relation of "coenzyme R" to biotin. *Science* 89:607–8
160. Weyler, W., Sweetman, L., Maggio, D. C., Nyhan, W. L. 1977. Deficiency of propionyl-CoA carboxylase and methylcrotonyl-CoA carboxylase in a patient with methylcrotonylglycinuria. *Clin. Chim. Acta* 76:321–28
161. Williams, M. L., Packman, S., Cowan, M. J. 1983. Alopecia and periorificial dermatitis in biotin-responsive multiple carboxylase deficiency. *J. Am. Acad. Dermatol.* 9:97–103
162. Williams, R. H. 1943. Clinical biotin deficiency. *N. Engl. J. Med.* 228:247–52
163. Wilson, J., Lorenz, K. 1979. Biotin and choline in foods—Nutritional importance and methods of analysis: A review. *Food Chem.* 4:115–29
164. Wolf, B., Grier, R. E., Allen, R. J., Goodman, S. I., Kien, C. L. 1983. Biotinidase deficiency: the enzymatic defect in late-onset multiple carboxylase deficiency. *Clin. Chim. Acta* 131:273–81
165. Wolf, B., Grier, R. E., Allen, R. J., Goodman, S. I., Kien, C. L., et al. 1983. Phenotypic variation in biotinidase deficiency. *J. Pediatr.* 103:233–37
166. Wolf, B., Grier, R. E., Heard, G. S. 1983. Hearing loss in biotinidase deficiency. *Lancet* 2:1365–66
167. Wolf, B., Grier, R. E., Parker, W. D., Goodman, S. I., Allen, R. J. 1983. Deficient biotinidase activity in late-onset multiple carboxylase deficiency. *N. Engl. J. Med.* 308:161
168. Wolf, B., Grier, R. E., Secor McVoy, J. R., Heard, G. S. 1985. Biotinidase deficiency: A novel vitamin recycling defect. *J. Inherit. Metab. Dis.* 8(Suppl. 1):53–58
169. Wolf, B., Heard, G. S., Jefferson, L. G., Proud, V. K., Nance, W. E., Weissbecker, K. A. 1985. Clinical findings in four children with biotinidase deficiency detected through a statewide neonatal screening program. *N. Engl. J. Med.* 313:16–19
170. Wolf, B., Heard, G. S., McVoy, J. R., Raetz, H. M. 1984. Biotinidase deficiency: The possible role of biotinidase

in the processing of dietary protein-bound biotin. *J. Inherit. Metab. Dis.* 7(Suppl. 2):121–22

171. Wolf, B., Hsia, Y. E., Sweetman, L., Feldman, G., Boychuk, R. B., et al. 1981. Multiple carboxylase deficiency: Clinical and biochemical improvement following neonatal biotin treatment. *Pediatrics* 68:113–18
172. Wolf, B., Hsia, Y. E., Sweetman, L., Gravel, R., Harris, D. J., Nyhan, W. L. 1981. Propionic acidemia: A clinical update. *J. Pediatr.* 99:835–46
173. Wolf, B., Secor McVoy, J. 1983. A sensitive radioassay for biotinidase activity: deficient activity in tissues of serum biotinidase-dcficient individuals. *Clin. Chim. Acta* 135:275–81
174. Wood, H. G., Barden, R. E. 1977. Biotin enzymes. *Ann. Rev. Biochem.* 46:385–413
175. Wright, L. D., Driscoll, C. A., Boger, W. P. 1954. Biocytinase, an enzyme concerned with hydrolytic cleavage of biocytin. *Proc. Soc. Exp. Biol. Med.* 86:335–37
176. Yatzidis, H., Koutsicos, D., Alaveras, A. G., Papastephanidis, C., Frangos-Plemenos, M. 1981. Biotin for neurologic disorders of uremia. *N. Engl. J. Med.* 305:764

*Ann. Rev. Nutr. 1986. 6:345–63*


# THE IMPACT OF CULTURE ON FOOD-RELATED BEHAVIOR

*M. L. Axelson*

Department of Food, Nutrition, and Institution Administration, University of Maryland, College Park, Maryland 20742

CONTENTS

INTRODUCTION ........ 345
THEORETICAL MODELS ........ 347
SOCIODEMOGRAPHIC DETERMINANTS ........ 348
*Income* ........ 348
*Household Size* ........ 349
*Education* ........ 351
*Gender and Age* ........ 352
*Wife's Employment Status* ........ 353
*Ethnicity and Race* ........ 355
PSYCHOSOCIAL DETERMINANTS ........ 358
*Nutrition Knowledge* ........ 358
*Attitudes* ........ 359
*Eating Types* ........ 359
SUMMARY ........ 360

## INTRODUCTION

Every day, people must procure, select, prepare, and consume food to sustain life. The manner in which they do this reflects complex interrelationships and interactions among the individuals, their culture, and the society in which they live. Linton (41) defines culture as the way of life of a society—that is, culture provides the societal members with "an indispensable guide in all affairs of life." This guide consists of the shared agreements among societal members about the way individuals should think, feel, and act. In other words, culture designates the socially standardized activities of people.



0199-9885/86/0715-0345$02.00

Those activities related to food are called *foodways*. A culture's foodways are exhibited by what substances are considered edible as well as the activities related to food selection, procurement, distribution, manipulation, storage, consumption, and disposal (10). One way of studying a culture's foodways is to examine the food-related behavior (commonly called food habits) of individuals within a society, because their behaviors are reflections of the culture. By definition then, *food-related behavior* is "the way in which individuals or groups of individuals, in response to social and cultural pressures, select, consume, and utilize portions of the available food supply" (17). Or, as the title of a recently published book succinctly states, *You Eat What You Are* (9).

Two points that are important to the topic of this chapter should be made about culture. First, culture is transmitted from generation to generation, which means that culture is learned. Second, individuals or groups of individuals participate differentially in their culture. Some socially standardized activities may only apply to certain groups because, for example, of their physiological status (gender or age) or social class. On the other hand, individuals may want to participate but cannot for some reason like income.

Already, the reader may be protesting that humans are biological creatures and that this fact cannot be ignored when studying food-related behavior. This author agrees and would like to orient the sociocultural determinants of behavior in relation to physiological determinants. Organisms need nourishment and must feed on a regular basis. Thus, for organisms to survive, sources of nourishment must meet minimal criteria; namely, these sources must be available and safe and nutritious enough so that reproduction can occur (i.e. the society can perpetuate itself). On the other hand, cultures do not define as edible all sources of nutrients that meet these criteria. Herman & Polivy (34) have developed a model that "attempts to provide an explicit place for both physiological and nonphysiological determinants of eating." The model is illustrated by a continuum of the amount or rate of food consumption. This continuum is divided into three ranges: hunger, appetitive control, and satiety. They hypothesize that hunger and satiety, the two end ranges, are predominantly under physiological control. The appetitive control in the center is seen as the zone of biological indifference, which is predominantly influenced by nonphysiological factors. Although these authors formulated their model to examine the regulation of eating of various types of eaters (e.g. dieters, binge eaters), it seems to provide a useful and cogent framework for understanding the relative relationship between the physiological and sociocultural determinants of food-related behavior.

The purpose of this chapter is to examine the sociocultural determinants of individuals' food-related behavior within their zone of biological indifference. The sociocultural variables (the predictor variables) are divided into two major categories—sociodemographic and psychosocial. The primary level of analysis of the influence of the sociocultural determinants will be food acceptance (the criterion variable) because this level seems to be the one with which nutritionists are most concerned.

Sociodemographic variables are thought to reflect an individual's access to socially mediated activities; these variables often are called external variables and include income, ethnicity, age, etc. Psychosocial variables are thought to reflect the individual's internal state, and commonly examined variables include knowledge, beliefs, and attitudes. Food acceptance has been conceptualized in two general ways: as a behavior and as an outcome of behavior. Behavioral measurements include types and amounts of food consumed and food expenditures. A commonly measured outcome of behavior is nutrient intake, or some dietary quality index (49). For this chapter, the literature examined is limited to studies conducted in the United States (US).

## THEORETICAL MODELS

Everyone seems to believe that the determinants of food-related behavior are complex and that a multidisciplinary approach is needed. The question then becomes, which determinants are the best predictors of behavior? To answer this question, various models have been proposed, although none have been studied extensively. These models, which vary in degree of specificity and thus testability, seem to be cited most often by researchers to justify studying variables like income and attitudes. These models lack the specificity expected in formal, theoretical models; however, they have provided an important framework for researchers in the comparatively young field of food-related behavior.

Dickens (21) presented four concepts (culture, social, personal, and situational) under which the determinants of food practices could be categorized. She viewed cultural causes as determining the food combinations eaten, and suggested that these cultural food patterns resulted from environmental conditions such as climate, technology, geography, and food availability. Social determinants included friends, relatives, and family members; personal factors included age, education, and psychological characteristics; situational factors were income and employment of homemaker. Leininger (39) conceptualized that differences in food practices are related to how people use food within a culture. People use food for nourishment, to express friendliness and maintain interpersonal relationships, to promote and maintain their social status, to cope with stress and tension, to influence others' behavior, and for religious and creative expression.

In his now classic "channel theory," Lewin (40) suggested that food moved through channels and that the person who was primarily responsible for the food for a household was the "gatekeeper" of the channels. He thought that the social and psychological characteristics of the "gatekeeper" should be examined to understand food acceptance because once the food was through the gate and on the table, it would be eaten by the household members.

Lund & Burk (42) published a framework for examining children's food consumption behavior and it included the following concepts: the child's biogenic, psychogenic, and sociogenic needs for food; his/her food-related knowledge, beliefs, attitudes, and values; and the school, home, and family environment, which influenced the child's needs and psychosocial characteristics. Similarly, Sims & co-workers (73) published a model for studying the final outcome of food consumption, i.e. the nutritional status of the child.

## SOCIODEMOGRAPHIC DETERMINANTS

### *Income*

The functional relationship between income and food consumption (most often measured as monetary value of food consumed) is expressed by the Engel demand curve. According to Engel's law, when there is an increase in personal income, there is a decrease in the relative importance of the sum of money spent on food purchases as compared to other expenses, but it may result in an absolute increase in expenditure (79). This relationship is usually expressed as either the marginal propensity to consume, which is defined as the change in food consumption resulting from a $1 increase in household income, or income elasticity, which is defined as the percentage change in food consumption resulting from a 1% change in income (52). For food in the US, the marginal propensity to consume or the income elasticity is very low (inelastic). Estimates of income elasticity for total food expenditures range from 0.17 (53) to 0.36 (62), which means that a 1% increase in household income produces a 0.17 to 0.36% increase in food expenditures. Thus, the relationship between income and food expenditures is not strong. The reason generally given is that food in the US is plentiful and relatively cheap compared to other countries.

Income elasticities also have been estimated for at-home and away-from-home food expenditures. Estimate of income elasticity for away-from-home food purchases is about 0.80 compared to 0.15 for at-home food purchases (62, 75). Findings from the US Department of Agriculture's 1977–1978 Nationwide Food Consumption Survey (NFCS) illustrate this point (58). Low-income households (below $5000) spent approximately 14% of their food dollar for food away from home, whereas high-income households ($20,000 or more) spent 29% of their food dollar on food away from home. High-income households spent approximately five times more on food away from home than the low-income households.

Most foods have income elasticities of less than 0.50. The foods that are considered staples like milk, bread, and eggs have extremely low income elasticities (values approach zero), but meats and fresh fruits and vegetables are generally considered to have higher income elasticities (52). More specifically, the food group containing meat, poultry, and fish had an estimated income elasticity of about 0.25, fruits had 0.25, vegetables 0.17, and milk products 0.16. In comparison, eggs' and cereal products' elasticities were close to zero, fresh milk 0.08, and bread 0.04 (2, 62, 75). Using the 1972–1973 Consumer Expenditure Survey, Blanciforti et al (12) calculated income elasticities for relatively more nutritious foods and relatively less nutritious foods, and found them to be equal.

The food usage pattern by income of individuals participating in the 1977–1978 NFCS was examined by Cronin et al (18). Food usage was defined as percentage of persons who reported using a food over a 3-day period. The pattern of food usage by income seems to reflect the pattern of the foods' income elasticities. Income was positively related to the usage of non-citrus fruits and "other" vegetables; cheese; meat, fish, and poultry; nuts; desserts, snack foods, and candy; and fats and salad dressings, whereas use of dried beans and peas, rice, and eggs was inversely related to income. Two other items of interest that were related positively to income were low-fat milk and whole-grain bread usage: these items probably are not related to income per se, but may reflect a growing concern about health in the higher socioeconomic groups.

Compared to the income–food expenditure relationship, less work has been done on the income–nutrient intake and food expenditure–nutrient intake relationships (19). In analyzing data from the 1965–1966 NFCS, Adrian & Daniel (3) found all nutrients except carbohydrate significantly and positively related to disposable income. Windham et al (84), however, did not find income related to the nutrient density of individuals' diets in the 1977–1978 NFCS. This may reflect measurement issues associated with using nutrient density as the criterion variable instead of using an indicator of dietary quality. Peterkin et al (50) examined over 4000 low-income households that took part in the 1977–1978 NFCS and found that the nutritional quality of the diets, as measured by the percentage of diets meeting the Recommended Dietary Allowances, increased as food costs increased. Higher incomes or food expenditures do not necessarily result in an adequate diet. Nevertheless, as personal income increases, the possibility of adequate nutrient intakes seems to increase.

## *Household Size*

Economists have observed that given the same income, larger households spend more on food than smaller households, but the value of the food purchased per person decreases with increasing household size. To assess the impact of household size on food expenditures, household size elasticities can be estimated. Household size elasticity (like income elasticity) is defined as the percentage change in food expenditures resulting from a 1% change in household size. Thus, a household size elasticity of more than 1.0 would indicate that a greater than 1% increase in food expenditure would result, and an elasticity of less than 1.0 means that a 1% increase in household size would result in less than a 1% increase in food expenditures (75). Because an increase in household size given the same income is in effect a decrease in income, an inverse relationship between income and household elasticities would be expected; that is, food items that are not responsive to income would be more responsive to changes in household size. Conversely, food products that are more responsive to income would have lower household size elasticities.

Using data from the 1977–1978 NFCS, Smallwood & Blaylock (75) examined food spending patterns by calculating both income and household size elasticities. For total food expenditures, income and household size elasticities were 0.32 and 0.57, respectively, which means that the addition of members to a household will cause a greater increase in food expenditures than will an increase in income. Household size elasticities for food at home and away from home were 0.73 and 0.11, respectively, whereas the income elasticities for food at home and away from home were 0.15 and 0.81, respectively. As expected, there was an inverse relationship between income and household size elasticities.

The food products most responsive to household size were fresh milk (household elasticity of 1.04) and dairy products (0.85); cereal products (1.10), bakery products (0.84), and bread (0.87); sugar products (1.00); potatoes (0.96); fats and oils (0.77), and eggs (0.75). Lower household size elasticities were estimated for fresh fruits (0.53), fresh vegetables (0.45), and juices (0.52). Although meats would be expected to have a relatively low household size elasticity because of its relatively high income elasticity, this was not the case. The household elasticities for beef (0.70) and poultry and fish (0.60) were higher than would be expected from their income elasticities—0.23 for beef and 0.17 for poultry and fish. In comparison, income elasticity for fresh vegetables was 0.18, with a household size elasticity of 0.45.

Windham et al (84) found household size to be significantly related to the nutrient density of individuals' diets. They found that households with 5+ members had a significantly lower nutrient density consumption of fat, but the mean difference was only 2 g/1000 kcal; households with 3+ members had a significantly higher nutrient density consumption of carbohydrate. These results correspond to the general pattern of the cereal products, sugar products, potatoes, bakery products, and breads having greater household size elasticities than fats and oils and meat. They also found vitamin C nutrient density consumption to be significantly and inversely related to household size, which corresponds to the lower household size elasticities of fresh fruits and vegetables. Vitamin $B_6$ was inversely related to household size, but vitamin $B_6$ is difficult to interpret because information on its content in foods and knowledge of bioavilability is limited.

## *Education*

Investigators have included level of formal education as a predictor variable when examining some aspect of food-related behavior. Depending on the study, the educational level of the individual, male head of household, or female head of household is examined. Using household data from the 1965–1966 NFCS, Abdel-Ghany & Schrimper (2) found that the educational level of the female head of household was positively related to total food expenditure in addition to expenditures for four out of nine food groups, even after accounting for income and other pertinent factors. Their calculated education elasticity was 0.12, compared to an income elasticity of 0.23. The education elasticities for fruits (0.32) and milk equivalents (0.18) were actually larger than their income elasticities, 0.25 and 0.11, respectively. The vegetable group and the meat, fish, and poultry group had education elasticities of 0.11 and 0.07, respectively. However, using data from the 1972–1973 Consumer Expenditure Survey, Abdel-Ghany & Foster (1) did not find a significant education elasticity (0.02). Both Adrian & Daniel (3), using the 1965–1966 NFCS, and Windham & co-workers (84), using the 1977–1978 NFCS, found the female head of household's educational level positively related to vitamin C consumption, which corresponds to the higher educational elasticity for fruit expenditures (2).

A number of investigators (4, 15, 23, 67, 90) have examined the relationship of mothers' (and sometimes fathers') educational levels to dietary quality, and they generally have found a positive, significant relationship. In addition, others (e.g. 66, 71) have found positive relationships (or trends) between women's educational levels and their dietary intake.

Although investigators have used educational level to predict food consumption and dietary quality, they often do not state explicitly how or why it should be related. Abdel-Ghany & Schrimper (2) hypothesized that the educational level of the female head of household may be related to food consumption patterns for three reasons: the educational experience may increase productive capabilities by increasing household-related knowledge and skills; may increase nutrition knowledge or at least a general concern for health; and may affect preferences and general life-style. Educational level has been found to be related to nutrition knowledge by a number of investigators (e.g. 23, 51, 71, 86, 89), with reported zero-order correlation coefficients ranging from 0.25 to 0.63. In addition, level of formal education has been found to be inversely related to the use of convenience foods (56, 57), directly related to the number of meals that a household eats together (48), but not related to the number of meals eaten away from home (48, 56).

## *Gender and Age*

Gender and age are physiological states that influence individuals' food consumption patterns. Cultures also may ascribe food patterns based on these physiological states. Consequently, the difficulty in examining differences between males and females of various ages is separating the physiological from the cultural effects.

Cronin & associates (18) found few differences in food usage between males and females participating in the 1977–1978 NFCS. For 54 out of 65 food groups examined, they found no difference in food usage. Of the remaining food groups, a greater percentage of women than men reported using citrus fruit, yogurt, coffee and tea, and low-calorie carbonated beverages in a 3-day period. A greater percentage of men reported using whole milk; luncheon meats; meat, fish, and poultry sandwiches; desserts, sugar, and sweet spreads. These differences, however, were not dramatic. The largest difference was in the use of luncheon meat, with 61% of the men versus 51% of the women reporting its use. These investigators also calculated the mean number of times per day that the foods were used by the individuals who reported using the food. Means between males and females did not differ for 21 out of 32 food groups, but females did report using foods in 11 groups fewer times per day. These food groups included breads and cereals; milk, yogurt, and cheese; meat, fish, poultry, and eggs; desserts, sugar, and sweet spreads.

Differences in food preferences (degree of liking) between males and females have been reported (e.g. 22, 87). A consistent finding is that women more than men prefer fruits and vegetables. However, the relationship between food preferences and consumption seems to be low to moderate in field studies within a culture (e.g. 54, 87). One explanation for these differences in food preferences is that women are socialized to like fruits and vegetables more than men are, but there appears to be no evidence to support this explanation. A more likely explanation is that adoption of a particular food consumption pattern (due perhaps to a physiological need) causes a greater exposure to particular foods, which may then enhance the preferences for them (59, 91).

Basically, because women are usually smaller and have less lean body mass than men, they need less energy; consequently, they eat less than men. As a result of the lower energy needs, the food consumption patterns of women may differ from men in three general ways: women may eat the same variety of foods but in smaller amounts than men, or they may eat a smaller variety of foods but in the same amounts, or they may show a combination of the two strategies. Even though Cronin et al (18) present data based on food usage and not food quantities consumed, the results still seem to indicate that women may be using the strategy of eating the same variety of foods as men, but in smaller amounts.

Most studies that consider age have cross-sectional research designs or just examine a particular age group at one point in time (teenagers and the elderly are especially popular). This type of study does not allow the partitioning of the effect due to aging or the effect due to cohort. As Garcia et al (27) point out, differences in food-related behavior among cohorts may come about because of technological, economic, and social changes in a society, and "any effects of generational patterns of eating must be accounted for if valid inferences are to be made as to the effects of aging per se on dietary intakes."

A few longitudinal studies (27, 47, 78) have been reported. Garcia et al (27) followed 35 women, born between 1873 and 1931, over an 18-year period. Four dietary intake measurements were collected between 1948 and 1969. Using multiple regression, they estimated the effects of cohort and aging on nutrient intake. With increasing age, the women reduced significantly their fat intake and increased significantly their calcium intake. There also was a downward trend ($p < 0.10$) in energy intake due to age. The cohort effect accounted for more of the variation in nutrient intake among the women. The younger the cohort, the higher the intakes of protein, calcium, phosphorus, iron, riboflavin, and niacin. Intakes of carbohydrate, thiamin, vitamin A, and ascorbic acid were not related to either cohort or age effects. These authors concluded that nutrient intakes do not change significantly from middle to old age. Investigators (47, 78) of other longitudinal studies reported similar results, in that a general decrease in food energy was observed with age, but not any dramatic changes in food consumption patterns; unfortunately, their lack of statistical analyses precludes more specific comment.

Windham et al (85) compared the nutrient densities (amount of nutrient/1000 kcal) of foods consumed by various sex-age groups. Comparing nutrient density rather than absolute amounts of nutrients corrects for the differences in energy needs due to gender or age. Using the 1977–1978 NFCS data, these investigators found that the nutrient densities of diets did not differ between males and females, with the exception that females consumed diets that contained more vitamin A and vitamin C per 1000 kcal than males. They also found no dramatic differences among age groups (range 4–65+), with again the exceptions of vitamins A and C. The younger and older age groups had diets more dense in these nutrients.

In our culture there seem to be virtually no dietary proscriptions based on gender or age; thus, physiologically based rather than culturally based reasons are more likely to explain most of the variance found in food consumption patterns between males and females within a cohort. On the other hand, differences found among age groups (cohorts) in food consumption patterns, after correcting for energy needs, seem to be more culturally based.

## *Wife's Employment Status*

Women in our culture perform most of the housework. Food-related activities like meal preparation are still the domain of women and account for a large proportion of time spent in housework (81). Because of the dramatic increase in women's employment outside the home, especially of married women with young children (81), investigators have turned their attention to studying the effect of wives' employment on households' food production and consumption. Contrary to the perception that husbands and wives are sharing more household-related tasks as a result of the changing sex roles in our society, working wives still perform most of the housework; in fact, Waite (81) reports that the hours spent in housework by working wives was six times greater than the hours spent by married men. Consequently, research has focused on the strategies used by working wives to satisfy the competing demands of their jobs and households.

Investigators (32, 45, 46, 76) have found that as the number of wives' employment hours increases, the number of hours they spend in housework decreases. More specifically, the more hours wives spent employed outside the home, the fewer hours they spent in meal preparation, with estimates of about 15–20 minutes per day less for employed wives compared to nonemployed wives (28, 29, 48). This inverse relationship between employment time and meal preparation time has generated speculation and investigation as to the means by which working wives decrease their meal preparation time.

Collective wisdom has attributed some of the increase in away-from-home food consumption in the US to the increased employment of women outside the home because purchasing meals would be an obvious way to decrease housework time. Goebel & Hennon (28, 29), controlling for income, found no relationship between wives' employment status (e.g. part time, full time) and expenditures for meals away from home, but they did find (28) a significant but low, positive correlation ($r = 0.14$) between number of hours employed and expenditures for food away from home. Ortiz et al (48) found the percentage of meals eaten away from home by households increased significantly when the female head of household worked full time (30 hr or more per week) but not when she worked part time. Similarly, hours of wives' employment were directly related to eating at fast-food establishments and school cafeterias, but not eating at other types of restaurants (45). The inconsistencies in findings are probably related to differences in the operationalization of the variables under study (e.g. hours of employment versus employment status). There does seem to be a trend for households with employed wives to eat more meals away from home; however, as Goebel & Hennon (28) comment, there is probably "no substantial substitution of money for time in the sense of purchasing meals away from home."

Another strategy women may use to decrease meal preparation time is to increase their use of convenience foods. Both Havlicek et al (33) and Redman (56), using national surveys, found employment of wives (or of primary meal planners) to be positively and significantly related to use of convenience foods.

When examining use of convenience foods by about 200 households in Wisconsin, Reilly (57) did not find a relationship between convenience food use and wives' employment status. A problem with studying convenience food use is trying to define convenience foods. Reilly seems to have used a more restricted definition (smaller number of foods) than Havlicek et al and Redman.

Wives' employment also has not been found to be related to food preparation style (as measured by number of food items per meal, difficulty of food preparation, frequency of preparing food ahead) (45) or to the number of meals eaten together by the household (29, 48). These factors seem to be more related to age of the children in the household. In addition, the nutritional implications of wive's employment status has been investigated (74, 84), and there appears to be no relationship between nutrient intakes of household members and female head of household's employment status.

### *Ethnicity and Race*

The literature related to cultural subgroups in the US can be divided according to the primary question that is addressed. There seem to be three basic questions: (*a*) What are the foodways of a particular ethnic group in the US? (*b*) How does a particular ethnic group's foodways in the US differ from the group's foodways in their culture of origin? (*c*) How does a particular ethnic group differ from the dominant cultural group?

Descriptions of cultural subgroups in the US dominate the literature. The method of examining one group at one point in time, however, has limitations. The food-related practices described are attributed either implicitly or explicitly to ethnicity, which may not be the case because alternative explanations (like income and geographic region) cannot be rejected. At the least, when studying ethnicity as a determinant of behavior, the ethnic group should be compared to a dominant cultural group that is similar in socioeconomic status and living in the same geographic area. Even though these descriptive studies of only one ethnic group contribute little to the understanding of ethnicity as a determinant of food-related behavior, they can provide, if current, useful information to health practitioners in the field working with particular cultural subgroups.

Because the US has so many ethnic groups, descriptions of each are not addressed in this chapter. The reader is referred to Sanjur's (64) book, where she describes from a nutritional point of view the ethnic food patterns of five major groups in the US: Puerto Ricans, Mexican Americans, Black Americans, Native Americans, and Asian Americans. Another recently published book, *Ethnic and Regional Foodways in the United States* (14), is a compilation of essays on the use of food as a marker of group identity and provides a more anthropological point of view.

When individuals immigrate to the US, what impact does the American culture have on their food-related behavior? The measured degree of cultural impact depends greatly on the level of analysis (e.g. food preparation methods, meal patterns, or foods consumed). To assess changes in the types and amounts of foods consumed, Dewey et al (20) provide a tripartite food categorization system: "traditional" foods—those that are more common in the culture of origin; "basic" foods—those that are common to both cultures; and "new" foods—those that are more common in the host culture.

Using this food categorization system, Dewey et al (20) examined the degree of acculturation of two groups (nonmigrants and migrants) of low-income, first-generation Mexican Americans. The food-use frequency of 54 foods was assessed. They found that even though both groups reported an increased use of both basic and new foods, the nonmigrants' (or more permanent groups') use of these foods was significantly greater than the migrants. The nonmigrants and migrants, however, were similar in their decreased use of traditional foods. Controlling for income and household size, Wallendorf & Reilly (82) examined the consumption of basic foods of urban Mexican Americans and urban Mexicans. They found that Mexican Americans ate fewer eggs but more meat, white bread, cereals, soft drinks, and caffeine-containing beverages than their counterparts in Mexico. The Mexican Americans continued using tortillas, but used more pre-prepared ones than did the Mexicans. Pattern of alcohol consumption differed, with Mexican Americans drinking more beer and wine and Mexicans more spirits.

The nutrient intakes of Puerto-Rico-born females who lived in Puerto Rico (nonmigrants), lived in the US (forward migrants), and lived in Puerto Rico after living in the US (return migrants) were compared (35). Even after controlling for socioeconomic variables, the forward migrants had better nutrient intakes than either the nonmigrants or return migrants. The authors also observed that the women who returned to Puerto Rico resumed their customary Puerto Rican diets.

First-generation Chinese Americans were asked about their food consumption of traditional and nontraditional foods available in the US when living in China and after living in the US (30, 88). Results, which were similar to the studies of Spanish-speaking populations, indicated a decreased use of traditional foods, even though they were available, and an increased use of basic and new foods. This trend also was identified by Jerome (37) in Blacks who had migrated from the southern to northern part of the US. Terry & Bass (80) found a positive correlation ($r = 0.37$) between the use of traditional Cherokee foods and degree of Indian genetic inheritance of the female household head. At a different level of analysis, however, acculturation is not evident. The food-related beliefs about appropriate foods for the elderly did not differ between Chinese and first-generation Chinese Americans (44). On the other hand, Freedman & Grivetti (26) found that the abandonment of traditional beliefs associated with diet and pregnancy was fairly complete by the third generation in a group of Greek American women.

These studies indicate that food-related behavior is modified by culture, and many of the observed changes in the amounts and types of foods consumed cannot be explained by availability of the foods or by change in socioeconomic status of the individuals. Although the types of foods consumed may change, some investigators (37, 80, 88) have observed that the characteristic food preparation methods of the culture of origin often are retained.

Do ethnic groups differ in their food-related behaviors from the dominant cultural group? Even though answers to this question are important to investigators of food-related behavior as well as to food and nutrition policymakers, there is a paucity of empirical research. Nevertheless, results of investigations that have controlled for sociodemographic variables indicate that there are differences between cultural subgroups and dominant cultural groups (e.g. 16, 43, 63, 82, 84).

According to data from the 1972–1974 Consumer Expenditure Survey, when compared to Whites, Blacks purchased more beef, pork, poultry, fish and seafood, but less cereal and bakery products, sugary products, dairy products, and nonalcoholic beverages (63). Other investigators (13) also have reported more meat purchases by Blacks than Whites. Rozin & Cines (60) found less use of coffee among Blacks compared to Whites and attributed the differences to socialization. Caster (16) compared low-income Black and White women living in the same geographic region on their food-use frequency of 150 foods in 3 groups—core diet (24% of the foods, which provided 69% of the diets' energy), secondary diet (33% foods and 27% energy), and peripheral diet (43% foods and 4% energy). The two groups did not differ in their core diets, but differences were found in their secondary diets. Because the peripheral diet was considered to be of little nutritional consequence, it was not analyzed.

Comparing Mexican Americans and Anglos (researchers' term), Wallendorf & Reilly (82) found that the Mexican Americans consumed more eggs, white bread, and tortillas and less dry cereals, pastries, wine, and beer than the Anglos, but the two groups consumed the same amount of convenience foods, soft drinks, and coffee and tea. They concluded that the Mexican Americans' consumption patterns were not like their culture of origin or their culture of residence. In fact, they felt that the Mexican American patterns were reminiscent of stereotypical American patterns of consumption before the widespread interest in food and health.

The nutrient density of calcium was found to be greater in the diets of Whites than of either Blacks or Spanish-speaking individuals. The nutrient density of vitamin A also differed among the groups, with Blacks having diets that were the most dense and Spanish-speaking individuals the least dense. Asians were found to have diets higher in carbohydrate but lower in fat, vitamin A, riboflavin, and calcium than Whites (43).

Cultural subgroups seem to exhibit food-related behavior unlike their culture of origin as well as unlike their culture of residence. Thus, ethnicity seems to be a significant predictor of food-related behavior. Within physiological constraints (e.g. lactose intolerance), however, this determinant probably becomes a poorer predictor for descending generations of immigrants and when social barriers are removed, which allows access to the dominant culture.

# PSYCHOSOCIAL DETERMINANTS

Psychosocial determinants of food-related behavior have been systematically studied only within the past 20 years. Interest seems to have grown out of the realization that the sociodemographic determinants accounted for a fairly low proportion of the variance observed in individuals' food consumption patterns. That is, even though individuals had the resources with which to obtain a good diet, they displayed food consumption patterns that, from the nutritionists' point of view, needed improving. It was hypothesized that if individuals increased their knowledge of nutrition, then desirable changes in their food-related behaviors would result. Thus, to increase knowledge and change attitudes through nutrition education programs, information was required about individuals' eating patterns (how they behave) and the knowledge (what they think) and attitudes (what they feel) related to their eating patterns.

## *Nutrition Knowledge*

Many investigators (e.g. 11, 15, 23, 31, 36, 51, 71, 86, 90) have examined nutrition knowledge and its relationship to food-related behavior. Nutrition knowledge (the predictor variable) was usually viewed as a unidimensional concept, meaning a person's nutrition knowledge was represented by the use of only one score. The food-related behavior (the criterion variable) was measured generally in either of two ways: as a specific behavior, e.g. participation in school lunch (90), or as an outcome of behavior, e.g. dietary intake (15).

Using meta-analytic techniques, Axelson et al (6) reviewed the relationship between dietary behavior (as measured by an overall dietary quality score) and nutrition knowledge. Meta-analytic techniques allow researchers conducting reviews to address quantitatively two questions: Is there a relationship between two variables? And, what is the strength (effect-size) of the relationship? They found a significant, positive relationship between nutrition knowledge and dietary intake, but the relationship was relatively small ($r = 0.10$). They concluded that there was a relationship between nutrition knowledge and dietary intake, but the effect-size was small because of the lack of specificity in measurements. Researchers who have more specifically defined the food-related behavior or the nutrition concepts in their studies have found a greater effect-size between the predictor and criterion variables—e.g. the relationship between percentage of presweetened cereals purchased and the mother's nutrition knowledge ($r = -0.35$) (51).

## *Attitudes*

Although the definitions of attitude vary, investigators for the most part have tried to identify individuals' organized sets of beliefs, feelings, and intentions associated with food and eating. The food- and nutrition-related attitudes that have been identified and studied include nutrition (7, 11, 23, 25, 31, 65, 71), general health and specific health apprehensions (8, 25, 31, 36, 38, 65, 68, 77), sensory-aesthetics (5, 7, 25, 38, 65), economics (5, 7, 8, 38, 65, 77), convenience (38, 65, 77), creative/adventuresomeness (7, 8, 68, 77), sociability and prestige (7, 8, 38, 69, 77), familiarity (38), and meal planning and preparation (15, 23, 68, 71). When using attitudes to predict behavior, investigators have used specific attitudes such as enjoyment in meal preparation (15, 23, 68, 71) or a general attitude such as nutrition is important (11, 23, 31, 71). Similarly, the criterion variables have been either more specific behaviors such as food-use frequencies (38, 55), food-purchase frequencies (68), and food purchasing practices (11) or outcomes of behavior such as nutrient intake (23, 31, 71) and dietary quality (15, 65).

Using meta-analytic techniques on the limited number of studies available, Axelson et al (6) found a significant relationship between food- and nutrition-related attitudes and dietary intake. Estimated effect-size of the relationship was $r = 0.18$. As with nutrition knowledge, they concluded that when the attitudes and behaviors under study are more specifically defined, a stronger relationship is usually found. For example, Jalso et al (36) found a relatively strong relationship ($r = 0.61$) between opinions about specific nutrition-related practices and practice scores. Likewise, the relationship between intention to eat at a fast-food restaurant and eating at such a restaurant was estimated to be $r = 0.41$ (5). Although attitudes as predictor variables have had limited success, researchers still feel that they are worth studying because the problem seems to be in the identification and measurement of the relevant attitudes and behaviors and not in the concept. The reader is referred to the article by Sims (72) for a more complete discussion of the issues related to attitude measurement in food and nutrition.

## *Eating Types*

Besides the obvious measurements of nutrient intake and of food consumption and expenditures, actual food-related behaviors have received little attention. Some investigators have begun examining food-related behaviors in an effort to identify eating patterns. The underlying hypothesis is that individuals who exhibit a particular pattern of food consumption or preference may have similar psychological and social characteristics.

The foods consumed by individuals participating in the Ten-State Nutrition Survey and Health & Nutrition Examination Survey I were factor analyzed, and seven eating patterns were identified: eating pattern I was characterized by the consumption of more dairy products and soups and less sugary foods and beverages; II by more nonsugary beverages and less dairy products; III by more eggs, legumes, nuts, and grain products; IV by more meats, fruit and vegetable products, and desserts; V by more poultry and less meat; VI by more protein-containing mixed dishes and shellfish; and VII by more fish, fats, and oils (70). Williams & Penfield (83) developed an instrument, the Food-Related Behavior Characterization Instrument, based on food consumption patterns that successfully predicted whether individuals were traditional eaters (consumed foods accepted by the dominant culture) or nontraditional eaters (excluded culturally accepted foods).

Grouping respondents according to their preferences for 68 foods, four types of eaters were identified: finicky eaters, health-conscious dieters, diverse diners, and high-calorie traditionalists (24). Similarly, Sadalla & Burroughs (61) found that when given five eating types—the vegetarian, the gourmet, the health food fan, the fast-food devotee, and the synthetic food user—respondents consistently identified particular foods with each type of eater. They concluded that food preference patterns are derived from the symbolism associated with foods, which means that individuals choose foods to present images to those around them.

## SUMMARY

Some of the sociodemographic and psychosocial determinants of individuals' food-related behaviors were examined in this chapter. The empirical research indicates that individuals do participate differentially in their culture. But, the reasons for why people eat what they eat are still incompletely understood, as evidenced by the inadequate predictive ability of the determinants examined.

### *Literature Cited*


1. Abdel-Ghany, M., Foster, A. C. 1982. Impact of income and wife's education on family consumption expenditures. *J. Consum. Stud. Home Econ.* 6:21–28
2. Abdel-Ghany, M., Schrimper, R. A. 1978. Food consumption expenditures and education of the homemaker. *Home Econ. Res. J.* 6:283–92
3. Adrian, J., Daniel, R. 1976. Impact of socioeconomic factors on consumption of selected food nutrients in the United States. *Am. J. Agric. Econ.* 58:31–38
4. Axelson, J. M. 1977. *Food Habits of North Florida Teenagers: Their Food Preferences, Meal Patterns, and Food and Nutrition Intakes.* Tallahassee, FL: Florida A & M Univ.
5. Axelson, M. L., Brinberg, D., Durand, J. H. 1983. Eating at a fast-food restaurant—A social-psychological analysis. *J. Nutr. Educ.* 15:94–98
6. Axelson, M. L., Federline, T. L., Brinberg, D. 1985. A meta-analysis of food- and nutrition-related research. *J. Nutr. Educ.* 17:51–54
7. Axelson, M. L., Penfield, M. P. 1983. Food- and nutrition-related attitudes of elderly persons living alone. *J. Nutr. Educ.* 15:23–27
8. Baird, P. C., Schutz, H. G. 1976. The marketing concept applied to "selling" good nutrition. *J. Nutr. Educ.* 8:13–17
9. Barer-Stein, T. 1979. *You Eat What You Are.* Toronto, Canada: McClelland & Stewart
10. Bass, M. A., Wakefield, L. M., Kolasa,

K. 1979. *Community Nutrition and Individual Food Behavior,* p. 1. Minneapolis, MN: Burgess

11. Beavers, I., Kelley, M., Flenner, J. 1982. Nutrition knowledge, attitudes, and food purchasing practices of parents. *Home Econ. Res. J.* 11:134–42
12. Blanciforti, L., Green, R., Lane, S. 1981. Income and expenditures for relatively more versus relatively less nutritious food over the life cycle. *Am. J. Agric. Econ.* 63:255–60
13. Brittin, H. C., Zinn, D. W. 1977. Meat-buying practices of Caucasians, Mexican-Americans, and Negroes. *J. Am. Diet. Assoc.* 71:623–28
14. Brown, L. K., Mussell, K. 1984. *Ethnic and Regional Foodways in the United States.* Knoxville, TN: Univ. Tenn. Press
15. Caliendo, M. A., Sanjur, D. 1978. The dietary status of preschool children: An ecological approach. *J. Nutr. Educ.* 10: 69–72
16. Caster, W. O. 1980. The core diet of lower-economic class women in Georgia. *Ecol. Food Nutr.* 9:241–46
17. Committee on Food Habits. 1945. *Manual for the Study of Food Habits,* p. 13, Bull. 111. Washington, DC: Natl. Acad. Sci.
18. Cronin, F. J., Krebs-Smith, S. M., Wyse, B. W., Light, L. 1982. Characterizing food usage by demographic variables. *J. Am. Diet. Assoc.* 81:661–73
19. Davis, C. G. 1982. Linkages between socioeconomic characteristics, food expenditure patterns, and nutritional status of low income households: A critical review. *Am. J. Agric. Econ.* 64:1017–25
20. Dewey, K. G., Strode, M. A., Fitch, Y. R. 1984. Dietary change among migrant and nonmigrant Mexican-American families in northern California. *Ecol. Food Nutr.* 14:11–24
21. Dickens, D. 1965. Factors related to food preferences. *J. Home Econ.* 57:427–30
22. Einstein, M. A., Hornstein, I. 1970. Food preferences of college students and nutritional implications. *J. Food Sci.* 35:429–36
23. Eppright, E. S., Fox, H. M., Fryer, B. A., Lamkin, G. H., Vivian, V. M. 1970. The North Central Regional Study of diets of preschool children. 2. Nutrition knowledge and attitudes of mothers. *J. Home Econ.* 62:327–32
24. Fetzer, J. N., Solt, P. F., McKinney, S. 1985. Typology of food preferences identified by Nutri-Food Sort. *J. Am. Diet. Assoc.* 85:961–65
25. Fewster, W. J., Bostian, L. R., Powers, R. D. 1973. Measuring the connotative meanings of foods. *Home Econ. Res. J.* 2:44–53
26. Freedman, M. R., Grivetti, L. E. 1984. Diet patterns of first, second and third generation Greek-American women. *Ecol. Food Nutr.* 14:185–204
27. Garcia, P. A., Battese, G. E., Brewer, W. D. 1975. Longitudinal study of age and cohort influences on dietary practices. *J. Gerontology* 30:349–56
28. Goebel, K. P., Hennon, C. B. 1982. An empirical investigation of the relationship among wife's employment status, stage in the family life cycle, meal preparation time, and expenditures for meals away from home. *J. Consum. Stud. Home Econ.* 6:63–78
29. Goebel, K. P., Hennon, C. B. 1983. Mother's time on meal preparation, expenditures for meals away from home, and shared meals: Effects of mother's employment and age of younger child. *Home Econ. Res. J.* 12:169–88
30. Grivetti, L. E., Paquette, M. B. 1978. Nontraditional ethnic food choices among first generation Chinese in California. *J. Nutr. Educ.* 10:109–12
31. Grotkowski, M. L., Sims, L. S. 1978. Nutritional knowledge, attitudes, and dietary practices of the elderly. *J. Am. Diet. Assoc.* 72:499–506
32. Hafstrom, J. L., Schram, V. R. 1983. Housework time of wives: Pressure, facilitators, constraints. *Home Econ. Res. J.* 11:245–55
33. Havlicek, J. Jr., Axelson, J. M., Capps, O. Jr., Pearson, J. M., Richardson, S. 1983. Nutritional and economic aspects of convenience and nonconvenience foods. In *Proc. Outlook '83. Agric. Outlook Conf.,* pp. 539–50. Washington, DC: US Dept. Agric.
34. Herman, C. P., Polivy, J. 1984. A boundary model for the regulation of eating. In *Eating and Its Disorders,* ed. A. Stunkard, E. Stellar, pp. 141–56. New York: Raven
35. Immink, M. D. C., Sanjur, D., Burgos, M. 1983. Nutritional consequences of U.S. migration patterns among Puerto Rican women. *Ecol. Food Nutr.* 13:139–48
36. Jalso, S. B., Burns, M. M., Rivers, J. M. 1965. Nutritional beliefs and practices. *J. Am. Diet. Assoc.* 47:263–68
37. Jerome, N. W. 1980. Diet and acculturation: The case of Black-American in-migrants. In *Nutritional Anthropology. Contemporary Approaches to Diet and Culture,* ed. N. Jerome, R. Kandel, G. Pelto, pp. 275–325. Pleasantville, NY: Redgrave
38. Lau, D., Hanada, L., Kaminskyj, O.,

Krondl, M. 1979. Predicting food use by measuring attitudes and preference. *Food Prod. Dev.* 13(5):66–72

39. Leininger, M. 1969. Some cross-cultural universal and nonuniversal functions, beliefs, and practices of food. In *Dimensions of Nutrition*, ed. J. Dupont, pp. 153–79. Boulder, CO: Colorado Assoc. Univ. Press.
40. Lewin, K. 1943. Forces behind food habits and methods of change. In *The Problem of Changing Food Habits. Report of the Committee on Food Habits*, pp. 35–65, Bull. 108. Washington, DC: Natl. Acad. Sci.
41. Linton, R. 1945. *The Cultural Background of Personality*, pp. 19–20. New York: Appleton-Century-Crofts
42. Lund, L. A., Burk, M. A. 1969. *A Multidisciplinary Analysis of Children's Food Consumption Behavior*. Univ. Minnesota Agric. Exp. Stn. Tech. Bull. 265
43. Netland, P. A., Brownstein, H. 1984. Acculturation and the diet of Asian-American elderly. *J. Nutr. Elderly* 3(3):37–56
44. Newman, J. M., Ludman, E. K. 1984. Chinese elderly: Food habits and beliefs. *J. Nutr. Elderly* 4(2):3–13
45. Nickols, S. Y., Fox, K. D. 1983. Buying time and saving time: Strategies for managing household production. *J. Consum. Res.* 10:197–208
46. Nickols, S. Y., Metzen, E. J. 1978. Housework time of husband and wife. *Home Econ. Res. J.* 7:85–97
47. Ohlson, M. A., Harper, L. J. 1976. Longitudinal studies of food intake and weight of women from ages 18 to 56 years. *J. Am. Diet. Assoc.* 69:626–31
48. Ortiz, B., MacDonald, M., Ackerman, N., Goebel, K. 1981. The effect of homemakers' employment on meal preparation time, meals at home, and meals away from home. *Home Econ. Res. J.* 9:200–6
49. Penfield, M. P., Axelson, M. L. 1984. State of the art: Food research. *Home Econ. Res. J.* 12:311–24
50. Peterkin, B. B., Kerr, R. L., Hama, M. Y. 1982. Nutritional adequacy of diets of low-income households. *J. Nutr. Educ.* 14:102–4
51. Phillips, D. E., Bass, M. A., Yetley, E. 1978. Use of food and nutrition knowledge by mothers of preschool children. *J. Nutr. Educ.* 10:73–75
52. Popkin, B. M., Haines, P. S. 1981. Factors affecting food selection: The role of economics. *J. Am. Diet. Assoc.* 79:419–25
53. Price, D. W. 1982. Political economics of U.S. food and nutrition policy: Discussion. *Am. J. Agric. Econ.* 64:1028–29
54. Randall, E., Sanjur, D. 1981. Food preferences—Their conceptualization and relationship to consumption. *Ecol. Food Nutr.* 11:151–61
55. Reaburn, J. A., Krondl, M., Lau, D. 1979. Social determinants in food selection. *J. Am. Diet. Assoc.* 74:637–41
56. Redman, B. J. 1980. The impact of women's time allocation on food expenditure for meals away from home and prepared foods. *Am. J. Agric. Econ.* 62:234–37
57. Reilly, M. D. 1982. Working wives and convenience consumption. *J. Consum. Res.* 8:407–18
58. Rizek, R. L., Peterkin, B. B. 1979. Food costs of U.S. households, Spring 1977. *Family Econ. Rev.* Fall, pp. 14–19
59. Rozin, P. 1984. The acquisition of food habits and preferences. In *Behavioral Health: A Handbook of Health Enhancement and Disease Prevention*, ed. J. Matarazzo, S. Weiss, J. Herd, N. Miller, S. Weiss, pp. 590–607. New York: Wiley
60. Rozin, P., Cines, B. M. 1982. Ethnic differences in coffee use and attitudes to coffee. *Ecol. Food Nutr.* 12:79–88
61. Sadalla, E., Burroughs, J. 1981. Profiles in eating. *Psychol. Today* 15(10):51–57
62. Salathe, L. E. 1979. *Household Expenditure Patterns in the United States*. Tech. Bull. 1603. Washington, DC: US Dept. Agric.
63. Salathe, L. E., Gallo, A. E., Boehm, W. T. 1979. *The Impact of Race on Consumer Food Purchases*. Rep. No. ESCS-68. Washington, DC: US Dept. Agric.
64. Sanjur, D. 1982. *Social and Cultural Perspectives in Nutrition*, pp. 233–84. Englewood Cliffs, NJ: Prentice-Hall
65. Schafer, R. B. 1978. Factors affecting food behavior and the quality of husbands' and wives' diets. *J. Am. Diet. Assoc.* 72:138–43
66. Schafer, R. B., Reger, R. A., Gillespie, A. H., Roderuck, C. E. 1980. Diet quality of selected samples of women and socio-demographic and social-psychological correlates. *Home Econ. Res. J.* 8:190–99
67. Schorr, B. C., Sanjur, D., Erickson, E. C. 1972. Teen-age food habits. *J. Am. Diet. Assoc.* 61:415–20
68. Schutz, H. G., Moore, S. M., Rucker, M. H. 1977. Predicting food purchase and use by multivariate attitudinal analysis. *Food Technol.* 31(8):85–92
69. Schutz, H. G., Rucker, M. H., Russell, G. F. 1975. Food and food-use classification systems. *Food Technol.* 29(3):50–64
70. Schwerin, H. S., Stanton, J. L., Riley, A. M., Schaefer, A. E., Leveille, G. A.,

et al. 1981. Food eating patterns and health: A reexamination of the Ten-State and HANES I surveys. *Am. J. Clin. Nutr.* 34:568–80

71. Sims, L. S. 1978. Dietary status of lactating women. 2. Relation of nutritional knowledge and attitudes to nutrient intake. *J. Am. Diet. Assoc.* 73:147–54
72. Sims, L. S. 1980. Measuring nutrition-related attitudes: State of the art. In *Attitude Theory and Measurement in Food and Nutrition Research. Proceedings of a Symposium,* pp. 69–76, Regional Project NE-73. University Park: Penn. State Univ.
73. Sims, L. S., Paolucci, B., Morris, P. M. 1972. A theoretical model for the study of nutritional status: An ecosystem approach. *Ecol. Food Nutr.* 1:197–205
74. Skinner, J. D., Ezell, J. M., Salvetti, N. N., Penfield, M. P. 1985. Relationships between mothers' employment and nutritional quality of adolescents' diets. *Home Econ. Res. J.* 13:218–25
75. Smallwood, D., Blaylock, J. 1981. *Impact of Household Size and Income on Food Spending Patterns.* Tech. Bull. 1650. Washington, DC: US Dept. Agric.
76. Stafford, K. 1983. The effects of wife's employment time on her household work. *Home Econ. Res. J.* 11:257–66
77. Steelman, V. P. 1976. Attitudes toward food as indicators of subcultural value systems. *Home Econ. Res. J.* 5:21–32
78. Steinkamp, R. C., Cohen, N. L., Walsh, H. E. 1965. Resurvey of an aging population—Fourteen-year follow-up. The San Mateo Nutrition Study. *J. Am. Diet. Assoc.* 46:103–10
79. Swagler, R. M. 1975. *Caveat Emptor! An Introductory Analysis of Consumer Problems.* Lexington, MA: Heath
80. Terry, R. D., Bass, M. A. 1984. Food practices of families in an eastern Cherokee township. *Ecol. Food Nutr.* 14:63–70
81. Waite, L. J. 1981. U.S. women at work. *Pop. Bull.* 36(2):1–43
82. Wallendorf, M., Reilly, M. D. 1983. Ethnic migration, assimilation, and consumption. *J. Consum. Res.* 10:292–302
83. Williams, A. C., Penfield, M. P. 1985. Development and validation of an instrument for characterizing food-related behavior. *J. Am. Diet. Assoc.* 85:685–89
84. Windham, C. T., Wyse, B. W., Hansen, R. G., Hurst, R. L. 1983. Nutrient density of diets in the USDA Nationwide Food Consumption Survey, 1977–1978: I. Impact of socioeconomic status on dietary density. *J. Am. Diet. Assoc.* 82:28–34
85. Windham, C. T., Wyse, B. W., Hurst, R. L., Hansen, R. G. 1981. Consistency of nutrient consumption patterns in the United States. *J. Am. Diet. Assoc.* 78:587–95
86. Woolcott, D. M., Kawash, G. F., Sabry, J. H. 1981. Correlates of nutrition knowledge in Canadian businessmen. *J. Nutr. Educ.* 13:153–56
87. Wyant, K. W., Meiselman, H. L. 1984. Sex and race differences in food preferences of military personnel. *J. Am. Diet. Assoc.* 84:169–75
88. Yang, G. I., Fox, H. M. 1979. Food habit changes of Chinese persons living in Lincoln, Nebraska. *J. Am. Diet. Assoc.* 75:420–24
89. Yetley, E. A., Roderuck, C. 1980. Nutritional knowledge and health goals of young spouses. *J. Am. Diet. Assoc.* 77:31–41
90. Yperman, A. M., Vermeersch, J. A. 1979. Factors associated with children's food habits. *J. Nutr. Educ.* 11:72–76
91. Zajonc, R. B. 1968. Attitudinal effects of mere exposure. *J. Pers. Soc. Psychol.* 9(2, P. 2):1–27

Ann. Rev. Nutr. 1986. 6:365–406


# THE BIOCHEMICAL FUNCTIONS OF ASCORBIC ACID

*Sasha Englard and Sam Seifter*

Department of Biochemistry, Albert Einstein College of Medicine, Bronx, New York 10461

CONTENTS

SCOPE OF THIS REVIEW ........ 365
BIOSYNTHESIS AND REQUIREMENTS OF ASCORBIC ACID ........ 366
METABOLISM OF ASCORBATE ........ 367
ACTIONS AND FUNCTIONS OF ASCORBATE ........ 368
DOPAMINE β-HYDROXYLASE ........ 372
PEPTIDYL GLYCINE α-AMIDATING MONOOXYGENASE ........ 373
4-HYDROXYPHENYLPYRUVATE DIOXYGENASE ........ 374
PROLYL AND LYSYL HYDROXYLASES FOR COLLAGENS ........ 376
HYDROXYLATION OF OTHER PROTEINS ........ 383
*Elastin* ........ 383
*C1q of Complement* ........ 384
DIOXYGENASE REACTIONS OF PYRIMIDINES AND NUCLEOSIDES ........ 385
CARNITINE PATHWAY HYDROXYLASES ........ 386
OTHER POSSIBLE FUNCTIONS OF ASCORBATE ........ 391
CONCLUDING REMARKS ........ 391

## SCOPE OF THIS REVIEW

This review is concerned primarily with functions of ascorbate that have been studied at the level of specific enzymatic reactions using in vitro systems. This approach excludes detailed consideration of many functions that become disturbed in the scorbutic animal if they have not also been studied in cell or organ culture systems or using isolated enzymes. In our final discussion we consider



0199-9885/86/0715-0365$02.00

whether, after all, the most important functions of ascorbate reside in other kinds of metabolism, as yet nondescript, for which none of the enzymatic reactions reviewed may be critical. In this article we also list other possible functions of ascorbate, referring only to reviews and a few primary articles. Several more general books and reviews on ascorbate are included in the bibliography (33, 39, 111, 120, 150, 152, 155, 180, 249, 284).

Although this article does not review the literature on the biosynthesis and metabolism of ascorbate per se, these subjects are discussed briefly to provide some background and perspective.

## BIOSYNTHESIS AND REQUIREMENTS OF ASCORBIC ACID

Among vertebrates from reptiles through mammals ascorbic acid is probably synthesized by this pathway:

α-D-glucose → → → → UDP-D-glucuronate ⟶ D-glucuronate ⟶ L-gulonate ⟶ L-gulono-γ-lactone ⟶ 2-keto-L-gulonolactone ⟶ L-ascorbic acid.

The first phase of ascorbate synthesis is part of a common pathway for converting glucose to UDP-glucuronate (34). The latter is also used for synthesis of certain glycosaminoglycans and for conjugation reactions in which glucuronides are formed. Diversion of the pathway toward specific synthesis of ascorbate would seem to be at the point where UDP-glucuronate is converted to D-glucuronate. The nature of that conversion is not known in animals, although liver UDP-glucuronyl transferases that catalyze the formation of glucuronides in the presence of a suitable glucuronyl acceptor may possibly hydrolyze UDP-glucuronate in the absence of an acceptor.

The C-1 aldehyde function of D-glucuronate is then reduced enzymatically with NADPH to a C-1 primary alcohol group giving L-gulonate. L-Gulonate lactonizes to form L-gulono-γ-lactone, which is then oxidized by L-gulono-γ-lactone oxidase to form ascorbate.

Humans and other primates, flying mammals, guinea pigs, and passeriformes birds do not synthesize ascorbate because they do not express a gene (if they have one) for synthesis of the last enzyme in the pathway, L-gulono-γ-lactone oxidase (39, 241). Although rats are known to synthesize ascorbate, a mutant strain of Wistar rats has been established that does not contain L-gulono-γ-lactone oxidase and must be administered ascorbate in order to develop and grow (184). The actual requirement for ascorbate (vitamin C) in a given species unable to synthesize it is almost impossible to determine, especially since the need may change with physiological status, daily variations, stress, and disease. Indeed some evidence exists that animals capable of synthesizing ascorbate can undergo induction of synthesis resulting in increased production (40). Thus, some drugs and anesthetics can induce increased synthesis. That circumstance strongly suggests that species requiring ascorbate in the diet also have a variable need for the vitamin, and that must be considered in the setting of recommended daily allowances. Depending on the margin of safety adopted, different recommendations have been made. In Great Britain the recommended daily allowance for ascorbate in the diets of adult humans is 30 mg, while in the United States it is 60 (227). Recently, despite the recommendation of a panel that the allowance be lowered, the National Academy of Sciences reaffirmed the amount at 60 mg of ascorbate (176).

A recent development that should be noted for its obvious interest and potential is the production by recombinant DNA technology of 2-keto-L-gulonic acid (6), which could be a key intermediate in the chemical synthesis of L-ascorbic acid.

## METABOLISM OF ASCORBATE

The main features of metabolism of ascorbate, particularly in vertebrates, are briefly summarized as follows:

$$\text{L-ascorbic acid} \xrightleftharpoons[+\text{le},\ +2\text{H}^+]{-\text{le},\ -2\text{H}^+} \begin{matrix}\text{L-ascorbate}\\ \text{free radical}\end{matrix} \xrightleftharpoons[+\text{le}]{-\text{le}}$$

$$\begin{matrix} & & \text{L-xylose} \nwarrow & \nearrow \text{L-threonic acid + oxalic acid} & & \\ \begin{matrix}\text{L-dehydroascorbic}\\ \text{acid}\end{matrix} & \longrightarrow & \begin{matrix}\text{2, 3-diketo-L}\\ \text{gulonic acid}\end{matrix} & & \longrightarrow & \begin{matrix}\text{L-xylonic and L-lyxonic.}\\ \text{Acid} \qquad \text{acid}\end{matrix}\end{matrix}$$

Ascorbate can be converted to L-dehydroascorbate by removing two electrons and two protons. Evidence suggests that this occurs in two stages, with a free radical formed intermediately by removal of one electron and two protons (18, 270). Semidehydroascorbate can then give up a second electron to yield L-dehydroascorbate. The free radical can also undergo disproportionation, in which two molecules form one of ascorbate and one of dehydroascorbate (18, 240).

In some plants, ascorbate is converted to L-dehydroascorbate irreversibly by an ascorbic acid oxidase that is a copper-requiring enzyme. In many cells of different species, including mammals, the conversion is reversible to some degree, and is catalyzed by a different enzyme, dehydroascorbate reductase. That enzyme uses reduced glutathione as a cosubstrate, and the products are ascorbate and oxidized glutathione. Should the reaction operate in reverse, oxidized glutathione would be reduced. In some of these cells another enzyme, glutathione reductase, utilizes NADPH for reduction of oxidized glutathione; one can then construct a cycle in which glutathione and NADPH are used in the overall reconversion of dehydroascorbate to ascorbate, allowing the last two to exist in equilibrium. If NADPH is then syphoned off for use in other reductions (for instance, in the reduction of folate to tetrahydrofolate or biopterin to tetrahydrobiopterin), one can visualize how ascorbate can be used as a source of electrons and protons.

The existence of the intermediate L-ascorbate free radical is incorporated into mechanisms proposed for certain hydroxylation reactions that appear to depend on ascorbate; for instance, such a mechanism has been proposed for the hydroxylation of dopamine to norepinephrine.

Other aspects of the above scheme apply to species that are able to open the lactone ring of L-dehydroascorbate to form 2,3-diketo-L-gulonate. This compound then can go through several possible degradation pathways, as shown above (34, 155, 170, 171, 270). The enzyme involved is a lactonase. If a species were to lack that enzyme, dehydroascorbate could either be reconverted to ascorbate, if mechanisms exist to perform that reaction, or be excreted in the urine. Species that apparently lack the lactonase are humans, other primates, and fishes (270). Significantly, the lactonase is present in the livers of guinea pigs. In theory, the presence or absence of lactonase in species such as the human and guinea pig, both of which cannot synthesize ascorbate, could influence the dietary requirement for the vitamin.

In considering the metabolism of ascorbate, one must recognize that it must be transported into cells and subcellular compartments where it performs its functions. Under physiological conditions ascorbate exists as a monoanion that cannot traverse most membranes readily. However, the subject of transport of ascorbate is only beginning to be studied. We refer to this matter further under our discussion of chromaffin cells of the adrenal glands in synthesis of norepinephrine.

## ACTIONS AND FUNCTIONS OF ASCORBATE

Actions and functions of a vitamin can be studied at two levels. First, using a dependent organism one can produce a deficiency disease and examine the disaffected functions and then determine whether these are restored to normal by administration of the vitamin. Second, one can identify specific biochemical reactions in which the vitamin or a cofactor form may act, isolate the enzymes involved, and determine the functions of the vitamin/cofactor in the reactions catalyzed by the enzymes. Reconciling the first and second approaches is frequently difficult. In vivo, observed functional changes may be secondary or even remote to the specific vitamin deficiency. The complexity of pellagra due to niacin deficiency is a case in point. In vitro, participation of the vitamin in a given reaction does not rule out that another factor operates in vivo. That is a possibility in some of the activities of ascorbate in isolated enzymatic reactions.

Although many physiological and biochemical processes appear to be influenced by ascorbate, the discrete biochemical reactions shown in Figure 1 are chief among those that have been studied sufficiently to warrant consideration here. Even in these reactions, one cannot say that the function of ascorbate is uniquely specific at the in vitro level, because other reductants such as glutathione, cysteine, tetrahydrofolate, tetrahydrobiopterin, dithiothreitol, and 2-mercaptoethanol frequently can be used in place of ascorbate. Still, ascorbate is most effective. If in the whole organism ascorbate is needed to produce another reductant that actually is used in an enzyme reaction, a decline in enzyme activity in scurvy would not be proof of direct participation of ascorbate in the reaction. Furthermore, in vivo, ascorbate could serve other functions to keep the enzyme in its optimal state of activity without directly participating in the mechanism of the reaction. We illustrate this possibility in our discussion of ascorbate and the activity of the prolyl hydroxylases.

Figure 1 is organized to present the known enzymatic reactions influenced by ascorbate according to the following conceptual division. First, the figure shows two monooxygenase reactions (reactions 1 and 2). Both require copper, molecular oxygen, and a reductant such as ascorbate. The ascorbate probably acts at the level of the metal to activate the oxygen and not directly on the substrate (dopamine in one case and a glycine-terminating peptide in the other). Second, a single reaction governed by a dioxygenase (reaction 3) is presented in which both atoms of a dioxygen molecule are incorporated into a single product, homogentisate. In that respect the enzyme involved, 4-hydroxyphenylpyruvate dioxygenase, differs from the other dioxygenases listed subsequently. Those dioxygenases (reactions 4–11) use α-ketoglutarate as a cosubstrate and incorporate one atom of oxygen into succinate and one into the product of oxidation of the specific substrate. All of the dioxygenases appear to be similar in requiring iron in the ferrous state. As we consider below, ascorbate may be required for maintaining iron in the ferrous state should it become adventitiously oxidized; in that case ascorbate would not participate directly in the mechanism of oxidation of the substrates.

A general mechanism for the α-ketoglutarate-dependent dioxygenases can be written as follows:

$$O_2 + \alpha\text{-ketoglutarate} + \text{specific substrate} \xrightarrow[\text{reductant}]{Fe^{2+}} \text{succinate} + CO_2 + \text{hydroxylated substrate.}$$

## MONOOXYGENASES

1. DOPAMINE $\beta$-HYDROXYLASE (EC 1.14.17.1)

3,4-DIHYDROXYPHENYLETHYLAMINE (DOPAMINE) → NOREPINEPHRINE

2. PEPTIDYLGLYCINE $\alpha$-AMIDATING MONOOXYGENASE

PEPTIDE WITH C-TERMINAL GLYCINE → C-TERMINAL AMIDATED PEPTIDE + GLYOXYLATE

## DIOXYGENASES

3. 4-HYROXYPHENYLPYRUVATE HYDROXYLASE (EC 1.13.11.27)

4-HYDROXYPHENYLPYRUVATE → HOMOGENTISATE

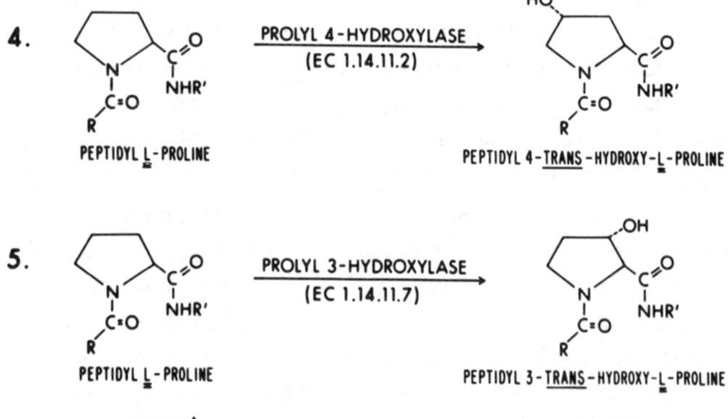


6. LYSYL HYDROXYLASE (EC 1.14.11.4)

PEPTIDYL L-LYSINE → PEPTIDYL 5-ERYTHRO-HYDROXY-L-LYSINE

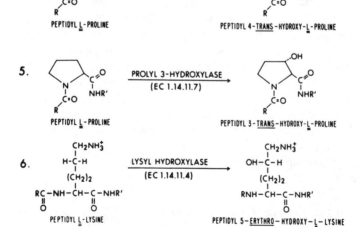

*Figure 1* Classification of specific enzymatic reactions in which ascorbate has been implicated. Reaction 3 is a dioxygenase, different from those shown in reactions 4–11 in that α-ketoglutarate is not required as a cosubstrate. Reactions 4–11 do require α-ketoglutarate. Reactions 4–6 are

DIOXYGENASES (Continued)

7. THYMINE —THYMINE 7-HYDROXYLASE (EC 1.14.11.6)→ 5-HYDROXYMETHYLURACIL → 5-FORMYLURACIL → URACIL-5-CARBOXYLIC ACID

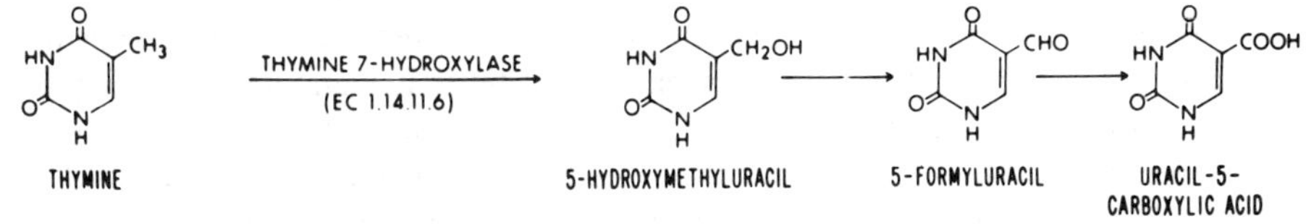

8. DEOXYURIDINE —PYRIMIDINE DEOXYRIBONUCLEOSIDE 2'-HYDROXYLASE (EC 1.14.11.3)→ URIDINE

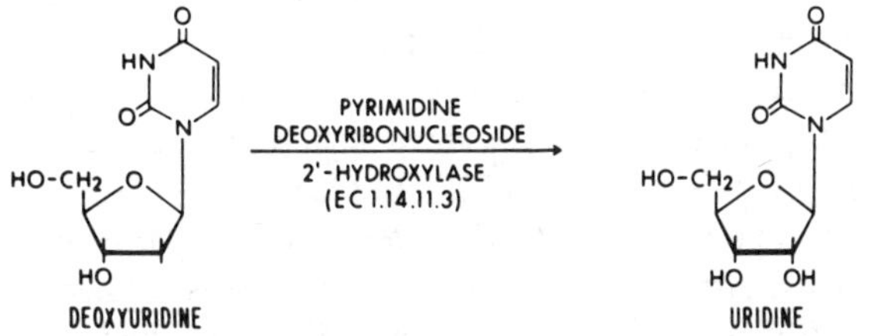

9. DEOXYURIDINE —DEOXYURIDINE (URIDINE) 1'-HYDROXYLASE→ [intermediate] → URACIL + DEOXYRIBONOLACTONE

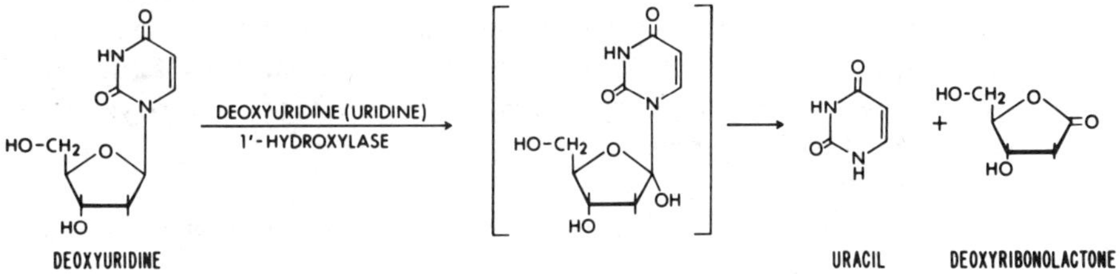

10. 6-N-TRIMETHYL-L-LYSINE —6-N-TRIMETHYL-L-LYSINE HYDROXYLASE (EC 1.14.11.8)→ ERYTHRO-3-HYDROXY-6-N-TRIMETHYL-L-LYSINE

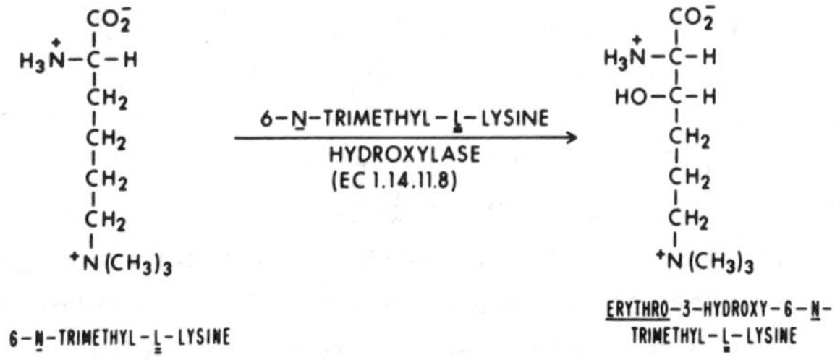

11. 4-N-TRIMETHYLAMINOBUTYRATE (γ-BUTYROBETAINE) —γ-BUTYROBETAINE HYDROXYLASE (EC 1.14.11.1)→ 3-HYDROXY-4-N-TRIMETHYLAMINOBUTYRATE (R-CARNITINE)

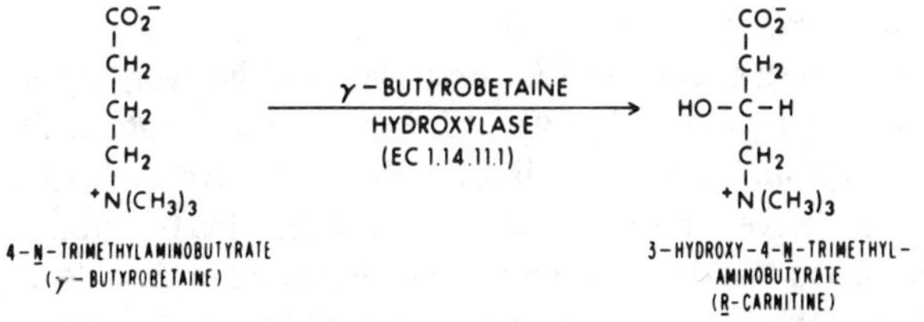

involved in posttranslational hydroxylation of procollagen chains in animal species. Reactions 7–9 are involved in pyrimidine and pyrimidine nucleoside metabolism in fungi. Reactions 10 and 11 are involved in the biosynthetic pathway of carnitine.

## DOPAMINE β-HYDROXYLASE

This enzyme catalyzes the final and probably a rate-determining reaction in the conversion of tyrosine to norepinephrine (reaction 1 in Figure 1). It occurs both as soluble and membrane-bound forms in catecholamine storage vesicles in nervous tissue, and specifically in granules of the chromaffin cells of the adrenal medulla. The enzyme was first purified from bovine adrenal medulla and its action studied (72, 148, 149). It is now known to consist of four identical subunits arranged as dimers joined by disulfide bonds. It has been reported to contain variously from 2 to 12 atoms of copper as $Cu^{2+}$ per tetramer (9, 119, 129, 232, 274), with 8 most probable. All of the above features of the enzyme are reviewed elsewhere in great detail (119, 152, 232, 255).

Ascorbate is considered to be a reductant in the dopamine β-hydroxylase reaction, and indeed the most effective agent when the enzyme is studied in vitro (72, 119, 148, 149). Belief that it may be the physiological reductant is strengthened by the fact that the adrenal medulla contains a very high concentration of ascorbate, exceeded only by adrenal cortex and pituitary in mammalian tissues (100, 121, 152, 177). Furthermore, in the enzymatic assay ascorbate is used stoichiometrically in relation to consumption of oxygen and formation of norepinephrine (72, 119):

$$\text{dopamine} + \text{ascorbate} + O_2 \longrightarrow \text{norepinephrine} + \text{dehydroascorbate} + H_2O.$$

The overall conversion of ascorbate to dehydroascorbate occurs with transfer of two electrons to a suitable acceptor. However, in the dopamine β-hydroxylase reaction some evidence has been obtained showing that the two electrons are donated one at a time in discrete steps, which requires that the ascorbate free radical (semidehydroascorbate) be an intermediate (52, 53, 255, 256, 274). It has been suggested that semidehydroascorbate in this mechanism could be acted on by a reductase to regenerate ascorbate (54), but a problem exists since that reductase occurs in the mitochondria and the hydroxylase is located in the chromaffin granules. Recent studies using mechanism-based inhibitors (44) and analysis of kinetic isotope effects (182) have probed the chemical mechanism of dopamine β-hydroxylase, but the function of ascorbate in reduction of the copper was not considered.

In the adrenal medulla, a further complication exists because the hydroxylase is inside the chromaffin granules (17, 122, 139, 143, 212) and most, but not all, of the ascorbate is found outside in the cytoplasm of the chromaffin cells (55, 108, 151, 266). This could be very important for understanding the function of ascorbate in the physiological reaction. The matter was discussed in great detail by Levine & Morita (152), who summarize several possibilities. For instance, ascorbate could be transferred from the extragranular to the intragranular space to replenish the ascorbate being consumed in the hydroxylation reaction or, alternatively, the granule membrane could contain an electron carrier system that specifically transports reducing equivalents from ascorbate outside the granules to an electron acceptor in the granules. In the latter case, ascorbate need not participate in the hydroxylation reaction per se, but could serve instead to generate another reductant for the reaction. Thus far no evidence exists for a system of active transport of ascorbate into the granules (269). However, some studies appear to support the concept that the action of ascorbate is related to the transfer of reducing equivalents into the granules, and Levine and his colleagues favor the idea (152, 153).

## PEPTIDYL GLYCINE α-AMIDATING MONOOXYGENASE

If one examines the structures of a number of peptides active as hormones, hormone-releasing factors, and neurotransmitters, one notes the frequency with which the carboxyl-terminal residue is amidated. Recently the nature of the amidation reaction was discovered (30, 31, 107, 128, 142). The process is catalyzed by a copper-requiring enzyme that oxidatively cleaves the carboxyl-terminal residue using molecular oxygen (62, 79, 80, 82, 173). This is not a simple hydrolytic cleavage of a peptide bond, because the amino group coming from the terminal residue is retained in the penultimate residue as a terminal amide group, while the remainder of the oxidized terminal residue leaves as an aldehyde (30). Most of the substrates studied in this class of reactions contain a carboxyl-terminal glycine residue, but other amino acid residues have been used in that position (128, 142). When a glycine-extended peptide is the substrate, one can write the reaction as shown in reaction 2 of Figure 1.

The peptides that may be amidated by this enzyme include bombesin (human gastrin-releasing peptide) (259), calcitonin (110), cholecystokinin (octapeptide) (51, 87), corticotropin-releasing factor (273), gastrin (25, 264, 286), growth-hormone-releasing factor (88), α- and γ-melanotropin (81, 195), metorphamide (278), neuropeptide Y (183), oxytocin (140), pancreatic polypeptide (24, 265), substance P (196), vasoactive intestinal peptide (109), and vasopressin (141). The parent precursor proteins of some of those peptides have been studied by molecular biological methods and, as noted in the listed references, their mRNA's reveal a sequence identical to that of the nonamidated peptide extended by a glycine residue.

Bradbury et al (30) proposed a mechanism in which two hydrogen atoms are abstracted from the peptide imino group and the α carbon of the glycine residue so that a double bond forms between the nitrogen and carbon atoms. They considered that the bond then was cleaved hydrolytically with formation of the carboxamide of the penultimate residue and release of glyoxylate.

With studies using a preparation from pituitary glands, Eipper et al (62) then showed that addition of ascorbate to the incubation medium caused a five-fold increase in amidation over the intrinsic activity. That was compared with a two-fold increase obtained with the best of other reductants used in place of ascorbate. That finding was of special significance since many of the peptides amidated are formed in tissues containing high concentrations of ascorbate, notably the pituitary glands, adrenal glands, and perhaps other nervous tissues.

A partially purified peptidyl amidating enzyme has been prepared from pituitary glands, and requirements for its in vitro assay have been determined (80). The intrinsic amidating activity, that is the activity without added ascorbate, can be diminished by treatment with plant ascorbate oxidase, which suggests that residual ascorbate is present in the preparation and that ascorbate is somehow required (82). On the other hand it has been found necessary to add catalase to the system, which indicates that hydrogen peroxide is formed that can inhibit the enzymatic action (62, 82). The function of catalase, as in the case of other oxygenases, would appear to be largely to protect the enzyme from oxidation by destroying hydrogen peroxide (20).

A nonenzymatic model system for amidation of peptides has been studied (13). This uses molecular oxygen, $Cu^{2+}$ ions and ascorbate. However, catalase added to the system *inhibits* the chemical reaction, which suggests that hydrogen peroxide is a requirement. The investigators proposed a mechanism for the model chemical reaction in which ascorbate is a direct reactant. Comparison of the enzymatic and nonenzymatic reactions therefore has at least one significant difference, the generation and use of hydrogen peroxide. This is a matter yet to be resolved.

Thus in addition to its importance in the formation of catecholamines, ascorbate is given considerably broader significance in the nervous and endocrine systems.

## 4-HYDROXYPHENYLPYRUVATE DIOXYGENASE

This enzyme catalyzes the conversion of 4-hydroxyphenylpyruvate to homogentisate as part of the pathway for completely oxidizing tyrosine to carbon dioxide and water. It has been purified from the livers of birds (275) and mammals (144, 194, 230) including humans (157). It has also been prepared from *Pseudomonas* sp. P.J. 874 (166). In its action the enzyme uses both atoms of dioxygen to catalyze the coupled oxidations within the same molecule as depicted in reaction 3 of Figure 1. One atom of oxygen is used for the oxidative decarboxylation of the sidechain pyruvate residue, thus leaving a sidechain acetate residue (156). The second oxygen atom of molecular oxygen is incorporated into a para hydroxy group as the acetate group moves to the ortho position; this occurs within a framework of the so-called NIH shift (156). The enzyme is truly a dioxygenase (156), and the similarity of its action with those of the α-ketoglutarate dioxygenases has been noted (3, 91), with a significant difference. In the latter group of enzymes the α-keto acid that becomes oxidatively decarboxylated is a separate external molecular substrate, whereas with the 4-hydroxyphenylpyruvate dioxygenase the α-keto acid is attached to the same molecule that becomes hydroxylated. All of the dioxygenases listed here share a requirement for ferrous iron (3, 91). Mechanistic studies have been performed with the 4-hydroxyphenylpyruvate dioxygenase (144, 235, 236). These have not advanced sufficiently to assign a specific function for the iron, although metal chelating agents inhibit the reaction (3, 91). No confirmatory evidence has yet been obtained for the proposed chemical mechanisms (3, 89, 91, 179, 238, 280).

Several reducing substances have been studied as activators for this enzyme, as in the case of the other dioxygenases (3, 83, 91, 288). However, in this reaction the clear superiority of ascorbate over all other reducing agents tried is not as evident. Reduced 2,6-dichlorophenolindophenol is almost as effective as ascorbate in assays done in vitro. The enzyme can be induced in *Pseudomonas* sp. P.J. 874 by inclusion of tyrosine in the medium, and then can be assayed in vitro using ascorbate (166, 167, 236). If the organism uses the induced enzyme in its metabolism of tyrosine, one wonders what the reductant is since it probably is not ascorbate.

That a relationship does exist between ascorbate and metabolism of tyrosine in mammals appears to be firmly established from experimental studies with scorbutic guinea pigs and from clinically related studies with children (83, 103, 130, 133, 137, 138). Scorbutic guinea pigs who are given either free or protein-bound tyrosine in their diets exhibit tyrosinemia and excrete metabolites of tyrosine in the urine, especially 4-hydroxyphenylpyruvate and 4-hydroxyphenyllactate (246–248). Human premature infants exhibit the same pattern: tyrosinemia and appearance of tyrosine metabolites in the urine (154). In both cases administration of ascorbate ameliorates the difficulty. As a matter of fact, since the work of Levine et al (154) and Nitowsky et al (199), premature infants in many nurseries are yet treated routinely with pharmacological doses of 100 to 200 mg ascorbate per day, and the results are clear. Kretchmer et al (134) studied the livers of premature infants for the enzymatic activity of 4-hydroxyphenylpyruvate dioxygenase, and found it to be greatly diminished. However, the activity was not elevated by including ascorbate in the incubation medium. The enzyme is now considered to be a "developmental" enzyme along with tyrosine aminotransferase (83, 133). That is to say, full development of adult enzymatic levels is not achieved until some time after birth. If, in premature infants, the dioxygenase is not yet expressed, one wonders why ascorbate has any effect since the aminotransferase does not require it, and furthermore it too is not fully expressed. There is some evidence that the 4-hydroxyphenylpyruvate that forms in the aminotransferase reaction is in itself an inhibitor for the dioxygenase, and that the ascorbate as a reductant overcomes the inhibition (3, 91, 167). If that indeed is the case, the action of ascorbate in the dioxygenase reaction again would be indirect and not critical to the mechanism per se.

## PROLYL AND LYSYL HYDROXYLASES FOR COLLAGENS

For general background on the subject of collagen structure and metabolism we have listed some representative books and reviews (23, 27, 69, 74, 75, 104, 202, 211, 217).

The known hydroxylases of collagen metabolism, prolyl 4-hydroxylase, prolyl 3-hydroxylase, and lysyl hydroxylase, are all α-ketoglutarate-dependent dioxygenases that require ferrous iron. They catalyze reactions 4, 5, and 6 shown in Figure 1. In their in vitro assay the enzymes require the presence of a reductant, the most effective being ascorbate. Because of the historical association of scurvy and recognized abnormalities of collagen metabolism, the finding that ascorbate is involved in those hydroxylations appeared to provide a logical basis for explaining the scurvy-collagen relationship. However, the subsequent detailed studies of effects of ascorbate on collagen metabolism are fraught with both apparent and real contradictions; and at present the evidence does not permit the conclusion that the main function of ascorbate is in the hydroxylation of prolyl and lysyl residues. Rather it would seem to be in the more nondescript but nevertheless very important effects of ascorbate on protein biosynthesis. Here we briefly trace the history of investigations that have led to this way of thinking.

Early studies in humans and guinea pigs demonstrated conclusively that scurvy is characterized by poor healing of wounds that can be rectified by administration of ascorbate. That, and the diminished patency of blood vessels resulting in bleeding, indicated that major pathology in scurvy is in the realm of the biochemistry of collagen (e.g. 147). About 25 years ago, when it was established that prolyl and lysyl residues in collagen are hydroxylated post-translationally (e.g. 250), the nature of the hydroxylating enzymes came under examination. A substrate called protocollagen was prepared by incubating collagen-forming tissues either in the presence of a metal chelator such as α,α'-bipyridyl or in the absence of oxygen (113, 216). Protocollagen is an underhydroxylated, operational, not biological form of collagen that can be used to study the hydroxylation reactions and to determine their requirements. Later, synthetic polypeptides were introduced as substrates. [Parenthetically, the instability of the underhydroxylated form of collagen led to the now-accepted conclusion that formation of a stable triple-helical procollagen molecule depends on the occurrence of hydroxyproline residues, thus for the first time giving a function for prolyl hydroxylation. Functions for lysyl hydroxylation are not as well established, except that hydroxylysyl residues, like those of lysine, take part in crosslinking of collagen, and that they make possible subsequent posttranslational modifications, namely glycosylation and the recently described phosphorylation (272c).]

The availability of protocollagen and peptide substrates allowed the preparation and characterization of the hydroxylases. Indeed, then, homogeneous preparations of prolyl 4-hydroxylase were made from chick embryo (17a, 197a, 271b), newborn rat tissues (41a, 228a), human tissues (135a), and cultured L-929 fibroblasts (116a). Prolyl 3-hydroxylase has not been isolated as a homogeneous protein but has been purified extensively (271a). Homogeneous preparations of lysyl hydroxylase have been made from chick embryos (272a) and from human placenta (272b). When the homogeneous preparations were studied, results obtained earlier with less pure preparations were confirmed, and it was established that the hydroxylases require ferrous iron and ascorbate, among other reductants, as activators. The requirement for ascorbate was increasingly more specific in relation to degree of purity of the enzyme.

From the results with ascorbate an impression emerged and seemed to flourish that the collagen "abnormality" in scurvy must be related in some way to poor hydroxylation of collagen. That idea has been expressed in some textbooks and scholarly review articles despite a lack of real supporting evidence. Several investigators, working before hydroxylation was discovered to be posttranslational, had failed to find the collagen of scorbutic guinea pigs to be relatively proline-rich and hydroxyproline-poor, so that no defect in hydroxylation was apparent (84, 86, 229). The seeming contradiction bothered workers in the field, if only subliminally, and studies continued to be made both in scorbutic animals and in cell culture systems to try to define the effect of ascorbate deficiency on collagen metabolism.

Barnes et al (10) found no difference in urinary hydroxyproline excretion in scorbutic as compared to normal guinea pigs. They concluded that even after collagen synthesis was impaired in scurvy no evidence could be found for occurrence of an underhydroxylated collagen. Thus no protein corresponding to protocollagen has been found to occur in scurvy.

In another study, Barnes et al (11) analyzed skin collagen from ascorbate-deficient guinea pigs that had been injected with tritiated proline. They studied a fraction of collagen that was soluble in hot trichloroacetic acid, nondiffusible, and degradable by bacterial collagenase. At several stages of ascorbate deficiency, measured ratios of proline : hydroxyproline indicated that the degree of proline hydroxylation was diminished from normal by only about 10%. The authors were aware that if underhydroxylated collagen formed and turned over more rapidly than normally hydroxylated collagen, the value of 10% decrease could be an underestimation; indeed they did find some diffusible peptide-bound hydroxyproline. In summary, studies from that laboratory indicated that scorbutic guinea pigs synthesized less collagen but that this was not seriously underhydroxylated.

We now summarize selectively the extensive literature on the effects of the presence or absence of ascorbate in culture media in which various cell lines and strains were grown. Collagen synthesis per se was *increased* in human skin fibroblasts (188, 190) and primary avian tendon cells (244, 245). An *increase* also was found in insoluble collagen in the extracellular matrix of neonatal rat aorta smooth muscle cells and in calf aorta smooth muscle cells (12, 242). *No effect* on collagen synthesis in presence of ascorbate was noted in other studies with human skin fibroblasts (26), human synovial cells (135), chick embryo tendon fibroblasts (207), L-929 cells (200, 208), mouse 3T6 cells (15, 200), and mouse 3T3 cells (207). *Decreased* collagen synthesis was found in human fetal lung fibroblasts (206).

With respect to the activity of prolyl hydroxylase in presence of ascorbate, the following variable results have been reported. *Decreased* activity was observed in cultured human skin fibroblasts (188, 190) and in human skin fibroblasts obtained from persons with Ehler-Danlos syndrome, in which the collagen is hydroxylysine-deficient (220). Hydroxylation was *unchanged* in either the presence or absence of ascorbate in cultured fibroblasts from chick embryo tendons (117). *Increased* activity was found in human skin fibroblasts (189), WI-38 human fetal lung fibroblasts (41), human synovial cells (135), 3T6 fibroblasts (146) and 3T3 fibroblasts (67), and L-929 fibroblasts (260).

With respect to lysyl hydroxylase activity in presence of ascorbate, the following has been reported. *Increased* activity was found in cultured human skin fibroblasts (188, 190). *No change* in activity was reported for human skin fibroblasts from persons with Ehler-Danlos syndrome in which the collagen is hydroxylysine-deficient (220).

Levels of hydroxyproline in collagens formed by cells in the *absence* of added ascorbate were found to range as follows. *Mildly decreased* levels were found in human skin fibroblasts (188), aging human fetal lung fibroblasts (206), primary cultures of chick tendon fibroblasts (118), and virally transformed BALB 3T3 cells (67). *Severely decreased* levels were observed in human skin fibroblasts (26), human fetal lung fibroblasts (68), skin fibroblasts from persons with Ehlers-Danlos syndrome in which collagen is hydroxylysine-deficient (221), chick embryo tendon fibroblasts (67, 207), rat smooth muscle cells (47), 3T6 fibroblasts (8, 14), and 3T3 fibroblasts (207).

Levels of hydroxylysine in collagens formed by cells in the *absence* of ascorbate showed the following. There was *no change* from when ascorbate was present in human skin fibroblasts (188) and in skin fibroblasts from persons with Ehlers-Danlos syndrome in which collagen is hydroxylysine-deficient (221). A *decreased* level was observed in 3T6 fibroblasts (8), the decrease being less than that observed for the hydroxyproline level in the same experiment.

In order to account for this wide variability, some investigators have searched for the presence of factors that could substitute for ascorbate in collagen metabolism. A reductant has been obtained from L-929 cells that could function in place of ascorbate in the prolyl hydroxylation reaction (178, 209). A different factor stimulating prolyl hydroxylation in cultured muscle cells was obtained from rat embryonic brain (114).

The variability and contradictions evident in the above recital of results are remarkable. Sometimes even in the same experiment measurement of two parameters that should be related gave puzzling results; for example, in some experiments the level of hydroxylation and the activity of hydroxylating enzymes are discordant. Before concluding that our understanding of the function of ascorbate is utterly confused, some probable reasons for the variability should be noted. Murad et al (188) and Schwarz & Bissell (244) and others have considered this matter. Thus one can point to the differences between human cell strains and animal cell lines. The former have finite life span in culture, the latter behave like transformed cells and show no limit in population doublings. The former are mostly diploid, the latter show considerable polyploidy. The human cell strains show density-dependent inhibition of growth in culture, while the animal cell lines do not. The two have different requirements for fetal calf serum. Primary cultures of chick tendon cells show inhibition of collagen synthesis when the serum concentration is greater than 0.5%, a concentration usually exceeded in many of the studies reported for cell lines. In most cases the precise origin of the cell being used is not known; thus even fetal lung fibroblasts or skin fibroblast cultures are grown out from explants of tissue that contain many types of cells. Even the cells that grow out may be of several kinds, making the culture a mixture. This is important because cells of different origin have variable capacity to express one or another collagen genes from the complete repertoire that occurs in most cells of an animal. Cell lines have largely lost the ability to synthesize collagen; whereas, for example, human skin fibroblasts and chick tendon cells in culture devote about 15 and 23% respectively of total protein synthesis to collagen, animal cell lines are much less devoted.

In addition to the above, studies with various cell populations have often employed different methodological approaches that have important influence on the interpretations. Some studies have used methods that do not distinguish between collagen synthesis and change in activity of prolyl hydroxylase. Even when methods are used to permit that distinction, time scales of experiments often differ, and no assurance is given that metabolic states of cells are comparable. For collagen synthesis to occur, an optimal pool of amino acids must be present, and some kinds of cells interconvert amino acids differently from other cells. Some cells have greater capacity than others to synthesize proline from glutamate and glutamine, and that could become a limiting factor in collagen synthesis (116, 254). Another factor is that cells in culture may not elaborate the peptidases required to process procollagen to extracellular collagen. Related to that is the fact that when procollagen is cleaved by those peptidases, extension propeptides are liberated to the medium. The latter feed information back to the cell, possibly at the transcription level, to regulate the synthesis of more procollagen (99, 131, 203, 279). In the studies of cell culture systems that we have enumerated, many of these factors are largely unmonitored and uncontrolled.

Using calf and rat embryo aortic smooth muscle cells, several studies have been performed to demonstrate that ascorbate greatly influences the synthesis and *deposition* of extracellular matrix conponents, including collagen (12, 242). The idea has been advanced that once the matrix is formed it can, in a kind of "dynamic reciprocity," cause the cells to modulate their protein synthesis in regard to components of the matrix, and the need for added ascorbate might diminish (242, 290). That view was tested by growing cells on a preformed matrix; under those conditions no added ascorbate was needed to maintain the level of collagen synthesis. The stimulation of protein synthesis in fetal calf smooth muscle cells by ascorbate was associated with an increase in the proportion of poly ($A^+$) RNA in the total RNA pool, perhaps in response to the matrix formed (290). Ascorbate was found not only to affect protein synthesis, but to have a measured effect on growth characteristics and morphology of thc cells.

Recently two groups of investigators have sought to develop ways to eliminate some of these many problems. They chose two model systems to study. Chojkier et al (42) returned to the study of the scorbutic guinea pig: they removed calvaria and maintained them in culture with and without ascorbate. After guinea pigs were on an ascorbate-free diet for two weeks, their calvaria showed a preferential decrease in rate of collagen synthesis dissociated in time from decreased hydroxylation of proline residues. Ascorbate added to cultures of calvaria from scorbutic animals restored the rate of prolyl hydroxylation to normal but did not affect the rate of collagen synthesis. Thus the decrease in collagen synthesis was not due to decrease in hydroxylation of prolyl residues in collagen, but must have been related to something else that happens to animals deprived of ascorbate. Chojkier et al (42) then were able to show that the decrease in collagen synthesis was linearly related to the decrease of body weight of the animals as they were continued on the ascorbate-free diet. The experimental protocol was then turned around, and animals were made to lose weight by food restriction while receiving ascorbate in the diet. Such animals showed an apparently specific decrease in collagen synthesis. In other experiments, collagen synthesis was found to decline in a number of different tissues when guinea pigs were starved for several days while being given ascorbate (258). Again the rate of decline of collagen synthesis was greater than that for other protein synthesis. All of those experiments point to the dissociation of hydroxylation from collagen synthesis, and the control of collagen synthesis by other metabolic events set into operation when an animal is deprived of ascorbate. The investigators thought that collagen mRNA levels were modulated downward in ascorbate-deficient states.

Schwarz and coworkers (244, 245) used cultures of primary avian tendon cells as a model system for studying the effects of ascorbate on collagen metabolism. In that model, maintenance of a large pool of procollagen within the cell would appear critical for regulating the synthesis of more procollagen. Addition of ascorbate to cultures at high cell density increased secretion rate and reduced the procollagen pool within the cell (243). The decreased pool size of procollagen was considered to trigger an increase in its additional synthesis. In other studies that laboratory found that the effect was at both the level of transcription and stability of the mRNA (172, 234).

In order to be able to relate all of the above findings obtained with scorbutic animals and cultured cells with what is known at the molecular level about ascorbate and hydroxylation reactions, we now consider the mechanisms of hydroxylation. Detailed reviews on that subject have appeared (38, 90, 123–126, 215). We refer also to selected primary articles pertinent to the discussion that follows (45, 48, 49, 174, 175, 191–193, 198, 218, 219, 222, 272).

A widely accepted mechanism for prolyl hydroxylation catalyzed by prolyl 4-hydroxylase (127), presumably operative in lysyl hydroxylation as well, is shown in Figure 2. The following can be stated concerning that mechanism.

1. In the overall hydroxylation reaction in vitro, ascorbate is used non-stoichiometrically. Thus, with all substrates and cofactors present, when one α-ketoglutarate is oxidatively decarboxylated concertedly with the hydroxylation of one proline residue of the substrate, the consumption of ascorbate is not stoichiometric.

2. The isolated purified prolyl 4-hydroxylase can go through a number of cycles of activity without added ascorbate before it loses activity (191, 198).

3. Kinetic evidence suggests a proposed mechanism in which the only action of ascorbate is to maintain the iron in the ferrous state (193, 272).

4. The enzyme can be made to carry out an uncoupled reaction: that is, α-ketoglutarate can be oxidized by molecular oxygen to produce succinate and carbon dioxide, without concomitant hydroxylation of prolyl residues in a suitable substrate (38, 45, 222). Under these conditions the ascorbate utilized is stoichiometric with the decarboxylation reaction (49, 192).

5. In the uncoupled reaction, the reactive ferryl-oxo complex decomposes to $Fe^{3+} + O\cdot$, and ascorbate reduces the enzyme-bound $Fe^{3+}$ to $Fe^{2+}$ (48, 49, 192).

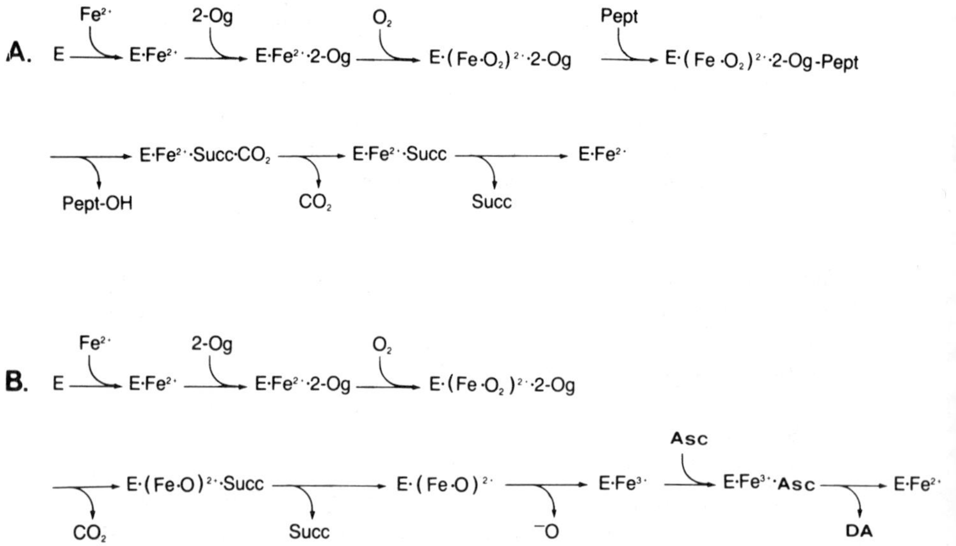

A. E —($Fe^{2+}$)→ E·$Fe^{2+}$ —(2-Og)→ E·$Fe^{2+}$·2-Og —($O_2$)→ E·$(Fe·O_2)^{2+}$·2-Og —(Pept)→ E·$(Fe·O_2)^{2+}$·2-Og-Pept

—(Pept-OH)→ E·$Fe^{2+}$·Succ·$CO_2$ —($CO_2$)→ E·$Fe^{2+}$·Succ —(Succ)→ E·$Fe^{2+}$

B. E —($Fe^{2+}$)→ E·$Fe^{2+}$ —(2-Og)→ E·$Fe^{2+}$·2-Og —($O_2$)→ E·$(Fe·O_2)^{2+}$·2-Og

—($CO_2$)→ E·$(Fe·O)^{2+}$·Succ —(Succ)→ E·$(Fe·O)^{2+}$ —($^{-}O$)→ E·$Fe^{3+}$ —(Asc)→ E·$Fe^{3+}$·Asc —(DA)→ E·$Fe^{2+}$

*Figure 2* Schematic representation of the mechanism for the prolyl 4-hydroxylase and lysyl hydroxylase reactions. The complete hydroxylation reaction is thought to proceed according to scheme *A*, in which the order of binding of $O_2$ and the peptide substrate and the order of release of the hydroxylated peptide and $CO_2$ are uncertain. In the absence of the peptide the enzymes catalyze an uncoupled decarboxylation of 2-oxoglutarate ($\alpha$-ketoglutarate) (scheme *B*). Certain peptides that do not become hydroxylated are known to increase the rate of the uncoupled decarboxylation. In the uncoupled reaction the reactive iron-oxo complex is probably converted to $Fe^{3+}$ and O·, and ascorbate is needed to reactivate the enzyme by reducing the $Fe^{3+}$ to $Fe^{2+}$ (*B*). E = enzyme; 2-Og = oxoglutarate; Pept-OH = hydroxylated peptide; Succ = succinate; Asc = ascorbate; DA = dehydroascorbate. [This figure and legend are reproduced with permission of the authors from an article in press by K. I. Kivirikko and R. Myllylä (127)].

Myllylä et al (192) state that since, even in the presence of a hydroxylatable substrate a number of unproductive decarboxylations may occur, inevitably the enzyme-bound iron becomes oxidized and requires a reductant, ascorbate being most effective.

A novel and fascinating series of experiments has been performed with ascorbate and its analogs to determine whether prolyl hydroxylase has a binding center for the reductant (K. I. Kivirikko, personal communication). Ascorbate was found to bind to the enzyme, its ring atoms but not its sidechain being required for that purpose. Thus D-isoascorbate and 5,6-*O*-isopropylidene ascorbate yielded $V_{max}$ and $K_m$ values almost identical to those of ascorbate. The investigators concluded that the binding site consists of two *cis*-positioned coordinated sites of the enzyme-bound iron, and is partially shared by the $\alpha$-ketoglutarate site of the enzyme, i.e. the site at which succinate and carbon dioxide are formed. In the uncoupled reaction, if that site is not occupied by ascorbate, the ferryl ion intermediate decomposes and the iron is oxidized to the trivalent state. This is consistent with the stoichiometric requirement of ascorbate in the uncoupled reaction.

The evidence that ascorbate is not required in the hydroxylation reaction per se may then explain much of the work with scorbutic guinea pigs showing that ascorbate deficiency does not produce severe underhydroxylation of collagen.

A different kind of presumptive evidence that ascorbate is concerned in collagen synthesis comes from studies with chick embryos (285). The chicken egg is a closed system. Until time of hatching, the chick egg-embryo system devotes much of its metabolism to the synthesis of collagenous structures. The fertile chick egg contains no detectable ascorbate until it is incubated; then synthesis of ascorbate increases rapidly, and simultaneously there is an increase of L-gulono-γ-lactone oxidase in the mesonephros, metanephros, and the yolk sac membrane. The yolk sac membrane synthesizes and accumulates the largest amount of ascorbate, and this increases throughout the incubation period as collagen synthesis also proceeds actively. (Of interest also is that the embryonic brain tissues contain high levels of ascorbate but do not appear to synthesize it. That might be of importance in relation to the neuroendocrine functions of ascorbate that were considered earlier in this review.)

In considering whether ascorbate is specific as a reductant in all collagen hydroxylations, it would be useful to know whether invertebrate species that manufacture collagens either synthesize ascorbate or concentrate it from their environment. For example, the gross composition of the collagen made by the sponge *Trematomus leonbergii* reveals large numbers of residues of 3-hydroxyproline, 4-hydroxyproline, and hydroxylysine (27). *Ascaris* cuticle collagen contains about 2% of its amino acid residues as those of 4-hydroxyproline, and earthworm cuticle collagen about 17% of its total residues as those of hydroxyproline (250). Neither of the cuticular collagens appears to contain hydroxylysine residues. The physiological reductant for those hydroxylations is not known.

## HYDROXYLATION OF OTHER PROTEINS

### *Elastin*

Barnes et al (11) studied the hydroxylation of proline residues in elastin of aortas of scorbutic animals. Elastins have about 1% of their proline residues as hydroxyproline. The investigators found no decrease in elastin from normal, but determined that the protein was underhydroxylated. Much later, Barone et al (12), studying cultured neonatal rat aortic smooth muscle cells with ascorbate present in the growth medium, found that the precursor tropoelastin appeared to be *overhydroxylated,* and the amount of insoluble elastin in the extracellular matrix was decreased from that found when no ascorbate was present in the medium. They considered the possibility that overhydroxylation interfered with subsequent posttranslational cross-linking reactions required to convert soluble tropoelastin to insoluble elastin. Taken together the studies on elastin seemed to indicate that in vivo ascorbate deficiency did not decrease elastin synthesis but did cause its underhydroxylation; whereas the *presence* of ascorbate in the in vitro experiment decreased the deposition of insoluble elastin, presumably because of the overhydroxylation of tropoelastin. Schwartz et al (242) did not find elastin in the extracellular matrix deposited by cultured calf aortic smooth muscle cells in either the presence or absence of ascorbate.

## *C1q of Complement*

At the beginning of the century, not long after discovery of the complement system, guinea pig serum (among many sera tested) was found to exhibit the highest titer of complement as assayed in a sheep erythrocyte hemolytic system. With the use of complement fixation tests for syphilis, many laboratories housed guinea pigs for bleeding as a source of serum complement. Several investigators found that complement activity was reduced during the winter months, and attributed that to a seasonal lack of leafy green vegetables in the diet and accordingly to a lack of vitamin C (60). Later a correlation was shown to exist between complement levels and ascorbate concentrations of guinea pig and human sera (59, 61). The practice was then adopted of feeding laboratory guinea pigs a diet containing sufficient lettuce, cabbage, or ascorbate per se. The effect of ascorbate on complement activity was considered to be related to its capacity as a reductant, and an interplay with another reductant, glutathione, was studied (58).

In the early 1970s, C1q, one of the subcomponents of the complement system, was shown to contain an assembly of polypeptide chains collagen-like in nature (213, 228). Those chains contain residues of hydroxyproline and hydroxylysine. Müller et al (187), studying C1q synthesis in guinea pig macrophages, noted that $\alpha,\alpha'$-bipyridyl reduced the secretion of C1q, and they inferred that the mechanism of hydroxylation of its prolyl and lysyl residues was the same as for collagen per se, particularly in sharing a requirement for $Fe^{2+}$. Bates et al (16) noted that scurvy in guinea pigs did not reduce their total C1 component as measured in a functional assay. That would imply that no change had occurred in C1q since it is a subcomponent of C1.

Those authors then tried to address the question why, in scurvy, collagen synthesis is affected whereas C1 synthesis (i.e. C1q) apparently is not. One consideration was that, even though both systems share collagen or collagen-like features, their individual synthesis might take place in different tissues or cells containing different concentrations of ascorbate. However, a cellular system that makes both collagen and C1q has been studied with and without addition of ascorbate to the culture medium. Morris & Paz (186) studied human fetal lung fibroblasts for the effect of ascorbate on C1q hydroxylation. They isolated C1q from the culture medium of cells grown with tritiated proline and analyzed collagenase-derived peptides for their contents of radiolabeled proline and hydroxyproline. They found that cells grown with ascorbate produced C1q with more hydroxyproline than those that had been grown without added ascorbate. Furthermore, in a functional test for C1q in which it was combined with C1r̄ and C1s̄, they found that the C1q produced in the absence of ascorbate, i.e. the underhydroxylated component, was considerably diminished in function; it did not bind as well to antigen-antibody-C4 complex.

The fact remains that overall complement activity in the animal may decrease in ascorbate-deficient states (16) even if C1q activity is unchanged. A similarity with the collagen situation in scurvy is possible. The synthesis of total collagen appears to decrease but the hydroxylation of the collagen is not seriously affected. One may infer that hydroxylation of C1q in ascorbate deficiency in animals is not affected since C1 is functionally unchanged, but perhaps synthesis of some other protein component of the complement system is diminished.

Note that another protein, acetylcholinesterase, also has a covalently attached assembly of collagen-like polypeptide chains; these anchor into basement membranes in certain kinds of neurons (233). That kind of acetylcholinesterase contains both hydroxyprolyl and hydroxylysyl residues. To our knowledge no studies have been made in scorbutic animals concerning the activity of acetylcholinesterase. That other proteins may be found to contain hydroxylysine is presaged by reports noting its occurrence in the precursor peptide of somatostatin of the anglerfish (7) and in bovine conglutinin (46a).

## DIOXYGENASE REACTIONS OF PYRIMIDINES AND NUCLEOSIDES

The reactions catalyzed by these dioxygenases are shown in Figure 1 as reactions 7, 8, and 9. They occur, as far as has been studied, in fungi. Reaction 9, the last to be described, occurs in *Rhodotorula glutinis* (263) and reactions 7 and 8 in *Neurospora crassa* (1, 2, 21, 22, 168, 169, 252, 253, 277) and *Rhodotorula glutinis* (263, 282). They are considered to be involved in so-called salvage or reutilization pathways for both the pyrimidines and the deoxyribose moiety of deoxynucleosides (251).

In the three reactions shown, the requirement for $Fe^{2+}$, molecular oxygen, and α-ketoglutarate appear to be absolute. The incorporation of $^{18}O_2$ has only been studied for the first and third steps in the sequence for the thymine 7-hydroxylase. In that case one atom of $^{18}O_2$ went into succinate and the other into 5-hydroxymethyluracil or into uracil 5-carboxylic acid (97). In reaction 9, the postulated intermediate shown then becomes cleaved to form uracil and a lactone (263).

The mechanisms of these reactions have not been explored in detail, but the purified enzymes are enhanced in their activities by the presence of one of several reducing agents, ascorbate being best. In reaction sequence 7, the thymine 7-hydroxylase catalyzes each of the three reactions, so that a total of three dioxygen molecules and three α-ketoglutarate molecules are used. Each of the three steps has been studied independently and show markedly different requirements for ascorbate (276). A puzzling aspect of the 7-hydroxylase reaction as studied with the purified enzyme is that nucleoside di- and triphosphates partially substitute for ascorbate (283).

Finally, the thymine 7-hydroxylase has been shown to catalyze the uncoupled decarboxylation of α-ketoglutarate in the absence of one of the hydroxylatable substrates and in the presence of a high concentration of uracil (101) or 5-fluorouracil (96). In the latter case, five times more ascorbate was required than when a hydroxylatable substrate was present. Those results appear to be somewhat comparable and strongly related to what was observed in the uncoupling of the prolyl and lysyl hydroxylases referred to earlier in this review. Thus, in both cases the requirement for ascorbate may be accessory to hydroxylation, the ascorbate perhaps being necessary for reduction of the iron atom if it gets oxidized in reactions not scheduled by the mechanism.

One should also add that the physiological reductant for these reactions is not known. Whether the species of fungi that contain these enzymes are able to synthesize ascorbate or at least concentrate it from their environment is not known. It is known that some yeasts are able to synthesize ascorbate from L-gulono-1,4-lactone and L-galactono-1,4-lactone (145). In addition, steady-state kinetic analysis and determination of intra- and intermolecular isotope effects in the reaction do not resolve the question of whether ascorbate is a direct participant (94, 95). Thus, as in the other dioxygenases requiring α-ketoglutarate, two possibilities exist concerning the need for ascorbate: either uncoupling of the reaction hardly occurs in vivo as it does in vitro, or it can use a reductant different from ascorbate if some unscheduled oxidation of the iron occurs.

## CARNITINE PATHWAY HYDROXYLASES

The metabolism of carnitine and its functions in humans are considered in another chapter of this volume (226) and its general aspects were reviewed in an earlier volume of this series (28). Our purpose here is to describe the effects of ascorbate on the two hydroxylation steps in the biosynthesis of carnitine (reactions 10 and 11 in Figure 1). However, for purposes of this discussion, we present a few broad statements about carnitine.

Carnitine is required in fatty acid metabolism for formation of acetyl and other acyl carnitine derivatives that can cross mitochondrial and peroxisomal membranes (32, 71, 73, 271). In particular, acyl carnitines are required for transport of fatty acids into mitochondria, where they can be oxidized. In carnitine deficiency states it is possible that fatty acids not oxidized are then converted to triacylglycerols, which would increase the amount of these.

The biosynthesis of carnitine is discussed in several reviews (e.g. 32, 71). Carnitine is derived ultimately from lysine, with an early step being the conversion of lysine to 6-*N*-trimethyl-L-lysine; the methyl donor is S-adenosyl methionine. Among a great many species that can make carnitine, there are two general ways in which 6-*N*-trimethyl-L-lysine can form. In *Neurospora crassa* the pathway from free lysine is direct (29, 223). However, in mammals this simple direct conversion does not occur. Rather, lysine must be incorporated into certain proteins, not yet adequately identified, in which specific lysine residues are then converted to 6-*N*-trimethyl-L-lysine residues (56, 136). Proteins in which 6-*N*-trimethyl-L-lysine has been found include histones, myosin, calmodulin, and cytochrome c. [Protein methylation is reviewed by Paik & Kim (204).] The residues of 6-*N*-trimethyl-L-lysine are then released by proteolytic cleavage. In either case, the free 6-*N*-trimethyl-L-lysine is converted stepwise to carnitine by processes including the separate hydroxylation steps. The first of these (reaction 10 in Figure 1) is the hydroxylation of 6-*N*-trimethyl-L-lysine to 3-hydroxy-6-*N*-trimethyl-L-lysine, which is of the *erythro* configuration (201). Cleavage between C-2 and C-3 of the latter compound forms glycine and 4-*N*-trimethylaminobutyraldehyde (92, 105). That compound is then oxidized to 4-*N*-trimethylaminobutyrate, known also as γ-butyrobetaine (106). Finally, γ-butyrobetaine is hydroxylated to yield carnitine (reaction 11). The first hydroxylation (reaction 10) has been studied in humans and rats, and found to occur in kidney, liver, heart, and skeletal muscle (105, 224, 237, 261, 262). In several species studied, the second hydroxylation (reaction 11) occurs almost exclusively in the liver (dog, guinea pig, mouse, and rat); however, in other species (cat, hamster, rabbit, monkey, and human) it occurs in both liver and kidney (64, 66, 162, 224).

The two hydroxylation reactions in this pathway are catalyzed by separate $Fe^{2+}$-requiring dioxygenases that also need α-ketoglutarate as a cosubstrate. Both enzymes have been studied in vitro for dependence upon a reductant; indeed a reductant is required, the most effective being ascorbate (105, 159–161, 164, 237, 261, 262). Of the two enzymes, only the γ-butyrobetaine hydroxylase has been isolated and studied extensively. That enzyme has been purified to homogeneity from calf liver (132) and from *Pseudomonas* sp. AK1 (161). It has also been prepared in highly purified but not homogeneous form from human kidney (163); in that tissue it exists in three isozymic species (165). The γ-butyrobetaine hydroxylase has also been partially purified from rat liver (159). A preparation of the bacterial enzyme was used to study $^{18}O$ incorporation from molecular oxygen (158). It was found that one of the oxygen atoms of dioxygen was incorporated into succinate formed by decarboxylation of α-ketoglutarate, but the incorporation of the second oxygen atom into carnitine was not studied. Holme et al (98) reported that during the in vitro hydroxylation of γ-butyrobetaine by the human kidney hydroxylase, uncoupling occurred to a significant extent, meaning that more α-ketoglutarate was converted to succinate than γ-butyrobetaine to carnitine. A similar event appeared to occur when the hydroxylase from *Pseudomonas* was used, but the degree of uncoupling was considerably less (98). In other experiments, when the human hydroxylase was incubated with α-ketoglutarate in the absence of γ-butyrobetaine but in the presence of added D-carnitine, the extent of uncoupling almost doubled, going from 20% in the first experiments to 36% in the last (98). Concerning those findings, Holme et al stated that the loosely coupled reaction observed for the human kidney enzyme has no obvious explanation.

The remainder of our discussion deals principally with the evidence concerning whether ascorbate is directly or indirectly involved in the hydroxylation steps of carnitine biosynthesis. On a historical note, Hughes et al (102) quote Woodall in 1639 and Lind in 1753 to the effect that lassitude is a central feature of scurvy in humans. In a classical study in which a human volunteer was kept for a considerable time on a diet deficient in ascorbate, the subject was found to experience similar lassitude and tiredness even before the clearly defined markers of frank scurvy were evident (46). The overall reasoning to explain those features of scurvy would be as follows. The biosynthesis of carnitine requires two hydroxylation reactions that are stimulated, at least in vitro, by ascorbate. Thus a deficiency of ascorbate could lead to decreased synthesis of carnitine, decreased oxidation of fatty acids in muscle, liver, and other tissues, and consequently fatigue and lassitude.

Bearing on that matter, Hughes et al (102) studied the levels of carnitine in muscle in normal and scorbutic guinea pigs. They found that a reduction of carnitine occurred in skeletal muscle, going from 1.15 to 0.59 μg per gram of tissue. Subsequently it was shown that administration of carnitine to scorbutic guinea pigs increased their survival time by about 10% (112).

In scurvy, decreased carnitine levels have been observed in skeletal muscle (57, 102, 197, 267), heart muscle (43, 57, 197), liver (57, 239, 267), and kidney (57). The carnitine concentration measured in other studies showed no differences between normal and scorbutic guinea pigs with respect to brain and serum (57) and liver (197). Yet another study showed an elevated level of carnitine in plasma of scorbutic guinea pigs (197).

Nelson et al (197) injected radiolabeled precursors of carnitine into normal and scorbutic guinea pigs to study the influence of ascorbate on the two hydroxylation reactions. In one series of experiments they injected 6-*N*-trimethyl-L-lysine, labeled in its methyl groups with $^{14}C$, into the inferior vena cavae of anesthetized guinea pigs. The amount of [$^{14}C$] γ-butyrobetaine produced by kidneys of either pair-fed or *ad libitum*–fed control guinea pigs was from 8 to 10 times greater than the amount produced by kidneys of scorbutic animals. Those results suggested that the activity of 6-*N*-trimethyl-L-lysine hydroxylase of the guinea pig is influenced by ascorbate concentration. In another series of experiments (197) they injected methyl-labeled γ-butyrobetaine and measured the appearance of methyl-labeled carnitine in the liver. The results appeared to indicate that formation of carnitine from its immediate precursor was no different in scorbutic guinea pigs from its formation in controls. The interpretation offered was that the concentration of ascorbate had no significant influence on hydroxylation of γ-butyrobetaine by the liver in vivo. It should be noted that in those experiments the livers of scorbutic animals showed no decreased carnitine levels when compared to controls. In contrast, Sandor et al (239) obtained results indicating that ascorbate concentration was important for maintaining normal carnitine levels in the liver; and later Dunn et al (57) obtained a similar result.

In a subsequent study (267) from the same laboratory of Nelson et al (197), guinea pigs were maintained on a scorbutic diet different in some respects from that used in the previous experiments. In addition, samples for analysis were obtained much earlier after injection of the radiolabeled precursors. Under those conditions, Thoma & Henderson (267) reported that liver carnitine levels were indeed significantly decreased in scorbutic guinea pigs as compared to controls, as was the in vivo conversion of γ-butyrobetaine to carnitine.

Dunn et al (57) isolated livers from scorbutic and normal animals and perfused them with asialofetuin that had been treated to convert some of its lysine residues to 6-*N*-trimethyl-L-lysine residues. Asialofetuin can be taken up by liver cells since these contain receptors that can combine with desialylated proteins and cause their endocytosis. Free 6-*N*-trimethyl-L-lysine is not taken up significantly by liver cells, and the use of trimethylated asialofetuin was a device, not unlike the physiological one, to introduce a precursor of carnitine into the liver cells. Dunn et al (57) also perfused the livers with suitably labeled γ-butyrobetaine. Furthermore, simultaneous perfusion of the livers with both of the labeled substrates allowed the investigators to determine the effects of ascorbate depletion and replenishment on both of the hydroxylases operating in concert within the same organ. They found that of the recovered radioactivity administered as [1,2,3,4–$^{14}$C] γ-butyrobetaine, 16% was present as γ-butyrobetaine and 84% appeared as carnitine for the control animals, while the scorbutic animals gave values of 51 and 49% respectively. Ascorbate-deficient livers treated to a prior perfusion with ascorbate subsequently showed that their capacity to convert γ-butyrobetaine to carnitine was restored completely.

For the same livers of scorbutic animals perfused with asialofetuin containing 6-*N*-trimethyl-L-lysine labeled in its methyl groups with $^{3}$H, no decrease was observed in production of metabolites beyond the step of hydroxylation of

6-*N*-trimethyl-L-lysine, that is, in the sum of γ-butyrobetaine plus carnitine plus acetylcarnitine. However, in that pool of metabolites, [$^3$H] carnitine constituted only 53% of the total radioactivity as compared to 83% obtained with livers of control animals and 85% obtained with livers of scorbutic animals first perfused with ascorbate. Thus livers of the ascorbate-deficient animals perfused either with methylated asialofetuin or with γ-butyrobetaine showed a decrease in production of carnitine as compared with controls, and that decrease was accompanied by an accumulation of γ-butyrobetaine in the liver.

Results obtained with livers perfused simultaneously with labeled methylated asialofetuin and γ-butyrobetaine strongly supported the conclusion that ascorbate deficiency in guinea pigs affects their livers in such a way that the rate of carnitine synthesis is limited by the activity of γ-butyrobetaine hydroxylase but not by the activity of 6-*N*-trimethyl-L-lysine hydroxylase. That implies a differential effect of ascorbate on the two hydroxylases involved in carnitine synthesis. Yet, in a personal communication to one of us (S.E.), Dr. Charles J. Rebouche has pointed out that some of these results are difficult to reconcile with other information. For example, rats fed 6-*N*-trimethyl-L-lysine but no carnitine, were found by Rebouche & Lehman (225) to excrete 100 times more carnitine than did rats fed no 6-*N*-trimethyl-L-lysine and no carnitine. That was interpreted to mean that the rat liver has an approximate 100-fold excess of γ-butyrobetaine hydroxylase activity, and this enzyme would not likely be the rate-limiting enzyme in carnitine biosynthesis perhaps even in scorbutic guinea pigs. The comparison of rat and guinea pig in this case would seem to be appropriate in view of a previous finding (66) that guinea pig liver has five times greater γ-butyrobetaine hydroxylase activity than rat liver.

Our present knowledge concerning the functions of ascorbate in carnitine biosynthesis can be summarized as follows. First, in vivo, ascorbate deficiency in guinea pigs results in a variable decrease in carnitine levels of several tissues studied. Second, most investigators agree that ascorbate-deficient guinea pigs show decreased activity of liver γ-butyrobetaine hydroxylase, which can be restored rapidly by injection of ascorbate. Third, in vivo, ascorbate deficiency in guinea pigs appears to diminish 6-*N*-trimethyl-L-lysine hydroxylase activity in kidney but not in liver. Fourth, in vitro, addition of ascorbate stimulates the activity of both of the hydroxylases. In addition to the above, based on experiments with γ-butyrobetaine hydroxylase preparations from calf liver and again from *Pseudomonas,* it was found possible to propose chemical mechanisms that do not require direct participation of ascorbate in the hydroxylation reactions (19, 65).

The fact that purified γ-butyrobetaine hydroxylase can catalyze the uncoupled decarboxylation of α-ketoglutarate (98) is reminiscent of the actions of prolyl and lysyl hydroxylases. Thus in this case, as with the collagen hydroxylases, unproductive cycles of activity may possibly occur. Should that happen, the iron atom may become oxidized and require ascorbate for its reduction to the active ferrous state.

## OTHER POSSIBLE FUNCTIONS OF ASCORBATE

The main focus of this review has been the possible participation of ascorbate in certain specific enzymatic reactions listed in Figure 1. We want now to categorize uncritically a number of biological and pathological processes that have been studied with relation to the vitamin. Study of these has not yet achieved sufficient scientific status at the enzymatic level to fit them into the scope of this review. That statement is not meant to diminish their possible importance; this may become evident as they receive further experimental investigation. Some of these postulated functions form the basis of controversy into which we are not competent to enter.

Antioxidant functions of ascorbate are reviewed by Johnson (111) and McCay (180). The participation of ascorbate in the metabolism of drugs is considered by Zannoni and his colleagues (287, 289). Some workers have implicated functions for ascorbate in cholesterol and lipid metabolism (70, 76–78, 85, 93, 210). The connection between immune function and ascorbate has received considerable attention over the years; we note only a few of relatively recent articles (4, 5, 50, 214, 268). A relationship appears to exist between iron metabolism and ascorbate (231). Many articles have appeared bearing on the ascorbate-cancer controversy; we call attention to a selected few (35–37, 115, 185, 205, 281).

## CONCLUDING REMARKS

Discoveries of the past four decades showing that ascorbate can participate as a reductant in perhaps more than a dozen different reactions performed in vitro generated optimism that its biological functions could be defined specifically, and that the pathophysiology of ascorbate-deficient states, including scurvy, might be explained satisfactorily. To the contrary, further study has raised questions about the unique specificity of ascorbate in those reactions, and the optimism has tended to wane. From investigations such as those reviewed in this article, one comes away with the impression that the vital functions of ascorbate are yet to be identified. A further impression is that some of the answers may yet lie in a closer understanding of the derangements of scurvy, and of how administered ascorbate rescues scorbutic guinea pigs and humans from certain death. From some of the experiments with collagen metabolism, one may infer strongly that ascorbate is concerned generally with protein biosynthesis and specifically with collagen biosynthesis. Yet only meager strategies for studying that problem are evident.

In relation to mammalian biology, the reactions that we have focused on are important in nervous and endocrine function, the metabolism of tyrosine, the biosynthesis of carnitine required for oxidation of fatty acids for energy, and posttranslational hydroxylations of residues in collagenous proteins (the various types of collagen, basement membranes, C1q, and possibly certain acetylcholinesterases) and elastin. If indeed ascorbate were absolutely and specifically required for those reactions, one should be able to rationalize many of the structural, regulatory, metabolic, and immune disorders associated with scurvy. At least two major difficulties have dampened that hope. First, examination of the in vitro evidence for direct participation of ascorbate in those reactions sometimes leads to the conclusion that, in fact, the participation is probably indirect. Second, the findings in scurvy often appear to contradict expectations coming from a postulated function of ascorbate. For instance, the participation of ascorbate in the in vitro hydroxylation of prolyl residues in collagen does not match the finding that the collagen of scorbutic animals is not substantially underhydroxylated.

Perhaps the strongest case for a direct function of ascorbate can be made for the two monooxygenase reactions that require copper as well. Thus, both the dopamine β-hydroxylase and peptidyl glycine α-amidation reactions occur in tissues in which ascorbate is concentrated to very high levels, providing circumstantial evidence for its requirement. Furthermore, one can write reaction mechanisms for both of these and, in at least one case, conduct model nonenzymatic reactions in which ascorbate has a direct function. Even for those reactions, however, alternative mechanisms, consistent with available experimental data, can be written without direct participation of ascorbate, thus weakening the case.

For 4-hydroxyphenylpyruvate dioxygenase, the in vivo evidence for participation of ascorbate seems at first examination to be quite convincing, but the in vitro evidence seems to be weakest for all of the reactions considered by us. With regard to the former, premature human infants who have not yet expressed fully the gene for the dioxygenase show evidences of diminished tyrosine catabolism as do scorbutic guinea pigs. In both cases administration of ascorbate restores tyrosine metabolism to normal. However, closer examination suggests that part of the effect of administered ascorbate may not be directly in the enzyme mechanism but on removal of substrate inhibition. In vitro studies with the dioxygenase show some other reductants to be almost as effective as ascorbate. Furthermore, even the precise function of the iron constituent of this enzyme is largely unknown, let alone the function of ascorbate.

With regard to prolyl 4-hydroxylase, evidence has been obtained that several cycles of hydroxylation can occur without participation of ascorbate. After that, some reductant is required to keep the enzyme actively working, ascorbate being best. It has been proposed, with considerable experimental back-up, that the ascorbate is needed in the in vitro reaction in a kind of subsidiary housekeeping function, that is, to bring the iron constituent back to the active ferrous form when it becomes oxidized fortuitously. Thus a chemical mechanism has been proposed for prolyl 4-hydroxylase, seemingly applicable to the other collagen hydroxylases as well, that does not require ascorbate directly. Experimentally, the requirement for ascorbate becomes stoichiometric when the decarboxylation of the α-ketoglutarate substrate is uncoupled from the hydroxylation of prolyl residues. When the enzyme functions in that way the reactive iron-oxo complex is probably converted to $Fe^{3+}$ and O·. At that point, presence of a reductant, particularly ascorbate, becomes necessary to keep the enzyme active by reducing the $Fe^{3+}$ to $Fe^{2+}$. If one considers that such uncoupling is an in vitro phenomenon, these considerations do not contradict the in vivo findings that collagen hydroxylation is not seriously compromised in scorbutic guinea pigs.

The effect of uncoupling of reactions in relation to the requirement for a reducing cofactor is discussed in a recent paper (55a) on the mechanism of phenylalanine hydroxylase action. The authors note that the enzyme can form a complex with $Fe^{2+}$, $O_2$, and tetrahydropterin. In the absence of the phenylalanine substrate, the enzyme complex catalyzes the uncoupled oxidation of the tetrahydropterin with formation of an enzyme·$Fe^{2+}$·OOH intermediate. This is unstable and can be converted to an enzyme·$Fe^{3+}$ intermediate that is no longer active enzymatically. For recovery of enzymatic activity, the $Fe^{3+}$ must be reduced to $Fe^{2+}$. This requires the investment of additional reduced cofactor (tetrahydropterin). The analogy with the uncoupled prolyl hydroxylase reaction and ascorbate requirement is striking.

In the case of carnitine, evidence has been obtained that its levels in several tissues fall below normal in scorbutic guinea pigs. The levels are restored by administration of ascorbate. Furthermore, perfusion of livers of scorbutic guinea pigs with precursors of carnitine, and examination of products, reveal deficiencies in the hydroxylation reactions involved in carnitine biosynthesis. Despite this, one can write chemical mechanisms for those hydroxylases without invoking direct participation of ascorbate, but assuming that the reductant is needed to restore the iron to its active ferrous form should it be oxidized accidentally—just as in the case of prolyl 4-hydroxylase.

Considering all of the above, one can say that none of the reactions has been shown in vitro to have an absolute requirement for ascorbate as opposed to other reductants, nor does the evidence permit the writing of unique chemical mechanisms involving direct participation of ascorbate. In the most pessimistic case, ascorbate in these reactions could be confined to the housekeeping role of restoring the metal constituents of the respective enzymes to the reduced state should they become oxidized adventitiously. In the more optimistic case, one can say that ascorbate may yet prove to have a direct function in the action of the monooxygenases.

If indeed these matters become settled in the way just described, one can rejoice that at least some issues will have been resolved, and then get on with the more difficult task of unraveling those as yet mystifying functions of ascorbate that make it necessary for sustaining life. Probably a good place to start is to determine how ascorbate functions at the molecular level in protein synthesis, specifically in collagen synthesis.

ACKNOWLEDGMENTS

We are grateful to Drs. Hartmut M. Hanauske-Abel, Paul M. Gallop, Norman Kretchmer, Julius Marmur, Eli Seifter, and Mercedes A. Paz for many helpful suggestions. We want also to express appreciation to Dr. Mark A. Levine for allowing us to read preprints of his two current reviews. We owe special thanks to Dr. Kari I. Kivirikko for permitting us to reproduce Figure 2 from a manuscript in press from his laboratory, and for allowing us to read an especially pertinent manuscript before publication. Our own research work reviewed in this article was supported by grants from the National Institutes of Health, 2R01 AM 21197 and 2P01 AG 00374.

*Literature Cited*

1. Abbott, M. T., Dragila, T. A., McCroskey, R. P. 1968. The formation of 5-formyluracil by cell-free preparation from *Neurospora crassa*. *Biochim. Biophys. Acta* 169:1–6
2. Abbott, M. T., Kadner, R. J., Fink, R. M. 1964. Conversion of thymine to 5-hydroxymethyluracil in a cell-free system. *J. Biol. Chem.* 239:156–59
3. Abbott, M. T., Udenfriend, S. 1974. α-Ketoglutarate-coupled dioxygenases. In *Molecular Mechanisms of Oxygen Activation*, ed. O. Hayaishi, pp. 167–214. New York/London: Academic
4. Anderson, R. 1981. Ascorbic acid and immune functions. In *Vitamin C: Ascorbic Acid*, ed. J. N. Counsel, D. H. Hornig, pp. 249–72. London: Applied Science
5. Anderson, R. 1984. The immunostimulatory, anti-inflammatory and anti-allergic properties of ascorbate. *Adv. Nutr. Res.* 6:19–45
6. Anderson, S., Berman-Marks, C., Lazarus, R., Miller, J., Stafford, K., et al. 1985. Production of 2-keto-L-gulonate, an intermediate in L-ascorbate synthesis, by a genetically modified *Erwinia herbicola*. *Science* 230:144–49
7. Andrews, P. C., Hawks, D., Shively, J. E., Dixon, J. E. 1984. Anglerfish preprosomatostatin II is processed to somatostatin-28 and contains hydroxylysine at residue 23. *J. Biol. Chem.* 259(24): 15021–24
8. Anttinen, H., Puistola, U., Pihlajaniemi, T., Kivirikko, K. I. 1981. Differences between proline and lysine hydroxylations in their inhibition by zinc or by ascorbate deficiency during collagen synthesis in various cell types. *Biochim. Biophys. Acta* 674:336–44
9. Ash, D. E., Papadopoulos, N. J., Colombo, G., Villafranca, J. J. 1984. Kinetic and spectroscopic studies of the interaction of copper with dopamine β-hydroxylase. *J. Biol. Chem.* 259:3395–98
10. Barnes, M. J., Constable, B. J., Kodicek, E. 1969. Excretion of hydroxyproline and other amino acids in scorbutic guinea-pigs. *Biochim. Biophys. Acta* 184:358–65
11. Barnes, M. J., Constable, B. J., Morton, L. F., Kodicek, E. 1970. Studies *in vivo* on the biosynthesis of collagen and elastin in ascorbic acid–deficient guinea pigs. Evidence for the formation and degradation of a partially hydroxylated collagen. *Biochem. J.* 119:575–85

12. Barone, L. M., Faris, B., Chipman, S. D., Toselli, P., Oakes, B. W., Franzblau, C. 1985. Alteration of the extracellular matrix of smooth muscle cells by ascorbate treatment. *Biochim. Biophys. Acta* 840:245–54
13. Bateman, R. C. Jr., Youngblood, W. W., Busby, W. H. Jr., Kizer, J. S. 1985. Nonenzymatic peptide α-amidation. Implication for a novel enzyme mechanism *J. Biol. Chem.* 260:9088–91
14. Bates, C. J., Prynne, C. J., Levene, C. I. 1972. The synthesis of underhydroxylated collagen by 3T6 mouse fibroblasts in culture. *Biochim. Biophys. Acta* 263:397–405
15. Bates, C. J., Bailey, A. J., Prynne, C. J., Levene, C. I. 1972. The effect of ascorbic acid on the synthesis of collagen precursor secreted by 3T6 mouse fibroblasts in culture. *Biochim. Biophys. Acta* 278:372–90
16. Bates, C. J., Levene, C. I., Oldroyd, R. G., Lachmann, P. J. 1978. Complement component C1q is insensitive to acute vitamin C deficiency in guinea pigs. *Biochim. Biophys. Acta* 540:423–30
17. Belpaire, R., Laduron, P. L. 1968. Tissue fractionation and catecholamines. *Biochem. Pharmacol.* 17:411–21
17a. Berg, R. A., Prockop, D. J. 1973. Affinity column purification of protocollagen proline hydroxylase from chick embryos and further characterization of the enzyme. *J. Biol. Chem.* 248:1175–82
18. Bielsky, B. H. J., Richter, H. W., Chan, P. C. 1975. Some properties of the ascorbate free radical. *Ann. NY Acad. Sci.* 258:231–38
19. Blanchard, J. S., Englard, S. 1983. γ-Butyrobetaine hydroxylase: primary and secondary tritium kinetic isotope effects. *Biochemistry* 22:5922–29
20. Blanchard, J. S., Englard, S., Kondo, A. 1982. γ-Butyrobetaine hydroxylase: A unique protective effect of catalase. *Arch. Biochem. Biophys.* 219:327–34
21. Blankel, L., Holme, E., Lindstedt, G., Lindstedt, S. 1972. Oxygenases involved in thymine and thymidine metabolism in *Neurospora crassa. FEBS Lett.* 21:135–38
22. Blankel, L., Lindstedt, G., Lindstedt, S. 1972. Thymidine 2'-hydroxylation in *Neurospora crassa. J. Biol. Chem.* 247:6128–34
23. Blumenfeld, O. O., Bienkowski, R. S., Schwartz, E., Seifter, S. 1983. Extracellular matrix of smooth muscle cells. In *Biochemistry of Smooth Muscle*, ed. N. L. Stephens, 2:137–87. Boca Raton, Fla: CRC
24. Boel, E., Schwartz, T. W., Norris, K. E., Fiil, N. P. 1984. A cDNA encoding a small common precursor for human pancreatic polypeptide and pancreatic icosapeptide. *EMBO J.* 3:909–12
25. Boel, E., Vuust, J., Norris, F., Norris, K., Wind, A., et al. 1983. Molecular cloning of human gastrin cDNA: evidence for evolution of gastrin by gene duplication. *Proc. Natl. Acad. Sci. USA* 80:2866–69
26. Booth, B. A., Polak, K. L., Uitto, J. 1979. Procollagen synthesis by cultured human skin fibroblasts. *Clin. Res.* 27:623 (Abstr.)
27. Bornstein, P., Traub, W. 1979. The chemistry and biology of collagen. In *The Proteins*, ed. H. Neurath, R. L. Hill, 4:411–632. New York: Academic
28. Borum, P. R. 1983. Carnitine. *Ann. Rev. Nutr.* 3:233–59
29. Borum, P. R., Broquist, H. P. 1977. Purification of *S*-adenosylmethionine: ε-*N*-L-lysine methyltransferase. The first enzyme in carnitine biosynthesis. *J. Biol. Chem.* 252:5651–55
30. Bradbury, A. F., Finnie, M. D. A., Smyth, D. G. 1982. Mechanism of C-terminal amide formation by pituitary enzymes. *Nature* 298:686–88
31. Bradbury, A. F., Smyth, D. G. 1983. Substrate specificity of an amidating enzyme in porcine pituitary. *Biochem. Biophys. Res. Commun.* 112:372–77
32. Bremer, J. 1983. Carnitine-metabolism and functions. *Physiol. Rev.* 63:1420–80
33. Burns, J. J., ed. 1961. Vitamin C. *Ann. NY Acad. Sci.*, Vol. 92. New York: NY Acad. Sci. 332 pp.
34. Burns, J. J. 1975. Overview of ascorbic acid metabolism. *Ann. NY Acad. Sci.* 258:5–6
35. Cameron, E. 1982. Vitamin C and cancer: an overview. *Int. Z. Vitam. Ernahrungsforsch.* 23:115–27
36. Cameron, E., Pauling, L. 1976. Supplemental ascorbate in the supportive treatment of cancer: prolongation of survival times in terminal human cancer. *Proc. Natl. Acad. Sci. USA* 73:3685–89
37. Cameron, E., Pauling, L., Leibovitz, B. 1979. Ascorbic acid and cancer: a review. *Cancer Res.* 39:663–81
38. Cardinale, G. J., Udenfriend, S. 1974. Prolyl hydroxylase. *Adv. Enzymol.* 41: 245–90
39. Chatterjee, I. B. 1978. Ascorbic acid metabolism. *World Rev. Nutr. Diet.* 30:69–87
40. Chatterjee, I. B., Majumder, A. K., Nandi, B. K., Subramanian, N. 1975. Synthesis and some major functions of

vitamin C in animals. *Ann. NY Acad. Sci.* 258:24–47

41. Chen, K. H., Evans, C. A., Gallop, P. M. 1977. Prolyl and lysyl hydroxylase activation and cofactor specificity in young and senescent WI-38 fibroblast cultures. *Biochem. Biophys. Res. Commun.* 74:1631–36

41a. Chen-Kiang, S., Cardinale, G. J., Udenfriend, S. 1977. Homology between a prolyl hydroxylase subunit and a tissue protein that crossreacts immunologically with the enzyme. *Proc. Natl. Acad. Sci. USA* 74:4420–24

42. Chojkier, M., Spanheimer, R., Peterkofsky, B. 1983. Specifically decreased collagen biosynthesis in scurvy dissociated from an effect on proline hydroxylation and correlated with body weight loss. *In vitro* studies in guinea pig calvarial bones. *J. Clin. Invest.* 72:826–35

43. Ciman, M., Rizzoli, V., Siliprandi, N. 1979. Deficiency of carnitine induced by scurvy. *J. Int. Res. Commun.* 7:253

44. Colombo, G., Rajashekhar, B., Giedroc, D. P., Villafranca, J. J. 1984. Mechanism-based inhibitors of dopamine β-hydroxylase: inhibition by 2-bromo-3-(*p*-hydroxyphenyl)-1-propene. *Biochemistry* 23:3590–98

45. Counts, D. F., Cardinale, G. J., Udenfriend, S. 1978. Prolyl hydroxylase half reaction: Peptidyl prolyl-independent decarboxylation of α-ketoglutarate. *Proc. Natl. Acad. Sci. USA* 75:2145–49

46. Crandon, J. H., Lund, C. G., Dill, D. B. 1940. Experimental human scurvy. *N. Engl. J. Med.* 223:353–69

46a. Davis, A. E., Lachmann, P. J. 1984. Bovine conglutinin is a collagen-like protein. *Biochemistry* 23:2139–44

47. DeClerck, Y. A., Jones, P. A. 1980. The effect of ascorbic acid on the nature and production of collagen and elastin by rat smooth-muscle cells. *Biochem. J.* 186: 217–25

48. DeJong, L., Albracht, S. P. J., Kemp, A. 1982. Prolyl 4-hydroxylase activity in relation to the oxidation state of enzyme-bound iron. The role of ascorbate in peptidyl proline hydroxylation. *Biochim. Biophys. Acta* 704:326–32

49. DeJong, L., Kemp, A. 1984. Stoichiometry and kinetics of the prolyl 4-hydroxylase partial reaction. *Biochim. Biophys. Acta* 787:105–11

50. Delafuente, J. C., Panush, R. S. 1980. Modulation of certain immunologic responses by vitamin C. *Int. J. Vitam. Nutr. Res.* 50:44–51

51. DeSchenes, R. J., Lorenz, L. J., Haun, R. S., Roos, B. A., Collier, K. J., Dixon, J. E. 1984. Cloning and sequence analysis of a cDNA encoding rat preprocholecystokinin. *Proc. Natl. Acad. Sci. USA* 81:726–30

52. Diliberto, E. J. Jr., Allen, P. L. 1980. Semidehydroascorbate as a product of the enzymic conversion of dopamine to norepinephrine: coupling of semidehydroascorbate reductase to dopamine-β-hydroxylase. *Mol. Pharmacol.* 17:421–26

53. Diliberto, E. J. Jr., Allen, P. L. 1981. Mechanism of dopamine β-hydroxylation. *J. Biol. Chem.* 256:3385–93

54. Diliberto, E. J. Jr., Dean, G., Carter, C., Allen, P. L. 1982. Tissue, subcellular and submitochondrial distributions of semidehydroascorbate reductase: possible role of semidehydroascorbate reductase in cofactor regeneration. *J. Neurochem.* 39:563–68

55. Diliberto, E. J. Jr., Heckman, G. D., Daniels, A. J. 1983. Characterization of ascorbic acid transport by adrenomedullary chromaffin cell. *J. Biol. Chem.* 258:12886–994

55a. Dix, T. A., Benkovic, S. J. 1985. Mechanism of "uncoupled" tetrahydropterin oxidation by phenylalanine hydroxylase. *Biochemistry* 24:5839–46

56. Dunn, W. A., Englard, S. 1981. Carnitine biosynthesis by the perfused rat liver from exogenous protein-bound trimethyllysine. Metabolism of methylated lysine derivatives arising from the degradation of 6-*N*-[methyl-$^3$H] lysine-labeled glycoproteins. *J. Biol. Chem.* 256:12437–44

57. Dunn, W. A., Rettura, G., Seifter, E., Englard, S. 1984. Carnitine biosynthesis from γ-butyrobetaine and from exogenous protein-bound 6-*N*-trimethyl-L-lysine by the perfused guinea pig liver. Effect of ascorbate deficiency on the *in situ* activity of γ-butyrobetaine hydroxylase. *J. Biol. Chem.* 259:10764–70

58. Ecker, E. E., Kalina, R., Pillemer, L. 1939. The explanation of an apparent inactivation of complement by alloxan. *Enzymologia* 7:307–9

59. Ecker, E. E., Pillemer, L. 1942. Complement. *Ann. NY Acad. Sci.* 53:63–84

60. Ecker, E. E., Pillemer, L., Wertheimer, D., Gradis, H. 1938. Ascorbic acid and complement function. *J. Immunol.* 34: 19–37

61. Ecker, E. E., Pillemer, L., Wertheimer, D. 1938. Complementing activity and ascorbic acid content of guinea-pig serums following ether anesthesia. *J. Immunol.* 34:39–43

62. Eipper, B. A., Mains, R. E., Glembotski, C. C. 1983. Identification in pituit-

ary tissue of a peptide α-amidation activity that acts on glycine-extended peptides and requires molecular oxygen, copper and ascorbic acid. *Proc. Natl. Acad. Sci. USA* 80:5144–48
63. Deleted in proof
64. Englard, S. 1979. Hydroxylation of γ-butyrobetaine to carnitine in human and monkey tissues. *FEBS Lett.* 102:297–300
65. Englard, S., Blanchard, J. S., Midelfort, C. F. 1985. γ-Butyrobetaine hydroxylase: stereochemical course of the hydroxylation reaction. *Biochemistry* 24:1110–16
66. Englard, S., Carnicero, H. H. 1978. γ-Butyrobetaine hydroxylation to carnitine in mammalian kidney. *Arch. Biochem. Biophys.* 190:361–64
67. Evans, C. A., Peterkofsky, B. 1976. Ascorbate-independent proline hydroxylation resulting from viral transformation of Balb 3T3 cells and unaffected by dibutyryl cAMP treatment. *J. Cell. Physiol.* 89:355–68
68. Faris, B., Snider, R., Levene, A., Moscaritolo, R., Salcedo, L., Franzblau, C. 1978. Effect of ascorbate on collagen synthesis by lung embryonic fibroblasts. *In Vitro* 14:1022–27
69. Fessler, J. H., Fessler, L. I. 1978. Biosynthesis of collagen. *Ann. Rev. Biochem.* 47:129–62
70. Fidanza, A., Audisio, M., Mastriacovo, P. 1982. Vitamin C and cholesterol. *Int. Z. Vitam. Ernahrungsforsch.* 23:153–71
71. Frenkel, R. A., McGarry, J. D., eds. 1980. *Carnitine Biosynthesis, Metabolism, and Functions*. New York/London: Academic. 356 pp.
72. Friedman, S., Kaufman, S. 1965. 3,4-Dihydroxyphenylethylamine β-hydroxylase. Physical properties, copper content, and role of copper in the catalytic activity. *J. Biol. Chem.* 240:4763–73
73. Fritz, I. B. 1963. Carnitine and its role in fatty acid metabolism. *Adv. Lipid Res.* 1:285–334
74. Gallop, P. M., Blumenfeld, O. O., Seifter, S. 1972. Structure and metabolism of connective tissue proteins. *Ann. Rev. Biochem.* 41:617–72
75. Gallop, P. M., Paz, M. A. 1975. Posttranslational protein modifications, with special attention to collagen and elastin. *Physiol. Rev.* 55:418–87
76. Ginter, E. 1975. Ascorbic acid in cholesterol and bile acid metabolism. *Ann. NY Acad. Sci.* 258:410–21
77. Ginter, E., Bobek, P., Jurcovicova, M. 1982. Role of L-ascorbic acid in lipid metabolism. See Ref. 249, pp. 381–93
78. Ginter, E., Cerna, O., Budlovsky, J., Balaz, V., Hruba, F., et al. 1977. Effect of ascorbic acid on plasma cholesterol in humans in long-term experiment. *Int. J. Vitam. Nutr. Res.* 47:123–34
79. Glembotski, C. C. 1984. The α-amidation of α-melanocyte stimulating hormone in intermediate pituitary requires ascorbic acid. *J. Biol. Chem.* 259:13041–48
80. Glembotski, C. C. 1985. Further characterization of the peptidyl α-amidating enzyme in rat anterior pituitary secretory granules. *Arch. Biochem. Biophys.* 241:673–83
81. Glembotski, C. C., Eipper, B. A., Mains, R. E. 1983. Adrenocorticotropin (1–14) OH-related molecules in primary cultures of rat intermediate pituitary cells. Identification and role in the biosynthesis of α-melanotropin. *J. Biol. Chem.* 258:7299–7304
82. Glembotski, C. C., Eipper, B. A., Mains, R. E. 1984. Characterization of a peptide α-amidation activity from rat anterior pituitary. *J. Biol. Chem.* 259: 6385–92
83. Goodwin, B. L. 1972. *Tyrosine Catabolism: The Biological, Physiological, and Clinical Significance of p-Hydroxyphenylpyruvate Oxidase*. Oxford/Clarendon: Oxford Univ. Press. 94 pp.
84. Gould, B. S., Manner, G., Goldman, H. M., Stolman, J. 1960. Some aspects of collagen formation. *Ann. NY Acad. Sci.* 85:385–98
85. Greene, Y., Harwood, H. J. Jr., Stacpoole, P. W. 1985. Ascorbic acid regulation of 3-hydroxy-3-methylglutaryl coenzyme A reductase activity and cholesterol synthesis in guinea pig liver. *Biochim. Biophys. Acta* 834:134–38
86. Gross, J. 1959. Studies on the formation of collagen. IV. Effect of vitamin C deficiency on the neutral salt-extractable collagen of skin. *J. Exp. Med.* 109:557–69
87. Gubler, U., Chua, A. O., Hoffman, B. J., Collier, K. J., Eng, J. 1984. Cloned cDNA to cholecystokinin mRNA predicts an identical preprocholecystokinin in pig brain and gut. *Proc. Natl. Acad. Sci. USA* 81:4307–10
88. Guillemin, R., Brazeau, P., Bohlen, P., Esch, F., Ling, N., Wehrenberg, W. B. 1982. Growth hormone–releasing factor from a human pancreatic tumor that caused acromegaly. *Science* 218:585–87
89. Hamilton, G. A. 1974. Chemical models and mechanisms for oxygenases. See Ref. 3, pp. 405–50
90. Hanauske-Abel, H. M., Günzler, V. 1982. A stereochemical concept for the

catalytic mechanism of prolylhydroxylase. Applicability to classification and design of inhibitors. *J. Theor. Biol.* 94:421–55

91. Hayaishi, O., Nozaki, M., Abbott, M. T. 1975. Oxygenases: dioxygenases. *Enzymes* 12:119–89
92. Hochalter, J. B., Henderson, L. M. 1976. Carnitine biosynthesis: The formation of glycine from carbons 1 and 2 of 6-*N*-trimethyl-L-lysine. *Biochem. Biophys. Res. Commun.* 70:364–66
93. Hodges, R. E., Hood, J., Canham, J. E., Sauberlich, H. E., Baker, E. M. 1971. Clinical manifestations of ascorbic acid deficiency in man. *Am. J. Clin. Nutr.* 24:432–43
94. Holme, E. 1975. A kinetic study of thymine 7-hydroxylase from *Neurospora crassa. Biochemistry* 14:4999–5003
95. Holme, E. 1982. Determination of intra- and intermolecular tritium isotope effects in the reaction of thymine 7-hydroxylase. *Biochim. Biophys. Acta* 707:259–66
96. Holme, E., Lindstedt, S. 1982. Studies on the partial reaction of thymine 7-hydroxylase in the presence of 5-fluorouracil. *Biochim. Biophys. Acta* 704:278–83
97. Holme, E., Lindstedt, G., Lindstedt, S., Tofft, M. 1971. $^{18}O$ Studies of the α-ketoglutarate-dependent sequential oxygenation of thymine to 5-carboxyuracil. *J. Biol. Chem.* 246:3314–19
98. Holme, E., Lindstedt, S., Nordin, I. 1982. Uncoupling in the γ-butyrobetaine hydroxylase reaction by D- and L-carnitine. *Biochem. Biophys. Res. Commun.* 107:518–24
99. Horlein, D., McPherson, J., Goh, S. H., Bornstein, P. 1981. Regulation of protein synthesis: translational control by procollagen-derived fragments. *Proc. Natl. Acad. Sci. USA* 78:6163–67
100. Hornig, D. 1975. Distribution of ascorbic acid, metabolites and analogues in man and animals. *Ann. NY Acad. Sci.* 258:103–18
101. Hsu, C.-A., Saewert, M. D., Polsinelli, L. F. Jr., Abbott, M. T. 1981. Uracils uncoupling of the decarboxylation of α-ketoglutarate in the thymine 7-hydroxylase reaction of *Neurospora crassa. J. Biol. Chem.* 256:6098–101
102. Hughes, R. E., Hurley, R. J., Jones, E. 1980. Dietary ascorbic acid and muscle carnitine (β-OH-γ-(trimethylamino) butyric acid) in guinea-pigs. *Br. J. Nutr.* 43:385–87
103. Huisman, T. H. J., Jonxis, J. H. P. 1957. Some investigations on the metabolism of phenylalanine and tyrosine in children with vitamin C deficiency. *Arch. Dis. Child.* 32:77–81
104. Hukins, D. W. L., ed. 1984. *Connective Tissue Matrix, Topics in Molecular and Structural Biology,* Vol. 5. Weinheim/ Deerfield Beach, Fla/Basel: Verlag Chemie. 245 pp.
105. Hulse, J. D., Ellis, S. R., Henderson, L. M. 1978. Carnitine biosynthesis. β-Hydroxylation of trimethyllysine by an α-ketoglutarate-dependent mitochondrial dioxygenase. *J. Biol. Chem.* 253: 1654–59
106. Hulse, J. D., Henderson, L. V. 1980. Carnitine biosynthesis. Purification of 4-*N*-trimethylaminobutyraldehyde dehydrogenase from beef liver. *J. Biol. Chem.* 255:1146–51
107. Husain, I., Tate, S. S. 1983. Formation of the COOH-terminal amide group of thyrotropin-releasing-factor. *FEBS Lett.* 152:277–81
108. Ingebretsen, O. C., Terland, O., Flatmark, T. 1980. Subcellular distribution of ascorbate in bovine adrenal medulla. *Biochim. Biophys. Acta* 628:182–89
109. Itoh, N., Obata, K. I., Yanaihara, N., Okamoto, H. 1983. Human preprovasoactive intestinal polypeptide contains a novel PHI-27-like peptide, PHM-27. *Nature* 304:547–49
110. Jacob, J. W., Goodman, R. H., Chin, W. W., Dee, P. C., Habener, J. F., et al. 1981. Calcitonin messenger RNA encodes multiple polypeptides in a single precursor. *Science* 213:457–59
111. Johnson, F. C. 1979. The antioxidant vitamins. *CRC Crit. Rev. Food Sci. Nutr.* 11:217–309
112. Jones, E., Hughes, R. E. 1982. Influence of oral carnitine on the body weight and survival time of avitaminotic-C guinea pigs. *Nutr. Rep. Int.* 25:201–4
113. Juva, K., Prockop, D. J. 1964. Puromycin inhibition of collagen synthesis as evidence for a ribosomal or post-ribosomal site for the hydroxylation of proline. *Biochim. Biophys. Acta* 91:174–76
114. Kalcheim, C., Duksin, D., Bachar, E., Vogel, Z. 1985. Collagen-stimulating factor from embryonic brain has ascorbate-like activity and stimulates prolyl hydroxylation in cultured muscle cells. *Eur. J. Biochem.* 146:227–32
115. Kamm, J. J., Dashman, T., Conney, A. H., Burns, J. J. 1973. Protective effect of ascorbic acid on hepatotoxicity caused by sodium nitrite plus amino pyrine. *Proc. Natl. Acad. Sci. USA* 70:747–49
116. Kao, F.-T., Puck, T. T. 1967. Genetics of somatic mammalian cells IV. Proper-

ties of Chinese hamster cell mutants with respect to requirement for proline. *Genetics* 55:513–24

116a. Kao, W. W. Y., Berg, R. A. 1979. Cell density–dependent increase in prolyl hydroxylase activity in cultured L-929 cells requires *de novo* protein synthesis. *Biochim. Biophys. Acta* 586: 528–36

117. Kao, W. W. Y., Berg, R. A., Prockop, D. J. 1975. Ascorbate increases the synthesis of procollagen hydroxyproline by cultured fibroblasts from chick embryo tendons without activation of prolyl hydroxylase. *Biochim. Biophys. Acta* 411:202–15

118. Kao, W. W. Y., Flaks, J. G., Prockop, D. J. 1976. Primary and secondary effects of ascorbate on procollagen synthesis and protein synthesis by primary cultures of tendon fibroblasts. *Arch. Biochem. Biophys.* 173:638–48

119. Kaufman, S., Friedman, S. 1965. Dopamine β-hydroxylase. *Pharmacol. Rev.* 17:71–100

120. King, C. G., Burns, J. J., eds. 1975. Second Conference on Vitamin C, *Ann. NY Acad. Sci.*, Vol. 258. New York: NY Acad. Sci. 552 pp.

121. Kirk, J. E. 1962. Variations with age in the tissue content of vitamins and hormones. *Vitam. Horm.* 20:67–139

122. Kirshner, N. 1962. Uptake of catecholamines by a particulate fraction of the adrenal medulla. *J. Biol. Chem.* 237:2311–17

123. Kivirikko, K. I., Myllylä, R. 1980. The hydroxylation of prolyl and lysyl residues. In *The Enzymology of Post-translational Modifications of Proteins*, ed. R. B. Freedman, H. C. Hawkins, 1:53–104. London/New York/Toronto: Academic

124. Kivirikko, K. I., Myllylä, R. 1982. Post-translational enzymes in the biosynthesis of collagen: intracellular enzymes. *Methods Enzymol.* 82(PA):245–304

125. Kivirikko, K. I., Myllylä, R. 1982. Post-translational modifications. In *Collagen in Health and Diseases*, ed. M. I. V. Jayson, J. B. Weiss, pp. 101–20. Edinburgh: Churchill Livingstone

126. Kivirikko, K. I., Myllylä, R. 1984. Biosynthesis of the collagens. See Ref. 211, pp. 83–118

127. Kivirikko, K. I., Myllylä, R. 1986. Post-translational processing of procollagens. *Ann. NY Acad. Sci.* In press

128. Kizer, J. S., Buzry, W. H. Jr., Cottle, C., Youngblood, W. W. 1984. Glycine-directed peptide amidation: presence in rat brain of two enzymes that convert *p*-GLU-HIS-PRO-GLY-OH into *p*-Glu-His-Pro-$NH_2$ (thyrotropin-releasing hormone). *Proc. Natl. Acad. Sci. USA* 81:3228–32

129. Klinman, J. P., Krueger, M., Brenner, M., Edmondson, D. E. 1984. Evidence for two copper atoms/subunit in dopamine β-monooxygenase catalysis. *J. Biol. Chem.* 259:3399–3402

130. Knox, W. E., Goswami, M. N. D. 1961. Ascorbic acid in tyrosine metabolism. *Ann. NY Acad. Sci.* 92:192–94

131. Koda, K., Wu, C. H., Wu, G. Y., Seifter, S. 1986. Inhibitory effect of type I procollagen carboxyterminal extension peptide on the synthesis of type I procollagen in human fibroblast culture. *Proc. Natl. Acad. Sci. USA*. In press

132. Kondo, A., Blanchard, J. S., Englard, S. 1981. Purification and properties of calf liver γ-butyrobetaine hydroxylase. *Arch. Biochem. Biophys.* 212:338–46

133. Kretchmer, N. 1959. Enzymatic patterns during development. *Pediatrics* 23: 606–17

134. Kretchmer, N., Levine, S. Z., McNamara, H., Barnett, H. L. 1956. Certain aspects of tyrosine metabolism in the young. I. The development of the tyrosine oxidizing system in human liver. *J. Clin. Invest.* 35:236–44

135. Kuttan, R., Parrott, D. P., Kaplan, S. R., Fuller, G. C. 1979. Effect of ascorbic acid on prolyl hydroxylase activity, collagen hydroxylation and collagen synthesis in human synovial cells in culture. *Res. Commun. Chem. Pathol. Pharmacol.* 26:337–45

135a. Kuutti, E. R., Tuderman, L., Kivirikko, K. I. 1975. Human prolyl hydroxylase purification, partial characterization and preparation of antiserum to the enzyme. *Eur. J. Biochem.* 57:181–88

136. LaBadie, J., Dunn, W. A., Aronson, N. N. Jr. 1976. Hepatic synthesis of carnitine from protein-bound trimethyl-lysine. Lysosomal digestion of methyl-lysine-labelled asialo-fetuin. *Biochem. J.* 160: 85–95

137. LaDu, B. N., Gjessing, L. R. 1972. Tyrosinosis and tyrosinemia. In *The Metabolic Basis of Inherited Diseases*, ed. J. B. Stanbury, J. B. Wyngaarden, D. S. Fredrickson, pp. 296–307. New York/ St. Louis/San Francisco: McGraw-Hill. 3rd ed.

138. LaDu, B. N., Zannoni, V. G. 1961. The role of ascorbic acid in tyrosine metabolism. *Ann. NY Acad. Sci.* 92:175–91

139. Laduron, P. L. 1975. Evidence for a localization of dopamine β-hydroxylase

within the chromaffin granules. *FEBS Lett.* 52:132–34
140. Land, H., Grez, M., Ruppert, S., Schmale, H., Rehbein, M., Richter, D., Schütz, G. 1983. Deduced amino acid sequence from the bovine oxytocin-neurophysin I precursor cDNA. *Nature* 302:342–44
141. Land, H., Schütz, G., Schmale, H., Richter, D. 1982. Nucleotide sequence of cloned cDNA encoding bovine arginine vasopressin—Neurophysin II precursor. *Nature* 295:299–303
142. Landymore-Lim, A. E. N., Bradbury, A. F., Smyth, D. G. 1983. The amidating-enzyme in pituitary will accept a peptide with C-terminal D-alanine as substrate. *Biochem. Biophys. Res. Commun.* 117: 289–93
143. Ledbetter, F. H., Kirshner, N. 1981. Quantitative correlation between secretion and cellular content of catecholamines and dopamine β-hydroxylase in cultures of adrenal medulla cells. *Biochem. Pharmacol.* 30:3246–49
144. Leinberger, R., Hull, W. E., Simon, H., Retey, J. 1981. Steric course of the NIH shift in the enzymic formation of homogentisic acid. *Eur. J. Biochem.* 117:311–18
145. Leung, C. T., Loewus, F. A. 1985. Concerning the presence and formation of ascorbic acid in yeasts. *Plant Sci.* 38:65–69
146. Levene, C. I., Aleo, J. J., Prynne, C. J., Bates, C. J. 1974. The activation of protocollagen proline hydroxylase by ascorbic acid in cultured 3T6 fibroblasts. *Biochem. Biophys. Acta* 388:29–36
147. Levenson, S. M., Seifter, E., Van Winkle, W. Jr. 1977. Nutrition. In *Fundamentals of Wound Management in Surgery,* ed. J. Englebert-Dunphy, T. K. Hunt, pp. 286–363. New York: Appleton-Century-Crofts
148. Levin, E. Y., Kaufman, S. 1961. Studies on the enzyme catalyzing conversion of 3,4-dihydroxyphenylethylamine to norepinephrine. *J. Biol. Chem.* 236:2043–49
149. Levin, E. Y., Levenberg, B., Kaufman, S. 1960. The enzymatic conversion of 3,4-dihydroxyphenylethylamine to norepinephrine. *J. Biol. Chem.* 235:2080–86
150. Levine, M. 1986. New concepts in the biology and biochemistry of ascorbic acid. *N. Engl. J. Med.* In press
151. Levine, M., Asher, A., Pollard, H., Zinder, O. 1983. Ascorbic acid and catecholamine secretion from cultured chromaffin cells. *J. Biol. Chem.* 258:13111–15
152. Levine, M., Morita, K. 1985. Ascorbic acid in endocrine systems. *Vitam. Horm.* 42:1–64
153. Levine, M., Morita, K., Pollard, H. 1986. Enhancement of norepinephrine biosynthesis by ascorbic acid in cultured bovine chromaffin cells. *J. Biol. Chem.* In press
154. Levine, S. Z., Gordon, H. H., Marples, E. 1941. A defect in the metabolism of tyrosine and phenylalanine in premature infants. II. Spontaneous occurrence and eradication by vitamin C. *J. Clin. Invest.* 20:209–19
155. Lewin, S. 1976. *Vitamin C: Its Molecular Biology and Medical Potential.* New York/London: Academic
156. Lindblad, B., Lindstedt, G., Lindstedt, S. 1970. The mechanism of enzymic formation of homogentisate from *p*-hydroxyphenyl pyruvate. *J. Am. Chem. Soc.* 92:7446–49
157. Lindblad, B., Lindstedt, G., Lindstedt, S., Rundgren, M. 1977. Purification and some properties of human 4-hydroxyphenyl pyruvate dioxygenase (I). *J. Biol. Chem.* 252:5073–84
158. Lindblad, B., Lindstedt, G., Tofft, M., Lindstedt, S. 1969. The mechanism of α-ketoglutarate oxidation in coupled enzymatic oxygenations. *J. Am. Chem. Soc.* 91:4604–6
159. Lindstedt, G. 1967. Hydroxylation of γ-butyrobetaine to carnitine in rat liver. *Biochemistry* 6:1271–82
160. Lindstedt, G., Lindstedt, S. 1970. Cofactor requirements of γ-butyrobetaine hydroxylase from rat liver. *J. Biol. Chem.* 245:4178–86
161. Lindstedt, G., Lindstedt, S., Nordin, I. 1977. Purification and properties of γ-butyrobetaine hydroxylase from *Pseudomonas* sp. AK1. *Biochemistry* 16: 2181–88
162. Lindstedt, G., Lindstedt, S., Nordin, I. 1980. Hydroxylation of γ-butyrobetaine. See Ref. 71, pp. 45–56
163. Lindstedt, G., Lindstedt, S., Nordin, I. 1982. γ-Butyrobetaine hydroxylase in human kidney. *Scand. J. Clin. Lab. Invest.* 42:477–85
164. Lindstedt, G., Lindstedt, S., Tofft, M. 1970. γ-Butyrobetaine hydroxylase from *Pseudomonas* sp. AK1. *Biochemistry* 9: 4336–42
165. Lindstedt, S., Nordin, I. 1984. Multiple forms of γ-butyrobetaine hydroxylase (EC 1.14.11.1). *Biochem. J.* 223:119–27
166. Lindstedt, S., Odelhög, B., Rundgren, M. 1977. Purification and some properties of 4-hydroxyphenylpyruvate dioxygenase from *Pseudomonas* sp. P.J. 874. *Biochemistry* 16:3369–77

167. Lindstedt, S., Rundgren, M. 1982. Inhibition of 4-hydroxyphenylpyruvate dioxygenase from *Pseudomonas* sp. strain P.J.874 by the *ENOL* tautomer of the substrate. *Biochim. Biophys. Acta* 704: 66–74
168. Liu, C. K., Hsu, C. A., Abbott, M. T. 1973. Catalysis of three sequential dioxygenase reactions by thymine 7-hydroxylase. *Arch. Biochem. Biophys.* 159:180–87
169. Liu, C. K., Shaffer, P. M., Slaughter, R. S., McKroskey, R. P., Abbott, M. T. 1972. Stoichiometry of the pyrimidine deoxyribonucleoside 2'-hydroxylase reaction and of the conversion of 5-hydroxymethyluracil to 5-formyluracil and of the latter to uracil-5-carboxylic acid. *Biochemistry* 11:2172–76
170. Loewus, F. A., Helsper, J. P. F. G. 1982. Metabolism of ascorbic acid in plants. See Ref. 249, pp. 249–61
171. Loewus, F. A., Wagner, G., Yang, J. C. 1975. Biosynthesis and metabolism of ascorbic acid in plants. *Ann. NY Acad. Sci.* 258:7–23
172. Lyons, B. L., Schwarz, R. I. 1984. Ascorbate stimulation of PAT cells causes an increase in transcription rates and decrease in degradation rates of procollagen mRNA. *Nucleic Acids Res.* 12:2569–79
173. Mains, R. E., Glembotski, C. C., Eipper, B. A. 1984. Peptide α-amidation activity in mouse anterior pituitary ALT-20 cell granules: properties and secretion. *Endocrinology* 114:1522–30
174. Majamaa, K., Hanauske-Abel, H. M., Günzler, V., Kivirikko, K. I. 1984. The 2-oxoglutarate binding site of prolyl 4-hydroxylase. Identification of distinct subsites and evidence for 2-oxoglutarate decarboxylation in a ligand reaction at the enzyme-bound ferrous ion. *Eur. J. Biochem.* 138:239–45
175. Majamaa, K., Turpeenniemi-Hujanen, T. M., Latipää, P., Günzler, V., Hanauske-Abel, H. M., et al. 1985. Differences between collagen hydroxylases and 2-oxoglutarate dehydrogenase in their inhibition by structural analogues of 2-oxoglutarate. *Biochem. J.* 229:127–33
176. Marshall, E. 1985. The academy kills a nutrition report. *Science* 230:420–21
177. Martin, G. R. 1961. Studies on tissue distribution of ascorbic acid. *Ann. NY Acad. Sci.* 92:141–47
178. Mata, J. M., Assad, R., Peterkofsky, B. 1981. An intramembranous reductant which participates in the proline hydroxylation reaction with intracisternal prolyl hydroxylase and underhydroxylated procollagen in isolated microsomes from L-929 cells. *Arch. Biochem. Biophys.* 206:93–104
179. Matsuura, T. 1977. Bio-mimetic oxygenation. *Tetrahedron* 33:2869–905
180. McCay, P. B. 1985. Vitamine E: interaction with free radicals and ascorbate. *Ann. Rev. Nutr.* 5:323–40
181. Deleted in proof
182. Miller, S. M., Klinman, J. P. 1985. Secondary isotope effects and structure-reactivity correlations in the dopamine β-monooxygenase reaction: evidence for a chemical mechanism. *Biochemistry* 24:2114–27
183. Minth, C. D., Bloom, S. R., Polak, J. M., Dixon, J. E. 1984. Cloning characterization, and DNA sequence of a human cDNA encoding neuropeptide. *Proc. Natl. Acad. Sci. USA* 81:4577–81
184. Mizushima, Y., Harauchi, T., Yoshizaki, T., Makinos, S. 1984. A rat mutant unable to synthesize vitamin C. *Experientia* 40:359–61
185. Moertel, C. G., Flemming, T. R., Creagen, E. T., Rubin, J., O'Connell, M. J., Ames, M. M. 1985. High-dose vitamin C versus placebo in the treatment of patients with advanced cancer who have had no prior chemotherapy. A randomized double-blind comparison. *N. Engl. J. Med.* 312:137–41
186. Morris, K. M., Paz, M. A. 1980. Post-translational hydroxylation of C1q: immunochemical and functional evidence for an effect of ascorbic acid. *8th Int. Complement Workshop* (Abstr.)
187. Müller, W., Hanauske-Abel, H., Loos, M. 1978. Reversible inhibition of C1q release from guinea pig macrophages by 2,2'dipyridyl. Evidence for a posttranslational hydroxylation step in the biosynthesis of C1q, a subcomponent of the first component of complement (C1). *FEBS Lett.* 90:218–22
188. Murad, S., Grove, D., Lindberg, K. A., Reynolds, G., Sivarajah, A., Pinnell, S. R. 1981. Regulation of collagen synthesis by ascorbic acid. *Proc. Natl. Acad. Sci.* 78:2879–82
189. Murad, S., Sivarajah, A., Pinnell, S. R. 1980. Prolyl and lysyl hydroxylase activities of human skin fibroblasts: effect of donor age and ascorbate. *J. Invest. Dermatol.* 75:404–7
190. Murad, S., Sivarajah, A., Pinnell, S. R. 1981. Regulation of prolyl and lysyl hydroxylase activities in cultured human skin fibroblasts by ascorbic acid. *Biochem. Biophys. Res. Commun.* 101:868–75
191. Myllylä, R., Kuutti-Savolainen, E. R., Kivirikko, K. I. 1978. The role of ascorbate in the prolyl hydroxylase reaction.

*Biochem. Biophys. Res. Commun.* 83: 441–48

192. Myllylä, R., Majamaa, K., Günzler, V., Hanauske-Abel, H. M., Kivirikko, K. I. 1984. Ascorbate is consumed stoichiometrically in the uncoupled reaction catalyzed by prolyl 4-hydroxylase and lysyl hydroxylase. *J. Biol. Chem.* 259:5403–5
193. Myllylä, R., Tuderman, L., Kivirikko, K. I. 1977. Mechanism of the prolyl hydroxylase reaction 2. Kinetic analysis of the reaction sequence. *Eur. J. Biochem.* 80:349–57
194. Nakai, C., Nozaki, M., Hayaishi, O., Saito, J., Matsuura, T. 1975. Studies on a possible reaction intermediate of *p*-hydroxyphenylpyruvate dioxygenase. *Biochem. Biophys. Res. Commun.* 67: 590–95
195. Nakanishi, S., Inoue, A., Kita, T., Nakamura, M., Chang, A. C. Y., et al. 1979. Nucleotide sequence of cloned cDNA for bovine corticotropin-β-lipotropin precursor. *Nature* 278:423–27
196. Nawa, H., Hirose, T., Takashima, H., Inayama, S., Nakanishi, S. 1983. Nucleotide sequences of cloned cDNAs for two types of bovine brain substance P precursor. *Nature* 306:32–36
197. Nelson, P. J., Pruitt, R. E., Henderson, L. L., Jenness, R., Henderson, L. M. 1981. Effect of ascorbic acid deficiency on the *in vivo* synthesis of carnitine. *Biochim. Biophys. Acta* 672:123–27

197a. Nietfeld, J. J., Kemp, A. 1980. Properties of prolyl 4-hydroxylase containing firmly-bound iron. *Biochim. Biophys. Acta* 613:349–58

198. Nietfeld, J. J., Kemp, A. 1981. The function of ascorbate with respect to prolyl 4-hydroxylase activity. *Biochim. Biophys. Acta* 657:159–67
199. Nitowsky, H. M., Govan, C. D. Jr., Gordon, H. E. 1953. Effect of hemopoietic and other agents on the hydroxyphenyluria of premature infants. *Am. J. Dis. Child.* 85:462–80
200. Nolan, J. C., Cardinale, G. J., Udenfriend, S. 1978. The formation of hydroxyproline in collagen by cells grown in the absence of serum. *Biochim. Biophys. Acta* 543:116–22
201. Novak, R. F., Swift, T. J., Hoppel, C. L. 1980. $N^6$-trimethyl-lysine metabolism. Structural identification of the metabolite 3-hydroxy-$N^6$-trimethyl-lysine. *Biochem. J.* 188:521–27
202. Olsen, B., Berg, R. A. 1979. Posttranslational processing and secretion of procollagen in fibroblasts. In *Secretory Mechanisms,* ed. C. R. Hopkins, C. J. Duncan, pp. 57–78. Cambridge: Cambridge Univ.
203. Paglia, L., Wilczek, J., Diaz DeLeon, L., Martin, G. R., Horlein, D., Muller, P. 1979. Inhibition of procollagen cell-free synthesis by amino-terminal extension peptides. *Biochemistry* 18:5030–34
204. Paik, W. K., Kim, S. 1980. *Protein Methylation*. New York: Wiley. 282 pp.
205. Pauling, L., et al. 1982. Workshop on vitamin C in immunology and cancer. *Int. Z. Vitam. Ernahrungforsch.* 23: 209–19
206. Paz, M. A., Gallop, P. M. 1975. Collagen synthesized and modified by aging fibroblasts in culture. *In Vitro* 11:302–12
207. Peterkofsky, B. 1972. Regulation of collagen secretion by ascorbic acid in 3T3 and chick embryo fibroblasts. *Biochem. Biophys. Res. Commun.* 49:1343–50
208. Peterkofsky, B. 1972. The effect of ascorbic acid on collagen polypeptide synthesis and proline hydroxylation during the growth cultured fibroblasts. *Arch. Biochem. Biophys.* 152:318–28
209. Peterkofsky, B., Kalwinsky, D., Assad, R. 1980. A substance in L-929 cell extract which replaces the ascorbate requirement in a tritium release assay for reducing cofactor; correlation of its concentration with the extent of ascorbate-independent proline hydroxylation and the level of prolyl hydroxylase activity in these cells. *Arch. Biochem. Biophys.* 199:362–73
210. Peterson, V. E., Crapo, P. A., Weiniger, J., Ginsberg, H., Olefsky, J. 1975. Quantification of plasma cholesterol and triglyceride levels in hypercholesterolemic subject receiving ascorbic acid supplements. *Am. J. Clin. Nutr.* 28:584–87
211. Piez, K. A., Reddi, A. H., eds. 1984. *Extracellular Matrix Biochemistry*. New York/Amsterdam/Oxford: Elsevier. 473 pp.
212. Pollard, H. B., Pazoles, C. J., Cruetz, C. C., Scott, J. H., Zinder, O., Hotchkiss, A. 1984. An osmotic mechanism for exocytosis from dissociated chromaffin cells. *J. Biol. Chem.* 259:1114–21
213. Porter, R. R., Reid, K. B. 1978. The biochemistry of complement. *Nature* 275:699–704
214. Prinz, W., Bortz, R., Bregin, B., Hersch, M. 1977. The effect of ascorbic acid supplementation on some parameters of the human immunological defense system. *Int. J. Vitam. Nutr. Res.* 47:248–57
215. Prockop, D. J., Berg, R. A., Kivirikko, K. I., Uitto, J. 1976. Intracellular steps in the biosynthesis of collagen. In *Biochemistry of Collagen,* ed. G. N. Ramachandran, A. H. Reddi, pp. 163–273. New York: Plenum.

216. Prockop, D. J., Juva, K. 1965. Synthesis of hydroxyproline *in vitro* by the hydroxylation of proline in a precursor of collagen. *Proc. Natl. Acad. Sci. USA* 53:661–68
217. Prockop, D. J., Tuderman, L. 1982. Posttranslational enzymes in the biosynthesis of collagens: extracellular enzymes. *Methods Enzymol.* 82(PA): 305–19
218. Puistola, U., Turpeenniemi-Hujanen, T. M., Myllylä, R., Kivirikko, K. I. 1980. Studies on the lysyl hydroxylase reaction I. Initial velocity kinetics and related aspects. *Biochim. Biophys. Acta* 611:40–50
219. Puistola, U., Turpeenniemi-Hujanen, T. M., Myllylä, R., Kivirikko, K. I. 1980. Studies on the lysyl hydroxylase reaction II. Inhibition kinetics of the reaction mechanism. *Biochim. Biophys. Acta* 611:51–60
220. Quinn, R. S., Krane, S. M. 1976. Abnormal properties of collagen lysyl hydroxylase from skin fibroblasts of siblings with hydroxylysine-deficient collagen. *J. Clin. Invest.* 57:83–93
221. Quinn, R. S., Krane, S. M. 1979. Collagen synthesis by cultured skin fibroblasts from siblings with hydroxylysine-deficient collagen. *Biochim. Biophys. Acta* 585:589–98
222. Rao, N. V., Adams, E. 1978. Partial reaction of prolyl hydroxylase. *J. Biol. Chem.* 253:6327–30
223. Rebouche, C. J., Broquist, H. P. 1976. Carnitine biosynthesis in *Neurospora crassa:* Enzymatic conversion of lysine to ε-*N*-trimethyllysine. *J. Bacteriol.* 126:1207–14
224. Rebouche, C. J., Engel, A. G. 1980. Tissue distribution of carnitine biosynthetic enzymes in man. *Biochim. Biophys. Acta* 630:22–29
225. Rebouche, C. J., Lehman, L. J. 1985. Availability of a dietary ε-*N*-trimethylysine for carnitine biosynthesis in growing rat. *Fed. Proc.* 44(3):763 (Abstr.)
226. Rebouche, C. J., Paulson, D. J. 1986. Carnitine metabolism and function in humans. *Ann. Rev. Nutr.* 6:41–66
227. *Recommended Daily Allowances*. 1980. Food and nutrition board, National Academy of Sciences, pp. 72–82. Washington, DC: Natl. Res. Council. 9th ed.
228. Reid, K. B. M., Porter, R. R. 1976. Subunit composition and structure of subcomponent C1q of the first component of human complement. *Biochem. J.* 155:19–23
228a. Risteli, J., Tuderman, L., Kivirikko, K. I. 1976. Intracellular enzymes of collagen biosynthesis in rat liver as a function of age and in hepatic injury induced by dimethylnitrosamine. Purification of rat prolyl hydroxylase and comparison of changes in prolyl hydroxylase activity with changes in immunoreactive prolyl hydroxylase. *Biochem. J.* 158:369–76
229. Robertson, W. B., Hewitt, J., Herman, C. 1959. The relation of ascorbic acid to the conversion of proline to hydroxyproline in the synthesis of collagen in the carrageenan granuloma. *J. Biol. Chem.* 234:105–8
230. Roche, P. A., Moorehead, T. J., Hamilton, G. A. 1982. Purification and properties of hog liver 4-hydroxyphenylpyruvate dioxygenase. *Arch. Biochem. Biophys.* 216:62–73
231. Roeser, H. P. 1983. The role of ascorbic acid in the turnover of storage iron. *Semin. Hematol.* 20:91–100
232. Rosenberg, R. C., Lovenberg, W. 1980. Dopamine β-hydroxylase. *Essays Neurochem. Neuropharmacol.* 4:163–209
233. Rosenberry, T. L., Richardson, J. M. 1977. Structure of 18S and 14S acetylcholinesterase. Identification of collagen-like subunits that are linked by disulfide bonds to catalytic subunits. *Biochemistry* 16:3550–58
234. Rowe, L. B., Schwarz, R. I. 1983. Role of procollagen mRNA levels in controlling the rate of procollagen synthesis. *Mol. Cell. Biol.* 3:241–49
235. Rundgren, M. 1982. Tritium isotope effects in the reaction catalyzed by 4-hydroxyphenylpyruvate dioxygenase from *Pseudomonas* sp. strain P.J. 874. *Biochim. Biophys. Acta* 704:59–65
236. Rundgren, M. 1983. Some kinetic properties of 4-hydroxyphenylpyruvate dioxygenase from *Pseudomonas* sp. strain P.J. 874. *Eur. J. Biochem.* 133:657–63
237. Sachan, D. S., Hoppel, C. L. 1980. Carnitine biosynthesis. Hydroxylation of $N^6$-trimethyl-lysine to 3-hydroxy-$N^6$-trimethyl-lysine. *Biochem. J.* 188:529–34
238. Saito, I., Yamane, M., Shimazu, H., Matsuura, T., Cahnmann, H. J. 1975. Biogenetic type conversion of *p*-hydroxyphenylpyruvic acid into homogentisic acid. *Tetrahedron Lett.* 1975:641–44
239. Sandor, A., Kispal, G., Kerner, J., Alkonyi, I. 1983. Combined effect of ascorbic acid deficiency and underfeeding on the hepatic carnitine level in guinea-pigs. *Experientia* 39:512–13
240. Sapper, H., Kang, S. O., Paul, H. H., Lohmann, W. 1982. The reversibility of the vitamin C redox system: Electrochemical reasons and biological aspects. *Z. Naturforsch. Teil C* 37:942–46

241. Sato, P., Udenfriend, S. 1978. Studies on ascorbic acid related to the genetic basis of scurvy. *Vitamin Horm.* 36:33–52
242. Schwartz, E., Bienkowski, R. S., Coltoff-Schiller, B., Goldfischer, S., Blumenfeld, O. O. 1982. Changes in the components of extracellular matrix and in growth properties of cultured aortic smooth muscle cells upon ascorbate feeding. *J. Cell. Biol.* 92:462–70
243. Schwarz, R. I. 1985. Procollagen secretion meets the minimum requirements for the rate-controlling step in the ascorbate induction of procollagen synthesis. *J. Biol. Chem.* 260:3045–49
244. Schwarz, R. I., Bissell, M. J. 1977. Dependence of the differentiated state on the cellular environment: Modulation of collagen synthesis in tendon cells. *Proc. Natl. Acad. Sci. USA* 74:4453–57
245. Schwarz, R. I., Mandell, R. B., Bissell, M. J. 1981. Ascorbate induction of collagen synthesis as a means for elucidating a mechanism for quantitative control of tissue-specific function. *Mol. Cell. Biol.* 1:843–53
246. Sealock, R. R., Goodland, R. L. 1951. Ascorbic acid, a coenzyme in tyrosine oxidation. *Science* 114:645–46
247. Sealock, R. R., Goodland, R. L., Summerwell, W. N., Brierly, J. M. 1952. The role of ascorbic acid in the oxidation of L-tyrosine by guinea pig liver extract. *J. Biol. Chem.* 196:761–67
248. Sealock, R. R., Silberstein, H. E. 1940. The excretion of homogentisic acid and other tyrosine metabolites by the vitamin C–deficient guinea pig. *J. Biol. Chem.* 135:251–58
249. Seib, P. A., Tolbert, B. M., eds. 1982. *Ascorbic Acid: Chemistry, Metabolism and Uses,* Adv. Chem. Ser. 200. Washington, DC: Am. Chem. Soc. 604 pp.
250. Seifter, S., Gallop, P. M. 1966. The structure of proteins. In *The Proteins,* ed. H. Neurath, 4:153–458. New York/ London: Academic. 2nd ed.
251. Shaffer, P. M., Hsu, C. A., Abbott, M. T. 1975. Metabolism of pyrimidine deoxyribonucleosides in *Neurospora crassa. J. Bacteriol.* 121:648–55
252. Shaffer, P. M., McCroskey, R. P., Abbott, M. T. 1972. Substrate specificity of the hydroxylase reaction in which thymidine is converted to thymine ribonucleoside. *Biochim. Biophys. Acta* 258: 387–94
253. Shaffer, P. M., McCroskey, R. P., Palmatier, R. D., Midgett, R. J., Abbott, M. T. 1968. The cell-free conversion of a deoxyribonucleoside to a ribonucleoside without detachment of the deoxyribose. *Biochem. Biophys. Res. Commun.* 33: 806–11
254. Shen, T. F., Strecker, H. J. 1975. Synthesis of proline and hydroxyproline in human lung (WI-38) fibroblasts. *Biochem. J.* 150:453–61
255. Skotland, T., LJones, T. 1979. Dopamine β-mono-oxygenase: Structure, mechanism and properties of the enzyme-bound copper. *Inorg. Perspect. Biol. Med.* 2:151–80
256. Skotland, T., LJones, T. 1980. Direct spectrophotometric detection of ascorbate free radical formed by dopamine β-monooxygenase and by ascorbate oxidase. *Biochim. Biophys. Acta* 630: 30–35
257. Deleted in proof
258. Spanheimer, R. G., Peterkofsky, B. 1985. A specific decrease in collagen synthesis in acutely fasted, vitamin C–supplemented guinea pigs. *J. Biol. Chem.* 260:3955–62
259. Spindel, E. R., Chin, W. W., Price, J., Rees, L. H., Besser, G. M., Habener, J. F. 1984. Cloning and characterization of cDNAs encoding human gastrin releasing peptides. *Proc. Natl. Acad. Sci. USA* 81:5699–5703
260. Stassen, F. I. H., Cardinale, G. J., Udenfriend, S. 1973. Activation of prolyl hydroxylase in L-929 fibroblasts by ascorbic acid. *Proc. Natl. Acad. Sci. USA* 70:1090–93
261. Stein, R., Englard, S. 1981. The use of a tritium release assay to measure 6-*N*-trimethyl-L-lysine hydroxylase activity: Synthesis of 6-*N*-[3-$^{3}$H]trimethyl-D,L-lysine. *Anal. Biochem.* 116:230–36
262. Stein, R., Englard, S. 1982. Properties of rat 6-*N*-trimethyl-L-lysine hydroxylases: Similarities among kidney, liver, heart, and skeletal muscle activities. *Arch. Biochem. Biophys.* 217:324–31
263. Stubbe, J.-A. 1985. Identification of two α-ketoglutarate-dependent dioxygenases in extracts of *Rhodotorula glutinis* catalyzing deoxyuridine hydroxylation. *J. Biol. Chem.* 260:9972–75
264. Sugano, K., Aponte, G. W., Yamada, T. 1985. Identification and characterization of glycine-extended post-translational processing intermediates of prograstin in porcine stomach. *J. Biol. Chem.* 260: 11724–29
265. Takeuchi, T., Yamada, T. 1985. Isolation of a cDNA clone encoding pancreatic polypeptide. *Proc. Natl. Acad. Sci. USA* 82:1536–39
266. Terland, O., Flatmark, T. 1975. Ascorbate as a natural constituent of chromaf-

fin granules from bovine adrenal medulla. *FEBS Lett.* 59:52–56
267. Thoma, W. J., Henderson, L. L. 1984. Effect of vitamin C deficiency on hydroxylation of trimethylaminobutyrate to carnitine in the guinea pig. *Biochim. Biophys. Acta* 797:136–39
268. Thomas, W. R., Holt, P. G. 1978. Vitamin C and immunity: An assessment of the evidence. *Clin. Exp. Immunol.* 32:370–79
269. Tirrell, J. G., Westhead, E. W. 1979. The uptake of ascorbic acid and dehydroascorbic acid by chromaffin granules of the adrenal medulla. *Neuroscience* 4:181–86
270. Tolbert, B. M., Ward, J. B. 1982. Dehydroascorbic acid. See Ref. 249, pp. 101–23
271. Tolbert, N. E. 1981. Metabolic pathways in peroxisomes and glyoxysomes. *Ann. Rev. Biochem.* 50:133–57
271a. Tryggvason, K., Majamaa, K., Risteli, J., Kivirikko, K. I. 1979. Partial purification and characterization of chick-embryo prolyl 3-hydroxylase. *Biochem. J.* 183:303–7
271b. Tuderman, L., Kuutti, E. R., Kivirikko, K. I. 1975. An affinity-column procedure using poly (L-proline) for the purification of prolyl hydroxylase. Purification of the enzyme from chick embryos. *Eur. J. Biochem.* 52:9–16
272. Tuderman, L., Myllylä, R., Kivirikko, K. I. 1977. Mechanism of the prolyl hydroxylase reaction. 1. Role of cosubstrates. *Eur. J. Biochem.* 80:341–48
272a. Turpeenniemi-Hujanen, T. M., Puistola, U., Kivirikko, K. I. 1980. Isolation of lysyl hydroxylase, an enzyme of collagen synthesis, from chick embryos as a homogeneous protein. *Biochem. J.* 189:247–53
272b. Turpeenniemi-Hujanen, T. M., Puistola, U., Kivirikko, K. I. 1981. Human lysyl hydroxylase: purification to homogeneity, partial characterization and comparison of catalytic properties with those of a mutant enzyme from Ehler-Danlos syndrome type VI fibroblasts. *Collagen Rel. Res.* 1:355–66
272c. Urushizaki, Y., Seifter, S. 1985. Phosphorylation of hydroxylysine residues in collagen synthesized by cultured aortic smooth muscle cells. *Proc. Natl. Acad. Sci. USA* 82:3091–95
273. Vale, W., Spiess, J., Rivier, C., Rivier, J. 1981. Characterization of a 41-residue ovine hypothalamic peptide that stimulates secretion of corticotropin and β-endorphin. *Science* 213:1394–97
274. Villafranca, J. J., Colombo, G., Ratashekhar, B., Giedroc, D., Baldoni, J. 1982. Dopamine β-hydroxylase: Studies of the $Cu^{+2}$ environment and development of suicide inhibitors. In *Oxygenases and Oxygen Metabolism,* ed. M. Nozaki, S. Yamamoto, Y. Ishimura, M. J. Coon, L. Ernster, R. W. Estabrook, pp. 125–35. New York/London/Paris: Academic
275. Wada, G., Fellman, J. H., Fujita, T. S., Roth, E. S. 1975. Purification and properties of avian liver *p*-hydroxyphenylpyruvate hydroxylase. *J. Biol. Chem.* 250:6720–26
276. Warn-Cramer, B. J., Macrander, L. A., Abbott, M. T. 1983. Markedly different ascorbate dependencies of the sequential α-ketoglutarate dioxygenase reactions catalyzed by an essentially homogeneous tymine 7-hydroxylase from *Rhodotorula glutinis. J. Biol. Chem.* 258:10551–57
277. Watanabe, M. S., McCroskey, R. P., Abbott, M. T. 1970. The enzymatic conversion of 5-formyluracil to uracil 5-carboxylic acid. *J. Biol. Chem.* 245: 2023–26
278. Weber, E., Esch, F. S., Bohlen, P., Patterson, S., Corbett, A. D., et al. 1983. Metorphamide: Isolation, structure, and biologic activity of an amidated opioid octapeptide from bovine brain. *Proc. Natl. Acad. Sci. USA* 80:7362–66
279. Wiestner, M., Krieger, T., Horlein, D., Glanville, R. W., Fietzek, P., Muller, P. K. 1979. Inhibiting effect of procollagen peptides on collagen biosynthesis in fibroblast cultures. *J. Biol. Chem.* 254: 7016–23
280. Witkop, B. 1973. In *Current Topics in Biochemistry,* ed. C. B. Anfinsen, A. N. Schechter, pp. 109–33. New York: Academic
281. Wittes, R. E. 1985. Vitamin C and cancer. *N. Engl. J. Med.* 312:178–79
282. Wondrack, L. M., Hsu, C.-A., Abbott, M. T. 1978. Thymine 7-hydroxylase and pyrimidine deoxyribonucleoside 2'-hydroxylase activities in *Rhodotorula glutinis. J. Biol. Chem.* 253:6511–15
283. Wondrack, L. M., Warn, B. J., Saewert, M. D., Abbott, M. T. 1979. Substitution of nucleoside triphosphates for ascorbate in the thymine 7-hydroxylase reaction of *Rhodotorula glutinis. J. Biol. Chem.* 254:26–29
284. Woodruff, C. W. 1975. Ascorbic acid—scurvy. *Prog. Food Nutr. Sci.* 1:493–506
285. Yew, M. S. 1985. Biosynthesis of ascorbic acid in chick embryos. *Experientia* 41:943–44
286. Yoo, O. J., Powell, C. T., Agarwal, K. L. 1982. Molecular cloning and nucle-

otide sequence of full-length cDNA coding for porcine gastrin. *Proc. Natl. Acad. Sci. USA* 79:1049–53

287. Zannoni, V. G., Holsztynska, E. J., Lau, S. S. 1982. Biochemical functions of ascorbic acid in drug metabolism. See Ref. 249, pp. 349–68
288. Zannoni, V. G., LaDu, B. N. 1959. The tyrosine oxidation system of liver. IV. Studies on the inhibition of *p*-hydroxyphenylpyruvic acid oxidase by excess substrate. *J. Biol. Chem.* 234:2925–31
289. Zannoni, V. G., Susick, R. L., Smart, R. C. 1984. Ascorbic acid as it relates to the metabolism of drugs and environmental agents. *Curr. Concepts Nutr.* 13:21–35
290. Zern, M. A., Schwartz, E., Giambrone, M.-A., Blumenfeld, O. O. 1985. Ascorbate-generated endogenous extracellular matrix affects cell protein synthesis in calf aortic smooth muscle cells. *Exp. Cell. Res.* 160:307–18

*Ann. Rev. Nutr. 1986. 6:407–32*


# LABILE METHYL GROUPS AND THE PROMOTION OF CANCER

*Paul M. Newberne and Adrianne E. Rogers*

Department of Pathology, Boston University School of Medicine, Boston, Massachusetts 02118

---

CONTENTS

INTRODUCTION ........ 407
DIETARY SOURCES OF LIPOTROPES ........ 408
INTERRELATIONSHIPS OF METHIONINE, FOLATE, AND VITAMIN $B_{12}$ METABOLISM ........ 409
EFFECT OF LIPOTROPE DEFICIENCY ON IMMUNE FUNCTION ........ 411
*Folic Acid* ........ 411
*Vitamin $B_{12}$* ........ 414
*Methionine and Choline* ........ 415
LIPOTROPES AND XENOBIOTIC METABOLISM ........ 417
LIPOTROPES AND CANCER ........ 420
*Human Studies* ........ 420
*Animal Studies* ........ 421
DISCUSSION ........ 425
CONCLUSIONS ........ 429

## INTRODUCTION

Lipotropes constitute a highly significant group of biologically active compounds, the major components of which are choline, methionine, vitamin $B_{12}$, and folic acid. These nutrients play a central role in cellular metabolism through their regulation of the transfer and utilization of one-carbon moieties (8). These are essential to the synthesis and methylation of DNA, the production of nucleoproteins and membranes, and the metabolism of lipids, all of which are required for cell proliferation and the maintenance of tissue integrity. Lipo-



0199-9885/86/0715-0407$02.00

tropes interact extensively with each other and with other nutrients. Figure 1 illustrates the role of folate, vitamin $B_{12}$, and methionine in the transfer of one-carbon units (17). There are a variety of reactions in which methyl groups are transferred, including (*a*) the formation of the purine ring; (*b*) pyrimidine biosynthesis; (*c*) amino acid interconversions; and (*d*) formate metabolism. This review concentrates on certain aspects of lipotropes and their role in the promotion of carcinogenesis; included are some of their immunoregulatory properties, their influence on xenobiotic metabolism, and proposed mechanisms for their interactions in the promotion of cancer.

# DIETARY SOURCES OF LIPOTROPES

Choline and folic acid are plentiful in both animal and plant foods; however, plants are low in methionine and do not contain vitamin $B_{12}$. Animal products and microorganisms are the sole dietary sources of vitamin $B_{12}$.

Each of the four lipotropic nutrients (methionine, choline, folic acid, and

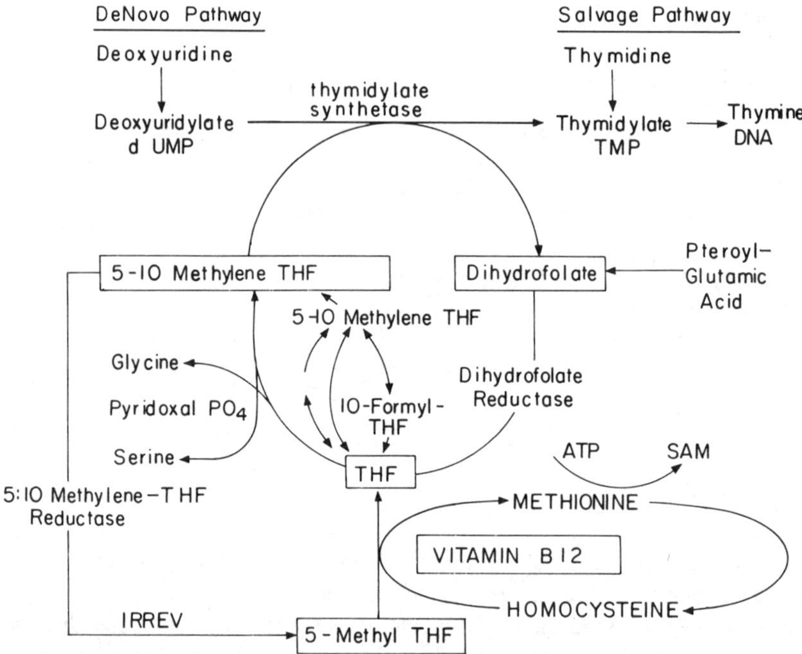


*Figure 1* The biochemistry of one-carbon units indicates the fundamental role of folic acid in the metabolism of nucleic acids, protein, amino acids, and phospholipids, all essential to mounting an effective immune response and to cell proliferation in general. Vitamin $B_{12}$ and methionine are integral components of the system as well as choline but the latter is less involved. From (17), with permission.

vitamin $B_{12}$) are stored in the body in given amounts in either pure or derivatized forms. They all turn over at specific rates. Vitamin $B_{12}$ has the largest store relative to its daily requirement. Methionine is stored in tissue proteins that turn over constantly; it is also present as its t-RNA derivative and in an activated form, *S*-adenosylmethionine, essential to transmethylation. Free methionine is also present in plasma and in small amounts in tissues.

The main storage form of choline is in the choline phospholipids, which are widely distributed in all tissues. Choline is not essential in most animal species but is conditionally essential in the young rat. Folic acid is stored in red cells and in other tissues in significant amounts, but its turnover is rapid.

Stores of folic acid last no more than a few months after intake ceases, and choline, as such, lasts only a few days or at most a few weeks. Like methionine, choline can be derived from tissue breakdown since it is a major component of cell membranes and it can also be synthesized from other tissue components, including glycine and serine. Nevertheless, the diet is the major source of all lipotropes and a dietary deficiency of any or all of these nutrients is a potential threat to health. A decrease in the pool of methyl groups may contribute to susceptibility to many diseases, including cancer. It is to the latter chronic disease that this review is addressed.

## INTERRELATIONSHIPS OF METHIONINE, FOLATE, AND VITAMIN $B_{12}$ METABOLISM

Before proceeding to the main subject relative to the influence of labile methyl groups and the promotion of cancer, a brief discussion of the interactions of lipotropes is appropriate.

Vitamin $B_{12}$ and folate are essential for growth and proliferation of mammalian cells. The metabolism and participation of these cofactors in a variety of reactions requiring transfer of 1-carbon intermediates have been extensively reviewed (19, 20, 65). Rapid availability of nucleotide precursors is particularly important in the lymphatic system, which depends on proliferation and cell division in response to a foreign stimulus. The same is true for growth of all cancerous cells and serves as a basis for chemotherapy of cancer with antifolates (26). Moreover, the megaloblastic anemia precipitated by either folate or vitamin $B_{12}$ deficiency appears to be caused by a common defect in thymidylate synthesis leading to a derangement of DNA synthesis. Menzies et al (36) found alterations in the chromosomes and abnormal DNA synthesis in bone marrow cells from patients with megaloblastic anemia. Other workers have reported a decrease in the number of megaloblasts synthesizing DNA, with some cells failing to exhibit any evidence for DNA synthesis (75).

Vitamin $B_{12}$ is involved in a number of reactions in bacteria, only two of which have been demonstrated in mammalian systems. These are (*a*) the isomerization of methylmalonate to succinate, which forms a link between carbohydrate and lipid metabolism, and (*b*) the methylation of homocysteine to methionine, the metabolic link between $B_{12}$, folate, and methionine metabolism.

A vitamin $B_{12}$–containing transmethylase is required for the conversion of homocysteine to methionine (Figure 1). In the process tetrahydrofolate (THF) is regenerated. Since methionine is available from other sources (diet and amino acid pools) it is thought that the importance of this reaction lies not in the synthesis of the amino acid but in the regeneration of THF.

As shown in Figure 1, folate coenzymes, carrying single-carbon units in different states of reduction, participate in a variety of reactions in which methyl groups are transferred. Cellular DNA synthesis depends on the availability of the four nucleotide precursors, and, although thymidylate can be formed directly from thymidine via a salvage pathway, most cells utilize the de novo path whereby *d*-uridine monophosphate (dUMP) is converted to TMP by the enzyme thymidylate synthetase. This is the rate-limiting step in DNA synthesis and requires 5,10-methylene THF as a cofactor, an observation made almost thirty years ago (12). In the process the cofactor is reduced to dihydrofolate (DHF), which can be further reduced via dihydrofolate reductase to THF.

An alternate way of regenerating THF is via the $B_{12}$-dependent methyl transferase reaction in which the methyl group is transferred from 5-methyl THF in the synthesis of methionine. As the folate-borne methyl groups go through successive stages of reduction, they are converted to 5,10-methylene THF, which can either serve as a cofactor for thymidylate synthetase or be further reduced via an irreversible reaction to 5-Me THF. This folate coenzyme must be converted to THF in order for the methyl group to reenter the methyl pool. In vitamin $B_{12}$ deficiency this conversion cannot take place and 5-Me THF accumulates (21). Patients with vitamin $B_{12}$ deficiency also exhibit an increase in the excretion of formiminoglutamic acid (64), formate (66), and 4(5)-amino-5(4)imidazole-carboxamide (35). These metabolites all require folate cofactors for further conversion and are restored to normal levels by the addition of dietary methionine (25).

Methionine, essential as a protein constitutent, also serves as a methyl donor in a large number of reactions. Mammalian liver systems have an enzyme for the direct methylation of homocysteine via betaine (8), but most cells utilize the $B_{12}$, 5-Me-THF-dependent methyl transferase reaction to synthesize methionine, which can then be further converted to *S*-adenosyl methionine (SAM). In addition to being an inhibitor of the 5-Me THF:homocysteine transmethylase reaction, SAM is a negative feedback inhibitor of 5,10-methylene THF reductase that reduces the amount of 5-Me THF formed and increases the availability of other folate cofactors (28).

Methionine also accelerates the conversion of formate into $CO_2$ (25). This reaction is catalyzed by the enzyme formyl tetrahydrofolate dehydrogenase. The normal concentration of 10-formyl THF is far below the $K_m$ of the enzyme (29); however, according to the scheme postulated by Krebs et al (25), an increase in dietary methionine increases SAM concentrations, causing a pile-up of 5,10-methylene THF that is at or near equilibrium with 10-formyl THF. Therefore, this latter intermediate would increase in concentration and thereby enhance the activity of the dehydrogenase. Krebs postulates that this pathway is important for disposing of excess one-carbon units and regenerating THF in the absence of vitamin $B_{12}$. This hypothesis is supported by the observations of others that added dietary methionine reduces the proportion of 5-methyl folate derivatives in rat liver and increases the 10-formyl monoglutamate (50) and polyglutamate (71) forms.

## EFFECT OF LIPOTROPE DEFICIENCY ON IMMUNE FUNCTION

### *Folic Acid*

It is not surprising that the immune response, which requires rapid proliferation of sensitized cells, is affected by a deficiency of folic acid and other sources for methyl group synthesis. Despite the significance of folate to the immune system there have been only a few systematic studies of this important deficiency on immunocompetence in either animal or human models. Table 1 summarizes the alterations in humoral and cell-mediated immunity in patients with megaloblastic anemia due to folate deficiency as well as the results of studies in folate-deficient animals. A few comments on the reports represented by Table 1 are appropriate.

HUMAN STUDIES The stress of infection, superimposed on low reserves of labile methyl groups, through inadequate nutrition and vitamin loss (through diarrhea, vomiting, etc), along with increased cell turnover, places the patient at risk for deficiency of folate and other nutrients (18, 19, 61). In an isolated case of peripheral lymphocyte response to mitogenic (phytohemagglutinin A, PHA) stimulation from a patient with megaloblastic anemia due to folate deficiency, Das & Hoffbrand (6) found a depressed incorporation of $^3$H-thymidine. Megaloblastic anemia was studied in Bantu patients in South Africa using dinitrochlorobenzene skin test and response of peripheral lymphocytes to PHA. These patients had normal levels of serum iron and vitamin $B_{12}$ except for two subgroups that were studied for iron deficiency and combined folate-iron deficiency (18). The results are presented in Table 2.

Prior to treatment, the folate-deficient groups exhibited a significant depression in skin reactivity to DNCB, compared to the purely iron-deficient and

**Table 1** Effects of folate deficiency on immune function[a]

- I. Human studies
  - A. Depressed peripheral lymphocyte response to PHA (6, 18)
  - B. No change in neutrophil function (24)
  - C. Increased incidence of folate deficiency in patients with hyperplastic candidosis (23)
  - D. Delayed cutaneous hypersensitivity is depressed (18)
- II. Animal studies
  - A. Guinea pig
    1. Decreased WBC (70)
    2. Increased susceptibility to Shigella infection (40)
  - B. Rats
    1. Decreased leukocytes and granulocytes (32)
    2. Decreased hemagglutination titers (53)
    3. Decreased number of antibody forming cells (27)
    4. Decreased number of T cells (77)
       Depressed cytotoxicity
       Depressed splenic PHA response
       Decreased delayed cutaneous hypersensitivity
    5. Increased susceptibility to parasitic infection (1)
  - C. Chickens
    1. Decreased bacterial agglutination titers (31)
    2. Increased susceptibility to viral infection

[a] From Nauss & Newberne (39) by permission. Numbers in parentheses are references.

control groups. Following therapy with folate supplements, 80% of the patients in the first three groups had a positive skin test response within 6–23 days. The PHA response of peripheral lymphocytes (as measured by $^3$H-thymidine incorporation) was one third that of the control or of the iron-deficient subjects and returned to normal values 7–14 days after therapy. Vitamin $B_{12}$ deficiency was ruled out in these patients by a negative Shilling test, which involves administration of a loading dose of the vitamin.

The remaining few studies in humans (10, 23, 24) have reported variable results.

ANIMAL STUDIES Selected nutrient deficiencies can be examined in animal models under rigidly controlled conditions. Impaired humoral (27, 32, 53) and cell-mediated (77) immune responses have been observed in rats on folate-deficient diets. Guinea pigs are particularly susceptible to folate deficiency (40, 70, 80).

Early studies showed that chicks raised on folate-deficient diets had decreased bacterial agglutination titers and increased susceptibility to viral infection (31). Folate-deficient rats were more susceptible to infection with *Trypanosoma lewisi* (1). The deficient animals had increased parasite levels in

**Table 2** Dinitrochlorobenzene skin test and PHA response before treatment in folic acid–deficient, iron-deficient, and control patients[a]

| Group[b] | Degree of dinitro-chlorobenzene skin test reaction (no. of patients) 0 | + | ++ | PHA stimulation of lymphocytes[b] (dpm) | Unstimulated lymphocytes[c] (dpm) |
|---|---|---|---|---|---|
| Folate-deficient | | | | | |
| nonobstetric | 11 | 0 | 0 | 8,800±3,600 (3,091–13,995) | 510 (219–1201) |
| obstetric | 6 | 6 | 1 | 6,800±2,900 (3,691–12,323) | 480 (176–1250) |
| Folate- and iron-deficient | 5 | 0 | 0 | 6,000±3,280 (3,527–10,049) | 330 (130–501) |
| Iron-deficient | 0 | 2 | 3 | 23,300±5,470 (15,005–28,896) | 390 (162–672) |
| Control | 1 | 4 | 8 | 26,340±5,680 (18,740–33,725) | 370 (130–719) |

[a] From (18), by permission.
[b] Uptake of $^3$H-thymidine; results are expressed in disintegrations per minute (dpm); mean ± S.D. and range.
[c] Uptake of $^3$H-thymidine by lymphocytes in presence of saline; results are expressed as disintegrations per minute (dpm); mean ± S.D.; and range.

their blood compared to control animals and remained infected for longer periods of time.

Table 3 lists results from studies (16, 77) conducted in our laboratories using weanling Sprague-Dawley rats, kept on a folate-deficient diet for three months. They had a decreased number of T cells (as measured by $^3$H-uridine labeling) in the spleen and peripheral blood. The cytotoxic activity of splenic lymphocytes of folate-deficient animals exposed to Brown Norway rat thymocytes decreased

**Table 3** Folic acid deficiency in rats[a]

| Immune parameter tested | Control | Folate-deficient |
|---|---|---|
| Delayed hypersensitivity (skin test response to PHA) | 3.8±0.4[b] | 1.6±0.4 |
| Lymphocyte-mediated cytotoxicity (% killing) | 29.1±3.7[c] | 5.2±1.5 |
| Spleen transformation (PHA response) | 19,398±1,014[d] | 4,263±579 |
| [$^3$H]-Uridine labeling of T cells | | |
| Spleen | 70±2.4[e] | 42±1.9 |
| Thymus | 82±1.5 | 73±2.0 |
| Blood | 67±1.7 | 44±2.8 |

[a] From (77) and (16), by permission.
[b] Histological grading based on degree of mononuclear cell infiltration: 0, no response; 4, severe response.
[c] Results expressed as mean ± S.E.
[d] Results expressed as cpm ± S.E.
[e] Results expressed as percentage of cells labeled.

significantly (percentage of killing was 29.1 ± 3.7 in controls compared to 5.2 ± 1.5 in folate-deficient rats) as did sensitivity to stimulation by the T-cell mitogen PHA (stimulation index of 14.8 in controls compared to 3.0 in folate-deficient rats). An in vivo measurement of cell-mediated immune function (skin test sensitivity to intradermal PHA injection) showed a depressed response in the deficient animals based on the degree of mononuclear cell infiltration.

Additional experiments demonstrated a profound defect in young animals (3 months) kept on a folate-deficient diet from weaning. Rats fed a folate-deficient diet from one month of age through a year exhibited interesting changes, with time, in the transformation response of lymphocytes from the spleen, thymus, and lymph nodes to a variety of mitogens (39). The results were quite similar to those observed in rats deficient in lipotrope (choline-methionine), described later. These deprivations during this period of rapid growth and development of the lymphatic system, even for short periods of time, caused a depressed mitogen transformation response in the first three weeks. However, after twelve months there were no longer significant differences between the experimental and control groups.

## *Vitamin $B_{12}$*

HUMAN STUDIES With the exception of autoimmune phenomena in pernicious anemia, studies relative to vitamin $B_{12}$ and immunocompetence are limited. Using the lymphocyte transformation test, Tai & McGuigan (69) showed that peripheral lymphocytes from patients with pernicious anemia were sensitized to a variety of gastric antigens. Using the leucocyte migration test, others have demonstrated in vitro delayed hypersensitivity to these antigens (11, 15). MacCuish et al (33) measured the lymphocyte transformation response to the mitogen PHA in 20 patients with pernicious anemia and an equal number of age- and sex-matched controls. The mean transformation response (as measured by $^{3}$H-thymidine uptake) of peripheral lymphocytes from patients with pernicious anemia was significantly lower than controls at the three doses tested. There were no significant differences in the percentages of B and T lymphocytes as measured by immunofluorescence and rosette techniques respectively.

ANIMAL STUDIES Rats and other laboratory animals do not develop clean-cut megaloblastic anemia when fed a vitamin $B_{12}$–deficient diet even though levels of serum $B_{12}$, methylmalonyl-CoA mutase activities, and tissue coenzyme levels may be reduced (20). This may explain why, with the exception of an early report on depressed complement-fixing antibodies in vitamin $B_{12}$–deficient rats (74), studies of vitamin $B_{12}$ deprivation in rat models have not demonstrated any effect on immune function (20). We showed that rats fed a

$B_{12}$-deficient diet from weaning until three months of age responded to Salmonella infection in a manner similar to control animals (45). Infection caused an identical increase in spleen weights and serum and globulin levels in control and deficient animals and there were no differences in the histopathology of the infected organs. However, if the $B_{12}$-deficient diets were fed during gestation and weaning, then infection with Salmonella at the age of three months caused a higher mortality (71% at 30 days compared to 25% in controls) in the vitamin $B_{12}$–deficient group (48). The resistance of this group improved appreciably when vitamin $B_{12}$ was added to the diet during the postweaning period. Other studies have focused on combined vitamin $B_{12}$/choline-methionine deficiencies and are discussed below.

## *Methionine and Choline*

Most clinical studies of nutrient modulation of immune function have dealt with patients suffering from kwashiorkor (protein-calorie malnutrition, PCM) or marasmus (starvation). Protein deprivation as well as protein-calorie imbalances, which are ubiquitous in Third World countries, play major roles in the immune response of individuals to infection. These studies (17) point to the importance of protein quality as well as quantity in the effective maintenance of the immune system. While not clearly established, these studies suggest the importance of amino acid balance and certain specific amino acids, particularly methionine, in the functional capacity of the immune mechanism. For an in-depth discussion of protein-calorie malnutrition, resistance to infection, and some of the perceived mechanisms, the reader is referred to (9, 17, 61, 68a). Briefly, it has been observed that all lymphoid organs, particularly the thymus, are reduced in size; active cell division is sharply decreased in these tissues; and the PCM patients are markedly susceptible to infection. There seems to be agreement that PCM does not appreciably diminish the B-cell population in number or function; in fact, humoral immunity may be enhanced. The major effect appears to be on the T-cell subset of lymphoid cells, especially the T-helper cells. Specific effects are described in (17).

Recent experiments have concentrated on the use of animal models to define the role of individual essential amino acids in modulating the cell-mediated or humoral immune response. Conflicting results with methionine deficiency on immune response are partially attributable to differences in species and time of initiation of the experimental diet.

The effect of a specific nutrient deficiency on the immune response depends on many parameters, including age of the animal, length of time on the diet, adequacy of other nutrients, and age at the time of challenge to the immune system. The importance of defining these parameters has been demonstrated in studies in our laboratories examining the effects of reduced methionine-choline levels at varying stages of development on the immunocompetence of rats or mice.

We have studied rats that were littered to dams fed diets marginally deficient in methionine and choline during gestation (39). Some of the animals were switched to an adequate diet at birth, others were maintained on the same diet the mother had received. One hundred days postweaning the animals were infected with *Salmonella typhimurium*. As seen in Table 4, rats fed the marginal methionine-choline diet had reduced body weight at three months of age and a high mortality rate following infection with Salmonella compared to the normal controls. Although supplementation in the postweaning period improved weight gain, it failed to alter the response to infection.

The thymus glands of the prenatally malnourished pups were smaller at birth than those of the pups adequately nourished *in utero* (Table 5). If the low lipotrope diets were continued to three months of age, the differences became even more marked. In addition to its decreased size, histological evaluation of the thymus showed a marked hypoplasia of tissue from not only this organ, but also the lymph nodes and spleen (44, 49).

The above-noted observations led to further studies (76), using a battery of mitogens. Response to the T-cell mitogen Con A was found to be depressed in spleen cells from rats fed diets low in methionine and choline. Depressed responsiveness to PHA and pokeweed mitogen (PWM) was seen in thymus cells (Table 6). It remains unclear whether the gestation or lactation period is the most critical; however, Figure 2, taken from later studies in our laboratory (39), clearly shows that the early period in life is a very sensitive period for the development of immunity and the thymolymphatic system.

Different periods of development of the immune system, including in-

**Table 4** Effect of lipotropes on response of rats to infection with *Salmonella typhimurium* three months postweaning

| Dietary treatment during average | | | |
|---|---|---|---|
| gestation and lactation | postweaning only | Weight at infection (g) | Mortality[a] (%) |
| Marginal methionine-choline $- B_{12}$ | Marginal methionine-choline $- B_{12}$ | 233±6 | 100 |
| Marginal methionine-choline $- B_{12}$ | Control | 240±8 | 100 |
| Marginal methionine-choline $+ B_{12}$ | Marginal methionine-choline $+ B_{12}$ | 248±5 | 91 |
| Marginal methionine-choline $+ B_{12}$ | Control | 285±7 | 90 |
| $B_{12}$-deficient | $B_{12}$-deficient | 260±3 | 71 |
| $B_{12}$-deficient | Control | 308±4 | 35 |
| Control | Control | 303±4 | 25 |

[a] Thirty days postinfection.

**Table 5** Lipotropes and development of the thymolymphatic system[a]

| | Control | Marginal lipotrope |
|---|---|---|
| Birth[b] | | |
| Body | 6.0 ± 0.5 | 5.6 ± 0.4 |
| Thymus | 25.0 ± 4.0 | 15.0 ± 2.0 |
| Spleen | 4.0 ± 0.3 | 3.0 ± 0.2 |
| Three months[b] | | |
| Body | 337.0 ± 12.0 | 292.0 ± 16.0 |
| Thymus | 590.0 ± 21.0 | 270.0 ± 8.0 |
| Spleen | 740.0 ± 27.0 | 420.0 ± 23.0 |

[a] Figures based on 20 animals per group. Taken from (44), by permission.
[b] Body weight given in g; thymus and spleen weights in mg.

trauterine and postnatal periods, vary in sensitivity and reversibility to deprivation (39, 44, 76). Much of this work was conducted in our own laboratories and these data combined with the results of others clearly indicate that lipotropes, similar to if not identical in many respects to human PCM, have a profound effect on immunocompetence, particularly during selected periods of growth and maturation of the thymolymphatic system. This may have some bearing on susceptibility to cancer (see below).

## LIPOTROPES AND XENOBIOTIC METABOLISM

In attempting to define how lipotrope deficiency promotes cancer, particularly of the liver, it is important to consider the influence of lipotropes on xenobiotic metabolism.

**Table 6** Marginal methionine-choline deprivation in rats[a]

| Assay | Control | Deprived during gestation and lactation |
|---|---|---|
| Splenic lymphocyte response to Con A (SI) | 47.2±19.5[b] | 18.7±16.0 |
| PFC/$10^5$ lymphocytes | 108.1±20.9 | 52.4± 9.3 |
| Hemagglutinin titer | 1:2560 | 1:640 |
| Hemolysin titer | 1:20560 | 1:640 |
| PHA skin test[c] response (4 mo.) | 3+ | 2+ |

[a] From 76.
[b] Results expressed ± S.D.
[c] Mononuclear cell infiltration scored from 0 (none) to 5 (severe).

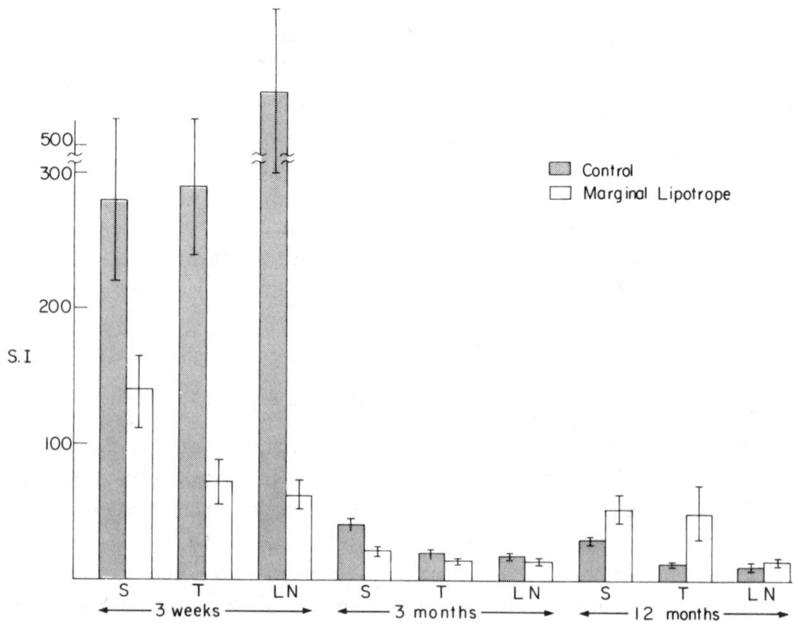


*Figure 2* The response to concanavalin A in rats fed normal diets and diets marginal in supplies of methyl groups. *S* = spleen; *T* = thymus; *LN* = lymph node. From (39), with permission.

Microsomal oxidase activity of the liver is highly sensitive to lipotrope deficiency (Table 7) and its decrease may be responsible for modification of carcinogenesis there or at other sites (58, 59). However, we demonstrated that microsomal enzymes are inducible by a potent hepatocarcinogen, aflatoxin $B_1$ ($AFB_1$), in the liver of rats fed low lipotrope diets. We also showed in other studies (4, 58) that the metabolism of chemicals by the lipotrope-deficient rat liver is modified; the time at which metabolic activity is measured will produce variable results, however, as noted in Table 7. While $AFB_1$ and other hepatocarcinogenic chemicals induce enzymes that result in metabolic activation or deactivation, the magnitude of induction is reduced in lipotropic deficiency.

Others have shown a shifting of target organ to the liver by the choline-deficient diet (56), probably associated with local tissue metabolism, but this is yet to be documented.

Studies in vivo indicate that lipotrope deficiency alters carcinogen metabolism. Rats fed the low lipotrope diet are more sensitive to the toxicity of repeated doses of most hepatocarcinogens, including $AFB_1$ (Table 8) (59). They are, however, highly insensitive to toxicity of a single dose of $AFB_1$ (58).

**Table 7** Lipotropes and microsomal enzyme activity[a]

| | Control[b] | Low lipotropes[b] |
|---|---|---|
| Microsomal protein | | |
| 90 days on diet | 24.4 ± 1.5 | 18.7 ± 1.1 |
| 90 days on diet then 3 weeks $AFB_1$ | 28.4 ± 1.7 | 25.2 ± 1.8 |
| Ethylmorphine *N*-demethylase | | |
| 90 days on diet | 787 ± 79 | 572 ± 40 |
| 90 days on diet then 3 weeks $AFB_1$ | 1123 ± 93 | 1063 ± 104 |
| Ethoxycoumarin *O*-dealkylase | | |
| 90 days on diet | 0.350 ± 0.09 | 0.215 ± 0.03 |
| 90 days on diet then 3 weeks $AFB_1$ | 0.590 ± 0.14 | 0.509 ± 0.11 |
| Cytochrome P450 | | |
| 90 days on diet | 1.8 ± 0.1 | 0.5 ± 0.1 |
| 90 days on diet then 3 weeks $AFB_1$ | 2.9 ± 0.4 | 2.1 ± 0.3 |
| Cytochrome C reductase | | |
| 90 days on diet | 66.2 ± 3.7 | 52.4 ± 3.5 |
| 90 days on diet then 3 weeks $AFB_1$ | 98.4 ± 5.2 | 88.6 ± 6.1 |

[a] Adapted from Campbell et al (4) and from additional studies conducted in our own laboratory). Details of diet composition are listed in Table 9 and references (41, 43, 58, 59).

[b] Microsomal protein measured in mg/kg; all others measured in nmole/mg protein.

This suggests that there is decreased metabolism of the chemical to its active, toxic form upon first exposure, but induction of metabolism by the carcinogen occurs following repeated exposures. This effect was not confirmed in the bacterial mutagenesis assays (68).

Other factors also impinge on the manner in which chemicals are activated or detoxified by biological systems. For example, it has been established that liver *S*-adenosylmethionine is decreased in lipotrope-deficient rats. GSH content of liver, however, does not appear to be affected (63). The reduction in SAM in rats fed the lipotrope-deficient diet is a direct result of the dietary treatment; this was confirmed by Mikol & Poirier (38) in rats fed diets deficient in one or more of the lipotropes. *S*-Adenosylmethionine may influence carcinogenesis by serving as a trap for electrophilic carcinogens or by playing a role in alkylation. Although the mechanisms of the interactions between methyl groups (lipotropes in general), xenobiotic metabolism, and neoplasia remain to be elucidated, the lipotropic regulatory role on metabolism of chemicals is likely of significance to cancer risk.

**Table 8** Chemical carcinogenesis in lipotrope deficiency[a]

| Carcinogen[b] | Tumor site | Tumor incidence (%) Control | Deprived |
|---|---|---|---|
| $AFB_1$ | Liver | 15 | 87 |
| DEN | Liver | 70 | 80 |
| DBN | Liver | 24 | 64 |
| | Bladder | 84 | 80 |
| DMN | Liver | 28 | 27 |
| | Kidney | 16 | 3 |
| AAF | Liver | 19 | 41 |
| | Mammary | 80 | 79 |
| FANFT | Bladder | 53 | 61 |
| DMBA | Mammary | 48 | 15 |
| DMH | Colon | 86 | 100 |

[a] From Rogers & Newberne (59), abridged.
[b] $AFB_1$, aflatoxin $B_1$; DEN, *N*-nitrosodiethylamine; DBN, *N*-nitrosodibutylamine; DMN, nitrosodimethylamine; AAF, *N*-2-fluorenylacetamine; FANFT, *N*-[4-(5-nitro-2-2furyl)-2-thiazolyl]formamide; DMBA, 7,12-dimethylbenz[*a*]anthracene; DMH, 1,2-dimethylhydrazine.

## LIPOTROPES AND CANCER

### *Human Studies*

There are numerous reports in the literature on the relationship of the lipotrope family to cancer in humans (26). A number of disorders in humans lead to modulation of lipotrope status and are associated with increased risk for cancer. The incidence of carcinoma of the stomach in patients with pernicious anemia is about three times that observed in the general population. Moreover, about 40% of patients with gastric cancer in one study had pernicious anemia (5). While it is not known that vitamin $B_{12}$ deficiency in pernicious anemia is causally related to the increased incidence of stomach cancer, the association is significant. Mucosal atrophy and achlorhydria must also be considered.

A number of other reports have suggested that selected types of cancer may be associated with deficiencies of some of the lipotropes (e.g. leukemia and vitamin $B_{12}$; esophageal cancer and the B complex of vitamins, particularly folate). The associations have been put forth but the linkages have not been established (7, 67, 72, 81–83). The etiologies would appear to be much more complex than simple lipotrope deficits but the latter may have some important impact on the overall incidence of some types of cancer.

The countries where liver cancer occurs in highest incidence are also those areas where malnutrition (particularly protein, methionine, and vitamin $B_{12}$, and folate deficiencies) is common (52). These areas also have concomitant hepatitis B or other types of infection in high incidence, which suggests diminished immunocompetence (2). These liver cancer patients are predominantly male and have cirrhosis as well as hepatocellular carcinoma. The former is associated with protein-calorie malnutrition, and exposure to hepatitis B virus, as well as dietary contamination (2, 51, 52).

There are a number of immune defects in patients with chronic liver disease (52). For example, hyperglobulinemia and depressed cell-mediated immunity are common to most forms of chronic liver disease and probably secondary to liver damage. The anergic state seems to be related to increased activity of prostaglandin-secreting monocytes, which have suppressor functions, but it may also be due in part to a loss of T-suppressor cells.

It has been shown that many of the host defense systems are impaired when patients with chronic liver disease develop cirrhosis, effects insufficient in themselves to result in a significant rate of tumor development. However, when there are increased levels of carcinogenic stimuli such as environmental toxins, viruses, etc the tendency is for a more severe immunodeficiency to result. This then makes malignant transformation and evasion of immune surveillance more likely. The case for nutritional effects on xenobiotic metabolism and drug disposition in humans has been made by Vesell (73). This area of concern undoubtedly is associated with risks in human populations.

## *Animal Studies*

A deficiency of lipotropes associated with cancer was first reported from the laboratory of W. D. Salmon at Auburn University about thirty years ago (60). Rats maintained on choline-deficient diets (methyl group deficiency) for long periods of time developed hepatocellular carcinoma, an observation of far-reaching significance since it was a first instance in which removing something from the diet, instead of adding something (a carcinogen), resulted in cancer. The lipotrope deficiency caused a series of alterations in liver structure and function, including fatty liver, parenchymal cell hyperplasia, fibrosis, cirrhosis, and ultimately hepatocellular carcinoma in some of the animals. Accompanying these changes, as noted above, are alterations in xenobiotic metabolism and immunocompetence.

The discovery made by Salmon and co-workers was largely ignored for more than thirty years. Our work (41, 43) with diets using amino acids and intact proteins free of aflatoxin and other carcinogenic contaminants confirmed the work of Salmon and co-workers (see 47, 59 for more complete references). Others have duplicated our studies with results that document a diet-induced malignancy in lipotrope-deficient animals without a carcinogen superimposed (13a, 37). It is clear, however, that a diet low in lipotropes enhances experimental liver cancer in rats and mice (41, 43, 59). The following summary of experimental carcinogeneis in lipotrope-deficient animals is not encyclopedic because of space limitations. However, some of the more salient features of results are described. Our apologies go to the dedicated scientists working in the area in recent years whose important papers could not be included. Most of the following data are drawn from our own experiences.

Table 9 lists the diets most often used for lipotrope studies. The casein–peanut meal diet, assayed and determined to be free of $AFB_1$, is an excellently balanced diet and is useful because the methionine level is at the lower limits of a range satisfactory for normal growth of the rat and mouse. This then permits manipulation of the other three important lipotropes (choline, folate, vitamin $B_{12}$) and allows for gradations in the severity of the deficiency from severe (cirrhogenic) to mild. A mild deficiency results in no histologic evidence for injury; the only major measurable biochemical change is a small increase in liver lipid content.

A number of strains of outbred and inbred rats have been used for investigations of lipotrope deficiency–induced cirrhosis and its relationship to sensitivity of the liver to carcinogenesis. Rats of all strains, fed a diet low in lipotropes, develop fatty liver and cirrhosis similar if not identical to alcoholic or Laennecs cirrhosis in humans, who are at high risk for liver cancer. Figure 3 illustrates the appearance of a human liver with cirrhosis and hepatocellular carcinoma; compare this with the photograph of a rat liver in Figure 4. Mice of the inbred strains are also susceptible (43). Generally, the rodents have been fed a choline-free diet from weaning until cirrhosis develops, a period ranging from 200 to 500 days. In this animal model it is important that the rats or mice

**Table 9** The diets most often used in lipotrope studies[a]

| | Feed content (g/kg) | |
|---|---|---|
| | Diet 1 (control) | Diet 2 (deficient) |
| Casein | 60 | 60 |
| Peanut meal | 250 | 250 |
| Sucrose | 467 | 470 |
| Vitamin mix[b] | 20 | 20 |
| Mineral mix | 50 | 50 |
| Fat | 150 | 150 |
| Choline | 3 | 0 |
| Vitamin $B_{12}$ | 50 μg | 0 |

[a] Amino acid diets have also been used for some studies (37, 46). The diet listed in Table 1 is a particularly good one because the combination of casein and peanut meal provides about 0.3 methionine, allowing for normal growth even in the choline-deprived group.

[b] Vitamin mix complete except for folic acid (in folate deficiency studies) and choline and vitamin $B_{12}$, which were added at time of mixing the diet.

consume the diet continuously from weaning until the study is terminated; starting the diet at a later period does not induce cirrhosis even though the liver is sensitized.

Using this regimen some rats succumb to the hemorrhagic kidney syndrome induced by choline deficiency, usually between 8 and 10 days following initiation of dietary treatment; beyond that time the clinical course is uneventful, although renal injury usually persists in most of the survivors. Mice (B6C3F1 strain), while resistant to the renal injury, do develop fatty liver, fibrosis, and hepatocellular carcinomas (43).

The development of cirrhosis in the acutely deficient rat or mouse proceeds through a series of histologically identifiable changes described in other publications (43, 46, 47). The earliest lesion in the liver is an accumulation of lipid in the centrilobular zone that occurs within a few days after initiating the diet. Lipid continues to increase and within 2–3 weeks has filled most cells of the lobule. This is accompanied by the appearance of bizarre nuclei, many of which contain intranuclear inclusions, and there is widespread single-cell necrosis throughout the lobe. It is at this point that mitotic figures and $^3$H-thymidine labeling increases rapidly (Figure 5), as do focal accumulations of hyperchromatic (basophilic) proliferating parenchyma. The progression of le-

*Figure 3* Photograph of human liver cancer accompanied by cirrhosis, which coexist in a large majority of such neoplasms. This type of cancer is associated with malnutrition, especially a deficit of protein and calories, with dietary contamination ($AFB_1$), and with infection, particularly hepatitis B virus.

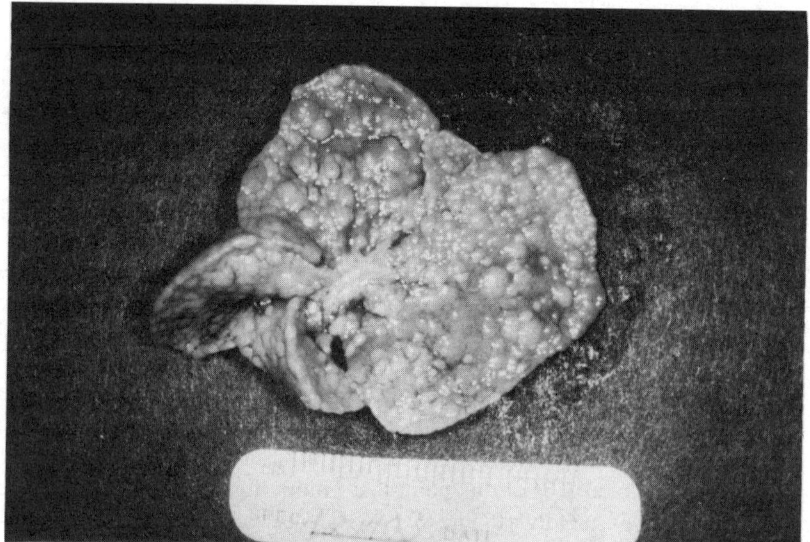

*Figure 4* Liver from a rat fed a diet low in methyl groups and given aflatoxin $B_1$, a carcinogen contaminating a high percentage of diets in areas of the world where human liver cancer is the most common form of neoplasia. Note the similarity between Figures 3 and 4.

sions then follows a predictable series of changes including a pale, nodular liver with marked fibrosis and cirrhosis and with nodules that may or may not contain fat. Some of the lesions progress through atypical nodular hyperplasia, usually without lipid, to hepatocellular carcinoma (Figure 4) and then often metastasize to the lungs. These changes have been documented and illustrated in much greater detail in many publications. Table 8 lists the types of responses observed in some of our studies.

We have conducted additional investigations in attempts to determine mechanisms for injury and development of neoplasms. We have documented (41) that a diet low in lipotropes is sufficient to induce neoplasms, without superimposing a chemical carcinogen, although such injured livers are more sensitive to a number of hepatocarcinogens, as noted in Table 8.

In the choline-deficient liver as fat increases the number of cells labeled by $[^3H]$-thymidine also increases (Figure 5). In addition, we found that choline deficiency alone causes a sharp increase in cell death, as others have also reported (13). Despite the lipotrope deficiency, there is increased DNA synthesis and cell turnover, both of which are essential components of hyperplasia of the liver parenchyma. This implies the synthesis of defective genetic material, cell membranes that are imperfect, and other aberrant factors that can interfere with normal cell proliferation.

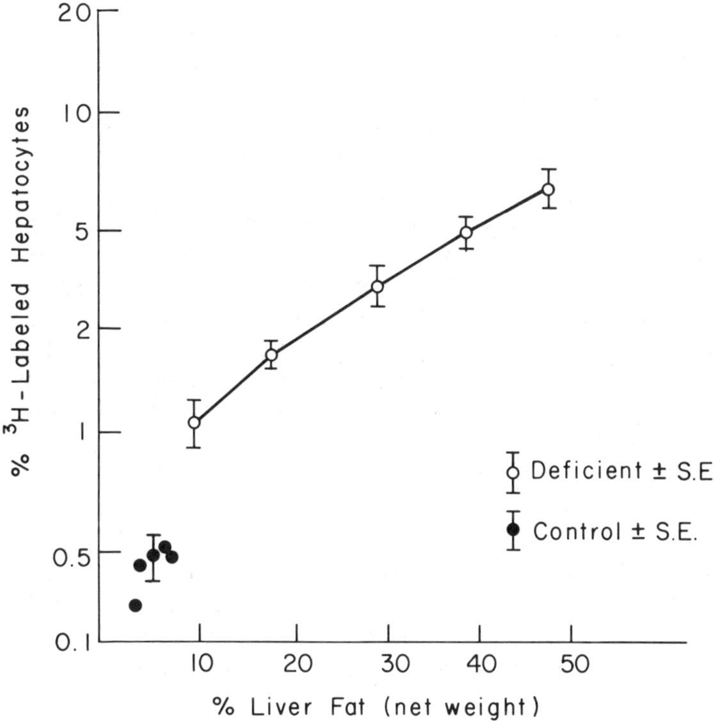


*Figure 5* A deficiency of methyl groups results in lipid accumulation in the liver, parenchymal cell death, and progressive increase in DNA synthesis, an indication of cell proliferation. Liver cell necrosis has been confirmed by microscopy.

## DISCUSSION

Chemical induction of hepatocarcinoma is governed in part by the level of DNA synthesis in hepatocytes at the time of carcinogen exposure, but also following exposure. Several models have been described and are being used to explore biochemical and morphological aspects of this relationship. While mechanisms are unclear, the lipotrope deficiency lesions leading to hepatocarcinoma may in some way be related to the hepatic proliferation inhibitor, a chalone expressed by adult rat liver (22), or to the hepatic stimulator substance expressed by fetal and neonatal rat liver (30). Both of these substances have been described recently and are now under intense study.

The significance of cell division to proliferative liver lesions and hepatocarcinoma in lipotrope-deficient rats has been questioned by other investigators

(62). Shinozuka and colleagues found that an increase in preneoplastic changes in the deficient liver did not correlate with cell division. The level of cell proliferation in deficient livers was decreased by feeding phenobarbital, but appearance of preneoplastic lesions was unchanged. In addition, by reducing the amount of fat in the deficient diet the number of preneoplastic lesions was decreased without altering hepatocyte hyperplasia. Both alterations of the model must be confirmed in carcinogenesis studies, since the significance of the putative preneoplastic lesions to liver cell cancer is not clear and a confirmed linkage is yet to be established.

The above-referenced study, in which lower fat content was fed, is particularly interesting because lower levels of dietary fat reduce the severity of lipotrope deficiency and would be expected to decrease both hepatic fat and DNA synthesis; neither occurred in the Shinozuka studies. Further, using the same carcinogen, *N*-nitrosodiethylamine (DEN), we have found that lipotrope and lipid effects interacted but in a complex way not as yet fully elucidated.

Carcinogenesis may be increased where DNA synthesis is increased. This can be achieved by partial hepatectomy, by necrogenic chemicals, and by choline deficiency. In the choline deficiency model, partial hepatectomy had no effect on tumor incidence when the carcinogen $AFB_1$ was administered at different times with respect to the partial hepatectomy (57). Both partial hepatectomy and the choline-deficient diet increase DNA synthesis. This may be a factor in the enhancement of liver cancer by choline deficiency but the mechanism for enhancement is unclear. We feel that the significance of cell division to carcinogenesis requires further study before attempting to draw sweeping conclusions.

Lipoperoxidation has been considered by some to be related to the initiation of transformation of hepatocytes and promotion of hepatocarcinogenesis (14). Our laboratory published such a relationship more than 15 years ago (42) and confirmed the observations with more sophisticated techniques a few years later (79). The synthetic antioxidants BHA and BHT protected the kidney and liver from choline deficiency and largely returned serum and tissue lipids nearly to control values. Furthermore, the free radical index (FRI) and TBA values of the lipotrope-deficient liver clearly demonstrated the presence of lipoperoxidation in livers sensitized to hepatocarcinogens by the diet (79).

The laboratory of Poirier has published important data relative to the effect of lipotrope deficiency on fundamental cellular metabolism (37, 38). An effect of lipotrope deficiency on the concentration of *S*-adenosylmethionine, the obligatory source of methyl groups essential to methylation of important bases in DNA, suggests that lipotropes are concerned with control of cell proliferation. Deprivation of choline, methionine, or both resulted in decreased liver concentrations of SAM and an increased ornithine decarboxylase (ODC) activity, the latter essential to polyamine synthesis and important in regulation of cell proliferation. Generally, there was an inverse relationship between SAM and ODC; this bears on the induction of liver injury and, perhaps, promotion of carcinogenesis.

Additional data from Poirier's laboratory (78) and from our own investigations (Table 10) point toward hypomethylation. Wilson et al observed a 10–15% decrease in 5-methyldeoxycytidine in the deficient liver, but only after about six months on diet. Our studies (P. Punyarit, P. M. Newberne, unpublished, 1985) essentially confirm the data of Wilson et al, although our methods for examining effects on methylation were slightly different from theirs. We maintained rats on diet for up to six months, performed a partial hepatectomy at different time points to generate new DNA (and accompanying methylation), and two weeks later sacrificed the animals for DNA analyses. In agreement with Wilson et al (78), it was only after several months of continuous exposure to the lipotrope-deficient diet that we found significant hypomethylation of cytosine. This suggests hypomethylation may be a slow process; if it is involved in liver carcinogenesis, which occurs in this model, hypomethylation very likely requires chronic derangement of liver genetic material over long periods of time. Conversely, our analytical techniques may be too insensitive to detect hypomethylation in early stages.

The association of malnutrition, infection (hepatitis B virus), and dietary contamination with human liver cancer seems to be a realistic concept in attempts to understand mechanisms for this form of cancer. In those areas of the world where hepatocellular carcinoma is highest, liver disease, infection, and dietary contaminants are indigenous. There are some features of the liver disease and cancer seen in these areas that are similar to the choline-deficient animal model for cirrhosis and liver cancer. Fatty liver, fibrosis, increased hepatocyte turnover, nodular regeneration, cirrhosis, and, in some cases,

**Table 10** Lipotropes and 5-methylcytosine in liver DNA[a]

| | 5-methylcytosine as % of cytosine | |
|---|---|---|
| Time on diet | Control | Deficient |
| 3 weeks | 4.8 ± 0.09 | 4.5 ± 0.11 |
| 3 months | 4.4 ± 0.13 | 4.7 ± 0.20 |
| 6 months | 4.5 ± 0.10 | 3.3 ± 0.06 |

[a] From P. Punyarit and P. M. Newberne, 1985, unpublished. Two weeks prior to sacrifice a 2/3 partial hepatectomy was performed. We are indebted to Dr. Ronald Shank, University of California, Irvine, for some of the DNA analyses listed in this table.

hepatocellular carcinoma are common to the human and animal disease. Thus the choline-deficient animal model may provide a means for identifying factors that modulate or influence this important form of cancer (1a, 51).

In western countries, and in particular, the United States, chronic alcoholism seems to be the most common condition associated with the genesis of both cirrhosis and liver cell cancer. The choline deficiency rat liver model for cirrhosis is histologically similar if not identical to alcoholic cirrhosis in human patients and, as such, provides a convenient means for exploring mechanisms by which cirrhosis and hepatocellular carcinoma develop in humans. It should be pointed out here again that malnutrition (lipotrope deficiency), liver injury (i.e. hepatitis B infection), and dietary contamination with aflatoxins and other hepatotoxins coexist in areas with the greatest frequency of human hepatocellular cancer. Figure 6 indicates our unifying concept of how a deficiency of lipotropes, represented by malnutrition, may interact with other important factors in the complex, probable etiology of liver cancer. It is through a thorough study of the phenomena represented in Figure 6 that we may elucidate the mechanisms for lipotrope deficiency enhancing carcinogenesis.

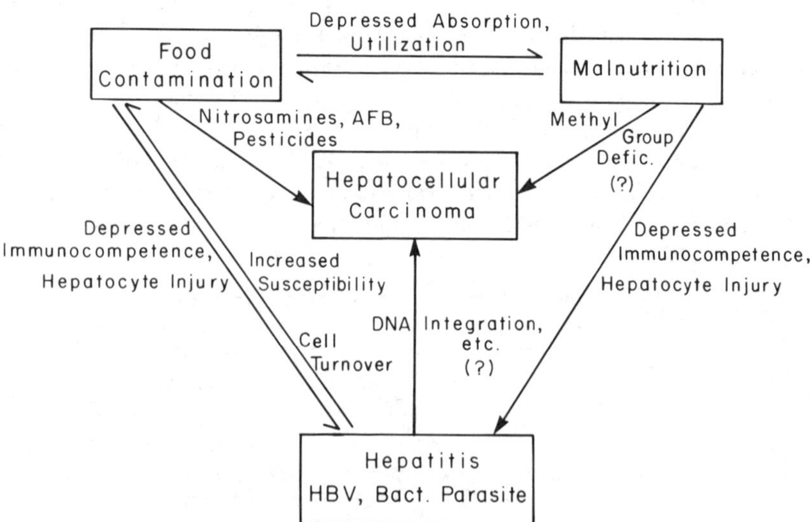


*Figure 6* This figure depicts a unifying concept of a triad of conditions that contribute to liver cell cancer in many areas of the world: food contamination, malnutrition with methyl group deficiency, and infection (especially with hepatitis B virus). With increased cell turnover but without adequate materials (methyl groups) for synthesis of macromolecules and other components, errors in replication of genetic material are more likely, with loss of control over cell proliferation.

# CONCLUSIONS

We do not know the mechanisms whereby lipotrope deficiency (and thus methyl group deficit) influences carcinogenesis. While the situation is unclear in human cancer, in animals the effects are more than promoting, however; at least three different laboratories have independently induced hepatocellular carcinoma in rodents with lipotrope deficiency alone. The deficient diets are characterized by marginal levels of certain essential amino acids, particularly methionine, in addition to deficiencies of choline, folate, and vitamin $B_{12}$. The relative importance of these factors in carcinogenesis varies with the carcinogen used to study them. Activity of *N*-2-fluorenylacetamide, a carcinogen used in many of the modeling studies cited above, is profoundly affected by choline and methionine but not detectably influenced by dietary fat content; $AFB_1$ and DEN results are affected by dietary fat content. Tumor induction varies considerably and yields complex results showing effects of lipotropes, amino acids, and fat, all of which interact in determining the final tumor incidence with these carcinogens.

Lipotropes influence immunocompetence and xenobiotic metabolism, and they are involved in the regulation of cell turnover in a number of tissues. A deficiency is also associated with a high incidence of liver disease, hepatitis B infection, and liver cancer in many areas of the world. We believe that the interactions between sensitive cells and carcinogens, resulting in the neoplastic change, are complex, not simple. Lipotropes impinge on a number of cell activities that can result in uncontrolled proliferation when lipotropes, and thus methyl groups, are in short supply.

## *Literature Cited*


1. Aboko-Cole, G. F., Lee, C. M. 1974. Interaction of nutrition and infection: Effect of folic acid deficiency on resistance to *Trypanosoma lewisi* and *Trypanosoma rhodesiense*. *Int. J. Biochem.* 5:693

1a. Anthony, P. P. 1979. Hepatic neoplasms. In *Pathology of the Liver*, ed. R. N. M. MacSween, P. P. Anthony, P. J. Scheuer, pp. 387–413, 258–271. Edinburgh: Churchill Livingstone

2. Beasley, R. P. 1982. Hepatitis B virus as the etiologic agent in hepatocellular carcinoma: Epidemiologic considerations. *Hepatology* 2:21S–26S

3. Beck, W. S. 1975. Metabolic features of cobalamin deficiency in man. In *Cobalamin-Biochemistry and Pathophysiology*, ed. B. M. Baboir, pp. 403–45. New York: Wiley Interscience

4. Campbell, T. C., Hayes, J. R., Newberne, P. M. 1978. Dietary lipotropes, hepatic microsomal mixed-function oxidase activities and in vivo covalent binding of aflatoxin $B_1$ in rats. *Cancer Res.* 38:4569–73

5. Chanarin, I. 1979. *The Megaloblastic Anemias*, pp. 332–50. Oxford: Blackwell. 2nd ed.

6. Das, K. C., Hoffbrand, A. V. 1970. Lymphocyte transformation in megaloblastic anaemia: Morphology and DNA synthesis. *Br. J. Haematol.* 19:459

7. Dormandy, K. M., Waters, A. H., Mollin, D. L. 1963. Folic-acid deficiency in coeliac disease. *Lancet* 1:632–35

8. DuVigneaud, V., Rachele, J. R. 1965. *Transmethylation and Methionine Biosynthesis*, ed. S. K. Shapiro, F. Schlenk, p. 1. Chicago: Chicago Press

9. Edelman, R. R., Suskind, R. E., Olson, R. E., Sirisinha, S. 1973. Mechanisms

of defective delayed cutaneous hypersensitivity in children with protein-calorie malnutrition. *Lancet* 1:506–8

10. Ferguson, M. M. 1975. Oral mucous membrane markers of internal disease: Part II, disorders of the endocrine system, the haemopoietic system and disorders of nutrition. In *Oral Mucosa in Health and Disease,* ed. A. E. Dolby. Oxford: Blackwell Scientific. 233 pp.
11. Finlayson, D. D. C., Fauconnet, M. H., Krohn, K. 1972. In vitro demonstration of delayed hypersensitivity to gastric antigens in pernicious anemia. *Dig. Dis.* 17:631
12. Friedkin, M. 1957. Enzymatic conversion of deoxyuridylic acid to thymidylic acid and the participation of tetrahydrofolic acid. *Fed. Proc.* 16:183
13. Ghoshal, A. K., Ahluwalia, M., Farber, E. 1983. The rapid induction of liver cell death in rats fed a choline-deficient, methionine-low diet. *Am. J. Pathol.* 113:309–14

13a. Ghoshal, A. K., Farber, E. 1983. Induction of liver cancer by a diet deficient in choline and methionine. *Proc. Am. Assoc. Cancer Res.* 24:98

14. Ghoshal, A. K., Rushmore, T., Lim, Y., Farber, E. 1984. Early detection of lipid peroxidation in the hepatic nuclei of rats fed a diet deficient in choline and methionine. *Cancer Res.* 25:94
15. Goldstone, A. H., Calder, E. A., Barnes, E. W., Irvine, W. J. 1973. The effect of gastric antigens on the in vivo migration of leukocytes from patients with atrophic gastritis and pernicious anemia. *Clin. Exp. Immunol.* 14:501
16. Gross, R. L., Newberne, P. M. 1976. Malnutrition, the thymolymphatic system and immunocompetence. In *The Reticuloendothelial System in Health and Disease: Immunologic and Pathologic Aspects,* ed. H. Friedman, M. R. Escobar, S. M. Reichard. New York: Plenum
17. Gross, R. L., Newberne, P. M. 1980. Role of nutrition in immunologic function. *Physiol. Rev.* 60:118
18. Gross, R. L., Reid, J. V. O., Newberne, P. M., Burgess, B., Marston, R., Hift, W. 1975. Depressed cell-mediated immunity in megaloblastic anemia due to folic acid deficiency. *Am. J. Clin. Nutr.* 28:225
19. Herbert, V. 1985. The inhibition and promotion of cancers by folic acid, vitamin $B_{12}$ and their antagonists. In *Xenobiotic Metabolism, Nutritional Effects,* ed. J. Finley, D. Schwass, Ser. 277:31–36. Washington, DC: Am. Chem. Soc.
20. Herbert, V., Das, K. C. 1976. The role of vitamin $B_{12}$ and folic-acid in hemato- and other -poiesis. *Vitam. Horm.* 34:1–30
21. Herbert, V., Zalusky, R. 1962. Interrelations of vitamin $B_{12}$ and folic acid metabolism: Folic acid clearance studies. *J. Clin. Invest.* 41:1263
22. Iype, P. T., McMahon, J. B. 1984. Hepatic proliferation inhibitor. *Mol. Cell Biochem.* 59:57–80
23. Jenkins, W. M. M., MacFarlane, T. W., Ferguson, M. M., Mason, D. K. 1977. Nutritional deficiency in oral candidiasis. *Int. J. Oral Surg.* 6:204
24. Kaplan, S. S., Basford, R. E. 1977. Effect of vitamin $B_{12}$ and folic acid deficiencies on neutrophil function. *Blood* 47:801
25. Krebs, H. A., Hems, R., Tyler, B. 1976. The regulation of folate and methionine metabolism. *Biochem. J.* 158:341
26. Krumdieck, C. L. 1983. Role of folate deficiency in carcinogenesis. In *Nutritional Factors in the Induction and Maintenance of Malignancy,* ed. C. E. Butterworth, M. L. Hutchinson, pp. 225–46. New York: Academic
27. Kumar, M., Axelrod, A. E. 1978. Cellular antibody synthesis in thiamin, riboflavin, biotin and folic acid-deficient rats. *Proc. Soc. Exp. Biol. Med.* 157:421
28. Kutzbach, C., Stokstad, E. L. R. 1967. Feedback inhibition of methylene-tetrahydrofolate reductase in rat liver by *S*-adenosylmethionine. *Biochim. Biophys. Acta* 139:217
29. Kutzbach, C. A., Stokstad, E. L. R. 1971. 10-Formyl tetrahydrofolate:NADP oxidoreductose. *Methods Enzymol.* 18B: 793
30. LaBrecque, D. R., Dachur, N. R. 1983. Hepatic stimulator substance: physiochemical characteristics and specificity. *Am. J. Physiol.* 242:G281–88
31. Little, P. A., Oleson, J. J., Roesch, P. K. 1950. The effect of pteroylglutamic acid on some immune responses of chicks. *J. Immunol.* 65:491
32. Ludovici, P. P., Axelrod, A. E. 1951. Circulating antibodies in vitamin deficiency states, pteroylglutamic acid, niacin-tryptophan, vitamins $B_{12}$, A and D deficiencies. *Proc. Soc. Exp. Biol. Med.* 77:526
33. MacCuish, A. C., Urbaniak, S. J., Goldstone, A. H., Irvine, W. J. 1974. PHA responsiveness and subpopulations of circulating lymphocytes in pernicious anemia. *Blood* 44:849
34. Deleted in proof
35. McGeer, P. L., Sen, N. P., Grant, D. A. 1965. Excretion of 4(5)-amino-5(4)-imidazole-carboxamide and formimino-L-glutamic acid in folic acid and vitamin

$B_{12}$ deficient rats. *Can. J. Biochem.* 43:1367

36. Menzies, R. C., Crossen, P. E., Fitzgerald, P. H., Gunz, F. W. 1966. Cytogenic and cytochemical studies on marrow cells in $B_{12}$ and folate deficiency. *Blood* 28:581
37. Mikol, Y. B., Hoover, K. L., Creasia, D., Poirier, L. A. 1983. Hepatocarcinogenesis in rats fed methyl-deficient, amino acid–defined diets. *Carcinogenesis* 4:1619–29
38. Mikol, Y. B., Poirier, L. A. 1981. An inverse correlation between hepatic ornithine decarboxylase and *S*-adenosylmethionine in rats. *Cancer Lett.* 13:195–201
39. Nauss, K. M., Newberne, P. M. 1981. Effects of dietary folate, vitamin $B_{12}$ and methionine/choline deficiency on immune function. In *Diet and Resistance to Disease,* ed. M. Phillips, A. Baetz, pp. 63–91. New York: Plenum
40. Nelson, J. D., Haltalin, K. C. 1972. Effect of neonatal folic acid deprivation on later growth and susceptibility to Shigella infection in the guinea pig. *Am. J. Clin. Nutr.* 25:992
41. Newberne, P. M. 1986. Lipotropic factors and oncogenesis. In *Single Nutrients and Carcinogenesis,* ed. L. Poirier, M. Pariza, P. M. Newberne. New York: Plenum
42. Newberne, P. M., Bresnahan, M. R., Kula, N. S. 1969. Effects of two synthetic antioxidants; vitamin E and ascorbic acid on the choline deficient rat. *J. Nutr.* 97:219–31
43. Newberne, P. M., deCamargo, J. L. V., Clark, A. J. 1982. Choline deficiency, partial hepatectomy and liver tumors in rats and mice. *Toxicol. Pathol.* 2:95–109
44. Newberne, P. M., Gebhardt, B. M. 1973. Pre- and postnatal malnutrition and responses to infection. *Nutr. Rep. Int.* 7:407
45. Newberne, P. M., Hunt, C. E., Young, V. R. 1968. The role of diet and the reticuloendothelial system in the response of rats to *Salmonella typhimurium* infection. *Br. J. Exp. Pathol.* 49:448
46. Newberne, P. M., Rogers, A. E., Bailey, C., Young, V. R. 1969. The induction of liver cirrhosis in rats by purified amino acid diets. *Cancer Res.* 29:230–35
47. Newberne, P. M., Rogers, A. E., Nauss, K. M. 1983. Choline, methionine, and related factors in oncogenesis. See Ref. 26, pp. 247–71
48. Newberne, P. M., Wilson, R. B., Williams, G. 1970. Effects of severe and marginal lipotrope deficiency on responses of postnatal rats to infection. *Br. J. Exp. Pathol.* 51:231
49. Newberne, P. M., Wilson, R. B. 1972. Prenatal malnutrition and postnatal responses to infection. *Nutr. Rep. Int.* 5:151
50. Noronha, J. M., Silverman, M. 1962. On folic acid, vitamin $B_{12}$, methionine and formiminoglutamic acid metabolism. In *Vitamin $B_{12}$ and Intrinsic Factor,* ed. H. C. Heinrich. Stuttgart: Enke. 728 pp.
51. Okuda, K., Mackay, I., eds. 1982. *Hepatocellular Carcinoma,* UICC Tech. Rep. Ser. No. 17, pp. 9–30. Geneva: UICC
52. Okuda, K., Mackay, I., eds. 1982. See Ref. 51, pp. 136–55
53. Pruzansksy, J., Axelrod, A. E. 1955. Antibody production to diptheria toxoid in vitamin deficiency status. *Proc. Soc. Exp. Biol. Med.* 89:323
54. Deleted in proof
55. Deleted in proof
56. Roebuck, B. D., Yager, J. D., Longnecker, D. S. 1981. Dietary modulation of azaserine-induced pancreatic carcinogenesis in the rat. *Cancer Res.* 41: 888–93
57. Rogers, A. E., Kula, N. S., Newberne, P. M. 1971. Absence of an effect of partial hepatectomy on $AFB_1$ carcinogenesis. *Cancer Res.* 31:491–95
58. Rogers, A. E., Newberne, P. M. 1971. Diet and aflatoxin $B_1$ toxicity in rats. *Toxicol. Appl. Pharmacol.* 20:113–21
59. Rogers, A. E., Newberne, P. M. 1980. Lipotrope deficiency in experimental carcinogenesis. *Nutr. Cancer* 2:104–12
60. Salmon, W. D., Copeland, D. H. 1954. Liver carcinoma and related lesions in chronic choline deficiency. *Ann. NY Acad. Sci.* 57:664–67
61. Scrimshaw, N. S., Taylor, C. E., Gordon, J. E. 1968. Interactions of nutrition and infection. *WHO Monogr. Ser.,* No. 57
62. Shinozuka, H., Lombardi, B. 1980. Synergistic effect of a choline-devoid diet and phenobarbital in promoting the emergence of foci of GGT-positive hepatocytes in the liver of carcinogen treated rats. *Cancer Res.* 40:3846–49
63. Shivapurkar, N., Poirier, L. A. 1983. Tissue levels of *S*-adenosylmethionine and *S*-adenosylhomocysteine in rats fed methyl-deficient, amino acid defined diets for one to five weeks. *Carcinogenesis* 4:1051–57
64. Silverman, M., Pitney, A. L. 1958. Dietary methionine and the excretion of formiminoglutamic acid by the rat. *J. Biol. Chem.* 233:1179
65. Stokstad, E. L. R. 1977. Regulation of

folate metabolism by vitamin $B_{12}$. In *Folic Acid—Biochemistry and Physiology in Relation to the Human Nutrition Requirement,* pp. 3–24. Washington, DC: Natl. Acad. Sci.

66. Stokstad, E. L. R., Webb, R. E., Shah, E. 1966. Effect of vitamin $B_{12}$ and folic acid on the metabolism of formiminoglutamate, formate and propionate in the rat. *J. Nutr.* 88:225
67. Strickland, G. T., Kostinas, J. E. 1970. *Am. J. Trop. Med. Hyg.* 19:910–15
68. Suit, J. L., Rogers, A. E., Jetten, M. E. R., Luria, S. E. 1977. Effects of diet on conversion of aflatoxin $B_1$ to bacterial mutagens by rats in vivo and by rat's hepatic microsomes in vitro. *Mutat. Res.* 46:313–23

68a. Suskind, R. M., Sirisinha, S., Vithayasai, V., Edelman, R., Damrongsak, D., et al. 1976. Immunoglobins and antibody response in children with protein-calorie malnutrition. *Am. J. Clin. Nutr.* 29:836–41

69. Tai, C., McGuigan, J. E. 1969. Immunologic studies in pernicious anemia. *Blood* 34:63
70. Thenen, S. W. 1978. Blood and liver folacin activity, formimino-glutamic acid excretion, growth and hematology in guinea pigs fed a folacin-deficient diet with and without sulfonamide. *J. Nutr.* 108:836
71. Thenen, S. W., Stokstad, E. L. R. 1973. Effect of methionine on supplemented rats. *J. Nutr.* 103:363
72. Tuyns, A. J., Pequignot, G., Abbatucci, J. S. 1979. Esophageal cancer and alcohol consumption. Importance of type of beverage. *Int. J. Cancer* 23:443–47
73. Vesell, E. S. 1985. Effects of dietary factors on drug disposition in normal human subjects. See Ref. 19, pp. 61–75
74. Wertman, K., Sarandria, J. L. 1952. Complement-fixing murine typhus antibodies in vitamin deficiency states. IV. $B_{12}$ deficiency. *Proc. Soc. Exp. Biol. Med.* 81:395
75. Wickramasinghe, S. N., Cooper, E. H., Chalmers, D. G. 1968. A study of erythropoiesis by combined morphologic quantitative cytochemical and autoradiographic methods. *Blood* 31:304
76. Williams, E. A. J., Gebhardt, B. M., Morton, B., Newberne, P. M. 1979. Effects of early marginal methionine-choline deprivation on the development of the immune system in the rat. *Am. J. Clin. Nutr.* 32:1214
77. Williams, E. A. J., Gross, R. L., Newberne, P. M. 1975. Effects of folate deficiency on the cell-mediated immune response in rats. *Nutr. Rep. Int.* 12:137
78. Wilson, M. J., Shivapurkar, N., Poirier, L. A. 1984. Hypomethylation of hepatic nuclear DNA in rats fed with a carcinogenic methyl-deficient diet. *Biochem. J.* 218:987–94
79. Wilson, R. B., Kula, N. S., Newberne, P. M., Conner, M. W. 1973. Vascular damage and lipid peroxidation in choline-deficient rats. *Exp. Mol. Pathol.* 18: 357–68
80. Woodruff, C. W., Clark, S. L. Jr., Bridgeforth, E. B. 1953. Folic acid deficiency in the guinea pig. *J. Nutr.* 51:23
81. World Health Organization. 1972. *Nutritional Anemias,* Rep. WHO Group of Experts, Ser. No. 503. Geneva: WHO Tech. Rep.
82. Wynder, E. L., Bross, I. G. 1961. A study of etiological factors in cancer of the esophagus. *Cancer* 14:389–413
83. Ziegler, J. L. 1981. Geographical distribution of lymphoma and malaria. *N. Engl. J. Med.* 305:735–45

*Ann. Rev. Nutr. 1986. 6:433–56*


# FOOD LIKES AND DISLIKES

*P. Rozin and T. A. Vollmecke*

Department of Psychology, University of Pennsylvania,
Philadelphia, Pennsylvania 19104

CONTENTS

INTRODUCTION ........ 433
THE ORIGINS OF FOOD PREFERENCES AND LIKES ........ 435
*Biological Factors* ........ 435
*Cultural Factors* ........ 437
*Individual (Psychological) Factors* ........ 437
*Interaction of Biological and Cultural Factors* ........ 438
A TAXONOMY OF PREFERENCES AND AVOIDANCES ........ 438
*Sensory Affective Motivation* ........ 439
*Anticipated Consequences* ........ 439
*Ideational Motivation* ........ 439
*Alternative Taxonomies* ........ 441
MECHANISMS OF ACQUIRED LIKES AND DISLIKES ........ 441
*Distasteful versus Dangerous Substances: Learning to Dislike Foods* ........ 442
*Good-Tasting versus Beneficial Substances: Learning to Like Foods* ........ 442
*Acquired Likes for Initially Unpalatable Substances* ........ 445
*Disgusting versus Inappropriate Substances* ........ 446
*Summary and Evaluation* ........ 446
THE TIME FRAME: LABILE AND STABLE LIKES ........ 447
*The Influence of Physiological State on Likes* ........ 447
*Temporary Changes in Likes: Sensory-Specific Satiety* ........ 448
*Relatively Stable Changes in Likes: Monotony* ........ 449
*The Influence of Context on Likes* ........ 450
CONCLUSIONS ........ 451

## INTRODUCTION

The mouth is the main route through which nutrients and most toxins enter the body. It is effectively the final point at which one decides whether or not to incorporate an item into one's body by swallowing (101). Consequently,



0199-9885/86/0715-0433$02.00

people have strong feelings about objects that enter the mouth and the sensations they produce. *Like* and *dislike* are affective words that humans apply easily in discussing most potential foods. The nature and origin of these likes and dislikes are the focus of this review.

In humans, things almost invariably get to the mouth by action of the hands. So, with the exception of infants and seriously handicapped people, it is through our own behavior that we acquire nutrients. Given this central role of behavior in nutrition, it is striking how little we know of how and why particular items are ingested and how they come to be liked or disliked (for general reviews, see 4, 6, 55, 57, 94, 97, 98, 117, 124). Our lack of knowledge results both from the difficulty of the problem and from a relative paucity of research efforts in the area.

Before reviewing the literature, we introduce six distinctions or qualifications. The first is the difference between foods and nutrients. People eat foods, not nutrients. Although foods stimulate the chemosensory, visual, thermal, and tactile senses, it is the mental representation invoked by this stimulation that is critical to humans' response: we respond to the mental representation of foods in order to identify particular items as either edible or not. The food itself is at once a source of nutrition, a source of harmful microorganisms or toxins, a great source of pleasure and satisfaction, and a vehicle for the expression of social relations and values.

A second set of distinctions must be made among *use, preference,* and *liking* (73, 96). The most common and "objective" measure of food selection is *use,* i.e. what and how much a person eats. It is largely determined by availability and cost, and is not directly considered in this review. *Preference* assumes the availability of at least two different items, and refers to the choice of one rather than the other. *Liking* refers to a set of hedonic (affective) reactions to a food, usually indexed directly by verbal reports or rating scales, but sometimes indirectly by facial expressions. Preference is ordinarily taken to be synonymous with liking, but this is not necessarily the case. Liking is only one of the motivations that may account for a preference. Perceived health value, convenience, and economic factors are potent influences on preference (59, 110) but may not affect liking. A dieter, for example, may prefer cottage cheese to ice cream, but like ice cream better. Nonetheless, in most cases, we prefer those foods that we like better. We focus here on literature that addresses the ways foods come to be liked or disliked. In practice, however, this assessment is sometimes made with data on preferences. While it is important to recognize the liking-preference distinction, it is also necessary to recognize that most data do not permit us to draw this distinction.

A third distinction concerns the time frame in which a preference (or liking) is cast. Some aspects of liking (e.g. liking lobster more than tuna fish) hold for any individual over periods of years or even a lifetime. Although one's general interest in food may vary with state of repletion, the relative standing of items within a food category (e.g. seafood) tends to be stable. Such stable likes contrast with more labile likes, as in the shift from breakfast foods to other foods as the day progresses, or shifts in the types of foods liked as a function of repletion.

Fourth, preference and liking are abstractions, easily made by humans when called for. But to say one likes lobster does not mean that one likes it for breakfast or smothered in whipped cream. A statement of preference or liking presumes an appropriate context. What constitutes an appropriate context is largely specified by culture.

Fifth, although it is tempting to account for individual differences in preferences in terms of sensory differences, efforts to do so have met with little success. Neither thresholds nor individual scaled intensity functions are good predictors of individual preferences (5, 73, 74a).

Sixth, almost all the data reported in this paper come from British or North American subjects. These represent a small percentage of humanity, and may differ significantly from much of the world's population. In India, for example, food assumes a much more important role in communication and in regulation of the social hierarchy (2). This should not be considered a deviant role. It is not restricted to India, but even if it were there are more people alive in India today than in all of North and South America.

## THE ORIGINS OF FOOD PREFERENCES AND LIKES

Besides availability and economic factors, all other determinants of food choice can be categorized as biological (genetically determined), cultural, or individual (psychological). These three categories can be applied to universals of human food preferences, to differences between cultures, and to individual differences within a culture.

### *Biological Factors*

Biological explanations are more likely for universal features of food choice than for individual differences. But in examining food preferences of humans cross-culturally, one notes an enormous diversity. Universals are few. This follows in part from the fact that humans are omnivorous. They have general-purpose dentition and digestive systems and are inclined to exploit a wide variety of those foods that are locally available to them. Since it is not possible to specify completely, in advance, which sensory properties predict particular nutrients or toxins, the omnivore must discover what is edible (94). That is, it is fundamental to omnivore biology to have few biological predispositions about foods. There are many important biological determinants in the background, such as the nutritional needs of the organism and the particular classes of chemicals that the nose and mouth can detect. With specific reference to food choice, there are three well-documented, genetically based, behavioral predispositions in many mammalian omnivores and in other generalists.

First are innate taste biases. There is an innate preference and liking for sweet tastes, present at birth and measurable either by enhanced acceptance of sweetened water or by positive facial expressions (31, 35, 120, 123). Similarly, among adults in virtually all cultures, there is a liking for sweet items, though the most liked level of sweetness varies greatly from person to person (70, 72, 74). The preference for sweetness has an adaptive basis since, in nature, most items with a sweet taste are sugars and thus sources of calories. There is good evidence for an innate dislike of bitter tastes (31, 120), which are correlated in nature with the presence of toxins. There are also some indications that strongly acid (sour) or irritant substances produce an innate rejection. Again, as with sweetness, although there may be more or less universal biases against these (bitter, sour, irritant) tastes, there is wide variation between individuals and across cultures (71). Judging by the great appeal of animal products cross-culturally and our carnivorous heritage, humans may also have a genetically based tendency to like meat even though it may not be expressed in early life. However, there is no definitive evidence for a genetically influenced preference for or avoidance of meat or of any nonirritant odor.

The second genetically based predisposition is an ambivalent response to potential new foods; a mixture of interest (neophilia) and fear (neophobia) (3b, 94). Biologically, this relates to the possible nutritive value of a potential new food, opposed to the possibility that it will contain toxins. In traditional settings, the interest-fear balance often tilts toward fear, which accounts for a general conservatism in cuisine and preferences.

The third predisposition involves special built-in abilities to alter preferences or likes in response to the delayed consequences of ingestion of a particular food (26, 94). This is particularly clear in the ability to avoid foods that cause illness (acquired taste aversions; 46) but also influences the acquisition of preferences or likings for nutritious foods.

Genetically determined abilities such as these might cause a hypothetical human child, uninfluenced by culture, to choose wisely among foods. Such a claim for the wisdom of the body was supported with a great deal of evidence from studies on rats in the laboratory by Curt Richter (85). Clara Davis (32, 33) carried out a classic demonstration of adaptive self-selection in human infants. She offered three infants, for a period of months to years immediately after weaning, an array of about a dozen foods to choose from at each meal. She reported that the children showed normal growth, even though what they ate was completely under their own control. However, these important findings do not establish a case for the biological wisdom of the body. All the foods offered to the children were of good nutritional value, so that random choice would probably also have led to normal growth. No refined products (e.g. sugar) or flavorings were added to the foods. Most critically, the preferred foods of the infants were milk and fruit, the two sweetest choices available.

Biological factors can explain some individual differences in food choice as well as some universals. There are well-documented, genetically based differences between people in sensitivity to some bitter compounds, and these show a weak relation to preferences for bitter foods. Those individuals with greater sensitivity to bitterness like bitter foods less (44). However, very little of the extensive differences in liking within a culture (74, 74a) can be attributed to genetically based sensory variations. Biological influences on individual variations in preference are probably more often manifested indirectly, as a result of inherited metabolic differences among individuals and ethnic groups (e.g. 56, 115). A case in point is lactose intolerance (114, 115): people carrying this inherited trait usually avoid moderate amounts of milk.

## *Cultural Factors*

The impact of culture on food preference is immense and varied (34, 56, 115; see also 3a). If one were interested in determining as much as possible about an adult's food preferences and could only ask one question, the question should undoubtedly be: "What is your culture or ethnic group?"

Culture has uncoupled the search for food from the ingestion of food, and has greatly extended the number of foods available through agriculture and importation. Traditions regulate the pattern of exposure to foods, the nature of foods, their flavoring and preparation (36, 93). Food takes on nonnutritional significance, perhaps most clearly in India, where the personal history of a particular food (who cooked or touched it) imbues it with social qualities that make it desirable for some and undesirable for others. Food is a medium of social expression in the Indian home, a way of establishing or confirming the social relations and importance of individuals in the family (2).

## *Individual (Psychological) Factors*

There are many differences in food likes among members of the same culture. We know almost nothing about the causes of these differences. Among functioning adults, after our first question (determining a target person's ethnic group or culture), there is no second question that is very informative about food likes. Gender (3, 65, 104) and biological factors such as differences in taste sensitivity account for very little of the variance. What about family influence? When culture is factored out, there are very low correlations (rarely above .30 and often below .15) between likes or preferences of parents and those of their children (16) even when the children are college students (80,

104). Resemblances among siblings are somewhat higher (81). Family resemblances provide an *upper* limit on the possible influence of family environment, since they can also arise from common genetic factors. Most twin studies on food preferences report minimal heritable components (e.g. 43, 50; but see 58 for substantial positive results). If we allow for some genetic effects, the influence of family experiences is even smaller than the low family resemblance correlations indicate.

Two further results add to the puzzlement. Mother-father correlations in preferences or likes are equal to or higher than parent-child correlations (104), and these correlations tend to increase with number of years married (84), which reveals an effect of mutual exposure and influence of the sort we would expect between parents and children. Furthermore, given the reasonable assumption that contact with a parent, especially in a feeding situation, would be the natural vehicle for transmitting likes, it is surprising that mother-child preference correlations are not consistently higher than father-child correlations (e.g. 28, 80, 104, 122). Selection of foods for the family by the food preparer (almost always the mother) may be more influenced by the father's preferences than by the mother's (122).

We presume that much of the unexplained within culture variance can be accounted for by social encounters with people outside the family, particularly peers and respected adults (30), and by the specific individual factors reviewed in the section on mechanisms of acquired likes (see below).

### *Interaction of Biological and Cultural Factors*

Biological and cultural factors establish constraints or predispositions, within which any individual develops a particular set of food likes. But these two types of constraints are not independent. Since culture is ultimately the product of individual humans, some of the biological predispositions we discussed have come to be embodied in cultural institutions (98). A clear example is the cultural evolution of techniques for sweetening foods, including sugar agriculture, refining, and the manufacture of artificial sweeteners, all of which are motivated by our innate liking for sweets (69). Such examples are limited in number (not surprisingly since there are a limited number of biological predispositions), and there are some cases in which cultural forces operate "against" our genetic heritage. Most notable is the culture-induced liking for innately disliked bitter or irritant foods such as coffee or chili (98).

## A TAXONOMY OF PREFERENCES AND AVOIDANCES

Liking can be thought of as one of a number of motives for ingestion. A structure of motives underlying food selection was developed for American adults through the use of interviews and questionnaires (41, 100, 101). This analysis suggests that there are three basic types of reasons for accepting or rejecting potential foods. Each of these reasons (Table 1) in one form motivates acceptance, and in its opposite form motivates rejection. This simplified scheme emphasizes the principal feature motivating acceptance or rejection. We review these features below.

## *Sensory-Affective Motivation*

Some items are rejected or accepted primarily because of the degree of pleasantness of the sensory effects in the mouth, or of their odor or appearance. Items accepted on these grounds can be called "good tastes" and those rejected "distastes." The sensory-affective motivation for acceptance is basically equivalent to liking or disliking a food. Individual differences on sensory-affective grounds (e.g. liking or disliking lima beans) probably account for most variations in food preference within a culture.

## *Anticipated Consequences*

Some substances are accepted or rejected primarily because of the anticipated consequences of ingestion. These could be rapid effects, such as nausea or cramps, or the pleasant feeling of satiation. More delayed effects involve beliefs or attitudes about the health value of substances (e.g. they provide vitamins, help one lose weight, contain carcinogens). Anticipated consequences may also be social, such as expected changes in social status as a consequence of eating a food. Foods accepted on the basis of anticipated consequences we label "beneficial," and foods rejected for similar reasons are "dangerous." One may have a distinct like or dislike for the sensory properties of these substances, but if present, this motivation is secondary to anticipated consequences.

## *Ideational Motivation*

Some substances are rejected or accepted primarily because of our knowledge of what they are and where they come from, or for their symbolic meaning. Ideational factors do not commonly play a role in food acceptances, but they do account for many rejections. Two clearly distinct subcategories of primarily ideational rejection can be distinguished.

REJECTION AS INAPPROPRIATE Inappropriate items are considered inedible within the culture and are refused simply on this basis. Grass, sand, and paper are examples in our culture. Typically, there is not a presumption that these items taste bad, and the items are usually considered inoffensive.

**Table 1** Psychological categories of acceptance and rejection[a]

| | Rejections | | | | Acceptances | | | |
|---|---|---|---|---|---|---|---|---|
| Dimensions | Distaste | Danger | Inappropriate | Disgust | Good Taste | Beneficial | Appropriate | Transvalued |
| Sensory-affective | — | | | — | + | | | + |
| Anticipated consequences | | — | | | | + | | |
| Ideational | | ? | — | — | | ? | + | + |
| Contaminant | | — | | — | | | | + |
| Examples | Beer, chili, spinach | Allergy foods, carcinogens | Grass, sand | Feces, insects | Saccharine | Medicines | Ritual foods | Leavings of heroes or deities |

[a]Source: Fallon & Rozin (41).

REJECTION AS DISGUSTING Disgusting items are considered offensive, and are rejected both on ideational and sensory-affective grounds. The taste, odor, and/or sight are disliked, and even the thought of eating the item may elicit nausea. Disgusting items are "contaminants" or "pollutants." The possibility of their presence in food, even in the tiniest amounts, makes the food unacceptable (101, 102). A few substances, such as feces, seem to be universally disgusting (1). Within American culture this category includes many animals such as insects and dogs.

### *Alternative Taxonomies*

The taxonomy offered in this review differs from other food taxonomies in that it includes all substances, edible and inedible, acceptable or unacceptable. Other taxonomies provide a finer-grained analysis within the framework of culturally acceptable foods (e.g. 8, 59, 111, 126). In general, flavor emerges as a central determinant of food use, classification, and liking (59, 110, 126, 129). Most of the factors extracted in these studies fall under anticipated consequences, including nutritive and health effects, and social effects (prestige). Two of these studies (8, 126) use a technique that elicits the dimensions that differentiate among foods from each subject, and thereby allows the creation of individualized food taxonomies.

## MECHANISMS OF ACQUIRED LIKES AND DISLIKES

In the first years of life, children must learn what is edible and what is not. Since infants and very young children tend to put almost anything in their mouths (33, 106), a basic task of early development is learning what *not* to eat. In this section we focus on adults and children after they have made the basic edible-inedible distinction, and we consider how foods come to be liked or disliked (to have positive or negative sensory properties). The acquisition of likes and dislikes is of special interest in the study of food selection for two reasons. First, it is particularly puzzling. We can understand that someone avoids a food because he has been told it will make him sick, but what makes him come to dislike its taste? Second, from the point of view of public health, it would be highly desirable if people could be induced to like what was good for them, and dislike what was harmful. Acceptance of a food based on liking is particularly stable because the food is then eaten for itself, rather than for some extrinsic reason.

We consider three contrasting pairs of categories (from Table 1). In each case, the first member of the pair involves an affective (like or dislike) response, and the second does not. The contrasts will be: (*a*) distasteful versus dangerous foods, (*b*) good-tasting vs beneficial foods, and (*c*) disgusting vs inappropriate items.

### *Distasteful versus Dangerous Substances: Learning to Dislike Foods*

Many foods that are initially neutral or liked come to be rejected as distasteful or dangerous. When ingestion of a food is followed by some types of malaise, humans (and rats) develop a strong aversion to that food (11, 45, 46, 64, 107). This distaste (called a taste aversion) often occurs after a single negative experience with an interval of some hours between ingestion and illness. There is a tendency to associate novel tastes with the illness. Taste aversions occur even if a person "knows" that the food he has eaten did not cause the illness.

Nausea and vomiting are especially potent as causes of acquired distastes (77). Other negative events such as headache, respiratory distress, hives, and cramps following eating usually induce avoidance motivated by danger rather than distaste. Even the lower gut cramps resulting from moderate levels of milk ingestion by lactose-intolerant people tend to produce a danger-based rejection, rather than a distaste for milk (77). This contrast can be illustrated by typical cases of two individuals who avoid peanuts. One has an allergy to peanuts and suffers rashes and/or difficulty breathing after eating them. This person avoids peanuts as dangerous but likes the taste. If his allergy could be cured he would be delighted to consume peanuts. The other person originally liked peanuts but got sick and vomited after eating them. She dislikes the taste of peanuts, while realizing they are not dangerous.

Individuals report many distastes, yet somewhat less than half of the people surveyed (45, 64, 77) could remember even one instance of a food-nausea experience. We presume that there are other important mechanisms for acquiring distastes, but none have yet been demonstrated. (See discussion below on sensory-specific satiety.)

### *Good-Tasting versus Beneficial Substances: Learning to Like Foods*

There is no single factor that clearly causes acquired likes in the way that nausea causes dislikes. Rather, there is evidence for weak contributions from the factors described below.

MERE EXPOSURE In general, exposure tends to increase liking, and Zajonc (131) has suggested that exposure is a sufficient condition for liking (mere exposure theory). Increased liking for foods with exposure has been demonstrated under controlled conditions for both adults (79) and children (21), with 1 to 20 exposures. There are circumstances under which "mere exposure" produces either no change in preference or decreases in preference (see section on sensory-specific satiety). Whether or not mere exposure is a sufficient condition for increased liking, exposure is surely critical in making it possible for other processes to operate that influence liking.

DISSIPATION OF NEOPHOBIA Exposure may allow fear of a new food to dissipate; one learns that the food is safe (96). For example, Torrance (121) found that liking for buffalo meat (pemmican) increased markedly from first to second exposure, even for those who found it unpleasant on the first exposure. However, it is not clear how dissipation of fear would produce a liking, as opposed to a lack of negative response.

PHYSIOLOGICAL CONSEQUENCES OF INGESTION Rapid satiety may enhance liking (26, 27). Booth and his colleagues offered hungry subjects meals of a high-calorie starch-based food (with flavor A) on some days and a low-calorie food (with flavor B) on other days. After only a few meals of each, hungry subjects showed a relative increase in liking for the flavor of the high-calorie food. However, a flavor associated with a high-calorie food will become *less* liked than a low-calorie flavor if it is consumed when the person is satiated. Unlike the nausea-produced decreases in liking, these changes are state dependent: flavor A paired with high calories in a hungry person is preferred only when the person is in the same hungry state. Insofar as one views rapid satiety as an upper-gastrointestinal "sensation," there is a parallel with the effectiveness of nausea on the negative side.

As with the specific effect of nausea on dislikes, the domain of physiological effects that induce liking is very limited. Oral medicines with distinctive tastes produce positive consequences, such as relief of headache, respiratory distress, heartburn, etc. These medicines are not highly favored as good tastes and there is no special potency of any particular medicinal consequences for enhanced liking. Even the upper-gastrointestinal pain relief produced by antacids is ineffective in promoting liking for their flavor (83).

ASSOCIATION OF A NEUTRAL OBJECT WITH A GOOD TASTE (PAVLOVIAN CONDITIONING) It has been demonstrated that liking for a variety of neutral, nonfood objects can be increased by associating them with positive events (67). In the food domain, sweetness is a convenient unconditioned stimulus, and has been used to produce enhanced preference for flavors on the part of rats (54), children (with chocolate as the unconditioned stimulus; 47), and adult humans. In a recent laboratory study, flavor A was served to young adults in a sweet (palatable) beverage, while flavor B was served equally often in an unsweetened, less palatable form. There was an enhanced liking for flavor A, even when both flavors were served in the unsweetened form (132). Without further research, we cannot evaluate the extent to which associations of this type alter liking or preferences under natural conditions. The acquisition of a liking for coffee may illustrate this mechanism, since at least in early encounters, coffee is usually drunk with a fair amount of sugar. Certainly cultural constraints are operative: for example with most staple foods very sweet tastes are generally rejected by American adults.

SOCIAL VALUATION Animal research indicates that preferences are much harder to establish than aversions (107, 130). Whereas a rat's innate preference for sweetened water can be reversed by one pairing with nausea, it is extremely difficult to produce preferences for innately unpalatable (e.g. bitter or irritant spicy) foods (105, but see 26). The relative weakness of acquired preferences in animals and the great strength of these preferences in humans suggests that some important factors operate only in humans. Sociocultural influences are the obvious candidates.

Social factors probably operate at two levels. First, social pressure (custom, the behavior of elders, the foods made available to the child) forces exposure, which may directly (mere exposure) or indirectly produce liking. Second, the perception that a food is valued by respected others (e.g. parents) may itself be a mechanism for establishment of liking (see 17 for a review).

Children increase their preferences for foods that are presented as preferred by elders, heroes, or peers (39, 66). Birch and her colleagues recently established a role for social influence in a rigorous and convincing way. Nursery school children show stable preference enhancements for foods chosen by their peers (15). Preference for a snack is enhanced if it is given to the child in a positive social context, e.g. used by the teacher as a reward (23, 51). The enhancement must be attributed to a social influence effect (the teacher's indication that she values the food) because if the same food is given to other children, at the same frequency, in a nonsocial context (e.g. left in their locker), there is no enhancement of preference (23). We do not know how social value is conveyed. It could be simply the voluntary use of the food by a respected other, or it could involve verbal or nonverbal (e.g. facial) expressions of positive affect in the respected other.

The importance of the perception of social value in acquired liking is emphasized by the converse phenomenon. A few studies show that liking for a food declines when a child perceives that respected others do not value that food for itself, and that the child (or others) must be bribed to eat it (e.g. rewarded, told how healthy it is). For example, preschool children who were rewarded for eating a particular food showed a drop in preference for that food for weeks after discontinuance of the reward (19; see also 22, 63).

These results are accounted for by self-perception theory (9). People "infer" their attitudes (e.g. liking a food) from their own behavior (e.g. choosing a food). If they ingest a food without clear extrinsic motivation, they tend to justify the behavior by increasing the food's value. However, this relation does not hold if they interpret their behavior as resulting from external causes (e.g. they were forced to eat a food). The decline in value of an object when extrinsic reward is employed is called the "overjustification effect" (62). The fact that people are less likely to come to like oral medicines than foods is consistent with this view, since medicine ingestion is determined by external factors: anticipated beneficial consequences and imposition of use by medical authorities or parents (83).

A relevant study compared a variety of techniques designed to increase adults' liking for grasshoppers (116). The most effective technique used the smallest financial reward and a communicator (person encouraging the ingestion) who was relatively cool and not especially likable. This technique inclines subjects to account for their ingestion of the grasshopper in terms of internal motivation, since external causes were minimal. As the theory predicts, the result is an increase in liking.

## *Acquired Likes for Initially Unpalatable Substances*

Some mechanisms of liking enhancement presume an initial negative response to the food in question. These apply particularly to innately distasteful substances, such as various forms of alcohol, tobacco, coffee, and the irritant spices—in short, some of the more popular ingestants of our species!

Chili pepper, the most widely consumed irritant spice, qualifies as a good taste for almost all users; it is eaten because people like the flavor and mouth "burn" it produces. This shift from dislike to like happens by age 5–8 years in many chili-eating cultures (108). The shift could result from some of the mechanisms outlined above (e.g. pairing with rapid satiety, social valuation) (95, 108) or from either of the special mechanisms discussed below, which may also account for the shift to liking for other initially unpalatable items.

CONSTRAINED RISK The mouth pain produced by chili may become pleasant as people realize that it does not cause harm. Liking for chili pepper may be a form of thrill-seeking (or "benign masochism"), in the same sense that the initial terror of a roller coaster ride or parachute jumping is replaced by pleasure. People come to enjoy the fact that their bodies are signaling danger but their minds know there really is none (108).

OPPONENT RESPONSES The many painful mouth experiences produced by chili in the novice eater may cause the brain to attempt to modulate the pain by secreting endogenous opiates (morphine-like substances produced in the brain). There is evidence that, like morphine, these brain opiates do reduce pain. At high levels, they might produce pleasure. In accordance with opponent process theory (118), hundreds of experiences of chili-based mouth pain may cause larger and larger brain opiate responses, resulting in a net pleasure response after many trials (99).

## *Disgusting versus Inappropriate Substances*

Why do disgusting items, primarily of animal origin (1), come to be offensive and disliked, while inappropriate items (primarily of vegetable or mineral nature) are treated as neutral? Three features of disgust seem to be universal: a characteristic facial expression, the inclusion of feces in the disgust category, and the fact that disgusting items serve as psychological contaminants (rendering otherwise good food undesirable after the slightest contact with the disgusting item) (1, 40, 102).

There is no evidence for an innate basis for disgust: infants do not manifest an aversion to feces, and decay odor does not seem to be innately aversive (78). Children in the United States do not develop the contamination response to disgusting objects until the first years of elementary school (42). We presume that the offensiveness of disgusting items is somehow conveyed to children by their parents, perhaps through facial and other forms of emotional expression. It seems reasonable that feces produce developmentally the first disgust, and that this arises through the process of toilet training, but there is no firm evidence on this point (101, 102), nor on the general issue of how ideas about the nature or origin of a substance lead to such powerful emotional responses to it. In contrast, children probably learn to avoid inappropriate items by being informed, in a more neutral emotional context, that such items are inedible.

## *Summary and Evaluation*

At this time, our list of mechanisms that lead to acquired likes and dislikes is incomplete. It is difficult to assign particular foods to particular mechanisms, partly because many substances are consumed for multiple reasons (111). People drink coffee because of the pleasant oral sensations, the positive pharmacological effects, to avoid withdrawal, to be social, to avoid eating, and/or out of habit (49). Individuals have multiple motivations, and the pattern of motives varies from one individual to another. Furthermore, ingestion of the same food at different times may have different motivations, as when someone drinks coffee in the morning to wake up and in the afternoon to be social. In this respect, chili pepper is simpler than coffee, since the motivation for consuming chili pepper is predominantly oral pleasure (98, 108).

It is essential to distinguish the current motivation for acceptance of a food from the historical cause of that acceptance. A typical chili pepper user is motivated by sensory pleasure, but his enjoyment may have come about through social valuation and physiological effects. The taxonomy we have presented deals with current motivations, but these same motivations constitute the set of causes of acquired changes in liking.

## THE TIME FRAME: LABILE AND STABLE LIKES

So far, we have emphasized the stability of preferences and likes. However, a person's liking for a particular food will vary with a number of factors, including the time of day, physiological state, recent past eating experience, and the context in which the food is presented. Many of these factors are subject to cultural influences. Some of them result in temporary, reversible changes in liking, and some in more permanent changes. In addition, whereas some of these factors influence likes for broad classes of foods, others result in a very specific change restricted to a particular food.

### *The Influence of Physiological State on Likes*

The physiological state of the organism is one factor that influences how much foods are liked (29). Organisms in a nutritionally deprived state will find almost *all* food more attractive than when they are not deprived. Cabanac has investigated this overall change in the perceived pleasantness of foods, termed *alliesthesia,* by observing changes in pleasantness ratings for sucrose solutions by initially hungry subjects who subsequently consume either nothing or a substantial amount of sucrose. Subjects ingesting sugar solutions showed a decline in their pleasantness rating of the solution over time whereas those without this caloric load showed no change in pleasantness rating.

Cabanac believes that sensory pleasure plays a homeostatic role, reflecting internal need states. Taste and olfaction, with their special involvement with food, should be closely linked to nutritional state. Thus, the liking for odors should change as a function of nutritive state. Accordingly, it has been found that manipulation of nutritional need influences the pleasantness of food odors but not of other odors (38). However, the assumption that nutritional state is the key variable has been questioned by observations of equivalent changes in pleasantness rating after ingestion of nonnutritive substances (125).

Physiological state (energy balance) also alters liking for particular foods in relation to their power to satiate. Booth and his colleagues (27) offered energy-deprived subjects separate meals of high- and low-calorie foods, with similar sensory characteristics, except that each type was marked with a different, arbitrary flavor. Over a series of meals, subjects learned the consequences for satiety of eating each of the foods (and associated flavors) offered. Subjects subsequently preferred the flavor of the high-calorie food when energy deprived, but the flavor of the low-calorie food when replete. Thus, liking for a particular food depends upon an interaction between the person's current physiological state (full or hungry) and past experience with the food in question.

There is abundant evidence that animal preferences for particular nutrients are affected by the availability of these nutrients in the body (85, 94). Evidence in humans is less extensive; the best comes from indications that human sodium preference is related to sodium deficiency and/or dietary sodium levels (7). Human preferences for high-carbohydrate versus high-protein foods may also be related to a specific physiological variable. Recent work on animals and humans by Blundell (24, 25), Wurtman (128), and their collaborators indicates that high brain levels of the neurotransmitter serotonin induce a relative preference for protein as opposed to carbohydrates. These findings are of particular interest because brain serotonin levels are influenced by serotonin precursors in the diet (127). It is possible that changes in protein/carbohydrate preferences in the course of meals may be related to changes in serotonin levels (25).

## *Temporary Changes in Likes: Sensory-Specific Satiety*

Le Magnen (61) observed that rats offered successive meals containing the same food but with varying odorants consumed more than rats offered a single-odorant food combination. He named this phenomenon "sensory-specific satiety" because the foods differed only in their chemosensory properties.

Sensory-specific satiety effects on consumption have been reliably observed in humans (82, 89–91), including children (20). Such effects are measured as a decrease in total consumption as the number of choices decreases, or as a drop in hedonic ratings of a food consumed repeatedly. For instance, subjects offered a variety of hot hors d'oeuvres, all at one time, ate more than subjects offered equal amounts of only their single favorite hors d'oeuvre (82). Variety in a meal resulting from multiple, successive courses also stimulates increased intake.

Most research on sensory-specific satiety in humans has been carried out by Rolls and her collaborators (see 88 for review), using this sequential food paradigm: Subjects offered four different courses (crackers with different spreads, different sandwiches, or yogurts differing in visual appearance, texture, and taste) eat more in the varied meal condition than they eat of their favorite food alone, presented over the same period of time (89, 91). The increase in consumption in the varied condition is large and seems to vary with the similarity of the different foods. For example, in the varied condition, sandwiches with fillings that differ in appearance, taste, and texture stimulate 33% greater intake, whereas yogurts, differing less in taste but more in appearance, stimulate 19.5% more consumption (90).

In humans, the change in liking accompanying the sensory-specific satiety effect on consumption can be assessed. A food that is eaten declines in liking relative to foods that have not been eaten (82, 90). In one experiment, subjects taste and rate seven different foods, one of which is subsequently eaten to satiety. The subjects show declines in liking for the eaten but not the uneaten foods immediately after eating and these changes remain stable over twenty minutes (89). The magnitude of changes in liking is greatest immediately after eating and then gradually declines over the course of an hour (88).

The time course suggests that the foods eaten diminish in pleasantness before they can exert postingestive effects. Further, since the pleasantness ratings do not continue to decrease with increased time for postingestive consequences, these ratings appear to be insensitive to the metabolic consequences of food consumption. Additional evidence suggesting the relatively minor role of nutritive consequences on changes in likes is the observation that the same magnitude of changes in liking occurs over the course of a low- or high-caloric meal (88). The changes in pleasantness correlate positively with consumption in a subsequent course (89). Thus, if sausage is eaten in one course, there will be a large drop in the pleasantness between pre- and post-ratings, a drop that predicts how much sausage the subject would eat if offered more.

The mechanism underlying the selective decrease in hedonic evaluation (liking) and consumption awaits further investigation. Neither alliesthesia (29) nor sensory adaptation (88) can account for the magnitude and specificity of sensory-specific satiety. One possibility meriting further exploration is that cognitive factors play a role. The pleasantness of a food may decrease according to the memory for how much of a food has been consumed.

## *Relatively Stable Changes in Likes: Monotony*

The effect of frequent repetitions of the same foods has been examined in army personnel (112). Rotation of only four daily menus over a five-week period led to a drop in hedonic ratings of meats and vegetables, but not of other foods. A subsequent study exposed university students to an alternation of only two daily menus (lunch and dinner) for up to six weeks (113). This treatment led to a decline in hedonic ratings for all types of foods served. The decreased liking persisted, with only minor improvement, at a retest four months after completion of the study. The decline in liking was *least* for the best-liked foods and, as in the first study, there was a tendency for main-dish items to decline most in liking.

The sensory-specific satiety, monotony, and mere exposure paradigms are essentially identical: in each case, the same foods are repeatedly consumed with no particular consequences. The result is either a decrease or increase in preference. On the basis of the data on food and other research on exposure effects (10, 52, 131) it seems that exposure is more likely to enhance liking when it occurs at moderate frequency, and when the stimuli are novel, relatively complex, or both. For many novel items, there may be enhanced liking at moderate levels of exposure, followed by decreased liking when exposure becomes more frequent. Decreased preference effects (e.g. sensory-specific satiety; see also 119) may in general be more transient, perhaps because they are often produced by a close bunching of experiences. Finally, the monotony studies suggest that how much a food is liked in the first place, as well as the particular kind of food it is, may affect its susceptibility to overexposure.

### *The Influence of Context on Likes*

A judgment about foods and flavors is, of necessity, made in a particular context. The context includes social setting, ideas of appropriateness, expectations, and, at the most elementary level, the foods accompanying and preceding the food in question. A meal can be described as a temporal sequence of complex flavor and texture experiences. Clearly, a momentary rating of strength of sensation or of liking will be strongly tied to this context.

The effect of context on food perception and evaluation has been studied in the laboratory, albeit under very simple conditions: only one flavor is experienced, and the context consists of recent prior experience with that flavor in different intensities. The question addressed is, how will the perception or evaluation of a standard flavor be influenced by prior exposure to relatively stronger or weaker instances of that flavor?

Psychophysical research in domains other than taste and smell demonstrates the potent influence of the intensity of prior experiences (context) on current sensory/perceptual (53, 76) and hedonic evaluations (109). Parducci (76) has shown that, in general, judgments are a function of both the range of stimuli perceived and the frequency of exemplars of each type. These principles of sensory/perceptual evaluation have been demonstrated by a number of investigators for both tastes and flavors.

The dependence of intensity evaluations on context is illustrated by the following manipulation of salt in soups (60). Subjects experienced salt in two different contexts—one high-salt and one low-salt—in two separate sessions. In each context they received three levels of salt, with the middle level appearing in both sessions. Subjects in the high-salt context (0.25, 0.35, 0.50 M NaCl) rated 0.25-M NaCl soup as less salty than subjects in the low-salt context (0.12, 0.18, 0.25 M NaCl). Similar effects were observed in other studies in which subjects evaluated the saltiness and pleasantness of soups (86).

Riskey et al (87) found that the *hedonic* evaluation of tastes and flavors follows the same contextual principles as evaluation of sensory/perceptual properties. Generally, people seem to prefer sugar concentrations in the middle of the range of rated sweetness (87).

The context effect does not seem to depend on a particular evaluation method. It has been demonstrated with category rating scales, magnitude estimation, method of comparison, and a mixing method (e.g. diluting a strong sample) (48, 60, 68, 86, 87). Peripheral sensory alterations cannot account for the effects. Although manipulations affecting sensory adaptation (e.g. rinsing, delays) alter the intensity of ratings (e.g. for saltiness in soups), they do not affect the magnitude of the context effect.

The short-term influences on food likes observed in these experimental studies could result from perceptual changes (changes in the perceived intensity of a beverage would affect one's evaluation of the beverage). The prior exposures that are part of these studies may also influence evaluation directly. For these temporal context effects to operate in normal food choice, outside the confines of a single meal, the context effects would have to endure for days, weeks, or longer. That this may indeed be the case is suggested by the observation that some subjects maintained for an extended period of time on a low-salt diet rate a given sample as more salty than they did before beginning the diet. They also show a shift in preference to lower salt concentrations, which may follow from the change in perceived intensity (12).

Context also includes attitudes about the appropriateness of particular combinations of foods and the appropriate time to consume foods. These contextual effects are heavily influenced by culture. For example, although Chinese prefer a lower level of sweetness in a beverage relative to North Americans, they prefer a higher level of sweetness in their crackers (13). Pangborn (73–75) has consistently emphasized the importance of simultaneous context in judgments of both intensity and pleasantness. Predictions about liking of salt or sugar in a particular medium (e.g. juice or soup) cannot be made on the basis of pleasantness ratings of NaCl or sucrose in water. For example, American adults find salt at moderate levels pleasant in soup but unpleasant in water (7), and preferred levels of sweetness in dairy products depend on the level of fat (37).

Other, more general cultural rules of appropriateness of foods have major effects on acceptability. Among Americans (even as young as three years of age), certain foods are more or less desirable for breakfast than for dinner (18). Some contextual attitudes are not acquired until later in childhood. For example, in American culture, certain combinations (e.g. meat and potatoes) are acceptable and others (e.g. hamburger and ice cream) are not. For adults, this attitude is somewhat independent of how much they like the component foods. Children under six years of age, however, unlike adults, appear to follow the rule that if they like both A and B, then they will like the combination of A and B (42, 103), even if A and B are hamburger and whipped cream.

## CONCLUSIONS

We are just beginning to understand the origins of food likes and dislikes. The complex multidetermination of likes and the massive role of culture have discouraged intensive investigation. But food likes and dislikes are such a powerful force in nutrition that they must be a focus for future research.

## *Literature Cited*

1. Angyal, A. 1941. Disgust and related aversions. *J. Abnorm. Soc. Psychol.* 36:393–412
2. Appadurai, A. 1981. Gastropolitics in Hindu South Asia. *Am. Ethnologist* 8:494–511
3. AuCoin, D., Haley, M., Rae, J., Cole, M. 1972. A comparative study of food habits: influence of age, sex and selected family characteristics. *Can. J. Publ. Health* 63:143–51

3a. Axelson, M. 1986. The impact of culture on food-related behavior. *Ann. Rev. Nutr.* 6:345–63

3b. Barnett, S. A. 1956. Behavior components in the feeding of wild and laboratory rats. *Behaviour* 9:24–43

4. Barker, L. M., ed. 1982. *Psychobiology of Human Food Selection.* Westport, Conn: AVI. 632 pp.
5. Bartoshuk, L. M. 1979. Preference changes: Sensory versus hedonic explanations. See Ref. 57, pp. 39–47
6. Beauchamp, G. K. 1981. Ontogenesis of taste preferences. In *Food, Nutrition and Evolution,* ed. D. Walcher, N. Kretchmer. New York: Masson
7. Beauchamp, G. K., Bertino, M., Engelman, K. 1983. Modification of salt taste. *Ann. Intern. Med.* 98:763–69
8. Bell, A. C., Stewart, A. M., Radford, A. J., Cairney, P. T. 1981. A method for describing food beliefs which may predict personal food choice. *J. Nutr. Educ.* 13:22–26
9. Bem, D. 1967. Self-perception: An alternative interpretation of cognitive dissonance phenomena. *Psychol. Rev.* 74: 183–200
10. Berlyne, D. E. 1970. Novelty, complexity and hedonic value. *Percept. Psychophys.* 8:279–86
11. Bernstein, I. L. 1978. Learned taste aversions in children receiving chemotherapy. *Science* 200:1302–3
12. Bertino, M., Beauchamp, G. K., Engelman, K. 1982. Long-term reduction in dietary sodium alters the taste of salt. *Am. J. Clin. Nutr.* 36:1134–44
13. Bertino, M., Beauchamp, G. K., Jen, K. L. C. 1983. Rated taste perception in two cultural groups. *Chem. Senses* 8:3–15
14. Birch, L. L. 1979. Preschool children's food preferences and consumption patterns. *J. Nutr. Educ.* 11:189–92
15. Birch, L. L. 1980. Effects of peer models' food choices and eating behaviors on preschooler's food preferences. *Child Dev.* 51:489–96
16. Birch, L. L. 1980. The relationship between children's food preferences and those of their parents. *J. Nutr. Educ.* 12:14–18
17. Birch, L. L. 1986. The acquisition of food acceptance patterns in children. In *Eating Habits,* ed. R. Boakes, D. Popplewell, M. Burton. Chichester, Engl: Wiley. In press
18. Birch, L. L., Billman, J., Richards, S. 1984. Time of day influences food acceptability. *Appetite* 5:109–12
19. Birch, L. L., Birch, D., Marlin, D. W., Kramer, L. 1982. Effects of instrumental consumption on children's food preference. *Appetite* 3:125–34
20. Birch, L. L., Deysher, M. 1986. Caloric compensation and sensory specific satiety: Evidence for self-regulation of food intake by young children. *Appetite.* In press
21. Birch, L. L., Marlin, D. W. 1982. I don't like it; I never tried it: Effects of exposure to food on two-year-old children's food preferences. *Appetite* 4:353–60
22. Birch, L. L., Marlin, D. W., Rotter, J. 1984. Eating as the "means" activity in a contingency: Effects on young children's food preferences. *Child Dev.* 55:432–39
23. Birch, L. L., Zimmerman, S. I., Hind, H. 1980. The influence of social-affective context on the formation of children's food preferences. *Child Dev.* 51:856–61
24. Blundell, J. E. 1984. Serotonin and appetite. *Neuropharmacology* 23:1537–51
25. Blundell, J. E., Rogers, P. J. 1980. Effects of anorexic drugs on food intake, food selection and preferences and hunger motivation and subjective experiences. *Appetite* 1:151–65
26. Booth, D. A. 1982. Normal control of omnivore intake by taste and smell. In *The Determination of Behavior by Chemical Stimuli. ECRO Symposium,* ed. J. Steiner, J. Ganchrow, pp. 233–43. London: Information Retrieval
27. Booth, D. A., Mather, P., Fuller, J. 1982. Starch content of ordinary foods associatively conditions human appetite and satiation, indexed by intake and eating pleasantness of starch-paired flavors. *Appetite* 3:163–84
28. Burt, J. V., Hertzler, A. A. 1978. Parental influence on the child's food preference. *J. Nutr. Educ.* 10:127–28
29. Cabanac, M. 1971. Physiological role of pleasure. *Science* 173:1103–7
30. Cavalli-Sforza, L. L., Feldman, M. W.,

Chen, K. H., Dornbusch, S. M. 1982. Theory and observation in cultural transmission. *Science* 218:19–27
31. Cowart, B. J. 1981. Development of taste perception in humans. Sensitivity and preference throughout the life span. *Psychol. Bull.* 90:43–73
32. Davis, C. 1928. Self-selection of diets by newly-weaned infants. *Am. J. Dis. Child.* 36:651–79
33. Davis, C. M. 1939. Results of the self-selection of diets by young children. *Can. Med. Assoc. J.* 41:257–61
34. de Garine, I. 1971. The socio-cultural aspects of nutrition. *Ecol. Food Nutr.* 1:143–63
35. Desor, J. A., Maller, O., Greene, L. S. 1977. Preference for sweet in humans: Infants, children and adults. See Ref. 123, pp. 161–72
36. Douglas, M., Nicod, M. 1974. Taking the biscuit: The structure of British meals. *New Society,* Dec. 19, pp. 744–47
37. Drewnowski, A., Greenwood, M. R. C. 1983. Cream and sugar: Human preferences for high-fat foods. *Physiol. Behav.* 30:629–33
38. Duclaux, R., Feisthauer, J., Cabanac, M. 1973. Effects of eating a meal on the pleasantness of food and non-food odors in man. *Physiol. Behav.* 10:1029–33
39. Duncker, K. 1938. Experimental modification of children's food preferences through social suggestion. *J. Abnorm. Soc. Psychol.* 33:489–507
40. Ekman, P., Friesen, W. V. 1975. *Unmasking the Face.* Englewood Cliffs, NJ: Prentice Hall. 212 pp.
41. Fallon, A. E., Rozin, P. 1983. The psychological bases of food rejections by humans. *Ecol. Food Nutr.* 13:15–26
42. Fallon, A. E., Rozin, P., Pliner, P. 1984. The child's conception of food: The development of food rejections with special reference to disgust and contamination sensitivity. *Child Dev.* 55:566–75
43. Faust, J. 1974. A twin study of personal preferences. *J. Biosociol. Sci.* 6:75–91
44. Fischer, R., Griffin, F., England, S., Garn, S. M. 1961. Taste thresholds and food dislikes. *Nature* 191:1328
45. Garb, J. L., Stunkard, A. 1974. Taste aversions in man. *Am. J. Psychiatry* 131:1204–7
46. Garcia, J., Hankins, W. G., Rusiniak, K. W. 1974. Behavioral regulation of the milieu interne in man and rat. *Science* 185:824–31
47. Gauger, M. E. 1929. The modifiability of response to taste stimuli in the preschool child. In *Teacher's College, Columbia University, Contributions to Education, Number 348.* New York: Bureau of Publ., Teacher's Coll., Columbia Univ.
48. Giovanni, M., Pangborn, R. M. 1983. Measurement of taste intensity and degree of liking of beverages by graphic scales and magnitude estimation. *J. Food Sci.* 48:1175–82
49. Goldstein, A., Kaizer, S. 1969. Psychotropic effects of caffeine in man. III. A questionnaire survey of coffee drinking and its effects in a group of housewives. *Clin. Pharmacol. Ther.* 10:477–88
50. Greene, L. S., Desor, J. A., Maller, O. 1975. Heredity and experience: their relative importance in the development of taste preference in man. *J. Comp. Physiol. Psychol.* 89:279–84
51. Harper, L. V., Sanders, K. M. 1975. The effect of adults' eating on young children's acceptance of unfamiliar foods. *J. Exp. Child Psychol.* 20:206–14
52. Harrison, A. A. 1977. Mere exposure. In *Advances in Experimental Social Psychology,* ed. L. Berkowitz, Vol. 10. New York: Academic
53. Helson, H. 1964. *Adaptation-level Theory: An Experimental and Systematic Approach to Behavior.* New York: Harper & Row
54. Holman, E. 1975. Immediate and delayed reinforcers for flavor preferences in rats. *Learn. Motiv.* 6:91–100
55. Kare, M. R., Maller, O., eds. 1977. *The Chemical Senses and Nutrition.* New York: Academic. 488 pp.
56. Katz, S. 1982. Food, behavior and biocultural evolution. See Ref. 4, pp. 171–88
57. Kroeze, J. A. H., ed. 1979. *Preference Behavior and Chemoreception.* London: Information Retrieval. 353 pp.
58. Krondl, M., Coleman, P., Wade, J., Miller, J. 1983. A twin study examining the genetic influence on food selection. *Hum. Nutr. Appl. Nutr.* 37:189–98
59. Krondl, M., Lau, D. 1982. Social determinants in human food selection. See Ref. 4, pp. 139–51
60. Lawless, H. 1983. Contextual effects in category ratings. *J. Test. Eval.* 11:346–49
61. Le Magnen, J. 1956. Hyperphagie provoquee chez le rat blanc par alteration du mécanisme de satieté periphérique. *C. R. Soc. Biol.* 150:32
62. Lepper, M. R. 1980. Intrinsic and extrinsic motivation in children: detrimental effects of superfluous social controls. In *Minnesota Symposium on Child Psychology,* ed. W. A. Collins, 14:155–214. Hillsdale, NJ: Erlbaum
63. Lepper, M., Sagotsky, G., Dafoe, J. L., Greene, D. 1982. Consequences of

superfluous social constraints: Effects on young children's social inferences and subsequent intrinsic interest. *J. Pers. Soc. Psychol.* 42:51–65

64. Logue, A. W., Ophir, I., Strauss, K. E. 1981. The acquisition of taste aversions in humans. *Behav. Res. Ther.* 19:319–33
65. Logue, A. W., Smith, M. E. 1986. Predictors of food preferences in adult humans. *Appetite*. In press
66. Marinho, H. 1942. Social influence in the formation of enduring preferences. *J. Abnorm. Soc. Psychol.* 37: 448–68
67. Martin, I., Levey, A. B. 1978. Evaluative conditioning. *Adv. Behav. Res. Ther.* 1:57–102
68. Mattes, R. D., Lawless, H. T. 1985. An adjustment error in optimization of taste intensity. *Appetite* 6:103–14
69. Mintz, S. 1985. *Sweetness and Power. The Place of Sugar in Modern History*. New York: Viking. 274 pp.
70. Moskowitz, H. R. 1977. Sensations, measurement and pleasantness: Confessions of a latent introspectionist. See Ref. 123, pp. 282–94
71. Moskowitz, H. R., Kumaraiah, V., Sharma, K. N., Jacobs, H. L., Sharma, S. D. 1975. Cross-cultural differences in simple taste preferences. *Science* 190:1217–18
72. Pangborn, R. M. 1970. Individual variation in affective responses to taste stimuli. *Psychon. Sci.* 21:125–26
73. Pangborn, R. M. 1980. A critical analysis of sensory responses to sweetness. In *Carbohydrate Sweeteners in Foods and Nutrition,* ed. P. Koivistoinen, L. Hyvonen, pp. 87–110. London: Academic
74. Pangborn, R. M. 1981. Individuality in response to sensory stimuli. See Ref. 117, pp. 117–219

74a. Pangborn, R. M., Pecore, S. D. 1982. Taste perception of sodium chloride in relation to dietary intake of salt. *Am. J. Clin. Nutr.* 35:510–520

75. Pangborn, R. M., Trabue, I. M. 1967. Detection and apparent taste intensity of salt-acid mixtures in two media. *Percept. Psychophys.* 2:503–9
76. Parducci, A. 1965. Category judgment: A range-frequency model. *Psychol. Rev.* 72:407–18
77. Pelchat, M. L., Rozin, P. 1982. The special role of nausea in the acquisition of food dislikes by humans. *Appetite* 3:341–51
78. Pető, E. 1936. Contribution to the development of smell feeling. *Br. J. Med. Psychol.* 15:314–20
79. Pliner, P. 1982. The effects of mere exposure on liking for edible substances. *Appetite* 3:283–90
80. Pliner, P. 1983. Family resemblance in food preferences. *J. Nutr. Educ.* 15:137–40
81. Pliner, P., Pelchat, M. L. 1986. Similarities in food preferences between children and their siblings and parents. *Appetite*. In press
82. Pliner, P., Polivy, J., Herman, C. P., Zakalusny, I. 1980. Short-term intake of overweight individuals and normal-weight dieters and non-dieters with and without choice among a variety of foods. *Appetite* 1:203–13
83. Pliner, P., Rozin, P., Cooper, M., Woody, G. 1985. Role of specific post-ingestional effects and medicinal context in the acquisition of liking for tastes. *Appetite* 6:243–52
84. Price, R. A., Vandenberg, S. G. 1980. Spouse similarity in American and Swedish couples. *Behav. Genet.* 10:59–71
85. Richter, C. P. 1943. Total self-regulatory functions in animals and human beings. *Harvey Lect. Ser.* 38:63–103
86. Riskey, D. R. 1982. Effects of context and interstimulus procedures in judgements of saltiness and pleasantness. In *Selected Sensory Methods: Problems and Approaches to Measuring Hedonics, Spec. Tech. Publ. 773* ed. J. T. Kuznicki, R. A. Johnson, A. F. Rutkiewiz. Philadelphia: ASTM
87. Riskey, D. R., Parducci, A., Beauchamp, G. K. 1979. Effects of context in judgment of sweetness and pleasantness. *Percept. Psychophys.* 26:171–76
88. Rolls, B. J., Hetherington, M., Burley, V., Van Duijvenvoorde, P. M. 1986. Changing hedonic response to foods during and after a meal. In *Interaction of the Chemical Senses with Nutrition,* ed. M. A. Kare, J. G. Brand, Vol. 5. New York: Academic. In press
89. Rolls, B. J., Rolls, E. T., Rowe, E. A., Sweeney, K. 1981. Sensory specific satiety in man. *Physiol. Behav.* 27:137–42
90. Rolls, B. J., Rowe, E. A., Rolls, E. T., Kingston, B., Megson, A., Gunary, R. 1981. Variety in a meal enhances food intake in man. *Physiol. Behav.* 26:215–21
91. Rolls, B. J., Rowe, E. A., Rolls, E. T. 1982. How sensory properties of foods affect human feeding behavior *Physiol. Behav.* 29:409–17
92. Rolls, B. J., Van Duijvenvoorde, P. M., Rolls, E. T. 1984. Pleasantness changes and food intake in a varied four-course meal. *Appetite* 5:337–48

93. Rozin, E. 1982. The structure of cuisine. See Ref. 4, pp. 189–203
94. Rozin, P. 1976. The selection of food by rats, humans and other animals. In *Advances in the Study of Behavior*, ed. J. Rosenblatt, R. A. Hinde, C. Beer, E. Shaw, 6:21–76. New York: Academic
95. Rozin, P. 1978. The use of characteristic flavorings in human culinary practice. In *Flavor: Its Chemical, Behavioral and Commercial Aspects*, ed. C. M. Apt, pp. 101–27. Boulder, Colo: Westview 229 pp.
96. Rozin, P. 1979. Preference and affect in food selection. See Ref. 57, pp. 289–302
97. Rozin, P. 1981. The study of human food selection and the problem of "Stage One Science." In *Nutrition and Behavior*, ed. S. Miller, pp. 9–18. Philadelphia: Franklin Inst.
98. Rozin, P. 1982. Human food selection: The interaction of biology, culture and individual experience. See Ref. 4, pp. 225–54
99. Rozin, P., Ebert, L., Schull, J. 1982. Some like it hot: A temporal analysis of hedonic responses to chili pepper. *Appetite* 3:13–22
100. Rozin, P., Fallon, A. E. 1980. The psychological categorization of foods and non-foods: A preliminary taxonomy of food rejections. *Appetite* 1:193–201
101. Rozin, P., Fallon, A. E. 1981. The acquisition of likes and dislikes for foods. See Ref. 117, pp. 35–48
102. Rozin, P., Fallon, A. E. 1986. A perspective on disgust. *Psychol. Rev*. In press
103. Rozin, P., Fallon, A. E., Augustoni-Ziskind, M. 1986. The child's conception of food: The development of categories of acceptable and rejected substances. *J. Nutr. Educ*. In press
104. Rozin, P., Fallon, A. E., Mandell, R. 1984. Family resemblance in attitudes to food. *Dev. Psychol*. 20:309–14
105. Rozin, P., Gruss, L., Berk, G. 1979. The reversal of innate aversions: Attempts to induce a preference for chili peppers in rats. *J. Comp. Physiol. Psychol*. 93: 1001–14
106. Rozin, P., Hammer, L., Oster, H., Horowitz, T., Marmora, V. 1986. The child's conception of food: Differentiation of categories of rejected substances in the 1.4 to 5 year range. *Appetite*. In press
107. Rozin, P., Kalat, J. W. 1971. Specific hungers and poison avoidance as adaptive specializations of learning. *Psychol. Rev*. 78:459–86
108. Rozin, P., Schiller, D. 1980. The nature and acquisition of a preference for chili pepper by humans. *Motiv. Emotion* 4:77–101
109. Sandusky, A., Parducci, A. 1965. Pleasantness of odors as a function of the immediate stimulus context. *Psychon. Sci*. 3:321–22
110. Schutz, H. G., Judge, D. S. 1984. Consumer perceptions of food quality. In *Research in Food Science and Nutrition. Food Science and Human Welfare*, ed. J. V. McLoughlin, B. M. McKenna, 4:229–42. Dublin: Boole
111. Schutz, H. G., Rucker, M. H., Russell, G. F. 1975. Food and food-use classification systems. *Food Technol*. 29:50–64
112. Schutz, H. G., Pilgrim, F. J. 1958. A field study of food monotony. *Psychol. Rep*. 4:559–65
113. Siegel, P. S., Pilgrim, F. J. 1958. The effect of monotony on the acceptance of food. *Am. J. Psychol*. 71:756–59
114. Simoons, F. J. 1978. The geographic hypothesis and lactose malabsorption: A weighing of the evidence. *Digest. Dis*. 23:963–80
115. Simoons, F. J. 1982. Geography and genetics as factors in the psychobiology of human food selection. See Ref. 4, pp. 205–24
116. Smith, E. E. 1961. The power of dissonance techniques to change attitudes. *Publ. Opin. Q*. 25:625–39
117. Solms, J., Hall, R. L., eds. 1981. *Criteria of Food Acceptance: How Man Chooses What He Eats*. Zurich: Forster. 461 pp.
118. Solomon, R. L. 1980. The opponent-process theory of acquired motivation. *Am. Psychol*. 35:691–712
119. Stang, D. J. 1975. When familiarity breeds contempt, absence makes the heart grow fonder: Effects of exposure and delay on taste pleasantness ratings. *Bull. Psychon. Soc*. 6:273–75
120. Steiner, J. E. 1977. Facial expressions of the neonate infant indicating the hedonics of food-related chemical stimuli. See Ref. 123, pp. 173–88
121. Torrance, E. P. 1958. Sensitization versus adaptation in preparation for emergencies: prior experience with an emergency ration and its acceptability in a simulated survival situation. *J. Appl. Psychol*. 42:63–67
122. Weidner, G., Archer, S., Healy, B., Matarazzo, J. D. 1985. Family consumption of low fat foods: Stated preference versus actual consumption. *J. Appl. Soc. Psychol*. 15:773–79
123. Weiffenbach, J. M., ed. 1977. *Taste and Development: The Genesis of Sweet Preference*, (DHEW Publ. No. NIH 77-

1068). Washington, DC: US GPO. 432 pp.
124. Wilson, C. S. 1973. Food habits: A selected annotated bibliography. *J. Nutr. Educ.* 5(Suppl. 1):38–72
125. Wooley, O. W., Wooley, S. C., Dunham, R. B. 1972. Calories and sweet taste: Effects on sucrose preferences in the obese and non-obese. *Physiol. Behav.* 9:765–68
126. Worsley, A. 1980. Thought for food: Investigations of cognitive aspects of food. *Ecol. Food Nutr.* 9:65–80
127. Wurtman, R. J., Heftl, F., Melamed, E. 1981. Precursor control of neurotransmitter synthesis. *Pharmacol. Rev.* 32:315–35
128. Wurtman, J. J., Wurtman, R. J. 1979. Drugs that enhance central serotonergic transmission diminish elective carbohydrate consumption by rats. *Life Sci.* 24:895–904
129. Yoshida, M. 1981. Trends in international and Japanese food consumption and desirable attributes of foods as assessed by Japanese consumers. See Ref. 117, pp. 117–37
130. Zahorik, D. 1979. Learned changes in preferences for chemical stimuli: Asymmetrical effects of positive and negative consequences, and species differences in learning. See Ref. 57, pp. 233–46
131. Zajonc, R. B. 1968. Attitudinal effects of mere exposure. *J. Pers. Soc. Psychol.* 9(Pt. 2):1–27
132. Zellner, D. A., Rozin, P., Aron, M., Kulish, C. 1983. Conditioned enhancement of human's liking for flavors by pairing with sweetness. *Learn. Motiv.* 14:338–50

*Ann. Rev. Nutr. 1986. 6:457–74*


# ALCOHOL AND NUTRITION: Caloric Value, Bioenergetics, and Relationship to Liver Damage

*Mack C. Mitchell and H. Franklin Herlong*

Alcohol Research Center and Department of Medicine, The Johns Hopkins University School of Medicine, Baltimore, Maryland 21205

---

CONTENTS

INTRODUCTION .......... 457
DIETARY SURVEYS OF ALCOHOL CONSUMPTION .......... 458
CALORIC VALUE OF ETHANOL .......... 460
BIOENERGETICS OF ETHANOL METABOLISM .......... 461
*General Considerations* .......... 461
*Effects on Hepatic ATP Content* .......... 463
*Effects on Hepatic "ATP-ase" Activity* .......... 463
*Effects on Oxidative Phosphorylation* .......... 464
*Effects of Acetaldehyde on Bioenergetics* .......... 465
ROLES OF ALCOHOL AND MALNUTRITION IN PATHOGENESIS OF CIRRHOSIS .......... 466
SUMMARY .......... 470

## INTRODUCTION

Alcoholic beverages contribute significantly to overall calories in the diet of most Western countries. Numerous effects of ethanol on intermediary metabolism and on nutrition have been described. This chapter reviews the dietary contribution of calories derived from alcoholic beverages and their metabolic utilization as a source of energy. The interaction between alcohol and nutrition in the development of alcoholic liver damage is discussed as an example of how ethanol and nutrition may contribute to the pathogenesis of disease in man.



0199-9885/86/0715-0457$02.00

In recent years, investigators have examined the composition of the diet in the United States and other Western countries. These investigations have been engendered by well-documented relationships between intake of various dietary components and the incidence of disease. In particular, there is interest in the extent to which ethyl alcohol contributes to the total caloric intake.

## DIETARY SURVEYS OF ALCOHOL CONSUMPTION

Total per capita alcohol consumption in the US increased slowly, but steadily, from 1934 to 1980 (67). Since 1980 alcohol consumption has leveled off and perhaps decreased slightly. Similar trends have been reported for other Western countries (86, 93). In 1955, alcoholic beverages accounted for 3.0% of total per capita caloric intake, rising to 5.7% in 1955, while in the US alcohol contributed 4.5% to the total intake of calories (81). These figures represent aggregate approximations derived from tax and census records and information regarding the national food supply. Children and abstainers were not excluded. Although census studies do not provide information about the distribution of alcohol consumption within the population, their advantage is that the data obtained are not influenced by subject recall and the results of alcohol beverage sales are known accurately.

Dietary surveys including assessment of alcohol consumption have been carried out in both alcoholic and nonalcoholic individuals. In one survey over 80% of male business executives and professionals drank alcohol on one or more of the study days. Within this group of drinkers, ethanol accounted for 5–10% of total calories in one fourth of the subjects, while in an additional one fourth ethanol averaged more than 10% of calories (5).

Similar results have been obtained in other nationwide surveys. A wide geographic variation was reported in prevalence of alcohol consumption in both men and women enrolled in nine Lipid Research Clinics between 1972 and 1975. The highest consumption was in southern California whereas the lowest was in Oklahoma. These surveys did not include weekend alcohol consumption. In drinkers, alcohol accounted for 6.5–15.2% of calories ingested by men and 6.0–18% by women in the 24 hours before the survey (27). In the National Food Consumption Survey, a national probability sample (99), alcoholic beverages contributed 17.0% for male drinkers and 21.9% for female drinkers. However, ethanol per se, accounted for only 5.3% of calories in the group after calories from carbohydrate and protein in beer were subtracted.

Although data from surveys are subject to the imperfections of recall and imprecise quantitation, the results obtained are similar to those obtained by weighing all food consumed by the crew of an oil tanker during an 8-day sea voyage. Total caloric intake in these British sailors was 3600 kcal/day, of which

13% was from ethanol. Again, there was a wide range, from 5 to 20% of total calories (29).

Despite this appreciable contribution of alcohol to total calories, protein intake is seldom changed, either as an absolute amount or as a percentage of total calories. However, consumption of fat and carbohydrates is more variable in drinkers (Table 1). In British sailors, alcohol calories tended to be substituted for fat. Fat accounted for 38% of the calories in light drinkers (5% calories as ethanol) vs 24% in moderate drinkers (20% ethanol). Furthermore, consumption of simple carbohydrates in the form of sugars and sweetened soft drinks was decreased in moderate drinkers (15, 29). Although there is often an inverse relationship between calories derived from ethanol and from fat or carbohydrate, some surveys have found that alcohol calories are added to the diet rather than replacing other foodstuffs. In the group surveyed by Bebb and colleagues, alcohol calories were added to the diet on drinking days compared with nondrinking days (5). In the Zutphen study of obesity and dietary intake, there was a significant positive correlation between the degree of fatness and alcohol intake, whereas the correlation between obesity and total caloric intake was negative (45). Obese men consumed almost twice as much alcohol as lean men. Although total calories ingested and alcohol consumption were not compared directly, the relationship would be inverse almost by necessity. More information regarding the relationships between caloric balance, dietary alcohol intake, and body weight in nonalcoholics would be important, particularly to assess utilization of alcohol as an energy source in moderate drinkers.

**Table 1** Dietary surveys including alcohol consumption in nonalcoholics

| | | | | % Total Calories | | | |
|---|---|---|---|---|---|---|---|
| Study | Method | Subjects (number) | Total kcal | EtoH | Prot | Fat | CHO |
| Bebb et al (5) | 3-day diary × 6 sets | men (114) | 2348 | 6.1 | 16.0 | 38.1 | 39.8 |
| | | drinkers (94) | 2391 | 6.2 | 15.0 | 38.0 | 38.8 |
| | | nondrinkers (20) | 2145 | 0 | 16.5 | 38.8 | 44.7 |
| Dennis et al (27) | 24-hr recall | men (1993) | 2400–3200 | 6–15[a] | ~15[b] | 36–43 | 43–46 |
| | Lipid Res. Clin. | women (1741) | 1650–2150 | 6–18[a] | ~15[b] | 36–43 | 40–45 |
| Eddy et al (29) | food | British seamen | 3600 | 13.0 | 12.0 | 35.0 | 40.0 |
| Kromhout (45) | cross-check | men (871) | | | | | |
| | usual intake | obese | 2916 | 1.6 | 11.5 | 42.1 | 43.4 |
| | 6–12 months | nonobese | 3193 | 0.6 | 11.8 | 43.1 | 45.5 |
| Windham et al (99) | 24-hr recall | Age > 14 yr (7061) | | | | | |
| | & 2-day dairy | drinkers | 2037 | 5.30 | 16.3 | 40.3 | 38.1 |
| | | nondrinkers | 1928 | 0 | 17.2 | 41.4 | 41.4 |

[a]Drinkers only.
[b]Men and women combined.

Not surprisingly, alcohol contributes an even greater percentage to the total caloric intake of alcoholics. Assessment of dietary intake and nutritional status of alcoholics is often confounded by socioeconomic variables and availability of nutrient intake. These factors must be controlled in order to assess accurately nutrition-alcohol interactions. Hurt and coworkers (37) at the Mayo Clinic found from dietary reports that total calories ingested by 12 employed alcoholics were almost identical to total calories consumed in the hospital during and after alcohol detoxification. These alcoholics replaced alcohol calories with carbohydrates while undergoing detoxification. Of interest, 88% of 59 alcoholics in this same study were at or above ideal body weight. Nutrient intakes in these individuals were equal to or greater than RDA for total protein, calories, and most other nutrients, despite an average consumption of 35% of calories as ethanol (approximately 150 g). Neville and coworkers (68) reported a similar caloric contribution of alcohol to the diets of lower middle class alcoholics. Percentages of protein, fat, and carbohydrate calories were decreased equally in alcoholics compared to controls. However, vitamin B intakes were similar to controls. Although urinary vitamin excretion increased slightly after abstinence in the hospital, there was no evidence of gross deficiencies.

Careful assessment of nutritional parameters including anthropometrics, serum proteins, and immunologic competence in alcoholics has shown evidence of malnutrition in most, but not all, patients (17, 58, 65, 84). In one study, tricep skin-fold thickness and mid-arm and muscle circumference were inversely correlated with alcohol consumption (84). Alcohol intake in these patients averaged 25–35% of total calories. It must be emphasized that these findings were obtained from alcoholics who were otherwise healthy and had no clinical or laboratory evidence of liver disease. As discussed later in this chapter, the incidence of malnutrition is much greater in patients with alcoholic liver diseases, particularly alcoholic hepatitis and cirrhosis.

## CALORIC VALUE OF ETHANOL

Ethanol yields 7.1 kcal/g upon complete combustion in a bomb calorimeter. To assess the effectiveness of alcohol as an energy source, two experimental approaches have been used. Metabolic studies directly measure thermogenesis and oxygen consumption to assess energy metabolism from ingested ethanol. The second approach correlates alcohol intake with body weight or anthropometric measurements. Both approaches have produced conflicting data. The classical report of Atwater & Benedict (3) demonstrated in three healthy nonalcoholic volunteers that 72 g of absolute ethanol per day was utilized as efficiently as fat or carbohydrate as a source of energy. In this study, energy utilization was measured by direct calorimetry. Only during vigorous exercise was there a suggestion that ethanol calories were not efficiently utilized and the difference was considered by the authors to be within experimental error. In support of the findings of Atwater & Benedict, Barnes and coworkers (4) did not observe an increase in oxygen consumption or thermogenic effects of 31.5 g ethanol per 65 kg body weight in nine normal subjects. In contrast, Perman (70) reported that administration of moderate doses of alcohol to normal subjects resulted in thermogenesis and increased oxygen consumption, which suggests inefficient caloric utilization of ethanol.

In some studies of alcohol feeding, subjects have lost weight while receiving alcoholic beverages (13, 57, 71, 72). In one study, weight loss occurred in volunteers when 35% of carbohydrate calories were replaced by ethanol and was maximal at 50%, the highest range tested (71). Furthermore, addition of ethanol to the diet resulted in a transient small increase in weight that returned to baseline in 10 days, whereas increases in dietary fat and carbohydrate calories resulted in greater weight gain that was sustained over a similar time. In addition, ethanol (unlike fat or carbohydrates) failed to stabilize weight in obese subjects on hypocaloric diets (13).

These important observations suggest that the caloric utilization of ethanol may be dose-related. At intakes less than 25–35% of calories, ethanol may be completely utilized as a source of energy, but at higher intake utilization may not be complete. At high doses ethanol may be metabolized by pathways other than those that metabolize low doses (32, 36, 49, 50, 60, 63, 64, 79, 83, 97). Furthermore, high concentrations of ethanol and its metabolites may affect ATP formation and turnover, as discussed later in this chapter. It is possible that effects of ethanol on caloric utilization might be mediated indirectly through inefficient utilization of other dietary components. For example, urinary nitrogen losses were higher in subjects receiving 25% of calories as wine compared with control periods (57).

Not all studies have shown a negative effect of alcohol on body weight. In several surveys alcoholics were at or above ideal body weight (17, 28, 45, 47, 58, 65, 84). In the Zutphen study a positive correlation was found between alcohol consumption and obesity. This observation is consistent with effective caloric utilization of ethanol in real-life situations, particularly in light of the lower total calories ingested by obese men in this study (45).

## BIOENERGETICS OF ETHANOL METABOLISM

### *General Considerations*

Alcohol dehydrogenase (ADH), a cytosolic enzyme that exists as several isoenzymes, is the major enzyme metabolizing ethanol (49, 61). ADH catalyzes the oxidation of ethanol to acetaldehyde while converting the cofactor $NAD^+$ to NADH. Acetaldehyde is further metabolized to acetate by aldehyde dehydrogenase (ALDH), which has both mitochondrial and cytosolic forms (49). NADH is generated from the cofactor $NAD^+$. These reactions are summarized as

$$\text{ethanol} + NAD^+ \rightleftarrows \text{acetaldehyde} + NADH \quad 1.$$

$$\text{acetaldehyde} + NAD^+ \rightleftarrows \text{acetate} + NADH. \quad 2.$$

Metabolism of ethanol by ADH and acetaldehyde by ALDH generates reducing equivalents (NADH) that can be used for mitochondrial ATP synthesis. The low $K_m$ for ADH (1 mM) makes it the principal enzyme for ethanol metabolism in vivo (49, 61).

Other enzymes are capable of metabolizing ethanol. Of these only the microsomal ethanol oxidizing system (MEOS) is believed to be active in vivo (32, 44, 49, 64, 83, 97). As implied by the name, this enzyme is bound to the smooth endoplasmic reticulum of hepatocytes and resembles the cytochrome P-450 mixed-function oxygenases in its catalytic activity. MEOS differs from ADH in several aspects. It has a higher $K_m$, on the order of 10 mM compared with 1 mM for ADH (49, 61). The higher $K_m$ of MEOS suggests that the enzyme would be active in vivo only at high ethanol concentrations. Secondly, its activity increases after chronic ethanol feeding due to induction of the enzyme in animals (40, 50, 63, 64) and in man (44, 64, 79). Thus, MEOS may be quantitatively more important in regular heavy drinkers. Recent evidence suggests that MEOS metabolizes ethanol in vivo in deermice, which lack ADH, and at high ethanol concentrations (83). Finally, NADPH rather than $NAD^+$ serves as a cofactor and $NADP^+$ is formed rather than reducing equivalents for potential ATP synthesis. Acetaldehyde is the product of MEOS-catalyzed oxidation of ethanol, just as in ADH-catalyzed ethanol oxidation:

$$\text{ethanol} + NADPH + H^+ + \tfrac{1}{2}\, O_2 \rightarrow \text{acetaldehyde} + NADP^+ + H_2O.$$

The acetaldehyde formed is further metabolized by ALDH.

Pirola & Lieber (71, 72) proposed that metabolism of ethanol by MEOS results in loss of energy (thermogenesis) without effective coupling to ATP synthesis. This hypothesis might explain the weight loss observed in subjects receiving 50% of dietary calories as ethanol (71). If correct, oxygen consumption should be higher during ethanol oxidation in animals chronically fed ethanol and in human alcoholics. Increased oxygen consumption has been observed after ethanol administration in man in some studies (41, 70, 92) but not in others (3, 4). Conflicting results have also been obtained in experimental animals and are discussed later in this chapter.

If ethanol oxidation is to provide useful energy for other cellular processes, it must be coupled in some way to ATP production. During ADH-catalyzed oxidation of ethanol, one mole of NADH is formed for each mole of ethanol oxidized. Since this NADH is formed in cytoplasm, it must be shuttled into the mitochondria for use in ATP synthesis. The major shuttle system for this transport is the malate-aspartate system (11, 19, 25, 26, 49, 76). In this context, several studies suggested that the shuttle might be limiting for ethanol metabolism (11, 76). However, more recent data provide evidence that the mitochondrial shuttle is capable of operating at rates in excess of those of ethanol metabolism (26). However, during fasting shuttle intermediates may become depleted, which would make mitochondrial transport and reoxidation of NADH rate limiting (19, 25). Thus, it seems unlikely that the shuttle system limits ethanol metabolism or mitochondrial access to NADH except possibly during fasting.

### *Effects on Hepatic ATP Content*

Through the processes of electron transport and oxidative phosphorylation, free energy gained during oxidation of both ethanol and acetaldehyde is used for synthesis of ATP, which may later be used to drive cellular processes such as biosynthesis and maintenance of electrochemical gradients. Within 15 min after administration of a single intraperitoneal dose of ethanol (approximately 0.5 g/kg) both the cytoplasmic and mitochondrial $NAD^+$/NADH ratios were decreased (94). There was a corresponding increase in the phosphorylation potential that was attributed, in part, to metabolism of ethanol beyond acetaldehyde. It is of note that the absolute levels of ATP did not decrease and were occasionally increased after single-dose ethanol administration to intact rats (33, 36, 94) or after perfusion of the isolated rat liver with 10-mM ethanol (98). Thus, acute administration of ethanol does not decrease hepatic ATP content, but may increase it slightly.

However, there is evidence to suggest that hepatic ATP content is reduced after chronic ethanol feeding (1, 8, 14, 33, 35, 85, 96). This decrease in hepatic ATP content could be due to either increased utilization of ATP in response to increases in hepatic "ATP-ase" activity or to decreased synthesis of ATP.

### *Effects on Hepatic "ATP-ase" Activity*

Increased activity of hepatic Na-K ATP-ase would be expected to increase ATP utilization by the liver, in effect creating a hypermetabolic state. This hypothesis was proposed by Israel and coworkers, who consistently observed increases in oxygen consumption in liver slices (95) and in perfused livers (9, 39, 91) from rats chronically fed ethanol. In these same animals, there was a corresponding increase in activity of the sodium pump (70%) and Na-K ATPase

(190%). Furthermore, the reported increase in $O_2$ consumption was completely eliminated by ouabain, an inhibitor of Na-K ATPase (9, 10).

On the basis of these observations, the investigators suggested that the increased metabolic demands might increase susceptibility of the alcoholic liver to damage from hypoxia (39). In other studies, oxygen consumption was unchanged in perfused livers (80) or in isolated hepatocytes (18) from fasted chronic ethanol-fed rats. Although hepatic vein $O_2$ tension was lower in fasted ethanol-fed baboons, it actually increased after ethanol administration (82). It has been suggested that changes in availability of substrates in fasted, ethanol-fed animals may account for the observed increases in $O_2$ consumption (2, 19, 22, 35). Other reports indicate that the magnitude of increase in Na-K ATPase is only 15% (35), an amount unlikely to account for changes in ATP levels.

## *Effects on Oxidative Phosphorylation*

Decreased synthesis of ATP has been reported in animals fed ethanol for more than one month (1, 14, 35, 85, 96). Gordon reported that ATP synthesis was decreased in rats with ethanol-induced fatty liver. This decrease resulted from accumulation of long-chain CoA derivatives of fatty acids, which impede translocation of ADP into mitochondria and thereby limit the rate of oxidative phosphorylation (35). Using isolated submitochondrial particles from the livers of rats fed ethanol for one month, Thayer & Rubin (89) observed a 35–40% decrease in ATP synthesis with each substrate tested (Table 2). These results suggested that the observed decreases in respiration were a consequence of alterations in the electron transport chain itself. Major decreases (40–50%) occur in activities of cytochrome oxidase, cytochrome b, and NADH dehydrogenase (7, 88–90).

Other studies have found decreases in respiration in intact mitochondria after chronic ethanol feeding (10, 14, 21, 85). In these studies, state-3 (ADP-stimulated) oxygen consumption was decreased in intact mitochondria from ethanol-fed rats, whereas state-4 (basal) oxygen consumption was unchanged (7, 21, 85). The decreases in ATP synthesis appear to be related to decreased catalytic activity of the ATP synthetase complex as measured by the ATP-$P_i$ exchange rate (14, 21), rather than to alterations in the proton gradient (14).

Similar changes have been observed in hepatic mitochondria obtained from baboons fed ethanol for up to 7 years. In these animals, there was a 50% decrease in state-3 respiration as well as a 25–40% decrease in enzyme activities of mitochondrial respiratory chain. Mitochondria from ethanol-fed baboons were larger than those from control animals and also exhibited morphologic evidence of damage, with disorganization of cristae even at the stage of fatty liver (2). Morphologic changes of this type have been frequently observed in experimental animals fed ethanol (34, 38, 43, 52) and in alcoholics (16, 42, 46, 54).

**Table 2** Effects of chronic ethanol ingestion on oxidative phophorylation by rat hepatic submitochondrial particles[a]

| Substrate | Parameter | Control | Ethanol[b] | Change (%) |
|---|---|---|---|---|
| NADH | Respiration rate[c] | 151 | 99 | −34 |
| | P/O ratio | 2.59 | 2.33 | −10 |
| | Phosphorylation rate[d] | 389 | 230 | −41 |
| Succinate | Respiration rate[c] | 145 | 104 | −28 |
| | P/O ratio | 1.55 | 1.37 | −12 |
| | Phosphorylation rate[d] | 225 | 146 | −35 |
| Ascorbate/phenzine methosulfate | Respiration rate[c] | 131 | 98 | −25 |
| | P/O ratio | .92 | .79 | −14 |
| | Phosphorylation rate[d] | 120 | 79 | −34 |

[a]Data are adapted from Thayer & Rubin (89).
[b]All results are significantly different from control ($p < 0.05$).
[c]Nanoatoms of oxygen/min/mg of protein.
[d]Nanomoles of ATP/min/mg of protein.

## *Effects of Acetaldehyde on Bioenergetics*

Several studies have assessed the effects of acetaldehyde on mitochondrial function to determine what role, if any, this potentially toxic metabolite of ethanol has in causing the decreased ATP synthesis observed in chronic ethanol-fed animals. High concentrations (3–30 mM) of acetaldhyde inhibit oxidative phosphorylation and ATP-$P_i$ exchange in freshly isolated hepatic mitochondria from untreated rats (20, 22). There was also decreased $Ca^{2+}$ uptake in the presence of acetaldehyde concentrations in excess of 12 mM. In addition, there was decreased $CO_2$ production from citric acid cycle intermediates in the presence of acetaldehyde (1.25–3.0 mM) (22). In vivo, inhibition of aldehyde dehydrogenase by calcium cyanamide caused a decrease in phosphorylation potential (ATP/ADP · $P_i$) during infusion of ethanol or acetaldehyde. The decrease was due almost entirely to increases in ADP and $P_i$ without significant decreases in ATP content (55). Although the results of these studies suggest that acetaldehyde may cause changes in mitochondrial energy production, the concentrations of acetaldehyde required to demonstrate these effects are far in excess of those occurring in the liver, even after ingestion of large amounts of ethanol.

It is of interest that the toxic effects of acetaldehyde on mitochondrial function can be prevented by addition of cysteine in vitro (23). The investigators attributed the protection in part to condensation of acetaldehyde with cysteine to form a stable adduct. Whether cysteine or other thiols such as glutathione are important in in vivo protection against acetaldehyde or ethanol-induced mitochondrial damage remains unknown.

Recent evidence suggests that acetate may alter energy utilization by increasing adenine nucleotide turnover (31, 74). Hyperuricemia and gout have long been associated with heavy ethanol consumption. In part, the increases in uric acid have been attributed to increased blood lactate levels (6, 56, 100). However, ethanol-induced elevation of urate production occurs as a result of increased turnover of ATP as well (74). The investigators hypothesized that increased turnover results from utilization of two moles of ATP for each mole of acetate converted to acetyl CoA:

$$\text{acetate} + \text{ATP} \rightarrow \text{PP}_i + \text{acetyl-AMP}$$

$$\text{acetyl-AMP} + \text{CoASH} \rightarrow \text{acetyl-CoA} + \text{AMP}.$$

The rate of acetate formation from ethanol exceeds the rate of hepatic acetate oxidation and thereby increases acetate loads to other tissues (74). Peripheral oxidation of acetate possibly contributes to the net increase in nucleotide turnover observed. Formation of acetate from ethanol could result in a net loss of ATP under these conditions.

## ROLE OF ALCOHOL AND MALNUTRITION IN PATHOGENESIS OF ALCOHOLIC CIRRHOSIS

A close relationship between prolonged alcohol consumption and liver disease has been recognized for many years. In the United States, alcohol abuse accounts for 75% of cases of cirrhosis. The spectrum of liver injury produced by alcohol includes fat accumulation, alcoholic hepatitis, and cirrhosis. These three morphologic conditions are not mutually exclusive and may coexist within the same liver.

The pathogenesis of alcohol-related liver disease is complex. Both the amount and duration of alcohol consumption are important factors (47). Although there is a clear relationship between alcohol consumption and alcoholic hepatitis or cirrhosis, total alcohol consumption alone does not explain why only 17–30% of heavy drinkers develop alcoholic liver injury (47, 49). For this reason, other factors including genetics, immune response, and nutrition have been studied to determine which ones might contribute to pathogenesis of alcohol-related liver injury.

The relationship between nutrition and alcoholic liver disease has received much attention, but the role of nutritional factors in pathogenesis of alcoholic liver disease remains controversial (48, 60). Before 1960 liver disease in patients consuming large quantities of alcohol was thought to be due solely to protein malnutrition. That alcoholic liver disease might be due to nutritional deficiencies was supported by experiments showing that alcohol administered in the drinking water of rats did not produce liver damage unless accompanied by a nutritionally deficient diet (12). Epidemiologic studies reporting a reduced intake of protein and other essential nutrients in alcoholics with liver disease also supported the nutritional hypothesis (69). Furthermore, in uncontrolled studies the clinical signs of liver disease improved in patients given high-protein, vitamin-supplemented diets despite continued consumption of more than 100 g of ethanol per day (30, 87), while the clinical signs of liver disease worsened in patients who continued to drink alcohol and ate low-protein diets.

In 1963 Lieber and coworkers (53) demonstrated that rats fed 36% of calories as ethanol with an otherwise nutritious diet developed fatty liver. In these experiments, the natural aversion of rodents to alcohol was overcome by administering ethanol in a totally liquid diet. These observations were extended to primates such as the baboon (51, 78). These animals were fed 4.5–8.3 g of ethanol/kg of body weight, while pair-fed controls were given diets with carbohydrates isocalorically substituted for 9 months to 4 years. This amount of alcohol represented 50% of the total calories consumed, the average consumption of alcohol by alcoholic patients (Table 3). The entire spectrum of alcoholic liver injury was initially reported to occur in these animals, including fatty liver, alcoholic hepatitis, and cirrhosis (51, 78). It was subsequently noted that the histologic appearance of the livers from these animals was similar to but not identical with the histologic lesion of alcoholic hepatitis in humans (73). In the baboons, hepatocytes were increased in size and there was some ballooning of cells associated with mononuclear inflammatory cells. There were, however, few polymorphonuclear cells in the inflammatory infiltrate, a characteristic feature of alcoholic hepatitis. By electron microscopy there was some clumping in the cytoplasm of the liver cells but no frank alcoholic hyalin was seen. In other studies, administration of ethanol as 50% of the calories to monkeys for 4 years resulted only in fatty liver (62).

Administration of ethanol as 50% of total calories combined with a nutritious diet to alcoholic patients and nonalcoholic volunteers for two weeks, resulted in fatty liver and ultrastructural changes in mitochondria (54, 74). The later stages of alcoholic liver disease were rarely, if ever, seen in these patients (77). Thus, just as a solely nutritional explanation for alcoholic liver disease proved untenable, direct hepatotoxicity from alcohol alone inadequately explained the clinical, biochemical, and histologic observations in humans with alcohol-related liver injury.

Clearly the daily amount of alcohol consumed and duration of excessive consumption are important in the etiology of liver injury, but nutritional factors may play a role in modulating the hepatotoxicity of alcohol. The prevalence of malnutrition in alcoholics with liver disease is so high that it may be impossible to isolate completely the contribution of each factor. Recently the Veterans Administration Cooperative Alcoholic Hepatitis Study Group reported the incidence of protein/calorie malnutrition in a large number of patients with alcoholic hepatitis (58). This study excluded patients with nonspecific changes

**Table 3** Dietary surveys in alcoholics with and without liver disease

| Study | Method | Alcoholic subjects (number) | Total kcal | % Total calories EtoH | Prot | Fat | CHO |
|---|---|---|---|---|---|---|---|
| Hurt et al (37) | 6-mo recall | not specified (58) | 3118 | 34.9 | 11.0 | 30.3 | 22.8 |
| Mendenhall et al (58) | 1-mo recall | liver disease (21) | 3722 | 41.5 | 8.1 | 18.5 | 30.8 |
| | | alcoholic hepatitis (95)[a] | 3104 | 50.0 | 7.0 | 15.1 | 28.0 |
| Mills et al (65) | 6-mo recall | liver disease (30) | 2452 | 52.0 | 9.5 | N.A. | N.A. |
| Neville et al (68) | | men[b] (26) | 2710 | 36.4 | 10.0 | 22.6 | 31.0 |
| | | women[b] (8) | 2578 | 22.0 | 11.2 | 27.6 | 39.2 |
| Patek et al (69) | 1-mo recall | w/o liver disease (69) | 3544 | 51.4 | 8.1 | N.A. | N.A. |
| | | cirrhosis (195) | 3394 | 54.9 | 5.9 | N.A. | N.A. |
| Simko et al (84) | 24-hr recall | w/o liver disease (20) | 3135 | 24.2 | 9.5 | N.A. | N.A. |
| | | liver disease (62) | 3093 | 34.6 | 8.4 | N.A. | N.A. |

[a]Clinically severe.
[b]18% had liver disease defined by prolonged BSP retention.

or fatty liver alone and patients who had cirrhosis without alcoholic hepatitis. In this study, complete nutritional assessment was performed in 284 patients. These patients were compared with a group of alcoholics matched for age and alcohol consumption, but without clinically evident liver disease. None of the patients with liver disease was completely free from malnutrition, although some indicators of malnutrition (e.g. decreased serum albumin) could arise from liver disease alone. In 62% of alcoholics without liver disease, one or more signs of malnutrition were present.

Alcohol consumption averaged 220 g/day and was similar in patients with and without liver disease. The amount of alcohol consumption did not correlate with the severity of liver disease. However, an inverse relationship was noted between nonalcoholic calorie consumption and the severity of liver disease. Nonalcoholic calorie consumption decreased from 2176 kcal in alcoholic patients without liver disease to 2015 kcal in patients with mild alcoholic hepatitis to 1552 kcal in patients with severe alcoholic hepatitis.

Despite this reduction in nonalcoholic calorie consumption, the mean consumption of protein exceeded 50 g/day, even in patients with severe alcoholic hepatitis. Similar results have been obtained in other dietary surveys comparing protein intake in alcoholics with and without serious liver disease. In several studies, protein intake was significantly lower in cirrhotics compared to alcoholics without liver disease. These results are summarized in Table 3. When expressed as grams per day, the protein intake was above the Recommended Dietary Allowance in most patients. Although dietary protein intake might be adequate, it is possible that protein requirements are increased in alcoholics. Factors that could contribute to malnutrition despite adequate dietary protein intake include malabsorption (59, 60) and azotorrhea (75), inhibition of protein synthesis by alcohol or acetaldehyde (24), and increased urinary excretion of nitrogen (57). Increased hepatic oxygen consumption, which may occur after chronic ethanol ingestion, is associated with increased protein degradation (41).

Nutritional deficiencies are common in alcoholics even in the absence of liver disease. However, these deficits were most severe in those patients with the most clinically severe liver disease (58). Furthermore, the clinical severity of liver disease is better correlated with nutritional parameters than with morphological changes seen on liver biopsy (28). In patients with moderately severe alcoholic hepatitis, Diehl and coworkers (28) found that patients consumed more calories per basal energy expenditure (BEE) than necessary to maintain weight, and met expected standards for protein intake as well. These patients were in the 99th percentile for ideal body weight. However, the following indicators of nutrition were uniformally suboptimal: creatinine-height index; arm muscle area; arm fat area; hematocrit; and plasma levels of short half-life visceral proteins (such as retinol binding protein), prealbumin, and longer half-life proteins (such as albumin) (28). These findings imply that patients with active alcoholic liver disease are unable to utilize dietary protein efficiently. In addition, alcohol itself may be an ineffective source of energy during times of high alcohol consumption, as mentioned earlier.

The prevalence of malnutrition in patients with advanced alcoholic disease has lead to several trials of specific nutritional therapy in patients with alcoholic hepatitis. Nasrallah & Galambos (66) reported decreased mortality from acute alcoholic hepatitis in patients receiving parenteral amino acid supplementation. In this study, patients received 51.6 g of protein as an amino acid infusion in addition to a high-calorie, high-protein diet. Significant reduction in mortality and improvement in biochemical parameters of liver function were observed in the treated group compared with controls. In a randomized controlled trial of parenteral amino acid therapy in 15 patients with biopsy-proven alcoholic hepatitis, Diehl and coworkers (28) found that parenteral amino acid therapy improved the clinical severity of liver disease more rapidly but, at the end of 30 days, was no more beneficial than standard therapy in improving creatinine-height index, arm muscle area, arm fat area, and plasma proteins. Amino acid treatment resulted in greater resolution of fat infiltration but did not otherwise affect hepatic histology. Thus, improvement in protein nutrition had more effect on the clinical than on the histological index of severity of liver disease.

Nutritional deficiencies, resulting from either decreased intake or increased nutritient requirements, are best correlated with clinical rather than histological severity of alcoholic liver disease (17, 28, 58). Certainly the daily amount of alcohol ingested and the duration of excessive drinking are the two most important determinants of the risk of developing serious alcoholic liver injury. Furthermore, cirrhosis can and does occur even in well-nourished individuals. Current evidence suggests that liver disease in alcoholics is not a result of malnutrition independent of the effects of alcohol, but the close relationship between clinical severity of liver disease and nutritional deficiencies, coupled with evidence that nutritional therapy is beneficial in improving the rate of recovery from alcoholic liver disease, suggests a definite role for nutritional parameters in modulating the course of alcoholic liver disease.

## SUMMARY

Alcoholic beverages contribute an appreciable percentage (4–6%) to the total caloric intake in Western societies. The caloric value of ethanol as fuel may be dose-related. Most evidence suggests that at moderate intake levels of less than 45 g/day (3 drinks) ethanol is efficiently utilized as a fuel by the liver. At high intakes, ethanol calories may not be utilized for cellular synthesis of ATP and maintenance of weight. The exact mechanism for this inefficient utilization remains unknown but may be related, in part, to metabolism of ethanol by the microsomal ethanol-oxidizing system, a reaction that does not contribute to generation of reducing equivalents for ATP synthesis.

Although ethanol is utilized for ATP synthesis after single-dose administration, chronic consumption leads to morphological changes in hepatic mitochondria and to decreased ATP synthesis. Reductions in the activities of the enzymes of the mitochondrial electron transport chain have been reported after alcohol feeding and may help to explain decreases in hepatic ATP synthesis. There is some evidence that ATP degradation by "Na-K ATPase" is increased after ethanol feeding and that hepatic $O_2$ consumption is likewise enhanced. However, other studies have failed to demonstrate enhanced $O_2$ consumption.

Current evidence suggests that malnutrition alone is not sufficient to explain the pathogenesis of chronic liver disease in alcoholics. Although the daily amount of alcohol consumed and the duration of excessive consumption are clearly important factors in the development of alcoholic hepatitis and cirrhosis, other factors, particularly nutritional deficiencies, may modulate the risk of developing alcohol-related liver damage. The prevalence of malnutrition is exceedingly high in alcoholics with clinically severe liver disease. Nutritional deficiencies are better correlated with a clinical index of severity than with histologic severity of alcoholic hepatitis. Prognosis and outcome of patients with alcoholic liver disease may be affected by nutritional deficiencies, which thus provides a rationale for aggressive nutritional management of these patients.

### ACKNOWLEDGMENTS

The authors would like to thank the Alcoholic Beverage Medical Research Foundation for their support, Dr. Esteban Mezey for his helpful comments in reviewing this manuscript, and Ms. Judith Hariton for her expert assistance in preparing this manuscript.

## *Literature Cited*


1. Ammon, H. P. T., Estler, C. J. 1967. Influence of acute and chronic administration of alcohol on carbohydrate breakdown and energy metabolism in the liver. *Nature* 216:158–59
2. Arai, M., Leo, M. A., Nakano, M., Gordon, E. R., Lieber, C. S. 1984. Biochemical and morphological alterations of baboon hepatic mitochondria after chronic ethanol consumption. *Hepatology* 4:165–74
3. Atwater, W. D., Benedict, F. G. 1902. An experimental inquiry regarding the nutritive value of alcohol. *Mem. Natl. Acad. Sci.* 8:235–397
4. Barnes, E. W., Cooke, N. J., King, A. J., Passmore, R. 1965. Observations on the metabolism of alcohol in man. *Br. J. Nutr.* 19:485–89
5. Bebb, H. T., Houser, H. B., Witschi, M. S., Littell, A. S., Fuller, R. K. 1971. Calorie and nutrient contribution of alcoholic beverages to the usual diets of 155 adults. *Am. Clin. Nutr.* 24:1042–52
6. Beck, L. H. 1981. Clinical disorders of uric acid metabolism. *Med. Clin. North Am.* 65:401–11
7. Bernstein, J. D., Penniall, R. 1977. Effect of chronic ethanol treatment upon rat liver mitochondria. *Biochem. Pharmacol.* 27:2337–42
8. Bernstein, J., Videla, L., Israel, Y. 1973. Metabolic alterations produced in the liver by chronic ethanol administration: Changes related to energetic parameters of the cell. *Biochem. J.* 134:515–21
9. Bernstein, J., Videla, L., Israel, Y. 1974. Role of the sodium pump in the regulation of liver metabolism in experimental alcoholism. *Ann. NY. Acad. Sci.* 242:560–72
10. Bernstein, J., Videla, L., Israel, Y. 1975. Hormonal influences in the development of the hypermetabolic state of the liver produced by chronic administration of ethanol. *J. Pharmac. Exp. Ther.* 192:583–91
11. Berry, M. N., Werner, H. V., Kun, E. 1974. Effects of bicarbonate on intercompartmental reducing-equivalent translocation in isolated parenchymal cells from rat liver. *Biochem. J.* 140: 355–61
12. Best, C. H., Hartroft, W. S., Lucas, C. C. 1949. Liver damage produced by feeding alcohol or sugar and its prevention by choline. *Br. Med. J.* 2:1101–6
13. Bortz, W. M., Howat, P., Holmes, W. S. 1969. Lack of effect of alcohol on rate of weight loss on a hypocaloric diet. *Am. J. Clin. Nutr.* 22:119–21
14. Bottenus, R. E., Spach, P. I., Filus, S., Cunningham, C. C. 1982. Effect of chronic ethanol feeding consumption on energy-linked processes associated with oxidative phosphorylation: Proton translocation and ATP-P exchange. *Biochem. Biophys. Res. Commun.* 105:1368–73
15. Bresard, M., Gombervaux, C. 1962. Enquête sur la consommation des boissons auprès des mineurs du bassin de la Loire. *Bull. Inst. Natl. Hyg. (Paris)* 17:217–65
16. Bruguera, M., Bertman, A., Bombi, J. A., et al. 1977. Giant mitochondria in hepatocytes. A diagnostic hint for alcoholic liver disease. *Gastroenterology* 73:1383–87
17. Bunout, D., Gattas, V., Iturriaga, H., Perez, C., Pereda, T., et al. 1983. Nutritional status of alcoholic patients: Its possible relationship to alcoholic liver damage. *Am. J. Clin. Nutr.* 38:469–73
18. Cederbaum, A. I., Dicker, E., Lieber, C. S., et al. 1978. Ethanol oxidation by isolated hepatocytes from ethanol-treated and control rats: Factors contributing to the metabolic adaptation after chronic ethanol consumption. *Biochem. Pharmacol.* 27:7–15
19. Cederbaum, A. I., Dicker, E., Rubin, E. 1977. Transfer and reoxidation in reducing equivalents as the rate-limiting steps in oxidation of ethanol by liver cells isolated from fed and fasted rats. *Arch. Biochem. Biophys.* 183:638–46
20. Cederbaum, A. I., Lieber, C. S., Rubin, E. 1974. The effect of acetaldehyde on mitochondrial function. *Arch. Biochem. Biophys.* 161:26–39
21. Cederbaum, A. I., Lieber, C. S., Rubin, E. 1974. Effects of chronic ethanol treatment on mitochondrial functions: damage to coupling site. *Arch. Biochem. Biophys.* 165:560–69
22. Cederbaum, A. I., Lieber, C. S., Rubin, E. 1976. Effect of chronic ethanol consumption and acetaldehyde on partial reactions of oxidative phosphorylation and $CO_2$ production from citric acid cycle intermediates. *Arch. Biochem. Biophys.* 176:525–38
23. Cederbaum, A. I., Rubin, E. 1976. Protective effect of cysteine on the inhibition of mitochondrial functions by acetaldehyde. *Biochem. Pharmacol.* 25:963–73
24. Chapman, S., Ward, L. C., Cooksley, W. G. 1979. Effect of ethanol on dietary

protein concentration and whole body protein synthesis rates in rats. *Nutr. Rep. Int.* 20:239–34
25. Crow, K. E., Cornell, N. W., Veech, R. L. 1978. Lactate-stimulated ethanol oxidation in isolated rat hepatocytes. *Biochem. J.* 172:29–36
26. Dawson, A. G. 1982. Rapid oxidation of NADH via the reconstituted malate-asparate shuttle in systems containing mitochondrial and soluble fractions of rat liver: implications for ethanol metabolism. *Biochem. Pharmacol.* 31:2733–38
27. Dennis, B. H., Haynes, S. G., Anderson, J. J., Liu-Chi, S. B. L., Hosking, J. D., et al. 1985. Nutrient intakes among selected North American populations in the lipid research clinics prevalence study: composition of energy intake. *Am. J. Clin. Nutr.* 41:312–29
28. Diehl, A. M., Boitnott, J. K., Herlong, H. F., Potter, J. J., Van Duyn, M. A., et al. 1985. Effect of parenteral amino acid supplementation in alcohol hepatitis. *Hepatology* 5:57–63
29. Eddy, T. P., Wheeler, E. F., Stock, A. L. 1971. Nutritional and environmental studies on an ocean-going oil tanker. 4. The diet of seamen. *Br. J. Ind. Med.* 28:342–52
30. Erenoglu, E., Edreira, J. G., Patek, A. J. 1964. Observations on patients with Laennec's cirrhosis receiving alcohol while on controlled diets. *Ann. Intern. Med.* 60:814–23
31. Faller, J., Fox, I. H. 1982. Ethanol-induced hyperuricemia. Evidence for increased urate production by activation of adenine nucleotide turnover. *N. Engl. J. Med.* 307:1598–1602
32. Feinman, L., Baraona, E., Matsuzaki, S., Korsten, M., Lieber, C. S. 1978. Concentration dependence of ethanol metabolism *in vivo* in rats and man. *Alcohol. Clin. Exp. Res.* 2:381–85
33. French, S. W. 1966. Effect of acute and chronic ethanol ingestion on rat liver ATP. *Proc. Soc. Exp. Biol. Med.* 121:681–85
34. French, S. W., Todoroff, T. 1970. Hepatic mitochondrial fragility and permeability. *Arch. Pathol.* 89:329–36
35. Gordon, E. 1977. ATP metabolism in an ethanol induced fatty liver. *Biochem. Pharmacol.* 26:1229–34
36. Guynn, R. W., Pieklik, J. R. 1975. Dependence on dose of the acute effects of ethanol on liver metabolism *in vivo*. *J. Clin. Invest.* 56:1411–19
37. Hurt, R. D., Higgins, J. A., Nelson, R. A., Morse, R. A., Dickson, E. R. 1981. Nutritional status of a group of alcoholics before and after admission to an alcoholism treatment unit. *Am. J. Clin. Nutr.* 34:386–92
38. Iseri, O. A., Lieber, C. S., Gottlieb, L. S. 1966. The ultrastructure of fatty liver induced by prolonged ethanol ingestion. *Am. J. Pathol.* 48:535–55
39. Israel, Y., Videla, L., Bernstein, J. 1975. Liver hypermetabolic state after chronic ethanol consumption. *Fed. Proc.* 34:2052–59
40. Joly, J. G., Villeneuve, J. P., Mavier, P. 1977. Chronic ethanol administration induces a form of cytochrome P-450 with specific spectral and catalytic properties. *Alcohol. Clin. Exp. Res.* 1:17–20
41. Kessler, B. J., Liebler, J. B., Bronfin, G. J., et al. 1954. The hepatic blood flow and splanchnic oxygen consumption in alcoholic fatty liver. *J. Clin. Invest.* 33:1338–45
42. Kiessling, K. H., Pilström, L., Strandberg, B., et al. 1965. Ethanol and the human liver. Correlation between mitochondrial size and degree of ethanol abuse. *Acta Med. Scand.* 178:633–38
43. Koch, O. R., Roatta, L. L., Bolanos, L. P., et al. 1978. Ultrastructural and biochemical aspects in liver mitochondria during recovery from ethanol-induced alterations. *Am. J. Pathol.* 90:325–44
44. Kostelnik, M. E., Iber, F. L. 1973. Correlation of alcohol and tolbutamide blood clearance rates with microsomal enzyme activity. *Am. J. Clin. Nutr.* 26:161–64
45. Kromhout, D. 1983. Energy and macronutrient intake in lean and obese middle-aged men (the Zutphen Study). *Am. J. Clin. Nutr.* 37:295–99
46. Lane, B. P., Lieber, C. S. 1966. Ultrastructural alterations in human hepatocytes following ingestion of ethanol with adequate diets. *Am. J. Pathol.* 49:593–603
47. Lelbach, W. K. 1975. Cirrhosis in the alcoholic and its relation to the volume of alcohol abuse. *Ann. NY Acad. Sci.* 252:85–105
48. Lieber, C. S. 1980. Alcohol, protein metabolism, and liver injury. *Gastroenterology* 79:373–90
49. Lieber, C. S. 1982. Metabolism of ethanol. In *Medical Disorders of Alcoholism*, ed. C. S. Lieber, pp. 1–65. Philadelphia: Saunders. 589 pp.
50. Lieber, C. S., De Carli, L. M. 1970. Hepatic microsomal ethanol oxidizing system: *in vitro* characteristics and adaptive properties *in vivo*. *J. Biol. Chem.* 245:2505–12
51. Lieber, C. S., DeCarli, L. M. 1975. Sequential production of fatty liver, hepati-

tis, and cirrhosis in sub-human primates fed ethanol with adequate diets. *Proc. Natl. Acad. Sci. USA* 72:437–41
52. Lieber, C. S., DeCarli, L. M., Gang, H., et al. 1972. Hepatic effects of long-term ethanol consumption in primates. In *Medical Primatology,* ed. E. I. Goldsmith, J. Moorjankowski, 3:270–78. Basel: Karger.
53. Lieber, C. S., Jones, D. P., DeCarli, L. M. 1965. Effects of prolonged ethanol intake: production of fatty liver despite adequate diets. *J. Clin. Invest.* 44:1009–20
54. Lieber, C. S., Rubin, E. 1968. Alcoholic fatty liver in man on a high protein and low fat diet. *Am. J. Med.* 44:200–6
55. Lindros, K. O., Stowell, A. 1982. Effects of ethanol-derived acetaldehyde on the phosphorylation potential and on the intramitochondrial redox state in intact rat liver. *Arch. Biochem. Biophys.* 218:428–37
56. Maclachlan, M. J., Rodnan, G. P. 1967. Effects of food, fast and alcohol on serum uric acid and acute attacks of gout. *Am. J. Med.* 42:38–57
57. McDonald, J. T., Margen, S. 1976. Wine versus ethanol in human nutrition. I. Nitrogen and calorie balance. *Am. J. Clin. Nutr.* 29:1093–1103
58. Mendenhall, C. L., Anderson, S., Weesner, R. E., Goldberg, S. J., Crolic, K. A. 1985. Protein-calorie malnutrition associated with alcoholic hepatitis. *Am. J. Med.* 76:211–22
59. Mezey, E. 1975. Intestinal function in chronic alcoholism. *Ann. NY Acad. Sci.* 252:215–77
60. Mezey, E. 1980. Alcoholic liver disease: roles of alcohol and malnutrition. *Am. J. Clin. Nutr.* 33:2709–18
61. Mezey, E. 1981. Actions and interactions of ethanol with drugs on intermediary metabolism. *Pharmacol. Ther.* 14:411–30
62. Mezey, E., Potter, J. J., French, S. W., Tamura, T., Halsted, C. H. 1983. Effect of chronic ethanol feeding on hepatic collagen in the monkey. *Hepatology* 3:41–43
63. Mezey, E., Potter, J. J., Reed, W. D. 1973. Ethanol oxidation by a component of liver microsomes rich in cytochrome P-450. *J. Biol. Chem.* 248:1183–87
64. Mezey, E., Tobon, F. 1971. Rates of ethanol clearance and activities of ethanol-oxidizing enzymes in chronic alcoholic patients. *Gastroenterology* 61:707–15
65. Mills, P. R., Shenkin, A., Anthony, R. S., McLelland, A. S., Main, A. N. H., et al. 1983. Assessment of nutritional status and *in vivo* immune response in alcohol liver disease. *Am. J. Clin. Nutr.* 38:849–59
66. Nasrallah, S. M., Galambos, J. T. 1980. Amino acid therapy of alcoholic hepatitis. *Lancet* 2:1276–77
67. National Institute on Alcohol Abuse and Alcoholism. 1984. *5th Spec. Rep. to Congr. on Alcohol and Health.* US Publ. Health Serv. DHHS Publ. No. (ADM) 84–1291. Washington, DC: GPO
68. Neville, J. N., Eagles, J. A., Samson, G., Olson, R. E. 1968. Nutritional status of alcoholics. *Am. J. Clin. Nutr.* 21: 1329–40
69. Patek, A. J., Toth, E. G., Saunders, M. G., Castro, A. M., Engel, J. J. 1975. Alcohol and dietary factors in cirrhosis. *Arch. Intern. Med.* 135:1053–57
70. Perman, E. S. 1962. Increase in oxygen uptake after small ethanol doses in man. *Acta Physiol. Scand.* 55:207–9
71. Pirola, R. C., Lieber, C. S. 1972. The energy cost of the metabolism of drugs, including ethanol. *Pharmacology* 7:185–96
72. Pirola, R. C., Lieber, C. S. 1976. Hypothesis: energy waste in alcoholism and drug abuse: possible role of hepatic microsomal enzymes. *Am. J. Clin. Nutr.* 29:90–93
73. Popper, H., Lieber, C. S. 1980. Histogenesis of alcoholic fibrosis and cirrhosis in the baboon. *Am. J. Pathol.* 98:695–716
74. Puig, J. G., Fox, I. H. 1984. Ethanol-induced activation of adenine nucleotide turnover. Evidence for a role of acetate. *J. Clin. Invest.* 74:936–41
75. Roggin, G. M., Iber, F. L., Kater, R. M., et al. 1969. Malabsorption in the chronic alcoholic. *Johns Hopkins Med. J.* 125:321–30
76. Rognstad, R. 1981. Control of ethanol utilization by rat liver hepatocytes. *Biochem. Biophys. Acta* 676:270–73
77. Rubin, E., Lieber, C. S. 1968. Alcohol-induced hepatic injury in non-alcoholic volunteers. *N. Engl. J. Med.* 278:869–76
78. Rubin, E., Lieber, C. S. 1974. Fatty liver, alcoholic hepatitis and cirrhosis produced by alcohol in primates. *N. Engl. J. Med.* 290:128–35
79. Sato, N., Kamada, T., Shichiri, M., et al. 1978. The levels of the mitochondrial and microsomal cytochromes in drinkers' livers. *Clin. Chem. Acta* 87:347–51
80. Schaffer, W. T., Denckla, W. D., Veech, R. L. 1981. Effects of chronic ethanol treatment on $O_2$ consumption in the whole body and perfused liver of the rat. *Alcohol. Clin. Exp. Res.* 5:192–97

81. Scheig, L. 1974. Effects of ethanol on the liver. *Am. J. Clin. Nutr.* 23:467–73
82. Shaw, S., Heller, E. A., Friedman, H. S., et al. 1977. Increased hepatic oxygenation following ethanol administration in the baboon. *Proc. Exp. Biol. Med.* 156:509–13
83. Shigeta, Y., Nomura, F., Iida, S., Leo, M. A., Felder, M. R., et al. 1984. Ethanol metabolism *in vivo* by the microsomal ethanol-oxidizing system in deermice lacking alcohol dehydrogenase (ADH). *Biochem. Pharmacol.* 33: 807–14
84. Simko, V., Connell, A. M., Banks, B. 1982. Nutritional status in alcoholics with and without liver disease. *Am. J. Clin. Nutr.* 35:197–203
85. Spach, P. I., Bottenus, R. E., Cunningham, C. C. 1982. Control of adenine nucleotide metabolism in hepatic mitochondria from rats with ethanol-induced fatty liver. *Biochem. J.* 202:445–52
86. Spring, J. A., Buss, D. H. 1970. Three centuries of alcohol in the British diet. *Nature* 270:567–72
87. Summerskill, W. H. J., Wolfe, S. J., Davidson, C. S. 1957. Response to alcohol in chronic alcoholics with liver disease. Clinical, pathological and metabolic changes. *Lancet* 1:335–40
88. Thayer, W. S., Ohnishi, T., Rubin, E. 1980. Characterization of iron-sulfur clusters in rat liver submitochondrial particles by electron paramagnetic resonance spectroscopy. *Biochim. Biophys. Acta* 591:22–36
89. Thayer, W. S., Rubin, E. 1979. Effects of chronic ethanol intoxication on oxidative phosphorylation in rat liver submitochondrial particles. *J. Biol. Chem.* 254:7717–23
90. Thayer, W. S., Rubin, E. 1981. Molecular alterations in the respiratory chain of rat liver after chronic ethanol consumption. *J. Biol. Chem.* 256:6090–97
91. Thurman, R. G., McKenna, W. R., McCaffrey, T. B. 1976. Pathways responsible for the adaptive increase in ethanol utilization following chronic treatment with ethanol. *Mol. Pharmacol.* 12:156–66
92. Tremolieres, J., Carre, L. 1961. Etudes sur les modalites d'oxydatoin de l'alcohol chez l'homme normal et alcoholique. *Rev. Alcool.* 7:202–27
93. Varela, G., Navarro, M. P., Andujar, M. M. 1981. Influence of ethanol on nutrients utilization. *Bibl. Nutr. Dieta* 30:139–60
94. Veech, R. L., Guynn, R., Veloso, D. 1971. The timecourse of the effects of ethanol on the redox and phosphorylation states of rat liver. *Biochem. J.* 127:387–97
95. Videla, L., Bernstein, J., Israel, Y. 1973. Metabolic alterations produced in the liver by chronic ethanol administration: Increased oxidative capacity. *Biochem. J.* 134:507–14
96. Walker, J. E. C., Gordon, E. R. 1970. Biochemical aspects associated with an ethanol-induced fatty liver. *Biochem. J.* 119:511–16
97. Wilkinson, P. K., Sedman, A. J., Dakmar, E., Earhart, R. H., Weidler, D. J., Wagner, J. G. 1976. Blood ethanol concentrations during and following constant rate intravenous infusion of alcohol. *Clin. Pharmacol. Ther.* 19:213–23
98. Williamson, J. R., Scholz, R., Browning, E. T., Thurman, R. G., Fukami, M. H. 1969. Metabolic effects of ethanol in perfused rat liver. *J. Biol. Chem.* 214:5044–54
99. Windham, C. T., Wyse, B. W., Hansen, R. G. 1983. Alcohol consumption and nutrient density of diets in the Nationwide Food Consumption Survey. *J. Am. Diet. Assoc.* 82:364–72
100. Yu, T. F., Sirota, J. H., Berger, L., Halpern, M., Gutman, A. B. 1957. Effect of sodium lactate infusion on urate clearance in man. *Proc. Soc. Exp. Biol. Med.* 96:809–13

*Ann. Rev. Nutr. 1986. 6:475–94*


# CALCIUM AND HYPERTENSION

*Njeri Karanja and David A. McCarron*

Oregon Health Sciences University, Division of Nephrology and Hypertension, Portland, Oregon 97201

---

CONTENTS

INTRODUCTION .......... 475
EPIDEMIOLOGY OF CALCIUM INTAKE AND HYPERTENSION .......... 476
DIETARY CALCIUM SUPPLEMENTATION IN ANIMALS .......... 479
DIETARY CALCIUM SUPPLEMENTATION IN HUMANS .......... 482
POSSIBLE DEFECTS OF CALCIUM METABOLISM IN HYPERTENSION .......... 484
*The Gastrointestinal Tract, the Kidney, and Bone* .......... 484
*Cellular Handling of Calcium* .......... 487
MECHANISMS ASSOCIATED WITH THE ANTIHYPERTENSIVE ACTION OF DIETARY CALCIUM .......... 488
CONCLUSIONS AND FUTURE RESEARCH .......... 490

## INTRODUCTION

The concept that hypertension can be managed through dietary means, first popularized by Kempner (1) and others, has re-evolved into an area of active research within the past 5 years. With the advent of potent antihypertensive agents in the 1950s, nutritional aspects of blood pressure regulation became less important as areas of investigation.

The current interest is a result of a number of developments. First, several decades of experience with antihypertensives medications indicate that, despite their ability to control hypertension effectively, they may precipitate untoward side effects. Some of the side effects such as hyperlipidemia and hyperglycemia are just as likely as hypertension itself to hasten the time course for developing cardiovascular complications. Secondly, individuals not normally classified as hypertensive carry a greater than normal risk of experiencing a cardiovascu-



0199-9885/86/0715-0475$02.00

lar-related event. The latter group of individuals includes adults with "high-normal" blood pressures and children with blood pressures in the upper deciles of normal for their respective age and size. The demographics of these subgroups are poorly defined; however, it is clear that they add substantially to the ranks of those likely to experience a cardiovascular-related event at some point in their lives. Consequently, they, along with those experiencing mild forms of hypertension, are prime candidates for dietary intervention to control their respective conditions, as dietary intervention may be most effective in lowering the very modest increases in blood pressure that they experience.

Most authorities agree that essential hypertension constitutes a genetic disorder characterized by increased peripheral vascular tone that may, or may not be accompanied by hemodynamic changes and enhanced sensitivity of the autonomic nervous system. It is further accepted that this disorder depends on environmental factors such as stress and diet for expression. These facts imply that stress management and/or dietary intervention can be used in a prophylactic manner to preempt the occurrence of hypertension or to control it once it has occurred.

As with anemia, it is now acknowledged that essential hypertension is not a single disorder. As such, it responds differently to different medications and may behave in the same manner where diet is concerned. Hence, some individuals may benefit from a single nutrient manipulation, while others may be harmed by such a manipulation. This insight has extended the dimension of blood pressure regulation by diet beyond sodium restriction as the only valid dietary maneuver in hypertension control. In synchrony with this idea, other nutrients and dietary factors such as fiber and alcohol are actively being investigated as blood-pressure-regulating agents. Among these, dietary calcium has commanded considerable attention within the last three years.

The purpose of this review is to summarize the data that have led to this interest, and to define directions of future research within this area. This approach is not intended to suggest that the role of other nutrients is less important; indeed, as will become clear throughout the review, the effect of calcium on blood pressure is probably mediated through the action of many other nutrients and nonnutrient factors.

## EPIDEMIOLOGY OF CALCIUM INTAKE AND HYPERTENSION

A link between calcium intake and blood pressure was postulated as early as 1930 in studies of gestational hypertension (2). Recent epidemiologic data indicate that women in societies where calcium consumption is 1000 mg or more experience low rates of preeclamptic hypertension, despite limited prenatal care and a diet generally poor in other respects (3–5). While such population observations have failed to control for confounding variables and utilized crude measures of calcium intake, they serve as a general stimulant for more precise analysis of the role of calcium in nongestational essential hypertension. They have further put into context the earlier epidemiologic work of Kobayashi (6) and Schroeder (7), who reported that cardiovascular mortalities in hard-water (high in calcium and magnesium) areas were lower relative to regions with soft water.

Table 1 is a summary of epidemiologic studies that have reported an inverse correlation between calcium intake and blood pressure (8–17). A distinct feature of these studies is that they used the ethnic and regional diversity of the United States as well as techniques that control for obvious confounders such as age, sex, race, and body mass index to draw their conclusions. Despite the variation in blood pressure definition, statistical approaches, and different methods of collecting intake data, these studies establish a statistical association between low levels of potassium, magnesium, phosphorus, and calcium with a greater risk of elevated blood pressure. In one report (8) that analyzed data from a cross-sectional sample of the entire US population, calcium was the strongest correlate of blood pressure. It was estimated that a person consuming less than 300 mg of calcium per day carried an 11–14% risk of developing hypertension. This chance was reduced 3–6% if the individual's intake was 1200 mg per day.

It is difficult to distinguish the singular effects of calcium on blood pressure from the effects of other nutrients that track closely with calcium in foods. Thus, in analyzing data from the Honolulu cardiovascular disease tracking program, Reed et al (14) could not separate the effects of protein, milk, and potassium from those of calcium on blood pressure. The authors attribute this to the fact that protein, potassium, and calcium all occur in relatively high proportions in dairy products. In any case, dairy products or calcium were found to be protective against hypertension.

An intriguing relationship between hypertension and the existence of mandibular interdental canals was recently reported. Patni et al (19), examining radiographs, found a higher incidence of interdental canals in 97 hypertensive patients compared to 111 normotensive individuals. Although these structures are considered normal by some investigators, others have correlated them with a variety of other conditions, among them, calcium deficiency. It would be instructive to examine further interrelationships involving calcium intake, bone loss syndromes, and hypertension.

Despite the strong negative association made by this body of data relating dietary calcium to hypertension, a number of epidemiologic studies have reported a positive correlation between serum total (12, 20) and ionized (21) calcium and blood pressure, while others have noted lower ionized calcium values in hypertension (21a). These findings would appear to be inconsistent

**Table 1** Epidemiological studies relating calcium intake to hypertension

| Ref. | Location | Dietary data[a] | Statistics[b] | Calcium source | BP Def. | Age (yr) | Sex | No. | Other nutrients[c] |
|---|---|---|---|---|---|---|---|---|---|
| 9 | Portland, OR | 24 hr | t-test | Dairy | MAP<105 | 25–65 | M,F | 96 | Mg |
| 8 | US/HANES I | 24 hr | DA | Dietary Ca | SPB>140, 160 | 18–74 | M,F | 10,419 | K, Vit C |
| 10 | San Diego, CA | Ques. | ANOVA t-test | Dairy prod. | DBP>95, SBP>160 | 30–79 | M,F | | Not reported |
| 11 | Puerto Rico | 24 hr | MR | Diet Ca/ milk | continuum | 45–64 | M | 7,932 | ETOH, coffee |
| 12 | US/HANES I | 24 hr | MR | Dietary Ca | continuum | 25–74 | M,F | 2,055 | ETOH, $PO_4$ |
| 13 | US/HANES II | 24 hr | MR | Dietary Ca | continuum | 25–74 | M,F | | ETOH |
| 14 | Honolulu, HI | 24 hr | MR | Dietary Ca milk | continuum | 46–65 | M | 6,496 | $PO_4$, protein |
| 15 | Chicago, IL | DH | MR | Dietary Ca | continuum | 40–56 | M | 1,976 | PUFA, ETOH |
| 16 | Zutphen, Netherlands | DH | MR | Dietary Ca | continuum | 45–70 | M | 605 | $PO_4$, ETOH |
| 17 | Pittsburgh, PA | FF | MR | Dietary Ca | continuum | 34–56 | M,F | 1,939 | Not reported |

[a]Dietary data: 24 hr = 24-hour recall; Ques. = questionnaire; DH = diet history; FF = food frequency; FR = food record.
[b]Statistics: MR = multiple regression; DA = discriminant analysis.
[c]Nutrients: ETOH = alcohol; PUFA = polyunsaturated fatty acid; K = potassium; $PO_4$ = phosphorus; MG = magnesium.

with the notion of a decreased calcium intake in hypertension. While no immediate explanation for this discrepancy is available, the most likely interpretation is that total calcium levels are dependent on plasma proteins, which are increased in hypertensives. It is also well established that serum calcium, especially the ionized component, is regulated by a variety of factors. Among these are bioavailability, as it may be affected by other dietary components (fiber, oxalates, phosphorus) and hormonal influences [PTH, calcitonin, 1,25,$(OH)_2D_3$]. The large sample sizes used in surveys make a complete appraisal of these modifiers logistically impossible. An example of these confounding variables is the influence of thiazide diuretics, which likely accounted for the increased serum ionized calcium in one study (21). Consequently, it is unlikely that this information can be used to negate the current interpretation of the previously outlined inverse associations between dietary calcium intake and blood pressure.

## DIETARY CALCIUM SUPPLEMENTATION IN ANIMALS

The hypothesis formulated from epidemiological associations that supplemental dietary calcium plays an ameliorative role in hypertension has been tested in animal models of hypertension and in humans. In interpreting the available data, it is important to distinguish between acute administration of calcium provided through intravenous infusions and graded exposure, as might be afforded by a high-calcium diet. Clearly, the two modes of administration engage different physiological pathways. As such, they cannot be expected to have comparable effects on blood pressure. As an example, acute calcium infusions appear to cause transient increments in blood pressure that return to baseline levels after infusion in patients with normal or mildly impaired renal function (22). In contrast, chronic dietary exposure to diets ranging in calcium content from 0.59 to 4.3% have repeatedly been shown to attenuate the rate at which blood pressure develops in normal, pregnant, and hypertensive rats, as well as in other species (25–37). Belizan and his coworkers (25) fed a diet deficient in calcium to pregnant Wistar rats and compared their blood pressures to those of pregnant rats maintained on 0.59% calcium diet for nine weeks. The animals on a calcium-deficient diet showed a steady increase in blood pressure that was significantly higher than that of rats fed adequate amounts of calcium. Similar results have been reported in normotensive Wistar rats (26) and in Wistar Kyoto (WKY) rats bred from the same stock as the spontaneously hypertensive rats (SHR) (27).

The greatest effects of dietary calcium on blood pressure, however, have been reported in animal models of hypertension. In weanling rats, supplemental calcium in the diet slows down the rate at which blood pressure rises with age. It is important to note that dietary calcium does not eliminate hypertension per se.

In a preliminary report (28) (Figure 1), the rate of blood pressure development as a function of increasing doses of dietary calcium was evaluated in post-weanling (6-week-old) rats. At a dietary concentration of 0.25%, the rate of increase was 7.14 mm Hg every two weeks, compared to 3.28 mm Hg at a dietary calcium concentration of 2.0%, during the first 18 weeks of life. Consequently, even though both groups became hypertensive by the end of this period, systolic pressure of the calcium-supplemented groups stabilized to lower levels than those of rats fed suboptimal amounts of calcium. This finding is in keeping with the earlier work of McCarron (32) indicating that early exposure to dietary calcium results in a greater attenuation in blood pressure compared to intervention initiated at a later time.

Recently, Hatton et al (31) expanded this concept even further. They evaluated blood pressure in SHR pups born to mothers receiving either 0.1 or 2% calcium during pregnancy. Pups born to mothers on the low-calcium diet were subsequently cross-suckled to mothers maintained on a high-calcium diet during pregnancy and vice versa. Mean arterial pressures, measured by intraarterial catheters, were higher in pups fostered to dams maintained on a low-calcium diet compared to pups fostered to mothers maintained on a high-calcium diet from gestation up until the pups were 21 days old (Table 2). Similarly, total and ionized calcium were higher in pups suckled to dams

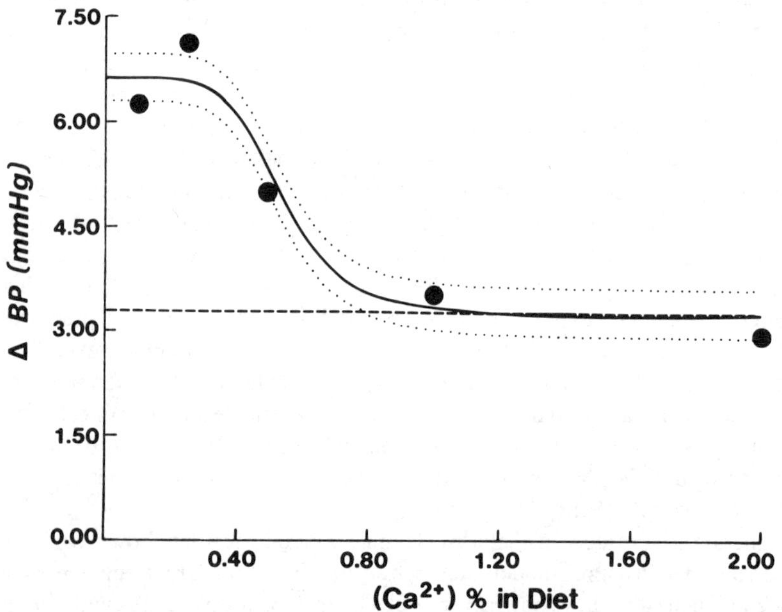


*Figure 1* The effect of dietary calcium concentration on blood pressure rise in SH rats. Each point represents the mean of seven rats. Dotted lines are the 95% confidence interval.

**Table 2** Blood pressure and serum calcium levels based on postnatal dietary $Ca^{2+}$ (mean ± SD)

| | Supplemented $n = 12$ | Restricted $n = 21$ |
|---|---|---|
| MAP (mm Hg) | 105 ± 15 | 135 ± 22[a] |
| Serum ionized $Ca^{2+}$ (mMol/liter) | 1.13 ± .13 | 0.92 ± .10[a] |
| Serum total calcium (mg/dl) | 10.20 ± .93 | 8.80 ± 1.15[a] |

[a]Significant difference between diet groups $p<0.01$.

maintained on a high-calcium diet. Presumably, intrauterine exposure to calcium does not influence the blood pressure of offspring as much as postnatal exposure through the mothers milk. Interestingly, total elimination of calcium from the diets of recently weaned rats produces a paradoxical decrease in blood pressure. Five-week-old SH rats fed 0% calcium have been reported to experience a rapid blood pressure rise, followed by a reversal of this trend after two weeks on the diet (33). This reduction in blood pressure occurs concomitantly with a severe curtailment in growth.

Supplemental dietary calcium may also lower blood pressure in rats with hypertension artificially induced with deoxycorticosterone acetate (DOCA) and sodium chloride (34) and in other species (35). Mature turkeys, *Meleagris gallopavo,* provided with twice (1.96%) the amount of calcium normally found in the diet of these birds experienced mean arterial pressures that were lower than turkeys fed normal levels (0.98%) of calcium. In addition to these pressure changes, mean total heart weights were lower in calcium-supplemented birds than in those receiving the regular diet. Similarly, the heterophil/lymphocyte ratio (a crude measure of stress in domestic avian species) was higher in the supplemental group (35). These results indicate that calcium may regulate blood pressure in part by reducing left ventricular hypertrophy and stress.

The notion that stress can be ameliorated by a high-calcium diet may be too presumptive at this point. Nevertheless, preliminary data appear to support such a notion. Spontaneously hypertensive rats and mice exposed to psychosocial stress through manipulation of group housing exhibit blood pressures that are higher than those of nonstressed animals. Spontaneously hypertensive rats exposed to similar stress were reported to have lower blood pressures when their diets contained 2% calcium than those whose diets contained 0.1% calcium (36). This concept requires further investigation.

Findings of an ameliorative role for dietary calcium supplementation are not unequivocal. Stern et al (38) evaluated blood pressures in post-weanling rats (6 weeks old) fed either 0.4 or 2.8% calcium. After 28 days of feeding, blood pressure values from both groups were not significantly different, even though the high-calcium diet increased serum ionized calcium. It is not clear why these reports differ from those of other workers. The possibility that the rapid weight gain associated with this phase of growth may have masked the hypotensive effects of calcium exists. Certainly, supplementation beyond this rapid growth phase would have made the results more comparable with those of others. Nevertheless, the bulk of experimental data in animals seems to support the view that dietary calcium modulates the rate at which hypertension develops. Still, conclusive statements regarding blood pressure and calcium can only come from experimental data in humans. This is true of calcium more than other nutrients because calcium requirements in most other species are considerably higher than in humans.

## DIETARY CALCIUM SUPPLEMENTATION IN HUMANS

Unlike the data generated from animals, data on calcium intervention in human hypertension are limited. To date, a total of five studies have supplemented the diets of normal (39), pregnant (40), or hypertensive (18, 18a, 41) subjects with calcium and reported significant decreases in blood pressure. Belizan et al (39) studied 57 normal volunteers aged 18–35 years in a double blind trial employing either 1 g of elemental calcium or placebo for 22 weeks. Blood pressure fluctuated for the first 9 weeks in women and 6 weeks in men. After this time, diastolic blood pressure stabilized to lower values in both sexes receiving supplemental calcium compared to those on placebo. For women, a 5% decrease in supine diastolic pressure was reported. The comparable value for males was 9%. Systolic blood pressures were not affected.

Blood pressure reductions of a magnitude similar to that seen in nonpregnant women have been reported in pregnant women given 1 or 2 g of calcium, compared to a group treated with placebo. The women given 1 g of calcium experienced lower diastolic and systolic blood pressure from 15 weeks of gestation until the end of the second trimester of pregnancy. After this time, 1 g calcium could not prevent the characteristic rise in blood pressure typical of the third trimester of pregnancy. In contrast, the blood pressures of women ingesting 2 g calcium remained low until delivery (40).

The first randomized, double-blind crossover trial of calcium as therapy for mild to moderate essential hypertension has recently been reported (41). In this study, 48 hypertensive and 32 matched normotensives received either 1 g of calcium per day (provided as calcium carbonate) or placebo for eight weeks. Treatments were then switched for an additional eight weeks after an interim "washout" period of four weeks when placebo was ingested. Compared to placebo (Figure 2), calcium significantly reduced average systolic pressure by 5.6 mm Hg and average diastolic blood pressure by 2.3 mm Hg in hypertensive subjects. As in the study by Belizan et al (39), steady changes did not become apparent until the 6th week of supplementation. After this time, blood pressure started to decline and was still declining when the study was terminated. As with any trial, some of the patients in this study did not respond to therapy

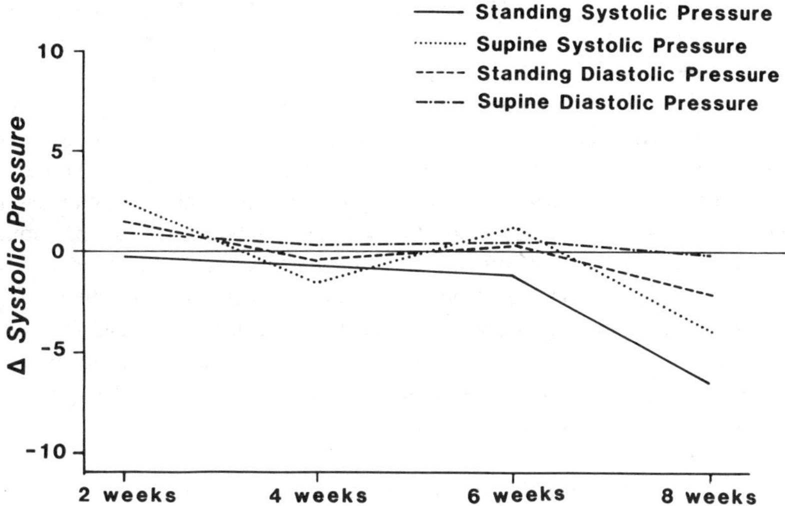


*Figure 2* Blood pressure change by week in 48 patients with hypertension receiving 1 g of calcium per day.

within the eight weeks of supplementation. At the inception of the trial, the authors defined response as a 10-mm Hg decrease in systolic blood pressure with calcium compared to placebo. Using this criterion, they found that 21 of 48 (44%) hypertensive participants experienced a decrease of 10 mm Hg or more. For normotensive subjects the response rate was 19%. The authors point out that these differential responses may reflect the etiological heterogeneity of hypertension.

Two other recent reports have also demonstrated an antihypertensive effect of supplemental calcium. Johnson and colleagues (18) reported that 16 hypertensive postmenopausal women who received 1.5 g/day of $Ca^{2+}$ for four years experienced a significant reduction in their systolic blood pressure compared to a control group of 18 women who received placebo. Luft et al (18a) supplemented 16 hypertensives for two weeks with 1 g of calcium and noted modest but significant decreases in blood pressure compared to the two weeks on placebo.

Collectively, these trials in humans indicate that calcium can reduce blood pressure in selected patients, and that these nonpharmacologic doses can theoretically be achieved through the diet (<2500 mg). Whether calcium actually supplied through dietary sources would have the same effects remains undetermined.

## POSSIBLE DEFECTS OF CALCIUM METABOLISM IN HYPERTENSION

A number of biochemical abnormalities associated with hypertension have been reported in both hypertensive animals and humans. These include decreased serum ionized calcium with attendant elevations in parathyroid hormone, and increased fractional and total urinary calcium excretion. As outlined in a recent review, however, these findings have not been found to exist in all studies to the same extent (24). While any number of explanations could be invoked for these discrepancies, it is likely that they are indicators of different stages of more profound disturbances of calcium metabolism, occurring within the major organ systems that regulate calcium balance and the vascular smooth muscle cell. Thus, subnormal handling of calcium in the gastrointestinal tract, the kidney, or bone will invariably affect the manner in which calcium is made available to the smooth muscle cell, the site at which cation appears to contribute to the regulation of vascular tone and thereby blood pressure. These possible defects are discussed in the next sections.

### *The Gastrointestinal Tract, the Kidney, and Bone*

Inasmuch as the gastrointestinal (GI) tract acts as the first delimiter of nutrient bioavailability, it is not surprising that this organ system is receiving considerable attention in the study of calcium balance in hypertension. In considering the complex mechanisms that govern calcium absorption, four loosely defined points can be identified where defects may occur.

First, the uptake of calcium across the brush border membrane into the cell may be impaired. The movement of calcium at this point is actively mediated and depends on the vitamin D status of the animal. Transport is further dependent on the ability of the cell to synthesize proteins, such as calcium binding protein, that act as carriers of calcium into the cell. Other nutrients such as sodium, magnesium, and phosphorus may further modify this process (42). Consequently studies attempting to identify defective calcium absorption in hypertension may need to characterize one or all of the following: (*a*) ability of the enterocyte to synthesize binding proteins, (*b*) number and capacity of cytosolic receptors for vitamin D and, (*c*) the activity of brush border membrane bound enzymes such as alkaline phosphatase.

Once calcium has penetrated the brush border membrane, the enterocyte must effectively translocate it to the basolateral membrane for extrusion into the blood stream (42). This phase constitutes a second point where calcium handling may be defective in hypertension. The ability of intracellular organelles successfully to buffer and move calcium to the basolateral membrane must therefore be examined.

Extrusion of calcium through the basolateral membrane is an energy-requiring process (42) thought to be mediated by a calcium-dependent ATPase and a non-ATP-dependent $Ca^{2+}/Na^{+}$ exchange mechanism (43–45). The activity of these enzymes needs to be investigated within the context of hypertension.

Lastly, calcium absorption occurs through nonenergy-, gradient-dependent, largely passive pathways that need to be characterized for possible defects.

Preliminary investigations into possible defects of calcium absorption have been reported. Studies suggest that active transport is impaired in the SHR. However, the nature of this impairment is controversial. In an initial study, Toraason & Wright (47) reported a higher serosal/mucosal (S/M) ratio of calcium concentration in duodenal sacs prepared from 12-week-old SHR relative to age-matched WKY rats. Calcium uptake was similarly higher in SHR compared to WKY rats in vivo. Administration of $1,25(OH)_2D_3$ elicited an increase in duodenal calcium transport in WKY but not SH rats. Whether this decreased transport of calcium was due to the high S/M ratio of calcium concentration demonstrated in the SHR or due to an impairment of the vitamin D adaptive process is not clear.

In a protocol similar to that used by Toraason et al, Schedl and his coworkers (48) reported opposite findings. Young (5-week-old) and older (12-week-old) SHR exhibited significantly lower S/M concentrations of $^{45}Ca$, compared to age-matched WKY rats. Furthermore, a kinetic analysis of calcium transport in in situ segments of the small intestine revealed that maximal velocity ($V_{max}$) for calcium was higher in WKY relative to SH rats. Despite these differences serum concentrations of $1,25(OH)_2D_3$ were similar in both strains. These findings suggest that the SHR may produce sufficient quantities of 1,25-dihydroxycholecalciferol, but its GI tract may be refractory to vitamin D's effects. It is noteworthy that both studies utilized dietary calcium and phosphorus levels that were more than adequate by NRC criterion.

In a recent communication Lucas et al (49) examined the vitamin D response in SHR and WKY rats fed low (0.1%) or adequate (2%) calcium diets from the age of 6 weeks up until they were 12–14 weeks old. Decreased levels of $1,25(OH)_2D_3$ were seen in SHR maintained on adequate amounts of calcium in relation to WKY rats. The calcium-deficient diet stimulated by 80% the level of serum $1,25(OH)_2D_3$ in both strains. However, the SHR's initial $1,25(OH)_2D_3$ were low, and absolute adaptive values were also lower than those of WKY rats. Accordingly, mucosal to serosal calcium flux rose nonsignificantly from $29.5 \pm 4.2$ on a 2.0% calcium diet to $37.2 \pm 8.1$ $nmol \cdot cm^{-2}hr^{-1}$ on the 0.1% calcium diet in an older (20–24-week-old) group of rats. Similar values were from $30.6 \pm 4.0$ to $83.1 \pm 10.5$ $nmol \cdot cm^{-2}hr^{-1}$ in WKY rats, which was a highly significant increase. Similar values were found by McCarron et al (50) but are not supported by calcium balance studies (37, 38).

Calcium fluxes have been examined in isolated enterocytes of SH and WKY rats. Preliminary evidence suggests that $^{45}$Ca efflux constants are lower in SHR than in WKY rats (51). The efflux rate constant reflects calcium ATPase activity in the basolateral membrane. This pump has been found to be deficient in other cells from hypertensive animals and humans. Calcium absorption has not been evaluated in human subjects with hypertension.

The kidney may also contribute to the biochemical abnormalities in hypertension, especially hypercalciuria. Unfortunately, the nature, characteristics, and cellular processess governing calcium reabsorption in the various segments of the nephron are not well understood and have been minimally studied in hypertension. Nevertheless, mechanisms of calcium reabsorption in the kidney are remarkably similar to those of calcium absorption in the GI tract. Consequently, defective calcium transport is likely to occur at those sites along the kidney where active transport is most prevalent. Within the proximal convoluted tubule, only about 12% of the filtered load of calcium is actively transported, with 48% moving passively following water and sodium reabsorption. Active transport similarly governs calcium reabsorption in the pars recta and in the distal convoluted tubule. About 20% of the filtered load of calcium is reabsorbed at these two latter sites. Theoretically then, only about 35% of the filtered calcium load is reabsorbed actively; the rest is absorbed passively through concentration or electrical gradients (52). As with the intestine, it is likely that a variety of enzyme systems responsible for calcium transport are partially ineffective as a result of either (*a*) diminished synthesis or diminished binding to receptors or (*b*) rapid degradation. A negative correlation between $Na^+/K^+$ ATPase activity and blood pressure has been reported in renal cortical segments of both SHR and WKY rats (22a). Investigations designed to explore further these aspects of calcium transport in the kidney in hypertension are therefore urgently needed.

The contribution of bone to overall calcium homeostasis in hypertension is poorly characterized. Based on the previously outlined defects in intestinal absorption and renal reabsorption, it can be anticipated that mineralization in the SHR is abnormal. In a preliminary study, Izawa et al reported that bone density was decreased in tibial trabecular bone of male SH relative to age-matched WKY rats. Although a similar difference could not be demonstrated for tibial cortical bone, mean femur dry weight and ash weight per unit of bone volume were significantly reduced in the SHR (53). Preliminary studies from our laboratory indicate that femoral cortical bone density in 54-week-old male SH rats is reduced (52a). This latter observation indicates that osteopenia is progressive in the SHR and may go undetected in cortical bone of younger rats (26 weeks old) such as those studied by Izawa et al. Nevertheless it is clear that some aspect of bone mineralization and modeling is defective in SHR. The precise nature of this defect and its contribution to the availability of calcium and blood pressure regulation require further experimentation.

## *Cellular Handling of Calcium*

Defects involving cellular calcium handling in hypertension have been partially characterized, and were reviewed in a recent publication (53a). Three basic abnormalities that contribute to increased basal active tension in the smooth muscle cell of hypertensive animals have been indentified. First, increased sensitivity to vasoactive substances such as norepinephrine has been noted in mesenteric resistance vessels from SHR compared to those from WKY rats. This increased sensitivity is associated with increased permeability to calcium in vascular smooth muscle cells (54–57). Secondly, the rate of relaxation after an agonist is removed is lower in arteries obtained from hypertensive rats relative to normotensive controls (58, 59). Lastly, red blood cells and adipocytes obtained from hypertensive rats and humans have higher than normal intracellular concentrations of calcium (60, 61, 64). These abnormalities are consistent with dysfunctional calcium influx, intracellular sequestration/release, and efflux pathways.

Increased permeability of the hypertensive membrane to calcium is thought to be due to a reduction of binding sites rather than a reduced affinity of these sites to calcium (53a). Theoretically possible sites where calcium may bind within the cell membrane include carboxylic acid residues of acidic amino acids (aspartate and glutamate) as well as negatively charged membrane phospholipids such as phosphotidylserine. To date, there is little evidence that these particular components are altered in hypertension. The composition of the main membrane lipids for example is similar in hypertensive and normotensive humans (64a). Secondly, despite the observation that band III protein, which constitutes ~30% of all erythrocyte proteins, is increased in SHR (53a), direct evidence for a reduction in glutamate and/or aspartate in hypertensive membranes is lacking. Irrespective of the precise nature of membrane alterations in hypertension, the increased permeability in these membranes (62) presumably destabilizes the membrane, which in turn promotes the entry of cations, especially calcium, into the cell.

The rate of relaxation and rebound of elastic elements depends upon rate of calcium efflux and sequestration by subcellular organelles. The calcium pump ATPase and the $Na^+/Ca^{2+}$ exchanger, present in both the plasma membrane and in subcellular membranes, are responsible for this phase.

Data on the operational nature of the $Na/Ca^{2+}$ exchanger in hypertension are lacking. The apparent absence of this enzyme in cells traditionally studied for calcium handling (erythrocytes, adipocytes, and hepatocytes) has resulted in a scarcity of knowledge regarding the role of this system on cellular calcium handling and distribution in hypertension. Nevertheless, the activity of the $Na^+/K^+$ ATPase is decreased in hypertensive rats and humans. While this enzyme does not directly regulate calcium transport in the VSMC, it causes sodium to accumulate within the VSMC and thereby hampers the ability of the $Na^+/Ca^{2+}$ exchanger to extrude calcium (63, 65, 66).

Recent reports indicate further that the more ubiquitous calcium pump ATPase is similarly hampered in hypertension. Microsomes harvested from aortas and mesenteric arteries of SHR, DOCA, and renovascular models of hypertension show diminished calcium pump ATPase activity (67–69). In humans, basal unstimulated activity of this enzyme in lysates of red blood cells (RBCs) is reduced in untreated hypertensive subjects compared to normotensives (70). These changes occur despite the observation that the calmodulin content and distribution of RBC's are normal (70a). Furthermore, the ability of calmodulin to activate calcium pump ATPase is reduced in hypertensive human subjects (70b). These observations are consistent with a basic defect in the manner in which this universal $Ca^{2+}$ binding protein interacts with calcium in hypertension. Postonov & Orlov (53a) postulate that factors that modify the calmodulin-$Ca^{2+}$-ATPase interaction, such as the release of calcium-dependent phospholipases and proteases, may play a role in the observed defects of this enzyme system. Presumably these enzyme modifications would in turn modify the hydrophobic regions of both calmodulin and $Ca^{2+}$-ATPase by altering the ratio of free to bound forms of unsaturated fatty acids and probably peptides (53a). Dysfunctions of the $Ca^{2+}$-ATPase system tend to occur in very young (3–5-wk-old) rats and may be absent in pregnancy-induced hypertension (71, 72). Furthermore, when renovascular hypertension is treated, these abnormalities disappear in rats with the latter form of hypertension compared to SHR (72). This latter observation indicates that the abnormalities of the $Ca^{2+}$-ATPase system are genetically determined.

## MECHANISMS ASSOCIATED WITH THE ANTIHYPERTENSIVE ACTION OF DIETARY CALCIUM

The precise nature of the antihypertensive action of dietary calcium is not known beyond the finding that additional calcium in the diet increases serum ionized calcium and does not exacerbate the calciuria. Two distinct theories for the antihypertensive action of dietary calcium have been advanced. Both are fraught with inconsistencies with the current knowledge and understanding of the hypertensive process and are subject to modification with additional research.

Feeding supplemental calcium causes marked decreases in serum and urine phosphorus levels in normal adult males, decreases that are accompanied by significant increases in fecal phosphorus (73). Similar changes in serum and urine, but not feces, phosphorus values have been noted in hypertensive rats and humans not receiving supplemental dietary calcium (74). Lau et al (29) tested the hypothesis that supplemental dietary $Ca^{2+}$ lowers blood pressure through decreasing serum and urine, and increasing fecal phosphate. Female SHR (22-wk-old) were fed a diet containing 4.3% calcium and given daily injections of $NaPO_4$ or sham injections of NaCl for ten days. Serum and urine phosphorus values remained normal in the calcium- and phosphate-supplemented group with no dectable change in blood pressure. The rats receiving NaCl and supplemental dietary calcium exhibited significantly lower urine and phosphorus values and lower blood pressure. Subsequent phosphate injections in this latter group for an additional 16 days reversed their phosphorus chemistries and increased blood pressures to levels similar to a control group receiving 1.2% dietary calcium.

Based on these findings, the authors concluded that dietary calcium lowered blood pressure by depleting phosphate. Two criticisms make this conclusion untenable at this point in time. First, the level of dietary calcium, and consequently the Ca: P ratio (9:1), was far in excess of levels required to lower blood pressure and therefore the phosphate "depletion" may have been a reflection of the unbalanced provision of the two nutrients. Secondly, injected phosphate is metabolized differently from ingested phosphate. Consequently, the implications for blood pressure regulation by this route are limited. Nevertheless, the theory is worthy of further research, especially as it may affect cellular energy utilization, since one of the major function of phosphorus is to provide the cell with sufficient energy.

The second theory proposes that dietary calcium may lower blood pressure through VSMC membrane stabilization. The theory is based on early in vitro observations that high concentrations of calcium are able to relax aortic preparations made to contract with norepinephrine (75). Similar results have been reported in the New Zealand strain of genetically hypertensive rats using lower ranges of calcium in hindlimb preparations (76). It is postulated that the observed relaxation occurs because excess extracellular calcium inhibits its own flux rate into the cell, in essence acting much in the same manner as the calcium channel blockers do. This postulate is strengthened by observations that the rate of calcium entry into VSMC (77) and cardiac cells (78) governs the release of intracellular calcium stores. By the same token, a decreased influx rate would presumably decrease intracellular calcium.

The major drawbacks of this theory are (*a*) the levels of calcium used are far in excess of what is physiologically attainable even with increased dietary calcium intake, and (*b*) in vitro preparations do not reflect steady-state conditions. While the latter criticism cannot be easily overcome, the first criticism can be. Recently, Bukoski et al (79) tested the hypothesis that dietary calcium can alter functional properties of aortic smooth muscle. Isometric force development, apparent membrane stability, and elastic properties were evaluated in SHR maintained on either a 2 or 1% diet from 6 weeks of agc cither until 13–14 weeks or until 20–23 weeks of age. While aortic properties remained essentially unchanged for the two diet groups in the younger rats, significant alterations were observed in aortas isolated from the rats maintained on the 2% diet for 15 weeks. The changes included a decrease in sensitivity to KCl, an increase in apparent membrane stability, and a normalization of vessel wall stiffness. These findings are consistent with an effect of dietary calcium intake on vascular smooth muscle. In a preliminary report utilizing a similar protocol, these results could not be substantiated in tail arteries isolated from 15-week-old SH rats maintained on either 0.4% or 2.8% $Ca^{2+}$ in the diet for 4 weeks (79a). The comparative value of these findings is limited by differences in the ages of the animal used. Further experimentation is required, however.

Calcium may also alter the activity of the sodium-potassium pump. Smooth muscle cells cultured from the carotid artery and incubated in a calcium-deficient media accumulate more sodium than do cells incubated in media containing 0.5, 2.0, or 4.0 mM calcium (80). In view of the effects of increased intracellular sodium on the $Ca^{2+}/Na^{+}$ exchange mechanism alluded to earlier, this aspect requires further experimentation with particular attention to dietary calcium intake.

## CONCLUSIONS AND FUTURE RESEARCH

The thesis that increased dietary calcium protects against pervasive hypertension has been tested intensely through epidemiological studies, animal experiments, and human clinical trials. Consideration of available data indicates that a causal relationship exists between lower dietary calcium intake and a higher risk of hypertension. Still, large areas of this relationship are not clearly delineated. Several aspects need to be evaluated further. Epidemiologically, it would be interesting to find out why the prevalence of hypertension is low in regions of the world where calcium intake is also low. Since this may be a reflection of the interaction of calcium with nutrients and/or environmental contaminants, it might help to define which nutrients should be experimentally studied. The relationship between hypertension, dietary calcium, and other calcium-losing syndromes (peridontal gum disease, osteoporosis, etc) needs clarification, especially in children and young adults.

In intervention trials, the role of dietary calcium as opposed to calcium from nonnutrient dietary supplements needs to be examined in humans. This is especially important as the nutrient mixtures in foods may modify the effects of calcium on blood pressure. The role of nutrients that track closely with calcium physiologically and in foods (such as magnesium, phosphorus, vitamin D, and potassium) and their effects on blood pressure also need clarification. The implied role of calcium in reactivity to environmental stress is another area where future research efforts should be directed.

Research is most critically needed in the area of physiological mechanisms associated with the antihypertensive action of dietary calcium. A clarification of these mechanisms would greatly advance our knowledge not only of how dietary calcium acts to reduce pressure, but also of how other nutrients may modify blood pressure. Until these issues are fully resolved, it is premature to make recommendations regarding dietary calcium intake other than supporting the current recommendation of the National Academy of Sciences (800 mg calcium per day). Unfortunately, the vast majority of adult women and over half of the adult males in the American society are below this level, thereby increasing their cardiovascular risk.

ACKNOWLEDGMENTS

The authors would like to thank Rick Delk for his assistance in preparing this manuscript. Studies reported from our laboratory were supported by the M. J. Murdock Charitable Trust; the R. Blaine Bramble Medical Research Center of the US Public Health Service; a research grant-in-aid from Miles Laboratories, Inc., Elkhart, Indiana; and by the National Dairy Council.

## *Literature Cited*

1. Kempner, W. 1944. Treatment of kidney disease and hypertensive vascular disease with rice diet. *NC Med. J.* 5:125–33
2. Belizan, J. M., Villar, J. 1980. The relationship between calcium intake and edema, proteinuria, and hypertension-gestosis: an hypothesis. *Am. J. Clin. Nutr.* 33:2202–10
3. Hamlin, R. H. J. 1962. Prevention of pre-eclampsia. *Lancet* 1:864–67
4. Chaudhuri, S. K. 1969. Calcium deficiency and toxemia of pregnancy. *J. Obstet. Gynecol. (India)* 19:313–16
5. Lechtig, A., Degado, H., Martorell, R., Yarbrough, C., Klein, R. E. 1978. Effect of food supplementation on blood pressure and on prevalence of edema and proteinuria during pregnancy. *J. Trop. Pediatr. Environ. Child Health* 24:70–74
6. Kobayashi, J. 1957. On geographical relationship between the chemical nature of river water and death rate from apoplexy. *Ber. Ohara. Inst. Landwirtsch. Biol. Okayama Univ.* 11:12–21
7. Schroeder, H. A. 1960. Relation between mortality from cardiovascular disease and treated water supplies. *J. Am. Med. Assoc.* 172(17):1902–8
8. McCarron, D. A., Morris, C. D., Henry, H. J., Stanton, J. L. 1984. Blood pressure and nutrient intake in the United States. *Science* 224:1392–98
9. McCarron, D. A., Morris, C. D., Cole, C. 1982. Dietary calcium in human hypertension. *Science* 217:267–69
10. Ackley, S., Barrett-Connor, E., Suarez, L. 1983. Dairy products, calcium and blood pressure. *Am. J. Clin. Nutr.* 38:457–61
11. Garcia-Palmieri, M. R., Costas, R. Jr., Cruz-Vidal, M., Sorlie, P. D., Tillotson, J., Havlik, R. J. 1984. Milk consumption, calcium intake and decreased hypertension in Puerto Rico Heart Health Program Study. *Hypertension* 6:322–28
12. Harlan, W. R., Hull, A. L., Schmouder, R. L., Landis, J. R., Thompson, F. E., Larkin, F. A. 1984. Blood pressure and nutrition in adults. *Am. J. Epidemiol.* 120:17–28
13. Harlan, W. R., Landis, J. R., Schmouder, R. L., Goldstein, N. G., Harlan, L. C. 1985. Blood lead and blood pressure: relationship in adolescent and adult U.S. population. *J. Am. Med. Assoc.* 253: 530–34
14. Reed, D., McGee, D., Yano, K., Hankin, J. 1985. Diet, blood pressure, and multicollinearity. *Hypertension* 7:405–11
15. Nichaman, M., Shekelle, R., Paul, O. 1984. Diet, alcohol, and blood pressure in the Western Electric Study. *Am. J. Epidemiol.* 120:469–70
16. Kromhout, D., Bosschieter, E. B., Coulander, C. D. L. 1985. Potassium, calcium, alcohol intake and blood pressure: the Zutphen study. *Am. J. Clin. Nutr.* 41:1299–1304
17. Yamamoto, M. E., Kuller, L. H. 1985. Does dietary calcium influence blood pressure? Evidence from the three area stroke mortality study (1971–1974). *Circulation* 72(Suppl. III):464 (Abstr.)
18. Johnson, N. E., Smith, E. L., Freudenheim, J. L. 1985. Effects on blood pressure of calcium supplementa-

tion of women. *Am. J. Clin. Nutr.* 42:12–17

18a. Luft, E., Aronoff, G. R., Sloan, R. S., Fienberg, N. S., Weinberger, M. H. 1986. Short-term augmented Ca intake has not effect on $Na^+$ homeostasis in man. *Clin. Pharmacol. Ther.* In press

19. Patni, V. M., Merchant, G. J., Dhooria, H. S. 1985. Incidence of nutrient canals in hypertensive patients: A radiographic study. *Oral Surg. Oral Med. Oral Pathol.* 59:206–11

20. Kesteloot, H., Geboers, J. 1982. Calcium and blood pressure. *Lancet* 1:813–15

21. Fogh-Andersen, N., Hedegaard, L., Thode, J., Siggaard-Anderson, O. 1984. Sex-dependent relation between ionized calcium and blood pressure. *Clin. Chem.* 30(1):116–18

21a. Folsom, A. R., Smith, C. L., Prineas, R. J., Grim, R. H. 1986. Serum calcium fractions in essential hypertensive and matched normotensive subjects. *Hypertension* 8:11–15

22. Marone, C., Beretta-Piccoli, C., Weidman, D. 1980. Acute hypercalcemic hypertension in man: role of hemodynamics, catecholamines and renin. *Kidney Int.* 20:92–96

22a. Wilson, P., Marconi, J., Levi, M. 1986. Effects of dietary calcium on blood pressure and Na,K-ATPase in the spontaneously hypertensive rat. *Kidney Int.* 29(1):262 (Abstr.)

23. Deleted in proof.

24. McCarron, D. A. 1985. Is calcium more important than sodium in the pathogenesis of essential hypertension? *Hypertension* 7(4):607–27

25. Belizan, J. M., Pineda, O., Sainz, E., Menendez, L. A., Villar, J. 1981. Rise of blood pressure in calcium-deprived pregnant rats. *Am. J. Obstet. Gynecol.* 141:163–69

26. Itokawa, Y., Tanaka, C., Fujiwara, M. 1974. Changes in body temperature on blood pressure in rats with calcium and magnesium deficiencies. *J. Appl. Physiol.* 37(6):835–39

27. McCarron, D. A. 1982. Blood pressure and calcium balance in the Wistar Kyoto rat. *Life Sci.* 30:683–89

28. Karanja, N., Metz, J. A., McCarron, D. A. 1985. Calcium dose analysis in hypertension of the SHR: A kinetic approach. *12th Int. Congr. Nutr.* C26:185 (Abstr.). Brighton, UK

29. Lau, K., Chen, S., Eby, B. 1984. Evidence for the role of $PO_4$ deficiency in antihypertensive action of a high $Ca^{2+}$ diet. *Am. J. Physiol.* 246:H324–31

30. Ayachi, S. 1979. Increased dietary calcium lowers blood pressure in the spontaneously hypertensive rat. *Metabolism* 28:1234–38

31. Hatton, D. C., Huie, P. E., Muntzel, M. S., Metz, J. A., Karanja, N., McCarron, D. A. 1985. Blood pressure development and serum calcium in suckling SHR pups: effects of maternal dietary calcium. *5th Int. Symp. SHR and Related Studies,* Kyoto, Japan (Abstr.). *J. Hypertension Suppl.* In press

32. McCarron, D. A. 1982. Calcium, magnesium and phosphorus balance in human and experimental hypertension. *Hypertension* 4(Suppl. III):27–33

33. Schleiffer, R., Pernot, F., Berthelot, A., Gairard, A. 1984. Low calcium diet enhances development of hypertension in the spontaneously hypertensive rat. *Clin. Exp. Hypertension* A6(4):783–93

34. Barry, G. D. 1977. Effect of increased dietary calcium on the development of experimental hypertension. *Fed. Proc.* 36:5492 (Abstr.)

35. Lee, J. C., McGrath, C. J., Leighton, A. T., Gross, W. B. 1984. Effect of dietary calcium on blood pressure of turkeys. *Poultry Sci.* 63:993–96

36. Huie, P. E., Hatton, D. C., Muntzel, M. S., Metz, J. A., McCarron, D. A. 1985. Dietary calcium, acute stress and hypertension in the spontaneously hypertensive rat. *Am. Soc. Nephrol.* 98A

37. Lau, K., Zikos, D., Spirnak, J., Eby, B. 1984. Evidence for an intestinal mechanism in hypercalciuria of spontaneously hypertensive rats. *Am. J. Physiol.* 247:E625–33

38. Stern, N., Lee, D. B. N., Silis, V., Beck, F. W. J., Manolagas, S. C., Sowers, J. R. 1984. Effects of high calcium intake on blood pressure and calcium metabolism in young SHR. *Hypertension* 6:639–46

39. Belizan, J. M., Pineda, O., et al. 1983. Reduction of blood pressure with calcium supplementation in young adults. *J. Am. Med Assoc.* 249:1161–65

40. Belizan, J. M., Villar, J., Salazar, A., Rojas, L., Chan, D., Bryce, G. F. 1983. Preliminary evidence of the effect of calcium supplementation on blood pressure in normal pregnant women. *Am. J. Obstet. Gynecol.* 146:175–80

41. McCarron, D. A., Morris, C. D. 1985. Blood pressure response to oral calcium in persons with mild to moderate hypertension: A randomized double-blind placebo controlled crossover trial. *Ann. Intern. Med.* 103(6):825–31

42. Levine, B. S., Walling, M. W., Coburn, J. W. 1982. Intestinal absorption of calcium: Its assessment, normal physiology,

and alterations in various disease states. In *Disorders of Mineral Metabolism: Calcium Physiology*, pp. 103–42. New York/London: Academic

43. Ghijsen, W. E. J. M., DeJonge, H. R., Van Os, C. 1980. Dissociation between $Ca^{2+}$ ATPase and alkaline phosphatase activity in plasma membranes of rat duodenum. *Biochim. Biophys. Acta* 599:538–51
44. DeJonge, H. R., Ghijsen, W. E. J. M., Van Os, C. 1981. Phosphorylated intermediates of $Ca^{2+}$ ATPase and alkaline phosphatase in plasma membranes from rat duodenal epithelium. *Biochim. Biophys. Acta* 647:140–49
45. Murer, H. J., Hildmann, B. 1981. Transcellular transport of calcium and inorganic phosphate in the small intestinal epithelium. *Am. J. Physiol.* 240:G409–16
46. Deleted in proof
47. Toraason, M. A., Wright, G. L. 1981. Transport of calcium by duodenum of spontaneously hypertensive rat. *Am. J. Physiol.* 4:G344–47
48. Schedl, H. P., Miller, D. L., Pape, J. M., Horst, R. L., Wilson, H. D. 1984. Calcium and sodium-transport and vitamin-D metabolism in the spontaneously hypertensive rat. *J. Clin. Invest.* 73:980–86
49. Lucas, P. A., Brown, R. C., Drüeke, T., Lacour, B., Metz, J. A., McCarron, D. A. 1986. Abnormal vitamin D metabolism and intestinal calcium transport in the spontaneously hypertensive rat: relation to bone calcium status. *J. Clin. Invest.* In press
50. McCarron, D. A., Lucas, P. A., Schneidman, R. J., Lacour, B., Drüeke, T. 1985. Blood pressure development of the spontaneously hypertensive rat after concurrent manipulations of dietary $Ca^{2+}$ and $Na^{+}$. *J. Clin. Invest.* 76: 1147–54
51. McCarron, D. A., Lucas, P. A., LaCour, B., Drüeke, T. 1985. $Ca^{2+}$ efflux rate constant in isolated enterocytes. *Am. Soc. Nephrol.* 52:103a (Abstr.)
52. Massry, S. G. 1982. Renal handling of calcium. See Ref. 42, pp. 103–42

52a. Izawa, Y., Sagara, K., Kadota, T., Makita, T. 1985. Bone disorders in spontaneously hypertensive rats. *Calcif. Tissue Int.* 37:605–7

53. Metz, J. A., Karanja, N., McCarron, D. A. 1984. Abnormal bone density in the spontaneously hypertensive rat: differential effect of dietary sodium and calcium. *Proc. Am. Soc. Nephrol.* 17:24a

53a. Postnov, Y. V., Orlov, S. N. 1985. Ion transport across plasma membrane in primary hypertension. *Physiol. Rev.* 65(4):904–45

54. Mulvany, M. J., Nyborg, N. 1980. An increased calcium sensitivity of mesenteric resistance vesicles in young and adult spontaneously hypertensive rats. *Br. J. Pharmacol.* 71:583–96
55. Mulvany, M. J., Korsgaard, J. N., Nyborg, N. 1981. Evidence that the increased calcium sensitivity of resistance vessels in spontaneously hypertensive rats in an intrinsic defect of their vascular smooth muscle. *Clin. Exp. Hypertension* 3:749–61
56. Jones, A. W. 1974. Altered ion transport in large and small arteries from spontaneously hypertensive rats and influence of calcium. *Circ. Res.* 34(S1)117–22
57. Jones, A. W., Hart, R. G. 1975. Altered ion transport in aortic smooth muscle during deoxycorticosterone acetate hypertension in the rat. *Circ. Res.* 37:333–41
58. Noon, J. P., Rice, P. J., Baldessarini, R. J. 1978. Calcium leakage as a cause of the high resting tension in vascular smooth muscle from the spontaneously hypertensive rat. *Proc. Natl. Acad. Sci. USA* 75:1605–7
59. Janis, R. A., Triggle, D. J. 1973. Effect of diazoxide on aortic reactivity to calcium in spontaneously hypertensive rats. *Can. J. Physiol. Pharmacol.* 51:621–26
60. Zidek, W., Vetter, H., Dorst, K. G., Zumkley, H., Losse, H. 1982. Intracellular $Na^{+}$ and $Ca^{2+}$ activities in essential hypertension. *Clin. Sci.* 63:413–35
61. Postnov, Y. V., Orlov, S. N., Pokudin, N. I. 1980. Alterations of intracellular calcium distribution in the adipose tissue of human patients with essential hypertension. *Pflügers Arch.* 388:89–91
62. Wei, J. M., Janis, R. A., Daniel, E. E. 1976. Studies on subcellular fractions from mesenteric arteries of spontaneously hypertensive rats: alterations in both calcium uptake and enzyme activities. *Blood Vessels* 13:293–308
63. Postnov, Y. V., Orlov, S. N., Shevchenko, A., Alder, A. M. 1977. Altered sodium permeability, calcium binding and Na-K-ATPase activity in the red blood cell. *Pflügers Arch.* 371:263–69
64. Postnov, Y. V., Orlov, S. N., Pokudin, N. I. 1979. Decrease of calcium binding by the red blood cell membrane in spontaneously hypertensive rats and in essential hypertension. *Pflügers Arch.* 379:191–95

64a. Preiss, R., Prümke, H. J., Sohr, R., Müller, E., Schmeck, G., Bonaschak, H.

1982. Sodium flux and lipid spectrum in the erythrocyte membrane in hypertension. *Int. J. Pharmacol. Ther. Toxicol.* 20:105–12

65. Scheid, C. R., Honeyman, T. W., Fay, F. S. 1979. Mechanism of $\beta$-adrenergic relaxation of smooth-muscle. *Nature* 277:32–36

66. Bhalla, R. C., Webb, R. C., Singh, D., Ashley, T. 1978. Calcium, fluxes, calcium binding and adenosine cyclic 3'5'-monophosphate-dependent protein kinase activity in aorta of spontaneously hypertensive rats. *Mol. Pharmacol.* 14:468–77

67. Webb, R. C., Bhalla, R. C. 1976. Altered calcium sequestration by subcellular fractions of vascular smooth muscle from spontaneously hypertensive rats. *J. Mol. Cell. Cardiol.* 8:651–60

68. Kwan, C. Y., Belbeck, L., Daniel, E. E. 1979. Abnormal biochemistry of vascular smooth muscle plasma membrane as an important factor in the initiation and maintainance of hypertension in rats. *Blood Vessels* 16:259–68

69. Kwan, C. Y., Belbeck, L., Daniel, E. E. 1980. Abnormal biochemistry of vascular smooth muscle plasma membrane isolated from hypertensive rats. *Mol. Pharmacol.* 17:137–40

70. Morris, C. D., Vincenzi, F., McCarron, D. A. 1985. *Kidney Int.* 27:197 (Abstr.)

70a. Postnov, Y. V., Orlov, S. N., Reznikova, M. B., Rjazhsky, G. G., Pokudin, N. I. 1984. Calmodulin distribution and $Ca^{2+}$ transport in the erythrocytes of patients with essential hypertension. *Clin. Sci.* 66:459–63

70b. Olorunsogo, O. O., Okudolo, B. E., Lawal, S. O. A., Falase, A. O. 1985. Erythrocyte membrane $Ca^{2+}$ pumping ATPase of hypertensive humans; reduced stimulation by calmodulin. *Biosci. Rep.* 5:525–31

71. Bramley, P. M., Millar, J. A., Wilson, P. D. 1985. Intracellular electrolytes and efflux kinetics in pregnancy-induced hypertension. *Proc. Univ. Otago Med. Sch.* 63:34–35

72. Kwan, C. Y., Belbeck, L., Daniel, E. E. 1980. Characteristics of arterial plasma membrane in renovascular hypertension in rats. *Blood Vessels* 17:131–40

73. Spencer, H., Kramer, L., Osis, D. 1984. Effect of calcium on phosphorus metabolism in man. *Am. J. Clin. Nutr.* 40:219–25

74. Hsu, C. H., Chen, P. S., Caldwell, R. 1984. Renal phosphate excretion in spontaneously hypertensive and normotensive Wistar Kyoto rats. *Kidney Int.* 25:789–95

75. Bohr, D. F. 1963. Vascular smooth muscle: dual effect of calcium. *Science* 139:597–99

76. Overbeck, H. 1984. Attenuated arteriolar dilator responses to calcium in genetically hypertensive rats. *Hypertension* 6:647–53

77. Hurwitz, L., McGuffee, L. J., Smith, P. M., Little, S. A. 1982. Specific inhibition of calcium channels by calcium ions in smooth muscle. *J. Pharmacol. Exp. Ther.* 220:382–88

78. Fabiato, A. 1983. Calcium-induced release of calcium from the cardiac sarcoplasmic reticulum. *Am. J. Physiol.* 245:C1–14

79. Bukoski, R. D., Plant, S. B., McCarron, D. A. 1985. *18th Ann. Meet. Am. Soc. Nephrol.* (Abstr.)

79a. Stern, N., Golub, M., Nyby, M., Berger, M., Tuck, M. L., et al. 1986. The hypotensive effect of high calcium intake is not mediated by decreased vascular reactivity. *Am. Fed. Clin. Res.* 34(1): 44A

80. Kino, M., Tokushige, A., Tamura, H., Hopp, L., Searle, B. M., et al. 1985. Cultured rat vascular smooth muscle cells: extracellular calcium on $Na^+$-$K^+$ regulation. *Am. J. Physiol.* 248:C436–41

Ann. Rev. Nutr. 1986. 6:495–526


# METABOLIC ADAPTATION TO LOW INTAKES OF ENERGY AND PROTEIN

*J. C. Waterlow*

Department of Community Health, London School of Hygiene and Tropical Medicine, Keppel Street, London WC1E 7HT, England.

---

CONTENTS

INTRODUCTION .......... 495
*Some General Characteristics of Adaptation* .......... 496
*Variability* .......... 497
*Changes in Body Weight and Size* .......... 499
ADAPTATION TO LOW ENERGY INTAKES .......... 501
*Introduction* .......... 501
*Basal Metabolic Rate* .......... 502
*Diet-Induced Thermogenesis* .......... 506
*Efficiency of Physical Work* .......... 507
*Conclusion* .......... 511
ADAPTATION TO LOW PROTEIN INTAKES .......... 512
*Nitrogen Balance* .......... 512
*Utilization of Urea* .......... 514
*Energy Intake* .......... 515
*Protein Turnover* .......... 515
*The Biochemical Basis of Nitrogen Economy* .......... 518
*Conclusion* .......... 520

## INTRODUCTION

Adaptation to low intakes of energy and protein is a very wide subject; the treatment of it here is inevitably superficial because of the limitations of space and of my own knowledge. The plan adopted has been to cover as many aspects as possible in short sections, which make no claim to be complete reviews of the



0199-9885/86/0715-0495$02.00

literature, but which may stimulate further inquiries. I do not define adaptation nor distinguish it formally from related concepts such as homeostasis, regulation, or acclimatization (see 154). However, to bring the subject into perspective a brief discussion of terminology and general characteristics may be useful.

## *Some General Characteristics of Adaptation*

1. Terminology: the word "normal" is used here, as in clinical and nutritional biochemistry, to describe the range of a given variable in a group of healthy people. It is therefore essentially a statistical concept, although "normal" in this sense does not necessarily coincide with Gaussian. "Acceptable" is a functional term and it must be a main objective of any study of adaptation to determine the acceptable range of the characteristic under consideration, according to whatever criteria are chosen. A "successful" adaptation is one that maintains the characteristic within the acceptable range. These are not offered as definitions but merely as descriptions of the commonsense usage adopted in this review.

2. Adaptations that are important for nutrition are of three kinds: biological/genetic; physiological/metabolic; behavioral/social. Here we are concerned with adaptations of the second kind, but the three cannot be completely separated. For example, peoples whose way of life is based on herds of animals and who drink a great deal of milk retain intestinal lactase activity into adulthood. This may be regarded as a metabolic adaptation, but the capacity to achieve it is genetically determined, perhaps by a single gene (80).

3. An adapted state is a stable state that is maintained as long as the stimulus that evokes it is maintained, often throughout life.

4. In classical physiology, adaptation and homeostasis are discussed in relation to particular variables, such as body temperature in hot or cold climates, oxygen transport at high altitudes, body fluid volumes, osmolarity, pH, etc. Unfortunately, in nutrition it is seldom possible to focus in this way on a single variable. Usually the criterion is vaguely described as the maintenance of an acceptable level of function. In principle, any discussion of an adaptive process should begin by defining "adaptation of what in response to what?".

5. One function may be maintained at the expense of another, so that, as has been said: "every adaptation has its cost." To put it in another way, the success or failure of an adaptation depends on the criteria adopted. It is seldom useful to discuss whether an adaptation is "successful" unless the criteria have been agreed, and here we enter the realm of subjective value judgments. A key question, for example, is whether or not maintenance of a constant body weight or of a normal rate of growth is a necessary and appropriate criterion.

In conclusion, it is almost impossible to discuss adaptation without making value judgments and without using indefinable concepts such as "normal," "healthy," "satisfactory," etc. D'Arcy Thompson said "sooner or later nature does everything that is physically possible" (146). Our problem is that what is physically possible may not be good enough.

### *Variability*

The concept of adaptation implies that there is an acceptable state maintained by adaptive processes. This immediately raises the question of the variability between individuals and the range of normal variation.

In relation to energy metabolism the variation between people takes two forms, which are perhaps two sides of the same coin: the large differences in recorded food intake between similar people engaged in similar activities (big and small eaters), and the fact that some people get fat and others remain slim on apparently similar intakes. Both kinds of difference are relevant to the question of adaptation, since one asks: how do they manage to be so economical of energy? The classical story is of an almost two-fold range between the highest and lowest intakes of a group of similar people (163). Harries et al (60) summarized results of studies published up to 1962, and their results in turn are summarized in Table 1. It might be supposed that the low intakes so often recorded in Third World countries (e.g. 100, 108) represent a subgroup of "survivors" from the lower end of the range of intakes in the West. In that case the coefficient of variation (CV) should be lower, but I know of no evidence for this. A large range of variation in recorded intakes seems to be universal.

Cross-sectional surveys of intakes exaggerate the differences between individuals because they ignore the variability within the individual. The pioneering work of Sukhatme & Margen (143) drew attention to the importance of intraindividual variation. Their analysis of earlier data on cadets whose intake and expenditure were measured for three weeks (32) showed that the CV of intakes in the same subject from day to day was of the order of 20% and was greater than that between subjects. They also showed a significant variation

**Table 1** Estimates of variability of energy intake and expenditure in subjects studied over 5 days or more[a]

| | No. of studies | Total no. of subjects | Mean[d] CV (%) |
|---|---|---|---|
| Adult males | | | |
| intake[b] | 26 | 1458 | 14.8 |
| expenditure[c] | 14 | 218 | 10.8 |
| Adult females | | | |
| intake[b] | 28 | 2247 | 18.3 |
| expenditure[c] | 6 | 99 | 10.8 |

[a]Summarized from Harries et al (60).
[b]Intakes were measured in each subject over 7 days or more except in 5 of the 54 studies.
[c]Expenditures were measured in each subject over 7 days or more except in 3 of the 20 studies.
[d]For each study, the mean is given of the CVs of the daily intake/expenditure of each individual. This column represents the overall mean of these mean CVs, without weighting for numbers.

**Table 2** Within-subject ranges of energy intake and expenditure[a]

| Subject | Days of study | Sex | BMI | Mean intake (kcal/d) | Range[b] | Mean expenditure (kcal/d) | Range[b] | Expenditure / Intake |
|---|---|---|---|---|---|---|---|---|
| 4 | 7 | M | 29.9 | 3602 | 1.81 | 3405 | 1.35 | 0.95 |
| 7 | 7 | M | 17.8 | 2417 | 1.19 | 2212 | 1.20 | 0.92 |
| JB | 7 | M | 25.4 | 3022 | 1.20 | 2900 | 1.13 | 0.96 |
| RM | 14 | M | 16.3 | 2432 | 1.74 | 2674 | 1.46 | 1.10 |
| 29 | 7 | F | 21.2 | 2419 | 1.07 | 2458 | 1.08 | 1.02 |
| 34 | 14 | F | 23.0 | 1595 | 1.77 | 1660 | 1.36 | 1.04 |
| | | | | | Mean: 1.46 | | 1.26 | 1.00 |

[a]Data of Booyens & McCance (10).
[b]Ratio of maximum/minimum intake or expenditure. Standard deviations are not given in this paper.

within subjects of the mean intake from week to week. In a study in Canada (7), in which intakes were estimated by dietary recall for one day on six occasions throughout the year, intra- and interindividual variation made roughly equal contributions to the total variance, each with coefficients of variation of 25–30%.

As is apparent from Table 1, the variability of energy expenditure (EE) seems in general to be less than that of intake. From the data of Booyens & McCance (10) the CV of lying, sitting, and standing rates of expenditure per $m^2$ surface area in 22 male subjects was 16% for all three rates. Their results for six subjects who were studied for 7–14 days are shown in Table 2. It shows that the within-subject variation of expenditure was less than that of intake, even though the expenditure was measured by the tedious and relatively inaccurate diary method. Analysis of a very large body of data (126) shows that the CV of BMR, adjusted for age, sex, and body weight, is 7–10%.

More precise methods give lower values for the variability of total EE. Calorimetric measurements of EE on nonobese subjects performing standardized activities over 24 h have given values of 6–7% for between-subject CV and 1.5–2.5% for within-subject CV (see 25, 44, 45). Admittedly, the conditions are far removed from those of real life. The method of measuring total EE over 10 days or more with doubly labelled water should greatly extend our knowledge. In a recent comparison (109) of measurements of EE by 24-h calorimetry and by the isotope method over 2–3 weeks, there was a significant rank order correlation between the two sets of results in 11 subjects. The interindividual CV of the isotope results was 24%, that of the calorimeter measurements 11.5%[1]. This difference may reflect the extent to which a measurement over 1 day is unrepresentative of a 2–3-week period.

[1]Values calculated from (109) as metabolic rates per kg body weight. When more than one set of measurements were made on a subject, only the first was used for estimating the CV. Two subjects were pregnant and two were obese. The data from one grossly obese woman were omitted.

There is less information about the variability of protein metabolism. It has been estimated from short-term balances that the average amount of protein needed for zero balance in groups of similar young men has a CV of 12.5% (37). Sukhatme & Margen's analysis of longer-term studies of nitrogen output on a fixed intake showed autocorrelated variations in time (142), although this effect has not been confirmed in other long-term studies (111). There is evidence of substantial interindividual differences in protein turnover (J. C. Waterlow, unpublished results). As with energy expenditure, intraindividual variation exists but appears to be less. In repeated measurements of nitrogen flux made on the same subjects over periods of up to four years, the intraindividual CV was only 4% (38). Data presented by Bier et al (8) on repeated measurements of amino acid flux in the same subjects show an average range of variation within the individual of about 10%.

Payne & Dugdale (104) proposed a model according to which the "*P* ratio," defined as the ratio of protein stored to total energy stored during weight gain, and conversely the ratio of protein lost to energy lost during weight loss, is characteristic and fixed for each person. This model attempts to link individual variability in protein and energy metabolism (62).

The important contribution of Sukhatme's thinking is that human beings should not be regarded as existing in a fixed and constant state. Nevertheless, even when allowance is made for the confounding effect of this variability, real differences between individuals remain, and there is increasing interest in the extent to which they are genetically determined. The genetic component in height has been analyzed in detail (117), and there have been a number of studies of the heritability of obesity (e.g. 12). A particularly interesting experiment, because it involves metabolic measurements, is that of Griffiths & Payne (57) showing that preschool children, not themselves overweight, who had an obese parent had lower food intakes, basal metabolic rates, and 24-h food intakes than the children of nonobese parents. More general discussions of genetic factors in nutrition are to be found in (149) and (167).

The large range of variation both between and within individuals provides an opportunity for the study of adaptive mechanisms of which more advantage could perhaps be taken.

## *Changes in Body Weight and Size*

Changes in body weight are an important part of long-term adaptation—perhaps the most important part (74). This review concentrates on adults, in spite of the fact that children are more sensitive to deficient intakes of energy and protein, precisely because in children the most obvious response to deficiency of any nutrient is a retardation of growth that tends to overshadow other adjustments.

"Low" intakes mean intakes that are low in relation to supposed requirements. Both for energy and protein, requirements vary with body weight. It is self-evident that a big person, unless obese, needs more food than a small one. The process of estimating requirements depends on the concept of balance—of determining the intake needed to balance the output or expenditure. It is implicit in measurements of energy or nitrogen balance that constant body weight should be maintained, and there are good practical reasons for this. For example, over a 10-day experimental period one can determine a negative nitrogen balance of −1 g of nitrogen per day with reasonable confidence. This loss corresponds to a decrease of about 300 g of lean body mass, a quantity too small to be measured with accuracy by methods currently available.

This experimental approach, which involves determining requirements at a particular body weight, does not necessarily imply that the body weight has to be fixed and constant. At any given height there is a range of body weight consistent with health. There is no reason, therefore, why a reduction in body weight should not be accepted as part of the process of adaptation to low intakes, provided that weight remains within acceptable limits. To adjust for height it is convenient to use the body mass index: BMI = $Wt(kg)/Ht(m)^2$. It has been proposed that the acceptable limits of BMI may be taken as 19–25 (11). The upper limit, with which we are not concerned here, has been reasonably well defined by studies on the excess morbidity and mortality of people who are overweight. The lower limit is much less clear. The evidence that morbidity risk increases if the BMI falls below about 19 may well be an artefact of conditions in Western societies (116). According to the analysis of Keys et al (77), death is likely to occur when 40% of body weight has been lost. This would correspond to a BMI of 13 in a person whose initial BMI was 22, and if Keys' analysis is correct, may be regarded as the absolute lower limit.

The more important question is to define a lower limit compatible with acceptable functional capacity. In many Third World countries the average BMI [calculated from average weight and average height (35)] is 18–19. If the coefficient of variation is taken as 10%, this would give a range (mean ± 2 SD) of BMI in these populations of about 15–23. Shetty (128) reported that poor Indian laborers were able to work and performed well in physiological fitness tests with a BMI of 15–16 and an estimated body fat content of 6%. Young women with anorexia nervosa may have a BMI as low as 14 (42, 120, 141), and such patients are often symptom-free and physically hyperactive. It may be suggested as a rule of thumb that a BMI of 15 be regarded as the absolute lower limit of what is acceptable. However, circumstances are clearly important. Shetty's laborers, after a lifetime of exposure to low intakes, were apparently functioning reasonably well at a BMI of 16 (and the same may be said of subject RM in Table 2), whereas Keys' volunteers, after 24 weeks of semistarvation, at a similar level of BMI were physically inactive and psychologically disturbed. In anorexia nervosa, the peculiar psychological motivation is presumably important.

The discussion so far has been in terms of BMI or weight for height. A further question is the significance in relation to adaptation of differences in height. In the Third World very large numbers of children are severely stunted in height, compared with international reference standards (76). The evidence summarized by Martorell (89) indicates that in schoolchildren in these countries there is a substantial difference in height between rich and poor, regardless of ethnic group, just as there used to be in industrialized countries such as the United Kingdom (18). It seems that height deficits in older children and adults are probably established in the first years of life. Satyanarayana et al (123) studied the growth of children who, at the age of five, were divided into groups described as well- or malnourished on the basis of height for age, the average difference in height between the extremes being 16.5 cm. This difference in height remained at the age of 17. It was remarkable, however, that the increment between 5 and 17 years was the same in both groups and equal to that found in American children. Thus the potential for growth was retained but it was not enough to overcome the original deficit.

Do these differences matter? Is it "smart to be small," or a handicap? There are some (e.g. 127, 140) who regard stunting in children as an adaptation: they need less food and are therefore more likely to survive. This, however, is not a sufficient criterion, since to survive without an acceptable level of functional capacity would not be a successful adaptation. Margen (88) has an interesting discussion on this subject. It is outside the scope of this review to examine the evidence on physical, mental, and immunological function in stunted children. However, in reply to those who maintain that stunting is a satisfactory adaptation one might invoke the UN Declaration of Human Rights, that everyone has a right to develop their full genetic potential (see also 56). This controversy illustrates the extent to which subjective value judgements may enter into a discussion of adaptation.

## ADAPTATION TO LOW ENERGY INTAKES

### *Introduction*

Several years ago I and others asked the rhetorical question "How much food does a man require?" (31). That letter pointed out the gross inadequacy of our knowledge on this subject. Since then much has been done, including the development in several countries of whole-body calorimeters capable of accurate measurements of energy expenditure over periods of 24 h or more. Nevertheless, as often happens, better methods have revealed further problems. For example, it has been estimated from calorimeter studies that the energy expenditure of subjects engaging in minimum physical activities is 1.4 × basal metabolic rate (BMR) (37). However, measurements of energy expenditure by the labelled-water method of British housewives in their homes, carrying out their normal activities, was 1.38 × BMR (109). Have we been consistently overestimating energy expenditure and needs in ordinary life (e.g. 30)? In the face of such uncertainties, it is very difficult to discuss adaptation to low intakes, if we cannot define a baseline in people who have not needed to adapt.

In the following sections I examine the possibilities for adaptation in the two main components of energy expenditure—basal metabolic rate and physical activity. Nothing will be said about growth because in children the cost of weight gain depends largely on the composition of the tissue deposited. Although the gap between observed intakes and estimated requirements is particularly large in pregnant and lactating women (108), not enough is known about the energy costs of human lactation or of the development of the fetus and adnexa for a worthwhile discussion of adaptation in these processes. All that can be said is that undernourished women tend to produce smaller babies and less milk.

There are four strategies for adaptation, which are probably usually combined:

1. Achieving and maintaining a low body weight, as discussed above.

2. A reduction in voluntary and conscious activity, whether occupational or discretionary (37). This type of adaptation may be regarded by definition as undesirable. Very little is known about the extent to which it actually occurs when people are faced with a restricted intake, for example in the hungry season in some countries. However, this is a subject for anthropological rather than metabolic inquiry.

3. Unconscious economy of activity. It has often been suggested that big eaters are able to remain thin because they are more "tense," habitually making unnecessary movements, etc, and anecdotal impressions have been recorded of the smoothness and economy of effort with which people seem to move in tropical countries. Certainly there are easy and difficult ways of doing the same task and much depends on training, habit, custom, and experience. These points are mentioned because they have to be borne in mind when one looks at physiological studies of the energy cost of work.

4. True metabolic adaptations. In order to establish the existence of such adaptive changes, energy expenditure must be related to body weight or, if possible, to lean body mass (LBM).

## *Basal Metabolic Rate*

The BMR is defined as the rate of energy expenditure in a subject who is fasting, and completely relaxed in a thermoneutral environment. The resting metabolic rate (RMR), in the post-absorptive state and physically at rest, is usually the best approximation that can be achieved in practice. The terms are used interchangeably here.

For most people in most occupations total energy expenditure (EE) is unlikely to be greater than twice the BMR (37). This is one reason why the BMR is so important in relation to adaptation. A second reason is that BMR or RMR is easier to measure than other components of EE.

In the following discussion the observed BMR is often compared with the expected BMR, calculated from body weight by equations recently published by Schofield et al (126) on the basis of an analysis of the world literature. These equations are simply descriptive of data from healthy populations. They do not claim to have the physiological significance of allometric equations (63).

The relationship of BMR, expressed as kcal per person per day, to body weight is not linear. In healthy people the BMR/kg rises as body weight falls and except at extremes this effect is independent of height (37). For example, from the Schofield equations a young adult male will have an expected BMR of 1750 kcal/d or 25 kcal/kg/d, whereas at 55 kg his expected BMR is 1520 kcal/d or 27.6 kcal/kg/d. However, on the basis of $Wt^{0.67}$ the two rates are the same (102 and 104 kcal/$wt^{0.67}$ respectively). This identity suggests at first sight that there can be no difference in body composition between the two subjects (63). Nevertheless, differences almost certainly do exist. The 55-kg man is likely to have a lower proportion of body fat and, at least in more extreme cases, to have a different make-up of his LBM (see below).

The available evidence for a metabolic adaptation in BMR is of three kinds, described in the next three subsections.

THE EFFECT OF WEIGHT LOSS There have been many studies, summarized by Apfelbaum et al (3) and by James (71), of the effect on BMR of restricted food intake and consequent weight loss. The results are rather variable. In general there is a rapid initial fall in BMR in response to severe and indeed artificial reduction of energy intake, as in the treatment of obese patients, followed by a slower fall that goes hand in hand with loss of weight. It is the second aspect that is of more interest in relation to long-term adaptation. Two examples may be given, one old, one new.

In the classical semistarvation experiment of Keys et al (77) the average weight of the subjects fell from 68 kg (BMI 21.4) initially to 52 kg (BMI 16.3) after 24 weeks of semistarvation. The BMR per kg fell during this time by 16%, most of this fall occurring in the first two weeks, whereas on the basis of body weight alone it would have been expected from the Schofield equations to rise by 12%. This, therefore, represents a very substantial reduction.

The second example comes from a study by Forbes and coworkers (42) of subjects with anorexia. They started with an average BMI of only 14.2; their BMR was 77% of expected and rose with treatment to 93, while the BMI was still only 16. However, in another series of anorexic patients with an even lower initial BMI, there was no reduction in resting metabolic rate per kg compared with standard values, for which the source is not given (141).

In severely malnourished children the BMR per kg weight or LBM has been found to be low (14, 93), but rapidly rises with treatment to levels that may be greater than normal. In these children (48, 157) and in rats (160) tissues such as muscle and skin, with a low metabolic rate, are preferentially lost, while the visceral tissues and brain, with a high metabolic rate, tend to be preserved. It is probable, therefore, that the person with a low body weight has, from a physiological point of view, a reduced metabolic rate per unit LBM, which is cancelled out by the effect of smaller body size per se. Admittedly this is an academic point, since from the nutritional point of view what matters is the overall expenditure, regardless of how it is made up.

COMPARISONS OF BIG AND SMALL EATERS Rose & Williams (118) investigated the hypothesis that if, with similar levels of physical activity, some people eat far more than others, they must differ in their efficiency of energy utilization. They studied two small groups of normal young men, one of which had a recorded energy intake nearly twice that of the other, but they found no difference in the BMR. Edmundson (33) made a similar comparison between two groups of Javanese workers with the same average weights and heights (BMI 20). One group had an energy intake 55% greater than the other. In the big eaters the average BMR/kg/d was 36.5 ± 6.5 kcal; in the small eaters it was 18.4 ± 2.7—a result totally different from that of Rose & Williams. The expected BMR in young men of the same body weight (52.5 kg) is 28.2 ± 2.9 kcal/kg/d, so that in one group the BMR was 30% greater than the expected level and in the other it was 35% less. This finding clearly needs to be substantiated.

STUDIES ON SUBJECTS WHO ARE PRESUMABLY HABITUATED TO LOW ENERGY INTAKES Schofield et al (126), in their review of the world literature on BMR, cite some 30 papers giving measurements on non-Europeans in developing countries, of which 20 come from India. They conclude that in Indians the BMR is significantly lower, by about 9%, than the expected rate, based on weight and height, of Europeans or North Americans. Many possible causes for this difference have been discussed in the literature—climate, ethnic group, diet—without any clear conclusions. Studies on Europeans in the tropics suggest that climate has only a small effect on BMR (119), and the more recent UN reports (36, 37) have removed the recommendation of previous committees that estimated energy requirements should be adjusted for environmental temperature.

A recent study by Shetty (128) throws some light on the relative importance of ethnic group and diet. Table 3 summarizes Shetty's results in poor Indian laborers, whose estimated daily energy intake was extremely low. The resting metabolic rate (RMR) of the laborers per kg was significantly lower than that of the Indian controls, particularly when related to lean body mass. It was some

**Table 3** Metabolic rates in Indian laborers and control subjects

| | Indian laborers[a] | Indian controls[a] | US volunteers[b] Initial | US volunteers[b] At 24 wk |
|---|---|---|---|---|
| Number | 14 | 14 | 32 | 32 |
| Intake (kcal/d) | 1540 | 2260 | 3490 | 1570 |
| Body wt (kg) | 45.8 | 61.4 | 69.4 | 52.6 |
| BMI | 16.6 | 20.7[d] | 21.4 | 16.3 |
| Body fat (%) | 6.1 | 14.3[d] | 13.9 | 5.2 |
| RMR (kcal/kg) | 25.1 | 26.5[d] | 23.1 | 19.3 |
| RMR (kcal/kg LBM) | 26.7 | 31.0[d] | 26.8 | 20.3 |
| Expected BMR (kcal/kg)[c] | 30.1 | 26.4 | 25.2 | 28.4 |
| Observed/expected BMR (%) | 83 | 100 | 92 | 68 |

[a]Data summarized from Shetty (128).
[b]From Keys et al (77).
[c]Expected BMR from Schofield et al (126).
[d]Difference between labourers and controls significant at $P = 0.01$ or less.

17% lower than the expected value for Caucasians at the same body weight. It is interesting to compare Shetty's laborers with Keys' subjects after 24 weeks of semistarvation. The BMI is the same in the two groups; the BMR per kg of Keys' volunteers was 68% of that expected on the basis of body weight. Thus the reduction was much greater in the Americans exposed to a low intake for a relatively short period than in the Indians, who were habituated to it. In this case adaptation seems to have achieved a successful compromise since the Indians were active and fit, but this could not be said of Keys' subjects.

Data from Third World countries other than India are scanty and are summarized in Table 4.

Finally, we have comparisons between different ethnic groups living in the same environment. Mahadeva et al (87) found no difference in the energy costs of walking and stepping between Europeans and Asians in Edinburgh. Geissler & Aldouri (51) compared European, Asian, and African students, matched for

**Table 4** Resting metabolic rates in different ethnic groups

| Subjects | Sex | No. | Food intake | BMI | RMR (kcal/kg/d) | BMR (% of expected) | Ref. |
|---|---|---|---|---|---|---|---|
| Chinese in Taiwan | M | 50 | normal | 19.6 | 25.75 ± 2.7 | 93 | 66 |
| Chinese in US | M | 6 | normal | 19.4 | 25.95 ± 3.9 | 95 | 66 |
| Jamaican | M | 5 | low | 19.6 | 24.5 ± 2.9 | 88 | 4 |
| Jamaican | F | 5 | low | | 25.8 ± 4.2 | 102 | 4 |
| Javanese | M | 5 | high | 19.8 | 36.5 ± 6.5 | 129 | 33 |
| Javanese | M | 6 | low | 20.2 | 18.35 ± 2.7 | 65 | 33 |
| New Guineans | M | 15 | normal | 24.6 | 25.4 ± 2.5 | 96 | 65 |
| Japanese | M | 10 | normal | 22.2 | 28.65 ± 4.7 | 112 | 65 |

weight and height, well nourished (average BMI 23.5), and presumably on an adequate diet. The lying metabolic rate was 17% lower in the Africans and Asians than in the Europeans. In a similar study in France, Dieng et al (29) found no difference in lying metabolic rate between Vietnamese refugees and French subjects. In both these studies the non-Europeans had been living in Europe for several months, so they may have lost any previous adaptation. These divergent results are difficult to interpret; perhaps the reason is that the lying metabolic rate was not precisely standardized.

In conclusion, the evidence is consistent with the hypothesis that there may be a significant reduction in BMR, of the order of 10%, in people on habitually low intakes. It is not clear how far and in what way this reduction is related to a fall in body weight. There is no evidence that ethnic differences are important, or that the low BMR is maintained when body weights and food intakes are within the normal range.

## *Diet-Induced Thermogenesis*

In recent years there has been a great deal of interest in diet-induced thermogenesis (DIT), particularly in relation to obesity (47, 72, 119, 129, 165). "Big eaters" appear to have a larger thermic response than others (94). There is some disagreement about the extent to which DIT may be reduced in obesity. James & Trayhurn (75) found an inverse relation between the body fat content and the thermic response to feeding fat, but not to protein or carbohydrate, whereas Garrow & Hawes (49) showed that the response depended on the energy content of the meal and not its composition. Garrow (47) concluded that a failure of thermogenesis is unlikely to play an important role in causing or maintaining obesity.

There is not much information about the effect on DIT of habitually low energy intakes. Diet restriction has been said to produce a reduction in DIT (3), but this effect has not always been found (71). In severely malnourished children, who have a low BMR (14, 93), there was no DIT in response to food, but it reappeared when appetite was restored, food intake increased, and the children began to gain weight. In these studies the magnitude of the thermic response was linearly related to the rate of weight gain (13). In anorectic patients undergoing treatment the thermic response to a glucose meal was unusually high (16%), as in the recovering children (141).

When these children begin to gain weight they show a large increase in the rate of whole-body protein synthesis (54). It therefore seemed reasonable to conclude that DIT is not a catabolic response, as used to be thought, but represents the energy cost of protein synthesis and the conversion of carbohydrate to fat (5). This interpretation is confirmed by the finding that when the rate of protein turnover was measured in normal adults over 24 h, during the day (when they were eating) the rate of protein synthesis was high and during the night (when they were fasting) it fell (23). One might, therefore, expect a reduction in DIT in conditions where protein turnover is depressed, as discussed below in the section on protein turnover.

DIT is usually about 10% of the energy value of a meal, so that over a whole day's intake it would amount to about 200 kcal. Thus a 50% fall in DIT, which, according to James (71) is the most that could be expected, would save some 100 kcal. This amount, though small, would still be a significant economy.

## *Efficiency of Physical Work*

Work efficiency may be considered at several levels—biochemical, physiological, and "real life." At the biochemical level, the mechanical efficiency of muscular contraction is the product of the coupling efficiency (work done per unit ATP hydrolyzed) and the efficiency of energy transduction to ATP by oxidation of substrate. This aspect is not considered here.

MECHANICAL EFFICIENCY I use this term to describe the ratio between mechanical work done and the energy expended in doing it. The simplest and most usual method of measuring efficiency so defined is on a bicycle ergometer with an electric brake so that the mechanical work done can be adjusted and known precisely, while oxygen consumption and respiratory exchange ratio are measured to determine the amount of energy used. The great advantage of the bicycle ergometer is that it does not involve lifting the body, so that efficiency should be independent of weight. However, even with this simple system there are problems. To determine the energy cost of the work itself it is necessary to subtract the energy expenditure when no work is being done. Often this has been taken as equal to the BMR, but it is more accurate to use as the baseline the expenditure at zero load, since this takes account of the energy cost of moving the legs (162). Another method is to determine efficiency as the slope of the line relating increase in work to increase in oxygen consumption.

In studies in which careful attention was paid to the question of baseline (43), the mechanical efficiency in healthy men was found to be 26–30%. In these experiments the relation between work load on the ergometer and $\dot{V}O_2$ was linear, indicating constant efficiency, over the range 200–800 kp·m/min. However, the authors point out that the literature on the relation between work load and efficiency is very contradictory, there being reports of increasing, decreasing, or unchanged efficiency with increasing load. This may be because inadequate attention was paid to the baseline, or because of failure to reach a steady state. Another factor is the speed of work. In the experiments of Gaesser & Brooks (43), efficiency at constant load fell off with increasing speed of pedalling. On the other hand, Bunc et al (15) reported that in subjects running on a treadmill, there was a linear relationship between speed and $\dot{V}O_2$ within the range 20–80% of $\dot{V}O_2$ max. The question of speed may be more important in relation to "real life" work (see below).

In spite of the carefully controlled conditions of the studies quoted, there is considerable variability between subjects. In the study by Whipp & Wasserman (162) the increase in $\dot{V}O_2$ for a fixed load showed a three-fold range in eight presumably normal men. In that of Gaesser & Brooks (43) the coefficients of variation were of the order of 8%, giving a range of 1.4 from +2 SD to −2 SD.

Measuring the amount of mechanical work done in other activities, even simple ones such as running or stepping up and down, is extremely complicated (68, 78, 110). In their study on athletes, Bunc et al (15) obtained the results shown in Table 5. It is interesting that in spite of the large differences in calculated mechanical efficiency, the energy cost of moving 1 kg over 1 m, which might be regarded as an example of "real-life" efficiency (see below) was very much the same in the different kinds of athletes and was only some 10% higher in untrained subjects. This fits in with the statement (6) that, contrary to the common misconception, training (as opposed to adaptation) does not produce any change in the metabolic efficiency of the muscles.

Perhaps a solution of this apparent paradox lies in a different pattern of muscle fiber types in subjects adapted to different speeds of work. Komi et al (78) performed muscle biopsies on subjects who subsequently ran a marathon. There was a positive correlation between the proportion of slow-twitch fibers and $\dot{V}O_2$ at the anerobic threshold—a measure of maximum working capacity. Slow-twitch fibers are said to be more efficient than fast-twitch ones, in terms of mechanical force development per unit ATP used (see 161a). The studies of Russell and coworkers (83, 120) showed that in malnourished patients there was an increase in the ratio of slow to fast fibers, mainly due to a reduction in the number of fast fibers, the slow being better preserved. The same effect has been found in hypothyroidism (164). One might venture the hypothesis that a possible mechanism of adaptation is a relative preservation of slow-twitch fibers or, perhaps more generally, the achievement of an optimum pattern for a

**Table 5** Work output and mechanical efficiency of different types of athletes[a]

| Subjects | BMI | Cost of work[b] (kJ/kg/m) | Mechanical[c] efficiency (%) |
|---|---|---|---|
| Middle-distance runners | 20.5 | 3.57 | 34.1 |
| Endurance runners | 20.1 | 3.63 | 32.4 |
| Marathon runners | 20.9 | 3.67 | 31.1 |
| Football players | 23.6 | 3.88 | 24.8 |
| Pentathletes | 23.6 | 3.95 | 22.6 |
| Untrained subjects | — | 4.0 | 19–20 |

[a]Data from Bunc et al (15).
[b]Energy cost of running on treadmill at 5% slope.
[c]Calculated according to Ito et al (68).

person's particular lifestyle. Bassey & Fentem (6) are cautious about the possibility of transformation of one fiber type to another, but they are discussing training rather than adaptation.

Attention has been drawn in this section to some technical points and to apparently contradictory results to emphasize the difficulty of establishing real differences between groups in the mechanical efficiency of muscular work.

PHYSIOLOGICAL EFFICIENCY What we are really interested in with respect to adaptation is the actual energy expenditure needed for a particular task or activity. In this context "efficiency" is often taken as the ratio (energy expended during work − energy expended at rest)/total energy expended while working. No attempt is made to estimate the actual mechanical work done. This might be called the "apparent efficiency." Very often, however, in comparisons between individuals and groups it is the gross rather than the net cost that is of greater real interest. It has been proposed (37) that the energy costs of activities and occupations should be expressed as multiples of the BMR since most common activities involve moving the body. It has been shown that for walking and running in normal subjects the cost per kg appears to be independent of body weight (55, 85, 165). Gross expenditure per kg is therefore probably the most useful parameter for comparisons between individuals or groups when one is looking at adaptive changes in working efficiency. In such comparisons it is clearly essential that activities should be standardized. When this condition has been strictly adhered to, no important differences between ethnic groups have emerged (29, 51, 87). However, in these cases, as mentioned above, the Asian and African subjects had been living in Europe for some time and might have lost any adaptation that they had acquired.

A study that has attracted much interest was made by Edmundson of working efficiency in Javanese farmers, comparing big and small eaters. In one experiment (33) the 24-h food intake and total energy expenditure were measured and an index of "relative efficiency" calculated as intake/output. This ratio varied from 0.6 in big eaters to 1.6 in small eaters. However, if these discrepancies between intake and output were real and habitual, there must in the long term have been changes in body weight, which were not recorded although the study lasted a year. In a second experiment (34) Edmundson measured the energy cost of work on a bicycle ergometer, and with work at 100 W found a significantly lower gross energy cost in small than in big eaters, although their weights and heights were the same. Norgan (99) has commented: "The net mechanical efficiencies are typical of values found in Europeans, except in the high intake group at high work loads (100 W), when the value of net efficiency was at the lower limit of the expected range (22 ± 4%). Thus a significant difference in work metabolism appears to arise from a low efficiency in the high intake group rather than from a high efficiency in those with a low intake." Spurr et al (135) reported no difference in gross efficiency of walking on a treadmill between marginally malnourished and normal boys.

The problem remains that activities usually cannot be standardized. How can one suppose that the mechanical work of digging, for example, is the same everywhere? For this reason Norgan et al in their classical study in New Guinea (100) cautiously refrained from comparing the energy costs of different activities with the standard values obtained in well-fed countries (103). When such comparisons have been made, e.g. in the Philippines (27) and in pregnant women in the Gambia (81), they have not shown any differences. Parizkova concluded: "The gross or net efficiency of *standardized* tasks [italics mine] appears not to increase with low food intakes" (102).

EFFICIENCY IN REAL LIFE One also has to consider that people differ in their patterns of activity and the ways in which they live and carry out their work. It has often been suggested that some people remain thin in spite of a large food intake because they are more tense and fidgety. Garrow & Webster (50) attempted to assess the cost of such minor thermogenic stimuli and concluded that on a 24-h basis they might increase energy expenditure by some 12%. Avoiding unnecessary movements may be an important form of adaptation. Lawrence et al (81), in their studies on pregnant women in the Gambia, observed that "most activities were performed with considerable economy of effort, i.e. there were few superfluous movements." Booyens & McCance (10) say of their subject RM, who had an exceptionally low expenditure in running and cycling: "RM is both a cyclist and a long-distance walker of great experience and has a highly developed sense of rhythm, and all unnecessary movements were probably eliminated from both occupations twenty five year ago."

The speed at which people work may also be important. If there is a given task to be done, is it more economical to perform it slowly or quickly? Ashworth (4) measured the energy cost of moving a certain number of bricks from point A to point B. The greater the number of bricks carried in one load, and hence the fewer the journeys, the less the expenditure for the total task. When the subjects carried the number of bricks that was natural to them, their expenditure fell in the middle of the range. In a study of this kind the result will depend on the relative cost of carrying the load and of walking the distance. Evidently in this experiment walking accounted for the greater part of the cost.

It is generally considered (103) that in walking a fixed distance the total energy cost is the same regardless of the speed, within certain limits. In the study of big and small eaters referred to earlier (118), the natural pace of the big eaters was faster than that of the small eaters, but their energy expenditure over a given distance was the same. However, there is divergent evidence in both directions. The data of Goldman & Iampetro (55) indicate that with varying loads and grades the cost of walking 5 miles would on average be about 10%

lower at 2.5 than at 3.5 mph. Imms, who has given a very full discussion of this subject (67), has put the most economical rate even lower, at 1.8 km per h. On the other hand extrapolation from the results of McDonald (85) suggests that, over a range of body weights, in order to cover a given distance, walking at 100 m/min would be 15–20% more efficient than walking at 40 m/min.

The influence of load may be important. Data quoted by Passmore & Durnin (103) show that, in walking with a load of 40 lb, energy expenditure increased more than linearly with speed. Thus at 3 km/h the expenditure was 4 kcal/min and at 6 km/h it was nearly 11 kcal/min.

Here again, therefore, although the observations are relatively straightforward, there seem to be many contradictions. Perhaps the most practically useful conclusion is that of Bassey & Fentem (6) that short alternating periods of work and rest allow the same amount of work to be done in a given time with a much lower heart rate and lactate level than if the work and rest periods are longer.

This observation raises the question of work capacity, which is not strictly relevant to that of work efficiency. Many studies have been made (for a summary, see 134) of maximum working capacity ($\dot{V}O_2$ max—an index of cardiorespiratory fitness) in adults and children in developing countries. In general, when poorer, so-called undernourished, people are compared with more privileged groups, their absolute $\dot{V}O_2$ max is lower, but indices of physical fitness, when corrected for body weight, may be equal (28, 136) or even higher (39). Only with very severe deficits in body weight has there been found a lower working capacity per kg (122). It has been argued that if a given task involves a certain absolute energy cost, a person with a lower $\dot{V}O_2$ max will be at a disadvantage, at least in endurance, since he will be working at a higher proportion of his maximum capacity. However, this argument loses much of its force if it is accepted that in most tasks, though admittedly not in all, the rate of energy expenditure is proportional to the body weight. Only when $\dot{V}O_2$ max per kg is low will there be a real handicap.

## *Conclusion*

The most important adaptation to a low energy intake is to have a low body weight. Beyond that, in the present state of knowledge it seems probable that any adaptation that occurs is the sum of several separate but small sources of economy. Of these the most important is a reduction in BMR, which is unlikely to be greater than 10%. There is no rigorous evidence of an increased efficiency of muscular work. However, there may perhaps be significant savings from a more economical pattern of work and lifestyle. In particular, for many tasks it may be more economical of energy to work slowly rather than quickly. This subject needs further study.

Possible biochemical mechanisms for economizing energy will be discussed in a future publication.

## ADAPTATION TO LOW PROTEIN INTAKES

The ability to achieve nitrogen balance over a wide range of intakes is probably the most clear-cut example of nutritional adaptation. This is the first line of defense against an inadequate intake and its objective, in teleological terms, is to maintain the constancy of the body's protein mass. Once the capacity to economize N is exhausted, the second line of defense is a reduction in lean body mass. All committees that have been concerned with the subject have assumed that the protein requirement is directly related to body weight, or more precisely to lean body mass, so that in adults in the absence of growth, a single figure can be given for the protein requirement per kg. In fact there is no evidence either for or against this assumption; it is entirely possible that the nitrogen requirement follows the same rules as the oxygen requirement, as indicated by the BMR, and that the requirement per kg increases with decreasing body weight. Such a relationship would make biological sense, but it would reduce the extent to which adaptation could be achieved by a fall in lean body mass.

In children, if the intake of protein or indeed of any other nutrient is inadequate, there is a fall-off in the rate of growth in weight, so that in them the second line of defense is to sacrifice growth. It has been suggested (53, 155) that growth in height may be particularly sensitive to protein supply and that stunting in height is perhaps a manifestation of protein deficiency. Pregnancy and lactation are often regarded as coming under the heading of growth, since new protein is deposited or secreted. Here, however, the priorities seem to be different, since these kinds of growth can be achieved, at least to some extent, at the expense of the mother's own tissues.

This section is concerned with the metabolic adaptation that constitutes the first line of defense, in which the central concept is that of nitrogen balance and the conservation of body nitrogen.

### *Nitrogen Balance*

At any given body weight the minimum N intake needed to secure balance, that is, the lower limit of adaptation, is determined by two factors: the obligatory N loss and the efficiency with which food protein is used to cover that loss.

OBLIGATORY LOSSES Numerous short-term balance studies, summarized by Bodwell et al (9) and in the most recent FAO/WHO/UNU report (37), have shown that in young North American men the average obligatory N loss in round figures is 60 mg/kg/d, of which 35–40 mg are excreted in urine, 15–20 mg in feces, and about 5 mg from the skin. The fecal component depends largely on the quality of the diet, being greater in diets high in fiber, such as those of Third World countries. Nitrogen is lost from the skin mainly as urea, and therefore this loss may be expected to be somewhat less on low-protein diets, when blood urea concentrations are low. However, skin loss is only a small part of the total. Any possibility for economy lies in reduction of the urinary N loss. Even on minimal protein intakes, about 50% of urinary N is in urea. The amount of ammonia excreted is determined by the need to maintain acid-base balance and tends to be lower on diets containing vegetable rather than animal protein, because they produce smaller amounts of acid. As Folin pointed out 80 years ago (40), the excretion of the other N-containing metabolites (such as uric acid, creatine, and free amino acids) appears to be remarkably constant regardless of the level of protein intake, and there is no evidence of any physiological mechanism for regulating this source of N loss.

A number of studies confirm that there is little scope for economizing N by reducing obligatory loss. Nicol & Phillips (97) showed that in Nigerian farmers the obligatory urinary N loss was very similar to that of North American men. In collaborative studies organized by the United Nations University (113) the obligatory losses in different population groups were very constant, although there is an indication that they may be slightly lower in oriental people (66).

EFFICIENCY OF UTILIZATION The efficiency of utilization is the slope of the line relating N balance to intake. In adults who are not growing and in whom one cannot expect a positive balance, the slope has to be determined at submaintenance levels of intake. The requirement is the intake at zero balance—that is, the intake needed to make good the obligatory losses. Although individuals may have the same obligatory losses, they may differ in the amounts needed to cover them. The UNU studies concluded that there was no difference between the average protein requirement of different ethnic groups; the mean requirement was 0.6 g protein/kg/d. As long ago as 1956 Phanselkar & Patwardhan (105) stated that the N requirement of Indians was strictly comparable to that of Americans habituated to a high intake. However, there is not complete agreement; more recent studies in India (1, 7a) on men and women on vegetarian diets led to somewhat lower estimates of average protein requirements. The very detailed investigations of Nicol & Phillips (98) suggested that Nigerian farmers utilized protein more efficiently than American men did.

The balance studies mentioned so far were all short-term and it may be objected that they did not allow enough time for adaptation. This problem is discussed in some detail in the 1985 report on energy and protein requirements (37) and by Rand et al (112). The report points out that after the first few days on a protein intake close to maintenance "because of day to day variation in urinary N excretion it is difficult to make accurate measurements of the subsequent slope or to prove that it is significantly different from zero." It concludes from the evidence available at that time (1981)—and there does not seem to be any new information since then—that when subjects are fed a fixed low-protein diet over long periods, some do and some do not show a slow drift toward a lower rate of urinary N excretion. Data from a long-term study on men fed 0.64 g protein/kg/day showed that urinary N continued to fall for at least 90 days

(168). The rate of decline after the first two weeks was about 0.01 g N/kg/d, which would be statistically undetectable in short-term studies. Even after 100 days the cumulative loss (about 1 g of N) would be too small to be determined by any existing method of measuring total body nitrogen. To get a general answer to the question of long-term adaptation, it would be necessary to study a large number of individuals for a very long time on a fixed protein intake slightly below that needed for maintenance. This is clearly not a practical proposition with human subjects.

As in the case of energy, convincing evidence about long-term adaptation to habitually low intakes can probably only be obtained by observations in the field. For example, a typical Kaul woman in New Guinea, as described by Norgan et al (100), would weigh 50 kg and have a protein intake of 24 g/d, of which only 3.5 g would be animal protein. If such an intake is habitual, and if this woman is in balance, as she must be to survive, her daily N output would be 77 mg/kg/d $(24 \times 1000)/(6.25 \times 50)$. If her obligatory losses were 60 mg/kg/d, this would give an efficiency of utilization of dietary protein of better than 80%, in spite of its being of low quality. Of course, it may be and indeed has been argued that such people are depleted. The classical experiments of Allison et al (2) showed that dogs depleted of N utilized dietary N much more efficiently than did control dogs. Children in Jamaica recovering from malnutrition utilized almost 100% of milk N when it was fed at a low level (21). However, the New Guinea woman or the Nigerian farmer, unlike Allison's dogs or the Jamaican infants, were in a steady state. Therefore in this context it is difficult to distinguish depletion from adaptation.

Twenty or 30 years ago such subjects, although in balance, would have been described as having depleted protein stores. The transition from a high to a low protein intake involves a net loss of so-called labile protein, which is proportionately greater in the rat than in man. In the rat the total loss amounts to 3–5% of total body N, initially from liver and viscera, later mainly from muscle and skin (160). In man the loss that occurs before a new steady state is reached is only about 1% of total body N. In malnourished infants, whose stores should be depleted, the loss on moving from a high to a low intake was no less than in well-nourished children (20). We do not know from what tissues this protein comes, but it seems likely that the loss is too small to be of any significance. The important point is that the concept of some kind of labile protein as a "store" is no longer valid. The losses or gains that occur when the dietary protein intake is changed are simply a by-product of the metabolic changes involved in shifting from one steady state to another.

## *Utilization of Urea*

In a person on a normal diet about 30% of the urea produced in the liver passes into the colon and is split to ammonia by bacterial urease (150). Part of this ammonia is recycled to urea and part of it is taken up into nonessential amino acids. Picou & Phillips (106) and Jackson et al (70) have examined the question whether on a low protein intake increased utilization of urea N might contribute to nitrogen economy. They found that on a low intake there was an increase in the proportion of urea produced that was utilized for amino acid synthesis, but no increase in the absolute amount taken up. Walser (150) has objected to the word "utilized" in this connection, since the shuttling of N between urea and amino acids essentially constitutes a futile cycle. This view is correct to the extent that the exchange of N between urea and amino acids does nothing to replace the carbon skeletons of the essential amino acids lost by oxidation. The only natural situation in which the recycling of urea could be useful is if the diet contains a relative excess of the essential amino acids, the limiting factor being nonessential N (132). This situation is unlikely to arise in real life in people on low protein intakes. Studies with $^{15}N$-labelled urea, showing that $^{15}N$ may be incorporated in plasma proteins (144), demonstrate uptake into amino acids and transamination of $NH_3$ derived from urea, but they provide no evidence of biosynthesis of the essential carbon skeletons.

It is a question for the future whether it may be possible to alter the colonic microflora to include strains of bacteria that synthesize essential amino acid, and whether they would be absorbed.

## *Energy Intake*

Energy balance has a profound effect on nitrogen balance. Within a certain range of intakes each extra kilocalorie reduces urinary N loss by about 1.5 mg. These original observations of Munro (95) and of Calloway & Spector (17) have since been confirmed many times (37). The N-sparing effect of increased availability of energy is well shown in the obese (41).

This effect of energy intake on N retention or loss would militate in two ways against the capacity to adapt to low protein intakes. The very people whose diet is marginally low in protein are those whose total food intake is most likely to be inadequate. These people will also have small stores of body fat, as is now very well recognized. Thus the full capacity to adapt to a low protein intake can only be achieved if energy intakes are adequate.

## *Protein Turnover*

One of the first questions that arose when interest in protein turnover was renewed in the 1960s concerned the relationship between N excretion and N flux. Is a constant fraction of the amino-N flux irreversibly oxidized to urea? Putting it in a different way: are alterations in N excretion determined by changes in the rates of protein synthesis and breakdown? The alternative hypothesis is that rates of protein turnover and of N excretion vary independently. Our earlier results suggested that the second hypothesis was correct (153). In studies on young children, changes in protein intake produced very little change in protein turnover. On a generous protein intake of 6 g/kg/d,

25% of the amino-N flux was excreted as urea, whereas on an intake of 1.2 g/kg/d the flux remained unchanged and only 4% of it was excreted (107). The body is therefore very efficient, reutilizing for protein synthesis almost, but not quite, all the amino acids entering the free amino acid pool. This leaves little scope for adaptive improvements in economy.

Later work has to some extent modified the view that the rate of protein turnover is independent of the intake. The early studies were done with protein intakes at or above the maintenance level. More recent work (summarized in 156) suggests that at submaintenance intakes rates of turnover are reduced. At the same intake the turnover rate is lower in children with kwashiorkor, who may be regarded as depleted, than in normal children (54). These malnourished children are also unable to increase their turnover rates in response to an infection and they excrete less nitrogen than infected children who are normally nourished (148). This finding recalls the old observation, that undernourished patients have a smaller "catabolic" response to trauma (24). It is difficult to decide whether this represents a protective mechanism to preserve body tissues or a failure to meet a challenge. The severely malnourished child has, at least in the acute stage, a reduced capacity to produce humoral antibodies and impaired cell-mediated immunity (22, 147). The evidence for impairment of these defense mechanisms is much weaker in moderate malnutrition (147), so that the point at which adaptation breaks down is not clearly defined.

Muscle plays an important part in the response of whole-body protein turnover to low protein intakes. Experiments in the rat have shown that there is a fall in both protein synthesis and breakdown, so that balance is achieved at a lower rate of turnover (46). The reduction in synthesis results from a fall in the cellular concentration of ribosomal RNA (RNA/DNA ratio), with little change in the efficiency of synthesis per unit RNA (92). In man it has been shown from measurements on biopsies that the diurnal changes in whole-body protein turnover in response to fasting and feeding (23) are accompanied by parallel changes in the rate of muscle protein synthesis (115). Malnourished children have a reduced rate of methylhistidine excretion (96), which suggests a fall in the rate of myofibrillar protein turnover (166). More detailed reviews of the effects of diet on protein turnover in individual tissues are to be found in (156) and (159).

Plasma albumin provides perhaps the clearest example of adaptive changes in protein turnover. The elegant study of James & Hay (73) in well- and malnourished children showed that when the protein intake was reduced there was an immediate fall in the rate of albumin synthesis, followed after a short lag by a fall in the rate of breakdown and a shift of albumin from the extravascular to the intravascular compartment. The result of these processes was to maintain the intravascular circulating albumin mass. Similarly, Hoffenberg et al. (64) in experiments on adults showed that lowering the dietary protein intake caused a fall of 36% in albumin turnover with a reduction of only 7% in plasma albumin concentration. Therefore, if it were possible to measure it routinely, the rate of albumin turnover would be a much more sensitive index of response to low protein intake than the classical measurement of albumin concentration. It has been claimed that the levels of other plasma proteins, particularly those with short half-lives such as transferrin and thyroxin-binding prealbumin, provide more sensitive "tests" of protein deficiency (for review, see 52, 130), but I know of no information about the effects of low protein intakes on their turnover rates. By contrast, the turnover rates of circulating immunoglobulins are not reduced in malnutrition.

From all this evidence it is well established that when amino acid supplies are limited the rate of protein turnover falls in many tissues and in the body as a whole. Because protein turnover is relatively less reduced in liver and visceral tissues (86) than in muscle, the fall in the body as a whole is modest. It is not possible to discuss here the mechanisms by which these effects are produced: how far they depend on changes in pattern of the many hormones that are known to influence protein synthesis and breakdown; or how far they are mediated by changes in free amino acid concentrations (159). However, in view of the important effects of thyroid hormones on the components of energy expenditure, it should be pointed out that these hormones also play a role in the regulation of protein turnover, at least in muscle. In the rat a linear relation has been found between the plasma concentrations of free T3 and the rate of muscle protein degradation, through control of the activity of lysosomal proteinases (90). The catabolic effects of T3 are reduced by protein depletion (16, 19). T3 also influences the rate of protein synthesis, apparently by regulation of ribosome production (91). It is only when the hormone is present in relatively large amounts that its catabolic effects predominate.

In conclusion, what advantage is it for protein turnover rates to be low? We have two nitrogen cycles, input/output and synthesis/breakdown, connecting through the free amino acid pool (155). If one is out of balance, the other must be also since alterations in the size of the free pool are small in relation to the flux (158). However, in the context of long-term adaptation both must be in overall balance, within which there are short-term fluctuations. There is no obvious direct connection between the two cycles when they are in balance, but there seem to be three indirect ways in which a reduction in the rate of protein turnover could make a positive contribution to adaptation. First, there is a small saving in energy. If the cost of protein turnover accounts for 15% of the BMR, a reduction of 30% in its rate would save some 70 kcal. The other two bonuses both arise from the diurnal rhythm of protein turnover that has already been mentioned. As Millward has suggested (90), if there is less net protein synthesis in response to the ingestion of food, there will be a smaller requirement for essential amino acids, so that survival will be possible on a dietary protein mixture of lower biological value. Secondly, if the increase in protein breakdown that occurs in the post-absorptive state is damped down, there will be a reduced influx of amino acids into the free pool and therefore fewer opportunities for them to be lost by oxidation. This aspect is considered in the next section. Whether or not any costs are attached to the lower rates of protein turnover is completely unknown.

### *The Biochemical Basis of Nitrogen Economy*

The foundation stone of our knowledge on this subject is the work of Schimke (124), who showed that in rats on a low-protein diet there was a reduction in the activity of the urea cycle enzymes, measured in liver homogenates in vitro. He later proved that in the case of arginase there was a fall in the actual amount of the enzyme and not merely a masking of its activity (125). Following this lead, Das & Waterlow (26) showed that after an increase or decrease in protein intake the time-course of changes in the four urea cycle enzymes followed quite closely that of the change in urinary N output. However, the correspondence is not exact. The rate-limiting enzyme in the urea cycle is probably argininosuccinate synthetase (ASS). Saheki and coworkers (121) found that when the protein intake was altered the change in ASS activity lagged behind that of urea formation, which suggests that other factors exert more immediate effects, such as the concentrations of ornithine and of *N*-acetyl glutamate, (145) although doubt has been cast on the role of the latter (84). These in turn depend on the supply of amino acids, particularly of glutamate (139) and of arginine. These metabolic relationships provide for rapid regulation of urea output in response to amino acid input (150). For long-term adaptation, changes in the amounts of the enzymes would at first sight seem to be more significant. Thus Saheki et al (121) found that the amount of the rate-limiting ASS, measured immunologically, was almost an order of magnitude lower in rats on 5% compared with 70% protein (0.69 versus 5.9 units/g).

However, this is not the end of the story. The real adaptive changes must be further up the line, controlling the input of amino-N to the urea cycle. The activity of many enzymes of amino acid metabolism is modified by the level of dietary protein intake. This is a subject that was much more intensively studied 10–20 years ago (e.g. 58, 133, 161) than it is now. The activities of some enzymes that have very short half-lives (151), such as tyrosine aminotransferase and tryptophan pyrrolase in the liver, show rapid and profound changes in response to a single meal (151). The activities of glutamic dehydrogenase and of aminotransferases in the liver change pari passu with those of the urea cycle enzymes (26). It seems still unknown how this coordinated control is achieved of enzymes some of which are cytosolic, others mitochondrial.

If urea production falls, there is a potentially toxic accumulation of ammonia unless it is removed by recycling to amino acids and uptake into protein.

Following this line of thought, we showed both in rats (137) and in children (138) that a reduction in urea cycle activity was accompanied by increased activity of what were then called the amino acid synthetases, now the amino-acyl-tRNA-transferases. Protein synthesis cannot occur unless all the essential amino acids are available in appropriate amounts. Therefore the real limiting factor is the rate of oxidation of the carbon skeletons of the essential amino acids.

A case could be made for the hypothesis that the key amino acids in this respect are the branched-chain amino acids (BCAs). Although the BCAs together contribute about 20% of the amino acid residues of most proteins, their concentrations in the amino acid pool are relatively low and particularly sensitive to the level of amino acid supply. The first step in their catabolism is transamination, mainly in muscle, followed by irreversible decarboxylation of the keto acids by the BCA dehydrogenase complex. In experiments some years ago, when it was still thought that the BCAs were oxidized exclusively in muscle, some evidence was obtained of a decrease in their rate of oxidation in rats on a low-protein diet (131), which suggested that enzymes in muscle could be induced or repressed, like those in liver.

It is now recognized that the BCA dehydrogenase complex is widely distributed in tissues (59), and that its activity in liver is probably more important than in muscle. There are several ways by which that activity is controlled. As Krebs (79) pointed out, the $K_m$ of the enzyme is close to the concentration of the substrate in the free pool, so that the activity is concentration dependent. The enzyme complex exists in an inactive phosphorylated form, which is activated by dephosphorylation (61). Finally, there is an activator protein that reactivates the enzyme without dephosphorylation (114). Both mechanisms contribute to a reduction in dehydrogenase activity when dietary protein is restricted. According to Randle (114), on low-protein diets the activity of the activator protein falls by 90%.

Most of the work in this area of metabolism relates to short-term responses. It remains a challenge to define the control mechanisms that are most important for long-term adaptation. It is clear that the body has a highly efficient capacity for responding rapidly to large variations in amino acid supply—to economize when they are in short supply and to dispose of them when in excess. This flexibility is necessary since there is no store of protein, like that of fat, to buffer the system during periods of shortage or glut of food. There is no evident disadvantage in operating at the lowest possible level of amino acid intake and oxidation, because the maintenance of protein turnover, even at a somewhat reduced rate, ensures that amino acids are always available for exchange between tissues, according to where they are most needed. Nevertheless, there are limits to the adaptive capacity; although Walser (150) states that "the stimulus to ureagenesis virtually ceases at a low value of circulating amino acid concentration," in our experience (152) even depleted children on very low protein intakes continue to excrete small amounts of urea.

## *Conclusion*

The body's mechanisms for reducing nitrogen loss on low intakes of protein are reasonably well defined. What is not yet clear is the extent to which long-term adaptation may lower the limit. This subject is exceedingly difficult to study experimentally in man without imposing totally artificial conditions. In epidemiological studies we come up against the problem that in most situations it is energy rather than protein that is likely to be limiting. However, more work might be rewarding on subjects whose dietary staple is starchy roots with a very low and unbalanced protein content. For example, the persistently negative nitrogen balances that yet appear to be compatible with health, described by Oomen (101) in sweet-potato eaters in New Guinea, have never been satisfactorily explained.

## *Literature Cited*


1. Agarwal, D. K., Agarwal, K. N., Shankar, R., Bhatia, B. D., Mishra, K. P., et al. 1984. Determination of protein requirements on vegetarian diet in healthy female volunteers. *Ind. J. Med. Res.* 79:60–67
2. Allison, J. B., Anderson, J. A., White, J. I. 1949. Evaluation of the nutritional value of proteins with normal and protein-deficient dogs. *Trans. Am. Assoc. Cereal Chem.* 7:24–33
3. Apfelbaum, M., Bostsarron, J., Brigant, L. 1969. La diminution de la consommation "basale" d'oxygene sous l'effet d'une restriction calorique chez des sujets en bilan d'azote equilibre. *Rev. Franc. Etud. Clin. Biol.* 14:361–72
4. Ashworth, A. 1968. An investigation of very low calorie intakes reported in Jamaica. *Br. J. Nutr.* 22:341–55
5. Ashworth, A. 1969. Metabolic rates during recovery from protein-calorie malnutrition: the need for a new concept of specific dynamic action. *Nature* 223: 407–9
6. Bassey, E. J., Fentem, P. H. 1981. In *The Principles and Practice of Human Physiology*, ed. O. G. Edholm, J. S. Weiner, pp. 19–130. London: Academic
7. Beaton, G. H., Milner, J., Corey, P., McGuire, V., Cousins, M., et al. 1979. Sources of variance in 24-hour dietary recall data: implications for nutrition study design and interpretation. *Am. J. Clin. Nutr.* 32:2546–59

7a. Bhatia, B. D., Agarwal, D. K., Agarwal, K. N. 1983. Determination of protein requirements in healthy male volunteers on vegetarian diet. *Ind. J. Med. Res.* 77:658–67

8. Bier, D. M., Motil, K. J., Matthews, D. E., Burke, J. F., Young, V. R. 1981. Energy intake and whole body protein dynamics in man. In *Nutrition and Child Health: Perspectives for the 1980s*, pp. 161–80. New York: Liss
9. Bodwell, C. E., Schuster, E. M., Kyle, E., Brooks, B., Womack, M., et al. 1979. Obligatory urinary and fecal nitrogen losses in young women, older men and young men and the factorial estimation of adult human protein requirements. *Am. J. Clin. Nutr.* 32:2450–59
10. Booyens, J., McCance, R. A. 1957. Individual variations in expenditure of energy. *Lancet* 1:225–29
11. Bray, G. A., ed. 1979. Obesity in America. *Proc. 2nd Fogarty Int. Cent. Conf. Obesity*. NIH Publ. 79. Washington, DC: US Dept. Health, Education, and Welfare
12. Brooke, C. G. D., Huntley, R. M. C., Slack, J. 1975. Influence of heredity and environment in determination of skinfold thickness in children. *Br. Med. J.* 2:719–21
13. Brooke, O. G., Ashworth, A. 1972. The influence of malnutrition on the postprandial metabolic rate and respiratory quotient. *Br. J. Nutr.* 27:407–15
14. Brooke, O. G., Cocks, T. 1974. Resting metabolic rate in malnourished babies in

relation to total body potassium. *Acta Paediatr. Scand.* 63:817–25

15. Bunc, V., Sprynarova, S., Pařizková, J., Leso, J. 1984. Effects of adaptation on the mechanical efficiency and energy cost of physical work. *Hum. Nutr. Clin. Nutr.* 38C:317–19
16. Burini, R., Santidrian, S., Moreyra, M., Brown, P., Munro, H. N., et al. 1981. Interaction of thyroid status and diet on muscle protein breakdown in the rat, as measured by $N^T$-methylhistidine excretion. *Metabolism* 30:679–87
17. Calloway, D. M., Spector, H. 1954. Nitrogen balance as related to calorie and protein intake in active young men. *Am. J. Clin. Nutr.* 2:405–12
18. Cameron, N. 1979. The growth of London schoolchildren 1904–1966: An analysis of secular trend and intracounty variation. *Ann. Hum. Biol.* 6:505–25
19. Carter, W. J., Benjamin, W. S., Faas, F. H. 1984. Effect of a protein-free diet on muscle protein turnover and nitrogen conservation in enthyroid and hyperthyroid rats. *Biochem. J.* 217:471–76
20. Chan, H. 1968. Adaptation of urinary nitrogen excretion in infants to changes in protein intake. *Br. J. Nutr.* 22:315–23
21. Chan, H., Waterlow, J. C. 1966. The protein requirement of infants at the age of about 1 year. *Br. J. Nutr.* 20:775–82
22. Chandra, R. K. 1983. Nutrition, immunity and infection: present knowledge and future directions. *Lancet* 1:688–91
23. Clugston, G. A., Garlick, P. J. 1982. The response of protein and energy metabolism to food intake in lean and obese man. *Hum. Nutr. Clin. Nutr.* 36C:57–70
24. Cuthbertson, D. P. 1954. Interrelationship of metabolic changes consequent to injury. *Br. Med. Bull.* 10:33–37
25. Dallosso, H. M., Murgatroyd, P. R., James, W. P. T. 1982. Feeding frequency and energy balance in adult males. *Hum. Nutr. Clin. Nutr.* 36C:25–39
26. Das, T. K., Waterlow, J. C. 1974. The rate of adaptation of urea cycle enzymes, aminotransferases and glutamic dehydrogenase to changes in dietary protein intake. *Br. J. Nutr.* 32:353–73
27. De Guzman, P. E. 1983. Energy allowances for the Philippine population. See Ref. 96, pp. 23–38
28. Desai, I. D., Waddell, C., Dutra, S., Dutra de Oliverra, S., Duarte, E., et al. 1984. Marginal malnutrition and reduced physical work capacity of migrant adolescent boys in Southern Brazil. *Am. J. Clin. Nutr.* 40:135–45
29. Dieng, K., Lemonnier, D., Bleiberg, F., Brun, T. 1980. Differences in the rate of energy expenditure of resting activities between European and African men. *Nutr. Rep. Int.* 21:183–88
30. Durnin, J. V. G. A. 1984. Is nutritional status endangered by virtually no extra energy intake during pregnancy? *Nestlé Found. Ann. Rep.*, pp. 31–42. Lausanne: Nestlé
31. Durnin, J. V. G. A., Edholm, O. G., Miller, D. S., Waterlow, J. C. 1973. How much food does man require? *Nature* 242:418
32. Edholm, O. G., Adam, J. M., Healy, M. J. R., Wolff, H. S., Goldsmith, R., et al. 1970. Food intake and energy expenditure of army recruits. *Br. J. Nutr.* 24:1091–1107
33. Edmundson, W. 1977. Individual variation in work output per unit energy intake in East Java. *Ecol. Food Nutr.* 6:147–51
34. Edmundson, W. 1979. Individual variations in basal metabolic rate and mechanical work efficiency in East Java. *Ecol. Food Nutr.* 8:189–95
35. Eveleth, P. B., Tanner, J. M. 1976. *Worldwide Variation in Human Growth.* Cambridge: Cambridge Univ. Press
36. FAO/WHO. 1973. *Energy and Protein Requirements.* Rep. Joint FAO/WHO Ad Hoc Expert Committee. FAO Nutr. Meet. Rep. Ser. 52. Rome: FAO
37. FAO/WHO/UNU. 1985. *Energy and Protein Requirements.* Rep. Joint FAO/WHO/UNU Meet. Tech. Rep. Ser. 000. Geneva: WHO
38. Fern, E. B., Garlick, P. J., Sheppard, H., Fern, M. 1984. The precision of measuring the rate of whole-body nitrogen flux and protein synthesis in man with a single dose of $^{15}$N glycine. *Hum. Nutr. Clin. Nutr.* 38C:63–73
39. Ferro-Luzzi, A., D'Amicis, A., Ferrini, A. M., Maiale, G. 1979. Nutrition, environment and physical performance of preschool children in Italy. *Bibl. Nutr. Dieta* 27:85–106
40. Folin, O. 1905. Laws governing the chemical composition of urine. *Am. J. Physiol.* 13:66–115
41. Forbes, G. B., Drenick, E. J. 1979. Loss of body nitrogen on fasting. *Am. J. Clin. Nutr.* 32:1570–74
42. Forbes, G. B., Kreipe, R. E., Lipinski, B. A., Hodgman, C. H. 1984. Body composition and changes during recovery from anorexia nervosa: comparison of two dietary regimes. *Am. J. Clin. Nutr.* 40:1137–45
43. Gaesser, G. E., Brooks, G. A. 1975. Muscular efficiency during steady-state exercise: effects of speed and work rate. *J. Appl. Physiol.* 38:1132–39
44. Garby, L., Lammert, O. 1984. Within-

subjects between-days-and-weeks variation in energy expenditure at rest. *Hum. Nutr. Clin. Nutr.* 38C:395–97
45. Garby, L., Lammert, O., Nielsen, E. 1986. 24-Hour energy expenditure on low physical activity programmes. *Hum. Nutr. Clin. Nutr.* 40C: In press
46. Garlick, P. J., Millward, D. J., James, W. P. T., Waterlow, J. C. 1975. The effect of protein deprivation and starvation on the rate of protein synthesis in tissues of the rat. *Biochim. Biophys. Acta* 414:71–84
47. Garrow, J. S. 1981. Thermogenesis and obesity in man. In *Recent Advances in Obesity Research,* ed. P. Bjorntorp, M. Cairella, A. N. Howard, 3:208–12. London: Libbey
48. Garrow, J. S., Fletcher, K., Halliday, D. 1965. Body composition in severe infantile malnutrition. *J. Clin. Invest.* 44:417–25
49. Garrow, J. S., Hawes, S. F. 1972. The role of amino acid oxidation in causing "specific dynamic action" in man. *Br. J. Nutr.* 27:211–19
50. Garrow, J. S., Webster, J. D. 1984. Thermogenesis to small stimuli. In *Human Energy Metabolism,* ed. A. J. M. Van Ess, pp. 215–24. Rep. Eur. Community Workshop, Wageningen, Netherlands
51. Geissler, C. A., Aldouri, M. S. H. 1985. Racial differences in the energy costs of standardized activities. *Ann. Nutr. Metab.* 29:40–47
52. Golden, M. H. N. 1982. Transport protein as indices of protein status. *Am. J. Clin. Nutr.* 35:1159–65
53. Golden, M. H. N. 1985. The consequences of protein deficiency in man and its relationship to the features of kwashiorkor. See Ref. 69, pp. 169–88
54. Golden, M. H. N., Waterlow, J. C., Picou, D. 1977. Protein turnover, synthesis and breakdown before and after recovery from protein-energy malnutrition. *Clin. Sci. Mol. Med.* 53:473–77
55. Goldman, R. F., Iampetro, P. F. 1962. Energy cost of load carriage. *J. Appl. Physiol.* 17:675–76
56. Gopalan, C. 1983. "Small is healthy"? For the poor, not for the rich! *Bull. Nutr. Found. India,* Oct.
57. Griffiths, M., Payne, P. R. 1976. Energy expenditure in small children of obese and non-obese parents. *Nature* 260:698–700
58. Harper, A. E. 1965. Effect of variations in protein intake on enzymes of amino acid metabolism. *Can. J. Biochem.* 43: 1589–1603
59. Harper, A. E., Benjamin, E. 1984. Relationship between intake and rate of oxidation of leucine and α-ketoisocaproate in vivo in the rat. *J. Nutr.* 114:431–40
60. Harries, J. M., Hobson, E. A., Hollingsworth, D. F. 1962. Individual variations in energy expenditure and intake. *Proc. Nutr. Soc.* 21:157–68
61. Harris, R. A., Paxton, R., Jenkins, P. 1985. Nutritional control of branched-chain α-ketoacid dehydrogenase in rat hepatocytes. *Fed. Proc.* 44:2463–68
62. Henry, C. J. K., Rivers, J. W. P., Payne, P. R. 1986. Hypothesis: does the pattern of tissue mobilization dictate protein requirements? *Hum. Nutr. Clin. Nutr.* 40C:87–92
63. Heusner, A. A. 1985. Body size and energy metabolism. *Ann. Rev. Nutr.* 5:267–93
64. Hoffenberg, R., Black, E., Brock, J. F. 1966. Albumin and γ-globulin tracer studies in protein depletion states. *J. Clin. Invest.* 45:143–52
65. Hori, S., Tsujita, J., Mayuzumi, M., Tanaka, T. 1980. Comparative studies on physical characteristics and resting metabolism between young male highlanders of Papua–New Guinea and young male Japanese. *Int. J. Biometerol.* 24: 253–61
66. Huang, P. C., Chong, H. E., Rand, W. M. 1972. Obligatory urinary and fecal nitrogen losses in young Chinese men. *J. Nutr.* 102:1605–14
67. Imms, F. J. 1981. In *The Principles and Practice of Human Physiology,* ed. O. G. Edholm, J. S. Weiner, p. 384. London: Academic
68. Ito, A., Komi, P. V., Sjödin, B., Bosco, C., Karlsson, J. 1983. Mechanical efficiency of positive work in running at different speeds. *Med. Sci. Sports Exercise* 15:299–308
69. Jackson, A. A. 1985. Nutritional adaptation in disease and recovery. In *Nutritional Adaptation in Man,* ed. K. Blaxter, J. C. Waterlow, pp. 111–26. London: Libbey
70. Jackson, A. A., Picou, D., Landman, J. 1984. The non-invasive measurement of urea kinetics in normal man by a constant infusion of $^{15}N^{15}N$-urea. *Hum. Nutr. Clin. Nutr.* 38C:339–54
71. James, W. P. T. 1981. Adaptation to different energy intakes: the mechanism, extent and social consequences. *Work. Pap. FAO/WHO/UNU Expert Consultation on Energy and Protein Requirements.* Rome: FAO
72. James, W. P. T. 1983. Energy requirements and obesity. *Lancet* 2:386–89
73. James, W. P. T., Hay, A. M. 1968. Albumin metabolism: effect of the nutri-

tional state and the dietary protein intake. *J. Clin. Invest.* 47:1958–72
74. James, W. P. T., Shetty, P. S. 1982. Metabolic adaptation and energy requirements in developing countries. *Hum. Nutr. Clin. Nutr.* 36C:331–36
75. James, W. P. T., Trayhurn, P. 1981. Thermogenesis and obesity. *Br. Med. Bull.* 37:43–48
76. Keller, W., Fillmore, C. M. 1983. Prevalence of protein-energy malnutrition. *World Health Stat. Q.* 36:129–67
77. Keys, A., Brožek, J., Henschel, A., Mickelson, O., Taylor, H. L. 1950. *The Biology of Human Starvation.* Minneapolis: Univ. Minn. Press
78. Komi, P. V., Ito, A., Sjödin, B., Wallenstein, R., Karlsson, J. 1981. Muscle metabolism, lactate breaking point and biomechanical features of endurance running. *Int. J. Sports Med.* 2:148–153
79. Krebs, H. A. 1972. Some aspects of the regulation of fuel supply in omnivorous animals. *Adv. Enzyme Regul.* 10:397–420
80. Kretchmer, N. 1981. Food: a selective agent in evolution. In *Food, Nutrition and Evolution,* ed. D. N. Walcher, N. Kretchmer, pp. 37–48. New York: Masson
81. Lawrence, M., Singh, J., Lawrence, F., Whitehead, R. G. 1984. Energy requirements of pregnancy and lactation: the energy cost of common daily activities in the Gambia. *Nestlé Found. Ann. Rep.*, pp. 43–52. Lausanne: Nestlé
82. Deleted in proof
83. Lopes, J., Russell, D. M., Whitwell, J., Jeejeebhoy, K. N. 1982. Skeletal muscle function in malnutrition. *Am. J. Clin. Nutr.* 36:602–10
84. Lund, P., Wiggins, D. 1984. Is *N*-acetylglutamate a short-term regulator of urea synthesis? *Biochem. J.* 218:991–94
85. McDonald, I. 1961. In *FAO/WHO/UNU Rep. Expert Consultation on Energy and Protein Requirements,* Annex 2. WHO Tech. Rep. Ser. 724 Geneva: WHO
86. McNurlan, M. A., Pain, V. M., Garlick, P. J. 1980. Conditions that alter rates of tissue protein synthesis in vivo. *Biochem. Soc. Trans.* 8:283–85
87. Mahadeva, K., Passmore, R., Woolf, B. 1953. Individual variations in the metabolic cost of standardized exercises: the effects of food, age, sex and race. *J. Physiol.* 121:225–37
88. Margen, S. 1984. Energy-protein malnutrition: the web of causes and consequences. In *Malnutrition and Behavior: Critical Assessment of Key Issues,* ed. J. Brožek, B. Schürch, pp. 20–31. Lausanne: Nestlé Found.
89. Martorell, R. 1985. Child growth retardation: a discussion of its causes and of its relationship to health. See Ref. 69, pp. 13–29
90. Millward, D. J. 1985. Human protein requirements: the physiological significance of changes in the rate of whole body protein turnover. In *Substrate and Energy Metabolism in Man,* ed. J. S. Garrow, D. Halliday, pp. 135–44. London: Libbey
91. Millward, D. J., Bates, P. C., Coyer, P., Cox, M., Dalal, S., et al. 1986. The effect of dietary energy and protein on growth as studied in animal models. In *Energy and Protein Needs during Infancy,* ed. S. J. Fomon, W. Heird. San Diego: Academic. In press
92. Millward, D. J., Brown, J. G., Odedra, B. 1981. Protein turnover in individual tissues, with special emphasis on muscle. In *Nitrogen Metabolism in Man,* ed. J. C. Waterlow, J. M. L. Stephen, pp. 475–94. London: Appl. Sci.
93. Montgomery, R. D. 1962. Changes in the basal metabolic rate of the malnourished infant and their relation to body composition. *J. Clin. Invest.* 41: 1653–63
94. Morgan, J. B., York, D. A., Wasilewska, A., Portman, J. 1982. A study of the thermic responses to a meal and to a sympathomimetic drug (ephedrine) in relation to energy balance in man. *Br. J. Nutr.* 47:21–32
95. Munro, H. N. 1951. Carbohydrate and fat as factors in protein utilization. *Physiol. Rev.* 31:449–88
96. Narasinga Rao, B. S. 1985. Metabolic adaptation to chronic malnutrition. See Ref. 90, pp. 145–54
97. Nicol, B. M., Phillips, P. G. 1976. Endogenous nitrogen excretion and utilization of dietary protein. *Br. J. Nutr.* 35:181–93
98. Nicol, B. M., Phillips, P. G. 1976. The utilization of dietary protein by Nigerian men. *Br. J. Nutr.* 36:337–51
99. Norgan, N. G. 1983. Adaptation of energy metabolism to level of energy intake. See Ref. 102, pp. 56–64
100. Norgan, N. G., Ferro-Luzzi, A., Durnin, J. V. G. A. 1974. The energy and nutrient intake and the energy expenditure of 204 New Guinean adults. *Philos. Trans. R. Soc. London Ser. B* 268:309–48
101. Oomen, H. A. P. C. 1970. Interrelationship of the human intestinal flora and protein utilization. *Proc. Nutr. Soc.* 29:197–206
102. Pařízková, J. 1983. *Energy Expenditure under Field Conditions,* p. 130. Prague: Charles Univ.

103. Passmore, R., Durnin, J. V. G. A. 1955. Human energy expenditure. *Physiol. Rev.* 35:801–40
104. Payne, P. R., Dugdale, A. E. 1977. A model for the prediction of energy balance and body weight. *Ann. Hum. Biol.* 4:425–35
105. Phanselkar, S. V., Patwardhan, V. N. 1956. Utilization of animal and vegetable proteins: nitrogen balances at marginal protein intakes and the determination of minimum protein requirements for maintenance in young Indian men. *Ind. J. Med. Res.* 44:1–10
106. Picou, D., Phillips, M. 1972. Urea metabolism in malnourished and recovered children receiving a high or low protein diet. *Am. J. Clin. Nutr.* 25:1261–66
107. Picou, D., Taylor-Roberts, T. 1969. The measurement of total protein synthesis and catabolism and nitrogen turnover in infants in different nutritional states and receiving different amounts of dietary protein. *Clin. Sci.* 36:283–96
108. Prentice, A. M. 1979. Variations in maternal dietary intake, birthweight and breast milk output in the Gambia. In *Maternal Nutrition during Pregnancy and Lactation,* ed. H. Aebi, R. G. Whitehead, pp. 167–83. Bern: Huber
109. Prentice, A. M., Coward, W. A., Davies, H. L., Murgatroyd, P. R., Black, A. E., et al. 1985. Unexpectedly low levels of energy expenditure in healthy women. *Lancet* 1:1419–22
110. Pudelski, J. 1968. Evaluation of the magnitude of work in the step test. *Ann. Med. Sect. Pol. Acad. Sci.* 13:109–33
111. Rand, W. R., Scrimshaw, N. S., Young, V. R. 1979. An analysis of temporal patterns in urinary nitrogen excretion of young adults receiving constant diets at two nitrogen intakes for 8–11 weeks. *Am. J. Clin. Nutr.* 32:1408–14
112. Rand, W. R., Scrimshaw, N. S., Young, V. R. 1981. Conventional (long-term) nitrogen balance studies for protein quality evaluation in adults: rationale and limitations. In *Protein Quality in Humans: Assessment and in vitro Estimations,* ed. C. E. Bodwell, J. S. Adkins, D. T. Hopkins, pp. 61–94. Westport, Conn: AVI
113. Rand, W. R., Uauy, R., Scrimshaw, N. S., eds. 1984. *Protein-Energy-Requirement Studies in Developing Countries: Results of International Research.* Tokyo: United Nations Univ.
114. Randle, P. J. 1984. Regulatory devices in metabolism and medicine. *J. R. Coll. Physicians London* 18:211–18
115. Rennie, M. J., Edwards, R. H. T., Halliday, D., Matthews, D. E., Wolman, S. L., et al. 1982. Muscle protein synthesis measured by stable isotope techniques in man: the effects of feeding and fasting. *Clin. Sci.* 63:519–23
116. Rhoads, G. G., Kagan, A. 1983. The relation of coronary disease, stroke and mortality to weight in youth and in middle age. *Lancet* 1:492–95
117. Roberts, D. F. 1981. Genetics of growth. *Br. Med. Bull.* 37:239–46
118. Rose, G. A., Williams, R. T. 1961. Metabolic studies on large and small eaters. *Br. J. Nutr.* 15:1–9
119. Rothwell, N. J., Stock, M. J. 1981. Regulation of energy balance. *Ann. Rev. Nutr.* 1:235–56
120. Russell, D. M., Prendergast, P. J., Darby, P. L., Garfinkel, P. E., Whitwell, J., et al. 1983. A comparison between muscle function and body composition in anorexia nervosa: the effect of refeeding. *Am. J. Clin. Nutr.* 38:229–37
121. Saheki, T., Tsuda, M., Takada, S., Kusumi, K., Katsunuma, T. 1980. Role of argininosuccinate synthetase in the regulation of urea synthesis in the rat and argininosuccinate synthetase–associated metabolic disorder in man. *Adv. Enzyme Regul.* 18:221–38
122. Satyanarayana, K., Naidu, A. N., Narasinga Rao, B. S. 1979. Nutritional deprivation in childhood and the body size, activity and physical work capacity of young boys. *Am. J. Clin. Nutr.* 32:1769–75
123. Satyanarayana, K., Naidu, A. N., Narasinga Rao, B. S. 1980. Adolescent growth spurt among rural Indian boys in relation to their nutritional status in early childhood. *Ann. Hum. Biol.* 7: 359–65
124. Schimke, R. T. 1962. Adaptive characteristics of urea cycle enzymes in the rat. *J. Biol. Chem.* 237:459–68
125. Schimke, R. T. 1964. The importance of both synthesis and degradation in the control of arginase levels in rat liver. *J. Biol. Chem.* 239:3808–17
126. Schofield, W. N., Schofield, C., James, W. P. T. 1985. Basal metabolic rate—review and prediction, together with an annotated bibliography of source material. *Hum. Nutr. Clin. Nutr.* 39C(Suppl. 1):5–41
127. Seckler, D. 1982. "Small but healthy": a basic hypothesis in the theory, measurement and policy of malnutrition. In *Newer Concepts in Nutrition and Their Implications for Policy,* ed. P. V. Sukhatme, pp. 127–37. Pune, India: Maharashtra Assoc. Cultivation Sci.
128. Shetty, P. S. 1984. Adaptive changes in

basal metabolic rate and lean body mass in chronic undernutrition. *Hum. Nutr. Clin. Nutr.* 38C:443–52
129. Shetty, P. S., Jung, R. T., James, W. P. T., Barrand, M. A., Callingham, B. A. 1981. Postprandial thermogenesis in obesity. *Clin. Sci.* 60:519–25
130. Shetty, P. S., Watrasiewicz, K. E., Jung, R. T., James, W. P. T. 1979. Rapid turnover transport proteins: an index of sub-clinical protein-energy malnutrition. *Lancet* 2:230–32
131. Sketcher, R. D., Fern, E. B., James, W. P. T. 1974. The adaptation in muscle oxidation of leucine to dietary protein and energy intake. *Br. J. Nutr.* 31:333–42
132. Snyderman, S. E., Holt, L. E. Jr., Dancis, J., Roitman, E., Boyer, A., et al. 1962. "Unessential" nitrogen: a limiting factor for human growth. *J. Nutr.* 78:57–72
133. Soberón, G. 1971. The physiological significance of tissue enzyme activities as affected by diet. In *Metabolic Adaptation and Nutrition,* pp. 45–72. Pan Am. Health Organ. Sci. Publ. No. 222. Washington, DC: PAHO
134. Spurr, G. B. 1984. Physical activity, nutritional status and physical work capacity in relation to agricultural productivity. In *Energy Intake and Activity,* ed. E. Pollitt, P. Amante, pp. 207–61. New York: Liss
135. Spurr, G. B., Barac-Nieto, M., Reina, J. C., Ramirez, R. 1984. Marginal malnutrition in school-aged Colombian boys: efficiency of treadmill walking in sub-maximal exercise. *Am. J. Clin. Nutr.* 39:452–59
136. Spurr, G. B., Reina, J. C., Dahners, H. W., Barac-Nieto, M. 1983. Marginal malnutrition in school-aged Colombian boys: functional consequences in maximum exercise. *Am. J. Clin. Nutr.* 37: 34–37
137. Stephen, J. M. L. 1968. Adaptive enzyme changes in liver and muscle of rats during protein depletion and refeeding. *Br. J. Nutr.* 22:153–63
138. Stephen, J. M. L., Waterlow, J. C. 1968. Effect of malnutrition on activity of two enzymes concerned with amino acid metabolism in human liver. *Lancet* 1:118–19
139. Stewart, P. M., Walser, M. 1980. Short-term regulation of ureagenesis. *J. Biol. Chem.* 255:5270–80
140. Stini, W. A. 1981. Body composition and nutrient reserve in evolutionary perspective. *World Rev. Nutr. Diet.* 37:55–83
141. Stordy, B. J., Marks, V., Kalucy, R. S., Crisp, A. H. 1977. Weight gain, thermic effect of glucose and resting metabolic rate during recovery from anorexia nervosa. *Am. J. Clin. Nutr.* 30:138–46
142. Sukhatme, P. V., Margen, S. 1978. Models for protein deficiency. *Am. J. Clin. Nutr.* 31:1237–56
143. Sukhatme, P. V., Margen, S. 1982. Autoregulatory homeostatic nature of energy balance. *Am. J. Clin. Nutr.* 35:355–65
144. Tanaka, N., Kubo, K., Shiraki, K., Koishi, H., Yoshimura, H. 1980. A pilot study on protein metabolism in the Papua New Guinea highlanders. *J. Nutr. Sci. Vitaminol.* 26:247–59
145. Tatibana, M., Sligesada, K. 1976. Regulation of urea biosynthesis by the acetylglutamate-arginine system. In *The Urea Cycle,* ed. S. Grisolia, R. Baguena, F. Mayor, p. 301. New York: Wiley
146. Thompson, D'A. W. 1952. *On Growth and Form,* p. 50. Cambridge: Cambridge Univ. Press. 2nd ed.
147. Tomkins, A. M. 1986. Protein energy malnutrition and risk of infection. *Proc. Nutr. Soc.* 45:In press
148. Tomkins, A. M., Garlick, P. J., Schofield, W. N., Waterlow, J. C. 1983. The combined effects of infection and malnutrition on protein metabolism in children. *Clin. Sci.* 65:313–24
149. Velasquez, A., Bourges, H., eds. 1984. *Genetic Factors in Nutrition.* New York: Academic
150. Walser, M. 1981. Urea metabolism. See Ref. 92, pp. 229–46
151. Watanabe, M., Potter, V. R., Pitot, H. C. 1968. Systematic oscillations in tyrosine transaminase and other metabolic functions in liver of normal and adrenalectomized rats on controlled feeding schedules. *J. Nutr.* 95:207–77
152. Waterlow, J. C. 1963. The partition of nitrogen in the urine of malnourished Jamaican infants. *Am. J. Clin. Nutr.* 12:235–40
153. Waterlow, J. C. 1968. Observations on the mechanism of adaptation to low protein intakes. *Lancet* 2:1091–97
154. Waterlow, J. C. 1971. The concept of "normal" in nutrition. See Ref. 133, pp. 76–80
155. Waterlow, J. C. 1978. Observations on the assessment of protein-energy malnutrition, with special reference to stunting. *Courrier* 28:455–60
156. Waterlow, J. C. 1984. Protein turnover with special reference to man. *Q. J. Exp. Physiol.* 69:405–38
157. Waterlow, J. C., Cravioto, J., Stephen, J. M. L. 1960. Protein malnutrition in man. *Adv. Prot. Chem.* 15:131–238
158. Waterlow, J. C., Fern, E. B. 1981. Free

amino acid pools and their regulation. See Ref. 92, pp. 1–16
159. Waterlow, J. C., Garlick, P. J., Millward, D. J. 1978. *Protein Turnover in Mammalian Tissues and in the Whole Body,* Chap. 7. Amsterdam: North Holland
160. Waterlow, J. C., Stephen, J. M. L. 1966. Adaptation of the rat to a low protein diet: the effect of a reduced protein intake on the pattern of incorporation of L($^{14}$C)-lysine. *Br. J. Nutr.* 20:461–84
161. Waterlow, J. C., Stephen, J. M. L. 1969. Enzymes and the assessment of protein nutrition. *Proc. Nutr. Soc.* 28:234–42
161a. Wendt, I. R., Gibbs, C. L. 1973. Energy production of rat extensor digitorum longus muscle. *Am. J. Physiol.* 224: 1081–86
162. Whipp, B. J., Wasserman, K. 1969. Efficiency of muscular work. *J. Appl. Physiol.* 26:644–48
163. Widdowson, E. M. 1962. Nutritional individuality. *Proc. Nutr. Soc.* 21:121–28
164. Wiles, C. M., Young, A., Jones, D. A., Edwards, R. H. T. 1979. Muscle relaxation rate, fibre-type composition and energy turnover in hyper- and hypo-thyroid patients. *Clin. Sci.* 57:375–84
165. Woo, W., Daniels-Kush, R., Horton, E. S. 1985. Regulation of energy balance. *Ann. Rev. Nutr.* 5:411–33
166. Young, V. R., Munro, H. N. 1978. *N*-methylhistidine (3-methylhistidine) and muscle protein turnover: an overview. *Fed. Proc.* 37:2291–2300
167. Young, V. R., Scrimshaw, N. S. 1979. Genetic and biological variability in human nutrient requirements. *Am. J. Clin. Nutr.* 32:486–500
168. Young, V. R., Taylor, Y. S. M., Rand, W. M., Scrimshaw, N. S. 1973. Protein requirements of man—efficiency of egg protein utilization at maintenance and submaintenance levels in young men. *J. Nutr.* 103:1164–74

*Ann. Rev. Nutr. 1986. 6:527–62*


# VITAMIN D RECEPTORS: NATURE AND FUNCTION

*Mark R. Haussler*

Department of Biochemistry, University of Arizona, College of Medicine, Tucson, Arizona 85724

---

## CONTENTS

PERSPECTIVES AND SUMMARY ..... 527
BACKGROUND AND SIGNIFICANCE ..... 529
*Vitamin D Metabolism and Biologic Functions* ..... 529
*Receptor Discovery and Evidence that it Mediates Vitamin D Action* ..... 530
*Occurrence and Subcellular Distribution of the Receptor* ..... 533
BIOCHEMICAL PROPERTIES AND STRUCTURE ..... 536
*Avian Receptors* ..... 536
*Mammalian Receptors* ..... 538
*Evolution of the Receptor* ..... 539
PHYSIOLOGICAL AND CLINICAL APPLICATIONS ..... 540
*Radioreceptor Assay of 1,25-Dihydroxyvitamin D* ..... 540
*Hereditary Vitamin D–Resistant Syndromes* ..... 541
NEW INSIGHTS ..... 542
*Monoclonal Antibodies* ..... 542
*Quantitative and Qualitative Modification of the Receptor* ..... 544
BIOLOGIC ROLES AS A MEDIATOR OF VITAMIN D FUNCTION ..... 546
*Calcium and Mineral Homeostasis* ..... 546
*Regulation of Vitamin D Metabolism* ..... 547
*Control of the Immune System, Bone Remodeling, and Mineralization* ..... 548
*Cell Proliferation, Differentiation, and Anticancer Actions* ..... 550
INTEGRATED MODEL FOR THE ACTION OF THE VITAMIN D RECEPTOR ..... 551
CONCLUSION ..... 552

## PERSPECTIVES AND SUMMARY

The discovery of receptors for vitamins, hormones, neurotransmitters, and other biological modifiers has contributed greatly to our understanding of the molecular aspects of nutrition, physiology, and medicine. Notable examples



0199-9885/86/0715-0527$02.00

are the receptors for LDL-cholesterol, estrogen, insulin, acetylcholine, and the opiates. In many cases, the characterization of receptors has yielded information about the nature and quantitation of the endogenous ligand, its biochemical mechanism of action, and the pathophysiology of its related disease states. Such is the case for the role of vitamin D in controlling calcium and bone metabolism. The vitamin D receptor was first revealed in 1969 as a chromosomal protein in intestinal mucosa nuclei that specifically bound the most active metabolite of the parent vitamin (80). This metabolite was later identified (90) as 1,25-dihydroxyvitamin $D_3$ [1,25$(OH)_2D_3$], the hormonal ligand that occupies the vitamin D receptor in vivo. The vitamin D story parallels other scenarios of the interface between nutrition and endocrine systems. For example, iodine is a crucial nutritional factor in thyroid hormone biosynthesis, and tetraiodothyronine is metabolized to its more active metabolite, triiodothyronine, which localizes in target cell nuclei via a receptor similar to that for 1,25$(OH)_2D_3$ (20). The receptor for 1,25$(OH)_2D_3$ has been employed in radioreceptor assays for circulating 1,25$(OH)_2D_3$ in animals and humans (14, 50), which gave new insight into both the physiology and pathology of the vitamin D–endocrine system (78). Recently, genetic defects have been discovered in the 1,25$(OH)_2D_3$ receptor that are manifested by a type of vitamin D resistance that clinically resembles classical rickets (117).

Biochemical studies of the 1,25$(OH)_2D_3$ receptor indicate that the mode of action of the vitamin D sterol is similar to that of steroid and thyroid hormones, with the active metabolite complexing with a selective high-affinity binding protein that concentrates the hormone in the nucleus. The occupied receptor is then postulated to regulate gene expression and induce proteins that alter the functions of target cells. The 1,25$(OH)_2D_3$ receptor is a DNA-binding protein (157) with biochemical properties remarkably similar to those of steroid and thyroid hormone receptors. 1,25$(OH)_2D_3$ receptor proteins have molecular weights between 50,000 and 60,000, they bind 1,25$(OH)_2D_3$ with very high affinity ($K_d = 10^{-11}$M) and selectivity over other vitamin D metabolites, and they possess essential sulfhydryl groups in both their hormone- and DNA-binding domains (75). Recent work suggests that the 1,25$(OH)_2D_3$ receptor is itself modulated, both quantitatively in that it is up-regulated by vitamin D metabolites (35) and qualitatively by phosphorylation in the presence of 1,25$(OH)_2D_3$ (160). Monoclonal antibodies generated against the receptor (39, 155, 159) have facilitated unequivocal identification of the monomeric protein through immunoblotting, and permitted the analysis of its biosynthesis in cultured cells or via translation of its mRNA in vitro. Using antibody screening of expression vector cDNA libraries, it may soon be possible to clone the vitamin D receptor gene, as has just been accomplished for estrogen (194) and glucocorticoid receptors (91). At this point, there is little doubt that the receptor mediates the actions of 1,25$(OH)_2D_3$ at the level of DNA and the goal of the future is to elucidate the chemical and physical details of this biochemical event.

Finally, using the $1,25(OH)_2D_3$ receptor as a marker for vitamin D target organs, surprising new sites for vitamin D function have been postulated, including a number of endocrine glands, skin, breast, brain, thymus, and bone marrow. Therefore, vitamin D apparently has a myriad of biological actions beyond those involved in traditional control of bone and mineral metabolism at the intestine, kidney, and bone. It is probable that $1,25(OH)_2D_3$, like the vitamin A metabolite retinoic acid, plays a basic role in cell differentiation—especially in the hematopoietic system (124). There are also indications that, by analogy with vitamin A, vitamin D may act as an anticancer agent in certain situations (28). Thus, what was originally considered an antirachitic vitamin is now recognized as the precursor to a powerful sterol hormone capable not only of effecting calcium and skeletal homeostasis, but also of fundamental actions on cell proliferation and differentiation. The current challenge is to characterize the detailed molecular mechanism of action of $1,25(OH)_2D_3$ in its spectrum of target cells and to integrate these individual functions into a picture of vitamin D–mediated cell development as well as nutritional and physiological adaptation.

## BACKGROUND AND SIGNIFICANCE

### *Vitamin D Metabolism and Biologic Functions*

The focus of the present chapter is the receptor protein for the vitamin D hormone, but it is necessary to review first the significant advances in our comprehension of vitamin D metabolism and actions that have occurred in the last 20 years. This material is outlined only briefly because it has been the subject of several extensive reviews (42, 78, 86, 142).

As summarized in Figure 1, the functional metabolism of vitamin $D_3$, the sunlight vitamin, consists of an initial 25-hydroxylation primarily in liver, followed by 1-hydroxylation of 25-hydroxyvitamin $D_3$ [$25(OH)D_3$] in the kidney. The $1,25(OH)_2D_3$ product is likely the sole biologically significant metabolite of the vitamin that acts in target cells (13, 71, 73, 81). Its main functions are the stimulation of intestinal calcium and phosphate absorption, mediation of bone remodeling, and conservation of minerals at the kidney. $1,25(OH)_2D_3$ also has biologic effects not directly related to mineral transport or mineralization, including affecting sterol metabolism in skin (52), stimulating macrophage differentiation (124), modifying T-lymphocyte activity (193), and influencing the secretion of a number of peptide hormones [e.g. parathyroid hormone (43), prolactin (200), and insulin (102)]. Predominantly in kidney, but probably to some degree in all target cells, $1,25(OH)_2D_3$ induces a 24-hydroxylase (24-OHase) enzyme that initiates a catabolic cascade for the side-chain oxidation, cleavage, and ultimate metabolic elimination of the $1,25(OH)_2D_3$ hormone (Figure 1) as well as its $25(OH)D_3$ precursor (21, 100, 130, 141). Considering that the renal production of $1,25(OH)_2D_3$ is strictly controlled by the calcium and phosphorus needs of the organism (Figure 1; see also 78), it is clear that the levels and actions of the $1,25(OH)_2D_3$ hormone are dynamically regulated. For instance, during nutritional calcium deprivation, $1,25(OH)_2D_3$ biosynthesis is enhanced by parathyroid hormone (PTH) and in part by low blood calcium itself (94). Intestinal calcium absorption is then accelerated to correct the hypocalcemia and spare skeletal mineral, while at the same time $1,25(OH)_2D_3$ initiates its own biodegradation via the 24-OHase cascade. In this fashion the metered production of $1,25(OH)_2D_3$ and its biochemical actions delicately coordinate the physiological adaptation of the organism to varying situations of mineral nutrition.

## *Receptor Discovery and Evidence that it Mediates Vitamin D Action*

The first insight that a biologically active vitamin D metabolite functions analogously to steroid hormones was obtained in 1968 when Haussler et al (79) demonstrated that this metabolite was localized in target tissue nuclear chromatin in a saturable and specific manner after vitamin D administration in vivo. It was next reported by Haussler & Norman (80) in 1969 that the vitamin D metabolite could be extracted from chromatin by KCl, with 50% extraction occurring at 0.2-M KCl. Significantly, the metabolite remained bound to a receptor-like protein in the KCl extract as demonstrated by ammonium sulfate precipitation and CsCl ultracentrifugation. In fact, gel filtration suggested a $M_r$ of 50,000–70,000 for the protease-sensitive metabolite receptor (80). These data constitute the discovery of the vitamin D receptor and, interestingly, predate the structural identification of the active vitamin D metabolite as $1,25(OH)_2D_3$ (90).

Tsai & Norman (192) next showed that $1,25(OH)_2D_3$ association with chromatin in reconstituted systems was facilitated by a soluble factor. This factor was conclusively shown to be receptor-like by Brumbaugh & Haussler (15–17), who reported the following three critical characteristics of the macromolecule: (*a*) binds vitamin D analogs in a rank order corresponding to their biologic potencies (15), (*b*) sediments at 3.0–3.5S in high salt-sucrose gradients, and (*c*) displays saturable high-affinity binding in vitro (17). These studies in 1973 and 1974 comprised the first pharmacological and biochemical identification of the receptor in vitro. An important property of the receptor was revealed in 1979 when Pike & Haussler (157) observed that it is a DNA-binding protein and the molecule was first purified utilizing DNA cellulose chromatography. Denaturing electrophoresis demonstrated that the purified chick intestinal $1,25(OH)_2D_3$ receptor consisted of several protein species of 50,000–65,000 daltons (157).

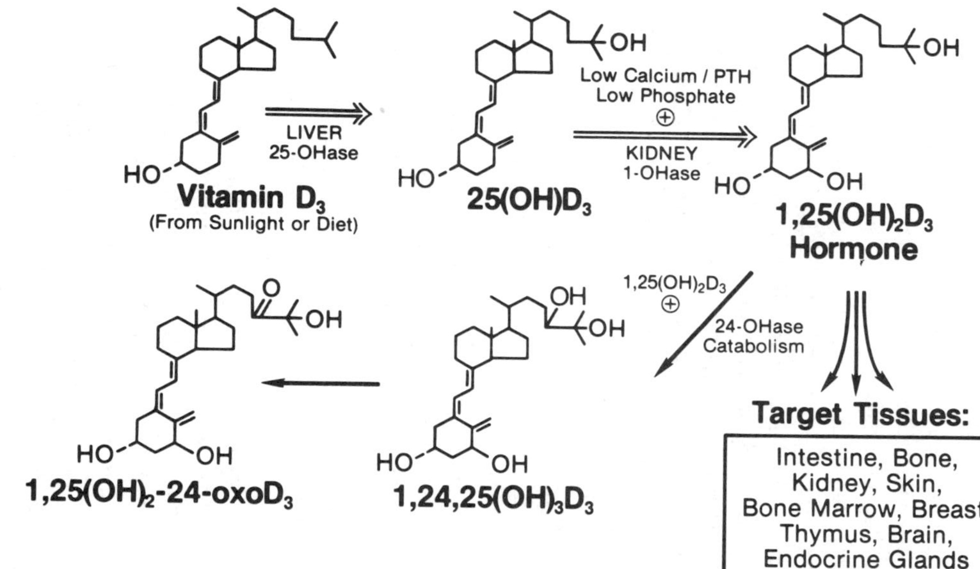


*Figure 1* The vitamin D endocrine system. The scheme for 24-OHase-initiated side-chain oxidation of 1,25(OH)$_2D_3$ also occurs with 25(OH)$D_3$ as a starting substrate, although for simplicity this pathway is not shown. 1,25(OH)$_2$-24-oxo$D_3$ is eventually converted via side-chain cleavage to calcitroic acid (1$\alpha$-hydroxy-23-carboxytetranorvitamin D), the probable excreted form of the hormone. Vitamin $D_2$ taken as a supplement or from diet is metabolized similarly to vitamin $D_3$.

There are now many lines of evidence indicating that the receptor protein mediates most, if not all, of the biologic functions of vitamin D. One of the more convincing of these is the strong positive correlation between binding potency of a series of vitamin D metabolites and analogs and their biological activity. This correlation holds when the analogs are assayed in vivo (70, 162), and in isolated systems such as calcium mobilization from bone in tissue culture (181). It is important to recognize that the relatively high association constant ($10^{11}$ $M^{-1}$) with which the intracellular receptor protein binds $1,25(OH)_2D_3$ compared to other metabolites like $25(OH)D_3$ is reversed in the case of the serum vitamin D–binding protein (DBP) (71, 81). Thus DBP binds $25(OH)D_3$ and 24,25-dihydroxyvitamin $D_3$ [$24,25(OH)_2D_3$] more avidly than the $1,25(OH)_2D_3$ hormone, which allows the intracellular receptor selectively to concentrate and retain $1,25(OH)_2D_3$ in vitamin D target cells (126).

The fact that the receptor was originally discovered in the major vitamin D target organ, namely intestinal mucosa, and was subsequently revealed in other sites of mineral translocation or regulation, i.e. parathyroid gland (19, 85), bone (110), and kidney (22, 29, 33), adds credence to its proposed role in vitamin D action. These tissues persist as locations with the highest concentrations of $1,25(OH)_2D_3$ receptor, but many new target tissues and cell types for $1,25(OH)_2D_3$ have been identified by biochemical detection of receptor and via autoradiographic localization of tritiated $1,25(OH)_2D_3$ in vivo (82, 184). Many of these new targets are mineral transport sites (shell gland, chorioallantoic membrane, etc), endocrine organs (pancreas, pituitary, ovary, testis, etc), and reproductive tissues (breast, placenta, uterus, etc). The skin, where the photobiosynthesis of vitamin D occurs, is also a location for the $1,25(OH)_2D$ receptor (54, 178).

These exciting findings do not negate the concept that the receptor is a marker for the calcium homeostatic actions of vitamin D, but instead bring to light the theory that vitamin D functions in a vast array of target cells, more akin to vitamin A and steroid hormones like the glucocorticoids. The physiologic significance of $1,25(OH)_2D_3$ action in its newly identified target cells has not been fully evaluated, but it is apparent that disorders of calcium absorption and bone mineralization dominate the clinical picture in simple vitamin D–deficient rickets or osteomalacia. In type II vitamin D–dependent rickets, which is a hereditary hypocalcemic syndrome characterized by resistance to $1,25(OH)_2D_3$, the receptor protein in fibroblasts from the affected patients is defective (49, 53, 117, 154). Despite the fact that these patients have excessive circulating levels of $1,25(OH)_2D_3$, they still display hypocalcemia and severe rickets. Since their genetic defect is presumably a point mutation destroying $1,25(OH)_2D_3$ receptor function, it is clear that this disease constitutes the most compelling evidence that the $1,25(OH)_2D_3$ receptor is obligatory and mediates the action of vitamin D to prevent rickets.

## *Occurrence and Subcellular Distribution of the Receptor*

As outlined above, it is now apparent that the distribution of the $1,25(OH)_2D_3$ receptor is broad, including a vast array of putative target cell types. In some cases these new target tissues were identified by classical ligand-binding experiments (19, 22, 29, 33, 42, 54, 82, 85, 110, 142, 156, 178).

However, two new developments in $1,25(OH)_2D_3$ binding studies have been the use of autoradiographic localization of $1,25(OH)_2D[^3H]D_3$ in vivo (183), and of cultured cell lines in vitro. Autoradiographic localization of the hormone has not only confirmed that $1,25(OH)_2D_3$ is concentrated in nuclei of target tissues like intestine, parathyroid, bone, and kidney, but has verified (and in some cases predicted) new target sites for the hormone. More importantly, autoradiographic techniques allow for the identification of individual cell types that localize and probably respond to the hormone. In this fashion, Stumpf and associates (183) demonstrated the following unique target cells for $1,25(OH)_2D_3$: neurons in brain and spinal cord, anterior pituitary thyrotrophs, gastric endocrine cells, pancreatic beta cells, bone marrow reticular cells, chondroblasts, and osteoblasts. Cultured cells also offer systems where homogeneous populations of cells can be probed for the $1,25(OH)_2D_3$ receptor. The receptor has been detected in human breast cancer cells (51), rat osteogenic sarcoma cells (44, 127), rat somatomammotrophic pituitary cells (77), human melanoma cells (32), human promyelocytic leukemia cells (124), human lymphoblasts (163), and embryonic mouse fibroblasts (158). These established cell lines are excellent systems for investigating the $1,25(OH)_2D_3$ receptor and its functions and are currently under intensive investigation in many laboratories. One caveat to using these model systems is that they are transformed cell lines that may have altered receptor dynamics because of their uncontrolled proliferation and relative state of dedifferentiation. However, studies to date seem to indicate that they are valid models that reflect the biochemistry of vitamin D action in their respective normal counterparts.

Table 1 presents a compilation of the known target locations for the $1,25(OH)_2D_3$ receptor, combining biochemical, autoradiographic and established cell line results. It should be noted that $1,25(OH)_2D_3$ receptors have also been detected in amphibians (82), as well as in specialized avian and fish tissues. Unique avian vitamin D receptor locations include the shell gland (37) and chorioallantoic membrane (38), while those in the fish are the gill, corpuscles of Stannius, and, surprisingly, the liver (128). Clearly, more tissues contain the $1,25(OH)_2D_3$ receptor than do not, although a clear pattern is emerging to indicate that vitamin D functions in select cell types, predomonantly to mediate mineral, endocrine, and reproductive actions. It is also apparent that, like other steroid hormones, $1,25(OH)_2D_3$ is potentially a neuromodulator and immune regulator. What must be determined is whether there is some common denominator in the action of $1,25(OH)_2D_3$ in all cells, such as intracellular calcium fluctuation, or whether $1,25(OH)_2D_3$ is a basic regulator of cell maturation. It is conceivable that vitamin D affects all cells during a certain period of their differentiation. Thus in fully differentiated intestinal epithelial cells, $1,25(OH)_2D_3$ is a potent inducer of calcium transport and this action correlates with the appearance and escalation of the receptor during embryonic and neonatal development in the chick (176) and rat (68), respectively. In contrast, adult avian and mammalian liver are not considered targets for vitamin D, but recent evidence from our laboratory (K. Yamaoka, S. L. Marion, J. W. Pike, and M. R. Haussler, unpublished information) suggests that early chick embryo liver possesses the $1,25(OH)_2D_3$ receptor and loses it during embryonic development. Do $1,25(OH)_2D_3$ and its receptor play some role in initial liver cell differentiation, or are such embryonic receptors vestigal? Answering this question is critical to evaluating the biological relevance of $1,25(OH)_2D_3$ receptor presence in embryonic and cancer cells as well as the significance of the wide receptor distribution detailed in Table 1. Perhaps there is a threshold number (e.g. 500 copies/cell) of receptors required to initiate a biological response, making quantitation of receptors as important as their qualitative presence in a cell.

In terms of the subcellular distribution of the vitamin D receptor, nuclear localization is supported indirectly by the striking nuclear occurrence of tritiated $1,25(OH)_2D_3$ via autoradiography (101, 182–184) and by original biochemical detection of the receptor protein in nuclear chromatin after administration of labeled vitamin D in vivo (79, 80). Subsequent biochemical fractionation of target tissues labeled with $1,25(OH)_2D[^3H]D_3$ in vitro, and studies in reconstituted systems (16–18), verified the predominant nuclear location of the occupied vitamin D receptor. Evidence was also gathered to suggest that the unoccupied receptor was primarily a cytosolic molecule, with the $1,25(OH)_2D_3$ receptor complex migrating to the nucleus upon hormone binding (17, 18). Thus, the $1,25(OH)_2D_3$ receptor system seemed to fit perfectly with the prevailing steroid hormone receptor dogma of a two-step process of hormone binding in cytoplasm and subsequent localization in the nucleus (78, 98).

Although nuclear localization of occupied $1,25(OH)_2D_3$ receptor remains undisputed, in vitamin D and several other steroid hormone systems the subcellular distribution of the unoccupied receptor is now less well defined. Initial data showing predominantly cytosolic receptors were obtained in experiments using homogenizing buffers of intermediate (17) or high (110) ionic strength. Walters and associates (197–199) have used low ionic strength buffers to reexamine the assumption that the unoccupied vitamin D receptor is cytosolic. They observed that as much as 90% of the unoccupied $1,25(OH)_2D_3$ receptor is associated with purified nuclei or chromatin under low ionic strength fractionation conditions. Thus, according to Walters et al (199), the nature of the $1,25(OH)_2D_3$ receptor may approach that of the thyroid hormone receptor,

**Table 1** Relevant tissues and cells that possess the $1,25(OH)_2D_3$ receptor[a]

| Category | Tissues | Specific cell types[b] | Established cell lines | References |
|---|---|---|---|---|
| Calcium control | Intestine | Absorptive epithelial | Intestine 407 (human) | 39, 80, 152 |
| | Bone/Cartilage | Osteoblast | ROS17/2.8 osteosarcoma (rat) | 27, 110, 127 |
| | | Chondroblast | — | 185 |
| | Kidney | Distal epithelial | LLC-$PK_1$ (pig) | 21, 22, 29, 33 |
| Endocrine | Parathyroid | Chief | — | 19, 85 |
| | Pancreas | β-cell | — | 29, 150, 156 |
| | Pituitary | Somatomammotroph | $GH_3$ tumor (rat) | 76, 77, 156 |
| | Ovary | ? | Chinese hamster ovary | 45 |
| | Testis | Sertoli/seminiferous tubule | — | 115, 136, 196 |
| | Thyroid | C-cell | — | 59 |
| Reproductive | Breast | Epithelial | MCF-7, T47D carcinoma (human) | 51, 58, 168, 177 |
| | Placenta | ? | — | 156 |
| | Uterus | ? | — | 195 |
| Other | Skin | Epidermal | 3T6 fibroblast (mouse)<br>G361 melanoma (human) | 32, 49, 54, 154, 158, 178 |
| | Muscle | Myoblast | G-8 myoblast (mouse) | 12, 180 |
| | Parotid | Acinar | — | 146 |
| | Brain | Certain neurons/hippocampus | — | 31, 182 |
| | Thymus | Reticular/T lymphocytes | HSB-2 lymphoblast (human) | 75, 163, 169 |
| | Bone marrow | Monocyte | HL-60 leukemia (human)<br>U937 monoblast (human) | 124, 138, 163, 188 |

[a]Receptor-positive tissues generally contain a concentration of ≥10 fmol/mg protein or approximately 500 copies per cell.
[b]Conclusions reached from autoradiography (183, 184) and biochemical studies in homogeneous populations of cultured cells.

which is an intrinsic nonhistone chromosomal protein (20). A general model has been proposed (199) to explain the $1,25(OH)_2D_3$ receptor in relation to steroid and thyroid hormone receptors. This model is based upon the concept that variations in the affinity of receptors for nuclear components account for apparent differences in subcellular distribution upon biochemical fractionation of the tissue. Unoccupied receptors are thought to have affinities for homologous nuclei in the following order: steroid hormones $<1,25(OH)_2D_3<$ thyroid hormones. These relative affinities for nuclear binding, plus the ionic strength and volume (free water content) of homogenizing buffers, explain the marked differences seen in the distribution of unoccupied hormone receptors in vitro. Recently, independent methodologies of immunocytochemistry and enucleation have been applied to determining the subcellular location of the unoccupied estrogen receptor (106, 202), with the surprising result that it is primarily a nuclear macromolecule. Thus, even this weakly nucleophilic macromolecule may reside principally in the nucleus in situ. Preliminary findings employing immunocytochemistry of the 1,25$(OH)_2D_3$ receptor (11, 31) also indicate nuclear localization of the unoccupied receptor in human breast cancer tissue, mouse osteoblasts and kidney, and rat hippocampus. The present working hypothesis is that the 1,25$(OH)_2D_3$ receptor, like other steroid receptors, is a loosely associated chromosomal protein, with affinity for nuclear components increasing upon hormone binding (96, 149, 158, 199). It is probable that a fraction of unoccupied receptors for 1,25$(OH)_2D_3$ exists in the cytoplasm—in equilibrium with the majority of unoccupied receptors on chromosomes. In any event, it does not seem to be critically important whether the receptor receives the 1,25$(OH)_2D_3$ hormone in the cytoplasm or while it is attached in the nucleus. What is significant is that the occupied receptor apparently is capable of translocating within the chromosome and recognizing upstream regulatory regions of vitamin D–controlled genes, with a resulting alteration in transcription.

In summary, based upon its tissue, cellular, and subcellular distribution, its pharmacologic profile for binding vitamin D congeners, and the clinical consequences of genetic defects in the molecule, it is reasonable to conclude that this protein is the biochemical mediator of 1,25$(OH)_2D_3$ action. Although extranuclear (nongenomic) actions of 1,25$(OH)_2D_3$ have not been ruled out (166), the properties of the vitamin D receptor convincingly place it in the family of genomic regulators with the thyroid and steroid receptors, but distinguish it from the smaller cellular vitamin A–binding proteins, which are not tightly associated with DNA or nuclei (83, 186).

## BIOCHEMICAL PROPERTIES AND STRUCTURE

### *Avian Receptors*

The most extensively studied 1,25$(OH)_2D_3$ receptor is that from chick intestinal mucosa (15–17, 109, 149, 157, 176, 201). The chick intestinal receptor is biochemically indistinguishable from that found in other avian tissues like parathyroid gland, bone, pancreas, and ovary. There is general agreement that the receptor is a macromolecule sedimenting at 3.0–3.7S and is present even in this richest known site at $\leq 0.001\%$ of the soluble protein. It is an acidic protein, with a pI of 6.2, has a Stokes radius of 36 Å, and possesses distinct domains for 1,25$(OH)_2D_3$ hormone binding ($K_d = 10^{-10}$–$10^{-11}$ M) and for association with DNA (5, 133). Both the 1,25$(OH)_2D_3$-binding region (36) and the DNA-binding domain (148) contain essential sulfhydryl groups. The receptor has been purified by multiple chromatographic steps including DNA-cellulose, gel filtration, and DEAE-cellulose to yield a protein of 63,000 daltons (179) or 64,000 daltons (159) via gel electrophoresis under denaturing conditions. This approximate molecular weight for the monomeric receptor is in reasonable agreement with recent immunoblot identification of the receptor as a 60,000-dalton species by Pike (152) in our laboratory. However, this molecular weight is not consistent with data suggesting that a form of larger size (95,000–110,000 daltons) exists in the presence of protease inhibitors (9, 96, 103) or dithiothreitol (67). Although the final resolution of this conflict will require the cloning and sequencing of the receptor gene, the studies with protease inhibitors and dithiothreitol involve crude preparations and probably reflect either the measurement of nonreceptor proteins or their complexing with the monomeric receptor. The more definitive denaturing electrophoresis of purified receptor and immunoblotting techniques are no doubt identifying the authentic receptor as a 60,000-dalton protein. Further characterization of the 60,000-$M_r$ chick intestinal receptor through amino acid sequencing has not been completed, but much additional information about the receptor has been obtained using impure or partially purified preparations.

The receptor is unstable and both hormone- and DNA-binding capacity decay in a time- and temperature-dependent fashion. Dithiothreitol (5 mM) preserves hormone binding to some degree but the DNA-binding function is quite labile and readily destroyed by endogenous proteolysis (57, 135). Recent data from our lab (E. A. Allegretto, K. Yamaoka, J. W. Pike, M. R. Haussler, unpublished information) reveal that an endogenous protease cleaves the 60,000-$M_r$ receptor into a fragment of $M_r$ 45,000 that binds hormone but not DNA. It is likely that this fragment is the "cytosolic" form of the receptor that has been reported not to bind DNA (139), which indicates that this species is a proteolytic product and not a novel form of unactivated receptor. As with other steroid receptors, molybdate appears to stabilize the 1,25$(OH)_2D_3$ receptor by interacting with its DNA-binding region (57, 140; K. Yamaoka, J. W. Pike, and M. R. Haussler, unpublished information).

Although most of the investigations have been carried out on monomeric chick intestinal receptor, there is evidence for aggregation and formation of multimeric configurations. In the case of well-characterized prokaryotic regulators of transcription, there is precedent for dimeric and tetrameric proteins constituting the active species (175). Accordingly, Wilhelm & Norman (203) have observed positive cooperativity in the binding of 1,25$(OH)_2D_3$ to its intestinal receptor protein in concentrated preparations. One possibility they propose to explain their data is that the receptor can form a homodimer, with the process of dimerization affecting the $K_d$ for the second 1,25$(OH)_2D_3$ bound. It is established that aggregation of the receptor to faster sedimenting forms in low-salt sucrose gradients requires an intact DNA-binding domain (57). Thus, it is reasonable to assume that, in its native form in association with DNA in situ, the receptor could exist as a homo- or heteropolymer.

Much additional information is now available about the DNA or polynucleotide binding characteristics of the chick intestinal 1,25$(OH)_2D_3$ receptor. The receptor elutes from DNA-cellulose with a higher salt concentration (0.22-M KCl) when occupied with 1,25$(OH)_2D_3$ than when unoccupied (0.16-M KCl) (96, 158). The intercalating agent, ethidium bromide, is a potent blocker of receptor-DNA association (164) and the receptor prefers double-stranded over single-stranded DNA. These data indicate that receptor-DNA interaction is not solely electrostatic, but involves hydrophobic interactions with the major and minor grooves of the DNA double helix (164). The receptor also interacts with RNA (56), but elutes at a lower KCl concentration than from DNA, which suggests that it may bind less avidly to RNA. Some base sequence selectivity is observed when polydeoxyribonucleotides are used instead of natural DNA, with adenine:thymine (AT) preference occurring when DNA interactions are assessed by competition assay (164). The polynucleotide binding domain of the receptor appears to be the site of interaction with triazinyl dye-ligands (132) and, like DNA-cellulose, resins such as blue dextran Sepharose are powerful tools in purifying the receptor (131). Clearly, specific amino acid sequence information will be required to characterize fully the DNA-binding domain and ultimately to identify its interactions with the regulatory regions of vitamin D–modulated genes. Another challenging question will be to determine how 1,25$(OH)_2D_3$ binding alters the conformation or activity of the DNA-binding domain to render it functional in controlling gene expression. Finally, the hormone-binding region of the receptor must be characterized, perhaps with the availability of photoaffinity probes such as recently reported by Ray et al (167).

### *Mammalian Receptors*

In addition to characterizing the rat intestinal mucosa receptor for 1,25$(OH)_2D_3$ (111), biochemical studies of mammalian receptors have included some unique tissue locations such as mouse colon (87) and rat yolk sac (41). Recently, mammalian vitamin D receptors have been intensely investigated in primary cultured cells and continuous cell lines (See Table 1). Mammalian receptors are remarkably similar to their avian counterparts, possessing corresponding dissociation constants for 1,25$(OH)_2D_3$ binding of $10^{-11}$–$10^{-10}$ M, and virtually identical specificity in that other prominent circulating vitamin D metabolites like 25$(OH)D_3$ and 24,25$(OH)_2D_3$ bind less than 4% as effectively as the hormone. The mammalian 1,25$(OH)_2D_3$ receptor has DNA-binding properties indistinguishable from the avian receptor, which reveals that both the hormone- and DNA-binding domains are conserved in these two species. Sucrose gradient centrifugation experiments do suggest that the mammalian receptor

(3.2–3.3S) is slightly smaller than the avian receptor, which is considered to be a 3.7S macromolecule (18, 109, 201), although sedimentation coefficients as low as 3.1–3.3S have been reported for the avian vitamin D receptor (19, 155). More definitive immunoblot data recently revealed that mammalian receptors are significantly smaller than the 60,000-dalton avian form. Employing immunoblotting of cultured cells, Pike (152) in our laboratory observed the following molecular weights for mammalian $1,25(OH)_2D_3$ receptors: mouse fibroblasts (3T6)=55,000; rat osteosarcoma (ROS 17/2.8)=54,000; porcine kidney ($LLC\text{-}PK_1$)=54,000; human leukemia (HL-60)=52,000. Similarly, Dame et al (39) identified the porcine intestinal receptor as a 55,000-dalton protein. Thus, mammalian $1,25(OH)_2D_3$ receptor monomers range in $M_r$ from 52,000 to 55,000 daltons, but are otherwise strikingly similar in biochemical properties to the 60,000-dalton avian protein.

## *Evolution of the Receptor*

The $1,25(OH)_2D_3$ receptor has been detected in vitamin D target cells in mammals (human, bovine, porcine, murine, and rat), birds, and amphibians, where it is prominent in such sites as skin, gut, and kidney (82). Fish also contain the $1,25(OH)_2D_3$ receptor in tissues like intestine, liver, pituitary, gills, and corpuscles of Stannius (47, 128, 159). These observations suggest that the vitamin D receptor is an evolutionarily ancient molecule. Biochemical properties such as $1,25(OH)_2D_3$-binding affinity and specificity, as well as DNA-binding characteristics, are indistinguishable for the receptor in all tissues from fish to humans. This indicates that the molecule is highly conserved and that similar mechanisms constitute the action of $1,25(OH)_2D_3$ in each of its target cells. The development of monoclonal antibodies to chick (155, 159) and porcine (39) receptors has strengthened this conclusion. Most, but not all, antibodies generated against the avian receptor cross-react with mammalian and fish vitamin D receptors (159), while virtually all antibodies to the porcine receptor react with other mammalian as well as avian receptors (40). Clearly the antigenic determinants in the receptor from various species are homologous and these regions of the molecule have undergone only minimal biochemical evolution. Because many of the epitopes are near or in the DNA-binding domain (40, 151), the conservation of this region and its potential functional significance are again highlighted. As with other hormone-receptor systems, the vitamin D receptor and its endogenous ligand have probably evolved new biological functions. Primitive but more fundamental roles of this system in cell proliferation and maturation may have preceded its more clinically significant involvement in stimulating mineral absorption and bone remodeling. Elucidating and cataloging the tissue-specific and specialized functions of the vitamin D receptor through evolution is obviously a significant problem for the future. Equally exciting will be the comparison of the amino acid sequence of the vitamin D receptor with other hormone receptors and proteins that modify DNA transcription to disclose any homology and perhaps point to a common ancestral gene or genes.

## PHYSIOLOGICAL AND CLINICAL APPLICATIONS

### *Radioreceptor Assay of 1,25-Dihydroxyvitamin D*

The renal production and blood level of $1,25(OH)_2D$ [i.e. $1,25(OH)_2D_3$ + $1,25(OH)_2D_2$] are affected by a number of physiologic and nutritional agents that influence mineral metabolism (78; see Figure 1). In addition to this physiological regulation, circulating $1,25(OH)_2D$ concentrations are altered in a number of diseases of bone and mineral metabolism, notably renal osteodystrophy, parathyroid disorders, and various types of heritable rickets (69, 78). Because of the importance of $1,25(OH)_2D$ in the pathophysiology of calcium metabolism, considerable effort has been directed toward development of assay methods for monitoring the hormone in biological fluids. The receptor has been the basis of most assay methodology because of its high affinity and specific binding of $1,25(OH)_2D$.

Brumbaugh et al (14) created the first competitive radioassay for $1,25(OH)_2D$ using the chick intestinal cytosol-chromatin receptor system and filtration to separate bound and free hormone. The procedure included a $1,25(OH)_2D$ purification scheme with Celite partition chromatography as the final step. Eisman et al (50) reported a conceptually similar method utilizing polyethylene glycol precipitation of soluble receptor to assess bound hormone and HPLC isolation of the sterol prior to assay. In the ensuing years modifications and improvements have been made in the radioreceptor assay of $1,25(OH)_2D$ in many laboratories (10, 48, 64, 93, 122, 134). Rapid extraction/purification procedures for the hormone have been devised and charcoal adsorption has been adopted as the method of choice for separating bound and free sterol. With the increased specific activity of $1,25(OH)_2D[^3H]D_3$ to $\geq$150 Ci/mmol and improved binding conditions to yield apparent dissociation constants approaching $10^{-11}$ M for the association of $1,25(OH)_2D_3$ with receptor, radioassays sensitive to 0.5–1 pg of $1,25(OH)_2D$ have been devised. The $1,25(OH)_2D_3$ receptor from chick intestine and more recently from calf thymus (170) are utilized in this clinically important assay. A variation on the radioreceptor assay, known as the cytoreceptor assay, has also been reported (125). Using intact rat osteosarcoma cells as a source of receptor and incubating in the presence of serum DBP to sequester interfering sterols like 25(OH)D and $24,25(OH)_2D$, Manolagas et al (125) were able to assay serum $1,25(OH)_2D$ with only minimal extraction and purification. Although the cytoreceptor assay is esthetically pleasing in that the receptor is employed for competition binding in its natural location within the cell, and although it is a rapid technique for clinical estimation of $1,25(OH)_2D$, it may not be as rigorous or accurate as radioreceptor assays involving HPLC purification and lipid equalization strategies (48). Regardless of the procedure chosen, it is evident that radioreceptor assay of $1,25(OH)_2D$ in animals and humans facilitated a quantum jump in our understanding of the pathophysiology of the vitamin D endocrine system (69, 78).

### *Hereditary Vitamin D–Resistant Syndromes*

In addition to nutritional rickets and osteomalacia, there are several inherited rachitic syndromes in which patients are resistant to physiologic doses of vitamin D and require massive supplements of vitamin D and/or minerals. Familial hypophosphatemic rickets, also known as vitamin D–resistant rickets, is characterized by a primary phosphate leak at the kidney that is also associated with a blunted adaptive increase in circulating $1,25(OH)_2D$ in response to the hypophosphatemia (120). Patients respond well to therapy with oral phosphate plus $1,25(OH)_2D_3$, which means that $1,25(OH)_2D_3$ responsiveness is intact (119), a conclusion supported by the presence of normal receptors and biochemical response in skin fibroblasts (4). There are two types of vitamin D–dependent rickets or hereditary hypocalcemic vitamin D–resistant rickets: (*a*) type I disease caused by a lack of adequate $1,25(OH)_2D_3$ production at the kidney, presumably because of a genetic error in the 1-OHase; and (*b*) type II disease resulting from tissue resistance to the $1,25(OH)_2D_3$ hormone (72).

Vitamin D–dependent rickets, type II (VDDR II), is a rare, heritable syndrome characterized clinically by hypocalcemia, secondary hyperparathyroidism, and rickets, all of which persist despite high circulating levels of $1,25(OH)_2D_3$. Patients also often display alopecia (53, 117). This constellation of features results from peripheral target organ resistance to $1,25(OH)_2D_3$ that is analogous to clinical disorders of resistance to glucocorticoids and androgens. Cultured skin fibroblasts from patients with VDDR II have been used to evaluate the underlying defects associated with this disorder. These studies showed that this disease is heterogeneous and arises primarily from defects in either the receptor's interaction with $1,25(OH)_2D_3$ or its site of action in the nucleus (53, 117). One particularly abundant phenotype identified in fibroblasts of a number of kindreds appears to be a receptor-deficient variant, as deduced by the absence of hormone-binding activity. There is a possibility that the syndrome is caused by an inherited deletion of the gene for the $1,25(OH)_2D_3$ receptor; we have recently evaluated this by using a radioligand immunoassay (46) to examine these fibroblasts for $1,25(OH)_2D_3$ receptors. Our results indicated the presence of normal amounts of material in these cells cross-reacting with the receptor antibody (154). This suggests that tissue resistance associated with phenotypes in which hormone binding is lacking may be caused by mutations in the hormone-binding domain of the receptor protein and is rarely the result of genetic deletion.

Two recent studies report on novel subtypes of VDDR II in which mutations selectively influence the DNA-binding domain of the vitamin D receptor, with a reduction in affinity for DNA and a presumed compromise in receptor biopotency (89, 118). These findings of cellular resistance to 1,25$(OH)_2D_3$ being associated with altered functional domains in the receptor provide dramatic confirmation of the biochemical results that point to the significance of the hormone- and DNA-binding regions of the receptor (153). The generality of the receptor defect in VDDR II fibroblasts is highlighted by reports that defective 1,25$(OH)_2D_3$ receptors also occur in keratinocytes (30), mononuclear cells (107), and cultured bone cells (116). Moreover, 1,25$(OH)_2D_3$ responsiveness in terms of vitamin D-24-OHase induction was shown to be absent or blunted in cells from patients with defective receptors, which proves a lack of functional bioresponsiveness to 1,25$(OH)_2D_3$ (26, 30, 53, 61, 107, 116). In one case, normal receptors were associated with impaired stimulation of 24-OHase(65), indicative of a variety of VDDR II with postreceptor resistance to 1,25$(OH)_2D_3$. As stated above, nature's experiment of VDDR II and its subtypes strengthens the conclusion that the 1,25$(OH)_2D_3$ receptor is an obligate mediator of vitamin D action in bone and mineral homeostasis. When the normal receptor gene is cloned, it should be possible to transfect it into genetically resistant cells and restore responsiveness to 1,25$(OH)_2D_3$.

Further study of vitamin D resistance will be facilitated by the use of certain cell culture and animal models. Kelly et al (105) have discovered that a monkey kidney cell line (LLC-$MK_2$) contains receptors with an abnormally low affinity for 1,25$(OH)_2D_3$ that is reflected by the need for pharmacologic doses of the hormone to induce the 24-OHase enzyme. An identical situation is seen in some patients with VDDR II (61), where excessive doses of 1,25$(OH)_2D_3$ cause a calcemic response in patients and elicit 24-OHase induction in cultured fibroblasts. Finally, as is the case with certain other steroid hormones, New World monkeys appear resistant to 1,25$(OH)_2D_3$ (3, 187). These primates have evolved with high circulating hormone levels and complementary low receptor levels, resulting in a situation of "adaptive resistance" to steroid hormones, including 1,25$(OH)_2D_3$.

## NEW INSIGHTS

### *Monoclonal Antibodies*

In order to characterize the vitamin D receptor fully, it was necessary to create immunochemical reagents. The low abundance of the receptor protein, its lability, and the resulting difficulties encountered in purifying it made this a formidable task. Pike et al (155, 159) extensively purified the receptor from 10 kg of chick intestinal mucosa, and were able to generate monoclonal antibodies to this highly enriched avian receptor. These antibodies displaced the native hormone-receptor complex in a sucrose gradient (155, 159) and, most importantly, were found to interact with both avian and mammalian $1,25(OH)_2D_3$ receptors with very high affinity ($K_d=10^{-11}$ M) (151). The latter property enabled our laboratory to develop immunoblot methodology capable of identifying the molecular mass of receptor proteins (152). Immunoblots of chick intestine high-salt extracts revealed a major immunoreactive protein in intestine at 60,000 daltons and a minor band at 58,000 daltons. We therefore concluded that the avian $1,25(OH)_2D_3$ receptor consists of two monomeric forms, a major species of 60,000 daltons and a minor form of 58,000 daltons. It is not known if both immunoreactive species in the avian intestine bind the $1,25(OH)_2D_3$ hormone and it is conceivable that the minor form arises through proteolytic degradation of the major receptor. Recent experiments involving the in vitro translation of chick intestinal mRNA similarly reveal a 60,000/58,000 dalton doublet of immunoprecipitable receptor (D. J. Mangelsdorf, J. W. Pike, and M. R. Haussler, unpublished information). Thus, these two forms of the receptor could result from alternative mRNA splicing or differing transcription start/termination sites, although proteolysis cannot be ruled out during the in vitro translation and subsequent immunoprecipitation procedures.

Recently, Dame et al (39) developed monoclonal antibodies to the highly enriched porcine intestinal receptor for $1,25(OH)_2D_3$. These workers employed a strategy similar to that of Pike et al (155, 159) to obtain monoclonal anti-receptor antibodies, most of which complexed with native receptors of mammalian as well as avian origin (40). As was detailed above, mammalian $1,25(OH)_2D_3$ receptors were identified by immunoblotting with monoclonal antibodies as single monomeric proteins of $M_r$ 52,000–55,000 (39, 152). In vitro translation of the respective mRNAs of mammalian $1,25(OH)_2D_3$ receptors followed by immunoprecipitation with monoclonal antibody has confirmed the molecular masses of the various mammalian receptors (D. J. Mangelsdorf, J. W. Pike, and M. R. Haussler, unpublished information). The $1,25(OH)_2D_3$ receptor monomer is therefore similar in size to the thyroid (20) and estrogen (194) receptors, which have molecular weights of 57,000 and 65,000 daltons, respectively. Also, as discussed above, like all thyroid and steroid hormone-binding proteins, the $1,25(OH)_2D_3$ receptor is a DNA-binding protein that now appears to be predominantly associated with the nucleus, even in the unoccupied state. However, in spite of the functional resemblance of the various receptors, and the fact that they likely are endowed with analogous structural motifs, each is unique in terms of the hormonal ligand. Antibodies to the vitamin D receptor do not cross-react with other receptors, such as those for estrogen and glucocorticoids (159). Hence if there is a superfamily of thyroid and steroid receptors that regulate gene expression, distinct immunologic epitopes are present in the individual proteins.

In summary, monoclonal antibodies have facilitated unequivocal identification of $1,25(OH)_2D_3$ receptors from various species through immunoblot analysis and immunoprecipitation of internally labeled products of in vitro mRNA translation. The ability to assess and possibly enrich receptor mRNA with the aid of in vitro translation, combined with antibody screening of cDNA libraries through expression vector technology, should ultimately lead to the cloning of the $1,25(OH)_2D_3$ receptor gene. In the meantime, monoclonal antibody immunoprecipitation is proving useful in investigating another exciting area—receptor regulation and covalent modification.

### *Quantitative and Qualitative Modification of the Receptor*

Cultured cells have provided excellent new model systems for studying the biochemical action of $1,25(OH)_2D_3$, especially as it relates to the receptor molecule and its possible modulation. Chen et al (27) first reported the existence of the $1,25(OH)_2D_3$ receptor in a cultured cell, namely primary mouse calvarial cells. Subsequently, Chen & Feldman (24) reported that the $1,25(OH)_2D_3$ receptor is regulated in culture in that levels correlate positively with the rate of cell division in primary bone cells. In LLC-$PK_1$ kidney cells, medium change caused a transient increase in $1,25(OH)_2D_3$ receptor followed by a decline to 40% of control values by 18 h (88). Glucocorticoids have been found to slow cell division in mouse cells and correspondingly reduce $1,25(OH)_2D_3$ receptor number (23). Conversely, in rat osteoblast-like cells, glucocorticoids stimulate cell division and enhance $1,25(OH)_2D_3$ receptor concentration. The significance of these results is unclear, but species dependence of the regulation of the receptor was recently highlighted by the demonstration that glucocorticoids administered to dogs in vivo double the intestinal $1,25(OH)_2D_3$ receptor level (108). The vitamin A metabolite retinoic acid has also been observed to modulate $1,25(OH)_2D_3$ receptors in cultured cells. Retinoic acid stimulates $1,25(OH)_2D_3$ receptors in rat osteosarcoma cells (147) and in mouse osteoblast-like cells (25), but it reduces receptor levels in primary rat osteoblast-like cells (25). These results emphasize the complexity of receptor control, with opposite effects of retinoic acid on receptor number in transformed vs primary (normal) rat bone cells, and species dependence as was observed in the case of glucocorticoid effects on the receptor.

Compounds such as glucocorticoids and retinoic acid are known to change the rate of cell proliferation and, in some instances, differentiation of cultured cells. Human promyelocytic leukemia (HL-60) cells are a good model system for studying $1,25(OH)_2D_3$ receptors during differentiation. These cells differentiate to macrophage-like cells when treated with the tumor promotor TPA and with $1,25(OH)_2D_3$; they also contain significant quantities of the 1, $25(OH)_2D_3$ receptor (up to 4000 copies per cell) (124). We have observed that differentiation of HL-60 cells to macrophages elicits an 80% reduction in $1,25(OH)_2D_3$ receptor number (M. R. Haussler, D. J. Mangelsdorf, C. A.

Donaldson, S. L. Marion, and J. W. Pike, unpublished information). It is also known that the receptor level increases dramatically in normal human T lymphocytes when they are activated (163). In our hands, the receptor copy number per T cell rises from 200 to 2000 when the cells are activated for 72 h with concanavalin A (75). Thus it is evident that the concentration of the 1,25$(OH)_2D_3$ receptor is critically dependent on the state of differentiation and/or activation of certain vitamin D target cells, probably to restrict or amplify the action of the hormone at various stages in the physiology of the cell.

The 1,25$(OH)_2D_3$ hormone also appears to alter the level of its receptor in certain cultured cell lines. Sher et al (177) reported that in T47D breast cancer cells 1,25$(OH)_2D_3$ induces processing of the receptor to a nonbinding form. Conversely, Costa et al (35) observed that 1,25$(OH)_2D_3$ causes a significant up-regulation of 1,25$(OH)_2D_3$ receptor binding activity in cultured kidney cells as well as other cell types. In our own studies involving immunoblot detection of the receptor in 1,25$(OH)_2D_3$-treated 3T6 mouse fibroblasts (J. W. Pike, N. M. Sleator, and M. R. Haussler, unpublished information) we found an enhancement in receptor levels as early as 4 h and as high as 10-fold within 48–72 h. Our data in 3T6 cells and those of Costa et al (35) may be explained by invoking the principle that 1,25$(OH)_2D_3$ influences receptor levels via an alteration of the proliferation and differentiation state of the cultured cells. However, in view of the rapidity of this event, it is more likely that the hormone is capable of altering the turnover rate of the receptor, either by enhancing its biosynthesis or by decreasing its degradation, or both. The mechanism whereby 1,25$(OH)_2D_3$ apparently up-regulates the level of its receptor in mouse 3T6 and other cells and the possible relevance of this finding to the biology of the receptor in mammalian systems in vivo are currently under study.

Recently, a striking qualitative modification in the receptor was observed in our laboratory (160) when mouse fibroblast (3T6) cells were exposed to the 1,25$(OH)_2D_3$ hormone. When a high-salt cytosol preparation from untreated 3T6 cells was immunoblotted, the receptor appeared as a band at 54,000 daltons. In contrast, after treatment of intact 3T6 cells with 1,25$(OH)_2D_3$ in culture for 90 min, the receptor extracted from the nucleus exhibited a small but significant reduction in electrophoretic mobility, with the upshifted form of the 3T6 cell 1,25$(OH)_2D_3$ receptor displaying an approximate molecular weight of 55,000. These data indicate that the occupied receptor isolated from the nuclear fraction had undergone covalent modification that caused it to migrate more slowly upon denaturing gel electrophoresis (160).

The hormone-dependent alteration in the receptor was further characterized by labeling the protein internally with [$^{35}$S]methionine in 3T6 cells. Metabolic labeling, immunoprecipitation, and denaturing electrophoresis confirmed the hormone-dependent upshift in electrophoretic mobility (160) that was seen via immunoblot analysis. An intense doublet appeared at 55,000 daltons representing the residual unmodified receptor and its upshifted derivative in the 3T6 total cell lysate (160). When cells were instead incubated with [$^{32}$P]orthophosphate in the presence or absence of 1,25$(OH)_2D_3$, no $^{32}$P was detected in the receptor without addition of 1,25$(OH)_2D_3$ to the cells, but significant and selective phosphorylation of the upshifted band occurred when 3T6 cells were treated for 4 h with 1,25$(OH)_2D_3$. Thus, the anomalous migration of the 1,25$(OH)_2D_3$ receptor was due to phosphorylation (160). Preliminary data indicate that phosphorylation in the presence of 1,25$(OH)_2D_3$ under these conditions (i.e. no phosphatase inhibitors) occurs on a serine residue(s) (J. W. Pike, N. M. Sleator, M. R. Haussler, N. Weigel, unpublished information). Results of in vitro translation of 3T6 cell mRNA followed by immunoprecipitation of biosynthesized receptors (D. J. Mangelsdorf, J. W. Pike, M. R. Haussler, unpublished information) are consistent with the upper receptor band being a posttranslationally modified form; only the lower nonphosphorylated receptor band at 54,000 daltons appears during in vitro translation.

A similar phosphorylation of the nuclear progesterone receptor in uterine slices was recently reported by Logeat et al (121). Therefore, the 1,25$(OH)_2D_3$ receptor and probably other steroid receptors become phosphorylated upon hormone binding in culture and perhaps in vivo. The interaction of the 1,25$(OH)_2D_3$ hormone with the receptor probably alters the conformation of the protein, rendering it a good substrate for a nuclear protein kinase. Because phosphorylation is an early, hormone-dependent event coinciding with nuclear localization, it is likely of functional importance. The phosphorylated receptor could be the form of the receptor that binds most avidly to upstream regulatory regions of vitamin D–controlled genes. In addition to functional activation, phosphorylation may act as a signal for receptor processing to inactive forms. Regardless of the role of 1,25$(OH)_2D_3$ receptor phosphorylation, this qualitative modification of the receptor is probably a key biochemical event in the mechanism of action of 1,25$(OH)_2D_3$.

## BIOLOGIC ROLES AS A MEDIATOR OF VITAMIN D FUNCTION

### *Calcium and Mineral Homeostasis*

In the case of stimulating intestinal calcium absorption, there is compelling evidence for the involvement of the 1,25$(OH)_2D_3$ receptor. In the developing neonatal rat, the receptor appears at a time coincident with 1,25$(OH)_2D_3$-elicited (active) calcium absorption (68). Moreover, exchange assays have been devised for quantitating both occupied and unoccupied 1,25$(OH)_2D$ receptors (97, 129, 165), exploiting the selective action of L-1-tosylamino-2-phenylethyl chloromethyl ketone (TPCK) on unoccupied receptors (97) or mersalyl to dissociate bound hormone (129, 165). Hunziker et al (95) have evaluated the dynamic equilibrium between in vivo occupied and unoccupied receptors and correlated this with differing vitamin D status and other physiologic conditions in the chick. These parameters were related also to a biologic response, the concentration of intestinal vitamin $D_3$–dependent calcium-binding protein (CaBP). Intestinal receptor occupancy correlated directly with serum $1,25(OH)_2D$, which indicates that the quantity of occupied receptor is determined by a simple equilibrium between serum $1,25(OH)_2D$ and unoccupied receptors. Under normal physiologic conditions, only 10–20% of the total receptor is occupied by ligand in both chicks (46, 95) and rats (129). Finally, under all experimental situations in chicks, there was a positive correlation between occupied receptor and CaBP levels (95). These data clearly support the participation of the occupied receptor in the calcium translocation response to $1,25(OH)_2D_3$.

## *Regulation of Vitamin D Metabolism*

In addition to its role in renal mineral conservation, a direct consequence of $1,25(OH)_2D_3$ action in the kidney is decreased production of $1,25(OH)_2D_3$ and, concomitantly, enhanced production of 24-hydroxylated vitamin $D_3$ metabolites (84, 143, 189, 191). This feedback regulatory action is known to result from the reciprocal action of $1,25(OH)_2D_3$ on the relative specific activities of the renal 1-OHase and 24-OHase enzymes. Substantial evidence has been accumulated to suggest that the expression/induction of the 24-OHase enzyme activity represents a classic steroid hormone action of $1,25(OH)_2D_3$. The presence of functional receptors for $1,25(OH)_2D_3$ has been demonstrated in a number of cultured cell systems and there is a good correlation between the presence of these receptors and $1,25(OH)_2D_3$-responsive 24-OHase activity.

In the established pig kidney line, LLC-$PK_1$, $1,25(OH)_2D_3$ receptors are present (21, 34) and have been correlated with the ability of $1,25(OH)_2D_3$ to induce the $25(OH)D_3$-24-OHase enzyme. The dose dependency of 24-OHase enhancement by $1,25(OH)_2D_3$ treatment in culture resembles the binding kinetics for the hormone to cytosol preparations from LLC-$PK_1$ cells. The time course of $1,25(OH)_2D$ action (2-h lag; 8-h maximal 24-OHase), plus the fact that actinomycin D blocks this effect of $1,25(OH)_2D_3$, indicates that 24-OHase increase is an induction event (21). Moreover, the occurrence of the $1,25(OH)_2D_3$ receptor in these cells and its recognized property of nuclear localization implicate the receptor as the mediator of the genomic effects of the hormone on 24-OHase enzyme levels. Impressive extensions of the data in kidney cells have been accomplished in the case of bone cells, circulating mononuclear cells, and fibroblasts. Osteoblast $1,25(OH)_2D_3$ receptors are significantly altered by treatment with retinoic acid and there is a positive correlation between receptor number in a particular circumstance and the magnitude of $1,25(OH)_2D_3$'s ability to induce the 24-OHase enzyme (25). Utilizing circulating mononuclear cells (107) or fibroblasts derived from patients with vitamin D–dependent rickets type II (26, 53, 61, 89), Feldman's and Liberman's groups observed a striking association between biochemically competent 1,25$(OH)_2D_3$ receptors and the induction of 24-OHase by the hormone. This association has even been extended to New World monkey fibroblasts (3), which display resistance to vitamin D caused by reduced 1,25$(OH)_2D_3$ receptor number. Taken together, these findings strongly suggest that the 1,25$(OH)_2D_3$ receptor mediates 24-OHase induction. But in all cell culture experiments reported thus far, there is only a correlation between the 1,25$(OH)_2D_3$ receptor and the bioresponse.

### *Control of the Immune System, Bone Remodeling, and Mineralization*

Because nonclassical sites for the 1,25$(OH)_2D_3$ receptor include cells derived from bone marrow and thymus, 1,25$(OH)_2D_3$ may be an immunomodulator like the glucocorticoids and other steroids. The most intensively investigated model system within the cell-mediated immune system is the differentiation of HL-60 leukemia cells. This leukemic line differentiates into macrophage-like cells when treated with 1,25$(OH)_2D_3$ in culture (7, 124, 188). Our laboratory has shown that saturation of the HL-60 nuclear receptor by 1,25$(OH)_2[^3H]D_3$ in complete culture medium correlates with the kinetics of 1,25$(OH)_2D_3$-induced FMLP (chemotaxin) receptors (124), which indicates that this expression of the differentiated phenotype can be mediated by the 1,25$(OH)_2D_3$ receptor protein. However, suppression of proliferation and differentiation of HL-60 cells into macrophages requires at least 72 h, even though the saturation of nuclear receptors with 1,25$(OH)_2D_3$ can be achieved as early as 4 h in suspended cells. One rapid action of 1,25$(OH)_2D_3$ in HL-60 cells that has been observed by Reitsma et al (171) is the attenuation of c-*myc* oncogene mRNA levels. While it is tempting to speculate that the 1,25$(OH)_2D_3$ receptor complex regulates c-*myc* transcription via direct binding in the c-*myc* gene regulatory region, it is plausible that this regulation is secondary and that the hormone-receptor complex controls the transcription of a key gene(s) whose product(s) in turn controls c-*myc* mRNA levels. Since 1,25$(OH)_2D_3$ regulates CaBP in traditional target cells, it is equally possible that intracellular calcium fluctuations modulated by CaBP represent a second messenger in 1,25$(OH)_2D_3$-induced differentiation of HL-60 cells. It should also be noted that a number of other compounds that differentiate HL-60 cells, such as retinoic acid and a phorbol ester tumor promoter (TPA), elicit suppressions in c-*myc* mRNA levels similar to that produced by 1,25$(OH)_2D_3$ (66). Thus, this effect on c-*myc* expression may reflect either a declining proliferation rate or possibly the general triggering of differentiation.

As noted above, there is an 80% reduction in the concentration of 1,25$(OH)_2D_3$ receptors that accompanies the process of macrophage differentiation. This may relate to the proposed role of monocytes and macrophages as osteoclast precursors (144). 1,25$(OH)_2D_3$ increases osteoclast number in vivo (190) and is proposed to mediate bone resorption, in part by increasing the differentiation of osteoclast progenitors, as illustrated in Figure 2. Osteoclasts do not possess $1,25(OH)_2D_3$ receptors (137) and therefore their number but not their activity is directly affected by $1,25(OH)_2D_3$. The observation that $1,25(OH)_2D_3$ receptor concentrations are dramatically reduced upon differentiation of HL-60 cells to macrophages could reflect the first stage in the attenuation of receptor expression that is presumably complete upon fusion of macrophages to multinucleate osteoclasts.

As illustrated in Figure 2, it is important to note that $1,25(OH)_2D_3$ indirectly augments the final stages of osteoclast differentiation through a newly recognized operation on T lymphocytes. T cells contain $1,25(OH)_2D_3$ receptors (163) and both $1,25(OH)_2D_3$ receptor number and lymphokine production are modulated by $1,25(OH)_2D_3$; at least one of the regulated lymphokines has been shown to elicit macrophage fusion to giant multinucleate osteoclast-like cells (2). A second T-cell-derived lymphokine acts synergistically with $1,25(OH)_2D_3$ in causing U937 monoblastic cells to elaborate IL-1 (6), which is itself a strong bone resorbing agent (63). Finally, $1,25(OH)_2D_3$ could cause bone resorption by binding to its well-known receptors in osteoblasts (27, 127) and bringing about the release of osteoblast-derived resorption factors, as depicted in Figure 2. $1,25(OH)_2D_3$-stimulated osteoblasts also presumably remineralize bone during the remodeling cycle.

Direct effects of $1,25(OH)_2D_3$ on osteoblast-like cells include enhanced vitamin K–dependent bone $\gamma$-carboxyglutamic acid (Gla) containing protein (BGP) (161) and alkaline phosphatase (123) biosynthesis, and suppressed collagen formation at the mRNA level (173). While the exact functions of these modulated proteins have not been characterized, attenuation of collagen

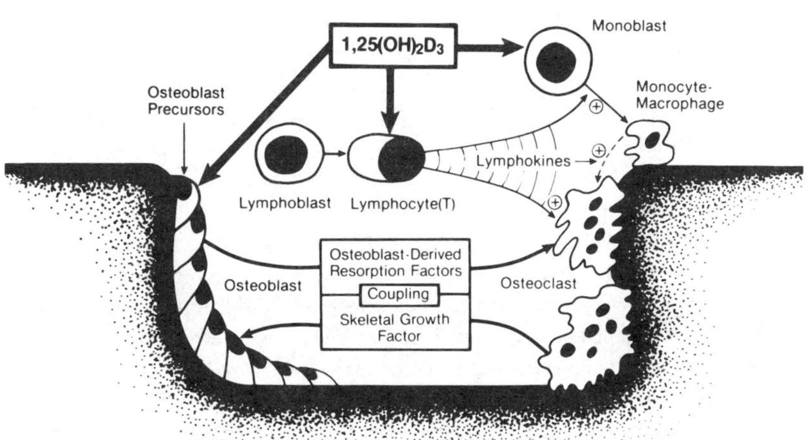


*Figure 2* Proposed function of $1,25(OH)_2D_3$ and its receptor in bone remodeling and immunomodulation.

biosynthesis and secretion could be the "final event" in 1,25$(OH)_2D_3$-induced mineralization of existing collagen. Similarly, 1,25$(OH)_2D_3$ has potent actions on blood mononuclear cells. The hormone suppresses immunoglobin production by activated human peripheral blood mononuclear cells, probably by inhibiting proliferation of antibody-producing B cells or helper T cells (113, 114). 1,25$(OH)_2D_3$ blocks phytohemagglutinin- and antigen-induced lymphocyte blast transformation, apparently via attenuation of IL-2 production (8, 113, 172, 193). All of this new information could have clinical relevance to osteoporosis, since T-cell subsets are abnormal in this disorder (60) and the regulation by 1,25$(OH)_2D_3$ and sex hormones of the immune system has been invoked to explain the etiology of postmenopausal osteoporosis (74). Therefore, it is clear that, along with its mediating receptor, 1,25$(OH)_2D_3$ accomplishes a complex yet elegant regulation of the bone remodeling cells. 1,25$(OH)_2D_3$-responsive cells of the immune system appear to play a central role in the function of 1,25$(OH)_2D_3$ on bone resorption, but this may be only one facet of a more general action of the hormone as a novel immunoregulator.

## *Cell Proliferation, Differentiation, and Anticancer Actions*

1,25$(OH)_2D_3$ has been found to inhibit proliferation in a number of cancer cell lines that possess the vitamin D receptor (32, 44, 55, 75, 124). In some cases, inhibition of cell growth is coupled to morphological changes (44, 55) and differentiation of the cells (1, 7, 24). Our laboratory has found that the 1,25$(OH)_2D_3$-elicited inhibition of colony formation by tumorigenic cells in soft agar is directly correlated to vitamin D receptor number (75). Clonal lines with low 1,25$(OH)_2D_3$ receptor numbers do not respond to 1,25$(OH)_2D_3$ in terms of growth regulation and morphological differentiation (44, 124). These results from cultured cells suggest that 1,25$(OH)_2D_3$ inhibits tumor cell growth and may even be capable of suppressing the malignant phenotype by initiating normal differentiation. Honma et al (92) extended these findings to the in vivo situation by showing that 1,25$(OH)_2D_3$ prolongs the survival time of *nude* mice inoculated with M1 leukemia cells. Also, 1$\alpha$-hydroxyvitamin $D_3$ [an efficient precursor of 1,25$(OH)_2D_3$] suppresses pulmonary metastases of Lewis lung carcinoma (174).

The above observations would seem to be consistent with preliminary data from a prospective study showing that colorectal cancer risk is inversely correlated with dietary vitamin D and calcium (62). Additionally, two groups (2, 205) have demonstrated that 1,25$(OH)_2D_3$ can inhibit phorbol ester–dependent chemical carcinogenesis in mouse skin. However, until more in vivo trials are performed, these data must be viewed with caution. For example, as with vitamin A compounds, in certain circumstances 1,25$(OH)_2D_3$ can act as a tumor enhancer (99, 112, 204; K. Yamaoka, S. L. Marion, A. Gallegos, and M. R. Haussler, unpublished information). Thus, it is premature to conclude that 1,25$(OH)_2D_3$ is a natural anticancer agent. What is evident is that, in combination with its receptor, $1,25(OH)_2D_3$ is a potent regulator of cell growth and maturation. Whether this bioeffect can be exploited in the prevention or treatment of certain malignancies is open to question.

## INTEGRATED MODEL FOR THE ACTION OF THE VITAMIN D RECEPTOR

In the integrated model of $1,25(OH)_2D_3$ receptor biochemistry and biology pictured in Figure 3, a fraction of the unoccupied receptor is hypothesized to be present in the cytoplasm, but the equilibrium probably favors the nuclear compartment, where the receptor exists as a loosely associated chromosomal protein. When complexed with the $1,25(OH)_2D_3$ hormone, the receptor is phosphorylated—possibly at multiple sites. The phosphorylated receptor is proposed to be the form that locates upstream regulatory regions of vitamin D–modulated genes in order to control transcription. These upstream activating sequences are analogous to those found for other steroid hormone receptors (104). Altered DNA transcription then results in enhanced or repressed levels of various mRNAs. The altered mRNA concentrations depicted in Figure 3 are hypothetical [i.e. extrapolated from $1,25(OH)_2D_3$-elicited protein changes] except for CaBP, which is increased (145), and c-*myc* and collagen, which are decreased (171, 173). The concept that the $1,25(OH)_2D_3$ receptor complex

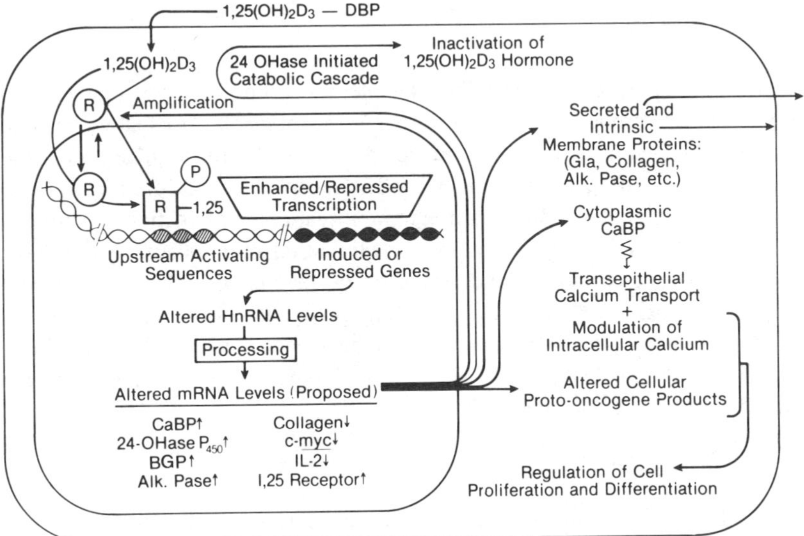


*Figure 3* Model for receptor-mediated actions of $1,25(OH)_2D_3$ at the molecular level. A hypothetical composite target cell for vitamin D is depicted. An R in a circle represents the unoccupied receptor, while an R in a square designates the occupied and phosphorylated receptor. BGP means bone Gla containing protein, CaBP is calcium-binding protein, and 24-OHase is 24-hydroxylase.

binds to regulatory/promotor sequences for each of the putative induced mRNAs is only one possible mechanism. Regardless of the exact sequence of events, there is little doubt that control of mRNA levels is the key manner in which $1,25(OH)_2D_3$ ultimately orchestrates the concentration of its bioactive proteins.

As summarized in Figure 3, there are a number of $1,25(OH)_2D_3$-induced proteins that occur in various target cells. Individual cell types are presumably preprogrammed to modulate certain of the induced proteins, which then effect the appropriate altered cell function. 3T6 fibroblasts would be an example of a cell type in which receptor up-regulation or amplification occurs. Other target cells, such as those of the kidney, may primarily inactivate $1,25(OH)_2D_3$ via the induced 24-OHase initiated cascade and still carry out transepithelial transport of minerals. Bone cells apparently respond to $1,25(OH)_2D_3$ by modulating an array of proteins (e.g. BGP, collagen, alkaline phosphatase, etc) required for the complex process of bone mineralization and remodeling. CaBP undoubtedly functions as a part of intestinal calcium transport, but could also modulate intracellular calcium in other targets. Along with control of oncogene products, intracellular calcium may act to regulate cell proliferation and differentiation. This is particularly true in certain hematopoietic and transformed cells that appear to respond to $1,25(OH)_2D_3$ by differentiation and suppression of the embryonic or malignant phenotype.

## CONCLUSION

Clearly, the $1,25(OH)_2D_3$ receptor is an integral part of the biochemical action of vitamin D. Perhaps the receptor protein is the molecular key that will enable us to unlock the mechanism through which vitamin D controls gene expression and ultimately influences cell function. The receptor is therefore important to basic science, but it also has significant ramifications for nutrition and clinical medicine. Analysis of the receptor and its use in radioreceptor assay have dramatically increased our understanding of several disorders of bone and mineral metabolism. Perhaps most exciting, potential new actions of vitamin D in the neuroendocrine and immune systems have been revealed. As a nutritional principle, vitamin D has assumed a pivotal position as the precursor of a biological modifier of major significance.

### Acknowledgments

The author deeply appreciates the support and assistance of Carol Donaldson and Paula Leece in preparing this review. Research in the author's laboratory quoted in this review was supported by NIH Grants AM-15781 and AM-33351 to M. R. Haussler and AM-32313 and AM-34750 to J. W. Pike.

## Literature Cited


1. Abe, E., Miyaura, C., Sakagami, H., Takeda, M., Konno, K., et al. 1981. Differentiation of mouse myeloid leukemia cells induced by $1\alpha$,25-dihydroxyvitamin $D_3$. *Proc. Natl. Acad. Sci. USA* 78:4990–94
2. Abe, E., Miyaura, C., Tanaka, H., Shiina, Y., Kuribayashi, T., et al. 1983. $1\alpha$,25-Dihydroxyvitamin $D_3$ promotes fusion of mouse alveolar macrophages both by a direct mechanism and by a spleen cell-mediated indirect mechanism. *Proc. Natl. Acad. Sci. USA* 80:5583–87
3. Adams, J. S., Gacad, M. A., Baker, A. J., Kheun, G., Rude, R. K. 1985. Diminished internalization and action of 1,25-dihydroxyvitamin $D_3$ in dermal fibroblasts cultured from New World primates. *Endocrinology* 116:2523–27
4. Adams, J. S., Gacad, M. A., Singer, F. R. 1984. Specific internalization and action of 1,25-dihydroxyvitamin $D_3$ in cultured dermal fibroblasts from patients with X-linked hypophosphatemia. *J. Clin. Endocrinol. Metab.* 59:556–60
5. Allegretto, E. A., Pike, J. W. 1985. Trypsin cleavage of chick 1,25-dihydroxyvitamin $D_3$ receptors. Generation of discrete polypeptides which retain hormone but are unreactive to DNA and monoclonal antibody. *J. Biol. Chem.* 260:10139–45
6. Amento, E. P., Bhalla, A. K., Kurnick, J. T., Kradin, R. L., Clemens, T. L., et al. 1984. $1\alpha$,25-Dihydroxyvitamin $D_3$ induces maturation of the human monocyte cell line U937, and, in association with a factor from human T lymphocytes, augments production of the monokine, mononuclear cell factor. *J. Clin. Invest.* 73:731–39
7. Bar-Shavit, Z., Teitelbaum, S. L., Reitsma, P., Hall, A., Pegg, L. E. 1983. Induction of monocytic differentiation and bone resorption by 1,25-dihydroxyvitamin $D_3$ *Proc. Natl. Acad. Sci. USA* 80:5907–11
8. Bhalla, A. K., Amento, E. P., Serog, B., Glimcher, L. H. 1984. 1,25-Dihydroxyvitamin $D_3$ inhibits antigen-induced T cell activation. *J. Immunol.* 133:1748–54
9. Bishop, J. E., Hunziker, W., Norman, A. W. 1982. Evidence for multiple molecular weight forms of the chick intestinal 1,25-dihydroxyvitamin $D_3$ receptor. *Biochem. Biophys. Res. Commun.* 108:140–45
10. Bishop, J. E., Norman, A. W., Coburn, J. W., Roberts, P. A., Henry, H. L. 1980. Studies on the metabolism of calciferol XVI. Determination of the concentration of 25-hydroxyvitamin D, 24,25-dihydroxyvitamin D and 1,25-dihydroxyvitamin D in a single two-milliliter plasma sample. *Mineral Electrolyte Metab.* 3:181–89
11. Boivin, G., Mesguich, P., Morel, G., Pike, J. W., Dubois, P. M., et al. 1985. Ultrastructural-immunocytochemical localization of 1,25-dihydroxyvitamin $D_3$ receptors in osteoblasts and osteocytes. In *Vitamin D. Chemical, Biochemical and Clinical Update,* ed. A. W. Norman, K. Schaefer, H.-G. Grigoleit, D. V. Herrath, pp. 93–94. Berlin/New York: de Gruyter
12. Boland, R., Norman, A., Ritz, E., Hasselbach, W. 1985. Presence of a 1,25-dihydroxyvitamin $D_3$ receptor in chick skeletal muscle myoblasts. *Biochem. Biophys. Res. Commun.* 128:305–11
13. Brommage, R., DeLuca, H. F. 1985. Evidence that 1,25-dihydroxyvitamin $D_3$ is the physiologically active metabolite of vitamin $D_3$. *Endocr. Rev.* 6:491–511
14. Brumbaugh, P. F., Haussler, D. H., Bursac, K. M., Haussler, M. R. 1974. Filter assay for $1\alpha$,25-dihydroxyvitamin $D_3$. Utilization of the hormone's target tissue chromatin receptor. *Biochemistry* 13: 4091–97
15. Brumbaugh, P. F., Haussler, M. R. 1973. $1\alpha$,25-Dihydroxyvitamin $D_3$ receptor: Competitive binding of vitamin D analogs. *Life Sci.* 13:1737–46
16. Brumbaugh, P. F., Haussler, M. R. 1974. $1\alpha$,25-Dihydroxycholecalciferol receptors in intestine. I. Association of $1\alpha$,25-dihydroxycholecalciferol with intestinal mucosa chromatin. *J. Biol. Chem.* 249:1251–57
17. Brumbaugh, P. F., Haussler, M. R. 1974. $1\alpha$,25-Dihydroxycholecalciferol receptors in intestine. II. Temperature-dependent transfer of the hormone to chromatin via a specific cytosol receptor. *J. Biol. Chem.* 249:1258–62
18. Brumbaugh, P. F., Haussler, M. R. 1975. Specific binding of $1\alpha$,25-dihydroxycholecalciferol to nuclear components of chick intestine. *J. Biol. Chem.* 250:1588–94
19. Brumbaugh, P. F., Hughes, M. R., Haussler, M. R. 1975. Cytoplasmic and nuclear binding components for $1\alpha$,25-dihydroxyvitamin $D_3$ in chick parathyroid glands. *Proc. Natl. Acad. Sci. USA* 72:4871–75

20. Casanova, J., Horowitz, Z. D., Cop, R. P., McIntyre, W. R., Pascual, A., et al. 1984. Photoaffinity labeling of the thyroid hormone nuclear receptors. Influence of *n*-butyrate and analysis of the half-lives of the 57,000 and 47,000 molecular weight receptor forms. *J. Biol. Chem.* 259:12084–91
21. Chandler, J. S., Chandler, S. K., Pike, J. W., Haussler, M. R. 1984. 1,25-Dihydroxyvitamin $D_3$ induces 25-hydroxyvitamin $D_3$–24-hydroxylase in a cultured monkey kidney cell line (LLC-$MK_2$) apparently deficient in the high affinity receptor for the hormone. *J. Biol. Chem.* 259:2214–22
22. Chandler, J. S., Pike, J. W., Haussler, M. R. 1979. 1,25-dihydroxyvitamin $D_3$ receptors in rat kidney cytosol. *Biochem. Biophys. Res. Commun.* 90:1057–63
23. Chen, T. L., Cone, C. M., Morey-Holton, E., Feldman, D. 1982. Glucocorticoid regulation of 1,25$(OH)_2$-vitamin $D_3$ receptors in cultured mouse bone cells. *J. Biol. Chem.* 257:13564–69
24. Chen, T. L., Feldman, D. 1981. Regulation of 1,25-dihydroxyvitamin $D_3$ receptors in cultured mouse bone cells. Correlation of receptor concentration with the rate of cell division. *J. Biol. Chem.* 256:5561–66
25. Chen, T. L., Feldman, D. 1985. Retinoic acid modulation of 1,25$(OH)_2$-vitamin $D_3$ receptors and bioresponse in bone cells: Species differences between rat and mouse. *Biochem. Biophys. Res. Commun.* 132:74–80
26. Chen, T. L., Hirst, M. A., Cone, C. M., Hochberg, Z., Tietze, H.-U., et al. 1984. 1,25-Dihydroxyvitamin D resistance, rickets, and alopecia: Analysis of receptors and bioresponse in cultured fibroblasts from patients and parents. *J. Clin. Endocrinol. Metab.* 59:383–88
27. Chen, T. L., Hirst, M. A., Feldman, D. 1979. A receptor-like binding macromolecule for 1$\alpha$,25-dihydroxycholecalciferol in cultured mouse bone cells. *J. Biol. Chem.* 254:7491–94
28. Chida, K., Hashiba, H., Fukushima, M., Suda, T., Kuroki, T. 1985. Inhibition of tumor promotion in mouse skin by 1$\alpha$,25-dihydroxyvitamin $D_3$. *Cancer Res.* 45:5426–30
29. Christakos, S., Norman, A. 1979. Studies on the mode of action of calciferol XVIII. Evidence for a specific high affinity binding protein for 1,25-dihydroxyvitamin $D_3$ in chick kidney and pancreas. *Biochem. Biophys. Res. Commun.* 89:56–63
30. Clemens, T. L., Adams, J. S., Horiuchi, N., Gilchrest, B. A., Cho, H., et al. 1983. Interaction of 1,25-dihydroxyvitamin-$D_3$ with keratinocytes and fibroblasts from skin of normal subjects and a subject with vitamin-D–dependent rickets, type II: A model for study of the mode of action of 1,25-dihydroxyvitamin $D_3$. *J. Clin. Endocrinol. Metab.* 56:824–30
31. Clemens, T. L., Zhou, X. Y., Pike, J. W., Haussler, M. R., Sloviter, R. S. 1985. 1,25-Dihydroxyvitamin D receptor and vitamin D–dependent calcium-binding protein in rat brain: Comparative immunocytochemical localization. See Ref. 11, pp. 95–96
32. Colston, K., Colston, M. J., Feldman, D. 1981. 1,25-dihydroxyvitamin $D_3$ and malignant melanoma: The presence of receptor and inhibition of cell growth in culture. *Endocrinology* 108:1083–86
33. Colston, K. W., Feldman, D. 1979. Demonstration of a 1,25-dihydroxycholecalciferol cytoplasmic receptor-like binder in mouse kidney. *J. Clin. Endocrinol. Metab.* 49:798–800
34. Colston, K., Feldman, D. 1982. 1,25-Dihydroxyvitamin $D_3$ receptors and functions in cultured pig kidney cells (LLC-$PK_1$). *J. Biol. Chem.* 257:2504–8
35. Costa, E. M., Hirst, M. A., Feldman, D. 1985. Regulation of 1,25-dihydroxyvitamin $D_3$ receptors by vitamin D analogs in cultured mammalian cells. *Endocrinology* 117:2203–10
36. Coty, W. A. 1980. Reversible dissociation of steroid hormone-receptor complexes by mercurial reagents. *J. Biol. Chem.* 255:8035–37
37. Coty, W. A. 1980. A specific, high affinity binding protein for 1$\alpha$,25-dihydroxyvitamin D in the chick oviduct shell gland. *Biochem. Biophys. Res. Commun.* 93:285–92
38. Coty, W. A., McConkey, C. L. Jr., Brown, T. A. 1981. A specific binding protein for 1$\alpha$,25-dihydroxyvitamin D in the chick embryo chorioallantoic membrane. *J. Biol. Chem.* 256:5545–49
39. Dame, M. C., Pierce, E. A., DeLuca, H. F. 1985. Identification of the porcine intestinal 1,25-dihydroxyvitamin $D_3$ receptor on sodium dodecyl sulfate/polyacrylamide gels by renaturation and immunoblotting. *Proc. Natl. Acad. Sci. USA* 82:7825–29
40. Dame, M. C., Pierce, E. A., Prahl, J. M., DeLuca, H. F. 1985. Monoclonal antibodies against the 1,25-dihydroxyvitamin $D_3$ receptor protein: Production and characterization. *Proc. Endocr. Soc. 67th Ann. Meet.*, Baltimore, p. 261 (Abstr.)

41. Danan, J.-L., Delorme, A.-C., Cuisinier-Gleizes, P. 1981. Biochemical evidence for a cytoplasmic $1\alpha$,25-dihydroxyvitamin $D_3$ receptor-like protein in rat yolk sac. *J. Biol. Chem.* 256:4847–50
42. DeLuca, H. F., Schnoes, H. K. 1983. Vitamin D: Recent advances. *Ann. Rev. Biochem.* 52:411–39
43. Dietel, M., Dorn, G., Montz, R., Altenahr, E. 1979. Influence of vitamin $D_3$, 1,25-dihydroxyvitamin $D_3$, and 24,25-dihydroxyvitamin $D_3$ on parathyroid hormone secretion, adenosine 3',5'-monophosphate release, and ultrastructure of parathyroid glands in organ culture. *Endocrinology* 105:237–45
44. Dokoh, S., Donaldson, C. A., Haussler, M. R. 1984. Influence of 1,25-dihydroxyvitamin $D_3$ on cultured osteogenic sarcoma cells: Correlation with the 1,25-dihydroxyvitamin $D_3$ receptor. *Cancer Res.* 44:2103–9
45. Dokoh, S., Donaldson, C. A., Marion, S. L., Pike, J. W., Haussler, M. R. 1983. The ovary: A target organ for 1,25-dihydroxyvitamin $D_3$. *Endocrinology* 112:200–6
46. Dokoh, S., Haussler, M. R., Pike, J. W. 1984. Development of a radioligand immunoassay for 1,25-dihydroxycholecalciferol receptors utilizing monoclonal antibody. *Biochem. J.* 221:129–36
47. Dokoh, S., Llach, F., Haussler, M. R. 1982. 25-Hydroxyvitamin D and 1,25-dihydroxyvitamin D: New ultrasensitive and accurate assays. In *Vitamin D, Chemical, Biochemical and Clinical Endocrinology of Calcium Metabolism,* ed. A. W. Norman, K. Schaefer, D. von Herrath, H.-G. Grigoleit, pp. 743–49. Berlin/New York: de Gruyter
48. Dokoh, S., Pike, J. W., Chandler, J. S., Mancini, J. M., Haussler, M. R. 1981. An improved radioreceptor assay for 1,25-dihydroxyvitamin D in human plasma. *Anal. Biochem.* 116:211–22
49. Eil, C., Liberman, U. A., Rosen, J. F., Marx, S. J. 1981. A cellular defect in hereditary vitamin-D-dependent rickets type II: Defective nuclear uptake of 1,25-dihydroxyvitamin D in cultured skin fibroblasts. *N. Engl. J. Med.* 304:1588–91
50. Eisman, J. A., Hamstra, A. J., Kream, B. E., DeLuca, H. F. 1976. A sensitive, precise, and convenient method for determination of 1,25-dihydroxyvitamin D in human plasma. *Arch. Biochem. Biophys.* 176:235–43
51. Eisman, J. A., MacIntyre, I., Martin, T. J., Moseley, J. M. 1979. 1,25-Dihydroxyvitamin-D receptors in breast cancer cells. *Lancet* 2:1335–36
52. Esvelt, R. P., DeLuca, H. F., Wichmann, J. K., Yoshizawa, S., Zurcher, J., et al. 1980. 1,25-Dihydroxyvitamin $D_3$ stimulated increase of 7,8-didehydrocholesterol levels in rat skin. *Biochemistry* 19:6158–61
53. Feldman, D., Chen, T., Cone, C., Hirst, M., Shani, S., et al. 1982. Vitamin D resistant rickets with alopecia: Cultured skin fibroblasts exhibit defective cytoplasmic receptors and unresponsiveness to $1,25(OH)_2D_3$. *J. Clin. Endocrinol. Metab.* 55:1020–22
54. Feldman, D., Chen, T., Hirst, M., Colston, K., Karasek, M., et al. 1980. Demonstration of 1,25-dihydroxyvitamin $D_3$ receptors in human skin biopsies. *J. Clin. Endocrinol. Metab.* 51:1463–65
55. Frampton, R. J., Omond, S. A., Eisman, J. A. 1983. Inhibition of human cancer cell growth by 1,25-dihydroxyvitamin $D_3$ metabolites. *Cancer Res.* 43:4443–47
56. Franceschi, R. T. 1984. Interaction of the $1\alpha$,25-dihydroxyvitamin $D_3$ receptor with RNA and synthetic polyribonucleotides. *Proc. Natl. Acad. Sci. USA* 81:2337–41
57. Franceschi, R. T., DeLuca, H. F., Mercado, D. L. 1983. Temperature-dependent inactivation of the nucleic acid binding and aggregation of the 1,25-dihydroxyvitamin $D_3$ receptor. *Arch. Biochem. Biophys.* 222:504–17
58. Freake, H. C., Abeyasekera, G., Iwasaki, J., Marcocci, C., MacIntyre, I., et al. 1984. Measurement of 1,25-dihydroxyvitamin $D_3$ receptors in breast cancer and their relationship to biochemical and clinical indices. *Cancer Res.* 44:1677–81
59. Freake, H. C., MacIntyre, I. 1982. Specific binding of 1,25-dihydroxycholecalciferol in human medullary thyroid carcinoma. *Biochem. J.* 206:181–84
60. Fujita, T., Matsui, T., Nakao, Y., Watanabe, S. 1984. T lymphocyte subsets in osteoporosis. Effect of 1-alpha hydroxyvitamin $D_3$. *Mineral Electrolyte Metab.* 10:375–78
61. Gamblin, G. T., Liberman, U. A., Eil, C., Downs, R. W., DeGrange, D. A., et al. 1985. Defective induction of 25-hydroxyvitamin $D_3$-24-hydroxylase by 1,25-dihydroxyvitamin $D_3$ in cultured skin fibroblasts. *J. Clin. Invest.* 75:954–60
62. Garland, C., Barrett-Connor, E., Rossof, A. H., Shekelle, R. B., Criqui, M. H., et al. 1985. Dietary vitamin D and calcium and risk of colorectal cancer: A 19-year prospective study in men. *Lancet* 1:307–9

63. Gowen, M., Wood, D. D., Ihrie, E. J., McGuire, M. K. B., Russell, R. G. G. 1983. An interleukin-1-like factor stimulates bone resorption in vitro. *Nature* 306:378–80
64. Gray, R. W., Wilz, D. R., Caldas, A. E., Lemann, J. Jr. 1977. The importance of phosphate in regulating 1,25(OH)$_2$-vitamin D levels in human studies in healthy subjects, in calcium-stone formers and in patients with primary hyperparathyroidism. *J. Clin. Endocrinol. Metab.* 45:299–306
65. Griffin, J. E., Zerwekh, J. E. 1983. Impaired stimulation of 25-hydroxyvitamin D–24-hydroxylase in fibroblasts from a patient with vitamin D–dependent rickets, type II. *J. Clin. Invest.* 72:1190–99
66. Grosso, L. E., Pitot, H. C. 1984. Modulation of c-myc expression in the HL-60 cell line. *Biochem. Biophys. Res. Commun.* 119:473–80
67. Guillemant, S., Eurin, J. 1983. Effect of dithiothreitol on the 1$\alpha$,25-dihydroxyvitamin D$_3$ chick intestinal receptor analyzed by polyacrylamide gel electrophoresis. *Biochem. Biophys. Res. Commun.* 113:687–94
68. Halloran, B. P., DeLuca, H. F. 1981. Appearance of the intestinal cytosolic receptor for 1,25-dihydroxyvitamin D$_3$ during neonatal development in the rat. *J. Biol. Chem.* 256:7338–42
69. Haussler, M. R., Brickman, A. S. 1982. Vitamin D: Metabolism, actions, and disease states. In *Disorders of Mineral Metabolism,* ed. F. Bronner, J. Coburn, 2:359–431. New York: Academic
70. Haussler, M. R., Brumbaugh, P. F. 1976. 1$\alpha$,25-dihydroxyvitamin D$_3$ receptors in intestine. In *Hormone-Receptor Interaction: Molecular Aspects,* ed. G. S. Levey, pp. 301–32. New York/Basel: Dekker
71. Haussler, M. R., Chandler, J. S., Pike, J. W., Brumbaugh, P. F., Speer, D. P., et al. 1980. Physiological importance of vitamin D metabolism. In *Progress in Biochemical Pharmacology. Hormones and the Kidney,* ed. G. S. Stokes, J. F. Mahony, R. Paoletti, 17:134–42. Basel/Munchen/Paris/London/New York/Sydney: S. Karger
72. Haussler, M. R., Dokoh, S., Liberman, U. A., Eil, C., Marx, S. J., et al. 1984. Receptor for 1,25-dihydroxyvitamin D$_3$: Its importance in measuring circulating vitamin D hormone and detection of a defective form in vitamin D-dependent rickets type II. In *Endocrine Control of Bone and Calcium Metabolism,* ed. D. V. Cohn, J. T. Potts, Jr., T. Fujita, pp. 11–13. Amsterdam/New York/Oxford: Excerpta Medica
73. Haussler, M. R., Dokoh, S., Mangelsdorf, D. J., Donaldson, C. A., Pike, J. W. 1983. Vitamin D metabolites: New physiologic and clinical insights. In *Clinical Disorders of Bone and Mineral Metabolism,* ed. B. Frame, J. T. Potts, Jr., pp. 68–71. Amsterdam/Oxford/-Princeton: Excerpta Medica
74. Haussler, M. R., Donaldson, C. A., Allegretto, E. A., Marion, S. L., Mangelsdorf, D. J., et al. 1984. In *Osteoporosis: Proc. Copenhagen Int. Symp. Osteoporosis,* ed. C. Christiansen, C. D. Arnaud, B. E. C. Nordin, A. M. Parfitt, W. A. Peck, B. L. Riggs, 2: 725–36. Denmark: Aalborg Stiftsbogtrykkeri
75. Haussler, M. R., Donaldson, C. A., Marion, S. L., Allegretto, E. A., Kelly, M. A., et al. 1986. Receptors for the vitamin D hormone: Characterization and functional involvement in 1,25-dihydroxyvitamin D$_3$ regulated events. In *The Role of Receptors in Biology and Medicine,* ed. A. M. Gotto, Jr., B. W. O'Malley, pp. 91–104. New York: Raven
76. Haussler, M. R., Manolagas, S. C., Deftos, L. J. 1980. Evidence for a 1,25-dihydroxyvitamin D$_3$ receptor-like macromolecule in rat pituitary. *J. Biol. Chem.* 255:5007–10
77. Haussler, M. R., Manolagas, S. C., Deftos, L. J. 1982. Receptor for 1,25-dihydroxyvitamin D$_3$ in GH$_3$ pituitary cells. *J. Steroid Biochem.* 16:15–19
78. Haussler, M. R., McCain, T. A. 1977. Basic and clinical concepts related to vitamin D metabolism and action. *N. Engl. J. Med.* 297:974–83, 1041–50
79. Haussler, M. R., Myrtle, J. F., Norman, A. W. 1968. The association of a metabolite of vitamin D$_3$ with intestinal mucosa chromatin *in vivo*. *J. Biol. Chem.* 243:4055–64
80. Haussler, M. R., Norman, A. W. 1969. Chromosomal receptor for a vitamin D metabolite. *Proc. Natl. Acad. Sci. USA* 62:155–62
81. Haussler, M. R., Pike, J. W., Chandler, J. S., Jones, P. G. 1980. Molecular mechanism of action of 1,25-dihydroxyvitamin D hormone. In *Endocrinology 1980,* ed. I. A. Cumming, J. W. Funder, F. A. O. Mendelsohn, pp. 448–51. Canberra: Aust. Acad. Sci.
82. Haussler, M. R., Pike, J. W., Chandler, J., Manolagas, S. C., Deftos, L. J. 1981. Molecular action of 1,25-dihy-

droxyvitamin $D_3$: New cultured cell models. *Ann. NY Acad. Sci.* 372:502–17
83. Haussler, M., Sidell, N., Kelly, M., Donaldson, C., Altman, A., et al. 1983. Specific high-affinity binding and biologic action of retinoic acid in human neuroblastoma cell lines. *Proc. Natl. Acad. Sci. USA* 80:5525–29
84. Henry, H. L. 1979. Regulation of the hydroxylation of 25-hydroxyvitamin $D_3$ *in vivo* and in primary cultures of chick kidney cells. *J. Biol. Chem.* 254:2722–29
85. Henry, H. L., Norman, A. W. 1975. Studies on the mechanism of action of calciferol VII. Localization of 1,25-dihydroxyvitamin $D_3$ in chick parathyroid glands. *Biochem. Biophys. Res. Commun.* 62:781–88
86. Henry, H. L., Norman, A. W. 1984. Vitamin D: Metabolism and biological actions. *Ann. Rev. Nutr.* 4:493–520
87. Hirst, M. A., Feldman, D. 1981. 1,25-Dihydroxyvitamin $D_3$ receptors in mouse colon. *J. Steroid Biochem.* 14:315–19
88. Hirst, M., Feldman, D. 1983. Regulation of $1,25(OH)_2$-vitamin $D_3$ receptor content in cultured LLC-$PK_1$ kidney cells limits hormone responsiveness. *Biochem. Biophys. Res. Commun.* 116:121–27
89. Hirst, M. A., Hochman, H. I., Feldman, D. 1985. Vitamin D resistance and alopecia: A kindred with normal 1,25-dihydroxyvitamin D binding, but decreased receptor affinity for deoxyribonucleic acid. *J. Clin. Endocrinol. Metab.* 60:490–95
90. Holick, M. F., Schnoes, H. K., DeLuca, H. F., Suda, T., Cousins, R. J. 1971. Isolation and identification of 1,25-dihydroxycholecalciferol. A metabolite of vitamin D active in intestine. *Biochemistry* 10:2799–2804
91. Hollenberg, S. M., Weinberger, C., Ong, E. S., Cerelli, G., Oro, A., et al. 1985. Primary structure and expression of a functional human glucocorticoid receptor cDNA. *Nature* 318:635–41
92. Honma, Y., Hozumi, M., Abe, E., Konno, K., Fukushima, M., et al. 1983. $1\alpha$,25-Dihydroxyvitamin $D_3$ and $1\alpha$-hydroxyvitamin $D_3$ prolong survival time of mice inoculated with myeloid leukemia cells. *Proc. Natl. Acad. Sci. USA* 80:201–4
93. Horst, R. L., Littledike, E. T., Riley, J. L., Napoli, J. L. 1981. Quantitation of vitamin D and its metabolites and their plasma concentrations in five species of animals. *Anal. Biochem.* 116:189–203
94. Hughes, M. R., Brumbaugh, P. F., Haussler, M. R., Wergedal, J. E., Baylink, D. J. 1975. Regulation of serum $1\alpha$,25-dihydroxyvitamin $D_3$ by calcium and phosphate in the rat. *Science* 190:578–80
95. Hunziker, W., Walters, M. R., Bishop, J. E., Norman, A. W. 1982. Effect of vitamin D status on equilibrium between occupied and unoccupied 1,25-dihydroxyvitamin D intestinal receptors in the chick. *J. Clin. Invest.* 69:826–34
96. Hunziker, W., Walters, M. R., Bishop, J. E., Norman, A. W. 1983. Unoccupied and *in vitro* and *in vivo* occupied 1,25-dihydroxyvitamin $D_3$ intestinal receptors. Multiple biochemical forms and evidence for transformation. *J. Biol. Chem.* 258:8642–48
97. Hunziker, W., Walters, M. R., Norman, A. W. 1980. 1,25-Dihydroxyvitamin $D_3$ receptors. Differential quantitation of endogenously occupied and unoccupied sites. *J. Biol. Chem.* 255:9534–37
98. Jensen, E. V., Mohla, S., Gorell, T., Tanaka, S., DeSombre, R. 1972. Estrophile to nucleophile in two easy steps. *J. Steroid Biochem.* 3:445–58
99. Jones, C. A., Callaham, M. F., Huberman, E. 1984. Enhancement of chemical-carcinogen-induced cell transformation in hamster embryo cells by $1\alpha$,25-dihydroxycholecalciferol, the biologically active metabolite of vitamin $D_3$. *Carcinogenesis* 5:1155–59
100. Jones, G., Kung, M., Kano, K. 1983. The isolation and identification of two new metabolites of 25-hydroxyvitamin $D_3$ produced in the kidney. *J. Biol. Chem.* 258:12920–28
101. Jones, P. G., Haussler, M. R. 1979. Scintillation autoradiographic localization of 1,25-dihydroxyvitamin $D_3$ in chick intestine. *Endocrinology* 104:313–21
102. Kadowaki, S., Norman, A. W. 1984. Dietary vitamin D is essential for normal insulin secretion from the perfused rat pancreas. *J. Clin. Invest.* 73:759–66
103. Kaetzel, D. M., Fu, I. Y., Christiansen, M. P., Kaetzel, C. S., Soares, J. H., et al. 1984. Isolation of a 110,000 molecular weight protein in the purification of the nuclear chick intestinal 1,25-dihydroxyvitamin $D_3$ receptor. *Biochim. Biophys. Acta* 797:312–19
104. Karin, M., Haslinger, A., Holtgreve, H., Richards, R. I., Krauter, P., et al. 1984. Characterization of DNA sequences through which cadmium and glucocorticoid hormones induce human metallothionein $II_A$ gene. *Nature* 308:513–19
105. Kelly, M. A., Marion, S. L., Donaldson, C. A., Pike, J. W., Haussler, M. R. 1985. A variant form of the 1,25-

dihydroxyvitamin $D_3$ receptor with low apparent hormone affinity in cultured monkey kidney cells (LLC-$MK_2$): A model for tissue resistance to vitamin D. *J. Biol. Chem.* 260:1545–49

106. King, W. J., Greene, G. L. 1984. Monoclonal antibodies localize oestrogen receptor in the nuclei of target cells. *Nature* 307:745–47

107. Koren, R., Ravid, A., Liberman, U. A., Hochberg, Z., Weisman, Y., et al. 1985. Defective binding and function of 1,25-dihydroxyvitamin $D_3$ receptors in peripheral mononuclear cells of patients with end-organ resistance to 1,25-dihydroxyvitamin D. *J. Clin. Invest.* 76: 2012–15

108. Korkor, A. B., Kuchibotla, J., Arrieh, M., Gray, R. W., Gleason, W. A. 1985. The effects of chronic prednisone administration on intestinal receptors for 1,25-dihydroxyvitamin $D_3$ in the dog. *Endocrinology* 117:2267–73

109. Kream, B. E., Jose, M. J. L., DeLuca, H. F. 1977. The chick intestinal cytosol binding protein for 1,25-dihydroxyvitamin $D_3$: A study of analog binding. *Arch. Biochem. Biophys.* 179:462–68

110. Kream, B. E., Jose, M., Yamada, S., DeLuca, H. F. 1977. A specific high-affinity binding macromolecule for 1,25-dihydroxyvitamin $D_3$ in fetal bone. *Science* 197:1086–88

111. Kream, B. E., Yamada, S., Schnoes, H. K., DeLuca, H. F. 1977. Specific cytosol-binding protein for 1,25-dihydroxyvitamin $D_3$ in rat intestine. *J. Biol. Chem.* 252:4501–5

112. Kuroki, T., Sasaki, K., Chida, K., Abe, E., Suda, T. 1983. 1$\alpha$,25-Dihydroxyvitamin $D_3$ markedly enhances chemically-induced transformation in Balb 3T3 cells. *Gann* 74:611–14

113. Lemire, J. M., Adams, J. S., Kermani-Arab, V., Bakke, A. C., Sakai, R., et al. 1985. 1,25-Dihydroxyvitamin $D_3$ suppresses human T helper/inducer lymphocyte activity in vitro. *J. Immunol.* 134:3032–35

114. Lemire, J. M., Adams, J. S., Sakai, R., Jordan, S. C. 1984. 1$\alpha$,25-Dihydroxyvitamin $D_3$ suppresses proliferation and immunoglobulin production by normal human peripheral blood mononuclear cells. *J. Clin. Invest.* 74:657–61

115. Levy, F. O., Eikvac, L., Jutte, N. H. P. M., Froysa, A., Tvermyr, S. M., et al. 1985. Properties and compartmentalization of the testicular receptor for 1,25-dihydroxyvitamin $D_3$. *J. Steroid Biochem.* 22:453–60

116. Liberman, U. A., Eil, C., Holst, P., Rosen, J. F., Marx, S. J. 1983. Hereditary resistance to 1,25-dihydroxyvitamin D: Defective function of receptors for 1,25-dihydroxyvitamin D in cells cultured from bone. *J. Clin. Endocrinol. Metab.* 57:958–62

117. Liberman, U. A., Eil, C., Marx, S. J. 1983. Resistance to 1,25-dihydroxyvitamin D. Association with heterogeneous defects in cultured skin fibroblasts. *J. Clin. Invest.* 71:192–200

118. Liberman, U. A., Eil, C., Marx, S. J. 1986. Receptor-positive hereditary resistance to 1,25-dihydroxyvitamin D: Chromatography of hormone-receptor complexes on deoxyribonucleic acid-cellulose shows two classes of mutation. *J. Clin. Endocrinol. Metab.* 62:122–26

119. Lobaugh, B., Burch, W. M. Jr., Drezner, M. K. 1984. Abnormalities of vitamin D metabolism and action in the vitamin D resistant rachitic and osteomalacic diseases. In *Vitamin D: Basic and Clinical Aspects,* ed. R. Kumar, pp. 665–720, Boston: Nijhoff

120. Lobaugh, B., Drezner, M. K. 1983. Abnormal regulation of renal 25-hydroxyvitamin D-1$\alpha$-hydroxylase activity in the X-linked hypophosphatemic mouse. *J. Clin. Invest.* 71:400–3

121. Logeat, F., LeCunff, M., Pamphile, R., Milgrom, E. 1985. The nuclear-bound form of the progesterone receptor is generated through a hormone-dependent phosphorylation. *Biochem. Biophys. Res. Commun.* 131:421–27

122. Lund, B., Lund, B., Sorensen, O. H. 1979. Measurement of circulating 1,25-dihydroxyvitamin D in man. Changes in serum concentrations during treatment with 1$\alpha$-hydroxycholecalciferol. *Acta Endocrinol.* 91:338–50

123. Majeska, R. J., Rodan, G. A. 1982. The effect of 1,25$(OH)_2D_3$ on alkaline phosphatase in osteoblastic osteosarcoma cells. *J. Biol. Chem.* 257:3362–65

124. Mangelsdorf, D. J., Koeffler, H. P., Donaldson, C. A., Pike, J. W., Haussler, M. R. 1984. 1,25-Dihydroxyvitamin $D_3$–induced differentiation in a human promyelocytic leukemia cell line (HL-60): Receptor-mediated maturation to macrophage-like cells. *J. Cell Biol.* 98:391–98

125. Manolagas, S. C., Culler, F. L., Howard, J. E., Brickman, A. S., Deftos, L. J. 1983. The cytoreceptor assay for 1,25-dihydroxyvitamin D and its application to clinical studies. *J. Clin. Endocrinol. Metab.* 56:751–60

126. Manolagas, S. C., Deftos, L. J. 1981. Comparison of 1,25-, 25-, and 24,25-

hydroxylated vitamin $D_3$ binding in fetal rat calvariae and osteogenic sarcoma cells. *Calcif. Tissue Int.* 33:655–61

127. Manolagas, S. C., Haussler, M. R., Deftos, L. J. 1980. 1,25-dihydroxyvitamin $D_3$ receptor-like macromolecule in rat osteogenic sarcoma cell lines. *J. Biol. Chem.* 255:4414–17
128. Marcocci, C., Freake, H. C., Iwasaki, J., Lopez, E., MacIntyre, I. 1982. Demonstration and organ distribution of the 1,25-dihydroxyvitamin $D_3$–binding protein in fish *(A. anguilla)*. *Endocrinology* 110:1347–54
129. Massaro, E. R., Simpson, R. U., DeLuca, H. F. 1983. Quantitation of endogenously occupied and unoccupied binding sites for 1,25-dihydroxyvitamin $D_3$ in rat intestine. *Proc. Natl. Acad. Sci. USA* 80:2549–53
130. Mayer, E., Bishop, J. E., Chandraratna, R. A. S., Okamura, W. H., Kruse, J. R., et al. 1983. Isolation and identification of 1,25-dihydroxy-24-oxo-vitamin $D_3$ and 1,23,25-trihydroxy-24-oxo-vitamin $D_3$. *J. Biol. Chem.* 258:13458–65
131. McCain, T. A., Haussler, M. R., Okrent, D., Hughes, M. R. 1978. Partial purification of the chick intestinal receptor for 1,25-dihydroxyvitamin D by ion exchange and blue dextran-Sepharose chromatography. *FEBS Lett.* 86:65–70
132. Mellon, W. S. 1984. Dye-ligand interactions with 1,25-dihydroxyvitamin $D_3$–receptor complexes from chicken intestine. *Mol. Pharmacol.* 25:79–85
133. Mellon, W. S. 1985. Analysis of hormone- and polynucleotide/histone-binding sites of the chicken intestinal 1,25-dihydroxyvitamin $D_3$ receptor by means of proteolysis. *Endocrinology* 116:1408–17
134. Mellon, W. S., DeLuca, H. F. 1979. An equilibrium and kinetic study of 1,25-dihydroxyvitamin $D_3$ binding to chicken intestinal cytosol employing high specific activity 1,25-dihydroxy[$^3$H-26,27] vitamin $D_3$. *Arch. Biochem. Biophys.* 197:90–95
135. Mellon, W. S., Franceschi, R. T., DeLuca, H. F. 1980. An *in vitro* study of the stability of the chicken intestinal cytosol 1,25-dihydroxyvitamin $D_3$–specific receptor. *Arch. Biochem. Biophys.* 202: 83–92
136. Merke, J., Hugel, U., Ritz, E. 1985. Nuclear testicular 1,25-dihydroxyvitamin $D_3$ receptors in sertoli cells and seminiferous tubules of adult rodents. *Biochem. Biophys. Res. Commun.* 127:303–9
137. Merke, J., Klaus, G., Waldherr, R., Ritz, E. 1986. No 1,25-dihydroxyvitamin $D_3$ receptors in osteoclasts (OC) of Ca-deficient chick despite demonstrable receptors in circulating monocytes. *J. Bone Mineral Res.* 1:151
138. Merke, J., Senst, S., Ritz, E. 1984. Demonstration and characterization of the 1,25-dihydroxyvitamin $D_3$ receptors in human mononuclear blood cells. *Biochem. Biophys. Res. Commun.* 120:199–205
139. Nakada, M., Simpson, R. U., DeLuca, H. F. 1984. Subcellular distribution of DNA-binding and non-DNA-binding 1,25-dihydroxyvitamin D receptors in chicken intestine. *Proc. Natl. Acad. Sci. USA* 81:6711–13
140. Nakada, M., Simpson, R. U., DeLuca, H. F. 1985. Molybdate and the 1,25-dihydroxyvitamin $D_3$ receptor from chick intestine. *Arch. Biochem. Biophys.* 238:517–21
141. Napoli, J. L., Pramanik, B. C., Royal, P. M., Reinhardt, T. A., Horst, R. L. 1983. Intestinal synthesis of 24-keto-1,25-dihydroxyvitamin $D_3$. *J. Biol. Chem.* 258:9100–7
142. Norman, A. W. 1979. In *Vitamin D, the Calcium Homeostatic Steroid Hormone*, ed. W. J. Darby. New York/San Francisco/London: Academic
143. Omdahl, J. L. 1978. Interaction of the parathyroid and 1,25-dihydroxyvitamin $D_3$ in the control of renal 25-hydroxyvitamin $D_3$ metabolism. *J. Biol. Chem.* 258:8474–78
144. Oursler, M. J., Bell, L. V., Clevinger, B., Osdoby, P. 1985. Identification of osteoclast-specific monoclonal antibodies. *J. Cell Biol.* 100:1592–1600
145. Perret, C., Desplan, C., Dupre, J. M., Thomasset, M. 1985. Control of cholecalcin (9000 MW cholecalciferol-induced CaBP) gene expression by $1,25(OH)_2D_3$ in rat intestine. See Ref. 11, pp. 365–66
146. Peterfy, C., Tenenhouse, A. 1982. Vitamin D receptors in isolated rat parotid gland acinar cells. *Biochim. Biophys. Acta* 721:158–63
147. Petkovich, P. M., Heersche, J. N. M., Tinker, D. O., Jones, G. 1984. Retinoic acid stimulates 1,25-dihydroxyvitamin $D_3$ binding in rat osteosarcoma cells. *J. Biol. Chem.* 259:8274–80
148. Pike, J. W. 1981. Evidence for a reactive sulfhydryl in the DNA binding domain of the 1,25-dihydroxyvitamin $D_3$ receptor. *Biochem. Biophys. Res. Commun.* 100: 1713–19
149. Pike, J. W. 1982. Interaction between 1,25-dihydroxyvitamin $D_3$ receptors and intestinal nuclei. Binding to nuclear

constituents *in vitro*. *J. Biol. Chem.* 257:6766–75

150. Pike, J. W. 1982. Receptors for 1,25-dihydroxyvitamin $D_3$ in chick pancreas: A partial physical and functional characterization. *J. Steroid Biochem.* 16:385–95
151. Pike, J. W. 1984. Monoclonal antibodies to chick intestinal receptors for 1,25-dihydroxyvitamin $D_3$. Interaction and effects of binding on receptor function. *J. Biol. Chem.* 259:1167–73
152. Pike, J. W. 1985. New insights into mediators of vitamin $D_3$ action. See Ref. 11, pp. 95–105
153. Pike, J. W., Allegretto, E. A., Kelly, M. A., Donaldson, C. A., Marion, S. L., et al. 1986. 1,25-Dihydroxyvitamin $D_3$ receptors: Altered functional domains are associated with cellular resistance to vitamin $D_3$. In *Advances in Biology and Experimental Medicine*. New York: Plenum. In press
154. Pike, J. W., Dokoh, S., Haussler, M. R., Liberman, U. A., Marx, S. J., Eil, C. 1984. Vitamin $D_3$–resistant fibroblasts have immunoassayable 1,25-dihydroxyvitamin $D_3$ receptors. *Science* 224: 879–81
155. Pike, J. W., Donaldson, C. A., Marion, S. L., Haussler, M. R. 1982. Development of hybridomas secreting monoclonal antibodies to the chicken intestinal $1\alpha$,25-dihydroxyvitamin $D_3$ receptor. *Proc. Natl. Acad. Sci. USA* 79:7719–23
156. Pike, J. W., Gooze, L. L., Haussler, M. R. 1980. Biochemical evidence for 1,25-dihydroxyvitamin D receptor macromolecules in parathyroid, pancreatic, pituitary, and placental tissues *Life Sci.* 26:407–14
157. Pike, J. W., Haussler, M. R. 1979. Purification of chicken intestinal receptor for 1,25-dihydroxyvitamin D. *Proc. Natl. Acad. Sci. USA* 76:5485–89
158. Pike, J. W., Haussler, M. R. 1983. Association of 1,25-dihydroxyvitamin $D_3$ with cultured 3T6 mouse fibroblasts. Cellular uptake and receptor-mediated migration to the nucleus. *J. Biol. Chem.* 258:8554–60
159. Pike, J. W., Marion, S. L., Donaldson, C. A., Haussler, M. R. 1983. Serum and monoclonal antibodies against the chick intestinal receptor for 1,25-dihydroxyvitamin $D_3$. Generation by a preparation enriched in a 64,000-dalton protein. *J. Biol. Chem.* 258:1289–96
160. Pike, J. W., Sleator, N. M. 1985. Hormone-dependent phosphorylation of the 1,25-dihydroxyvitamin $D_3$ receptor in mouse fibroblasts. *Biochem. Biophys. Res. Commun.* 131:378–85
161. Price, P. A., Baukol, S. A. 1980. 1,25-Dihydroxyvitamin $D_3$ increases synthesis of the vitamin K–dependent bone protein by osteosarcoma cells. *J. Biol. Chem.* 255:11660–63
162. Procsal, D. A., Okamura, W. H., Norman, A. W. 1975. Structural requirements for the interaction of $1\alpha$,25-$(OH)_2$-vitamin $D_3$ with its chick intestinal receptor system. *J. Biol. Chem.* 250:8382–88
163. Provvedini, D. M., Tsoukas, C. D., Deftos, L. J., Manolagas, S. C. 1983. 1,25-Dihydroxyvitamin $D_3$ receptors in human leukocytes. *Science* 221:1181–83
164. Radparvar, S., Mellon, W. S. 1982. Characterization of 1,25-dihydroxyvitamin $D_3$–receptor complex interactions with DNA by a competitive assay. *Arch. Biochem. Biophys.* 217:552–63
165. Radparvar, S., Mellon, W. S. 1984. An exchange assay for quantitation of 1,25-dihydroxyvitamin $D_3$ receptors. *J. Steroid. Biochem.* 20:807–15
166. Rasmussen, H., Matsumoto, T., Fontaine, O., Goodman, D. B. P. 1982. Role of changes in membrane lipid structure in the action of 1,25-dihydroxyvitamin $D_3$. *Fed. Proc.* 41:72–77
167. Ray, R., Rose, S., Holick, S. A., Holick, M. F. 1985. Evaluation of a photolabile derivative of 1,25-dihydroxyvitamin $D_3$ receptor in chick intestinal cytosol. *Biochem. Biophys. Res. Commun.* 132:198–203
168. Reinhardt, T. A., Conrad, H. R. 1980. Specific binding protein for 1,25-dihydroxyvitamin $D_3$ in bovine mammary gland. *Arch. Biochem. Biophys.* 203:108–16
169. Reinhardt, T. A., Horst, R. L., Littledike, E. T., Beitz, D. C. 1982. 1,25-Dihydroxyvitamin $D_3$ receptor in bovine thymus gland. *Biochem. Biophys. Res. Commun.* 106:1012–18
170. Reinhardt, T. A., Horst, R. L., Orf, J. W., Hollis, B. W. 1984. A microassay for 1,25-dihydroxyvitamin D not requiring high performance liquid chromatography: Application to clinical studies. *J. Clin. Endocrinol. Metab.* 58:91–98
171. Reitsma, P. H., Rothberg, P. G., Astrin, S. M., Trial, J., Bar-Shavit, Z., et al. 1983. Regulation of *myc* gene expression in HL-60 leukaemia cells by a vitamin D metabolite. *Nature* 306:492–94
172. Rigby, W. F. C., Stacy, T., Fanger, M. W. 1984. Inhibition of T lymphocyte mitogenesis by 1,25-dihydroxyvitamin $D_3$ (calcitriol). *J. Clin. Invest.* 74:1451–55
173. Rowe, D. W., Kream, B. E. 1982. Regu-

lation of collagen synthesis in fetal rat calvaria by 1,25-dihydroxyvitamin $D_3$. *J. Biol. Chem.* 257:8009–15

174. Sato, T., Takusagawa, K., Asoo, N., Konno, K. 1982. Antitumor effect of 1$\alpha$-hydroxyvitamin $D_3$. *Tohoku J. Exp. Med.* 138:445–46
175. Schnarr, M., Ouyet, J., Granger-Schnarr, M., Duane, M. 1985. Large-scale purification, oligomerization equilibria, and specific interaction of the lex A repressor of *Escherichia coli. Biochemistry* 24:2812–18
176. Seino, Y., Yamaoka, K., Ishida, M., Yabuuchi, H., Ichikawa, M., et al. 1982. Biochemical characterization of $1,25(OH)_2D_3$ receptors in chick embryonal duodenal cytosol. *Calcif. Tissue Int.* 34:265–69
177. Sher, E., Frampton, R. J., Eisman, J. A. 1985. Regulation of the 1,25-dihydroxyvitamin $D_3$ receptor by 1,25-dihydroxyvitamin $D_3$ in intact human cancer cells. *Endocrinology* 116:971–77
178. Simpson, R. U., DeLuca, H. F. 1980. Characterization of a receptor-like protein for 1,25-dihydroxyvitamin $D_3$ in rat skin. *Proc. Natl. Acad. Sci. USA* 77:5822–26
179. Simpson, R. U., Hamstra, A., Kendrick, N. C., DeLuca, H. F. 1983. Purification of the receptor for 1$\alpha$,25-dihydroxyvitamin $D_3$ from chicken intestine. *Biochemistry* 22:2586–94
180. Simpson, R. U., Thomas, G. A., Arnold, A. J. 1985. Identification of 1,25-dihydroxyvitamin $D_3$ receptors and activities in muscle. *J. Biol. Chem.* 260:8882–91
181. Stern, P. H. 1981. A monolog on analogs: In vitro effects of vitamin D metabolites and consideration of the mineralization question. *Calcif. Tissue Int.* 33:1–4
182. Stumpf, W. E., Sar, M., Clark, S. A., DeLuca, H. F. 1982. Brain target sites for 1,25-dihydroxyvitamin $D_3$. *Science* 215:1403–5
183. Stumpf, W. E., Sar, M., DeLuca, H. F. 1981. Sites of action of $1,25(OH)_2$-vitamin $D_3$ identified by thaw-mount autoradiography. In *Hormonal Control of Calcium Metabolism,* ed. D. V. Cohn, R. V. Talmage, J. L. Matthews, pp. 222–29. Amsterdam/Oxford/Princeton: Excerpta Medica
184. Stumpf, W. E., Sar, M., Reid, F. A., Tanaka, Y., DeLuca, H. F. 1979. Target cells for 1,25-dihydroxyvitamin $D_3$ in intestinal tract, stomach, kidney, skin, pituitary, and parathyroid. *Science* 206:1188–90
185. Suda, S., Takahashi, N., Shinki, T., Horiuchi, N., Yamaguchi, A., et al. 1985. 1$\alpha$,25-Dihydroxyvitamin $D_3$ receptors and their action in embryonic chick chondrocytes. *Calcif. Tissue Int.* 37:82–90
186. Sundelin, J., Anundi, H., Tragardh, L., Erikson, U., Lind, P., et al. 1985. The primary structure of rat liver cellular retinol-binding protein. *J. Biol. Chem.* 260:6488–93
187. Takahashi, N., Suda, S., Shinki, T., Horiuchi, N., Shiina, Y., et al. 1985. The mechanism of end-organ resistance to 1$\alpha$,25-dihydroxy-cholecalciferol in the common marmoset. *Biochem. J.* 227:555–63
188. Tanaka, H., Abe, E., Miyaura, C., Kuribayashi, T., Konno, K., et al. 1982. 1$\alpha$,25-dihydroxycholecalciferol and a human myeloid leukaemia cell line (HL-60). *Biochem. J.* 204:713–19
189. Tanaka, Y., DeLuca, H. F. 1974. Stimulation of 24,25-dihydroxyvitamin $D_3$ production by 1,25-dihydroxyvitamin $D_3$. *Science* 183:1198–1200
190. Tinkler, S. M. B., Williams, D. M., Johnson, N. W. 1981. Osteoclast formation in response to intraperitoneal injection of 1$\alpha$-hydroxycholecalciferol in mice. *J. Anat.* 133:91–97
191. Trechsel, V., Bonjour, J.-P., Fleisch, H. 1979. Regulation of the metabolism of 25-hydroxyvitamin $D_3$ in primary cultures of chick kidney cells. *J. Clin. Invest.* 64:206–17
192. Tsai, H. C., Norman, A. W. 1973. Studies on calciferol metabolism. VIII. Evidence for a cytoplasmic receptor for 1,25-dihydroxyvitamin $D_3$ in the intestinal mucosa. *J. Biol. Chem.* 248: 5967–75
193. Tsoukas, C. D., Provvedini, D. M., Manolagas, S. C. 1984. 1,25-Dihydroxyvitamin $D_3$: A novel immunoregulatory hormone. *Science* 224:1438–40
194. Walter, P., Green, S., Greene, G., Krust, A., Bornert, J.-M., et al. 1985. Cloning of the human estrogen receptor cDNA. *Proc. Natl. Acad. Sci. USA* 82:7889–93
195. Walters, M. R. 1981. An estrogen-stimulated 1,25-dihydroxyvitamin $D_3$ receptor in rat uterus. *Biochem. Biophys. Res. Commun.* 103:721–26
196. Walters, M. R. 1984. 1,25-Dihydroxyvitamin $D_3$ receptors in the seiminiferous tubules of the rat testis increase at puberty. *Endocrinology* 114:2167–74
197. Walters, M. R., Hunziker, W., Norman, A. W. 1980. Unoccupied 1,25-dihydroxyvitamin $D_3$ receptors. Nuclear/cytosol ratio depends on ionic strength. *J. Biol. Chem.* 255:6799–6805

198. Walters, M. R., Hunziker, W., Norman, A. W. 1981. Apparent nuclear localization of unoccupied receptors for 1,25-dihydroxyvitamin $D_3$. *Biochem. Biophys. Res. Commun.* 98:990–96
199. Walters, M. R., Hunziker, W., Norman, A. W. 1981. 1,25-Dihydroxyvitamin $D_3$ receptors: Intermediate between triiodothyronine and steroid hormone receptors. *Trends Biochem. Sci.* 6:268–71
200. Wark, J. D., Tashjian, A. H. 1982. Vitamin D stimulates prolactin synthesis by $GH_4C_1$ cells incubated in chemically defined medium. *Endocrinology* 111: 1755–57
201. Wecksler, W. R., Ross, F. P., Mason, R. S., Norman, A. W. 1980. Biochemical properties of the 1,25-dihydroxyvitamin $D_3$ cytosol receptors from human and chicken intestinal mucosa. *J. Clin. Endocrinol. Metabl.* 50:152–57
202. Welshons, W. V., Lieberman, M. E., Gorski, J. 1984. Nuclear localization of unoccupied oestrogen receptors. *Nature* 307:747–49
203. Wilhelm, F., Norman, A. W. 1985. Biochemical characterization of positive cooperativity in the binding of $1\alpha$,25-dihydroxyvitamin $D_3$ to its chick intestinal chromatin receptor. *J. Biol. Chem.* 260:10087–92
204. Wood, A. W., Chang, R. L., Huang, M.-T., Baggiolini, E., Partridge, J. J., et al. 1985. Stimulatory effect of $1\alpha$,25-dihydroxyvitamin $D_3$ on the formation of skin tumors in mice treated chronically with 7,12-dimethylbenz[a]anthracene. *Biochem. Biophys. Res. Commun.* 130: 924–31
205. Wood, A. W., Chang, R. L., Huang, M.-T., Uskokovic, M., Conney, A. H. 1983. $1\alpha$,25-Dihydroxyvitamin $D_3$ inhibits phorbol ester-dependent chemical carcinogenesis in mouse skin. *Biochem. Biophys. Res. Commun.* 116:605–11

*Ann. Rev. Nutr. 1986. 6:563–97*


# METABOLISM AND FUNCTION OF *myo*-INOSITOL AND INOSITOL PHOSPHOLIPIDS

*Bruce J. Holub*

Department of Nutritional Sciences, University of Guelph, Guelph, Ontario, Canada N1G 2W1

---

## CONTENTS

INTRODUCTION .................... 564
DIETARY SOURCES AND BIOLOGICAL FORMS .................... 564
METABOLISM OF INOSITOL AND INOSITOL PHOSPHOLIPIDS .................... 566
*Digestion and Absorption* .................... 566
*Biosynthesis and Catabolism of Inositol* .................... 567
*Cellular Uptake of Inositol* .................... 568
*Incorporation of Inositol into Phospholipid* .................... 570
*Formation of 1-Stearoyl 2-Arachidonoyl Phosphatidylinositol* .................... 571
*Phosphatidylinositol Transfer Proteins* .................... 572
EFFECTS OF DIETARY INOSITOL .................... 573
*Alteration of Cellular Levels of Inositol and Phosphatidylinositol* .................... 573
*Dietary Inositol Deficiency and Triacylglycerol Accumulation in Liver* .................... 574
*Dietary Inositol Deficiency and Intestinal Lipodystrophy* .................... 576
*Dietary Inositol and the Lung* .................... 577
CELLULAR FUNCTIONS OF PHOSPHATIDYLINOSITOL AND POLYPHOSPHOINOSITIDES IN MAMMALIAN CELLS .................... 578
*Membrane Structure and Function* .................... 578
*Source of Free Arachidonic Acid for Eicosanoid Production* .................... 579
*Involvement in Mediation of Cellular Responses to External Stimuli* .................... 580
*Source of the Second Messenger 1,2-Diacylglyerol and Phosphatidate* .................... 582
*Source of the Second Messenger Inositol Trisphosphate* .................... 583
*Degradation of Inositol Trisphosphate* .................... 583
ABNORMAL METABOLISM OF INOSITOL AND INOSITOL PHOSPHOLIPIDS IN DISEASE STATES .................... 584
*Diabetes* .................... 584
*Renal Disorders* .................... 586
*Other Disease States* .................... 587
SUMMARY AND CONCLUSIONS .................... 588



0199-9885/86/0715-0563$02.00

## INTRODUCTION

Inositol (*myo*-inositol) and its various biochemical derivatives are broadly distributed in mammalian tissues and cells, higher plants, fungi, and some bacteria where they provide important biological functions. The metabolism of *myo*-inositol has been extensively studied in mammalian cells, particularly in relation to the biosynthesis and degradation of the *myo*-inositol-containing phospholipids associated with biological membranes. The formation and function of the 1-stearoyl 2-arachidonoyl molecular species that greatly predominates in the membrane phosphoinositides of most mammalian cells has been a topic for active research.

*myo*-Inositol is an essential growth factor for many cells in tissue culture (47) and is capable of promoting the growth of young rats in a manner dependent on the diet composition (125). *myo*-Inositol is a required nutrient in the diet of the female gerbil (85) and other animals under certain conditions. Much of the nutritionally related work on dietary *myo*-inositol in the past has been directed toward a documentation of its role as a lipotropic factor for various animal species. More recently, the influence of dietary *myo*-inositol on the levels of free *myo*-inositol and its phospholipid derivatives in mammalian cells and the metabolic basis for the accumulation of triacylglycerol in the liver or intestine resulting from a *myo*-inositol deficiency have been of considerable interest. One of the most exciting developments in the field of *myo*-inositol functions in the cell has arisen very recently with the recognition of a dynamic role for membrane phosphoinositides in providing for the release of the second messengers 1,2-diacylglycerol and inositol trisphosphate in stimulated cells. These latter events may well play a central role in signal transmission for various hormones, neurotransmitters, growth factors, etc. Abnormalities in the metabolism of *myo*-inositol and/or inositol phospholipids have been documented and implicated in various disease states, including diabetes, renal disorders, and cancer.

This review highlights in an abbreviated manner many of those recent advances in the metabolism and function of *myo*-inositol and inositol phospholipids that are likely to be of interest to individuals with a combined concern for the nutritional, biochemical, and clinical aspects.

## DIETARY SOURCES AND BIOLOGICAL FORMS

*myo*-Inositol is found in the mixed diets of humans (diets that include animal and plant food sources) in its free form, as inositol-containing phospholipid, and as phytic acid (inositol hexaphosphate). The cyclitols include the inositols, of which there are nine possible isomers of hexahydroxycyclohexane. Of the latter, *myo*-inositol greatly predominates in mammalian tissues and cells and is the form of primary nutritional and metabolic interest. Articles are available that discuss the appropriate nomenclature and structures for inositol and the inositol-containing phospholipids (2, 118, 215). In this relatively brief review, the *myo*-isomer is the one considered unless otherwise indicated in the text and, for simplicity, the term "inositol" is used in place of *myo*-inositol.

It has been estimated that a mixed North American diet provides the human adult with approximately 1 g of total inositol per day (65). Inositol is a common constituent of plant foodstuffs, where a considerable portion of it is present as phytic acid. In the seeds of some cereals, inositol hexaphosphate can represent a major source of the total phosphorus present (183). Considerable data is available on the phytic acid contents of various plant products such as seeds, cereal grains, fruits, and vegetables (164, 184). In animal products such as fish, poultry, meats, and dairy products, inositol is present (143, 184) both in its free form and as inositol-containing phospholipid (primarily phosphatidylinositol, PI). The concentration in cow's milk of *myo*-inositol is approximately 30–80 mg/l (143); inositol is added to some infant formulas at a level of 0.01%. This cyclitol has also been given GRAS status, which indicates that no evidence currently implicates it as a dietary hazard to the public when used at current levels.

The organs of the male reproductive tract are particularly rich in free inositol (50). High concentrations have been confirmed in the testis, epididymal, vesicular, and prostatic fluids of the rat (63, 134, 210). Mammalian semen is a rich source of free inositol, with the seminal plasma having concentrations several-fold greater than in blood. Unbound inositol levels in the brain, cerebrospinal fluid, and choroid plexus are also higher than in plasma (194). Burton et al (23) reported the levels of free inositol in rat plasma (72-day-old animals) to be 50 $\mu$M when animals were fed a control diet containing inositol. The plasma concentration of free inositol in normal human subjects is approximately 30 $\mu$M (99). The concentration of inositol is about 0.6 mM at 3–7 months of lactation in human breast milk (24). Interestingly, Naccarato & Wells (157) reported the presence of a disaccharide form of inositol, 6-$\beta$-galactinol, in human and rat milk in addition to rat mammary gland. This latter sugar was found to represent approximately 17% of the total nonlipid inositol in rat milk on the 18th day of lactation (156). In contrast to the liver where lipid-bound inositol predominates, the levels of free inositol in the small intestine, kidney, and cerebrum from a 72-day-old rat were greater than those of inositol-containing phospholipid (23). Chu & Geyer (32) reported a significant predominance of free inositol over lipid-bound inositol (mainly PI) in the brain, kidney, and lung of both male and female gerbils fed a stock diet containing 0.3% total inositol. A predominance of inositol phospholipid was found in the pancreas, heart, liver, and muscle, whereas nearly equal amounts of free and lipid-bound inositol were found in the plasma and intestine.

In mammalian tissues and cells, inositol exists primarily in its free form and bound covalently to phospholipid as phosphatidylinositol. Much lower concentrations of the polyphosphoinositides (PI 4-phosphate and PI 4,5,-bisphosphate) also exist. The structures for free *myo*-inositol and the three phospholipid forms are given in Figure 1. In view of their metabolic lability, considerable degradation of PI 4-phosphate (PIP) and PI 4,5-bisphosphate ($PIP_2$) can occur during tissue handling prior to lipid extraction and analysis (79). PI represents 2–12% of the total phospholipid in various mammalian tissues (216). Concentrations of the polyphosphoinositides tend to be higher in nervous tissue; quantitation of inositol phospholipids of rat forebrain obtained by a freeze-blowing method revealed the levels of PIP and $PIP_2$ to be 30 and 70%, respectively, of that for PI (161). PI represents 3% of the total phospholipid in rat brain (8). In the human platelet, PI, PIP, and $PIP_2$ represent approximately 5, 1, and 0.3%, respectively, of the total membrane phospholipid (145, 149).

Inositol pentaphosphate is a predominant organic phosphate in the erythrocytes of most avian species (121). In contrast, the major organic phosphate in the erythrocyte of the adult ostrich is inositol tetraphosphate (116). Inositol diphosphate has been isolated and identified in erythrocytes from lungfish (117) and inositol pentaphosphate in the red blood cells of elasmobranch fishes (21). These compounds may play a role in regulating the oxygen affinity of the hemoglobins.

## METABOLISM OF INOSITOL AND INOSITOL PHOSPHOLIPIDS

### *Digestion and Absorption*

Phytic acid present in plant foodstuffs is hydrolyzed in the gut of monogastric animals by the enzyme phytase. This enzyme has been found in plant material and also in the intestinal mucosa of various animals (97, 164) where it is capable of releasing free inositol, orthophosphate, and intermediary products including the mono-, di-, tri-, tetra-, and pentaphosphate esters of inositol. Several investigators have reported that dietary phytic acid can reduce the bioavailability and utilization of both calcium and zinc. Nahapetian & Young (158) compared the effect of low and high dietary calcium intakes on the in vivo metabolic fate of oral doses of [$^{14}$C]phytate or [$^{14}$C]inositol in the rat. The high-calcium diet was found to increase significantly the loss of radioactivity in the feces and to reduce the appearance of radioactivity in expired air and in body tissues following [$^{14}$C]phytate administration; however, the high calcium intake did not affect the fate of [$^{14}$C]inositol. The authors further suggested that phytate or derivatives are almost quantitatively absorbed when the calcium intake is low. House et al (111) reported the respective values for apparent and

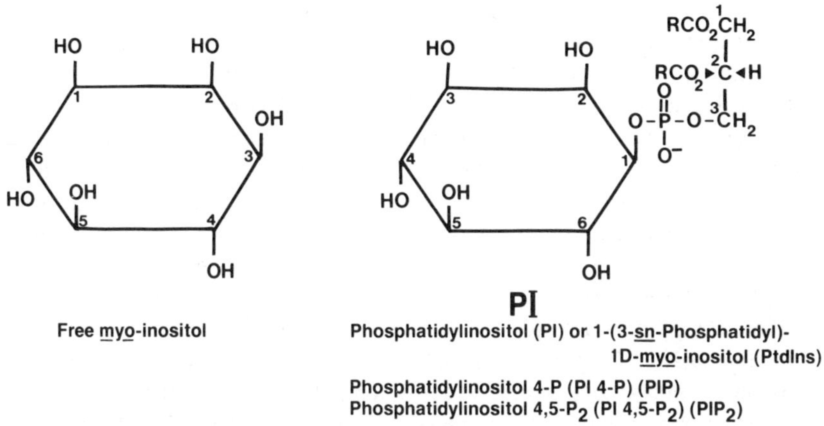

*Figure 1* Structures of free *myo*-inositol and the phosphoinositides.

true absorption of zinc to be approximately 30% lower in rats fed a diet containing phytate as compared to those fed a basal diet.

Research on the mode of absorption of free inositol in segments of hamster small intestine (29) has revealed that inositol is actively transported. Uptake and accumulation occur against a concentration gradient in a $Na^+$- and energy-dependent manner. The pathway by which inositol crossed the brush border membrane appeared not to be identical to the D-glucose pathway since phlorizin interacted competitively with the inositol binding site with an affinity considerably less than that for the common glucose binding site. Despite the fact that a considerable portion of the ingested inositol is consumed in the form of PI, little attention has been paid to the mode of digestion and absorption of this lipid form of dietary inositol. If the pathway for PI digestion should be analogous to that for dietary phosphatidylcholine (133), dietary PI may be hydrolyzed by a pancreatic phospholipase A in the intestinal lumen. The resulting lyso PI may then be reacylated via acyltransferase activity upon entering the intestinal cell or further hydrolyzed with the release of glycerylphosphorylinositol. Free inositol is transported in human blood plasma at a concentration of approximately 30 μM in normal subjects (99). PI is also present in small but significant amounts in association with the circulating serum lipoproteins (22, 30).

## *Biosynthesis and Catabolism of Inositol*

The pioneering work of Eisenberg & Bolden (49) as well as of Hauser & Finelli (80) indicated a biosynthetic capacity of rat testis, brain, kidney, and liver to synthesize inositol from glucose. Clements & Diethelm (36) attempted to assess the in vivo rate of inositol formation in the human kidney. The rate of endogenous synthesis from one normal human kidney was estimated to approach 2 g/day, thereby providing for 4 g of newly synthesized inositol per day in the binephric human; this is significantly above the daily dietary intake. Extrarenal tissues can also contribute to the endogenous production of inositol in the human and in experimental animals. Spector & Lorenzo (194) estimated that approximately one half of the unbound inositol in rabbit brain is synthesized from glucose in situ, with the remainder being transported into the brain from the blood. The conversion of glucose 6-phosphate to inositol 1-phosphate by the inositol 1-phosphate synthase, followed by a dephosphorylation reaction catalyzed by inositol 1-phosphatase activity (48), provides for the enzymatic biosynthesis of inositol. The stereospecificity of the synthase for nicotinamide adenine dinucleotide has been investigated in detail (28). Recently, Wong & Sherman (221) found the testicular inositol 1-phosphate synthase to have at least a 5-fold preference for the $\beta$-anomer of its natural substrate D-glucose 6-phosphate. Maeda & Eisenberg (152) have purified the inositol 1-phosphate synthase to homogeneity.

The early work of Howard & Anderson (112) led to the conclusion that the kidney is the only organ of importance in inositol catabolism, since [2-$^{14}$C]inositol was not degraded to respiratory $^{14}CO_2$ if rats were nephrectomized. In confirmation and extension of this early work, Lewin and colleagues (137) observed that bilaterally nephrectomized rats were essentially unable to convert inositol into $CO_2$ as compared to controls, which catabolized 16% of the injected [2-$^{14}$C]inositol to $^{14}CO_2$ in 5 hr. Since less than 1% of the administered radioactive inositol was released into the urine over the same time period, the catabolism of inositol by the kidney was of much greater significance than its excretion in the urine.

In animals, the initial committed step in the metabolism of inositol occurs exclusively in the kidney and involves cleavage of the ring to yield D-glucuronic acid (112). Through subsequent metabolic steps, D-xylulose 5-phosphate is produced and enters the pentose phosphate cycle. Reddy and colleagues (177, 178) purified the inositol oxygenase to homogeneity from hog kidney and found the enzyme to be specific for *myo*-inositol as a substrate, with some analogs being inhibitory. In human subjects, urinary excretion was found to account for only a small fraction of the disposal of inositol by the kidney (36). The kidney appears to be an important regulator of plasma inositol concentrations in human subjects. Interestingly, Fliesler et al (55) have suggested that inositol can be catabolized systemically to precursors utilized for glycerol lipid biosynthesis in the frog retina.

## *Cellular Uptake of Inositol*

The metabolic fate of radioactive inositol has been studied (137) in mature male rats following intraperitoneal injection. Within a few hours after injecting [2-$^{14}$C]inositol to control animals, the spleen, liver, pituitary gland, kidney, and notably the thyroid glands were found to concentrate the labelled cyclitol from the blood actively. Despite having high levels of endogenous inositol, the testes did not concentrate radioactive inositol from the blood. Muscle tissues (diaphragm and heart) concentrated little inositol, and no significant concentration was observed in the brain and epididymal fat pad. The vas deferens, epididymis, coagulating gland, seminal vesicle, and prostate had radioactivity levels that were approximately 10- to 30-fold those in blood serum. Most of the radioactivity was found in the aqueous trichloroactic acid extract—largely as free inositol in most organs with the exception of the liver, where the lipid fraction contained the majority of the radiolabelled inositol. The majority of the hepatic radioactivity was found to be associated with membrane fractions, including microsomal and mitochondrial (136).

The uptake of inositol by kidney slices appears to occur against a concentration gradient by means of a $Na^+$- and energy-dependent active transport (78, 203). A specific inositol transport system has been demonstrated in a plasma membrane fraction from rat kidney that contained brush border membranes (202). Inositol uptake by the membrane exhibited similarities to that by slices and was temperature dependent, pH sensitive, stereospecific, and inhibited by phlorizin. Both the binding and transport of inositol by brush border membranes of rat kidney were dependent on $Na^+$ (204).

The choroid plexus has been implicated as a locus of inositol transport from plasma to the cerebrospinal fluid. Spector (193), using isolated brain slices, characterized a saturable uptake system for inositol that was considered to be an active transport system and potentially capable of explaining the large inositol concentration differential between brain and cerebrospinal fluid. Warfield et al (211) obtained contrasting results in rat brain synaptosomes, where inositol was taken up via an unsaturable process that did not provide a concentration gradient indicative of active transport. Furthermore, the latter workers suggested that the uptake system in rabbit brain slices may reflect a species difference or uptake by a component of the slice other than neuron.

Recently, Segal et al (185) found the uptake of radiolabelled inositol by Schwann cells isolated from the sciatic nerve of very young rats to occur by a saturable, $Na^+$-dependent, phlorizin-inhibited mechanism with an apparent $K_m$ of 30 $\mu$M. In isolated rat liver parenchymal cells, it was concluded that inositol uptake is nonactive and occurs by a carrier-mediated process different from that for glucose (175). The intracellular concentration of inositol never exceeded the extracellular concentration, and uptake was not affected by inhibitors of mitochondrial ATP synthesis. Very recently, Auchus et al (6) have found the 5-hydroxyl of inositol to be essential for uptake into mouse fibrosarcoma cells. The 5-deoxy-inositol analog could not replace inositol as an essential growth factor and was not incorporated into the cellular phospholipid or accumulated in the cytoplasm of these cells.

## *Incorporation of Inositol into Phospholipid*

Two established biochemical mechanisms can provide for the entry of radiolabelled free inositol directly into cellular PI (Figure 2). The de novo biosynthesis of PI (167) involves the reaction of inositol with the liponucleotide, CDP-diacylglycerol, in the presence of the enzyme CDP-diacylglycerol:inositol phosphatidyltransferase (PI synthetase). This enzyme, which resides mainly in the microsomal fraction, has been solubilized and purified from rat brain and liver (176,200). Recently, Ghalayini & Eichberg (64) purified the PI synthetase from rat brain homogenate by approximately 250-fold and found the enzyme to exhibit a $K_m$ of 4.6 mM for inositol.

Alternatively, free inositol can react with endogenous phospholipid and enter PI by a $Mn^{2+}$-stimulated exchange reaction found in microsomes (93, 167). When rat liver microsomes were prelabelled with [$^{14}$C]choline in phosphatidylcholine, [$^{14}$C]ethanolamine in phosphatidylethanolamine, or [$^{3}$H]inositol in PI and chased with cold inositol under conditions that would activate the exchange reaction, support was forthcoming that PI is the preferred substrate for this reaction (94). Studies on the partially purified exchange enzyme from rat liver have also indicated (201) that choline- and ethanolamine-containing phospholipids do not play a role as acceptors for the exchange enzyme. The apparent $K_m$ for the $Mn^{2+}$-stimulated incorporation of free inositol into PI in rat liver microsomes was found to be 0.024 mM for the exchange reaction (93), which was generally similar to the $K_m$ value of 0.04 mM reported (201) for the partially purified exchange enzyme.

In the presence of CMP, the PI synthetase can operate in the reverse direction, which forms CDP-diacylglycerol and inositol from PI (7, 19, 92). The subsequent formation of PIP and $PIP_2$ from PI is catalyzed by the ATP:PI

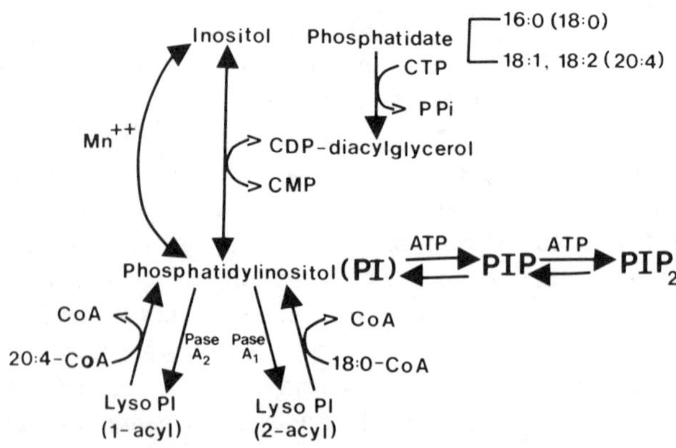


*Figure 2* Pathways for the entry of *myo*-inositol into the phosphoinositides and the formation of the 1-stearoyl 2-arachidonoyl molecular species.

4-phosphotransferase (PI kinase) and ATP:PIP 5-phosphotransferase (PIP kinase), respectively (40). The PI and PIP kinases are present on the cytosolic surface of the human erythrocyte membrane (58). Cellular phosphomonoesterases (phosphatases) have been reported (44, 144, 192) that can hydrolyze $PIP_2$ and PIP to yield PIP and PI, respectively, by sequential dephosphorylation.

## *Formation of 1-Stearoyl 2-Arachidonoyl Phosphatidylinositol*

The fatty acid compositions and distributions in PI, PIP, and $PIP_2$ are rather unique as compared to other phospholipids in most mammalian tissues and cells in that these phospholipids tend to be most enriched in stearic and arachidonic acids (96, 105). Stearate is found predominantely in the *sn*-1-position and arachidonate in the *sn*-2-position of the *sn*-glycero(3) backbone in the phosphoinositides (105, 205). Extensive molecular species analyses have revealed that the 1-stearoyl 2-arachidonoyl species predominates in PI from sources such as rat liver (102), bovine brain (105), human platelets (145), and also in the PIP and $PIP_2$ (105) from bovine brain (see Table 1). It is apparent that the PI from rat liver and human platelets is much more enriched in the 1-stearoyl 2-arachidonoyl species as compared to phosphatidylcholine, phosphatidylethanolamine, or phosphatidylserine isolated from the corresponding sources (104, 145). Tetraenoic species (mainly stearoyl arachidonoyl) also predominate (82% of total PI) in pig lymphocytes (197). Some exceptions to this predominance of the 1-stearoyl 2-arachidonoyl species in the inositol-containing phospholipids do exist; for example, monoenoic and not tetraenoic species predominate in lamb liver PI (141). Interestingly, the preferential pairing of arachidonate in the 2-position with stearate (over palmitate) in the 1-position has been found to be much more restrictive than when oleate resides in the 2-position of PI, PIP, or $PIP_2$ (102, 105).

**Table 1** Levels of 1-stearoyl 2-arachidonoyl molecular species in inositol-containing phospholipids

| Phospholipid | Source | Mol % of phospholipid | Ref. |
|---|---|---|---|
| Phosphatidylinositol | rat liver | 77 | 102 |
| Phosphatidylcholine | rat liver | 21 | 102 |
| Phosphatidylethanolamine | rat liver | 35 | 102 |
| Phosphatidylinositol | bovine brain | 60 | 105 |
| Phosphatidylinositol 4-phosphate | bovine brain | 43 | 105 |
| Phosphatidylinositol 4,5-bisphosphate | bovine brain | 42 | 105 |
| Phosphatidylinositol | human platelets | 71 | 145 |
| Phosphatidylcholine | human platelets | 10 | 145 |
| Phosphatidylethanolamine | human platelets | 47 | 145 |
| Phosphatidylserine | human platelets | 41 | 145 |

Tracer studies in vivo using radioactive glycerol, orthophosphate, and inositol suggested (96, 103) that the distributions of radioactivity among the newly synthesized species of rat liver PI could not account for the preponderance of tetraenoic molecular species in this phospholipid. Over later times following injection of these isotopes, evidence was provided for the transfer of radioactivity from monoenoic plus dienoic molecular species formed via de novo synthesis to tetraenoic species by way of deacylation-reacylation pathways. The in vivo results with radioactive inositol suggested that the reaction of free inositol with endogenous arachidonoyl CDP-diacylglycerol catalyzed by PI synthetase could account for approximately one half of the natural abundance of tetraenoic PI in rat liver (96), whereas the other half may originate by a retailoring cycle involving lyso PI intermediates (as outlined in Figure 2). Endogenous rat liver phosphatidate is enriched in palmitate in the 1-position and in oleate and linoleate in the 2-position (172) and is limited with respect to stearic and arachidonate in the 1- and 2-positions, respectively.

In vitro studies (106) have indicated that the CDP-diacylglycerol formed from the phosphatidate derived from the acylation of glycero(3)phosphate in rat liver microsomes is not enriched in arachidonate. Thompson & MacDonald (206) reported that rat liver CDP-diacylglycerol has levels of stearic and arachidonic acids that are intermediary between phosphatidic acid and PI. It is possible that a portion of the stearoyl arachidonoyl species in CDP-diacylglycerol may be derived via the back reaction catalyzed by the PI synthetase (and thereby derived indirectly via deacylation-reacylation reactions at the level of PI itself). The existence of phospholipases $A_1$ and $A_2$, which can deacylate PI in mammalian tissues and generate the intermediary lyso derivatives of PI depicted in Figure 2, have been reported (66, 89, 151, 189).

The predominant formation of tetraenoic species of PI from radioactive lyso(1-acyl) PI in the presence of ATP, CoA, and $Mg^{2+}$ has been demonstrated in rat liver homogenates and microsomal preparations (95) as has the existence of microsomal acyltransferases with affinities for arachidonoyl-CoA (95) and stearoyl-CoA (108) as acyl donors with lyso(1-acyl) PI and lyso(2-acyl) PI as acyl acceptors, respectively. The acyl-CoA: lyso(1-acyl) PI acyltransferase in rat brain (9) and human platelet microsomes (124) exhibits a selectivity toward arachidonoyl-CoA. Subcellular distribution studies (170) revealed that the lyso(1-acyl) PI acyltransferase activity in rat brain resides mainly in the endoplasmic reticulum.

## *Phosphatidylinositol Transfer Proteins*

Since PI biosynthesis is localized in the endoplasmic reticulum of eukaryotic cells, much research has been devoted recently to the mechanisms by which PI is transported at the intracellular level. There is increasing evidence to suggest that PI exchange proteins found in the cytosol of several tissues and cells might provide this function. Early work in this area revealed a net transfer of PI from microsomes and mitochondria to liposomes as catalyzed by transfer proteins isolated from beef brain and rat liver (73, 224). Helmkamp (87) discussed in some detail the PI transfer proteins with respect to their structure, catalytic activity, and possible physiological functions. These proteins may play key roles in the transfer of PI from the endoplasmic reticulum to other cellular fractions that apparently lack the potential for PI synthesis, such as the mitochondria and plasma membrane. Laffont and colleagues (132) have described the presence of a PI transfer protein in the cytosol of porcine platelets; George & Helmkamp (60) recently reported upon the purification and some characteristics of such a transfer protein from human platelets. The protein preferentially transferred PI, with phosphatidylcholine and phosphatidylglycerol being transferred to a lesser extent and no transfer being apparent for phosphatidylethanolamine.

It will be of considerable interest in the near future to determine the potential role of such PI transfer proteins in PI function at the membrane level. Furthermore, the characterization of transfer proteins with affinities for PIP and possibly also $PIP_2$ will likely be topics for future research. It will be of additional interest to compare the relative suitability of the 1-stearoyl 2-arachidonyl relative to other molecular species of PI as substrates for the PI transfer proteins in mammalian cells.

## EFFECTS OF DIETARY INOSITOL

### *Alteration of Cellular Levels of Inositol and Phosphatidylinositol*

The effect on tissue inositol levels of feeding inositol-depleted and -supplemented diets to the neonatal and developing rat was extensively investigated by Burton et al (23). The level of free inositol in all tissues studied (testis, liver, plasma, heart, lens, lung, kidney, and small intestine) with the exception of the cerebrum and cerebellum was significantly reduced when inositol-depleted diets were fed as compared to controls. The liver was the only tissue studied in which the inositol-containing phospholipid was lowered along with the free inositol levels.

The effect of inositol deprivation in pregnant and lactating rats on the inositol status in the circulation and in selected tissues was studied by Burton & Wells (25) in fetal and postnatal offspring. In these experiments, the pups were fed the corresponding diets after weaning until three months of age. A close correlation between the free inositol content in the diet and in the milk was obtained. At day 8 of lactation, the levels of free inositol in mammary gland and milk, and also of the 6-$\beta$-galactinol derivative in milk, were several-fold higher in animals receiving the supplemented diet as compared to those fed the inositol-deficient diet. The levels of free inositol in plasma, liver, kidney, and intestine of pups at all ages studied increased significantly with dietary inositol supplementation.

Using the female gerbil as an experimental animal model, Chu & Geyer (33) reported that animals fed an inositol-deficient diet for three weeks showed significantly depressed levels of both free and lipid-bound inositol in the intestine and liver, but only a depression in free inositol in the kidney and pancreas, relative to control animals receiving a diet containing inositol at the level of 0.1%; the levels of free and lipid-bound inositol were not significantly different in the brain of control or deficient gerbils. The hepatic level of PI was 68% lower (101) in rainbow trout fed an inositol-deficient diet for eight weeks relative to control animals receiving a supplement of dietary inositol (500 mg/kg diet); absolute liver weights were not significantly different in the two groups.

Inositol-deficient diets have also been found to reduce the level of free inositol in the urine of male rats (188). Oral doses of supplementary inositol can significantly elevate plasma inositol concentrations in human subjects (37) despite the capacity for certain tissues to synthesize this cyclitol. The fatty acid patterns of cellular PI can be significantly altered by dietary change (97); for example, the level of eicosapentaenoic acid in human platelet PI increased (from 0.1 to 0.5 mol %) when this fatty acid was ingested (100). Unfortunately, little information is available to date on the potential for dietary inositol levels and fatty acids to influence the concentrations and molecular species compositions of the polyphosphoinositides (PIP and $PIP_2$) in mammalian tissues and cells and their turnover upon cell stimulation.

## *Dietary Inositol Deficiency and Triacylglycerol Accumulation in Liver*

The pioneering work of Gavin & McHenry (59) indicated that inositol could serve as a lipotropic factor. Furthermore, the development of the fatty liver in inositol-deficient rats was particularly evident when the diet was devoid of choline. Many of the nutritional experiments used in early experiments to produce an inositol-dependent response in the rat utilized the feeding of a low-protein depletion diet free of B vitamins and fat before administrating the B vitamins with or without supplementary inositol (128). Subsequently, Hayashi and colleagues (82) reported upon an inositol-deficient experimental diet containing phthalylsulfathiazole that resulted in an inositol-responsive accumulation of triacylglycerol in rat liver when highly saturated fats were fed. The drug was added to inhibit the growth of intestinal bacteria that can synthesize inositol. After only 7 days of dietary treatment, rats fed a basal diet containing 10% by weight of hydrogenated cottonseed oil without inositol had liver triacylglycerol concentrations that were 158% higher than those in animals fed the control diet containing 0.5% inositol.

Subsequent work has revealed (3) that in the rat the type of dietary triglyceride can influence the function of dietary inositol as a lipotrope in a manner not simply related to the degree of saturation of the fat. Dietary conditions have been reported in the young rat (5) that can give rise to a significant elevation in hepatic triglyceride concentrations with the exclusion of inositol from the basal diet even when the regimen contains sufficient quantities of all the essential nutrients (including protein, B vitamins, choline, and essential fatty acids) and does not contain a sulfathiazole drug. Fatty acid analyses have revealed that the weight percentage of linoleic acid is reduced in the phospholipid while the relative abundance of palmitoleic tends to be elevated in the triacylglycerol when inositol-deficient diets producing an accumulation of rat liver triacylglycerol are fed (3, 4). Using lactating rats as the experimental animal model, Burton & Wells (25) reported that inositol-deprived dams developed severe fatty livers that were improved by dietary inositol supplementation or by terminating lactation. Triacylglycerol and esterified cholesterol levels were greatly elevated in inositol-deficient dams after 14 days of lactation, although liver free cholesterol and phospholipid levels (particularly PI) were significantly decreased (26). An increase in the size and number of fat droplets in the livers of the deficient dams was observed upon electron microscopy.

It has been of continued interest during the past several years to elucidate the metabolic basis for the accumulation of liver triacylglycerols in experimental animals under conditions of inositol deficiency. The early work of Hasan and colleagues (74, 75) suggested that the transport of lipoproteins containing triacylglycerol from liver into plasma is impeded when inositol-deficient diets are consumed since inositol was found to promote the synthesis of PI, which increases the synthesis of lipoprotein in liver and its secretion. Hepatic triacylglycerol secretion rates have been measured in vivo in rats in relation to the dietary inositol status following the injection of Triton, which coats very-low-density lipoproteins (159) so as to prevent their degradation by lipoprotein lipase. Using this technique, secretion rates were found to be significantly lower in inositol-deficient gerbils as compared to controls (109), which thereby implicates an inadequate release of lipoprotein as a causative factor in the hepatic lipid accumulation. In further support of this concept, a depression in the levels of total plasma lipoprotein lipid, very-low-density lipoprotein, high-density lipoprotein, total phospholipid, and plasma PI in inositol-deprived dams during lactation has been observed (26). In addition, lactating rats supplemented with inositol exhibited a greater loss of radioactivity from liver triacylglycerol (27) concomitant with a more rapid appearance in serum triacylglycerols following the intravenous injection of labelled palmitic acid as compared to animals given an inositol-deficient diet.

As an alternative explanation for the hepatic triacylglycerol accumulation in inositol deficiency, Hayashi and colleagues (83) have concluded that an increased mobilization of fatty acid from adipose depots to the liver in the inositol-deficient rat may be an important causative factor. In support of this concept, they found the transfer of radioactivity from epididymal fat pads prelabelled with radioactive palmitic acid to the liver lipids to be almost 3-fold higher in the inositol-deficient animals as compared to controls. Subsequent work by these investigators (81) suggested that the increased lipolysis associated with an inositol-deficient state may result from an activation of hormone-sensitive lipase in adipose tissue. The concentration of plasma epinephrine, a potential activator of the lipase, was higher in the inositol-deficient animals. The enhanced lipolysis was attributed to an excitation of the sympathetic nerve terminals innervating the adipose tissues, not to an elevation of serum epinephrine released from the adrenals, since adrenalectomy did not influence the hepatic triacylglycerol accumulation caused by inositol deficiency.

The elevation of serum free fatty acids and liver triacylglycerol levels in the inositol-deficient condition was inhibited by treatment with sympathetic nervous blockers such as bupranolol and hexamethonium. This led to the suggestion that the central autonomic discharge to the adipose tissue may be increased in the deficient rat. These investigators also suggested that the decreased levels of inositol in the brain and especially of the hypothalamus in the deficient animal may link an excitation of this region to certain metabolic alterations associated with a dietary deficiency of inositol.

Since the lipogenic enzymes of rat liver undergo large alterations in activity with dietary alterations, Beach & Flick (11) studied the effect of feeding inositol-sufficient and -deficient diets as described by Hayashi et al (82) on the activities of fatty acid synthetase and acetyl-CoA carboxylase. The specific activities of these two enzymes were elevated approximately 2-fold in the inositol-deficient group over controls within 3–4 days of feeding the experimental diets. The rates of fatty acid synthetase synthesis in the inositol-deficient animals were significantly higher than controls after 12–18 hr of feeding, as measured by [$^3$H]leucine incorporation into immunoprecipitable fatty acid synthetase polypeptide, and then declined to control levels by one day. These authors have suggested that the hepatic lipodystrophy observed during inositol deficiency in rats may be partly due to an elevation in the levels of the lipogenic enzymes during the early stages of the developing deficiency. The relative quantitative contribution of the various biochemical mechanisms to the hepatic triacylglycerol accumulation in inositol deficiency remains to be further investigated.

## *Dietary Inositol Deficiency and Intestinal Lipodystrophy*

Hegsted et al (86) documented the high sensitivity of female gerbils toward the development of a pronounced intestinal lipodystrophy (characterized by the accumulation of fat in the intestinal mucosal cells) when fed a diet containing coconut oil. The syndrome was prevented by the inclusion of inositol in the diet. In the chronic condition, there was a progressive loss of body weight associated with alopecia, which was further complicated by an exudative dermatitis and inanition. The small intestine from the inositol-deficient gerbils was greatly enlarged and the serosal surface was unusually white, with the exposed mucosa appearing swollen, corrugated, and equally whitened at necroscopy. Kroes et al (130) subsequently observed that dietary triacylglycerols rich in lauric, capric, or myristic acids produced the maximum accumulation of gut lipid upon feeding inositol-deficient diets. Additional research led to the concept that dietary inositol deprivation restricts the transport of saturated fat by the mucosal cells more than that of unsaturated lipid (213).

The intestinal lipodystrophy induced by dietary fat in female gerbils was reversed to normal (31) by inositol given in the diet or by injection within 1–4 days. Plasma chylomicron and lipid levels increased before the rapid disappearance of accumulated fat from the intestine. In addition, dietary inositol promoted an increase in triacylglycerol release from everted gut sacs. These and subsequent results by Chu & Geyer (32) led to the suggestion that a reduced biosynthesis of PI owing to a limited inositol availability may well be responsible for the impaired chylomicron assembly and secretion and intestinal lipid clearance in the gerbil consuming an inositol-depleted diet. A comparative study (34) using *M. unguiculatus* and *M. libycus* revealed that both species of gerbils developed an intestinal lipodystrophy due to a dietary deficiency of inositol.

The lower susceptibility of male gerbils to inositol deficiency may be due to the contribution of inositol biosynthesis in the testis, as shown by differences between intact and castrated animals (33). Like the rat, a gerbil testis contains high activities of both inositol 1-phosphate synthase and phosphatase. The activities of the two inositol biosynthetic enzymes were not significantly different in the liver, intestinal mucosa, kidney, and brain of male versus female animals, nor was the activity of the inositol degrading enzyme, inositol oxygenase, located in the kidney. Furthermore, the various enzyme activities were not significantly modified by dietary inositol supplementation.

### *Dietary Inositol and the Lung*

Since extracellularly derived inositol influences the metabolism of type II cells from the lung, Hallman (71) has studied the ability of inositol to promote differentiation and growth. Dietary inositol doubled the already high fetal serum inositol concentrations between fetal days 26 and 28 but had no detectable effects on the lung. The administration of inositol together with glucocorticoid decreased the glucocorticoid-induced decrease in lung dry weight when compared to controls. Inositol also potentiated a glucocorticoid-induced increase in the lavageable surfactant phospholipids. In an organ culture system, the addition of inositol increased the incorporation of glucose and acetate into the fatty acid moiety of surfactant phosphatidylcholine. Hallman (71) has proposed that the high level of extracellular inositol in immature fetuses provides an environment that promotes both the hormone-stimulated lung differentiation and growth.

## CELLULAR FUNCTIONS OF PHOSPHATIDYLINOSITOL AND POLYPHOSPHOINOSITIDES IN MAMMALIAN CELLS

### *Membrane Structure and Function*

In view of their intimate association with biological membranes, a plethora of membrane functions related to the inositol-containing phospholipids (PI, PIP, and $PIP_2$) have been documented in mammalian cells and tissues. These functions may be related to the preponderance of 1-stearoyl 2-arachidonoyl species that commonly reside in these three phospholipids, discussed earlier in this review. As seen in Table 2, the PI, PIP, and $PIP_2$ residing in purified plasma membrane from human platelets are greatly enriched in stearic acid (41–43 mol % of total) and arachidonic acid (42–46 mol % of total). It has been reported that most of the PI pool is localized on the luminal side of the endoplasmic reticulum (160), although results from specific hydrolysis of PI confirmed an essentially symmetric distribution across the liver microsomal and the Golgi vesicle membranes (198). It has been proposed that the pattern of phospholipid asymmetry observed in the erythrocyte membrane is not a general feature of biological membranes (181). Perret et al (168) found PI to be situated mainly at the internal face of the plasma membrane from human platelets. Recently, Herbette et al (88) found 88% of the PI to be localized in the inner monolayer of the sarcoplasmic reticulum lipid bilayer.

A function for PI in regulating enzyme activity and transport processes is supported by evidence of specific interactions between this phospholipid and protein. Mandersloot and colleagues (148) have shown PI to be the endogenous activator of the ($Na^+$ + $K^+$)-adenosine trisphosphatase (ATPase) in microsomes isolated from rabbit kidney. The enzymes alkaline phosphatase and 5'-nucleotidase appeared to exhibit a specific association with PI in the plasma membrane (140). Rothman (180) has proposed that specific electrostatic interactions between the polar head group of PI and protein could provide for the formation of complexes that are important for the passage of proteins through membranes. The nonpolar aliphatic fatty acyl chains of the phospholipid may provide a hydrophobic microenvironment for the proteins. Interestingly, PI has been reported as an essential constituent of the acetyl-CoA carboxylase from rat liver (84); PI was found to have a controlling influence on the kinetic properties of citrate activation of the enzyme. PI has also been found to have potent effects

**Table 2** Fatty acid composition of phosphoinositides from plasma membrane of human platelets[a]

| Fatty Acid | Phosphatidylinositol | Phosphatidylinositol 4-phosphate | Phosphatidylinositol 4,5-bisphosphate |
|---|---|---|---|
| 16:0 | 2.6±0.8 | 2.9±0.2 | <1.0 |
| 18:0 | 41.3±0.9 | 41.5±1.8 | 43.4±0.4 |
| 18:1 | 6.7±0.2 | 6.4±0.9 | 7.9±0.4 |
| 18:2 | 1.2±0.7 | 0.6±0.2 | 2.6±1.1 |
| 20:4 | 46.0±0.9 | 43.3±1.8 | 41.9±1.0 |

[a]Unpublished data of Holub, Mahadevappa, and Belkhode. Values are given in mol % of total fatty acids and represent means ± S.E. for three separate experiments. Other minor fatty acids have been omitted from the table.

on tyrosine hydroxylase, an enzyme that catalyzes the rate-limiting step in the biosynthesis of catecholamines, dopamine, and norepinephrine (139). Very recently, Futerman and colleagues (57) provided evidence to support the concept that PI is involved in anchoring acetylcholinesterase to the plasma membrane of *Torpedo*.

## *Source of Free Arachidonic Acid for Eicosanoid Production*

The release of arachidonic acid from membrane 1-stearoyl 2-arachidonoyl PI is of considerable importance in controlling the formation of the eicosanoids (via cyclooxygenase/lipoxygenase activities) including prostaglandins, thromboxanes, leukotrienes, and other metabolites in mammalian tissues and cells. Arachidonic acid is also found in the choline-, ethanolamine-, and serine-containing phospholipids, and the former two, in particular, can also be of considerable significance in providing for the release of free arachidonic acid. There are a number of metabolic pathways that may contribute to the release of free arachidonic acid from the turnover of membrane PI in both resting and agonist-stimulated cells (98). As discussed above, PI can be directly deacylated via phospholipase $A_2$ activity with the release of arachidonic acid; alternatively, deacylation via phospholipase $A_1$ activity and subsequent hydrolysis of the lyso(2-acyl) PI by lysophospholipase activity (115) can also provide for the release of the eicosanoid precursor. Cellular PI can be degraded directly via a phospholipase C type cleavage (by phosphodiesterase activity) (42, 114) or by its conversion to the polyphosphoinositides, which can be hydrolyzed also to 1,2-diacylglycerols via phosphodiesterase activity (126). The intermediary 1,2-diacylglycerol (enriched in stearic and arachidonic acids) can be hydrolyzed by diacylglycerol lipase with the formation of 2-monoacylglycerol (containing arachidonic acid); the latter lipid can then be cleaved by monoacylglycerol lipase to release free arachidonic acid (12, 146). Alternatively, the transient diacylglycerol can be phosphorylated via diacylglycerol kinase to form phosphatidic acid enriched in arachidonate at the 2-position (107). Billah et al (17) reported a particulate phospholipase $A_2$ enzyme that appears to act selectively on phosphatidic acid to release arachidonic acid.

### *Involvement in Mediation of Cellular Responses to External Stimuli*

The pioneering work of Hokin & Hokin (91), which demonstrated that acetylcholine stimulates the incorporation of radioactive inorganic orthophosphate into the inositol phospholipid of pancreas slices, suggested a possible physiological function for this accelerated metabolism. Considerable interest in this area has arisen from the discussions of Michell (153, 154) and accompanying experimental evidence suggesting that an accelerated metabolism and degradation of membrane PI by phospholipase C (phosphodiesterase) activity may be intimately related to the regulation of calcium fluxes that accompany cellular responses to external stimuli such as hormones and neurotransmitters.

An enhancement of PI metabolism in appropriate target tissues may occur, with stimuli having the ability to produce rapid physiological responses (muscarinic cholinergic, $\alpha$-adrenergic, etc) as well as those that bring about longer-term stimulation of cell proliferation (phytohemagglutinin and other mitogens, etc). This "PI effect" appeared to involve an initial degradation of membrane PI (154) and control cell surface $Ca^{2+}$ permeability, thereby giving rise to an elevation in intracellular $Ca^{2+}$ concentration (119). Kirk and colleagues (127) provided evidence for a relationship between enhanced PI metabolism and the activation of glycogen phosphorylase in hepatocytes exposed to vasopressin and related peptides. A role for PI turnover in stimulus-secretion coupling has also been provided with respect to $Ca^{2+}$-mediated histamine secretion in antigen-sensitized rat peritoneal mast cells stimulated with a number of ligands (38). Pickard & Hawthorne (169) have implicated the possible role of PI turnover in transmitter release by showing that electrical stimulation of synaptosomes labelled with radioactive phosphate in vivo caused a loss of radioactivity from the PI associated with the synaptic vessicles. A role for stimulated PI turnover in secretagogue-stimulated secretion was also revealed by in vitro work with rat pancreatic tissues (191).

There is now increasing evidence to suggest that direct PI hydrolysis by phospholipase C during agonist action may not be responsible for the initiation of calcium mobilization. The work of Abdel-Latif et al (1), which demonstrated the stimulatory effect of acetylcholine on the breakdown of prelabelled $PIP_2$ in iris smooth muscle, and subsequent investigations suggested that alterations in the polyphosphoinositides may be associated with receptor activation. According to this concept, receptor occupancy would exert primary control over the hydrolysis of $PIP_2$ via phosphodiesterase activity at the plasma membrane level, such that the disappearance of PI would be a consequence of its utilization for the replenishment of $PIP_2$ (16). A number of thoughtful reviews have been written very recently on the involvement of $PIP_2$ in relation to PI and PIP in mediating cellular responses to various agonists (for example, 16, 51, 54, 90, 147, and 155). A most timely and important conference was recently convened in Dallas by Drs. Bleasdale, Eichberg, and Hauser and reported upon (18).

A brief summarization of the possible involvement of PI and the polyphosphoinositides (particularly $PIP_2$) in receptor-mediated cellular responses is shown in Figure 3. Although the PI greatly predominates in quantity over PIP and $PIP_2$ in mammalian cells, and also in the very few studies on plasma membrane preparations characterized to date, research on stimulated blowfly salivary glands and other cells (14, 15) indicates that the accumulation of inositol trisphosphate precedes that of inositol 1-phosphate. This suggests that the degradation of $PIP_2$ and not PI may well be an initial event occurring upon receptor occupancy. Based on work in human platelets, Vickers et al (209) have suggested that the formation of diacylglycerol and inositol phosphates, and not $PIP_2$ decreases, may be the important change in platelet activation by thrombin. In vitro enzyme studies indicate that the hydrolysis of all three inositol-containing phospholipids is stimulated by $Ca^{2+}$, although only the polyphosphoinositides were hydrolyzed in the presence of EGTA (218). These results support the concept that the hydrolysis of $PIP_2$ is favored at low $Ca^{2+}$ concentrations (prior to $Ca^{2+}$ flux) such that the elevation in cytoplasmic $Ca^{2+}$ provides for the $Ca^{2+}$-dependent hydrolysis of PI by phospholipase C (14, 146, 218). Quantitative analysis revealed a significant decrease in the mass of stearoyl arachidonoyl PI from the plasma membrane of thrombin-stimulated human platelets (190), which may be of importance in mediating cellular

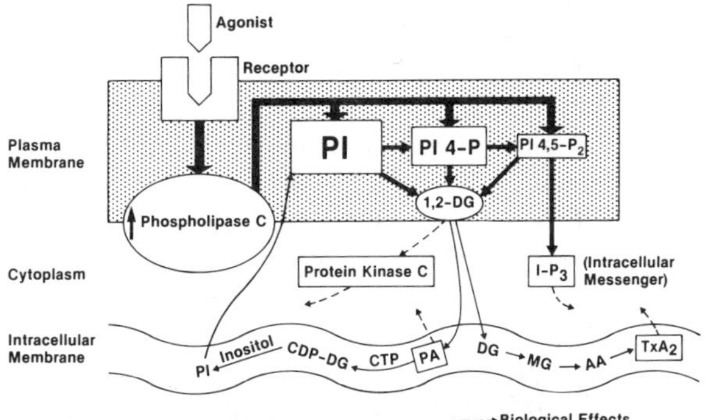


*Figure 3* Proposed mechanisms for receptor-mediated cellular responses involving phosphatidylinositol. In addition to providing for the formation of inositol trisphosphate (I-$P_3$), 1,2-diacylglycerol (1,2-DG), and phosphatidic acid (PA), the accelerated phosphoinositide metabolism can provide for the release of free arachidonic acid and its active metabolites [e.g. thromboxane $A_2$ ($TxA_2$) is a potentiator of platelet aggregation and a vasoconstrictor]. As discussed in the text, the action of phospholipase $A_2$ on PI and PA can also release free arachidonic acid.

responses to external stimuli including the formation of arachidonoyl diacylglycerol.

## *Source of the Second Messenger 1,2-Diacylglycerol and Phosphatidate*

In addition to providing a source of arachidonic acid for eicosanoid production (discussed in the previous section), the released diacylglycerol in stimulated cells may play an important messenger role in the cellular responses. Although the relative direct contribution of phospholipase C hydrolysis of $PIP_2$, PIP, and PI to the 1,2-diacylglycerol pool that accumulates at various times following receptor occupation has not been elucidated in various mammalian cells, Wilson et al (220) have concluded that the bulk of the PI breakdown in thrombin-stimulated platelets occurs via the direct hydrolysis of PI by phospholipase C to release diacylglycerol. Haslam & Davidson (77) have suggested that a GTP-binding protein may play a role in receptor-induced diacylglycerol formation based on work in permeabilized platelets. There is supporting evidence to suggest that the diacylglycerol that is transiently produced from the inositol phospholipids upon cellular stimulation may have an important second messenger function in activating protein kinase C to phosphorylate specific proteins (162). This function of diacylglycerol as a signal for the transmembrane control of protein phosphorylation is a complex process requiring both calcium and phosphatidylserine as cofactors, and it may mediate various physiological processes such as secretion and proliferation. For example, this metabolic sequence appears to be associated with 40 kDa protein phosphorylation and the release reaction in platelets (162). Cooper et al (41) observed that a 16-kDa protein present in a purified rat liver plasma membrane fraction and also in the cytosol can be phosphorylated by the endogenously activated protein kinase C.

Interestingly, tumor-promoting phorbol esters may substitute for diacylglycerol and permanently activate protein kinase C when they are intercalated into the cell membrane (163). The phosphorylation of diacylglycerol to phosphatidic acid by diacylglycerol kinase activity can provide for the marked elevations in cellular phosphatidate levels that often accompany cellular activation (52). Phosphatidate is able to complex with calcium and transport this cation as an ionophore (207). For example, Gerrard et al (61, 62) have suggested that the formation of phosphatidate and its monoacyl derivative may serve to initiate an intracellular flux of calcium by releasing the cation from an intracellular store and may contribute to the elevation in cytoplasmic calcium concentrations associated with platelet responses such as aggregation. In addition, the phosphatidate can be reconverted back to PI via de novo synthesis in the intracellular membrane. The PI transport proteins (see earlier section) may be important for the transfer of the newly synthesized PI to the plasma membrane site to replenish the degraded PI.

## *Source of the Second Messenger Inositol Trisphosphate*

There is now considerable evidence to indicate that the mobilization of calcium from intracellular stores is an early and important event following the extracellular stimulation of various mammalian cells. Considerable excitement has been generated in the field of inositol functioning at the cellular level with the mounting evidence to support the concept that the formation and function of inositol trisphosphate (1,4,5-trisphosphate), as derived from $PIP_2$, may link receptor occupancy to the mobilization of calcium from internal stores (15, 16). Berridge & Irvine (16) have described a number of tissues that might well respond to various external stimuli by such a mechanism. There is experimental evidence from stimulated salivary glands and other cells to indicate that the rapid appearance of inositol trisphosphate precedes calcium mobilization (16). In this way, inositol trisphosphate functions as an intracellular messenger in mammalian cells that are activated by calcium-mobilizing stimuli such as hormones, secretagogues, and other agonists. Berridge (15) discussed the potential synergistic interactions between the diacylglycerol and calcium signal pathways.

Using permeabilized pancreatic acinar cells, Streb et al (196) found that micromolar concentrations of inositol trisphosphate cause the release of calcium from a nonmitochondrial storage site. These latter findings have been confirmed in a number of other cellular systems (123, 174). In vitro studies have demonstrated that addition of inositol trisphosphate can induce the release of calcium from microsomal fractions of rat liver and insulinoma (43, 173). In the case of rat insulinoma, no release of calcium from mitochondria or secretory granules was found in response to inositol trisphosphate (173). Interestingly, inositol 1,3,4-trisphosphate was released in carbachol-stimulated rat parotid glands after an initial lag period; in addition, the level of inositol 1,4,5-trisphosphate was increased early (113). Potential sources and functions for the inositol 1,3,4-trisphosphate remain to be investigated. Very recently, Wilson and colleagues (219) demonstrated that the water-soluble products of polyphosphoinositide cleavage by purified ram seminal vesicle phospholipase C enzymes also contain cyclic phosphates, which may play a role in phosphoinositide-derived signal transduction.

## *Degradation of Inositol Trisphosphate*

Because inositol trisphosphate may play an important role as a second messenger for the mobilization of intracellular calcium, interest has arisen regarding the biochemical steps responsible for degrading this intermediate as potential sites in metabolic regulation. Seyfred et al (186) found the specific activity of the D-inositol 1,4,5-trisphosphate phosphatase to be highest in the plasma membrane fraction from rat liver, whereas the D-inositol 1,4-bisphosphate phosphatase activity was highest in the cytosolic and microsomal fractions.

These findings have been supported by other investigators (122). Storey et al (195) have also characterized the stepwise enzymatic dephosphorylation of inositol 1,4,5-trisphosphate to inositol in liver. Very recently, a phosphomonoesterase has been isolated from human platelets (39) that specifically hydrolyzes the 5-phosphate of inositol 1,4,5-trisphosphate. Other water-soluble inositol phosphates as well as phosphorylated sugars were not hydrolyzed; the only inositol-containing phospholipid cleaved was $PIP_2$ and at a rate less than 1% that for inositol trisphosphate. Research is needed on the control of inositol trisphosphate degradation in relation to the accelerated hydrolysis of $PIP_2$ upon receptor occupation in target cells.

## ABNORMAL METABOLISM OF INOSITOL AND INOSITOL PHOSPHOLIPIDS IN DISEASE STATES

### *Diabetes*

Diabetics are known to exhibit decreased peripheral motor and sensory nerve conduction velocities without evidence of polyneuropathy. The relationship of inositol to impaired functioning of the peripheral nervous system in rats with acute streptozotocin-induced diabetes has been studied by Greene and colleagues (67). Experimental diabetes rendered these animals unable to maintain normal concentrations of free inositol in the peripheral nerve, which was related to a decreased motor nerve conduction velocity. The free inositol levels in the nerve diminished despite the fact that circulating levels of free inositol were similar in normal and diabetic rats. Insulin treatment prevented the decrease in nerve inositol levels and the impaired nerve conduction velocity in the diabetic rats. Dietary inositol supplementation, which elevates plasma inositol levels, has proven beneficial in ameliorating the motor nerve conduction velocity in the acute streptozotocin-diabetic rat (70). Interestingly, an excessive elevation in plasma inositol levels induced by feeding a diet containing 3% (rather than 1%) inositol decreased the motor nerve conduction velocity in both normal and diabetic animals (67).

Structural changes in nerve membrane in diabetes and their reversal by inositol and insulin administration have been revealed by electron microscopy (56). The specific activity of the inositol 1-phosphate synthase involved in inositol biosynthesis was found to be lower in the testis but not in the sciatic nerve of diabetic rats relative to controls (217). Clements & Reynertson (37) suggested that hyperglycemia in the untreated human diabetic may impede inositol transport, thereby resulting in a widespread intracellular deficiency in human subjects. The inositoluria observed in human diabetes may arise from the inhibitory effect of glucose on renal tubular reabsorption of inositol. Consequently, urinary inositol excretion can account for a significant fraction of the dietary inositol intake of the untreated diabetic; the urinary excretion is lowered toward normal levels with insulin treatment. The activity of the kidney inositol oxygenase that degrades inositol was markedly decreased in experimental diabetes. This may contribute to the elevated concentrations of inositol in the diabetic kidney and the increased clearance of inositol (166, 217).

Greene & Lattimer (68) studied the phospholipid-dependent membrane-bound ($Na^+ + K^+$)-ATPase in an attempt to provide a potential mechanism that would link defects in diabetic peripheral nerve to the abnormal inositol metabolism. The enzyme activity was found to be reduced in homogenates of sciatic nerve in experimental diabetes. This reduction in enzyme activity was selectively prevented by 1% inositol supplementation, which restored normal nerve conduction. These authors suggested that dietary inositol may correct diabetic nerve conduction by changing enzyme activity, and this may be mediated via alterations in inositol-containing phospholipids. Subsequent work demonstrated that sorbinil treatment, which preserves normal nerve inositol contents (53), prevents the fall in nerve ($Na^+ + K^+$)-ATPase activity that has been linked to conduction slowing in the diabetic rat (69).

During the past few years, attention has been directed toward the levels and metabolism of inositol-containing phospholipids in relation to diabetes. The rate of labelled inositol entry into PI falls in intact nerve segments from diabetic rats but not in broken cell preparations (110). This suggests a depression in inositol transport occurring in diabetes. Palmano et al (166) reported a lowered concentration of lipid-bound inositol in the nerves of acutely diabetic animals. Biochemical analyses on sciatic nerves removed postmortem from diabetic patients and normal subjects have revealed the concentrations of both inositol phospholipid and free inositol to be significantly lower in nerves from the diabetics (150). Bell and colleagues (13) observed an increased turnover of $PIP_2$ in sciatic nerve from streptozotocin-diabetic rats that appears relatively early and persists throughout the course of the disease. These authors suggested that this metabolic alteration may be related to a primary defect responsible for the accompanying deficient peripheral nerve function. Further research is needed on the enzyme-catalyzed steps associated with the turnover of the phosphoinositides in diabetic as compared to normal animals. Clements & Reynertson (37) demonstrated that a 3-g oral load of inositol could significantly elevate plasma inositol concentrations in human subjects, with diabetics showing a greater response. These investigators suggested that oral inositol supplementation might be of benefit in the prevention and treatment of certain complications associated with human diabetes mellitus. The effect of inositol on neurophysiological measurements in diabetic patients has been investigated by Salway et al (182). The administration of a 0.5-g oral dose of inositol twice a day for two weeks increased the amplitude of the evoked action potentials of the median, sural, and popliteal nerves by an average of 76, 160, and 40% respectively. Their results suggested a therapeutic role for inositol in diabetic neuropathy.

## *Renal Disorders*

Significant abnormalities in inositol metabolism accompanying renal failure have been well documented in human patients and are manifested in a dramatic hyperinositolemia (35, 135, 171). For example, patients with chronic renal failure have been reported to have circulating inositol levels 7-fold greater than those for controls (99) (240 versus 33 $\mu$M). It has been suggested that an impaired renal oxidation of inositol to D-glucuronate may contribute to the abnormally elevated plasma inositol levels in uremic patients (35) since the kidney is the major site for inositol catabolism in the body. A decreased glomerular filtration rate and a disturbed inositol reabsorption are also present in advanced forms of glomerulonephritis (171). Consequently, the estimation of serum and urinary inositol may have advantages in the evaluation of kidney function. Plasma inositol levels show a moderate decrease during hemodialysis in patients with chronic renal failure but to a lesser extent than the plasma urea nitrogen. Clements & Diethelm (36) reported that the half-life of inositol disappearance, which was prolonged in patients with chronic renal failure, was obviated following successful renal transplantation based on experiments in which [$^3$H]inositol was injected into an antecubital vein of fasting subjects.

Research has been conducted on the potential toxic effects of abnormally high levels of circulating inositol in both experimental animals and human subjects. Large doses of inositol given to rats increase PI levels in the endoplasmic reticulum of liver with no obvious deleterious effects (222). Doses of inositol did not produce any appreciable change in the liver or kidney of male and female rats when studied morphologically by light microscopy (76). The sciatic nerve motor neuron conduction velocity markedly decreased when normal male rats were placed on a diet enriched in inositol for one week (35). The condition improved when the animals were restored to a normal diet. These and subsequent experiments have supported the idea that hyperinositolemia may contribute to the pathogenesis of the uremic polyneuropathy in subjects with chronic renal failure (46).

Reznek and colleagues (179) showed that rises in plasma inositol concentrations were related to a depression of sural nerve conduction velocity based on experiments with uremic patients, but a relationship with clinically evident neuropathy was not a established. Liveson et al (138) observed the development of cytoplasmic abnormalities following the exposure of dorsal root ganglion cells to inositol. Neurotoxicity was revealed at an inositol concentration as low as 109 $\mu$M, which is considerably below the levels found in many uremic patients (99). Other work in this area will be greatly enhanced by the application of suitable animal models for studying the interrelationship between abnormalities in inositol and inositol phospholipid metabolism and chronic kidney disorders. Interestingly, measurement of the levels of free inositol in the early effluent perfusate appears to offer an accurate method for evaluating the viability of preserved kidneys and predicting graft functioning after renal transplantation (131).

## Other Disease States

Alterations in inositol and inositol phospholipid metabolism have also been implicated in various other disease states, although, in most cases, no definitive associations have been established. Shastri and colleagues (187) reported that only the PI (as a percentage of total phospholipid) was significantly higher in the blood platelets from type II hypercholesterolemic patients relative to normal subjects. The absolute concentration of arachidonoyl PI ($\mu$mol per $10^9$ platelets) was also found to be elevated in the hypercholesterolemic gerbil and human platelets, primarily because of the higher amounts of this phospholipid and not because of differences in the percentage contribution of arachidonate to the total fatty acids in PI (100). These findings may be relevant to the hypersensitivity of platelets from hypercholesterolemic human subjects to pro-aggregating agents, which may contribute to their increased risk for arterial thrombosis. Cholesterol feeding has been reported to influence the rapid metabolism of PI in the pig and monkey aorta (20, 45).

Galactitol concentration is elevated and free and lipid-bound inositol levels are depressed in the brains of galactosemic infants or animals subjected to experimental galactose toxicity (214). The PI response to acetylcholine is impaired in synaptosomes from galactose-fed rats, which suggests that these animals may be deficient in the number of acetylcholine receptors or have a defect in the step between receptor-neurotransmitter interaction and PI breakdown (212). Analysis of a biopsy specimen from the liver of an adult patient with hepatosplenomegaly and hyperlipidemia revealed a marked elevation of PI (223). Since an immunologic abnormality appears to be involved in the pathogenesis of multiple sclerosis, it is of interest that the lymphocytes from such patients incorporate less labelled inositol into PI than those from control patients when stimulated by phytohemagglutinin (165). Hallman and colleagues (72) have reported that the abnormality in surfactant phospholipids in adult respiratory distress syndrome is usually associated with low PI and low plasma inositol levels. The metabolism of inositol lipids has also been implicated in cell proliferation and cancer. PI turnover has been proposed to be regulated by the oncogene protein kinases either directly by acting as PI kinases or indirectly as tyrosine kinases (142).

Reduced inositol levels have been reported in cerebrospinal fluid from patients with affective disorders (10), but fluid levels of inositol in schizophrenic patients were not significantly different from healthy controls (199). The defective phosphoinositide metabolism observed in the erythrocyte membrane of the spontaneously hypertensive rat was not a consequence of the blood pressure elevation and may be related to the pathogenesis of hypertension

(129). Significant differences have also been reported in the fatty acid composition of PI from total and subcellular fractions of liver as compared to hepatoma (208). Interestingly, soybean PI (enriched in linoleic acid in the 2-position) but not animal PI (enriched in arachidonic acid in the 2-position) can exert cytotoxicity toward tumor cells from cultured cell lines without affecting normal cell lines (120).

It will be of considerable interest in the future to elucidate the abnormalities in the metabolism of $PIP_2$, PIP, and PI in various disease states. Since the concentrations of these cellular inositol phospholipids and their various component molecular species are subject to significant nutritional modifications, it will also be of interest to determine whether restoring the inositol lipid patterns to normal by dietary or other intervention may be used clinically to prevent and treat disease states involving abnormalities in inositol phospholipid-mediated physiological responses.

## SUMMARY AND CONCLUSIONS

Alterations in the level of dietary inositol can significantly influence the concentration of free inositol and inositol-containing phospholipid in the circulation and in selected mammalian tissues and cells. The 1-stearoyl 2-arachidonoyl molecular species that commonly predominates in cellular phosphoinositides may be of considerable importance for the functioning of these phospholipids in biological membranes. Retailoring reactions subsequent to the de novo biosynthesis of PI involving the acylation of lyso(1-acyl) PI allow for the preferential enrichment of this phospholipid in arachidonic acid. The impaired release of plasma lipoprotein, increased fatty acid mobilization from adipose tissue, and enhanced fatty acid synthesis in liver have all been implicated as causative factors in the hepatic triacylglycerol accumulation occurring with experimental inositol deficiency. The severe intestinal lipodystrophy that develops in female gerbils consuming inositol-deficient diets is likely mediated by a reduced synthesis of PI and the associated impairment of chylomicron assembly and secretion.

Membrane PI can potentially regulate enzyme activities and transport processes as well as providing a source of free arachidonic acid for production of the eicosanoids. There has been mounting evidence recently to indicate that an accelerated turnover of the phosphoinositides may play a key role in mediating cellular responses to external stimuli. The transient rise of phosphoinositide-derived 1,2-diacylglycerol in stimulated cells may serve as a signal for the transmembrane control of protein phosphorylation by activating protein kinase C. Receptor occupancy also elicits the phosphodiesterase-catalyzed release of the second messenger inositol 1,4,5-trisphosphate, which appears to provide for the mobilization of calcium from internal stores.

Subnormal levels of free inositol and inositol phospholipid, as found in the nerves of animals with experimental diabetes and in sciatic nerves removed postmortem from diabetic patients, have been implicated in the impaired nerve conduction of human diabetics. Patients with renal failure exhibit a dramatic hyperinositolemia that may have clinical significance. Nutritional intervention may offer an approach for counteracting abnormalities in inositol and inositol phospholipid profiles and associated physiological responses in certain disease states.

ACKNOWLEDGMENTS

The assistance of Mrs. Frances Graziotto, Ms. Andra Hinds, and Ms. Tanya Fawcett in the processing of this manuscript is gratefully acknowledged. I wish to thank Dr. R. Parthasarathy for clarifying the stereochemistry of inositol and its derivatives (Parthasarathy, R., Eisenberg, F. Jr. 1986. *Biochem. J.* 235:1–10). The author's research described herein was supported by grants from the Medical Research Council of Canada, the Heart and Stroke Foundation of Ontario, and the Natural Sciences and Engineering Research Council of Canada.

## *Literature Cited*

1. Abdel-Latif, A. A., Akhtar, R. A., Hawthorne, J. N. 1977. Acetylcholine increases the breakdown of triphosphoinositide of rabbit iris muscle prelabelled with [$^{32}$P]phosphate. *Biochem. J.* 162:61–73
2. Agranoff, B. W. 1978. Cyclitol confusion. *Trends Biochem. Sci.* 3:283–85
3. Andersen, D. B., Holub, B. J. 1976. The influence of dietary inositol on glyceride composition and synthesis in livers of rats fed different fats. *J. Nutr.* 106:529–36
4. Andersen, D. B., Holub, B. J. 1980. *Myo*-inositol-responsive liver lipid accumulation in the rat. *J. Nutr.* 110: 488–95
5. Andersen, D. B., Holub, B. J. 1980. The relative response of hepatic lipids in the rat to graded levels of dietary *myo*-inositol and other lipotropes. *J. Nutr.* 110:496–504
6. Auchus, R. J., Wilson, D. B., Covey, D. F., Majerus, P. W. 1985. The 5-hydroxyl of *myo*-inositol is essential for uptake into $HSDM_1C_1$ mouse fibrosarcoma cells. *Biochem. Biophys. Res. Commun.* 130:1139–46
7. Baker, R. R., Chang, H.-Y. 1985. The CMP-stimulated production of diacylglycerol and CDP-diacylglycerol in neuronal nuclei labelled with radioactive arachidonate. *Biochim. Biophys. Acta* 835:221–30
8. Baker, R. R., Thompson, W. 1972. Positional distribution and turnover of fatty acids in phosphatidic acid, phosphoinositides, phosphatidylcholine and phosphatidylethanolamine in rat brain *in vivo*. *Biochim. Biophys. Acta* 270:489–503
9. Baker, R. R., Thompson, W. 1973. Selective acylation of 1-acyl-glycerophosphorylinositol by rat brain microsomes. *J. Biol. Chem.* 248:7060–65
10. Barkai, A. I., Dunner, D. L., Gross, H. A., Mayo, P., Fieve, R. R. 1978. Reduced *myo*-inositol levels in cerebrospinal fluid from patients with affective disorders. *Biol. Psychiatry* 13:65–72
11. Beach, D. C., Flick, P. K. 1982. Early effect of *myo*-inositol deficiency on fatty acid synthetic enzymes of rat liver. *Biochim. Biophys. Acta* 711:452–59
12. Bell, R. L., Kennerly, D. A., Stanford, N., Majerus, P. W. 1979. Diglyceride lipase: a pathway for arachidonate release from human platelets. *Proc. Natl. Acad. Sci. USA* 76:3238–41
13. Bell, M. E., Peterson, R. G., Eichberg, J. 1982. Metabolism of phospholipids in peripheral nerve from rats with chronic streptozotocin-induced diabetes: increased turnover of phosphatidylinositol-4,5-bisphosphate. *J. Neurochem.* 39: 192–200
14. Berridge, M. J. 1983. Rapid accumulation of inositol trisphosphate reveals that agonists hydrolyze polyphosphoinositides instead of phosphatidylinositol. *Biochem. J.* 212:849–58
15. Berridge, M. J. 1984. Inositol trisphos-

phate and diacylglycerol as second messengers. *Biochem. J.* 220:345–60

16. Berridge, M. J., Irvine, R. F. 1984. Inositol trisphosphate, a novel second messenger in cellular signal transduction. *Nature* 312:315–21
17. Billah, M. M., Lapetina, E. G., Cuatrecasas, P. 1981. Phospholipase $A_2$ activity specific for phosphatidic acid. *J. Biol. Chem.* 256:5399–403
18. Bleasdale, J. E., Eichberg, J., Hauser, G., eds. 1985. *Inositol and Phosphoinositides: Metabolism and Regulation.* Clifton, NJ: Humana
19. Bleasdale, J. E., Wallis, P., MacDonald, P. C., Johnston, J. M. 1979. Characterization of the forward and reverse reactions catalyzed by CDP-diacylglycerol:inositol transferase in rabbit lung tissue. *Biochim. Biophys. Acta* 575:135–47
20. Borensztajn, J., Getz, G. S., Wissler, R. W. 1973. The *in vitro* incorporation of $[^3H]$thymidine into DNA and of $^{32}P$ into phospholipids and RNA in the aorta of Rhesus monkeys during early atherogenesis. *Atherosclerosis* 17:269–80
21. Borgese, T. A., Nagel, R. L. 1978. Inositol pentaphosphate in fish red blood cells. *J. Exp. Zool.* 205:133–40
22. Breckenridge, W. C., Palmer, F. B. St. C. 1982. Fatty acid composition of human plasma lipoprotein phosphatidylinositols. *Biochim. Biophys. Acta* 712:707–11
23. Burton, L. E., Ray, R. E., Bradford, J. R., Orr, J. P., Nickerson, J. A., Wells, W. W. 1976. *myo*-Inositol metabolism in the neonatal and developing rat fed a *myo*-inositol-free diet. *J. Nutr.* 106:1610–16
24. Burton, L. E., Wells, W. W. 1974. Studies on the developmental pattern of the enzymes converting glucose-6-phosphate to *myo*-inositol in the rat. *Dev. Biol.* 37:35–42
25. Burton, L. E., Wells, W. W. 1976. *myo*-Inositol metabolism during lactation and development in the rat. The prevention of lactation-induced fatty liver by dietary *myo*-inositol. *J. Nutr.* 106:1617–28
26. Burton, L. E., Wells, W. W. 1977. Characterization of the lactation-dependent fatty liver in *myo*-inositol deficient rats. *J. Nutr.* 107:1871–83
27. Burton, L. E., Wells, W. W. 1979. *Myo*-inositol deficiency: Studies on the mechanism of lactation-dependent fatty liver formation in the rat. *J. Nutr.* 109:1483–91
28. Byun, S. M., Jenness, R. 1981. Stereospecificity of L-*myo*-inositol-1-phosphate synthase for nicotinamide adenine dinucleotide. *Biochemistry* 20:5174–77
29. Caspary, W. F., Crane, R. K. 1970. Active transport of *myo*-inositol and its relation to the sugar transport system in hamster small intestine. *Biochim. Biophys. Acta* 203:308–16
30. Chapkin, R. S., Haberstroh, B., Liu, T., Holub, B. J. 1983. Characterization of the individual phospholipids and their fatty acids in serum and high-density lipoprotein of the renal patient on long-term maintenance hemodialysis. *J. Lab. Clin. Med.* 101:726–35
31. Chu, S. W., Geyer, R. P. 1981. *myo*-Inositol action on gerbil intestine. Reversal of a diet-induced lipodystrophy and change in microsomal lipase activity. *Biochim. Biophys. Acta* 664:89–97
32. Chu, S. W., Geyer, R. P. 1982. *myo*-Inositol action on gerbil intestine. Association of phosphatidylinositol metabolism with lipid clearance. *Biochim. Biophys. Acta* 710:63–70
33. Chu, S. W., Geyer, R. P. 1983. Tissue content and metabolism of *myo*-inositol in normal and lipodystrophic gerbils. *J. Nutr.* 113:293–303
34. Chu, S. W., Hegsted, D. M. 1980. *myo*-Inositol deficiency in gerbils: comparative study of the intestinal lipodystrophy in *Meriones unguiculatus* and *Meriones libycus*. *J. Nutr.* 110:1209–16
35. Clements, R. S. Jr., DeJesus, P. V. Jr., Winegrad, A. I. 1973. Raised plasma-myoinositol levels in uremia and experimental neuropathy. *Lancet* 1:1137–41
36. Clements, R. S. Jr., Diethelm, A. G. 1979. The metabolism of *myo*-inositol by the human kidney. *J. Lab. Clin. Med.* 93:210–19
37. Clements, R. S. Jr., Reynertson, R. 1977. *myo*-Inositol metabolism in diabetes mellitus: effect of insulin treatment. *Diabetes* 26:215–21
38. Cockcroft, S., Gomperts, B. D. 1979. Evidence for a role of phosphatidylinositol turnover in stimulus-secretion coupling. *Biochem. J.* 178:681–87
39. Connolly, T. M., Bross, T. E., Majerus, P. W. 1985. Isolation of a phosphomonoesterase from human platelets that specifically hydrolyzes the 5-phosphate of inositol 1,4,5-trisphosphate. *J. Biol. Chem.* 260:7868–74
40. Cooper, P. H., Hawthorne, J. N. 1976. Phosphatidylinositol kinase and diphosphoinositide kinase of rat kidney cortex. *Biochem. J.* 160:97–105
41. Cooper, R. H., Kobayashi, K., Williamson, J. R. 1984. Phosphorylation of a 16-kDa protein by diacylglycerol-

activated protein kinase C *in vitro* and by vasopressin in intact hepatocytes. *FEBS Lett.* 166:125–30

42. Dawson, R. M. C., Freinkel, N., Jungalwala, F. B., Clarke, N. 1971. The enzymatic formation of *myo*-inositol 1:2-cyclic phosphate from phosphatidylinositol. *Biochem. J.* 122:605–7
43. Dawson, A. P., Irvine, R. F. 1984. Inositol(1,4,5)trisphosphate-promoted $Ca^{2+}$ release from microsomal fractions of rat liver. *Biochem. Biophys. Res. Commun.* 120:858–64
44. Dawson, R. M. C., Thompson, W. 1964. The triphosphoinositide phosphomonoesterase of brain tissue. *Biochem. J.* 91:244–50
45. Day, A. J., Bell, F. P., Schwartz, C. J. 1974. Lipid metabolism in focal areas of normal-fed and cholesterol-fed pig aortas. *Exp. Mol. Pathol.* 21:179–93
46. DeJesus, P. V. Jr., Clements, R. S. Jr., Winegard, A. I. 1974. Hypermyoinositolemic polyneuropathy in rats: A possible mechanism for uremic polyneuropathy. *J. Neurol. Sci.* 21:237–49
47. Eagle, H., Oyama, V. I., Levy, M., Freeman, A. E. 1957. *myo*-Inositol as an essential growth factor for normal and malignant human cells in tissue culture. *J. Biol. Chem.* 266:191–205
48. Eisenberg, F. Jr. 1967. D-*myo*-inositol 1-phosphate as product of cyclization of glucose-6-phosphate and substrate for a specific phosphatase in rat testis. *J. Biol. Chem.* 242:1375–82
49. Eisenberg, F. Jr., Bolden, A. H. 1963. Biosynthesis of inositol in rat testis homogenate. *Biochem. Biophys. Res. Commun.* 12:72–77
50. Eisenberg, F. Jr., Bolden, A. H. 1964. Reproductive tract as site of synthesis and secretion of inositol in the male rat. *Nature* 202:599–600
51. Exton, J. H. 1985. Role of calcium and phosphoinositides in the actions of certain hormones and neurotransmitters. *J. Clin. Invest.* 75:1753–57
52. Farese, R. V. 1983. The phosphatidate-phosphoinositide cycle: an intracellular messenger system in the action of hormones and neurotransmitters. *Metabolism* 32:628–41
53. Finegold, D., Lattimer, S. A., Nolle, S., Bernstein, M., Greene, D. A. 1983. Polyol pathway activity and *myo*-inositol metabolism. A suggested relationship in the pathogenesis of diabetic neuropathy. *Diabetes* 32:988–92
54. Fisher, S. K., Van Rooijen, L. A. A., Agranoff, B. W. 1984. Renewed interest in the polyphosphoinositides. *Trends Biochem. Sci.* 9:53–56
55. Fliesler, S. J., Kelleher, P. A., Anderson, R. E. 1985. Catabolism of *myo*-inositol to precursors utilized for *de novo* glycerolipid biosynthesis. *J. Neurochem.* 44:171–74
56. Fukuma, M., Carpentier, J. L., Orci, L., Greene, D. A., Winegrad, A. I. 1977. An alteration in internodal myelin membrane structure in large sciatic nerve fibres in rats with acute streptozotocin diabetes and impaired nerve conduction velocity. *Diabetologia* 15:65–72
57. Futerman, A. H., Low, M. G., Ackermann, K. E., Sherman, W. R., Silman, I. 1985. Identification of covalently bound inositol in the hydrophobic membrane-anchoring domain of *Torpedo* acetylcholinesterase. *Biochem. Biophys. Res. Commun.* 129:312–17
58. Garrett, R. J., Redman, C. M. 1975. Localization of enzymes involved in polyphosphoinositide metabolism on the cytoplasmic surface of the human erythrocyte membrane. *Biochim. Biophys. Acta* 238:58–64
59. Gavin, G., McHenry, E. W. 1941. Inositol: a lipotropic factor. *J. Biol. Chem.* 139:485
60. George, P. Y., Helmkamp, G. M. Jr. 1985. Purification and characterization of a phosphatidylinositol transfer protein from human platelets. *Biochim. Biophys. Acta* 836:176–84
61. Gerrard, J. M., Butler, A. M., Peterson, D. A., White, J. G. 1978. Phosphatidic acid releases calcium from a platelet membrane fraction *in vitro*. *Prostag. Med.* 1:387–96
62. Gerrard, J. M., Kindom, S. E., Peterson, D. A., Peller, J., Krantz, K. E., White, J. G. 1979. Lysophosphatidic acids: influence on platelet aggregation and intracellular calcium flux. *Am. J. Pathol.* 96:423–38
63. Ghafoorunissa. 1975. Effect of dietary protein on the biosynthesis of inositol in rat testes. *J. Reprod. Fertil.* 42:233–38
64. Ghalayini, A., Eichberg, J. 1985. Purification of phosphatidylinositol synthetase from rat brain by CDP-diacylglycerol affinity chromatography and properties of the purified enzyme. *J. Neurochem.* 44:175–82
65. Goodhart, R. S. 1973. Bioflavonoids. In *Modern Nutrition in Health and Disease*, ed. R. S. Goodhart, M. E. Shils, pp. 259–67. Philadelphia: Lea & Febiger
66. Gray, N. C. C., Strickland, K. P. 1982. The purification and characterization of a phospholipase $A_2$ activity from the $106000 \times g$ pellet (microsomal fraction) of bovine brain acting on phosphatidylinositol. *Can. J. Biochem.* 60:108–17

67. Greene, D. A., DeJesus, P. V. Jr., Winegrad, A. I. 1975. Effects of insulin and dietary *myo*-inositol on impaired peripheral motor nerve conduction velocity in acute streptozotocin diabetes. *J. Clin. Invest.* 55:1326–36
68. Greene, D. A., Lattimer, S. A. 1983. Impaired rat sciatic nerve sodium-potassium adenosine triphosphatase in acute streptozocin diabetes and its correction by dietary *myo*-inositol supplementation. *J. Clin. Invest.* 72:1058–63
69. Greene, D. A., Lattimer, S. A. 1984. Action of sorbinil in diabetic peripheral nerve. *Diabetes* 33:712–16
70. Greene, D. A., Lewis, R. A., Lattimer, S. A., Brown, M. J. 1982. Selective effects of *myo*-inositol administration on sciatic and tibial motor nerve conduction parameters in the streptozotocin-diabetic rat. *Diabetes* 31:573–78
71. Hallman, M. 1984. Effect of extracellular *myo*-inositol on surfactant phospholipid synthesis in the fetal rabbit lung. *Biochim. Biophys. Acta* 795:67–78
72. Hallman, M., Spragg, R., Harrell, J. H., Moser, K. M., Gluck, L. 1982. Evidence of lung surfactant abnormality in respiratory failure. *J. Clin. Invest.* 70:673–83
73. Harvey, M. S., Helmkamp, G. M. Jr., Wirtz, K. W. A., Van Deenen, L. L. M. 1974. Influence of membrane phosphatidylinositol content on activity of bovine brain phospholipid transfer protein. *FEBS Lett.* 46:260–62
74. Hasan, S. H., Kotaki, A., Yagi, K. 1970. Studies on myoinositol. VI. Effect of myoinositol on plasma lipoprotein metabolism of rats suffering from fatty liver. *J. Vitaminol.* 16:144–48
75. Hasan, S. H., Nakagawa, Y., Nishigaki, I., Yagi, K. 1974. Studies on myoinositol. VIII. The incorporation of $^3$H-myoinositol into phosphatidylinositol of fatty liver. *J. Vitaminol.* 17:159–62
76. Hasan, S. H., Nishigaki, I., Tsutsui, Y., Yagi, K. 1974. Studies on myoinositol. IX. Morphological examination of the effect of massive doses of myoinositol on the liver and kidney of rat. *J. Nutr. Sci. Vitaminol.* 20:55–58
77. Haslam, R. J., Davidson, M. M. L. 1984. Receptor-induced diacylglycerol formation in permeabilized platelets; possible role for a GTP-binding protein. *J. Recept. Res.* 4:605–29
78. Hauser, G. 1969. *myo*-Inositol transport in slices of rat kidney cortex. II. Effect of the ionic composition of the medium. *Biophys. Acta* 173:267–76
79. Hauser, G., Eichberg, J., Gonzalez-Sastre, F. 1971. Regional distribution of polyphosphoinositides in rat brain. *Biochim. Biophys. Acta* 248:87–95
80. Hauser, G., Finelli, V. N. 1963. The biosynthesis of free and phosphatide *myo*-inositol from glucose by mammalian tissue slices. *J. Biol. Chem.* 238:3224–28
81. Hayashi, E., Maeda, T., Hasegawa, R., Tomita, T. 1978. The effect of *myo*-inositol deficiency on lipid metabolism in rats. III. The mechanism of an enhancement in lipolysis due to *myo*-inositol deficiency in rats. *Biochim. Biophys. Acta.* 531:197–205
82. Hayashi, E., Maeda, T., Tomita, T. 1974. The effect of *myo*-inositol deficiency on lipid metabolism in rats. I. The alteration of lipid metabolism in *myo*-inositol-deficient rats. *Biochim. Biophys. Acta* 360:134–45
83. Hayashi, E., Maeda, T., Tomita, T. 1974. The effect of *myo*-inositol deficiency on lipid metabolism in rats. II. The mechanism of triacylgycerol accumulation in the liver of *myo*-inositol-deficient rats. *Biochim. Biophys. Acta* 360:146–55
84. Heger, H. W., Peter, H. W. 1977. Phosphatidylinositol as essential constituent of the acetyl-CoA carboxylase from rat liver. *Int. J. Biochem.* 8:841–46
85. Hegsted, D. M., Gallagher, A., Hanford, H. 1974. Inositol requirement of the gerbil. *J. Nutr.* 104:588–92
86. Hegsted, D. M., Hayes, K. C., Gallagher, A., Hanford, H. 1973. Inositol deficiency: an intestinal lipodystrophy in the gerbil. *J. Nutr.* 103:302–7
87. Helmkamp, G. M. Jr. 1985. Phosphatidylinositol transfer proteins: structure, catalytic activity, and physiological function. *Chem. Phys. Lipids* 38:3–16
88. Herbette, L., Blasie, J. K., Defoor, P., Fleischer, S., Bick, R. J., et al. 1984. Phospholipid asymmetry in the isolated sarcoplasmic reticulum membrane. *Arch. Biochem. Biophys.* 234:235–42
89. Hirasawa, K., Irvine, R. F., Dawson, R. M. 1981. The catabolism of phosphatidylinositol by an EDTA-insensitive phospholipase $A_1$ and calcium-dependent phosphatidylinositol phosphodiesterase in rat brain. *Eur. J. Biochem.* 120:53–58
90. Hokin, L. E. 1985. Receptors and phosphoinositide-generated second messengers. *Ann. Rev. Biochem.* 54:205–35
91. Hokin, L. E., Hokin, M. R. 1955. Effects of acetylcholine on the turnover of phosphoryl units in individual phospholipids as pancreas slices and brain cortex slices. *Biochim. Biophys. Acta* 18:102–10
92. Hokin-Neaverson, M., Sadeghian, K., Harris, D. W., Merrin, J. S. 1977. Syn-

thesis of CDP-diglyceride from phosphatidylinositol and CMP. *Biochem. Biophys. Res. Commun.* 78:364–71

93. Holub, B. J. 1974. The $Mn^{2+}$-activated incorporation of inositol into molecular species of phosphatidylinositol in rat liver microsomes. *Biochim. Biophys. Acta* 369:111–22
94. Holub, B. J. 1975. Role of cytidine triphosphate and cytidine diphosphate choline in promoting inositol entry into microsomal phosphatidylinositol. *Lipids* 10:483–90
95. Holub, B. J. 1976. Specific formation of arachidonoyl phosphatidylinositol from 1-acyl-*sn*-glycero-3-phosphorylinositol in rat liver. *Lipids* 11:1–5
96. Holub, B. J. 1978. Studies on the metabolic heterogeneity of different molecular species of phosphatidylinositols. In *Cyclitols and Phosphoinositides,* ed. W. W. Wells, F. Eisenberg Jr., pp. 523–34. New York: Academic
97. Holub, B. J. 1982. The nutritional significance, metabolism, and function of *myo*-inositol and phosphatidylinositol in health and disease. *Adv. Nutr. Res.* 4:107–41
98. Holub, B. J. 1984. Altered phospholipid metabolism in thrombin-stimulated human platelets. *Can. J. Biochem. Cell Biol.* 62:341–51
99. Holub, B. J. 1984. Nutritional, biochemical, and clinical aspects of inositol and phosphatidylinositol metabolism. *Can. J. Physiol. Pharmacol.* 62:1–8
100. Holub, B. J. 1985. Nutritional regulation of the composition, metabolism, and function of cellular phosphatidylinositol. See Ref. 18, pp. 31–47
101. Holub, B. J., Celi, B., Bergeron, T., Woodward, B. 1982. The effect of inositol deficiency on the hepatic neutral lipid and phospholipid composition of rainbow trout. *J. Nutr.* 112:xxi
102. Holub, B. J., Kuksis, A. 1971. Structural and metabolic interrelationships among glycerophosphatides of rat liver *in vivo. Can. J. Biochem.* 49:1347–56
103. Holub, B. J., Kuksis, A. 1972. Further evidence for the interconversion of monophosphoinositides *in vivo. Lipids* 7:78–80
104. Holub, B. J., Kuksis, A. 1978. Metabolism of molecular species of diacylglycerophospholipids. *Adv. Lipid Res.* 16:1–125
105. Holub, B. J., Kuksis, A., Thompson, W. 1970. Molecular species of mono-, di- and triphosphoinositides of bovine brain. *J. Lipid Res.* 11:558–64
106. Holub, B. J., Piekarski, J. 1976. Biosynthesis of molecular species of CDP-diglyceride from endogenously-labeled phosphatidate in rat liver microsomes. *Lipids* 11:251–57
107. Holub, B. J., Piekarski, J. 1978. Suitability of different molecular species of 1,2-diacylglycerols as substrates for diacylglycerol kinase in rat brain microsomes. *J. Neurochem.* 31:903–8
108. Holub, B. J., Piekarski, J. 1979. The formation of phosphatidylinositol by acylation of 2-acyl-*sn*-glycero-3-phosphorylinositol in rat liver microsomes. *Lipids* 14:529–32
109. Hoover, G. A., Nicolosi, R. J., Corey, J. E., El Lozy, M., Hayes, K. C. 1978. Inositol deficiency in the gerbil: altered hepatic lipid metabolism and triglyceride secretion. *J. Nutr.* 108:1588–94
110. Hothersall, J. S., McLean, P. 1979. Effect of experimental diabetes and insulin on phosphatidylinositol synthesis in rat sciatic nerve. *Biochem. Biophys. Res. Commun.* 88:477–84
111. House, W. A., Welch, R. M., Van Campen, D. R. 1982. Effect of phytic acid on the absorption, distribution, and endogenous excretion of zinc in rats. *J. Nutr.* 112:941–53
112. Howard, C. F. Jr., Anderson, L. 1967. Metabolism of *myo*-inositol in animals. II. Complete catabolism of *myo*-inositol-$^{14}C$ by rat kidney slices. *Arch. Biochem. Biophys.* 118:332–39
113. Irvine, R. F., Anggard, E. E., Letcher, A. J., Downes, C. P. 1985. Metabolism of inositol 1,4,5-trisphosphate and inositol 1,3,4-trisphosphate in rat parotid glands. *Biochem. J.* 229:505–11
114. Irvine, R. F., Dawson, R. M. C. 1978. The distribution of calcium-dependent phosphatidylinositol-specific phosphodiesterase in rat brain. *J. Neurochem.* 31:1427–34
115. Irvine, R. F., Hemington, N., Dawson, R. M. C. 1978. The hydrolysis of phosphatidylinositol by lysosomal enzymes of rat liver and brain. *Biochem. J.* 176:475–84
116. Isaacks, R. E., Harkness, D. R., Sampsell, R. N., Alder, J. L., Roth, S., et al. 1977. Studies on avian erythrocyte metabolism. Inositol tetrakisphosphate: the major phosphate compound in the erythrocytes of the ostrich *(Struthio camelus camelus). Eur. J. Biochem.* 77:567–74
117. Isaacks, R. E., Kim, H. D., Harkness, D. R. 1978. Inositol diphosphate in erythrocytes of the lungfish, *Lepidosiren paradoxa,* and 2,3-diphosphoglycerate in erythrocytes of the armored catfish, *Pterygoplichtys* sp. *Can. J. Zool.* 56:1014–16
118. IUPAC-IUB Commission on Biochemical Nomenclature. 1977. Nomenclature

of phosphorus-containing compounds of biochemical importance (recommendations, 1976). *Proc. Natl. Acad. Sci. USA* 74:2222–30

119. Jafferji, S. S., Michell, R. H. 1976. Effects of calcium-antagonistic drugs on the stimulation by carbamoylcholine and histamine of phosphatidylinositol turnover in longitudinal smooth muscle of guinea-pig ileum. *Biochem. J.* 160:163–69
120. Jett, M., Alving, C. R. 1983. Selective cytotoxicity of tumor cells induced by liposomes containing plant phosphatidylinositol. *Biochem. Biophys. Res. Commun.* 114:863–69
121. Johnson, L. F., Tate, M. E. 1969. Structure of phytic acids. *Can. J. Chem.* 47:63–73
122. Joseph, S. K., Williams, R. J. 1985. Subcellular localization and some properties of the enzymes hydrolysing inositol polyphosphates in rat liver. *FEBS Lett.* 180:150–54
123. Joseph, S. K., Williams, R. J., Corkey, B. E., Matschinsky, F. M., Williamson, J. R. 1984. The effect of inositol trisphosphate on $Ca^{2+}$ fluxes in insulin-secreting tumor cells. *J. Biol. Chem.* 259:12952–55
124. Kameyama, Y., Yoshioka, S., Imai, A., Nozawa, Y. 1983. Possible involvement of 1-acyl-glycerophosphorylinositol acyltransferase in arachidonate enrichment of phosphatidylinositol in human platelets. *Biochim. Biophys. Acta* 752:244–50
125. Karasawa, K. 1972. The effect of carbohydrate and inositol on the growth of rats. *Jpn. J. Nutr.* 30:3–11
126. Keough, K. M. W., Thompson, W. 1972. Soluble and particulate forms of phosphoinositide phosphodiesterase in ox brain. *Biochim. Biophys. Acta* 270:324–36
127. Kirk, C. J., Rodrigues, L. M., Hems, D. A. 1979. The influence of vasopressin and related peptides on glycogen phosphorylase activity and phosphatidylinositol metabolism in hepatocytes. *Biochem. J.* 178:493–96
128. Kotaki, A., Sakurai, T., Kobayashi, M., Yagi, K. 1968. Studies on myoinositol. IV: Effects of *myo*-inositol on the cholesterol metabolism of rats suffering from experimental fatty liver. *J. Vitaminol.* 14:87–94
129. Koutouzov, S., Marche, P., Girard, A., Meyer, P. 1983. Altered turnover of polyphosphoinositides in the erythrocyte membrane of the spontaneously hypertensive rat. *Hypertension* 5:409–14
130. Kroes, J. F., Hegsted, D. M., Hayes, K. C. 1973. Inositol deficiency in gerbils: dietary effects on the intestinal lipodystrophy. *J. Nutr.* 103:1448–53
131. Kuzuhara, K., Uchima, T., Muto, M., Horiuchi, T., Sugimoto, H., et al. 1982. A new method for evaluating the viability of preserved kidney by determining free *myo*-inositol levels in the early effluent perfusate. *Transplant. Proc.* 14:231–37
132. Laffont, F., Chap, H., Soula, G., Douste-Blazy, L. 1981. Phospholipid exchange proteins from platelet cytosol possibly involved in phospholipid effect. *Biochem. Biophys. Res. Commun.* 102:1366–71
133. Le Kim, D., Betzing, H. 1976. Intestinal absorption of polyunsaturated phosphatidylcholine in the rat. *Hoppe-Seyler's Z. Physiol. Chem.* 357:1321–31
134. Lewin, L. M., Beer, R. 1973. Prostatic secretion as the source of *myo*-inositol in human seminal fluid. *Fertil. Steril.* 24:666–70
135. Lewin, L. M., Melmed, S., Bank, H. 1974. Rapid screening test for detection of elevated *myo*-inositol levels in human blood serum. *Clin. Chim. Acta* 54:377–79
136. Lewin, L. M., Sulimovici, S. 1975. The distribution of radioactive *myo*-inositol in the reproductive tract of the male rat. *J. Reprod. Fertil.* 43:355–58
137. Lewin, L. M., Yannai, Y., Sulimovici, S., Kraicer, P. F. 1976. Studies on the metabolic role of *myo*-inositol. *Biochem. J.* 156:375–80
138. Liveson, J. A., Gardner, J., Bornstein, M. B. 1977. Tissue culture studies of possible uremic neurotoxins: *myo*-inositol. *Kidney Int.* 12:131–36
139. Lloyd, T. 1979. The effects of phosphatidylinositol on tyrosine hydroxylase: stimulation and inactivation. *J. Biol. Chem.* 254:7247–54
140. Low, M. G., Finean, J. B. 1978. Specific release of plasma membrane enzymes by a phosphatidylinositol-specific phospholipase. *Biochim. Biophys. Acta* 508:565–70
141. Luthra, M. G., Sheltawy, A. 1972. The fractionation of phosphatidylinositol into molecular species by thin-layer chromatography on silver nitrate–impregnated silica gel. *Biochem. J.* 126:1231–39
142. Macara, I. G. 1985. Oncogenes, ions, and phospholipids. *Am. J. Physiol.* 248:C3–C11
143. Machlin, L. J., ed. 1984. *Handbook of Vitamins; Nutritional, Biochemical, and Clinical Aspects*. New York: Marcel Dekker
144. Mack, S. E., Palmer, F. B. St. C. 1984. Evidence for a specific phosphatidylinositol 4-phosphate phosphatase in human

erythrocyte membranes. *J. Lipid Res.* 25:75–85
145. Mahadevappa, V. G., Holub, B. J. 1982. The molecular species composition of individual diacyl phospholipids in human platelets. *Biochim. Biophys. Acta* 713:73–79
146. Majerus, P. W., Neufeld, E. J., Wilson, D. B. 1984. Production of phosphoinositide-derived messengers. *Cell* 37:701–3
147. Majerus, P. W., Wilson, D. B., Connolly, T. M., Bross, T. E., Neufeld, E. J. 1985. Phosphoinositide turnover provides a link in stimulus-response coupling. *Trends Biochem. Sci.* 10:168–71
148. Mandersloot, J. G., Roelofsen, B., De Gier, J. 1978. Phosphatidylinositol as the endogenous activator of the ($Na^+ + K^+$)-ATPase in microsomes of rabbit kidney. *Biochim. Biophys. Acta* 508:478–85
149. Mauco, G., Dangelmaier, C. A., Smith, B. J. 1984. Inositol lipids, phosphatidate and diacylglycerol share stearoylarachidonoylglycerol as a common backbone in thrombin-stimulated human platelets. *Biochem. J.* 224:933–40
150. Mayhew, J. A., Gillon, K. R. W., Hawthorne, J. N. 1983. Free and lipid inositol, sorbitol and sugars in sciatic nerve obtained post-mortem from diabetic patients and control subjects. *Diabetologia* 24:13–15
151. McMurray, W. C., Magee, W. L. 1972. Phospholipid metabolism. *Ann. Rev. Biochem.* 41:129–60
152. Maeda, T., Eisenberg, F. Jr. 1980. Purification, structure, and catalytic properties of L-*myo*-inositol-1-phosphate synthase from rat testis. *J. Biol. Chem.* 255:8458–64
153. Michell, R. H. 1975. Inositol phospholipids and cell surface receptor function. *Biochim. Biophys. Acta* 415:81–147
154. Michell, R. H. 1979. Inositol phospholipids in membrane function. *Trends Biochem. Sci.* 4:128–31
155. Michell, R. H., Kirk, C. J., Jones, L. M., Downes, C. P., Creba, J. A. 1981. The stimulation of inositol lipid metabolism that accompanies calcium mobilization in stimulated cells: defined characteristics and unanswered questions. *Philos. Trans. R. Soc. London Ser. B* 296:123–37
156. Naccarato, W. F., Ray, R. E., Wells, W. W. 1975. Characterization and tissue distribution of 6-O-$\beta$-D-galactopyranosyl *myo*-inositol in the rat. *J. Biol. Chem.* 250:1872–76
157. Naccarato, W. F., Wells, W. W. 1974. Identification of 6-0-$\beta$-D-galactopyranosyl *myo*-inositol: a new form of *myo*-inositol in mammals. *Biochem. Biophys. Res. Commun.* 57:1026–31
158. Nahapetian, A., Young, V. R. 1980. Metabolism of $^{14}C$-phytate in rats: effect of low and high dietary calcium intakes. *J. Nutr.* 110:1458–72
159. Nicolosi, R. J., Herrera, M. G., El Lozy, M., Hayes, K. C. 1976. Effect of dietary fat on hepatic metabolism of $^{14}C$-oleic acid and very low density lipoprotein triglyceride in the gerbil. *J. Nutr.* 106:1279–85
160. Nilsson, O. S., Dallner, G. 1977. Transverse asymmetry of phospholipids in subcellular membranes of rat liver. *Biochim. Biophys. Acta* 464:453–58
161. Nishihara, M., Keenan, R. W. 1985. Inositol phospholipid levels of rat forebrain obtained by freeze-blowing method. *Biochim. Biophys. Acta* 835:415–18
162. Nishizuka, Y. 1983. Phospholipid degradation and signal translation for protein phosphorylation. *Trends Biochem. Sci.* 8:13–16
163. Nishizuka, Y. 1984. The role of protein kinase C in cell surface signal transduction and tumour promotion. *Nature* 308:693–98
164. Oberleas, D. 1973. Phytates. In *Toxicants Occurring Naturally in Foods*, pp. 363–71. Washington, DC: Natl. Acad. Sci.
165. Offner, H., Konat, G., Clausen, J. 1974. Effect of phytohemagglutinin, basic protein and measles antigen on *myo*-(2-$^3H$)inositol incorporation into phosphatidylinositol of lymphocytes from patients with multiple sclerosis. *Acta Neurol. Scand.* 50:791–800
166. Palmano, K. P., Whiting, P. H., Hawthorne, J. N. 1977. Free and lipid *myo*-inositol in tissues from rats with acute and less severe streptozotocin-induced diabetes. *Biochem. J.* 167:229–35
167. Paulus, H., Kennedy, E. P. 1960. The enzymatic synthesis of inositol monophosphatide. *J. Biol. Chem.* 235:1303–11
168. Perret, B., Chap, H. J., Douste-Blazy, L. 1979. Asymmetric distribution of arachidonic acid in the plasma membrane of human platelets. *Biochim. Biophys. Acta* 556:434–46
169. Pickard, M. R., Hawthorne, J. N. 1978. The labelling of nerve ending phospholipids in guinea-pig brain *in vivo* and the effect of electrical stimulation on phosphatidylinositol metabolism in prelabelled synaptosomes. *J. Neurochem.* 30:145–55
170. Pik, J. R., Thompson, W. 1978. Subcellular distribution of lysophosphatidylinositol and lyosphosphatidylcholine acyltransferases in rat brain. *Can. J. Biochem.* 56:765–68

171. Pitkanen, E. 1976. Changes in serum and urinary *myo*-inositol levels in chronic glomerulonephritis. *Clin. Chim. Acta* 71:461–68
172. Possmayer, F., Scherphof, G. L., Dubbelman, T. M. A. R., Van Golde, L. M. G., Van Deenen, L. L. M. 1969. Positional specificity of saturated and unsaturated fatty acids in phosphatidic acid from rat liver. *Biochim. Biophys. Acta* 176:95–110
173. Prentki, M., Biden, T. J., Janjic, D., Irvine, R. F., Berridge, M. J., Wollheim, C. B. 1984. Rapid mobilization of $Ca^{2+}$ from rat insulinoma microsomes by inositol-1,4,5-trisphosphate. *Nature* 309:562–64
174. Prentki, M., Wollheim, C. B., Lew, P. D. 1984. $Ca^{2+}$ homeostasis in permeabilized human neutrophils. *J. Biol. Chem.* 259:13777–82
175. Prpic, V., Blackmore, P. F., Exton, J. H. 1982. *myo*-Inositol uptake and metabolism in isolated rat liver cells. *J. Biol. Chem.* 257:11315–22
176. Rao, R. H., Strickland, K. P. 1974. On the solubility, stability and partial purification of CDP-diacyl-*sn*-glycerol:inositol transferase from rat brain. *Biochim. Biophys. Acta* 348:306–14
177. Reddy, C. C., Pierzchala, P. A., Hamilton, G. A. 1981. *Myo*-inositol oxygenase from hog kidney. II. Catalytic properties of the homogenous enzyme. *J. Biol. Chem.* 256:8519–24
178. Reddy, C. C., Swan, J. S., Hamilton, G. A. 1981. *Myo*-inositol oxygenase from hog kidney. I. Purification and characterization of the oxygenase and of an enzyme complex containing the oxygenase and D-glucuronate reductase. *J. Biol. Chem.* 256:8510–18
179. Reznek, R. H., Salway, J. G., Thomas, P. K. 1977. Plasma *myo*-inositol concentrations in uraemic neuropathy. *Lancet* 1:675–76
180. Rothman, S. S. 1978. Cymotrypsinogen-inositol phosphatide complexes and the transport of digestive enzyme across membranes. *Biochim. Biophys. Acta* 509:374–83
181. Rothman, J. E., Lenard, J. 1977. Membrane asymmetry. *Science* 195:743–53
182. Salway, J. G., Finnegan, J. A., Barnett, D., Whitehead, L., Karunanayaka, A., Payne, R. B. 1978. Effect of *myo*-inositol on peripheral-nerve function in diabetes. *Lancet* 2:1282–84
183. Schulz, V. E., Oslage, H. J. 1972. Untersuchungen zur intestinalen hydrolyse von inositphosphorsaureester und zur absorption von phytinphosphor beim schwein. *Z. Tierphysiol.* 30:76–91
184. Sebrell, W. H. Jr., Harris, R. S., eds. 1967. *The Vitamins*. Vol. III. New York: Academic
185. Segal, S., Hwang, S. M., Stern, J., Pleasure, D. 1984. Inositol uptake by cultured isolated rat Schwann cells. *Biochem. Biophys. Res. Commun.* 120:486–92
186. Seyfred, M. A., Farrell, L. E., Wells, W. W. 1984. Characterization of D-*myo*-inositol 1,4,5-trisphosphate phosphatase in rat liver plasma membranes. *J. Biol. Chem.* 259:13204–8
187. Shastri, K. M., Carvalho, A. C. A., Lees, R. S. 1980. Platelet function and platelet lipid composition in the dyslipoproteinemias. *J. Lipid Res.* 21:467–72
188. Shepherd, N. D., Taylor, T. G. 1974. A re-assessment of the status of *myo*-inositol as a vitamin. *Proc. Nutr. Soc.* 33:63A–64A
189. Shum, T. Y. P., Gray, N. C. C., Strickland, K. P. 1979. The deacylation of phosphatidylinositol by rat brain preparations. *Can. J. Biochem.* 57:1359–67
190. Skeaff, C. M., Holub, B. J. 1985. Altered phospholipid composition of plasma membranes from thrombin-stimulated human platelets. *Biochim. Biophys. Acta* 834:164–71
191. Slaby, F., Bryan, J. 1976. High uptake of *myo*-inositol by rat pancreatic tissue *in vitro* stimulates secretion. *J. Biol. Chem.* 251:5078–86
192. Smith, C. D., Wells, W. W. 1984. Characterization of a phosphatidylinositol 4-phosphate-specific phosphomonoesterase in rat liver envelopes. *Arch. Biochem. Biophys.* 235:529–37
193. Spector, R. 1976. Inositol accumulation by brain slices *in vitro*. *J. Neurochem.* 27:1273–76
194. Spector, R., Lorenzo, A. V. 1975. The origin of *myo*-inositol in brain, cerebrospinal fluid and choroid plexus. *J. Neurochem.* 25:353–54
195. Storey, D. J., Shears, S. B., Kirk, C. J., Michell, R. H. 1984. Stepwise enzymatic dephosphorylation of inositol 1,4,5-trisphosphate to inositol in liver. *Nature* 312:374–76
196. Streb, H., Irvine, R. F., Berridge, M. J., Schulz, I. 1983. Release of $Ca^{2+}$ from a nonmitochondrial intracellular store in pancreatic acinar cells by inositol-1,4,5-triphosphate. *Nature* 306:67–69
197. Sugiura, T., Waku, K. 1984. Enhanced turnover of arachidonic acid–containing species of phosphatidylinositol and phosphatidic acid of concanavalin A–stimulated lymphocytes. *Biochim. Biophys. Acta* 796:190–98

198. Sundler, R., Sarcione, S. L., Alberts, A. W., Vagelos, P. R. 1977. Evidence against phospholipid asymmetry in intracellular membranes from liver. *Proc. Natl. Acad. Sci. USA* 74:3350–54
199. Swahn, C. G. 1985. Gas chromatographic-mass spectrometric determination of *myo*-inositol in human cerebrospinal fluid. *J. Neurochem.* 45:331–34
200. Takenawa, T., Egawa, K. 1977. CDP-diglyceride:inositol transferase from rat liver. *J. Biol. Chem.* 252:5419–23
201. Takenawa, T., Egawa, K. 1980. Phosphatidylinositol:*myo*-inositol exchange enzyme from rat liver: partial purification and characterization. *Arch. Biochem. Biophys.* 202:601–7
202. Takenawa, T., Tsumita, T. 1974. *myo*-Inositol transport in plasma membrane of rat kidney. *Biochim. Biophys. Acta* 303:106–14
203. Takenawa, T., Tsumita, T. 1974. Properties of scyllitol transport in rat kidney slices. *Biochim. Biophys. Acta* 373:490–94
204. Takenawa, T., Wada, E., Tsumita, T. 1977. *myo*-Inositol binding and transport in brush border membranes of rat kidney. *Biochim. Biophys. Acta* 464:108–17
205. Thompson, W. 1969. Positional distribution of fatty acids in brain polyphosphoinositides. *Biochim. Biophys. Acta* 187:150–53
206. Thompson, W., MacDonald, G. 1977. Synthesis of molecular classes of cytidine diphosphate diglyceride by rat liver *in vivo* and *in vitro*. *Can. J. Biochem.* 55:1153–58
207. Tyson, C. A., Vande Zande, H., Green, D. E. 1976. Phospholipids as ionophores. *J. Biol. Chem.* 251:1326–32
208. Upreti, G. C., deAntueno, R. J., Wood, R. 1983. Membrane lipids of hepatic tissue. II. Phospholipids from subcellular fractions of liver and hepatoma 7288CTC. *J. Natl. Cancer Inst.* 70:567–73
209. Vickers, J. D., Kinlough-Rathbone, R. L., Mustard, J. F. 1984. Accumulation of the inositol phosphates in thrombin-stimulated, washed rabbit platelets in the presence of lithium. *Biochem. J.* 224:399–405
210. Voglmayr, J. K., Amann, R. P. 1973. The distribution of free *myo*-inositol in fluids, spermatozoa, and tissues of the bull genital tract and observations on its uptake by the rabbit epididymis. *Biol. Reprod.* 8:504–13
211. Warfield, A., Hwang, S. M., Segal, S. 1978. On the uptake of inositol by rat brain synaptosomes. *J. Neurochem.* 31:957–60
212. Warfield, A. S., Segal, S. 1978. *myo*-Inositol and phosphatidylinositol metabolism in synaptosomes from galactose-fed rats. *Proc. Natl. Acad. Sci. USA* 75:4568–72
213. Watkins, T. R., Hegsted, D. M. 1979. Tissue inositol metabolism in gerbil lipodystrophy. *Fed. Proc.* 38:279
214. Wells, H. J., Wells, W. W. 1967. Galactose toxicity and *myo*-inositol metabolism in the developing rat brain. *Biochemistry* 6:1168–73
215. Wells, W. W. 1984. Vitamins (Inositol). In *Encyclopedia of Chemical Technology*, 24:50–58. New York: Wiley
216. White, D. A. 1973. The phospholipid composition of mammalian tissues. In *Form and Function of Phospholipids*, ed. G. Ansell, R. Dawson, J. Hawthorne, pp. 441–82. Amsterdam: Elsevier
217. Whiting, P. H., Palmano, K. P., Hawthorne, J. N. 1979. Enzymes of *myo*-inositol lipid metabolism in rats with streptozotocin-induced diabetes. *Biochem. J.* 179:549–53
218. Wilson, D. B., Bross, T. E., Hofmann, S. L., Majerus, P. W. 1984. Hydrolysis of polyphosphoinositides by purified sheep seminal vesicle phospholipase C enzymes. *J. Biol. Chem.* 257:11718–24
219. Wilson, D. B., Bross, T. E., Sherman, W. R., Berger, R. A., Majerus, P. W. 1985. Inositol cyclic phosphate are produced by cleavage of phosphatidylphosphoinositols (polyphosphoinositides) with purified sheep seminal vesicle phospholipase C enzymes. *Proc. Natl. Acad. Sci. USA* 82:4013–17
220. Wilson, D. B., Neufeld, E. J., Majerus, P. W. 1985. Phosphoinositide interconversion in thrombin-stimulated human platelets. *J. Biol. Chem.* 260:1046–51
221. Wong, Y. H., Sherman, W. R. 1985. Anomeric and other substrate specificity studies with *myo*-inositol-1-P-synthase. *J. Biol. Chem.* 260:11083–90
222. Yagi, K., Kotaki, A. 1969. The effect of massive doses of *myo*-inositol on hepatic phospholipid metabolism. *Ann. NY Acad. Sci.* 165:710–25
223. Yamamoto, A., Adachi, S., Ishibe, T., Shinji, Y., Kaki-Uchi, Y., et al. 1970. Accumulation of acidic phospholipids in a case of hyperlipidemia with hepatosplenomegaly. *Lipids* 5:566–71
224. Zborowski, J., Wojtczak, L. 1975. Net transfer of phosphatidylinositol from microsomes and mitochondria to liposomes catalyzed by the exchange protein from rat liver. *FEBS Lett.* 51:317–20

# AUTHOR INDEX


A

Abbatucci, J. S., 420
Abbott, M. T., 375, 376, 385, 386
Abdel-Ghany, M., 349, 351
Abe, E., 535, 548-50
Abe, I., 230
Abel, G. G., 309
Abeles, F. B., 138
Abeles, R. H., 192
Abels, J. C., 332
Abeyasekera, G., 535
Abraham, A., 290
Abramson, J. H., 145
Abroms, I. F., 198
Ackerman, N., 351, 354, 355
Ackermann, K. E., 579
Ackley, S., 477, 478
Ackrell, B. A. C., 21
Adachi, S., 587
Adair, W. T. Jr., 252
Adam, J. M., 497
Adamany, A. M., 252
Adams, A. J., 122, 123
Adams, E., 381
Adams, J. S., 541, 542, 548, 550
Adams, R. J., 57
Adcock, K. J., 146
Adeshina, H., 146
Adilgireieva, L. K., 291
Adler, B., 30
Adolph, R. J., 20
Adrian, J., 349, 351
Adron, J. W., 227, 228, 230-32, 236-39
Agarwal, D. K., 513
Agarwal, K. L., 373
Agarwal, K. N., 24, 513
Agranoff, B. W., 565, 581
Agras, W. S., 309
Aguilar, T. S., 184, 185
Ahluwalia, M., 424
Ahmed, M., 115
Akagi, R., 189, 190, 197
Akazawa, S., 44
Akene, J., 146
Akers, A., 285
Aksamit, R. R., 185
Alaveras, A. G., 334
Albert, M. J., 162, 165, 172
Alberti, K. G. M. M., 52, 211, 216
Alberts, A. W., 578
Albracht, S. P. J., 381
Alder, A. M., 487
Alder, J. L., 566
Aldinger, C. E., 211, 213, 214
Aldo-Benson, M. A., 140
Aldouri, M. S. H., 505, 509
Alejandre, M. J., 264
Aleo, J. J., 378
Alkonyi, I., 48, 388, 389
Allan, L., 329
Allardyce, D. B., 45, 334
Allegretta, M., 140
Allegretto, E. A., 528, 535, 536, 542, 545, 550
Allen, J., 42
Allen, O. W. Jr., 232, 237, 238, 240
Allen, P. L., 372
Allen, R. J., 57, 328-31
Alliot, E., 228, 230, 231
Allison, J. B., 2, 514
Allison, M. J., 156, 164
Alloway, K. D., 126
Almi, C. R., 119
Altay, C., 19, 30, 31
Altenahr, E., 529
Altman, A., 536
Alving, C. R., 588
Amann, R. P., 565
Ambruso, D. R., 31
Amento, E. P., 549, 550
Ames, B. N., 68, 82, 84, 164
Ames, M. M., 391
Amin, S., 82
Ammann, A. J., 329, 330
Ammon, H. P. T., 463, 464
Amundson, C. H., 234, 236-38
Andelman, M. B., 33, 144
Andersen, D. B., 575
Anderson, G. H., 114
Anderson, J. A., 514
Anderson, J. J., 458, 459
Anderson, J. W., 215, 216
Anderson, L., 568
Anderson, R., 19, 30-33, 391
Anderson, R. A., 218
Anderson, R. E., 568
Anderson, R. J., 227
Anderson, S. M., 115, 367, 460, 461, 467-69
Anding, R. H., 313
Ando, M., 69
Ando, T., 325
Andolz, P., 54, 57
Andres, R., 218
Andrewes, A. G., 276
Andrews, A. W., 82
Andrews, B. F., 24
Andrews, J. W., 228
Andrews, P. C., 385
Andriola, M., 56
Andrus, L. B., 115
Andujar, M. M., 458
Angel, A., 49
Angelini, C., 42, 51, 56
Anggard, E. E., 583
Angus, C. W., 142
Annison, E. F., 101
Anthony, P. P., 428
Anthony, R. S., 460, 461, 468
Antonucci, A., 196
Anttinen, H., 378
Anundi, H., 536
Anver, M. R., 139
Aoe, H., 230
Apfelbaum, M., 503, 506
Apling, E. C., 215
Aponte, G. W., 373
Appadurai, A., 435, 437
Aquino, H., 320
Arai, M., 464
Arai, N., 328
Arai, S., 227, 230, 231
Arbeter, A., 144
Archer, S., 438
Arebalo, R. E., 255
Argenzio, R. A., 160
Arimoto, S., 76
Armitt, G. M., 288
Arnold, A. J., 535
Aro, A., 216
Aron, M., 443
Aronoff, G. R., 482, 483
Aronson, N. N. Jr., 43, 387
Arrieh, M., 544
Arthur, R., 168
Artwohl, J. E., 160
Arya, S., 56
Asakura, M., 69, 73
Asamizu, J., 195, 196
Asgärd, T., 279
Ash, D. E., 372
Ash, R. W., 160
Ashenbrucker, H., 146
Asher, A., 372
Ashkenazi, R., 26, 28
Ashley, T., 487
Ashoor, S. H., 68
Ashworth, A., 505, 506, 510
Asoo, N., 550
ASPLUND, J. M., 95-112; 96, 97, 100, 101, 103-6, 109
Assad, R., 379
Assan, R., 54, 57
Astrin, S. M., 548, 552
Astrom, J., 117
Atlas, R. M., 162
Atwater, W. D., 460, 462
Aubia, J., 54, 57

Auchus, R. J., 569
AuCoin, D., 437
Audisio, M., 391
Auestad, N., 56
Augereau, C., 330
Augustoni-Ziskind, M., 451
Auron, P. E., 137
Austern, B. M., 288
Austreng, E., 279, 281
Avedovech, N. A., 195, 198
Avigan, J., 254, 257, 259
Awad, W. M. Jr., 186-88
Axelrod, A. E., 412
Axelson, J. M., 351, 354
AXELSON, M. L., 345-63; 347, 358, 359, 437
Ayachi, S., 479
Ayers, J. W., 305
Aziz, N., 9, 8
Azran, F., 254

B

Babcock, M., 157, 167, 168
Babior, B. M., 30
Bach, B., 264
Bachar, E., 379
Backlund, P. S. Jr., 190, 192
Bacon, S., 215, 216
Baggiolini, E. G., 318, 550
Bailey, A. J., 378
Bailey, C., 422, 423
Bailey-Wood, R., 22, 23, 25
Baillod, R. A., 54, 57
Baily, E. J., 81, 83, 85
Baird, P. C., 359
Baker, A. J., 542, 548
Baker, E. G., 284
Baker, E. M., 391
Baker, H., 320, 322, 327-30, 333, 334
Baker, L., 307
Baker, R. R., 566, 570, 572
Baker, S. J., 162, 165, 172
Bakke, A. C., 550
Balarin, J. D., 228
Balascio, J. R., 168
Balasubramanian, S., 259, 260
Balaz, V., 391
Balch, C. C., 97
Baldessarini, R. J., 487
Baldoni, J., 372
Balgobin, L., 323
Baliga, B. S., 32
Balińska, M., 188
Balnave, D., 335
Bamji, M. S., 43, 44
Bank, H., 586
Banks, B., 460, 461, 468
Bannister, D. W., 335
Banta, C. A., 161
Banwell, J. G., 163
Barac-Nieto, M., 509, 511
Baracos, V., 138, 139
Barak, A. J., 188
Baraona, E., 461, 462
Barber, T. A., 193
Barbosa, J., 211
Barden, R. E., 320
Bardenheuer, H., 185
Barer-Stein, T., 346
Barkai, A. I., 587
Barker, H. M., 216
Barker, L. M., 434
Barlow, D. H., 309
Bar-Mein, S., 170
Barnes, E. W., 414, 461, 462
Barnes, M. J., 377, 383
Barnes, N. D., 323
Barness, L. A., 333
Barnett, D., 585
Barnett, H. L., 375
Barnett, S. A., 436
Barone, L. M., 378, 380, 383
Barrand, M. A., 506
Barratt, K. H., 313
Barrett-Connor, E., 477, 478, 550
Barrucand, L., 57
Barry, D. M. J., 147
Barry, G. D., 479, 481
Bar-Shani, S., 24
Bar-Shavit, Z., 548, 550, 552
Bartel, L. L., 54, 55
Bartlett, K., 52, 323-26, 328, 330, 331
Bartoshuk, L. M., 435
Bartsch, H., 68
Barua, A. B., 281, 283
Basford, R. E., 412
Basile, C., 54, 57
Bass, M. A., 346, 351, 356-58
Basset, P., 194
Bassey, E. J., 508, 509, 511
Bassoe, H. H., 304
Basu, S. K., 248
Baswell, D. L., 334
Bateman, R. C. Jr., 374
Bates, C. J., 378, 384, 385
Bates, L. S., 227
Bates, P. C., 517
Bates, S. P., 325, 328
Batshaw, M. L., 52, 57, 58
Battese, G. E., 353
Battistella, P. A., 54, 57
Bauchop, T., 156, 157, 160-62
Bauernfeind, J. C., 274, 284, 286
Baugh, C. M., 332
Baukol, S. A., 549
Baumgartner, E. R., 321, 328, 330, 331
Bausch, J., 321, 331
Baylink, D. J., 530
Bayliss, C. E., 168
Baynes, J. W., 215
Bazer, F. W., 8
Bazin, M., 290
Bazzato, G., 54
Beach, D. C., 576
Beard, J., 20, 28, 29
Bearne, C. A., 157, 171
Beasley, R. P., 421
Beaton, G. H., 498
Beatty, P. W., 190
Beauchamp, G. K., 434, 448, 450, 451
Beavers, I., 358, 359
Bebb, H. T., 458, 459
Beck, F. W. J., 481, 485
Beck, L. H., 466
Beck, P. W., 190, 196-98
Beckenhauer, H. C., 188
Becking, G. C., 34
Becroft, D. M. O., 147
Bedenko, V., 82, 84
Beekman, R. P., 56
Beemer, F. A., 198, 323, 328
Beer, R., 565
Beg, Z. H., 251
Behar, D., 122, 123
Beinert, H., 23
Beisel, W. R., 14, 32, 33, 131, 133, 134, 138, 139, 142
Beitz, D. C., 535
Bekaert, J., 58
Belanger, L., 180
Belbeck, L., 488
Belizan, J. M., 476, 479, 482
Bell, A. C., 441
Bell, F. P., 587
Bell, L. V., 548
Bell, M. E., 585
Bell, R. L., 579
Bell, R. M., 299
Beller, D. I., 137
Bellinghieri, G., 54
Bellinghieri, L. G., 54
Belpaire, R., 372
Bem, D., 444
Bender-Götze, C., 33
Benderly, A., 52
Bendich, A., 289
Benedict, F. G., 460, 462
Benevenga, N. J., 105, 184, 185, 188-90, 192, 193
Benezra, R., 194
Benford, S., 213
Benjamin, E., 519
Benjamin, L. R., 195
Benjamin, W. S., 517
Benkovic, S. J., 393
Bennet, M., 330
Bennett, F. C., 115
Bennett, M. J., 323, 328
Bennett, R. A., 191
Ben-Shachar, D., 26, 28
Benson, M. D., 140
Ben-Uriah, Y., 27

Beratis, N. G., 190
Berchtold, P., 216
Beresford, C. H., 33
Beretta-Piccoli, C., 479
Berg, C. J., 121-23
Berg, R. A., 376-78, 381
Bergen, W. G., 99-102
Berger, E., 320
Berger, H., 276
Berger, L., 466
Berger, M., 490
Berger, R., 25
Berger, R. A., 583
Bergeron, T., 574
Bergot, F., 228
Bergrem, H., 53
Bergstrom, J. D., 248
Berk, G., 444
Berlit, P., 334, 335
Berlow, D., 58
Berlow, S., 188, 193, 334
Berlyne, D. E., 449
Berman-Marks, C., 367
Bernar, J., 53, 56
Bernardini, I., 53
Bernhard, K., 276
Bernstein, G., 211
Bernstein, I. L., 442
Bernstein, J. D., 463, 464
Bernstein, M., 585
Berridge, M. J., 580, 581, 583
Berry, M. N., 463
Berryman, G. H., 322
Bershad, S., 261
Berthelot, A., 479, 481
Bertino, M., 448, 451
Bertman, A., 464
Bertoli, M., 54, 57
Besser, G. M., 373
Best, C. H., 466
Bethell, D., 190, 191
Betzing, H., 567
Beumont, P. J. V., 306, 311
Beutler, B., 141-43
Beutler, B. A., 141
Beutler, E., 14, 18, 21
Beyer-Mears, A., 213
Bhagavan, H. N., 318, 322
Bhalla, A. K., 549, 550
Bhalla, R. C., 487, 488
Bhaskaram, C., 19, 30, 32
Bhat, P., 165, 172
Bhatia, B. D., 513
Bhattathiry, E. P. M., 258
Bick, R. J., 578
Bickerman, H. A., 118
Bickers, D. R., 291
Biden, T. J., 583
Bieber, L. L., 42, 47, 53, 56
Biederbick, K., 320
Bielsky, B. H. J., 367
Bienkowski, R. S., 376, 378, 380, 384
Bier, D. M., 56, 499
Bierkamper, G. G., 254
Bikel, I., 190
Billah, M. M., 579
Billheimer, J. T., 249
Billings, R. E., 187
Billman, J., 451
Bingham, A., 276
Birch, D., 444
Birch, L. L., 437, 442, 444, 448, 451
Birtwell, A. J., 215
Bischoff, T. L. W., 4
Bishop, A. J., 186
Bishop, J. E., 530, 536-38, 540, 546, 547
Bissell, M. J., 378, 379, 381
Bistrian, B. R., 218
Bittar, N., 57
Bizzi, A., 54
Bjeldanes, L. F., 87
Bjørneklett, A., 166-71
Black, A. E., 498, 502
Black, A. L., 100
Black, E., 516
Black, J., 3
Black, K. A., 187
Black, P. H., 148
Blackburn, G. L., 133, 218
Blackmore, P. F., 569
Blair, A., 227, 228, 230, 231
Blair, D., 324
Blake, I. G., 155, 156
Blakely, R., 189
Blakemore, W. S., 133, 134
Blanc, D., 229
Blanchard, J. S., 374, 387, 390
Blanciforti, L., 349
Blankel, L., 385
Blasie, J. K., 578
Blass, J. P., 122, 126
Blaxter, K. L., 98
Blaylock, J., 348-50
Blayney, L., 22, 23, 25
Blayney, L. M., 25
Bleasdale, J. E., 570, 581
Bleiberg, F., 506, 509
Bloch, K., 254
Blom, W., 324
Bloom, S. R., 373
Bloomfield, M. R., 25, 27, 28
Blot, I., 24
Blotman, M. J., 215, 216
Blouin, A. G., 118, 122, 123
Blumenfeld, O. O., 376, 378, 380, 384
Blundell, J. E., 448
Boas, M. A., 318
Bobek, P., 391
Boda, J. M., 96
Boden, G., 214
Bodwell, C. E., 512
Bodzay, J., 290
Boehm, W. T., 357
Boel, E., 373
Boger, W. P., 320
Bohan, T. P., 47
Bohlen, P., 373
Bøhmer, T., 53, 166-71
Bohr, D. F., 489
Boitnott, J. K., 461, 469
Boivin, G., 536
Bokkenheuser, V. D., 157, 160
Boland, R., 535
Bolanos, L. P., 464
Bolaños, O., 165, 172
Bolden, A. H., 565, 567
Boldt, D. H., 163
Boling, J. A., 102
Bolkenius, F. N., 190
Bolli, G., 214
Bolognesi, R., 57
Bombi, J. A., 464
Bonaschak, H., 487
Bond, J. H., 167
Bonjour, J.-P., 321, 328, 331, 334, 335, 547
Bonner, M. J., 261
Bookchin, R. M., 214
Boonjawat, J., 282
Booth, B. A., 378
Booth, D. A., 436, 443, 444, 447
Booth, F. W., 17
Booth, G. D., 156
Booth, R. F. G., 25
Booyens, J., 498, 510
Borch, G., 276
Borchardt, R. T., 192
Borek, C., 69, 73
Borensztajn, J., 587
Borgers, M., 256
Borgese, T. A., 566
Bornert, J.-M., 528, 543
Bornstein, M. B., 586
Bornstein, P., 376, 380, 383
Bortz, R., 391
Bortz, W. M., 461
Borum, P. R., 42, 48, 49, 52, 386, 387
Bosco, C., 508
Boss, G. R., 185
Bosschieter, E. B., 477, 478
Bostian, L. R., 359
Bostsarron, J., 503, 506
Bothwell, T. H., 24
Bottenus, R. E., 463, 464
Boulding, E. T., 160, 168
Bourges, H., 499
Boussingault, J. B., 4
Bouvet, W., 118
Bouzrara, A., 119
Boychuk, R. B., 327, 328
Boyer, A., 515
Bradbury, A. F., 373
Bradford, J. R., 565, 573

Bradley, N. W., 102
Braekken, O. R., 283
Bramley, P. M., 488
Branch, W. J., 168
Brass, E. P., 58
Braunstein, A. E., 197
Bray, G. A., 500
Brazeau, P., 373
Breckenridge, W. C., 567
Bregin, B., 391
Bremel, D. H., 106
Bremer, J., 42, 55, 387
Brengelmann, G. L., 28, 29
Brenner, M., 372
Brenner, W., 302
Brent, B. E., 106
Bresard, M., 459
Breslow, J. L., 214
Bresnahan, M. R., 426
Bressler, R., 57, 196
Breton-Gorius, J., 31
Brew, K., 8
Brewer, H. B., 251, 261
Brewer, W. D., 353
Brewster, T., 327
Breznak, J. A., 156
Brickman, A. S., 540, 541
Bridgeforth, E. B., 412
Briedis, A. V., 264
Brierly, J. M., 375
Brigant, L., 503, 506
Briggs, A. P., 332
Brinberg, D., 358, 359
Bring, V. W., 261
Brittenham, G. M., 14, 26, 29, 30, 118
Brittin, H. C., 357
Britton, G., 274, 287, 288
Broch, O. J., 185
Brock, J. F., 516
Brodie, J. D., 186
Brody, K. R., 320
Brody, S., 97
Broitman, S. A., 164
Brommage, R., 529
Bronfin, G. J., 462, 469
Brooke, C. G. D., 499
Brooke, M. H., 56
Brooke, O. G., 504, 506
Brookes, I. M., 102
Brooks, B., 512
Brooks, D. E., 45
Brooks, G. A., 20-23, 507, 508
Brooks, O. G., 33
Broquist, H. P., 42, 44, 48, 387
Bross, I. G., 420
Bross, T. E., 581, 583, 584
Brostoff, J., 120
Brown, C., 264
Brown, D. A., 228
Brown, D. S., 102
Brown, E. B., 20-23
Brown, G. M., 306
Brown, J. A. H., 144
Brown, J. G., 516
Brown, L. K., 355
Brown, M. J., 584
Brown, M. S., 246, 248-51, 253, 254
Brown, P., 517
Brown, R. C., 485
Brown, R. E., 102
Brown, T. A., 533
Brown, W. J., 56
Browning, E. T., 463
Brownstein, H., 357
Brožek, J., 303, 500, 503, 505
Brümmer, W., 320
Brubakk, O., 304
Bruce, W. R., 164
Bruch, H., 301
Bruckheimer, S. M., 214
Bruckner, G., 160
Bruguera, M., 464
Brumbaugh, P. F., 528-30, 532-36, 539, 540
Brun, T., 506, 509
Brunetti, P., 214
Brunner, F. P., 54
Brush, A. H., 284
Bryan, J., 580
Bryan, M. H., 49
Bryant, M. P., 171
Bryant, S. L., 27
Bryce, G. F., 482
Brynger, H., 54
Buch, M., 48, 49, 57
Bücker, M., 86
Buchecker, R., 276, 278-80
Buchwald, H., 167, 215
Bucklin, J. A., 156
Budlovsky, J., 391
Budowski, P., 282
Buhler, D. R., 228
Bukoski, R. D., 489
Bull, N. L., 321, 322
Bullen, C. L., 165-67
Bunc, V., 507, 508
Bunn, H. F., 214
Bunout, D., 460, 461, 469
Buoncristiani, U., 55
Burch, W. M. Jr., 541
Burgess, B., 411-13
Burget, D., 58
Burgos, M., 356
Burini, R., 517
Burk, M. A., 348
Burke, G. T., 186
Burke, J. F., 499
Burke, K. A., 106
Burley, V., 448, 449
Burman, D., 33, 144
Burns, J. J., 366, 368, 391
Burns, M. M., 358, 359
Burri, B. J., 326-30
Burridge, S. M., 170
Burris, W. R., 102
Burroughs, J., 360
Bursac, K. M., 528, 540
Burstein, S., 257
Burt, J. V., 438
Burton, L. E., 565, 573, 575
Busby, W. H. Jr., 374
Buss, D. H., 321, 322, 458
Bussmann, Y. L., 324
Butler, A. M., 582
Butler, J. L., 139
Buts, J.-P., 24
Butterworth, C. E., 332
Buttery, P. J., 105
Buzry, W. H. Jr., 373
Byun, S. M., 568

C

Caballero, B., 124
Cabanac, M., 447, 449
Cagliero, E., 215
Cahill, G. F. Jr., 133
Cahnmann, H. J., 375
Cain, J. R., 165, 172
Cairney, P. T., 441
Caldas, A. E., 540
Calder, E. A., 414
Caldwell, J., 122-24
Caldwell, L., 122-24
Caldwell, R., 488
Caliendo, M. A., 351, 358, 359
Callaham, M. F., 550
Callaway, E., 120
Callingham, B. A., 506
Calloway, D. M., 515
Cameron, D. P., 217
Cameron, E., 391
Cameron, N., 501
Campanati, G., 329
Campbell, A. H., 261
Campbell, T. C., 418, 419
Canale-Parola, E., 168
Canham, J. E., 391
Cann, H., 326, 327
Cannon, J. G., 137
Canterbury, W. J. Jr., 135, 139
Cantoni, G. L., 185
Cantwell, R. J., 144
Capper, B. S., 231, 234, 237, 240
Capps, O. Jr., 354
Caprino, D., 330
Cardinale, G. J., 377, 378, 381
Carini, C., 120
Carlstedt-Duke, B., 164
Carney, M., 198
Carnicero, H. H., 387, 390
Carobi, C., 55
Carpenter, S., 42
Carpentier, J. L., 584
Carré, G., 330
Carre, L., 462

Carroll, J. E., 56
Carroll, K. K., 259
Carroll, P., 213, 214
Carson, D. A., 182, 190, 192
Carson, D. D., 252
Cartechini, M. G., 214
Carter, C. M., 120, 372
Carter, R. D., 216
Carter, W. J., 517
Cartwright, G. E., 146
Caruso, U., 54, 57
Carvalho, A. C. A., 587
Casanova, J., 528, 535, 543
Casciani, C. U., 54, 57
Case, G. L., 184, 192, 193
Caspary, W. F., 567
CASPER, R. C., 299-316; 302, 305-7, 310, 311
Castegnara, M., 68
Castell, D. O., 305
Caster, W. O., 357
Castro, A. M., 467, 468
Caswell, N. M., 326-30
Caterini, H., 322
Catto, E., 182, 193
Catz, C. S., 34
Cavallini, D., 196
Cavalli-Sforza, L. L., 438
Cavenee, W. K., 250, 256
Cazee, C. R., 261
Cederbaum, A. I., 463-65
Cederbaum, S. D., 56
Cederblad, G., 45, 54, 55, 58
Celi, B., 574
Cenedella, R. J., 254
Centore, J. M., 126
Cerami, A., 140-43, 214, 215
Cerami, A. C., 143
Cerelli, G., 528
Cerna, O., 391
Cha, C.-J., 138
Chadwick, V. S., 166, 167
Chalifour, L. E., 321
Chalmers, D. G., 409
Chalmers, M. I., 100
Chalmers, R. A., 47, 52, 324, 325
Chalupa, W., 102
Chan, D., 482
Chan, G., 48
Chan, H., 514
Chan, L., 264
Chan, M. K., 54, 57
Chan, P. C., 367
Chanard, J., 54, 57
Chanarin, I., 187, 420
Chance, R. E., 226, 234, 235, 237, 240
Chand, S., 24
Chandler, J. E., 102
Chandler, J. S., 529, 530, 532, 533, 535, 539-41, 547
Chandler, S. K., 530, 535, 547
Chandra, R. K., 19, 30-33, 516
Chandraratna, R. A. S., 530
Chang, A. C. Y., 373
Chang, C. C. Y., 249, 250
Chang, C. F., 180
Chang, C. P., 192
Chang, H.-Y., 570
Chang, K., 214
Chang, R. L., 550
Chang, T.-Y., 249, 250, 254, 257
Chantler, C., 54
Chap, H., 573
Chap, H. J., 578
Chapin, H. N., 309
Chapkin, R. S., 567
Chapman, S., 468
Chapoy, P. R., 56
Charles, B. M., 330
Charlton, R. W., 24
Charpentier, C., 330
Chatagner, F., 194, 195
Chatterjee, I. B., 366, 367
Chatterton, R. T., 307
Chaudhuri, S. K., 476
Chaykovsky, M., 190, 197
Chedid, L., 139
Chekrygina, Z. P., 291
Chen, H. W., 250, 256
Chen, K. H., 378, 438
Chen, M. S., 229
Chen, P. S., 488
Chen, S., 23, 479, 488
Chen, S.-H., 53
Chen, S. Y., 192
Chen, T. L., 532, 533, 535, 541, 542, 544, 547, 549, 550
Chen-Kiang, S., 377
Chesney, R. W., 196
Cheta, D., 217
Chew, H., 87
Chiang, P. K., 185
Chiao, F. F., 187
Chichester, C. O., 227, 228, 231, 277, 278, 284
Chida, K., 529, 550
Chiel, H. J., 122
Chin, D. J., 248-50
Chin, W. W., 373
Chiou, J. Y., 228
Chipman, S. D., 378, 380, 383
Chittenden, R. H., 4
Cho, H., 542
Choi, E., 68, 82, 84
Chojkier, M., 380
Chong, H. E., 505, 513
Choubert, G., 284
Christakos, S., 532, 533, 535
Christenson, H. N., 217
Christiansen, M. P., 537
Christopherson, R. J., 97
Chu, F. S., 68
Chu, S. W., 565, 574, 577
Chua, A. O., 373
Chua, T., 227, 228
Chun, R., 58
Chung, D., 49
Church, D. C., 108
Chused, T. M., 140
Ciborowski, C. J., 215
Ciliv, G., 19, 30, 31
Ciman, M., 54, 58, 388
Cines, B. M., 357
Cini, M., 54
Clark, A. J., 419, 421-23
Clark, J. B., 25
Clark, J. H., 99, 102, 105
Clark, J. L., 24
Clark, S. A., 534, 535
Clark, S. L. Jr., 412
Clarke, C. F., 250, 264
Clarke, N., 579
Clarke, R. T. J., 156, 166
Clarke, S., 180
Clausen, J., 587
Claverie, N., 185, 186, 191
Clayton, B., 328, 330
Cleator, I., 58
Clemens, E. T., 161
Clemens, T. L., 535, 536, 542, 549
Clements, R. S. Jr., 213, 567, 568, 574, 584-86
Clevinger, B., 548
Cline, J. H., 99
Clinkenbeard, K. D., 248
Clowes, G. H. A. Jr., 137, 138
Clugston, G. A., 507, 516
Coakley, G., 189
Coates, M. E., 158
Coates, P. M., 51, 52, 57, 58
Coburn, J. W., 484, 485, 540
Cockcroft, S., 580
Cockett, B., 216
Cocks, T., 504, 506
Codegoni, A. M., 54
Cohen, A., 32
Cohen, A. M., 215, 217
Cohen, B. I., 86, 160, 257
Cohen, D. W., 57
Cohen, L. M., 193
Cohen, M. P., 213-15
Cohen, N. D., 321
Cohen, N. L., 353
Cohen, P. A., 190
Cohen, R., 145
Cohn, M. S., 191
Cohn, R., 326, 327
Cole, C., 477, 478
Cole, M., 437
Cole, R. A., 214
Coleman, P., 438
Colette, C., 215, 216
Coli, U., 54
Colley, K. J., 215

Collier, K. J., 373
Colombo, G., 372
Coloso, R. M., 231, 232, 237, 239
Colston, K., 532, 533, 535, 547, 550
Colston, K. W., 532, 533, 535
Colston, M. J., 533, 535, 550
Colten, H. R., 139
Coltoff-Schiller, B., 378, 380, 384
Commoner, B., 68
Compagnucci, P., 214
Cone, C. M., 532, 541, 542, 544, 547
Conerly, E. B., 193, 198
Confalone, P. N., 318
Connell, A. M., 460, 461, 468
Conner, M. W., 426
Conners, C. K., 118, 122-24
Conney, A. H., 391, 550
Connolly, T. M., 581, 584
Conrad, H. R., 535
Consolo, F., 54
Constable, B. J., 377, 383
Constable, R. J., 321
Contois, J. H., 122-24
Cook, H. M., 164
Cook, J. D., 14, 17, 18, 32
Cooke, A. R., 146
Cooke, N. J., 461, 462
Cooke, R. J., 49
Cooksley, W. G., 468
Cools, W., 256
Coombs, M. M., 84, 86
Coon, M. J., 320
Cooney, T. E., 113, 125
Cooper, A. D., 260
Cooper, A. G., 262
Cooper, B. A., 186
Cooper, D., 163
Cooper, E. H., 409
Cooper, M., 443, 445
Cooper, P. H., 571
Cooper, P. J., 310
Cooper, R. H., 56, 582
Cop, R. P., 528, 535, 543
Copeland, D. H., 421
Corbett, A. D., 373
Corey, E. J., 254
Corey, J. E., 575
Corey, P., 498
Corkey, B. E., 51, 52, 583
Corkin, S., 126
Cornatzer, W. E., 185, 186
Cornblath, M., 122, 123
Cornelissen, F., 256
Cornell, N. W., 463
Correia, M. A., 34
Corrigal, W., 96, 97, 103
Corsi, M., 54, 57
Cortner, J. A., 51, 52
Corvaja, E., 54
Coryell, M. E., 186, 322
Coryell, M. N., 322
Costa, E. M., 528, 545
Costas, R. Jr., 477, 478
Costerton, J. W., 163
Cotisson, A., 329, 330
Cottle, C., 373
Cottom, D., 325
Cotton, E. K., 24
Cottrall, K., 324
Coty, W. A., 533, 536
Coudé, F. X., 329, 330
Coulander, C. D. L., 477, 478
Counts, D. F., 381
Cousins, M., 498
Cousins, R. J., 528, 530
Covey, D. F., 569
Cowan, M. J., 327-30
Coward, J. K., 191, 192
Coward, W. A., 498, 502
Cowart, B. J., 436
Cowey, C. B., 227, 228, 230-32, 236-39
Cox, M., 517
Coyer, P., 517
Cozolino, L., 115, 123
Craig, A., 118, 123
Craig, M. C., 259
Craik, J. C. A., 289
Cramer, E., 31
Crandon, J. H., 388
Crane, R. K., 567
Crapo, P. A., 216, 217, 391
Cravioto, J., 504
Cravotto, E., 54, 57
Crawhall, J. C., 198
Crayton, J. W., 119
Creagen, E. T., 391
Creasia, D., 421, 422, 426
Creba, J. A., 581
Creed, R. H., 283
Crenshaw, M. C., 214
Criqui, M. H., 550
Crisp, A. H., 299-301, 305, 500, 503, 506
Crnic, L. S., 18, 116
Crolic, K. A., 460, 461, 467-69
Cronin, F. J., 349, 352
Cronk, C., 117
Crook, W., 122
Crooks, H., 321
Crossen, P. E., 409
Crow, K. E., 463
Crozier, G. F., 276
Cruetz, C. C., 372
Cruse, R. P., 56
Crutchfield, M., 305
Cruz, E., 213
Cruz-Vidal, M., 477, 478
Cuadra, M., 148
Cuatrecasas, P., 579
Cubeddu, L., 28, 29
Cuca, G. C., 68
Cucchini, F., 57
Cuisinier-Gleizes, P., 538
Cullen, J. A., 335
Culler, F. L., 540
Cummings, J. H., 166-68, 171
Cummings, M., 122-24
Cummins, R. W., 120
Cunningham, C. C., 463, 464
Curnow, R. T., 133
Curran, J. S., 50
Currier, B. E., 167
Curry, B., 19
Curry, E., 47, 48, 57
Cuthbertson, D. P., 516
Cuthbertson, O. P., 100
Cutler, R. G., 7

D

Dabbagh, S., 196
Dabrowski, K., 227
Dabrowski, K. R., 231, 237, 239
Dachur, N. R., 425
Dafoe, J. L., 444
Dagg, J. H., 19
Dahlqvist, A., 77
Dahners, H. W., 511
Dakmar, E., 461, 462
Dakshinamurti, K., 318, 321, 329
Dalakas, M., 53
Dalal, S., 517
Dale, G., 328, 330, 331
Dal Lago, A., 58
Dallman, M. F., 27
DALLMAN, P. R., 13-40; 14, 16-25, 27, 28, 32-34
Dallner, G., 578
Dallosso, H. M., 498
Dame, M. C., 528, 535, 539, 543
D'Amicis, A., 511
Damrongsak, D., 415
Danan, J.-L., 538
Dancis, J., 515
Dangelmaier, C. A., 566
Daniel, E. E., 487, 488
Daniel, R., 349, 351
Daniels, A. J., 372
Daniels, K. M., 195, 196, 199
Daniels-Kush, R., 506, 509
Danielson, H., 264
Danzin, C., 185, 186, 191
Darby, P. L., 500, 508
Dark, K. A., 120
Das, K. C., 409, 411, 412, 414
Das, R. C., 283
Das, T. K., 518
Dashman, T., 391
da Silva, J. A. F., 57
Dasmahaptra, A., 213, 214
Datiles, M., 213

Daubner, S. C., 187
Davidson, C. S., 467
Davidson, F., 145
Davidson, M. M. L., 582
Davies, B. H., 274, 285, 288
Davies, B. W., 285
Davies, H. L., 498, 502
Davies, K. J. A., 20-22
Davis, A. E., 385
Davis, C. G., 349, 436
Davis, C. L., 105
Davis, C. M., 436, 441
Davis, J. E., 214
Davis, J. M., 302, 305, 307, 310, 311
Davis, W., 68
Dawson, A. G., 463
Dawson, A. P., 583
Dawson, J., 312
Dawson, K. A., 164
Dawson, R. M. C., 571, 572, 579
Day, A. J., 587
Day, H. E., 27
Day, J. F., 215
Deacon, R., 187
Dean, G., 372
Dean, P. D. G., 254
DeAngelis, B., 322
deAntueno, R. J., 588
deCamargo, J. L. V., 419, 421-23
De Carli, L. M., 461, 462, 467
DeClerck, Y. A., 378
Dee, P. C., 373
De Feo, P., 214
Defoor, P., 578
Deftos, L. J., 532, 533, 535, 539, 540, 545, 549
Degado, H., 476
de Garine, I., 437
Degen, J. L., 191
De Gier, J., 578
DeGrange, D. A., 542, 547
De Guzman, P. E., 510
Deiss, A., 15
DeJesus, P. V. Jr., 584, 586
DeJong, L., 381
DeJonge, H. R., 485
de Kalbermatten, N., 219
Dekeyser, N., 24
de Klerk, J. B. C., 56
Delacroix, D. L., 24
Delafuente, J. C., 391
De La Rosa, J., 194-97
DeLoach, H. L., 228
DeLong, D. C., 226, 227, 229-31, 237, 239
DeLorimer, A. A., 334
Delorme, A.-C., 538
Deltour, G., 58
DeLuca, H. F., 261, 262, 528-30, 532-40, 543, 546, 547
Demetriou, A. A., 191
Dempsey, M. E., 264
Dempsey, R. A., 140
Denckla, W. D., 464
den Daas-Slagt, H., 156, 167, 168
Deneke, S. M., 291
Denko, C. W., 322
Dennis, B. H., 458, 459
Denniston, J. C., 133
Dent, R. G., 305
Denton, R. M., 56
Derefeldt, T., 117
Desai, I. D., 511
de Sak Melo, T., 290
DeSchenes, R. J., 373
Deshimaru, O., 277
DeSombre, R., 534
Desor, J. A., 436, 438
Desplan, C., 551
DeVaughn, N. M., 332
DeVivo, D. C., 56, 324
deVos, N. M., 156, 167, 168
Dewey, K. G., 356
Dews, P. B., 116
Deysher, M., 448
Dhanamitta, S., 44
Dhar, A. K., 257
Dhooria, H. S., 477
Diamond, L. K., 24
Diamond, L. S., 148
Diaz DeLeon, L., 380
Dickens, D., 347
Dicker, E., 463, 464
Dickie, M., 56
Dickson, E. R., 460, 468
DiDonato, S., 47, 56
Dieckmann, B., 142, 143
Diehl, A. M., 461, 469
Dieng, K., 506, 509
Dietel, M., 529
Diethelm, A. G., 567, 568, 586
Dietschy, J. M., 258, 263
Digman, L., 115, 123
Dikun, P. P., 81
Diliberto, E. J. Jr., 372
DiLisa, F., 57
Dill, D. B., 388
Dillmann, E., 27-29
DiMauro, S., 51, 54, 56, 58
Dimitriadis, G. D., 216
Dinarello, C. A., 135-40
Dinterman, R., 138
Dinterman, R. E., 134, 135, 138, 139
DiPaolo, I. V., 55
DiStefano, C., 54
Ditchfield, J., 119
Ditzel, J., 214
Dix, M. R., 147
Dix, T. A., 393
Dixit, R., 291
Dixon, C., 84, 86
Dixon, J. E., 373, 385
Dixon, J. L., 193
Dixon, K., 312
Djordjević, V., 188
Dodd, P., 326, 327
Dodek, P., 47, 58
Dohan, F. C., 119
Dokoh, S., 529, 532, 533, 535, 539-41, 547, 550
Dolby, A. E., 19, 30, 32, 145
Doll, R., 67
Dolora, P., 68
Domschke, W., 164
Donaldson, C. A., 528, 529, 533, 535-37, 539, 542-45, 548, 550
Donckerwolcke, R. A., 54
Donlevy, S. C., 48
Donovan, C. M., 20-22
Donzelli, F., 49, 50, 57
Dormandy, K. M., 420
Dorn, G., 529
Dornbusch, S. M., 438
Dörner, M. H., 8
Dorogokupla, A. C., 291
Dorst, K. G., 487
Døskeland, S. O., 185
Douglas, M., 437
Douste-Blazy, L., 573, 578
Downes, C. P., 581, 583
Downie, E. D., 7
Downs, R. W., 542, 547
Draffan, G. H., 324, 328
Dragila, T. A., 385
Drake, M. R., 195, 197
Drasar, B. S., 171
Drenick, E. J., 515
Drewnowski, A., 451
Drezner, M. K., 541
Driscoll, C. A., 320
Drüeke, T., 485, 486
Duane, M., 537
Duarte, E., 511
Dubbelman, T. M. A. R., 572
Dube, D. P., 289
Dubertret, L., 290
Dubois, A., 305
DuBois, E. F., 133
Dubois, P. M., 536
Duclaux, R., 447
Ducluzeau, R., 163
Dudman, N. P. B., 188
Duerden, B. I., 165, 166, 171
Duerre, J. A., 185, 186
Dugan, R. E., 259, 264
Dugdale, A. E., 499
Duksin, D., 379
Duncan, C. A. H., 47
Duncan, D. B., 99
Duncker, K., 444
Dungal, N., 81, 83, 85
Dunham, R. B., 447
Dunn, P. J., 214

Dunn, W. A., 43, 387-89
Dunner, D. L., 587
Dupre, J. M., 551
Dupré, S., 196
Dupree, H. K., 230, 231
Duque, E., 165, 172
Duran, M., 56, 198, 323, 328
Durand, J. H., 359
Durnin, J. V. G. A., 497, 501, 510, 511, 514
Duthie, M., 326
Dutra de Oliverra, S., 511
Dutra, S., 511
Dyerberg, J., 214

E

Eagen, A. R., 105, 192, 193
Eagle, H., 564
Eagles, J. A., 460, 468
Eakin, R. E., 318-20
Earhart, R. H., 461, 462
Earl, D. C. N., 213, 216
Ebert, L., 446
Ebert, M. H., 183, 186, 189, 305
Eby, B., 479, 485, 488
Echeverri, L., 144
Eckbert, C. D., 217
Ecker, E. E., 384
Eckert, E. D., 302, 310-12
Eddington, C. L., 138
Eddy, T. P., 459
Edelman, R., 415
Edelstein, D., 258
Eder, H. A., 258
Edgerton, V. R., 27
Edholm, O. G., 497, 501
Edmond, J., 248
Edmonds, C. J., 166, 167
Edmondson, D. E., 372
Edmonson, P. F., 45
Edmundson, W., 504, 505, 509
Edreira, J. G., 467
Edwards, B. B., 24
Edwards, C. A., 171
Edwards, P. A., 248-50, 264
Edwards, R. H. T., 508, 516
Edwards, W. A., 193, 198
Edwin, E. E., 106
Eells, J. T., 187
Egan, H., 68
Egawa, K., 570
Egger, J., 120
Ehle, F. R., 169-71
Ehrenberg, A., 19, 32
Eichberg, J., 566, 570, 581, 585
Eichelman, B., 115
Eichhorn, H. H., 5
Eiklid, K., 53
Eikvac, L., 535
Eil, C., 528, 532, 535, 541, 542, 547
Einstein, M. A., 352
Eipper, B. A., 373, 374
Eisenberg, F. Jr., 565, 567, 568, 589
Eisenberg, M. A., 318
Eisman, J. A., 528, 533, 535, 540, 545, 550
Ekman, P., 446
Ekman, R., 24
Elahi, D., 218
Eldjarn, L., 324
Elian, E., 24
Elias, P. R. P., 57
Elishkorvsky, R., 145
Elliott, J. G., 261
Ellis, P. R., 215
Ellis, S. R., 387
Ellison, R. C., 214
Ellman, G., 120
El Lozy, M., 575
Ellwood, K. C., 217
Eloranta, T. O., 185, 186, 191
Elsden, S. R., 161
Elson, C., 54, 55, 57
Elwyn, D., 5
Emaus, R., 42, 53, 56
Emery, J. L., 335
Emoto, S., 318
Emshanova, A. V., 81
Eng, J., 373
Engel, A. G., 42-47, 49-52, 54, 56, 387
Engel, J. J., 467, 468
Engelman, K., 448, 451
Engerman, R. L., 213
England, P. J., 56
England, S., 437
ENGLARD, S., 365-406; 43, 374, 387-90
Englert, G., 284, 285
Engstrom, M. A., 190
Enzi, G., 49, 50, 57
Eppright, E. S., 351, 358, 359
Epstein, J. H., 291
Erbland, J. F., 261
Erde, P., 52
Erdman, J. W. Jr., 261
Erenoglu, E., 467
Erickson, E. C., 351
Erickson, S. K., 260
Erikson, U., 536
Eriksson, B., 118
Erlichman, M., 333
Ervin, F. R., 125
Esca, S. A., 302
Esch, F., 373
Esch, F. S., 373
Eskelson, C. D., 261
Estler, C. J., 463, 464
Esvelt, R. P., 529
Etzioni, A., 52
Eugster, C. H., 276, 278
Eurin, J., 537
Evans, C. A., 378
Eveleth, P. B., 500
Exton, J. H., 569, 581
Eyssen, H., 160
Ezell, J. M., 355

F

Faas, F. H., 517
Fabiato, A., 489
Fabry, P., 217
Fagher, B., 54, 55, 57
Fagius, J., 213
Fahey, T. H., 21
Fairbanks, V. F., 14, 18
Fairburn, C. G., 310, 313
Fairlamb, A. H., 141
Falase, A. O., 488
Falk, J. R., 310
Falko, J. M., 312
Falkoff, R. J. M., 139
Faller, J., 465
Fallon, A. E., 433, 437-41, 446, 451
Fanger, M. W., 550
Fant, M. E., 7
Farber, E., 421, 424, 426
Farese, R. V., 582
Faris, B., 378, 380, 383
Farkas, W. R., 162
Farmer, B. B., 57
Farmer, K., 147
Farrell, L. E., 583
Farrell, S., 42, 53, 56
Farrington, A. J., 313
FARTHING, M. J. G., 131-54; 32
Fauci, A. S., 139
Fauconneau, B., 236
Fauconnet, M. H., 414
Fausa, O., 166-71
Faust, J. R., 248-51, 253, 254, 438
Fay, F. S., 487
Feather, M. S., 68
Febvre, A., 230, 231
Federici, G., 196
Federline, T. L., 358, 359
Fehling, C., 187
Feighner, J. P., 300
Feingold, B. F., 115
Feingold, S., 320, 322
Feinman, L., 461, 462
Feisthauer, J., 447
Felber, J. P., 219
Felder, M. R., 461, 462
Feldman, D., 528, 532, 533, 535, 538, 541, 542, 544, 545, 547, 549, 550
Feldman, G. L., 326-28
Feldman, M. W., 438
Fell, R. D., 20-23

Fellman, J. H., 195, 196, 198, 374
Felton, J. S., 81
Fenderson, C. L., 102
Fentem, P. H., 508, 509, 511
Ferguson, H. B., 122-24
Ferguson, K. A., 99
Ferguson, M. M., 412
Fern, E. B., 499, 517, 519
Fern, M., 499
Fernandes-Costa, F., 187
Fernstrom, J. D., 125
Ferrari, R., 57
Ferrini, A. M., 511
Ferro, A. J., 185, 192
Ferro-Luzzi, A., 164, 497, 510, 511, 514
Fessler, J. H., 376
Fessler, L. I., 376
Fetzer, J. N., 360
Fewster, W. J., 359
Fidanza, A., 391
Field, R. B., 254
Fielden, H., 216
Fienberg, N. S., 482, 483
Fietzek, P., 380
Fieve, R. R., 587
Fiil, N. P., 373
Fillmore, C. M., 501
Filus, S., 463, 464
Finch, C. A., 6, 14, 16-18, 20, 21, 24, 25, 28, 29, 31, 32
Finean, J. B., 578
Finegold, D., 585
Finegold, S. M., 156, 165, 166, 172
Finelli, V. N., 567
Finer-Moore, J., 248
Finger, S., 119
Fink, R. M., 385
Finkelstein, J. D., 180, 185-90, 193
Finlayson, D. D. C., 414
Finnegan, J. A., 585
Finnie, M. D. A., 324, 373
Fischer, R., 437
Fiser, R. H., 133
Fisher, S. K., 581
Fitch, Y. R., 356
Fitzgerald, P. H., 409
Fitzpatrick, T. B., 291
Flaks, J. G., 378
Flatmark, T., 372
Fleisch, H., 547
Fleischer, S., 578
Fleming, S. E., 169-71
Flemming, T. R., 391
Flenner, J., 358, 359
Fletcher, J., 19, 30, 145
Fletcher, K., 504
Flick, P. K., 576
Flickinger, S. A., 227
Fliesler, S. J., 568
Flore, R., 57, 58
Flug, D., 145
Fogelman, A. M., 249, 250, 264
Fogh-Andersen, N., 477, 479
Fohlin, L., 304, 305
Foldager, J., 100
Folin, O., 513
Folkers, K., 318
Folsom, A. R., 477
Folts, J. D., 57
Fomon, S. J., 24
Fontaine, O., 536
Forbes, G. B., 500, 503, 515
Foreman, J. W., 329
Forness, S. R., 119
Forsythe, S. J., 163
Fort, P., 303
Fortier, N., 28
Foss, J. G., 164
Foss, P., 279, 281
Foster, D. W., 42, 58
Fowler, B., 188, 197
Fowles, N. O., 20
Fox, D. L., 286
Fox, H. M., 351, 356-59
Fox, I. H., 185, 192, 465-67
Fox, K. D., 354, 355
Frampton, R. J., 535, 545, 550
Franceschi, R. T., 537, 538
Franco, D., 144
Francoual, J., 24
Frangos-Plemenos, M., 334
Frank, O., 320, 322
Frankena, H., 196, 199
Franzblau, C., 378, 380, 383
Freake, H. C., 535, 539
Freed, D. L. J., 119
Freed, M., 322
Freedland, R. A., 197
Freedman, M. H., 32
Freedman, M. R., 356
Freedman, Z. R., 215
Freeman, A. E., 564
Freiberg, J. M., 218
Freier, S., 333
Freinkel, N., 579
French, S. W., 463, 464, 467
Frendo, J., 198
Frenkel, R. A., 387
Frerman, F. E., 52, 57, 58
Freudenheim, J. L., 477, 482, 483
Frezal, J., 330
Friedkin, M., 410
Friedman, H. S., 464
Friedman, S., 372
Frienden, E., 135
Friesen, W. V., 446
Fritz, I. B., 387
Froesch, E. R., 216
Frohlich, J., 45, 47, 58
Frohman, L. A., 306
Fronk, T. J., 107
Froysa, A., 535
Fryer, B. A., 351, 358, 359
Fu, I. Y., 537
Fujii, O., 195
Fujikawa, K., 69, 74
Fujimori, E., 292
Fujioka, M., 185, 193
Fujita, T. S., 196, 280, 374, 550
Fujita, Y., 69, 87
Fujiwara, M., 479
Fukami, M. H., 463
Fuki, H., 213
Fukui, T., 254
Fukuma, M., 584
Fukushi, S., 213
Fukushima, M., 529, 550
Fuller, G. C., 378
Fuller, J., 443, 447
Fuller, R., 160
Fuller, R. K., 458, 459
Fung, B., 254
Furcht, L. T., 215
FURIHATA, C., 67-94; 87, 88
Furuichi, M., 228
Futerman, A. H., 579

G

Gabbay, K. H., 213, 214
Gabuzda, T., 290
Gacad, M. A., 541, 542, 548
Gaesser, G. E., 507, 508
Gahimer, G. D., 231, 239
Gahl, W. A., 53
Gainer, J. L., 292
Gairard, A., 479, 481
Galambos, J. T., 469
Gale, C., 28, 29
Gallagher, A., 564, 576
Galler, J. R., 116, 117
Galli-Kienle, M., 182, 193
Gallin, J. I., 135, 139
Gallo, A. E., 357
Gallop, P. M., 214, 376, 378, 383
Gallup, E. M., 312
Galyean, M. L., 96
Gamblin, G. T., 542, 547
Gamel, W. G., 258
Gang, H., 464
Ganguly, J., 259
Gannon, M. C., 115
Garattini, S., 54
Garavaglia, B., 47, 56
Garb, J. L., 442
Garber, D., 57
Garbers, D. L., 192
Garby, L., 498
Garcia, J., 436, 442
Garcia, P. A., 353

Garcia-Palmieri, M. R., 477, 478
Garcia-Peregrin, E., 264
Gardner, G. W., 27
Gardner, J., 322, 586
Garfinkel, P. E., 500, 508
Gargiulo, M., 117
Garland, C., 550
Garlick, P. J., 499, 507, 516, 517
Garling, D. L. Jr., 227, 228, 231, 232, 237
Garn, S. M., 437
Garrett, R. J., 571
Garrigan, O., 264
Garrigus, U. S., 102
Garrow, J. S., 504, 506, 510
Garza, C., 118
Gasparotto, M. L., 54, 57
Gassull, M. A., 216
Gattas, V., 460, 461, 469
Gaudry, M., 330, 331
Gauger, M. E., 443
Gauldie, J., 139
Gaull, G. E., 180, 190
Gavey, K. L., 249
Gavin, G., 574
Gawienowski, A. M., 288
Gay, P. E., 126
Gayen, A. K., 254, 255
Gaylor, J. L., 249, 250
Gebhardt, B. M., 416, 417
Geboers, J., 477
Gehrig, D., 320
Geiger, J. W., 133, 134
Geisert, J., 330
Geissler, C. A., 505, 509
Gelenberg, A. J., 126
Gelfand, E. W., 32
Genovese, S., 215
Genuth, S. M., 47
George, B. C., 137, 138
George, D. T., 133, 138
George, P. Y., 573
Georgieff, M., 218
Gerard, J., 216
Gerich, J. E., 216
Gerner, R. H., 312
Gerrard, J. M., 582
Gersovitz, M., 117
Gery, I., 137
Geser, C., 219
Gettelman-Klein, R., 120
Getz, G. S., 587
Geyer, R. P., 565, 574, 577
Ghafari, H., 216
Ghafoorunissa, 565
Ghalayini, A., 570
Gherardini, F., 157, 167, 168
Ghijsen, W. E. J. M., 485
Ghneim, H. K., 323, 326, 328
Ghosh, S. R., 228
Ghoshal, A. K., 421, 424, 426
Giacco, A., 215
Giambrone, M.-A., 380
Giannella, R. A., 164
Gibbons, G. F., 250, 256
Gibbs, C. L., 508
Gibson, C. J., 126
Gibson, D. M., 251
Gibson, G. E., 122, 126
Gibson, G. J., 52
Gidwani, G. P., 305
Giedroc, D. P., 372
Gil, G., 248, 249
Gilbert, E. F., 42, 56
Gilbert, R., 121
Gilchrest, B. A., 542
Giles, C., 144
Gililand, K., 115
Gill, F. A., 148
Gillam, B. M., 189
Gillespie, A. H., 351
Gillespie, C. A., 27
Gillon, K. R. W., 585
Gilmour, R. F. Jr., 57
Ginsberg, H., 391
Ginter, E., 391
Giorcelli, G., 54, 57
Giovanella, B. C., 180
Giovanni, M., 450
Girard, A., 588
Giroux, A., 28
Giulidori, P., 182, 193
Gjessing, L. R., 375
Gladis, M., 313
Glanville, R. W., 380
Glasgow, A. M., 46, 47, 51, 56
Glass, T. L., 157, 160
Glassman, A. H., 313
Glatt, H. R., 86
Glazenburg, E. J., 193, 196
Gleason, W. A., 544
Glembotski, C. C., 373, 374
Glenson, R. E., 214
Glimcher, L. H., 550
Glinz, E., 280-84
Glover, J., 27
Gluck, L., 587
Go, V. L. W., 216
Goebel, K. P., 351, 354, 355
Goff, D. V., 216
Goff, G. M., 310
Goh, E. H., 260
Goh, S. H., 380
Golbus, M. S., 327-29
Gold, C., 164
Gold, P. H., 252
Goldberg, A., 19
Goldberg, A. C., 260, 264
Goldberg, A. L., 138, 139
Goldberg, D. P., 119
Goldberg, S. C., 302, 310, 311
Goldberg, S. J., 460, 461, 467-69
Golden, M. H. N., 506, 512, 516, 517
Golden, R., 126
Goldfarb, S., 259, 264
Goldfischer, S., 378, 380, 384
Goldman, H. M., 377
Goldman, J. A., 122-24
Goldman, P., 164
Goldman, R. F., 509, 510
Goldsmith, R., 497
Goldstein, A., 446
Goldstein, J. D., 248
Goldstein, J. L., 246, 248-51, 253, 254
Goldstein, N. G., 477, 478
Goldstein, R., 333
Goldstone, A. H., 414
Golub, M., 490
Gombervaux, C., 459
Gomperts, B. D., 580
Gompertz, D., 323-25, 328
Gonen, B., 214
Gonzalez, A. M., 213, 214
Gonzalez, J. L., 123
Gonzalez-Rios, M. D. C., 326, 327
Gonzalez-Sastre, F., 566
Goodey, P. A., 325
Goodhart, R. S., 565
Goodland, R. L., 375
Goodman, D. B. P., 536
Goodman, D. S., 261, 291
Goodman, J. R., 22, 25, 34, 155, 156
Goodman, R. H., 373
Goodman, S. I., 52, 57, 58, 328-31, 334
Goodson, J. D., 215
Goodwin, B. L., 375
GOODWIN, T. W., 273-97; 274, 279, 281, 282, 284-90
Gooze, L. L., 533, 535
Gopalan, C., 501
Gordon, A. H., 137
Gordon, E. R., 463, 464
Gordon, H. A., 137, 138
Gordon, H. E., 375
Gordon, H. H., 160, 375
Gordon, J. E., 131, 145, 411, 415
Gordon, S. S., 214
Gorell, T., 534
Gorelova, N. D., 81
Gorski, J., 536
Goryachenkova, E. V., 197
Goss, H., 106
Goswami, B. C., 281, 283
Goswami, M. N. D., 375
Goswami, U. C., 283
Gotoh, Y., 259, 260
Gottlieb, L. S., 464
Gotto, A. M. Jr., 259
Gould, B. S., 377

Gould, R. G., 251, 264
Govan, C. D. Jr., 375
Gowen, M., 549
Grace, R., 21, 25
Gracey, M., 158, 163, 164, 172
Grad, G., 303
Gradis, H., 384
Graf, R. J., 214
Graham, P. J., 120
Grahame-Smith, D. G., 25, 27, 28
Gram, T. E., 33
Granda, A. M., 285
Granger-Schnarr, M., 537
Grant, D. A., 410
Gräslund, A., 17, 32
Gravel, R., 323, 324, 328
Gravel, R. A., 326, 327, 329
Gravina, E., 58
Gravina-Sanvitale, G., 58
Gray, G. E., 114
Gray, L. K., 114
Gray, N. C. C., 572
Gray, R. W., 540, 544
Greden, J., 121
Green, A. R., 25, 27, 28, 328, 330
Green, D. E., 582
Green, N. M., 319
Green, R. S., 313, 349
Green, S., 528, 543
Green, W., 20, 28, 29
Greenberg, A., 333
Greenberg, G. R., 146
Greene, D. A., 213, 214, 444, 584, 585
Greene, G. L., 528, 536, 543
Greene, L. S., 436, 438
Greene, Y., 391
Greenfield, D. B., 119
Greenwald, D., 125
Greenwood, M. R. C., 451
Greim, G., 164
Grenier, A., 180
Grez, M., 373
Grier, R. E., 320, 328-31
Griffin, F., 437
Griffin, J. E., 542
Griffith, O. W., 194, 195
Griffiths, C., 115
Griffiths, M., 499
Griggs, R. C., 24
Grilli, M., 57, 58
Grim, R. H., 477
Grishaver, M. S., 197
Grivas, S., 77
Grivetti, L. E., 356
Groat, R., 313
Groeneveld, D., 28
Grof, P., 290
Gross, C. J., 45
Gross, E. G., 261
Gross, H. A., 305, 587
Gross, J., 282, 377
Gross, M. D., 122, 305
Gross, R. L., 408, 411-13, 415
Gross, W. B., 479, 481
Grosso, L. E., 548
Grotkowski, M. L., 358, 359
Grove, D., 378, 379
Grove, J., 191
Growden, J. H., 126
Grubb, D. A., 96, 97, 103
Grundy, S. M., 263, 264
Grundy, W. E., 322
Gruss, L., 444
Grzelakowska-Sztabert, B., 188
Gschnait, F., 302
Guarini, L., 190
Guarnieri, G., 54
Gubler, U., 373
Gudjonsson, H., 45
Guha, S. K., 191
Guillemant, S., 537
Guillemin, R., 373
Guion-Rain, M.-C., 194
Gull, W. W., 299
Gumby, D., 120
Gump, F. E., 5
Gunary, R., 448
Gunz, F. W., 409
Günzler, V., 381, 382
Gupta, A., 256-58, 261
Gupta, I., 164
Gupte, S., 57
Gusmano, R., 54, 57
Gusowski, N., 196
Gustafsson, B. E., 156, 158, 164, 165, 196
Guthrow, C. E., 215
Gutman, A. B., 466
Gutterberg, T. J., 148
Gutteridge, J. M. C., 9
Guynn, R. W., 461, 463
Guze, S. B., 300
Gwirtsman, H. E., 312
György, P., 318-20

H

Habener, J. F., 373
Haberstroh, B., 567
Hadley, C., 250
Hafstrom, J. L., 354
Hagel, H.-J., 164
Haguet, M., 54, 57
Hahn, D. A., 186
Hahn, P., 45, 47-50, 58
Haines, P. S., 348, 349
Hajj, S. N., 145
Hale, D. E., 51, 52, 57, 58
Haley, M., 437
Hall, A., 301, 548, 550
Hall, C. L., 52
Hall, R. L., 434
Hall, W. K., 186
Haller, A., 3
Haller, R. D., 228
Haller, R. G., 42
Hallert, C., 117, 119
Hallfrisch, J., 217
Hallgren, B., 166
Halliday, D., 504, 516
Halliwell, B., 9
Hallman, M., 577, 578, 587
Halloran, B. P., 534, 546
Halmi, K. A., 302, 310, 311
Halpern, M., 466
Halsted, C. H., 467
Haltalin, K. C., 412
HALVER, J. E., 225-44; 226-31, 233-35, 237, 239, 240
Halvorson, P. A., 310
Hama, M. Y., 349
Hamil, B. M., 322
Hamilton, G. A., 374, 375, 568
Hamilton, J. W., 45
Hamlin, R. H. J., 476
Hammer, L., 441
Hamprecht, B., 264
Hamstra, A. J., 528, 537, 540
Hanada, L., 359
Hanauske-Abel, H. M., 381, 382, 384
Handelsman, D. J., 214
Haney, D. N., 214
Hanford, H., 564, 576
Hankin, J. H., 67, 477, 478
Hankins, W. G., 436, 442
Hannonen, P., 191
Hansch, D. B., 57
Hansen, R. G., 349-51, 353, 355, 357, 458, 459
Hansen, R. I., 217
Hantman, E., 115, 122
Hanwell, M. A., 214
Hara, M., 76
Harada, Y., 57
Harashima, K., 286, 287
Harauchi, T., 366
Harber, L. C., 291
Harding, D. E., 231, 232, 237, 238
Hardinge, M. G., 321
Hardison, W. G. M., 195
Harkness, D. R., 566
Harlan, L. C., 477, 478
Harlan, W. R., 477, 478
Harlow, D. R., 148
Harner, C. J., 118
Harper, A. E., 184, 185, 518, 519
Harper, L. J., 353
Harper, L. V., 444
Harpey, J.-P., 186
Harrell, J. H., 587
Harries, J. M., 497
Harriman, G. A., 287
Harris, B. J., 185-88

Harris, C. J., 168
Harris, D. J., 323, 328
Harris, D. W., 570
Harris, J. W., 24
Harris, M. E., 322
Harris, R. A., 519
Harris, R. S., 565
Harris, S. A., 318
Harrison, A. A., 449
Harrison, C., 145, 148
Harrison, H. E., 213, 216
Hart, R. G., 487
Hartmann, E., 125
Hartroft, W. S., 466
Harval, C. M., 255
Harvey, M. S., 573
Harwood, H. J., 251
Harwood, H. J. Jr., 391
Hasan, S. H., 575, 586
Hasegawa, H., 69, 75
Hasegawa, R., 576
Hashiba, H., 529
Hashimoto, S., 158
Hashimoto, Y., 69, 230, 231
Haslam, R. J., 582
Haslinger, A., 551
Hasselbach, W., 535
Hasty, K., 214
Hata, Masahiro, 277-80, 283
Hata, Mitsuo, 277-80, 283
Hatfield, E. E., 101, 102
Hathaway, R. A., 54
Hatsukami, D., 312
Hatton, D. C., 479-81
Haun, R. S., 373
Hauser, G., 566, 567, 569, 581
Hauser, S., 264
Haussler, D. H., 528, 540
HAUSSLER, M. R., 527-62; 528-30, 532-36, 539-41, 545, 547, 550
Haveland-Smith, R. B., 290
Havlicek, J. Jr., 354
Havlik, R. J., 477, 478
Hawes, S. F., 506
Hawks, D., 385
Hawthorne, J. N., 571, 580, 584, 585
Hay, A. M., 516
Hayaishi, O., 374-76
Hayashi, E., 574-76
Hayashi, H., 57
Hayashi, K., 68
Hayatsu, H., 76
Hayes, J. P., 145
Hayes, J. R., 418, 419
Hayes, K. C., 575-77
Hayford, J. T., 123
Haymond, M. W., 324
Haynes, S. G., 458, 459
Heal, D. J., 25, 27, 28
Healy, B., 438
Healy, M. J. R., 497
Healy, S. K., 81
Heard, G. S., 320, 322, 330, 331
Hecht, S. S., 82, 84
Heckman, G. D., 372
Hedegaard, L., 477, 479
Heersche, J. N. M., 544
Heftl, F., 448
Hegenauer, J., 14, 20, 23
Heger, H. W., 578
Hegsted, D. M., 564, 576, 577
Heimberg, M., 260
Heimdahl, A., 164
Heiner, D. C., 24
Heininger, H. J., 250, 256
Heinrich, H. C., 33
Helland, S., 185, 186
Heller, E. A., 464
Helmkamp, G. M. Jr., 573
Helson, H., 450
Helsper, J. P. F. G., 368
Helu, B., 29, 118
Hemington, N., 579
Hemken, R. W., 106
Hempel, S., 44
Hems, D. A., 580
Hems, R., 187, 410, 411
Henderson, A., 22, 23, 25
Henderson, C. R., 322
Henderson, K., 133, 134
Henderson, L. L., 388, 389
Henderson, L. M., 43, 45, 387-89
Henderson, S., 20-22
Henderson, S. A., 23
Hendricks, D. G., 33
Hendrickse, R. G., 145, 148
Hennon, C. B., 354, 355
Henry, C. J. K., 499
Henry, H. J., 477, 478
Henry, H. L., 261, 262, 529, 532, 533, 535, 540, 547
Henry, M. J., 256
Henschel, A., 303, 500, 503, 505
Hentges, D. J., 155
Hepner, G. W., 196
Herbert, V., 409-11, 414
Herbette, L., 578
Heremans, J. F., 135
HERLONG, H. F., 457-74; 461, 469
Herman, C. P., 346, 377, 448
Hermann, M., 82, 84, 86
Herrera, M. G., 575
Herring, C., 185, 192
Hersch, M., 391
Hershfield, M. S., 185
Hershko, C., 15
Hersio, K., 216
Hertzler, A. A., 438
Herzog, D. B., 305
Hespell, R. B., 163
Hess-Sander, U., 320
Hetherington, M., 448, 449
Heusner, A. A., 503
Hewitt, D., 100
Hewitt, J., 377
Hibasami, H., 190-92
Hidaka, T., 286, 287
Hift, W., 411-13
Higashi, T., 190
Higgins, J. A., 460, 468
Higginson, J., 67
Higgs, J. M., 31, 145
Higuchi, D. A., 20-23
Hikichi, S., 280
Hikita, K., 190
Hildmann, B., 485
Hill, L., 196
Hill, M. J., 164
Hill, O. W., 300
Hill, R. L., 8
Hill, R. P., 323, 328
Hillier, V. F., 119
Hillman, R. E., 323
Hilton, J. W., 228
Himberg, J.-J., 191
Himms-Hagen, J., 217
Hind, H., 444
Hindhede, M., 4
Hinds, M. W., 67
Hirakawa, T., 69, 73
Hirano, S., 160
Hirao, S., 276
Hirasawa, K., 572
Hirasawa, M., 190
Hirayama, T., 76
Hirmo, T., 280, 281
Hirode, K., 29, 30
Hirono, I., 68, 69, 75
Hirose, T., 373
Hirota, N., 84
Hirsch, E., 138
Hirschberger, L. L., 195
Hirst, M. A., 528, 532, 533, 535, 538, 541, 542, 544, 545, 547, 549
Hitchcock, M. W. S., 161
Hitzel, F. N., 228
Ho, Y. K., 250
Hoag, M. S., 24
Hobson, E. A., 497
Hochalter, J. B., 387
Hochberg, Z., 542, 547
Hochman, H. I., 542, 547
Hockaday, T. D. R., 211, 216
Hodges, R. E., 391
Hodgman, C. H., 500, 503
Hoensch, H., 34
Hoffbrand, A. V., 411, 412
Hoffenberg, R., 516
Hoffman, B. J., 373
Hoffman, D. R., 185, 186
Hoffman, J. L., 180, 191
Hoffmann, D., 82, 84

Hoffmeister, F., 216
Hofmann, A. F., 160, 196
Hofmann, K., 318
Hofmann, S. L., 581
Hoganson, G. E., 58
Hokin, L. E., 580, 581
Hokin, M. R., 580
Hokin-Neaverson, M., 570
Holdeman, L. V., 171
Holick, M. F., 528, 530, 538
Holick, S. A., 538
Holland, A. J., 301
Hollenberg, S. M., 528
Hollingsworth, D. F., 497
Hollis, B. W., 540
Holloszy, J. O., 17, 21, 22
Hollowell, J. G. Jr., 186
Holman, E., 443
Holman, R. T., 334
Holmberg, L., 24
Holme, E., 385, 386, 388, 390
Holmes, C. S., 123
Holmes, W. S., 461
Holmlund, C. E., 254
Holmquist, W. R., 214
Holst, P., 542
Holsztynska, E. J., 391
Holt, L. E. Jr., 515
Holt, P. G., 391
Holtgreve, H., 551
HOLUB, B. J., 563-97; 264, 565-67, 570-72, 574, 575, 579, 581, 586, 587, 581
Homolka, J., 333
Honda, M., 68
Honeyman, T. W., 487
Hong, J-X., 139
Hong, R., 334
Honig, A. S., 29, 118
Honma, Y., 550
Hood, J., 391
Hood, R. L., 322, 335
Hoogkamp-Korstanje, J. A. A., 156, 167, 168
Hook, E. W., 148
Hoover, G. A., 575
Hoover, K. L., 421, 422, 426
Hopkins, D., 191
Hopp, L., 489
Hoppel, C. L., 47, 52, 58, 387
Hoppner, K., 321, 322
Hori, C., 191
Hori, S., 505
Horiuchi, N., 535, 542
Horiuchi, T., 587
Horlein, D., 380
Horne, D. W., 42
Horney, F. D., 99
Hornig, D., 372
Hornstein, I., 352
Horowitz, T., 441
Horowitz, Z. D., 528, 535, 543
Horsmans, Y., 24
Horst, R. L., 485, 530, 535, 540
Horton, E. S., 506, 509
Horwitz, D. L., 214, 215
Hosaka, N., 69, 75
Hosfield, W., 313
Hosking, G., 330
Hosking, J. D., 458, 459
Hoskins, L. C., 160, 168
Hosokawa, H., 227, 228
Hosokawa, Y., 194-96
Hotchkiss, A., 372
Hotez, P. J., 141
Hothersall, J. S., 585
House, W. A., 566
Houser, H. B., 458, 459
Houston, A. P., 168
Houston, H., 168
Hovell, F. D. DeB., 97
Høverstad, T., 166-71
Howanitz, P., 29, 118
Howard, C. F. Jr., 568
Howard, J. E., 540
Howard, R. B., 117, 163
Howat, P., 461
Hozumi, M., 550
Hruba, F., 391
Hsia, Y. E., 323, 327, 328
Hsu, C.-A., 385, 386
Hsu, C. H., 488
Hsu, W.-J., 278
Huang, M.-T., 550
Huang, P. C., 505, 513
Huber, J. T., 100
Huberman, E., 550
Hudson, J. I., 313
Hudson, R. A., 285
Huebers, E., 6
Huebers, H., 6
Huebers, H. A., 16, 24, 25
Hueper, W. C., 81
Hugel, U., 535
Hughes, D. E., 320
Hughes, M. R., 530, 532, 533, 535, 538, 539
Hughes, R. E., 388
Hughes, S. G., 231, 233-35
Huie, P. E., 479-81
Huisman, T. H. J., 375
Hukins, D. W. L., 376
Hull, A. L., 477, 478
Hull, D., 323-25, 328
Hull, W. E., 374, 375
Hulse, J. D., 387
Hulsmann, W. C., 58
Humbert, J. R., 30, 31, 143
Humphreyes, M., 115
Humphreys, S. R., 146
Hunt, C. E., 415
Huntington, G. B., 98
Huntley, R. M. C., 499
Hunziker, W., 534-38, 546, 547
Huovinen, J. A., 196
Hurley, R. J., 388
Hurst, R. L., 349-51, 353, 355, 357
Hurt, R. D., 460, 468
Hurwitz, L., 489
Hurxthal, K., 215
Husain, I., 373
Hussein, S., 145
Hussey, J. L., 54, 55
Huxtable, R., 196
Hwang, S. M., 569
Hyde, J., 328, 330
Hylemon, P. B., 157, 160
Hyman, E. S., 25
Hynie, I., 47, 58

I

Iampetro, P. F., 509, 510
Iber, F. L., 462, 468
Ichikawa, M., 534, 536
Ida, S., 196
Ide, T., 259, 260
Idell-Wenger, J., 57
Idell-Wenger, J. A., 57
Igarashi, Y., 328
Ihrie, E. J., 549
Iida, S., 461, 462
Iio, T., 264
Iizasa, T., 182
Ikeda, Y., 141
Iles, M., 5
Im, Y. S., 185
Imai, A., 572
Imai, H., 256
Imamura, A., 47, 57
Immink, M. D. C., 356
Imms, F. J., 511
Inagaki, E., 69, 74
Inamdar, A. R., 20, 21, 25, 28
Inayama, S., 373
Ingebretsen, O. C., 372
Ingebritsen, T. S., 251
Innis, S. M., 334
Inoue, A., 373
Inoue, T., 76
Ionescu-Tirgoviste, C., 217
Irreverre, F., 193
Irvine, R. F., 572, 579-81, 583
Irvine, W. J., 414
Irving, R. A., 290
Isaacks, R. E., 566
Isbell, H., 332
Iseri, O. A., 464
Ishi, K., 69
Ishibe, T., 587
Ishida, M., 534, 536
Ishii, K., 69
Ishikawa, T., 69, 74
Ishimoto, Y., 197
Ishizuka, B., 115
Ismond, D. R., 121
Israel, Y., 463, 464

Ito, A., 508
Itoh, N., 373
Itokawa, Y., 479
Iturriaga, H., 460, 461, 469
Iwasaki, J., 535, 539
Iype, P. T., 425
Izawa, Y., 486
Izumi, Y., 318

J

Jackson, A. A., 515
Jackson, A. J., 231, 234, 237, 240
Jackson, J. M., 19
Jacob, J. W., 373
Jacob, R. A., 302, 305
Jacobi, H. P., 261
Jacobs, A., 14, 19, 22, 23, 25, 27, 30, 32, 145
Jacobs, H. L., 436
Jafferji, S. S., 580
Jägerstad, M., 77, 187
Jahring, P. B., 138
Jakobs, C., 328
Jalso, S. B., 358, 359
James, M. J., 252
James, W. P. T., 498, 499, 503-7, 516, 517, 519
Jameson, S., 213
Janik, Z., 198
Janis, R. A., 487
Janjic, D., 583
Jänne, J., 191
Jansson, L. T., 20-24
Jarrett, R. J., 211
Jaudes, P., 214
Jauncey, K., 227, 228
Javaid, J., 119
Javitt, N. B., 257
Jeejeebhoy, K. N., 508
Jeevanandum, M., 133
Jefferson, L. G., 322, 331
Jellum, E., 324
Jen, K. L. C., 451
Jenkins, A. L., 216
Jenkins, D. J. A., 115, 171, 215, 216
Jenkins, P., 519
Jenkins, W. M. M., 412
Jenness, R., 388, 389, 568
Jennings, K. P., 311
Jennings, P., 187
Jensen, D. O., 103
Jensen, E. V., 534
Jensen, N. J., 69, 74
Jensen, N. S., 168
Jequier, E., 219
Jerome, N. W., 356, 357
Jett, M., 588
Jetten, M. E. R., 419
Jewett, D. L., 115
Jilge, B., 161
Joder-Ohlenbusch, A.-M., 191
Johnson, A. R., 322, 335
Johnson, B. C., 106
Johnson, C., 33
Johnson, D. G., 28, 29
Johnson, F. C., 366, 391
Johnson, H. C., 322
Johnson, J. D., 57
Johnson, J. L., 198
Johnson, L. F., 566
Johnson, N. E., 477, 482, 483
Johnson, N. W., 548
Johnson, R. B. Jr., 31
Johnston, D. A., 135, 285
Johnston, J. L., 114
Johnston, J. M., 185, 570
Joly, J. G., 462
Jonas, J. M., 313
Jones, A. W., 487
Jones, C., 312
Jones, C. A., 550
Jones, D. A., 508
Jones, D. P., 467
Jones, E., 388
Jones, G., 530, 544
Jones, I. R., 215
Jones, J. R., 292
Jones, L. M., 581
Jones, O. W., 197
Jones, P. A., 378
Jones, P. G., 529, 532, 534
Jones, P. J., 146
Jones, R. L., 214
Jonxis, J. H. P., 375
Jordan, S. C., 550
Jose, M. J. L., 532-36, 539
Joseph, S. K., 583, 584
Josephson, A. M., 122
Josephson, B. M., 24
Joynson, D. H. M., 19, 30, 32, 145
Juchau, M. R., 34
Judge, D. S., 434, 441
Jung, R. T., 506, 517
Jungalwala, F. B., 579
Jurcovicova, M., 391
Jutte, N. H. P. M., 535
Juva, K., 376

K

Kabra, P., 28
Kada, T., 76, 290
Kadar, P., 213
Kader, M. M. A., 57
Kadlecek, T., 326, 327
Kadner, R. J., 385
Kadota, T., 486
Kadowaki, S., 529
Kaetzel, C. S., 537
Kaetzel, D. M., 537
Kagamiyama, H., 194
Kagan, A., 500
Kaisyo, T., 227, 228
Kaizer, S., 446
Kajander, E. O., 185, 186, 191
Kajiyama, H., 227, 228
Kakimoto, Y., 44
Kaki-Uchi, Y., 587
Kaladhar, M., 26, 28
Kalager, T., 304
Kalat, J. W., 442, 444
Kalcheim, C., 379
Kalina, R., 384
Kaltwasser, J. P., 24
Kalucy, R. S., 299, 300, 500, 503, 506
Kalwinsky, D., 379
Kamada, T., 461, 462
Kamata, T., 277
Kamataki, T., 69
Kamatani, N., 190, 192
Kameyama, Y., 572
Kamikawa, T., 57
Kamin, S., 214
Kaminetzky, H. A., 322
Kaminski, J., 101, 102
Kaminski, M. V., 138
Kaminskyj, O., 359
Kamm, J. J., 391
Kampschmidt, R. K., 138, 140
Kan, T., 164
Kanada, T., 68
Kanarek, K. S., 50
Kanazawa, A., 227
Kandutsch, A. A., 250, 252, 256, 257
Kane, F. J., 116, 126
Kang, S. O., 367
Kanisawa, M., 256
Kano, K., 191, 530
Kantak, K. M., 115
Kao, F.-T., 380
Kao, W. W. Y., 377, 378
Kapadia, C. R., 165, 172
Kaplan, I. I., 332
Kaplan, S. R., 378
Kaplan, S. S., 412
Kappel, L. C., 101, 103, 105
Karabula, C., 333
KARANJA, N., 475-94; 479, 480, 486
Karasawa, K., 564
Karasek, M., 532, 533, 535
Karayalcin, G., 24
Kare, M. R., 434
Karin, M., 551
Karlsson, J., 508
Karnaukhov, V. N., 288
Karpati, G., 42
Karras, T. J., 57
Karunanayaka, A., 585
Kasai, H., 68, 70, 71, 77-79, 81, 86, 87
Kass, E. H., 145, 291
Kasselberg, A. G., 52

Katayama, T., 227, 228, 231, 277, 284
Katcher, M. L., 56
Kater, R. M., 468
Kato, R., 69
Kato, Y., 69, 73
Katsunuma, T., 518
Katsuyama, M., 276, 277, 280, 281
Kattamis, C., 333
Katz, J., 19, 30-33
Katz, S., 437
Katze, J. R., 162
Kaucher, M., 322
Kaufman, S., 372
Kaufmann, R. L., 134, 142
Kaushik, S., 231, 233, 234, 240
Kaushik, S. J., 229, 236
Kavale, K. A., 119
Kawachi, T., 68, 69, 71, 73-76, 80
Kawai, A., 80
Kawai, Y., 158, 164
Kawajiri, K., 69
Kawakami, M., 140-42
Kawamura, N., 47, 57
Kawase, A., 47
Kawash, G. F., 351, 358
Kay, R. M., 167
Kay, S. R., 119
Kaye, D., 148
Kayes, T. B., 234, 236-38
Kayser, H., 278, 286, 287
Kearney, E. B., 21, 194
Keating, J. N., 186
Keating, J. P., 323
Keenan, R. W., 566
Keeton, B. R., 324
Keister, D. B., 148
Keith, M. L., 251
Kelleher, P. A., 568
Keller, R. K., 252
Keller, U., 216
Keller, W., 501
Kelley, M., 358, 359
Kelly, E., 318
Kelly, M. A., 528, 535, 536, 542, 545, 550
Kemmer, F., 216
Kemp, A., 377, 381
Kendrick, N. C., 537
Kennedy, E. P., 570
Kennelly, P. J., 249, 251
Kennerly, D. A., 579
Keough, K. M. W., 579
Kerbey, A. L., 56
Kermani-Arab, V., 550
Kern, T. S., 213
Kerner, J., 47, 48, 388, 389
Kerr, R. L., 349
Kerr, S. J., 185
Kessler, B. J., 462, 469
Kesteloot, H., 477
Ketola, H. G., 231, 234, 236-38
Keup, V., 216
KEUSCH, G. T., 131-54; 32, 131, 133, 134, 143
Keys, A., 303, 500, 503, 505
Khan-Siddiqui, L., 43, 44
Khanna, S., 24
Kheun, G., 542, 548
Kiehm, T. G., 215
Kien, C. L., 328-31, 334
Kienholz, E. W., 227
Kiessling, K. H., 464
Kikuchi, K., 54, 55
Kikuchi, R., 276
Killingley, M., 170
Kilzer, P., 214
Kim, B. M., 133
Kim, D. N., 264
Kim, H. D., 566
Kim, I.-K., 185
Kim, K. I., 234, 236-38
Kim, S., 43, 387
Kimball, E. S., 137
Kimber, C., 24
Kimura, H., 197
Kindom, S. E., 582
King, A. J., 461, 462
King, C. G., 118, 366
King, K. M., 198
King, W. J., 536
Kingston, B., 448
Kinley, L. J., 261
Kinlough-Rathbone, R. L., 581
Kinney, J. M., 5, 133, 134
Kino, M., 489
Kinoshita, J. H., 213
Kinuta, M., 189, 190, 197
Kirk, C. J., 580, 581, 584
Kirk, J. E., 372
Kirschner, B., 302, 305
Kirshner, N., 372
Kirsner, J. B., 158
Kispal, G., 388, 389
Kissonerghis, A.-M., 84, 86
Kita, T., 373
Kitagawa, T., 69, 74
Kitahara, T., 281
Kitajima, C. G., 280
Kitamura, K., 281
Kitamura, S., 230
Kitts, W. D., 96
Kivirikko, K. I., 377, 378, 381, 382
Kizer, J. S., 373, 374
Kjellberg, J., 303
Klaus, G., 549
Kleiber, M., 100
Klein, A., 27
Klein, M. I., 57
Klein, R. E., 476
Klein, R. G., 234, 240
Kleinman, J., 119
Klempner, M. S., 135, 139
Klidjian, A. M., 311
Klinman, J. P., 372
Klipstein, F. A., 172
Kloppel, T. M., 239
Kluger, M. J., 137, 139
Knappe, J., 320
Knize, M. G., 81
Knödgen, B., 190
Knox, D., 231, 232, 237, 239
Knox, G., 213
Knox, W. E., 375
Kobayashi, A., 57
Kobayashi, J., 477
Kobayashi, K., 582
Kobayashi, M., 574
Kobayashi, Y., 164
Koch, O. R., 464
Kochanowski, B. A., 32, 33
Kochen, W., 335
Koch-Weser, J., 191
Koda, K., 380
Kodicek, E., 377, 383
Koeffler, H. P., 529, 533, 535, 544, 548, 550
Koenig, R. J., 214
Kögl, F., 318
Kohashi, N., 194, 195
Kohler, E., 334
Kohner, E. M., 211
Koishi, H., 515
Koivusalo, M., 320
Koj, A., 198
Kojima, K., 158
Kok, E., 257
Koke, J. R., 57
Kolasa, K., 346
Kolb, R., 264
Kolonel, L. N., 67
Kolterman, O. G., 217
Komi, P. V., 508
Komoi, T., 280, 281
Konat, G., 587
Kondo, A., 374, 387
Kondo, S., 69, 74
Konno, K., 535, 548, 550
Konosu, S., 280
Kontro, P., 195
Koraćević, D., 188
Koren, R., 542, 547
Korhonen, T., 216
Kori, Y., 194, 195
Korkor, A. B., 544
Korsgaard, J. N., 487
Korsten, M., 461, 462
Kosnai, I., 24
Kostelnik, M. E., 462
Kostinas, J. E., 420
Kosuge, T., 68-71, 77-80, 87
Kosugi, A., 87
Kotaki, A., 574, 575, 586
Kotarski, S. F., 157, 167, 168
Kothari, H. R., 261
Koutouzov, S., 588

Koutsicos, D., 334
Kovaks, A., 290
Kovalskys, J., 29
Kradin, R. L., 549
Kraicer, P. F., 568
Kramer, L., 444, 488
Krane, S. M., 378
Krantz, K. E., 582
Kratz, R., 56
Kraus, J., 188, 197
Kraus, J. P., 188
Krause, H. P., 216
Krause, K.-H., 334, 335
Krause, R. F., 261
Krauter, P., 551
Kream, B. E., 528, 532-36, 538-40, 549, 552
Krebs, H. A., 187, 410, 411, 519
Krebs-Smith, S. M., 349, 352
Kredich, N. M., 185
Kreipe, R. E., 500, 503
Krepinsky, J. J., 164
Kretchmer, N., 375, 496
Kreuger, J. M., 139
Krieger, T., 380
Kriegsmann, E. A., 115
Krijgsheld, K. R., 193, 196, 199
Krinsky, M. M., 161
Krinsky, N., 290, 291
Krinsky, N. I., 292
Kripke, B., 126
Krishnamachari, K. A. V. R., 19, 30, 32
Kroes, J. F., 577
Kroeze, J. A. H., 434
Krohn, K., 414
Kromhout, D., 459, 461, 477, 478
Krondl, M., 359, 434, 438, 441
Kronfield, D. S., 97
Kronsberg, S., 122-24
Krueger, K. K., 318
Krueger, M., 372
KRUESI, M. J. P., 113-30; 122-24
Krumdieck, C. L., 409, 420
Kruse, J. R., 530
Krust, A., 528, 543
Krymkiewicz, N., 86
Krzeminski, K., 115
Ku, L., 213
Kubo, K., 515
Kuchibotla, J., 544
Kudoh, Y., 54, 55
Kuitonen, P., 24
Kuksis, A., 571, 572
Kula, N. S., 426
Kulapongs, P., 30, 32
Kulish, C., 443
Kuller, L. H., 477, 478, 482
Kumar, M., 412
Kumaraiah, V., 436
Kumeno, K., 86
Kun, E., 463
Kunert, K. J., 291
Kung, M., 530
Kunstýr, I., 160
Kunz, L. J., 148
Kuratsune, M., 81, 83, 85
Kuribayashi, T., 535, 548-50
Kuritza, A., 168
Kuriyama, K., 196
Kurnick, J. T., 549
Kuroda, Y., 69, 73
Kuroki, T., 529, 550
Kurt-Jones, E. A., 137
Kusama, K., 69, 75
Kusumi, K., 518
Kutscher, J., 257
Kuttan, R., 378
Kutzbach, C., 187
Kutzbach, C. A., 410, 411
Kuutti, E. R., 377
Kuutti-Savolainen, E. R., 381
Kuvibidila, S. R., 32
Kuwabara, T., 213
Kuzuhara, K., 587
Kwan, C. Y., 488
Kyle, E., 512
Kyle, W. E., 180, 185-88

L

LaBadie, J., 43, 387
LaBrecque, D. R., 425
Lacey, J. H., 305, 313
LaChance, P. A., 261
Lachmann, P. J., 384, 385
Lacour, B., 54, 57, 485, 486
LaDu, B. N., 375
Laduron, P. L., 372
Laffont, F., 573
Lafourcade, J., 186
Lahey, M. E., 24
Lak, N. D., 197
Laleli, Y., 19, 30, 31
Lalich, J., 193
Lambert, G. F., 100
Lambertsen, G., 283
Lamkin, G. H., 351, 358, 359
Lammert, O., 498
Lampi, B., 321, 322
Lan, S.-F., 249, 250
Land, H., 373
Land, J. M., 25
Landini, S., 54
Landis, J. R., 477, 478
Landman, A. D., 321
Landman, J., 515
Landymore-Lim, A. E. N., 373
Lane, B. P., 24, 138, 464
Lane, D. M., 248
Lane, M. D., 141, 142, 319
Lane, S., 349
Lange, H. W., 44
Lanzkowsky, P., 24
Lapar, V., 264
Lapetina, E. G., 579
Larin, R., 125
Larkin, F. A., 477, 478
Larrick, J. W., 25
Lasègue, D., 299
Laser Reuterswärd, A., 77
Lashford, L. S., 323, 328
Lasser, N. L., 258
Laster, L., 193
Latipää, P., 381
Lattimer, S. A., 213, 214, 584, 585
Lau, D., 359, 434, 441
Lau, K., 479, 485, 488
Lau, S. S., 391
Lau, S. Y. M., 288
Lauritsen, M. A., 146
Lauwers, W. F., 256
LaVoie, E., 84
LaVoie, E. J., 82
Lawal, S. O. A., 488
Lawless, H., 450
Lawless, H. T., 450
Lawrence, F., 510
Lawrence, M., 510
Lawson, A. M., 325
Lazarus, R., 367
Le, N., 261
Le, P. T., 331
Lease, J. G., 318
Leavengood, H., 211, 213
Lebwohl, P., 305
Lechtig, A., 476
Leckie, M. P., 324
LeCunff, M., 546
Ledbetter, F. H., 372
Lederman, H. M., 32
Lee, D. B. N., 481, 485
Lee, D. J., 228
Lee, D. L., 230, 231
Lee, J. B., 290
Lee, J. C., 479, 481
Lee, J. W. W., 32
Lee, K. T., 264
Lee, R., 290
Leedle, J. A. Z., 157, 160, 166-68
Leeds, A. R., 216
Lees, R., 215, 216
Lees, R. S., 587
Leets, I., 28, 29
Lefebvre, P. J., 216
Legenstein, E., 215
Lehman, L. J., 49, 390
Lehnert, W., 330
Lehrer, G. M., 251
Lehrman, M., 214
Leibel, R. L., 26, 30, 119
Leiberman, H. R., 126
Leibold, E. A., 8

Leibovitz, B., 391
Leighton, A. T., 479, 481
Leinberger, R., 374, 375
Leininger, M., 347
Leitenberg, H., 309
Le Kim, D., 567
Lelbach, W. K., 461, 466
Le Magnen, J., 448
Lemann, J. Jr., 540
Lemire, J. M., 550
Lemm, C. A., 228
Lemonnier, D., 506, 509
Lemons, R., 330
Lenard, J., 578
Lencner, A. A., 156
Lenfant, C., 20
Lennarz, W. J., 252
Lennon, D. L. F., 46
Lentz, R., 312
Leo, M. A., 461, 462, 464
Leonard, J. V., 328, 330
Leonard, Y., 24
Lepe-Zuniga, J. L., 137
Lepper, M. R., 444, 445
Leprince, C., 158
LeQuesne, P. W., 256
Lerdvuthisopon, N., 44
Lerman, R. H., 122-24
Lerner, E., 57
Leslie, C. A., 289
Lesmes, H., 48, 57
Leso, J., 507, 508
Letcher, A. J., 583
Le Trang, N., 141
Leuenberger, F., 286
Leuenberger, F. J., 276, 280-85
Leung, C. T., 386
Leuthardt, F., 320
Leveille, G. A., 360
Levenberg, B., 372
Levene, A., 378
Levene, C. I., 378, 384, 385
Levenson, S. M., 376
Levey, A. B., 443
Levi, E., 333
Levi, M., 486
Levin, E. Y., 372
Levin, P., 218
Levin, P. A., 312
Levine, A. S., 311
Levine, B. S., 484, 485
Levine, M., 366, 372, 373
LEVINE, R., 211-24
Levine, S., 28
Levine, S. Z., 375
Levinson, S. M., 291
Levitt, M. D., 167
Levy, F. O., 535
Levy, H. L., 186, 187, 190, 193
Levy, J., 52
Levy, M., 564
Lew, P. D., 583
Lewin, K., 347
Lewin, L. M., 565, 568, 569, 586
Lewin, S., 366, 368
Lewis, D., 101, 103, 104
Lewis, G., 106
Lewis, M. J., 19, 30, 145
Lewis, N. S., 118
Lewis, R. A., 584
Li, B. U. K., 45
Liaaen-Jensen, S., 276, 279, 281
Liau, M. C., 180
Liberato, D. J., 47
Liberman, A., 24
Liberman, U. A., 528, 532, 535, 541, 542, 547
Licini, L., 54
Lieber, C. S., 461-67
Lieberman, M. E., 536
Liebholz, J., 100
Liebig, J. von, 4
Liebler, J. B., 462, 469
Liebman, P. A., 285
Liebman, W. M., 334
Liedtke, A. J., 57
Lifshitz, F., 303
Light, L., 349, 352
Lijinsky, W., 81-83, 85, 87
Lim, C., 227
Lim, P., 227, 228
Lim, Y., 426
Limanek, J. S., 249, 250
Lin, K., 254
Lin, Y. Y., 257
Lincoln, S. D., 53
Lind, P., 536
Lindberg, B., 138
Lindberg, K. A., 378, 379
Lindblad, B. S., 156, 165, 374, 387
Linder, M. C., 8
Lindner, J. G. E. M., 156, 167, 168
Lindros, K. O., 465
Lindsay, D. B., 105, 160
Lindstedt, G., 44, 374, 385, 387
Lindstedt, S., 44, 45, 374-76, 385-88, 390
Ling, N., 373
Linkswiler, H. M., 190
Linton, R., 345
Lipinski, B. A., 500, 503
Lipsky, P. E., 139
Lipton, M. A., 116, 126
Liscum, L., 248, 250
Lisper, H. O., 118
Littell, A. S., 458, 459
Little, C. O., 100
Little, P. A., 412
Little, P. J., 145
Little, S. A., 489
Littledike, E. T., 535, 540
Liu, C. K., 385
Liu, T., 567
Liu-Chi, S. B. L., 458, 459
Livesey, G., 192, 193
Liveson, J. A., 586
Livingston, D. M., 190
LJones, T., 372
Llach, F., 539
Llorach, M., 54, 57
Lloveras, J., 54, 57
Lloyd, T., 579
Lobaugh, B., 541
Lobley, G. E., 97
Locke, A., 146
Lockhart, H. B., 100
Lockley, W. J. S., 287
Loda, M., 138
Loewus, F. A., 368, 386
Logeat, F., 546
Logue, A. W., 437, 442
Lohmann, W., 367
Lollar, D., 318
Lombardi, B., 426
Lombardini, J. B., 180
Long, C. A., 8
Long, C. L., 133, 134
Long, C. S., 42
Long, E., 320
Longley, R., 288
Longnecker, D. S., 418
Lonsdale, D., 180
Loos, M., 384
Lopes, J., 508
Lopez, E., 539
Lorenz, K., 321
Lorenz, L. J., 373
Lorenzi, M., 215
Lorenzo, A. V., 565, 568
Loriette, C., 195
Losse, H., 487
Lotero, H., 165, 172
Lou, M. F., 44
Louria, D. B., 322
Lousberg, R. J. J. C., 287
Lousley, S., 216
Lovenberg, W., 372
Lovric, V. A., 144
Low, A. G., 215
Low, M. G., 578, 579
Lowe, J. E., 160
Lowell, W. E., 116
Löwer, R., 44
Lozoff, B., 14, 26, 29, 30, 118
Lubec, G., 215
Lucas, C. C., 466
Lucas, P. A., 485, 486
Luckey, T. D., 156
Ludman, E. K., 356
Ludovici, P. P., 412
Ludwig, U., 33
Luft, E., 482, 483
Luger, T. A., 140
Luisada-Opper, A. V., 320
Lukes, J., 28

Lukton, A., 233
Lumb, M., 187
Lund, B., 540
Lund, B., 540
Lund, C. G., 388
Lund, C. J., 24
Lund, D. B., 68
Lund, L. A., 348
Lund, P., 192, 193, 518
Lundström, U., 24
Luquet, P., 227, 229, 231, 232, 234, 237, 284
Luria, S. E., 419
Lusk, G., 2
Luskey, K. L., 248-50
Luthra, M. G., 571
Luyck, A. S., 216
Lynen, F., 264
Lynn, R., 126
Lyons, B. L., 381

M

Ma, A., 217
Macara, I. G., 587
MacCuish, A. C., 414
MacDonald, G., 572
MacDonald, I. A., 164
MacDonald, M. R., 185, 192, 351, 354, 355
MacDonald, P. C., 570
MacDonald, R. J., 249
Macdougall, L. G., 19, 30-33
MacFarlane, S. B. J., 145, 148
MacFarlane, T. W., 412
MacGregor, J. T., 68
Mach, K., 302
Machlin, L. J., 565
MacIntyre, I., 533, 535, 539
Mack, D. L., 45, 46
Mack, S. E., 571
Mackay, H. M. M., 144
Mackay, I., 421, 428
Mackler, B., 20, 21, 24, 25, 28, 29, 31
Mackowiak, P. A., 165
Maclachlan, M. J., 466
Macleod, N. A., 97
MacPhail, A. P., 24
MacRae, J. C., 97
Macrander, L. A., 386
Macy, I. G., 322
Madden, M., 46
Mader, J. A., 164
Madsen, J. A., 126
Madyastha, P., 68
Maebashi, M., 47, 57
Maeda, T., 568, 574-76
Maeder, E., 219
Maetzke, G., 49, 57
Magee, P. N., 68
Magee, W. L., 572
Magee, W. T., 227
Magendie, F., 3
Maggio, D. C., 325
Maglio, M., 155, 156
Maguire, J. J., 21, 22
Mahadeva, K., 505, 509
Mahadevappa, V. G., 566, 571
Mahnken, C., 284
Mahoney, A. W., 33
Mahoney, J., 141
Mahoney, J. R. Jr., 141
Maiale, G., 511
Main, A. N. H., 460, 461, 468
Main, E. R., 146
Mains, R. E., 373, 374
Majamaa, K., 377, 381, 382
Majerus, P. W., 569, 579, 581-84
Majeska, R. J., 549
Majumder, A. K., 367
Makar, A. B., 187
Makinos, S., 366
Makita, M., 76
Makita, T., 486
Malhotra, S., 29, 30
Mallamace, A., 54
Maller, O., 115, 123, 434, 436, 438
Mallett, A. K., 157, 171
Malone, J. H., 332
Malone, J. I., 211, 213
Mamont, P. S., 191
Manchester, K. L., 191
Mancini, J. M., 540, 541
Mandel, P., 194, 195
Mandell, R., 198, 437, 438
Mandell, R. B., 378, 381
Mandersloot, J. G., 578
Mange, M. S., 327
Mangelsdorf, D. J., 529, 533, 535, 544, 548, 550
Mangum, J. H., 186-88
Manies, E. C., 17, 25, 28
Mann, J. I., 216
Manner, G., 377
Manns, J. E., 96
Manoharan, K., 161
Manolagas, S. C., 481, 485, 529, 532, 533, 535, 539, 540, 545, 549, 550
Maoka, T., 276, 280, 281
Mapes, C. A., 135, 138, 139
Marcelis, J. H., 156, 167, 168
Marche, P., 588
Marcocci, C., 535, 539
Marconi, J., 486
Margen, S., 461, 469, 497, 499, 501
Marinho, H., 444
Marion, D. W., 185, 186
Marion, S. L., 528, 535, 537, 539, 542, 543, 545, 550
Markkanen, T., 322
Marks, P., 304
Marks, V., 500, 503, 506
Marks-Katz, M., 303
Marlin, D. W., 442, 444
Marmora, V., 441
Marone, C., 479
Marples, E., 375
Marquet, A., 331
Marsac, C., 330, 331
Marshall, E., 367
Marshall, R. A., 161
Marston, R., 411-13
Marthinsen, D., 170, 171
Martin, A. W., 6
Martin, D. C., 27
Martin, G. R., 372, 380
Martin, I., 443
Martin, J. C., 27-29
Martin, J. J., 180, 185-89
Martin, T. J., 533, 535
Martin, W. G., 196
Martinez, A., 108
Martinez-Torres, C., 28, 29
Martorell, R., 476, 501
Marusich, W. L., 284, 286
Marvel, J., 214
Marx, S. J., 528, 532, 535, 541, 542
Masaki, M., 68
Masawe, A. E. J., 146
Mason, D. K., 412
Mason, E., 116
Mason, J. I., 256
Mason, R. S., 536, 539
Masramon, J., 54, 57
Massaro, E. R., 546, 547
Masson, P. L., 135
Massry, S. G., 486
Master, R. W., 214
Masterson, B. J., 311
Mastriacovo, P., 391
Masuda, I., 230
Masuda, M., 69, 75
Masuda, N., 160
Masuda, Y., 81, 83, 85
Masumura, Y., 57
Mata, J. M., 379
Matarazzo, J. D., 438
Mathan, V. I., 162, 165, 172
Mather, J., 19, 30, 145
Mather, P., 443, 447
Mathews, M. M., 289
Mathews-Roth, M. M., 289-92
Mathisen, G. E., 156, 165, 166, 172
Matoth, Y., 24
Matsaniotis, N., 333
Matschinsky, F. M., 583
Matson, C. F., 134, 142
Matsui, I., 190, 191
Matsui, T., 550
Matsukura, N., 69, 75
Matsumoto, T., 68, 70, 71, 77-79, 536

Matsuno, T., 276-81
MATSUSHIMA, T., 67-94; 68, 77, 81, 87, 88
Matsushita, H., 79
Matsutaka, H., 276
Matsuura, T., 374, 375
Matsuzaki, S., 461, 462
Matsuzaki, T., 70, 71
Mattes, J. A., 120
Mattes, R. D., 450
Matthews, D. E., 499, 516
Matthews, R. G., 187
Matushima, T., 69, 75
Mauco, G., 566
Maurer, H., 86
Mavier, P., 462
Mayberry, W. R., 164
Mayer, E., 530
Mayer, J. H., 213, 214
Mayer, T. K., 215
Mayhew, J. A., 585
Mayo, P., 587
Mayoral, L. G., 165, 172
Mayuzumi, M., 505
Mazid, M. A., 227, 228, 231
McAdam, K. P. W. J., 139
McAllen, A. B., 99
McAllister, H. C., 320
McBee, R. H., 161, 162
McCaffrey, T. B., 463
McCain, T. A., 528-30, 534, 538, 540, 541
McCance, R. A., 498, 510
McCann, J., 68, 82, 84
McCann, P. P., 190
MCCARRON, D. A., 475-94; 477-82, 484-86, 488, 489
McCarthy, D. O., 137
McCarthy, K. D., 195
McCarthy, R. E., 157, 167, 168
McCay, P. B., 366, 391
McClain, C. J., 334
McClelland, S., 115
McConkey, C. L. Jr., 533
McCroskey, R. P., 385
McDonald, D. P., 213, 214
McDonald, I., 509, 511
McDonald, J. M., 214
McDonald, J. T., 461, 469
McDonald, R., 20
McDonough, K., 57
McDougal, D. B., 324
McElroy, L. W., 106
McFarlane, H., 146
McGarry, J. D., 42, 58, 387
McGee, D., 477, 478
McGeer, P. L., 410
McGovern, R. F., 259
McGrath, C. J., 479, 481
McGuffee, L. J., 489
McGuigan, J. E., 414
McGuire, D. M., 264
McGuire, M. K. B., 549
McGuire, V., 498
McHenry, E. W., 574
McIntosh, J. E. A., 45
McIntyre, W. R., 528, 535, 543
McKay, R. H., 20-23
McKenna, W. R., 463
McKinney, S., 360
McKroskey, R. P., 385
McLane, J. A., 21, 22
McLean, P., 213, 214, 585
McLelland, A. S., 460, 461, 468
McLennan, S., 215
McMahon, J. B., 425
McMurray, W. C., 572
McNab, G. M., 19, 30-33
McNamara, D. J., 264
McNamara, H., 375
McNeil, N. I., 166, 170
McNurlan, M. A., 517
McNutt, K. W., 216
McPherson, J. Jr., 186, 380
McRae, K. R., 254
McVoy, J. R. S., 320, 331
Meade, R. J., 190
Mecca, G., 54
Meenan, A., 250
Megson, A., 448
Mehlman, M. A., 57
Meiselman, H. L., 352
Mekhjian, H. S., 160
Melamed, E., 448
Melby, K. L., 148
Mellon, W. S., 536-38, 540, 546
Melmed, S., 586
Melville, D. B., 318
Mendenhall, C. L., 460, 461, 467-69
Menendez, L. A., 479
Menzies, R. C., 409
Mercado, D. L., 537
Mercer, E. I., 274
Mercer, N. J. H., 264
Merchant, G. J., 477
Merke, J., 535, 549
Merola, L. O., 213
Merrill, I. M., 146
Merrin, J. S., 570
Mertz, E. T., 226, 227, 229-31, 234, 235, 237, 239, 240
Mesbah, M. M., 101, 103
Mesguich, P., 536
Messaritakis, J., 333
Metailler, R., 230, 231
Metz, J., 187, 188
Metz, J. A., 479-81, 485, 486
Metzen, E. J., 354
Meyer, D. B., 285
Meyer, H., 161
Meyer, P., 588
Meyers, J., 163
Mezey, E., 461, 462, 466-68
Meznik, E., 215
Mezzina, C., 54
Michaelis, O. E. IV, 217
Michaelsson, G., 290
Michell, R. H., 580, 581, 584
Mickelson, O., 161, 303, 500, 503, 505
Midelfort, C. F., 390
Midgett, R. J., 385
Midtvedt, T., 156, 163-66
Mier, J. W., 140
Miettinen, T. A., 264
Mihalache, N., 217
Mikel'Saar, M. E., 156
Miki, W., 280
Mikol, Y. B., 419, 421, 422, 426
Milgrom, E., 546
Milich, R., 122-24
Millar, J. A., 488
Miller, B., 163
Miller, B. F., 261
Miller, D. L., 485
Miller, D. S., 501
Miller, F., 24
Miller, J. M., 214, 367, 438
Miller, L. R., 20, 21, 24, 25, 28, 29
Miller, R. S., 168
Miller, S. J., 251, 322
Miller, S. M., 372
Miller, T. L., 168, 171
Millikin, M. R., 227-29
Millington, D. S., 47
Mills, J. T., 252
Mills, P. R., 460, 461, 468
Millward, D. J., 516, 517
Milner, J., 498
Milsark, I. W., 143
Milton, J. T. B., 108
Mincu, I., 217
Miner, R. A., 122
Mingardi, G., 54
Minth, C. D., 373
Minty, B., 187
Mintz, S., 438
Miranda, P. M., 215
Mirouze, J., 215, 216
Mirrlees, D. J., 213, 216
Mishra, K. P., 513
Misiewicz, J. J., 216
Missala, K., 26, 28
Mitchell, A. D., 184, 192, 193
Mitchell, B. D., 25, 27, 28
Mitchell, G. E., 100
Mitchell, J. E., 310-13
MITCHELL, M. C., 457-74
Mitchell, R. M., 103, 104
Mitropoulos, K. A., 259, 260, 264
Mitschellen, J. J., 264, 265
Miyaura, C., 535, 548-50
Miyazawa, T., 68, 71, 79, 81

Mizel, S. B., 137, 139
Mizusaki, S., 68, 70, 81
Mizushima, Y., 366
Mock, D. M., 334
Modler, S., 168, 170
Moël, G. L., 186
Moertel, C. G., 391
Mogami, M., 69, 75
Mogensen, C. E., 213
Mohan, P., 48
Mohla, S., 534
Moldawer, L. L., 218
Mollin, D. L., 420
Molnar, G. D., 215
Moncion, A., 330
Mondon, C. E., 217
Monkus, E. F., 48-50, 57
Monnier, L. H., 215, 216
Monnier, M. P., 215, 216
Monnier, V. M., 215
Monro, J., 120
Montano, R. M., 255
Montgomery, R. D., 504, 506
Monti, M., 54, 55, 57
Montz, R., 529
Moody, J. B., 145, 148
Moore, L. L., 30, 31, 143
Moore, P., 191
Moore, S. M., 359
Moore, T., 281
Moore, W. E. C., 171
Moorehead, T. J., 374
Moorhead, J. F., 54, 57
Moorthy, A. V., 55
Moosa, A., 324
Mora, M., 56
Moreau, M.-C., 163
Morel, G., 536
Moretti, P., 329
Morey-Holton, E., 544
Moreyra, M., 517
Morgan, E. H., 18
Morgan, J. B., 506
Mori, K., 81, 83, 85
Mori, M., 76
Moriarty, R. J., 213, 214
Morino, K., 69, 75
Morishima, T., 216
Morishita, H., 47
Morita, K., 76, 366, 372, 373
Morley, J. E., 311
Morotomi, M., 158, 164
Morris, C. D., 477, 478, 482, 488
Morris, D. R., 191
Morris, K., 215
Morris, K. M., 384
Morris, P. M., 348
Morrison, A. D., 213, 214
Morrow, C. J., 255
Morrow, G. III, 186, 187
Morse, R. A., 460, 468
Morton, B., 416, 417
Morton, L. F., 377, 383
Morton, R. A., 283
Mosbach, E. H., 160, 264
Moscaritolo, R., 378
Moseley, J. M., 533, 535
Moser, K. M., 587
Moshang, T., 307
Mosher, D., 138
Mosher, H. S., 276
Moskowitz, H. R., 436
Moss, D., 217
Moss, J., 319
Motil, K. J., 499
Moyer, A. W., 318
Moyer, E. D., 140
Moyer, E. Z., 322
Mozingo, R., 318
Mucci, S. F., 137
Mudd, S. H., 183, 186, 187, 189, 190, 193, 198
Mueller, R. E., 106, 109
Mueller, R. L., 164
Muindi, J. M., 146
Muir, C. S., 67
Muir, J., 22, 23, 25
Muir, J. R., 25
Muirhead, P. A., 155, 156
Mukhtar, H., 291
Mulder, G. J., 3, 193, 196, 199
Muller, P., 380
Muller, P. K., 380
Müller, E., 487
Müller, R. K., 276
Müller, W., 384
Mulvany, M. J., 487
Mummery, R., 286
Munnich, A., 329-31
Munoz, R., 300
MUNRO, H. N., 1-12; 2, 3, 5-10, 515-17
Munson, D., 144
Muntzel, M. S., 479-81
Murad, S., 378, 379
Muraguchi, A., 139
Muramatsu, M., 81
Murer, H. J., 485
Murgatroyd, P. R., 498, 502
Muroya, H., 264
Murphy, P. A., 139
Murray, A. B., 146-48
Murray, C. J., 146-48
Murray, M. B., 146, 147
Murray, M. J., 146-48
Murray, M. W., 228
Murray, R. M., 301
Mursgin, R. A., 259
Murton, C. R., 216
Mussell, K., 355
Mustard, J. F., 581
Mutai, M., 158, 159, 161, 164
Muto, M., 587
Muto, Y., 6
Myant, N. B., 264
Myllylä, R., 381, 382
Myrtle, J. F., 530, 534

N

Naccarato, W. F., 565
Nagao, M., 68-71, 73, 76-80, 86, 87
Nagata, S., 276, 278, 279, 281
Nagaya, S., 47
Nagel, R. L., 566
Nagle, F. J., 46
Nahapetian, A., 566
Naidu, A. N., 501, 511
Naik, P., 29, 30
Naiman, J. L., 24
Nair, S., 68
Nakada, M., 537
Nakagawa, H., 197
Nakagawa, Y., 575
Nakai, C., 374
Nakajima, T., 47
Nakamura, M., 373
Nakanishi, S., 373
Nakano, M., 464
Nakao, Y., 550
Nakatsuru, Y., 69, 75
Nakayasu, M., 69, 73
Nakazato, F., 69, 73
Nalder, B. N., 33
Namba, T., 76
Nambudiri, A. M. D., 251, 253, 254
Nance, W. E., 322, 331
Nandi, B. K., 367
Nanno, M., 164
Napoli, J. L., 530, 540
Narasinga Rao, B. S., 501, 511, 516
Narisawa, K., 328
Narita, K., 71
Narita, M., 54, 55
Naruse, A., 190
Naso, A., 54, 57
Nasrallah, S. M., 469
Nathan, D. M., 215
Nauss, K. M., 32, 412, 414, 416-18, 421, 423
Navarro, M. P., 458
Nawa, H., 373
Neale, R. J., 33
Nedelec, J., 228
Neely, J. R., 46, 56, 57
Neer, R. M., 305
Negishi, C., 77, 81
Negishi, T., 76
Neill, C., 51, 54, 56, 58
Neims, A. H., 116, 121
Nellis, S. H., 57
Nelson, J. A., 254, 255
Nelson, J. D., 412
Nelson, P. J., 43, 388, 389

Nelson, R. A., 460, 468
Nelson, S. E., 24
Nesheim, M. C., 231, 233-35
Ness, G. C., 252
Nestel, P., 216
Netland, P. A., 357
Neudoerffer, T. S., 99
Neufeld, E. J., 579, 581, 582
Neufeld, H. A., 138
Neuman, P. A., 310
Neville, J. N., 460, 468
NEWBERNE, P. M., 407-32; 408, 411-24, 426
Newman, J. M., 356
Ney, K. A., 215
Ng, H., 328, 330
Nichaman, M., 477, 478
Nickerson, J. A., 565, 573
Nickols, S. Y., 354, 355
Nicod, M., 437
Nicol, B. M., 513
Nicolai, J. H., 97
Nicolette, J. A., 192
Nicolosi, R. J., 575
Nielsen, E., 498
Nietfeld, J. J., 377, 381
Nieuwenhuis, J., 139
Nilsson, O. S., 578
Nilsson-Ehle, P., 54, 55, 57
Nimrick, K., 101, 102
Nineham, R., 215, 216
Nisenson, A., 333
Nishigaki, I., 575, 586
Nishihara, M., 566
Nishimura, S., 68-70, 77-79, 86
Nishizuka, Y., 582
Nitowsky, H. M., 375
Nitzan, M., 52
Niwa, T., 69
Noack, K., 284, 285
Nogami, Y., 310
Noker, P. E., 187
Nolan, J. C., 378
Noland, B. J., 249
Nolle, S., 585
Nomura, F., 461, 462
Nomura, H., 80
Noon, J. P., 487
Nord, C. E., 164
Nordbro, S. A. N., 148
Nordin, I., 44, 387, 388, 390
Nordstrom, J. L., 264, 265
Norgan, N. G., 497, 509, 510, 514
Norin, K. E., 156, 165
Norman, A. W., 261, 262, 528-30, 532-40, 546, 547
Noronha, J. M., 411
Norris, F., 373
Norris, K. E., 373
North, J. A., 186
Nose, T., 227, 230, 231, 234, 235, 237, 240
Novak, M., 48-50, 57, 58
Novak, R. F., 387
Nozaki, M., 194, 374-76
Nozawa, Y., 572
Nussbaum, S. R., 305
Nussli, M., 191
Nuttall, F. Q., 115
Nyborg, N., 487
Nyby, M., 490
Nyhammar, T., 77
NYHAN, W. L., 317-43; 323, 325-31, 333

O

Oakes, B. W., 378, 380, 383
Obata, K. I., 373
Oberleas, D., 565, 566
Obert, K. A., 254
O'Brien, M., 167, 168
O'Brien, M. M., 211, 213
Ochs, H., 31
O'Connell, M. J., 391
Oddino, N., 330
O'Dea, K., 216
Odedra, B., 516
Odelhög, B., 374, 375
Odell, M., 133, 134
Oden, K. L., 180
Oei, J., 324
Oertel, W. H., 194
Oesch, F., 86
Offner, H., 587
Ogata, K., 318
Ogawa, H., 193
Ogier, H., 329-31
Ogino, C., 227-29
Ohara, Y., 76
Ohgaki, H., 69, 75
Ohira, Y., 23
Ohkuma, S., 196
Ohlson, M. A., 353
Ohlsson, A., 327
Ohnishi, E., 286, 287
Ohnishi, T., 464
Ohno, T., 286, 287
Ohrui, H., 318
Oikawa, A., 69, 70, 73
Oimatsu, H., 54, 55
Oja, S. S., 195
Oka, T., 191
Okada, G., 180
Okamatsu, H., 259
Okamoto, H., 68, 77, 373
Okamoto, T., 68-71, 77-79
Okamura, W. H., 530, 532
Okrent, D., 538
Okubadejo, M., 146
Okuda, K., 421, 428
Okudolo, B. E., 488
Oldroyd, R. G., 384, 385
Olefsky, J. M., 216, 217, 391
Oleggini, R., 54, 57
Oleinik, O. E., 191
Oleson, J. J., 412
Olorunsogo, O. O., 488
Olsen, B., 376
Olsen, W. A., 45
Olson, A. C., 170
Olson, J. A., 282
Olson, R. E., 30, 32, 248, 252, 415, 460, 468
Olsson, K., 77
Olsson, L., 54, 55, 57
Olsson, R., 77
O'Malley, K., 34
Omdahl, J. L., 547
Omond, S. A., 550
Onci, L., 261, 262
O'Neil, I. K., 68
Ong, A., 69, 73
Ong, E. S., 528
Onishi, T., 283
Ono, T., 254
Onstad, G. R., 334
Oo, M., 304
Oomen, H. A. P. C., 520
Ophir, I., 442
Opie, L. H., 55
Oppel, T. W., 322
Oppenheim, J. J., 137, 139, 140
Oppenheimer, S. J., 145, 148
Oppitz, K. H., 33
Orci, L., 584
Orf, J. W., 540
Orlov, S. N., 487, 488
Orme, L. E., 228
Oro, A., 528
O'Rourke-Locasio, S., 160
Orr, J. P., 565, 573
Ortiz, B., 351, 354, 355
Ortiz de Montellano, P. R., 254
Orzali, A., 49, 50, 57
Osaki, S., 135
Osborn, M., 119
Osborne, T. F., 248, 249
Osdoby, P., 548
Osis, D., 488
Oski, F. A., 24, 26, 28, 29, 118, 144
Oslage, H. J., 565
Öste, R., 77
Oster, H., 441
Oster, J. R., 311
Ott, D. B., 261
Oursler, M. J., 548
Ouyet, J., 537
Overbeck, H., 489
Owen, O. E., 214
Owens, D. R., 215
Owens, F. N., 96, 101, 102
Oyama, V. I., 564
Oyler, J. R., 118

P

Pace, J. G., 138
Pacioni, D., 215
Packard, C. J., 259
Packer, L., 20-22
Packman, S., 188, 197, 326-30, 335
Padilla, M., 196
Page, J. W., 228, 237, 238
Page, M. G., 211, 213
Paglia, L., 380
Pagliara, A. S., 324
Paik, W. K., 43, 387
Pain, V. M., 517
Pajula, R.-L., 191
Palella, T. D., 185, 192
Palmano, K. P., 584, 585
Palmatier, R. D., 385
Palmer, F. B. St. C., 567, 571
Palmer, J. K., 168
Palmer, R. L., 299, 300
Palossy, B., 304
Palti, H., 30
Pamphile, R., 546
Pande, H., 324
Pangborn, R. M., 434-37, 450, 451
Panini, S. R., 247, 248, 251, 254, 255, 257, 259
Panush, R. S., 391
Paolucci, B., 348
Papadopoulos, N. J., 372
Papastephanidis, C., 334
Pape, J. M., 485
Papiernik, E., 24
Paquet, S., 24
Paquette, M. B., 356
Parducci, A., 450
Parish, E. J., 255
Pařísková, J., 507, 508, 510
Pariza, M. W., 68
Parker, D., 56
Parker, D. S., 163
Parker, I. D., 137
Parker, R. A., 251
Parker, T. S., 264
Parker, W. D., 42, 329, 331
Parks, J. S., 307
Parrott, D. P., 378
Parsons, H. T., 318, 322
Parsons, N. D., 116
Parthasarathy, R., 589
Partridge, J. J., 550
Pasantes-Morales, H., 195
Pascal, T. A., 189
Pascoe, G. A., 34
Pascu, F., 48
Pascual, A., 528, 535, 543
Pascual, F. P., 227
Pask, H. T., 56
Pasqua, J. J., 215
Passmore, R., 461, 462, 505, 509-11
Pastoureaud, A., 228
Patek, A. J., 467, 468
Patel, A. K., 57, 116, 288
Paternita, J. R. Jr., 261
Pathak, M. A., 290, 291
Patni, V. M., 477
Patsch, J. R., 259
Patterson, S., 373
Patwardhan, V. N., 513
Paul, H. H., 367
Paul, O., 477, 478
Paul, R., 259
Pauling, L., 391
PAULSON, D. J., 41-66; 58, 386
Paulus, H., 570
Pavlatos, T. N., 190
Paxton, R., 519
Payne, P. R., 499
Payne, R. B., 585
Paz, M. A., 376, 378, 384
Pazoles, C. J., 372
Pearce, J., 335
Pearson, D. J., 120
Pearson, J. M., 354
Pearson, M. A., 144
Peck, G. L., 261
Pecore, S. D., 435, 437, 451
Pecsuvac, K., 48
Peeke, H. V. S., 120
Peffley, D., 250
Pegg, A. E., 185, 190-92
Pegg, L. E., 548, 550
Pekala, P., 141
Pekala, P. H., 141, 142
Pekarek, R., 138, 139
Pekarek, R. S., 134, 138
Pelchat, M. L., 438, 442
Peller, J., 582
Pelucchetti, D., 56
Penfield, M. P., 347, 355, 359, 360
Peng, S. K., 262
Penn, D., 48-50, 54, 57
Penn-Walker, D., 50
Penniall, R., 464
Pentlow, B. D., 305
Pequignot, G., 420
Pereda, T., 460, 461, 469
Perez, C., 460, 461, 469
Perfumo, F., 54, 57
Perkkiö, M. V., 20-24
Perman, E. S., 461, 462
Perman, J. A., 168, 170
Pernot, F., 479, 481
Perret, B., 578
Perret, C., 551
Perry, J., 187
Perry, L. W., 56
Persaud, J. W., 54, 57
Person, R., 20, 21, 25, 28, 31
Peter, H. W., 578
Peterfy, C., 535
Peterkin, B. B., 348, 349
Peterkofsky, B., 378-81
Peters, H. A., 56
Peterson, C. M., 214
Peterson, D. A., 582
Peterson, M. J., 211, 213, 214
Peterson, R. G., 585
Peterson, R. M., 333
Peterson, V. E., 391
Peterson, W. H., 318, 320, 322
Petkovich, P. M., 544
Petó, E., 446
Peto, R., 67
Petrelli, F., 329
Pevsner, B., 30
Pfeffer, E., 228
Phanselkar, S. V., 513
Philippot, J. R., 262
Philips, S. M., 160
Phillips, A. M. Jr., 228
Phillips, B. P., 148
Phillips, D. E., 351, 358
Phillips, M., 515
Phillips, P. G., 513
Phillips, W. A., 254
Phillipson, A. T., 161
Phirwa, S., 250, 254, 255, 257
Pick, A.-M., 188
Pickard, M. R., 580
Pickeral, S. F., 137
Picou, D., 506, 515, 516
Piekarski, J., 572, 579
Pieklik, J. R., 461, 463
Pieper, A., 228
Pierce, E. A., 528, 535, 539, 543
Pierre, Y., 195
Pierzchala, P. A., 568
Piez, K. A., 376
Pihl, R. O., 125
Pihlajaniemi, T., 378
Piik, K., 191
Pik, J. R., 572
Pikaar, N. A., 170
Pike, D. A., 214
Pike, J. W., 528-30, 532, 533, 535, 536, 539-44, 547, 548, 550
Pilgrim, F. J., 449
Pilistine, S. J., 7
Pillemer, L., 384
Pilström, L., 464
Pilz, R. B., 185
Pineda, O., 479, 482
Pinkos, J. A., 106
Pinnell, S. R., 378, 379
Pirola, R. C., 461, 462
Pispa, J., 320
Pitkanen, E., 586
Pitney, A. L., 410
Pitot, H. C., 259, 264, 518, 548

Pizzo, S. V., 215
Pizzolato, G., 318
Plant, S. B., 489
Plaut, A. G., 166
Playfair, L., 4
Pleasant, J. R., 160, 162
Pleasure, D., 569
Pliner, P., 437, 438, 442, 443, 445, 446, 448, 451
Poe, W. E., 232-35, 237, 238, 240
Poirier, L. A., 419, 421, 422, 426, 427
Pokudin, N. I., 487, 488
Pola, P., 54, 57, 58
Polak, J. M., 373
Polak, K. L., 378
Poliak, S. C., 261
Polivy, J., 346, 448
Pollak, A., 215
Pollard, H., 372, 373
Pollard, H. B., 372
Pollard, S., 285
Pollitt, E., 26, 30, 117-19
Pollitt, R. J., 323, 328, 330
Pollycove, M., 24
Polsinelli, L. F. Jr., 386
Ponniah, J., 165, 172
Poole, J. R., 183, 186, 189, 193, 198
Popa, E., 217
Pope, H. G., 313
Pope, J. A., 227, 228
Popjak, G., 250
Popkin, B. M., 348, 349
Popper, H., 467
Porte, D., 214
Portemer, C., 194, 195
Porter, J. W., 259, 264, 322
Porter, P. N., 197
Porter, R. R., 384
Portman, J., 506
Pösö, H., 191
Possmayer, F., 572
Post, G., 239
Postnov, Y. V., 487, 488
Postolnikov, S. F., 291
Poston, H. A., 236-39
Potkin, S. G., 119
Potter, J. E. R., 252
Potter, J. F., 218
Potter, J. J., 461, 462, 467, 469
Potter, V. R., 518
Powanda, M. C., 133, 138-40
Powell, C. T., 373
Powers, P. S., 309
Powers, R. D., 359
Prahl, J. M., 539, 543
Pramanik, B. C., 530
Prasad, J. S., 19, 30-32
Prather, E. S., 217
Preiss, B., 248
Preiss, R., 487
Prendergast, P. J., 500, 508
Prentice, A. M., 497, 498, 502
Prentki, M., 583
Preti, G., 326, 327
Price, D. W., 348
Price, J., 373
Price, P. A., 549
Price, R. A., 438
Prineas, R. J., 477
Prins, R. A., 157, 160, 161, 163
Printz, A. M., 299
Prinz, R. J., 115, 122, 123
Prinz, W., 391
Prior, R. L., 98
Pritchard, P. H., 185
Prockop, D. J., 376-78, 381
Procsal, D. A., 532
Proffitt, J. H., 195
Proud, V. K., 322, 331
Provvedini, D. M., 529, 533, 535, 545, 549, 550
Prpic, V., 569
Pruitt, R. E., 388, 389
Prümke, H. J., 487
Pruzansksy, J., 412
Prynne, C. J., 378
Pryzwansky, K. B., 31
Puck, T. T., 380
Pudelski, J., 508
Pugliese, M. T., 303
Puig, J. G., 465-67
Puistola, U., 377, 378, 381
Pullinger, C. R., 250, 256
Puls, W., 216
Purkiss, P., 187
Purser, D. B., 99
Putnam, G. B., 228
Pyle, R. L., 310-13
Pyzyrembel, H., 180

Q

Quackenbush, F. W., 259
Quigley, M. E., 115
Quinn, R. S., 378

R

Rachal, E., 255
Rachele, J. R., 407, 410
Radcliffe, B. C., 105
Raddino, R., 57
Radford, A. J., 441
Radparvar, S., 538, 546
Radziuk, J., 216
Rae, J., 437
Raetz, H. M., 320
Raffin, S. B., 34
Ragin, R., 190, 197
Ragione, F. D., 185, 192
Rahbar, S., 214
Rahman, M. A., 227, 228
Raibaud, P., 163
Raina, A. M., 185, 186, 191
Rainbird, A. L., 215
Raines, P. S., 288
Rajagopalan, K. V., 198
Rajamäki, P., 191
Rajan, D., 165, 172
Rajaram, R., 55
Rajashekhar, B., 372
Ramadori, G., 139
Ramakrishnan, R., 33
Ramamurti, L., 321
Ramesha, C. S., 259
Ramirez, H., 264
Ramirez, R., 509
Ramjit, H. G., 47
Ramos, A. C. M. F., 57
Ramsey, F., 116, 117
Rand, W. M., 505, 513, 514
Rand, W. R., 499, 513
Randall, E., 352
Randall, H. T., 138
Randle, P. J., 56, 519
Ranganathan, S., 251, 253, 254
Ranney, H. M., 214
Ransom, D. H., 194
Rao, B. S. N., 26, 28
Rao, N. G. S., 228
Rao, N. V., 381
Rao, R. H., 570
RAPOPORT, J. L., 113-30; 117, 121-24
Rappaport, U., 228
Rapport, M. M., 27
Rasch, C. A., 24
Rasmussen, B., 54, 55
Rasmussen, H., 536
Rasmussen, K., 325
Ratashekhar, B., 372
Rau, J. H., 313
Rau, W., 274
Raub, T. J., 8
Ravid, A., 542, 547
Ravussin, E., 219
Rawberg, A. H., 142
Ray, R., 538
Ray, R. E., 565, 573
Rayfield, E. J., 133
Reaburn, J. A., 359
Read, N. W., 171
Reaven, G. M., 217
Rebec, G. V., 126
REBOUCHE, C. J., 41-66; 42-47, 49, 51, 54, 56, 386, 387, 390
Recasens, M., 194
Reddi, A. H., 376
Reddi, A. L., 215
Reddy, B. S., 160
Reddy, C. C., 568
Reddy, S., 146
Reddy, V., 19, 30, 32
Redman, B. J., 351, 354
Redman, C. M., 571

Reed, D. J., 190, 477, 478
Reed, W. D., 248, 461, 462
Rees, L. H., 373
Reeve, A. W., 147
Refino, C., 18-22
Refino, C. A., 19, 21, 23, 27
Refino, C. J., 20-22
Reger, R. A., 351
Rehbein, M., 373
Reichard, P., 19, 32
Reid, F. A., 532, 534, 535
Reid, J. V. O., 411-13
Reid, K. B. M., 384
Reid, R. L., 108
Reilly, M. D., 351, 355-57
Reina, J. C., 509, 511
Reiner, J. M., 264
Reinhardt, T. A., 530, 535, 540
Reinitz, G. L., 228
Reiser, S., 217
Reitsma, P., 548, 550
Reitsma, P. H., 548, 552
Reizenstein, P., 303
Remmer, H., 33
Rennie, M. J., 516
Renström, B., 276
Rérat, A., 161
Resing, K., 191
Retey, J., 374, 375
Rettura, G., 291, 388, 389
Revelle, W., 115
Rey, A., 24
Reynertson, R., 574, 584, 585
Reyniers, J. P., 162
Reynolds, G. A., 248, 378, 379
Reznek, R. H., 586
Reznikova, M. B., 488
Rhoads, C. P., 332
Rhoads, G. G., 500
Rhode, T. D., 215
Ricard, C. A., 261
Riccardi, G., 215
Ricci, G., 196
Rice, P. J., 487
Rich, A., 137
Richards, H. H., 185
Richards, R. I., 551
Richards, S., 451
Richardson, E. N., 216
Richardson, J. M., 385
Richardson, S., 354
Richardson, W., 138
Richter, B. G., 101, 103
Richter, C. P., 436, 447
Richter, D., 373
Richter, H. W., 367
Riddle, D. B., 123
Rifkin, H., 211
Rigby, W. F. C., 550
Rigotti, N. A., 305
Riis, R. C., 238
Riley, A. M., 360
Riley, J. L., 540
Rimoldi, M., 47, 56
Ringler, D. H., 139
Ringler, M. B., 261
Ringold, G. M., 142, 143
Ringrose, R. C., 228
Riottot, M., 158
Riskey, D. R., 450
Risteli, J., 377
Ritz, E., 535, 549
Rivellese, A., 215
Rivers, J. M., 358, 359
Rivers, J. W. P., 499
Rivier, C., 373
Rivier, J., 373
Rix, K. J. B., 119, 120
Rizek, R. L., 348
Rizzo, W. B., 53
Rizzoli, V., 388
Rjazhsky, G. G., 488
Roatta, L. L., 464
Robert, C. H., 124
Roberton, A. M., 168
Roberts, A. B., 261, 291
Roberts, D. F., 499
Roberts, P. A., 540
Roberts, R. M., 8
Roberts, W. A., 115, 122
Robertson, J. B., 169-71
Robertson, W. B., 377
Robey, C., 213, 214
Robins, E., 300
Robinson, B. H., 324, 326, 327
Robinson, E. H., 232-35, 237, 238, 240
Robinson, I. M., 156
Robles-Valdes, C., 58
Rocco, M. D., 330
Roche, P. A., 374
Rochman, H., 214
Rød, T. O., 164
Rodan, G. A., 549
Rodemann, H. P., 138, 139
Roderuck, C., 322, 351
Roderuck, C. E., 351
Rodnan, G. P., 466
Rodrigues, L. M., 580
Rodriguez, D. B., 277, 278
Rodriguez, M. A., 169-71
Rodwell, V. W., 249, 251, 264, 265
Roe, C. R., 47, 52
Roebuck, B. D., 418
Roediger, W. E. W., 170
Roelofsen, B., 578
Roesch, P. K., 412
Roeser, H. P., 391
ROGERS, A. E., 407-32; 418-23, 426
Rogers, A. I., 311
Rogers, D. H., 247, 248, 251, 264
Rogers, J., 8
Rogers, L. S., 198
Rogers, P. J., 448
Roggin, G. M., 468
Rognstad, R., 463
Roheim, P. S., 258
Roitman, E., 515
Rojas, L., 482
Rollman, O., 290
Rolls, B. J., 448, 449
Rolls, E. T., 448, 449
Romshe, C. A., 46, 47, 51
Rönneberg, H., 276
Roos, B. A., 373
Roose, S. P., 313
Root, A. W., 56
Rosbach, D. O., 146
Rose, C. S., 318, 319
Rose, G. A., 504, 510
Rose, S., 538
Rose, W. C., 100
Rosemann, E., 215
Rosen, J. F., 532, 535, 542
Rosenberg, L. E., 188, 197
Rosenberg, R. C., 372
Rosenberry, T. L., 385
Rosenblatt, D. S., 186
Rosenblatt, S., 138
Rosenblum, M., 55
Rosenstreich, D. L., 139
Rosenwasser, L. J., 137, 139, 140
Ross, F. C., 261
Ross, F. P., 536, 539
Ross, H., 211
Ross, J. P., 96
Rossi, C. S., 58
Rossio, J. L., 137
Rossof, A. H., 550
Roth, E. S., 195, 196, 374
Roth, J., 261, 262
Roth, K. S., 326, 327, 329
Roth, S., 566
Rothberg, P. G., 548, 552
Rothman, J. E., 578
Rothman, R., 329
Rothman, S. S., 578
Rothwell, N. J., 217, 504, 506
Rotimi, V. O., 165, 166
Rotter, J., 444
Rotter, M. A., 194-96
Rout, M., 228
Rouzer, C. A., 140, 215
Rovetto, M. J., 57
Rowe, D. W., 549, 552
Rowe, E. A., 448, 449
Rowe, L. B., 381
Rowland, I. R., 157, 171
Rowold, E., 214
Roy, C., 186
Royal, P. M., 530
Roy-Byrne, P., 312
Rozin, E., 437
ROZIN, P., 433-56; 352, 357, 433-47, 451

Rubaltelli, F. F., 49, 50, 57
Rubenstein, A. H., 214
Rubin, E., 463-65, 467
Rubin, J., 391
Rubinstein, A., 261
Rucker, M. H., 359, 441, 446
Rude, R. K., 542, 548
RUDNEY, H., 245-72; 247, 248, 251, 253-59, 261
Rumsey, G. L., 231, 233-39
Rumsey, J. M., 117, 121
Rundgren, M., 374-76
Rupp, W. M., 215
Ruppert, S., 373
Ruppin, H., 164, 170
Rushmore, T., 426
Rusiniak, K. W., 436, 442
Russell, D. M., 500, 508
Russell, G. F. M., 301, 311, 359, 441, 446
Russell, M., 120
Russell, R. G. G., 549
Rutherford, D., 3
Rutledge, M. M., 322
Rüttimann, A., 276
Ryan, J. L., 139
Ryder, R. E. J., 215
Rydning, A., 53
Ryo, H., 69, 74

S

Sabaut, J. J., 227, 231, 234, 237
Sabine, E. J. R., 248, 313
Sabry, J. H., 351, 358
Sachan, D. S., 387
Sacks, J. C., 145
Saco-Pollitt, C., 30
Sacquet, E., 158
Sadalla, E., 360
Sadeghian, K., 570
Saeki, H., 70
Saeshima, M., 277
Saewert, M. D., 386
Sagara, K., 486
Sages, R., 213, 214
Sagotsky, G., 444
Saheki, T., 518
Sainz, E., 479
Saito, H., 81
Saito, I., 375
Saito, J., 374
Saito, K., 227
Saito, T., 230
Saito, Y., 81
Sakaguchi, S., 279
Sakai, R., 550
Sakai, T., 191
Sakakibara, S., 194-96
Sakamoto, H., 69, 73
Sakamoto, M., 227
Sakamoto, Y., 190
Sakata, T., 159
Sakate, M., 280
Sakati, N. A., 327
Sakurai, T., 164, 574
Salanitro, J. P., 155, 156
Salathe, L. E., 348, 349, 357
Salazar, A., 482
Salcedo, L., 378
Saleh, J. W., 305
Salfeld, J., 8
Saliternik, R., 217
Salmon, H. A., 21-23, 25
Salmon, W. D., 421
Saltman, P., 14, 20, 23
Salvetti, N. N., 355
Salway, J. G., 585, 586
Salyers, A. A., 157, 160, 166-68
Samejima, K., 191
Sampsell, R. N., 566
Samson, G., 460, 468
Sanadi, D. R., 57
Sander, J. E., 335
Sander, S., 217
Sanders, K. M., 444
Sandor, A., 48, 388, 389
Sandstead, H., 302, 305
Sandusky, A., 450
Sanjur, D., 351, 352, 355, 356, 358, 359
Santeusanio, F., 214
Santidrian, S., 517
Santoro, L., 196
Santus, R., 290
Sapienza, D. A., 106
Sapper, H., 367
Sar, M., 532-35
Sarandria, J. L., 414
Saravis, C. A., 137, 138
Sarcione, S. L., 578
Sarett, H. P., 322
Sasaki, K., 550
Sasaki, M., 69, 73
Sass, N. L., 196
Satake, M., 280
Satchell, P. M., 214
Satia, B. P., 227
Sato, M., 47, 57
Sato, N., 461, 462
Sato, P., 366
Sato, S., 68, 69, 75-77, 81, 87
Sato, T., 550
Sato, Y., 87
Satoh, T., 328
Satyanarayana, K., 501, 511
Sauberlich, H. E., 391
Saucier, S. E., 250, 257
Saudek, C., 214
Saudek, C. D., 214
Sauder, D. N., 139
Saudubray, J.-M., 329, 330
Saunders, M., 324, 326, 327, 329
Saunders, M. E., 326
Saunders, M. G., 467, 468
Saunders, W., 312
Saurat, J. H., 330
SAVAGE, D. C., 155-78; 155-60, 162-66, 171, 172
Savage, W. E., 145
Savi, L., 57, 58
Savica, V., 54
Savilahti, E., 24
Sawachika, T., 286, 287
Scallen, T. J., 249, 255
Scandurra, R., 196
Schaefer, A. E., 360
Schafer, K. H., 33
Schafer, R. B., 351, 359
Schaffer, W. T., 464
Schaffner, F., 180
Schanche, J.-S., 185
Schecter, M. D., 121
Schedl, H. P., 485
Scheid, C. R., 487
Scheig, L., 458
Schelling, G. T., 102
Schenk, E. A., 172
Scherphof, G. L., 572
Schiavoni, E. S. Jr., 254
Schiedt, K., 276, 280-85
Schiff, D., 48
Schiller, D., 445, 446
Schiller, W. R., 133, 134
Schimke, R. T., 518
Schimmel, S., 56
Schleiffer, R., 479, 481
Schlenk, F., 190
Schmale, H., 373
Schmechel, D. E., 194
Schmeck, G., 487
Schmid, R., 34
Schmidt, I. M., 305
Schmidt, P. J., 284
Schmidt-Sommerfeld, E., 48-50, 54, 57
Schmitt, M. G. Jr., 170
Schmouder, R. L., 477, 478
Schnackenberg, R. C., 121
Schnarr, M., 537
Schneider, D. L., 196
Schneider, J. F., 199
Schneidman, R. J., 485
Schnoes, H. K., 261, 262, 528-30, 533, 538
Schofield, C., 498, 503-5
Schofield, W. N., 498, 503-5, 516
Scholte, H. R., 56, 324
Scholtens, E., 193, 196, 199
Scholz, R., 463
Schonfeld, G., 260, 264
Schorr, B. C., 351
Schotman, A. J. H., 139
Schrader, J., 185

Schram, V. R., 354
Schrimper, R. A., 349, 351
Schroeder, H. A., 477
Schroeder, M.-L., 186
Schroeder, W. A., 214
Schroepfer, G. J. Jr., 251, 256
Schuab, E., 122-24
Schubert, W. K., 24
Schubik, P., 81, 83, 85, 87
Schuh, S., 186
Schull, J., 446
Schultz, F., 122-24
Schultz, L. H., 107
Schultz, S. G., 159
Schulz, I., 583
Schulz, V. E., 565
Schuster, E. M., 512
Schuster, G. S., 261
Schütz, G., 373
Schutz, H. G., 359, 434, 441, 446, 449
Schütz, W., 185
Schwachman, H., 24
Schwartz, C. J., 587
Schwartz, E., 310, 376, 378, 380, 384
Schwartz, H. C., 20-25
Schwartz, T. W., 373
Schwarz, R. I., 378, 379, 381
Schwerin, H. S., 360
Scott, D., 333
Scott, G. C., 102
Scott, J. H., 372
Scott, J. M., 186, 187
Scott, M. L., 237, 238
Scott, P., 68
Scott, S., 217
Scribner, J. D., 83
Scrimshaw, N. S., 30, 131, 145, 411, 415, 499, 513, 514
Scriver, C. R., 183, 186, 189
Seakins, J. W. T., 324, 328, 330
Sealock, R. R., 375
Searle, B. M., 489
Sebrell, W. H. Jr., 565
Seccombe, D. W., 47, 48, 58
Seckler, D., 501
Secor McVoy, J. R., 320, 331
Sedman, A. J., 461, 462
Sedvall, G., 117
Segal, S., 326, 327, 329, 569, 587
Seib, P. A., 366
Seidenfeld, J., 192
SEIFTER, S., 365-406; 43, 291, 376, 377, 380, 383, 388, 389
Seiler, K., 20, 21
Seiler, N., 190
Seino, Y., 68, 71, 534, 536
Seitonen, O., 216
Seitz, C. P., 118
Sells, C. J., 115
Semenza, G., 320
Sen, N. P., 410
Sen, P. R., 228
Senst, S., 535
Serdarevich, B., 259
Sered, B. R., 33, 144
Serog, B., 550
Serricchio, M., 57, 58
Service, F. J., 215
Seshadri, S., 29, 30
SEXTON, R. C., 245-72; 254-59, 261
Seyfred, M. A., 583
Seyfried, C. E., 191
Shaffer, P. M., 385
Shafrir, E., 217
Shah, E., 410
Shamberger, R. J., 291
Shane, B., 187
Shani, S., 532, 541, 542, 547
Shankar, R., 513
Shanks, A. M., 228
Shanks, W. E., 231, 239
Shantakumari, S., 165, 172
Shapiro, J. J., 264
Shapiro, R., 86
Shapiro, S., 289
Sharer, N., 187
Sharma, K. N., 436
Sharma, S. D., 436
Shastri, K. M., 587
Shaw, S., 464
Shears, S. B., 584
Sheets, J. J., 256
Shefer, S., 264
Sheffy, B. E., 161
Shekelle, R., 477, 478
Shekelle, R. B., 550
Sheltawy, A., 571
Shen, T. F., 380
Shenai, J. P., 48, 49
Shenkin, A., 460, 461, 468
Shennan, A. T., 49
Shepard, T. H., 24, 25
Shepherd, J., 259
Shepherd, N. D., 574
Sheppard, H., 499
Sher, E., 535, 545
Sherman, A. R., 32, 33
Sherman, W. R., 568, 579, 583
Shertzer, H., 258
Sherwood, W. G., 326, 327
Shetty, P. S., 499, 500, 504-6, 517
Shevchenko, A., 487
Shichiri, M., 461, 462
Shidoji, Y., 6
Shigehisa, S., 195, 196
Shigeta, Y., 461, 462
Shih, V. E., 198
Shiina, Y., 542, 549, 550
Shimada, M., 69
Shimaya, M., 277
Shimazu, H., 375
Shimeno, S., 227, 228, 280
Shimomura, M., 197
Shin, H. K., 190
Shinji, Y., 587
Shinki, T., 535, 542
Shinnar, S., 186
Shinomiya, A., 227
Shinozuka, H., 426
Shiomi, T., 68, 71, 77-79, 81
Shirahata, A., 191
Shirai, A., 68
Shiraki, K., 515
Shishibori, T., 254
Shiuey, S.-J., 86
Shivapurkar, N., 419, 427
Shively, J. E., 385
Shoji, T., 54, 55
Shone, C. C., 288
Shorter, R. G., 158
Shott, R. J., 24
Shown, E. P., 250
Shrago, E., 46, 54, 55, 57
Shudo, K., 68-71, 77-79
Shug, A. L., 45, 51, 54-58
Shulman, R., 118
Shum, T. Y. P., 572
Shuman, C. R., 214
Shumate, J. B., 56
Shuttleworth, K., 191
Siat, M., 191
Sidell, N., 536
Siegel, J. E., 158, 160
Siegel, P. S., 449
Siena, M., 44
Siggaard-Anderson, O., 477, 479
Sigman, G., 27
Siimes, M. A., 14, 17-20, 24, 25, 28, 32
Silbergeld, E. K., 115
Silberstein, H. E., 375
Siliprandi, D., 58
Siliprandi, N., 54, 57, 58, 388
Silis, V., 481, 485
Silman, I., 579
Silva, M., 119
Silverio, J., 48, 57
Silverman, J. A., 302
Silverman, M., 410, 411
Sima, A. A. F., 213
Simeon, J. G., 122-24
Simko, V., 460, 461, 468
Simmonds, M., 306
Simon, H., 374, 375
Simon, L., 115
Simoons, F. J., 437
Simpson, H. C. R., 216
Simpson, K. L., 227, 228, 231, 277, 278, 284
Simpson, R. C., 197

Simpson, R. U., 532, 533, 535, 537, 546, 547
Simpson, R. W., 216
Sims, L. S., 348, 351, 358, 359
Sin, A. W., 228
Sinensky, M., 250
Singal, S. A., 332
Singer, D. E., 215
Singer, F. R., 541
Singer, H. S., 186
Singer, T. P., 194
Singh, B. B., 261
Singh, D., 487
Singh, H. T., 283
Singh, J., 510
Singh, M. M., 119
Singla, P. N., 24
Sinnhuber, R. O., 228
Sintu, E., 217
Sipe, J. D., 139
Siperstein, M. D., 248, 250, 258
Sipple, H. L., 216
Sirisinha, S., 415
Sirota, J. H., 466
Sisler, H. D., 256
Sisson, T. R. C., 24
Sistrom, W. R., 289
Sivarajah, A., 378, 379
Sivén, V. C., 4
Sjödin, B., 508
Skarz˙yn, B., 198, 199
Skeaff, C. M., 581
Sketcher, R. D., 519
Skiba, W. E., 187, 188
Skinner, J. D., 355
Skotland, T., 372
Skovby, F., 188
Skulberg, O., 276
Skyler, J., 213
Slaby, F., 580
Slack, J., 499
Slag, M. F., 115
Slakey, L. L., 259, 264
Slaughter, R. S., 385
Sleator, N. M., 528, 545, 546
Sligesada, K., 518
Slinger, S. J., 228
Sloan, R. S., 482, 483
Slocu, L. A., 68
Slonim, A. E., 52
Slordahl, S., 148
Sloviter, R. S., 535, 536
Smallwood, D., 348-50
Smart, R., 102
Smart, R. C., 391
Smeets, H. G. W., 28
Smith, A. H., 100
Smith, B. J., 566
Smith, C. D., 571
Smith, C. J., 163
Smith, C. L., 477
Smith, D. C., 321, 322
Smith, E. E., 445
Smith, E. L., 477, 482, 483
Smith, J. L., 47
Smith, J. S., 96, 97, 103
Smith, L. C., 264
Smith, L. L., 257
Smith, M. E., 437
Smith, M. R., 186
Smith, P. M., 489
Smith, R. A., 190, 192
Smith, R. H., 99, 104, 105
Smith, S., 125
Smolen, J. S., 140
Smolin, L. A., 188, 190, 193
Smyth, D. G., 373
Snedden, W., 324
Snell, E. E., 318, 319
Snellen, J. E., 158, 160
Snider, R., 378
Snoswell, A. M., 186-88
Snow, P., 216
Snyder, L. M., 28
Snyderman, S. E., 515
Soares, J. H., 537
Soberón, G., 518
Sobocinski, P. Z., 135, 138, 139
Sochor, M., 213, 214
Soeldner, J. S., 214
Soemantri, A. G., 30
Soergel, K. H., 170
Sohr, R., 487
Solberg, H. E., 53
Solimano, G., 116, 117
Solinas, S., 196
Solinek, V. A., 81
Solms, J., 434
Solomon, R. L., 445
Soloway, A. H., 256
Solt, P. F., 360
Soothill, J. F., 120
Sorensen, O. H., 540
Sorlie, P. D., 477, 478
Sorrell, M. F., 320
Soula, G., 573
Sourkes, T. L., 26, 28
Sours, J. A., 305
Southgate, D. A. T., 168
Southworth, M., 160
Sowers, J. E., 190
Sowers, J. R., 481, 485
Spach, P. I., 463, 464
Spady, D. K., 258, 263
Spaeth, D. G., 196
Spanheimer, R., 380
Spanheimer, R. G., 381
Spector, H., 515
Spector, R., 189, 565, 568, 569
Speer, D. P., 529, 532
Spellacy, E., 324
Spencer, H., 488
Spencer, J. A., 254
Spencer, R. P., 320
Spencer, T. A., 250, 254, 255, 257
Spiess, J., 373
Spiller, G. A., 167
Spindel, E. R., 373
Spinelli, J., 284
Spingarn, N. E., 68
Spires, H. E., 105
Spirito, R. A., 17
Spirnak, J., 479, 485
Sporn, M. B., 261, 291
Spragg, R., 587
Spring, B. J., 115, 123, 126
Spring, J. A., 458
Sprynarova, S., 507, 508
Spurr, G. B., 509, 511
Srikantia, S. G., 19, 30, 32
Sriratanaban, A., 24
Stacewicz-Sapuncakis, M., 288
Stacey, T. E., 47, 52
Stacpoole, P. W., 391
Stacy, T., 550
Stafford, K., 354, 367
Stanford, N., 579
Stang, D. J., 450
Stange, E. F., 263
Stangler, R. S., 299
Stanley, C. A., 51, 52, 57
Stanley, P. A., 305
Stanley, R. A., 168
Stanton, J. L., 360, 477, 478
Stassen, F. I. H., 378
Steckbeck, S. R., 254
Steele, R. D., 192, 193, 195
Steelman, V. P., 359
Stein, R., 387
Steinberg, A. D., 140
Steinberg, D., 257, 259
Steiner, J. E., 436
Steinkamp, R. C., 353
Stekel, A., 14, 17, 18, 29, 32
Stephen, A. M., 166
Stephen, J. M. L., 504, 514, 518, 519
Stern, C. M. M., 324
Stern, J., 569
Stern, N., 481, 485, 490
Stern, P. H., 532
Stevens, B., 248
Stevens, C. E., 160
Stevens, D. L., 52
Stevens, V. J., 215
Stevenson, I. H., 34
Stewart, A. M., 441
Stewart, D. N., 100
Stewart, J. T., 313
Stewart, M. G., 165-67
Stewart, P. M., 518
Stewart, W. E., 97
Stickney, R. R., 227, 228
Stiff, J. E., 56
Stini, W. A., 501

STIPANUK, M. H., 179-209; 189, 190, 194-99
Stirk, H.-J., 326
Stock, A. L., 459
Stock, M. J., 217, 504, 506
Stockard, C. P., 213
Stockland, W. L., 190
Stockman, J. A., 26, 28
Stoddart, C., 122-24
Stokke, O., 324
Stokstad, E. L. R., 187, 409-11
Stolman, J., 377
Stoloff, L., 68
Stonehill, E., 305
Stordy, B. J., 500, 503, 506
Storebakken, T., 279, 281
Storey, D. J., 584
Storm, E., 101, 102
Stowell, A., 465
Strachan, I., 330
Stramentinoli, G., 182, 193
Strandberg, B., 464
Stratman, F. W., 46
Strause, L., 23
Strauss, K. E., 442
Strauss, R. G., 14, 32, 33
Streb, H., 583
Strecker, H. J., 380
Streiff, K., 281
Stribling, D., 213, 216
Strickland, G. T., 420
Strickland, K. P., 570, 572
Strode, M. A., 356
Stroud, R. M., 248
Stuart, M. J., 26, 28
Stubbe, J.-A., 385
Stuckey, S. R., 285
Stumbo, P., 122-24
Stumpf, D. A., 42
Stumpf, W. E., 532-35
Stunkard, A., 442
Sturgeon, P., 24
Sturman, J. A., 190, 195, 196
Suarez, L., 477, 478
Suarez, S., 213, 214
Subramanian, N., 367
Subramanyam, V., 256
Sucec, A., 20
Suchy, S. F., 320
Suda, S., 535, 542
Suda, T., 528-30, 550
Sudaie, Y., 290
Sufrin, J. R., 180
Suga, T., 254
Sugano, K., 373
Sugano, M., 259, 260
Sugawara, R., 69, 70, 73
Sugimoto, H., 587
Sugimura, K., 69, 73
Sugimura, T., 67-71, 73-80, 87
Sugiura, T., 571
Sugiyama, N., 47
Sugiyama, T., 248
Suit, J. L., 419
Sukhatme, P. V., 497, 499
Sukhawongs, S., 227
Sulimovici, S., 568, 569
Sullivan, D. M., 180
Summerskill, W. H. J., 467
Summerwell, W. N., 375
Sundelin, J., 536
Sundler, R., 578
Sunshine, P., 24
Suormala, T., 321, 328, 330, 331
Superti-Furga, A., 330
Surh, L., 326, 333
Surma, M., 215
Susick, R. L., 391
Suskind, R., 30, 32, 415
Suskind, R. M., 32
Sutter, V. L., 156, 165, 166, 172
Suwa, Y., 87
Suzuki, K., 164
Suzuki, Y., 54, 55, 57
Švejcar, J., 333
Swagler, R. M., 348
Swahn, C. G., 587
Swai, G. B. R., 146
Swan, J. S., 568
Swartz, M. N., 148
Sweeney, K., 448, 449
SWEETMAN, L., 317-43; 325-31, 333, 334
Swendseid, M. E., 191
Swick, H. M., 329
Swift, T. J., 387
Swyryd, E. A., 251
Sydenstricker, V. P., 332
Symes, A. L., 26, 28
Synge, R. L. M., 100
Szczepkowski, T. W., 198, 199
Sztein, M. B., 139


T


Tabata, T., 264
Tabor, C. W., 190, 191
Tabor, H., 190, 191
Tack, P. I., 227, 228, 233
Tacon, A. G. J., 227, 228, 232
Tada, K., 328
Tada, M., 69, 70, 73
Tada, M., 69
Tagashira, Y., 69
Tai, C., 414
Taitz, L. S., 330
Takada, K., 70, 80
Takada, S., 518
Takahashi, N., 535, 542
Takahashi, S., 68
Takahashi, Y., 76-78, 86
Takane, T., 280
Takashima, H., 373
Takata, Y., 185
Takayama, S., 69, 73-75
Takeda, K., 79
Takeda, M., 227, 228, 280
Takenawa, T., 569, 570
Takeuchi, T., 227, 228, 373
Takusagawa, K., 550
Tallan, H. H., 180, 189
Tamir, H., 27
Tamura, G., 164
Tamura, H., 489
Tamura, J., 196
Tamura, T., 467
Tanaka, C., 479
Tanaka, H., 535, 548-50
Tanaka, K., 52
Tanaka, M., 69, 73, 264
Tanaka, N., 515
Tanaka, R. D., 249, 250
Tanaka, S., 534
Tanaka, T., 259, 260, 505
Tanaka, Y., 227, 228, 231, 532, 534, 535, 547
Tanega, S., 214
Tang, K.-C., 191
Tanner, J. M., 500
Tanphaichitr, V., 42, 44
Tao, R. C., 96, 101, 103, 105
Tappaz, M. L., 194
Tappel, A. L., 291
Tarka, S., 196
Tarsio, J. F., 215
Tashjian, A. H., 529
Tate, M. E., 566
Tate, S. S., 373
Tateishi, N., 190
Tatematsu, M., 87
Tatibana, M., 518
Tattersall, R. B., 214
Taue, S., 68
Taunton, O. D., 259
Taylor, C. B., 262
Taylor, C. E., 131, 145, 411, 415
Taylor, F. R., 250, 254, 255, 257
Taylor, H. L., 303, 500, 503, 505
Taylor, M. P., 187, 188
Taylor, R. H., 115, 216
Taylor, T. G., 574
Taylor, W. F., 215
Taylor, Y. S. M., 514
Taylor-Roberts, T., 516
Tchernia, G., 24
Tchobroutsky, G., 213
Tearle, P. V., 165-67
Tedesco, T. A., 213
Tedford, C. E., 187
Teitelbaum, A., 217
Teitelbaum, S. L., 548, 550
Tenenhouse, A., 535
Teng, J. I., 257
Teng, S., 227, 228

Tephly, T. R., 187
Terada, M., 69, 73
Teraoka, H., 180
Terashima, T., 164
Terland, O., 372
Ternouth, J. H., 108
Terry, R. D., 356, 357
Teshima, S., 227
Tessari, P., 216
Testa, U., 31
Thayer, W. R., 24
Thayer, W. S., 464, 465
Theander, S., 301
Thebault, H., 231, 237
Thelander, L., 17, 32
Thelander, M., 17, 32
Thenen, S. W., 411, 412
Therriault, D. G., 57
Thibault, L. H., 82
Thind, I. S., 322
Thissen, J. T. N. M., 170
Thode, J., 477, 479
Thoene, J., 329, 330
Thoene, J. G., 330
Thoma, R. W., 320
Thoma, W. J., 388, 389
Thomas, G., 216
Thomas, G. A., 535
Thomas, M., 321
Thomas, P. J., 196
Thomas, P. K., 586
Thomas, W. A., 264
Thomas, W. R., 391
Thomasset, M., 551
Thommen, H., 286
Thompson, D., 185, 192
Thompson, D'A. W., 496
Thompson, F. E., 477, 478
Thompson, P. A., 139
Thompson, R. C., 320
Thompson, W., 566, 571, 572, 579
Thomsen, J. H., 57
Thomson, A. D., 320
Thornber, J. M., 217
Thorpe, S. R., 215
Thurman, R. G., 463
Thurston, J., 304
Thysell, H., 54, 55, 57
Tietze, H.-U., 542, 547
Tillotson, J., 477, 478
Timmons, G. D., 121
Tinker, D. O., 544
Tinkler, S. M. B., 548
Tirrell, J. G., 373
Tisdale, M. J., 191
Tjuri, M. E., 156
Tobey, T. A., 217
Tobon, F., 461, 462
Todo, T., 69, 74
Todoroff, T., 464
Tofft, M., 385, 387
Togawa, K., 76
Tohda, H., 69, 70, 73
Tohyama, K., 158, 159, 161, 164
Tokushige, A., 489
Tolbert, B. M., 366-68
Tolbert, N. E., 387
Toledo, S., 215
Tolosa, E. A., 197
Tomita, H., 77-79
Tomita, T., 574-76
Tomkins, A. M., 516
Tomlinson, D. R., 213, 214
Tondi, P., 58
Tonkin, S., 147
Tönnis, B., 318
Toraason, M. A., 485
Torget, R., 250
Torrance, E. P., 443
Torrance, J. D., 24
Torti, F. M., 142, 143
Toselli, P., 378, 380, 383
Toth, E. G., 467, 468
Towfighi, J., 56
Towle, H. C., 264
Townsend, J. J., 335
Toyoda, T., 230
Trabue, I. M., 451
Trackman, P. C., 192
Tragardh, L., 536
Traub, W., 318, 376, 383
Traxler, J., 58
Trayhurn, P., 506
Trechsel, V., 547
Tremolieres, J., 462
Trevisan, C., 56
Trial, J., 548, 552
Triggle, D. J., 487
Tripp, M. E., 56, 57
Trippestad, A., 163
Troitzkaia, E. G., 291
Trousseau, A., 146
Truex, R., 196
Tryggvason, K., 377
Trzaskos, J. M., 250
Tsai, H. C., 530
Tsoukas, C. D., 529, 533, 535, 545, 549, 550
Tsuda, M., 76, 77, 518
Tsuji, K., 68, 70, 71, 80
Tsujita, J., 505
Tsukada, K., 180
Tsumita, T., 569
Tsutsui, Y., 586
Tuboi, S., 197
Tuck, M. L., 490
Tuderman, L., 376, 377, 381
Tuma, D. J., 188
Turley, S. D., 258, 263
Turnbull, D. M., 52
Turner, J. B., 320
Turner, M. W., 120
Turpeenniemi-Hujanen, T., 377, 381
Turtle, J. R., 214, 215
Tutikawa, T., 290
Tuyns, A. J., 420
Tvermyr, S. M., 535
Tyler, B., 187, 410, 411
Tyrrell, P. A., 188
Tyson, C. A., 582

U

Uauy, R., 513
Ubuka, T., 197
Uchibori, M., 69, 74
Uchima, T., 587
Udall, J. N., 122-24
Udenfriend, S., 366, 375-78, 381
Ueda, I., 194-96
Ueland, P. M., 185, 186
Uitto, J., 378, 381
Ulbrecht, J., 213, 214
Ullrey, D. E., 227, 228, 233
Umemura, S., 197
Umesaki, Y., 159, 161
Umezawa, K., 68
Unanue, E. R., 137
Upchurch, H. F., 138, 140
Upreti, G. C., 588
Urbaniak, S. J., 414
Urdanivia, E., 215
Uren, J. R., 190, 197
Urrutia, J. J., 29, 118
Urushizaki, Y., 377
Uskoković, M., 550
Uskoković, M. R., 318
Utiger, R. D., 307
Uusitupa, M., 216
Uyeta, M., 68
Uziel, G., 47

V

Vacha, G. M., 54, 57
Vagelos, P. R., 578
Vahlquist, A., 290
Vaidya, V., 307
Valadon, L. R. G., 286
Vale, W., 373
Väljaots, M. E., 156
Valkner, K., 42, 53, 56
Valle, D., 51, 54, 56, 58
Vallotton, M., 320
Vanaman, T. C., 8
Van Campen, D. R., 566
Vance, D. E., 185
van Cutsem, J. M., 256
Van Deenen, L. L. M., 572, 573
Vandenberg, S. G., 438
Van den Bossche, H., 256
Vander, A. J., 137
Vanderbark, A. A., 185, 192

van der Westhuyzen, J., 187, 188
Vande Zande, H., 582
Van Dokkum, W., 170
Van Duijvenvoorde, P. M., 448, 449
Van Duin, C. T. M., 139
Van Duyn, M. A., 461, 469
van Eijk, H. G., 24
van Eys, J., 216
Van Golde, L. M. G., 572
Van Miert, A. S. J. P. A., 139
Van Os, C., 485
Van Rooijen, L. A. A., 581
Van Snick, J. L., 135
Van Soest, P. J., 169-71
Van Winkle, W. Jr., 376
Van Zuiden, P. E., 260
Varat, M. A., 20
Varela, G., 458
Varghese, Z., 54, 57
Varley, C., 122
Vary, T. C., 46
Vass, J. K., 8
Vawter, G. F., 24
Vecchi, M., 276, 280-85
Veech, R. L., 463, 464
Velasquez, A., 499
Velez, H., 144
Veloso, D., 463
Venkatesan, S., 259, 260
Vercellotti, J. R., 168
Vergani, L., 54, 57
Verheijden, J. H. M., 139
Verhulst, A., 160
Vermeersch, J. A., 351, 358
Vesell, E. S., 421
Vetter, H., 487
Vickers, J. D., 581
Vickers, S., 47
Vidal, A. J., 187
Videla, L., 463, 464
Vila, J. P., 158
Villafranca, J. J., 372
Villar, J., 476, 479, 482
Villee, C. A. Jr., 137, 138
Villeneuve, J. P., 462
Villeval, J.-L., 31
Vince, A. J., 170
Vincenzi, F., 488
Vine, W., 141
Viola, S., 228
Virkkunen, M., 122, 123
Virtanen, A. I., 99
Visioli, O., 57
Vitahyathil, A. J., 68
Vitale, J., 144
Viteri, F. E., 29, 30, 118
Vithayasai, V., 30, 32, 415
Vivian, V. M., 351, 358, 359
Vogel, S. N., 139
Vogel, Z., 379
Voglmayr, J. K., 565
Voit, C., 4
Volanakis, J. E., 140
VOLLMECKE, T. A., 433-56
Volpe, J. J., 254
von Bassewitz, D. B., 180
von Liebig, J., 4
Voorhess, M. L., 26, 28
Vorhaus, L. J., 305
Voutilainen, E., 216
Vrana, A., 217
Vranic, M., 216
Vuolo, L. L., 68
Vuust, J., 373
Vyas, D., 19, 30

W

Waaler, P. E., 324
Waber, L. J., 51, 54, 56, 58
Wada, E., 569
Wada, G. H., 374
Waddell, C., 511
Wade, J., 438
Wadman, S. K., 56, 323, 328
Wagner, A., 28
Wagner, C., 183, 184, 187
Wagner, D. G., 96
Wagner, G., 368
Wagner, J., 185, 186, 191
Wagner, J. G., 461, 462
Wahlquist, M. L., 216
Wainer, A., 197
Waite, L. J., 354
Wakabayashi, K., 68-71, 73, 76-81, 87
Wakefield, L. M., 346
Wakeling, A. E., 101, 313
Waksman, D., 119
Waku, K., 571
Waldherr, R., 549
Walker, D. M., 19, 30, 32, 145
Walker, J. E. C., 463, 464
Wall, S., 327, 328
Wallach, D. F. H., 262
Wallenburg, H. C. S., 24
Wallendorf, M., 356, 357
Wallenstein, R., 508
Waller, G. R., 68
Wallerstein, R. O., 24
Wallick, E. T., 57
Walling, M. W., 484, 485
Wallis, D. A., 292
Wallis, P., 570
Walser, M., 514, 515, 518, 519
Walsh, B. T., 313
Walsh, H. E., 353
Walter, J., 139
Walter, P., 528, 543
Walter, T., 29
Walters, M. R., 534-38, 546, 547
Walton, M. J., 231, 232, 236-39
Wang, K. W., 227
Wang, Y. M., 216
Wannemacher, R. W., 133, 134, 138
Wannemacher, R. W. Jr., 134, 138
Wara, D. W., 329, 330
Ward, C., 97, 101, 103
Ward, J. B., 367, 368
Ward, J. D., 211
Ward, K., 215, 216
Ward, L. C., 468
Warfield, A., 569
Warfield, A. S., 587
Wark, J. D., 529
Warn, B. J., 386
Warn-Cramer, B. J., 386
Warshaw, J. B., 22, 25, 47, 48, 57
Wasilewska, A., 506
Wass, D. F., 190
Wasserman, K., 507, 508
Wastell, H., 326, 331
Watanabe, J., 69
Watanabe, K., 197
Watanabe, M. S., 385, 518
Watanabe, S., 550
Watanabe, T., 164, 227, 228, 280
Watanabe, Y., 180
Waterlow, J., 4, 9
WATERLOW, J. C., 495-526; 496, 501, 504, 506, 512, 514-20
Waters, A. H., 420
Watkins, T. R., 577
Watrasiewicz, K. E., 517
Watson, J. A., 255
Watters, G., 42
Watts, J. L., 324, 328
Watts, R. W. E., 325
Waud, W. R., 198
Waxler, C., 122-24
Weaver, G. A., 171
Webb, A. C., 137
Webb, J., 6
Webb, R. C., 487, 488
Webb, R. E., 410
Weber, A., 276
Weber, E., 373
Weber, F. L. Jr., 163
Weber, M., 198, 199
Webster, A. J. F., 96-98, 103
Webster, J. D., 510
Wecksler, W. R., 536, 539
Wee, K. L., 227, 228
Weesner, R. E., 460, 461, 467-69
Wehrenberg, W. B., 373
Wei, J. M., 487
Weidler, D. J., 461, 462
Weidman, D., 479
Weidner, G., 438
Weiffenbach, J. M., 436

Weinberg, E. D., 33, 143, 146, 148
Weinberg, J., 28
Weinberger, C., 528
Weinberger, D., 119
Weinberger, M. H., 482, 483
Weiner, H., 306, 307
Weiniger, J., 391
Weintraub, L. R., 24
Weir, D. G., 186, 187
Weis, H. J., 258
Weisburger, J. H., 68
Weise, V. K., 194
Weisman, Y., 542, 547
Weiss, U., 287
Weissbecker, K. A., 322, 331
Welch, R. M., 566
Wells, H. J., 587
Wells, M. S., 187, 188
Wells, R. S., 31, 145
Wells, W. W., 565, 571, 573, 575, 583, 587
Welshons, W. V., 536
Welt, S. I., 214
Wendt, I. R., 508
Wergedal, J. E., 530
Werner, H. V., 463
Wertheimer, D., 384
Werthessen, N. T., 256
Wertman, K., 414
West, P. M., 318
West, S. E. H., 168
Westhead, E. W., 373
Westley, J., 199
Weydart, J. A., 123
Weyler, W., 325
Wheeler, E. F., 459
Whipp, B. J., 507, 508
White, D. A., 566
White, J. G., 582
White, J. I., 514
White, L. K., 126
White, L. W., 248
White, R. W., 160
White, S. D., 47
Whitehead, L., 585
Whitehead, R. G., 510
Whitehouse, S., 56
Whiteman, E. H., 57
Whitesell, L. F., 57
Whiting, G., 19, 30, 145
Whiting, P. H., 584, 585
Whitman, V., 57
Whitmer, J.-T., 57
Whitney, P. L., 187
Whitt, D. D., 158-60
Whitwell, J., 500, 508
Wichmann, J. K., 529
Wick, H., 321, 328, 330, 331
Wickramasinghe, S. N., 409
Widdowson, E. M., 497
Wieser, P. B., 48
Wiestner, M., 380
Wiggins, D., 518
Wiggins, H. S., 168
Wigness, B., 215
Wilcken, B., 188
Wilcken, D. E. L., 188
Wilczek, J., 380
Wiles, C. M., 508
Wilhelm, F., 537
Wilkie, D. W., 276
Wilkins, T. D., 168
Wilkinson, P. K., 461, 462
Will, H., 8
Willams, R. J., 320
Willard, S. G., 313
Willemsen, G., 256
Willhardt, I. H., 197
Williams, A. C., 360
Williams, A. P., 100
Williams, D. M., 548
Williams, E. A. J., 412, 413, 416, 417
Williams, E. S., 57
Williams, G., 415
Williams, H. H., 322
Williams, J. C., 323
Williams, M. L., 329
Williams, P. R., 50
Williams, R. H., 332
Williams, R. J., 318, 319, 583, 584
Williams, R. T., 504, 510
Williams, S., 215
Williams-Ashman, H. G., 192
Williamson, J. R., 463, 582, 583
Wills, R. E., 20
Wilmshurst, E. G., 216
Wilson, C. S., 434
Wilson, D. B., 569, 579, 581-83
Wilson, D. M., 46, 47, 51
Wilson, H. D., 485
Wilson, J. D., 258, 321, 328, 330
Wilson, J. F., 24, 120, 192
Wilson, M. J., 427
Wilson, P., 486
Wilson, P. D., 488
Wilson, P. W., 318
Wilson, R. B., 415, 416, 426
WILSON, R. P., 225-44; 227, 228, 231-35, 237, 238, 240
Wilson, T., 292
Wilton, D. C., 253
Wilz, D. R., 540
Wind, A., 373
Winder, W. W., 20-23
Windham, C. T., 349-51, 353, 355, 357, 458, 459
Winegrad, A. I., 213, 584, 586
Winfree, R. A., 227, 228
Winokur, G., 300
Winstead, D. K., 313
Winter, J., 157, 160
Wintrobe, M. M., 146
Wirtz, K. W. A., 573
Wise, A., 157
Wissler, R. W., 587
Witkop, B., 375
Witschi, M. S., 458, 459
Wittels, B., 57
Wittes, R. E., 391
Wittwer, A. J., 183, 184
Wixom, R. L., 100
Wogan, G. N., 68
Wojcik, J. D., 126
Wojtczak, L., 573
Wolever, T. M. S., 115, 215, 216
Wolf, A. W., 29, 118
Wolf, B., 320, 322, 323, 326-31
Wolf, D. E., 318
Wolf, G., 261
Wolf, H., 48-50, 57
Wolfe, S. J., 467
Wolff, H. S., 497
Wolff, S. M., 137-39
Wolfrom, G. W., 100, 103
Wolin, M. J., 156, 157, 161, 166-68, 170, 171
Wollheim, C. B., 583
Wolman, S. L., 516
Womack, M., 512
Wondrack, L. M., 385, 386
Wong, C. A., 248
Wong, Y. H., 568
Woo, C. H., 34
Woo, W., 506, 509
Wood, A. W., 550
Wood, C., 81
Wood, C. A., 195
Wood, C. M., 170
Wood, D. D., 549
Wood, H. G., 320
Wood, J. D., 261
Wood, R., 588
Woodruff, C. W., 24, 366, 412
Woodruff, R. A., 300
Woods, H. F., 28
Woodson, R. D., 20
Woodward, B., 574
Woody, G., 443, 445
Woolcott, D. M., 351, 358
Wooley, O. W., 447
Wooley, S. C., 447
Woolf, B., 505, 509
Woolraich, M., 122-24
Worsley, A., 441
Worth, H. G. J., 323, 328
Worth, W., 146
Worwood, M., 14
Wostmann, B. S., 158-60, 162
Wozny, M. A., 171
Wright, D. W., 217
Wright, G. L., 485
Wright, L. D., 320

Wrobel, N. C., 192
Wrong, O. M., 166, 167, 170
Wu, C. H., 380
Wu, G. Y., 380
Wu, H. L. C., 57
Wuebbles, B. J., 81
Wurtman, J., 115, 123
Wurtman, J. J., 448
Wurtman, R. J., 122, 124-26, 448
Wyant, K. W., 352
Wynder, E. L., 420
Wyse, B. W., 349-53, 355, 357, 458, 459

X

Xue, G.-P., 186-88

Y

Yabana, F., 310
Yabuuchi, H., 534, 536
Yaffe, S. J., 34
Yager, J., 312
Yager, J. D., 418
Yagi, K., 574, 575, 586
Yagi, T., 194
Yagihashi, S., 213
Yahagi, T., 68, 71
Yajima, T., 158, 159, 161
Yamada, J., 276
Yamada, M., 76
Yamada, S., 532-35, 538
Yamada, T., 373
Yamaguchi, A., 535
Yamaguchi, K., 70, 77, 78, 80, 194-96, 280
Yamaizumi, Z., 68, 70, 71, 77-79, 81, 86
Yamamoto, A., 587
Yamamoto, M. E., 477, 478, 482
Yamamoto, T., 70, 80
Yamane, M., 375
Yamanishi, T., 197
Yamanoha, B., 191
Yamaoka, K., 534, 536
Yamasaki, E., 68, 82, 84
Yamazaki, N., 54, 55, 57
Yamazoe, Y., 69
Yanaihara, N., 373
Yandrasitz, J., 326, 327
Yang, G. I., 356, 357
Yang, J. C., 368
Yang, M. G., 161
Yang, W., 329
Yannai, Y., 568
Yano, K., 477, 478
Yao, K., 189, 190, 197
Yap, V. U., 57
Yarbrough, C., 476
Yarrow, M., 122-24
Yates, P., 164
Yatzidis, H., 334
Yazawa, K., 164
Yefremova, L. L., 197
Yeh, Y.-Y., 49, 58, 59
Yehuda, S., 27
Yellin, A. M., 122
Yen, S. S. C., 115
Yergey, A. L., 47
Yetgin, S., 19, 30, 31
Yetley, E., 351, 358
Yetley, E. A., 351
Yew, M. S., 383
Yip, R., 33
Yland, M. J., 19, 21
Yogman, M. W., 125
Yokogoshi, H., 124
Yokokura, T., 158
Yokota, M., 71
Yokoyama, M., 228
Yokoyama, S., 68, 71, 79, 81
Yonace, A., 313
Yone, Y., 227, 228, 231
Yonekawa, H., 69
Yonekura, R., 264
Yoo, M. A., 69, 74
Yoo, O. J., 373
York, C. M., 48
York, D. A., 506
Yoshida, D., 68, 70, 71, 77-79, 81
Yoshida, M. A., 69, 73, 441
Yoshida, S., 54, 55, 88
Yoshimura, H., 515
Yoshimura, R., 70, 71
Yoshinaga, K., 47, 57
Yoshino, M., 329, 330
Yoshioka, S., 572
Yoshizaki, T., 366
Yoshizawa, S., 529
Youdim, M. B. H., 25-28
Young, A. W., 102, 508
Young, S. N., 125
Young, V. R., 415, 422, 423, 499, 513, 514, 516, 566
Youngblood, W. W., 373, 374
Yperman, A. M., 351, 358
Yu, T. C., 228
Yu, T. F., 466
Yuasa, S., 197
Yudkoff, M., 57
Yue, D. K., 214, 215
Yunis, F., 30
Yurgelun-Todd, D., 313

Z

Zahn, T. P., 121
Zahorik, D., 444
Zajonc, R. B., 352, 442, 449
Zakalusny, I., 448
Zalusky, R., 410
Zamcheck, N., 164
Zamenhof, S., 5
Zannoni, V. G., 375, 391
Zavaroni, I., 217
Zborowski, J., 573
Zebrowski, T., 215
Zech, L. A., 261
Zee, P., 49
Zehringer, N. V., 261
Zeisel, S. H., 125
Zeitoun, I. H., 227, 228, 233
Zellner, D. A., 443
Zenda, H., 80
Zenser, T. V., 138
Zern, M. A., 380
Zerwekh, J. E., 542
Zhou, X. Y., 535, 536
Zidek, W., 487
Ziegler, E. E., 24
Ziegler, J. L., 420
Zielinska, B., 331
Zierler, K. L., 48
Zikos, D., 479, 485
Zimmerman, S. I., 444
Zinder, O., 372
Zinn, D. W., 357
Zipes, D. P., 57
Zs-Nagy, I., 288
Zumkley, H., 487
Zuo, P. P., 196
Zurcher, J., 529
Zweens, J., 196, 199

# SUBJECT INDEX


A

Acarbose
diabetes mellitus and, 216
Acetaldehyde
bioenergetic effects of, 465-66
ethanol metabolism and, 461-62
Acetic acid
microbial metabolism and, 161
Acetoacetate
infection and, 134
Acetoacyl CoA synthase
cholesterol biosynthesis and, 248-50
Acetonemia
ruminants and, 97
Acetylcarnitine
citric acid cycle and, 56
Acetyl-CoA
carnitine and, 56
Acetyl-CoA carboxylase
fatty acid synthesis and, 141
Acidemia
carnitine deficiency and, 52
Acidosis
3-methylcrotonyl-CoA carboxylase deficiency and, 323
Aciduria
biotin deficiency and, 334
biotinidase deficiency and, 329
carnitine deficiency and, 52-53
Actinic reticuloid
carotenoid therapy and, 289-90
Acyl-CoA/CoA ratio
carnitine and, 42-43
Acyl-CoA dehydrogenase deficiency
carnitine deficiency and, 52
Adenosine triphosphate
biotin and, 319
cytochromes and, 15
ethanol oxidation and, 463
iron deficiency and, 21, 23
S-Adenosylhomocysteine
metabolism of, 185-86
S-Adenosylmethionine
carcinogenesis and, 419
carnitine and, 43
decarboxylation of
polyamine pathway and, 190
methionine metabolism and, 180-83
transmethylation and, 409
Adenylcyclase
dopamine receptors and, 26
AdoMet decarboxylase
regulation of, 191
Adonirubin, 280
Age
food-related behavior and, 352-53
Aging
myocardial carnitine deficiency and, 57
nutrition and, 9-10
peroxidation and, 7
Alanine
muscle/viscera exchange of, 7
Albumin
biotin and, 320
body size/metabolism and, 7
protein turnover and, 516-17
Alcohol
cirrhosis and, 466-70
consumption of
dietary surveys of, 458-60
nutrition and, 457-70
Alcohol dehydrogenase
ethanol metabolism and, 461-62
Alcoholism
malnutrition and, 460
vitamin deficiency and, 126
Aldose reductase
diabetes mellitus and, 214
glucose metabolism and, 213
Alopecia
biotin deficiency and, 333-34
biotinidase deficiency and, 329-30
vitamin D–dependent rickets and, 541
Amines
See specific type
Amino acids
behavioral effects of, 125-26
body size/metabolism and, 7
central plasma clearance rate for
protein synthesis and, 138-39
dietary requirements of, 6
ruminants and, 99-106
liver/muscle exchange of, 7
protein turnover and, 517
pyrolysates of
carcinogenicity of, 68
requirements in fishes, 229-39
sulfur-containing
metabolism of, 179-200
synthesis of
biotin and, 319
uptake by liver
interleukin-1 and, 138
Amitriptyline
bulimia nervosa and, 313
α-Amylase
pancreatic
acarbose and, 216
Anemia
anorexia nervosa and, 305
megaloblastic
folate deficiency and, 409
Animals
calcium supplementation in, 479-82
carotenoid synthesis in, 287-88
evolution of
nutrition and, 5-9
nitrogenous principles of, 3
Anisocytosis
anorexia nervosa and, 305-6
Anorexia
fever-induced, 137
recurrent infection and, 131
Anorexia nervosa, 300-309
differential diagnosis of, 300
Anoxia
carnitine and, 43
Anthraquinones
carcinogenicity of, 68
Antibacterial agents
nutritional deficiency and, 164
Anticonvulsant agents
biotin deficiency and, 334
Antitrypsin
interleukin-1 and, 140
Apoferritin
structure of, 15-16
Arachidonic acid
eicosanoid production and, 579-80
interleukin-1 and, 137
Arginine
requirements in fishes, 233, 236
requirements in ruminants, 100, 103
Aromatic hydrocarbons
polynuclear
mutagenicity/carcinogenicity of, 81

Ascorbate
carnitine pathway hydroxylases and, 386-91
dioxygenase reactions and, 385-86
dopamine β-hydroxylase and, 372-73
functions of, 368-69
antioxidant, 391
4-hydroxyphenylpyruvate dioxygenase and, 374-76
metabolism of, 367-68
peptidyl glycine α-amidating monooxygenase and, 373-74
prolyl and lysyl hydroxylases and, 376-83
protein hydroxylation and, 383-85
Ascorbic acid, 365-94
biosynthesis of, 366-67
nutrient requirements of, 366-67
Asialofetuin, 389-90
Aspartame
behavioral effects of, 124-25
Aspartate aminotransferase
cysteinesulfinate pathway and, 194
Astaxanthin
absorption in birds, 284
chirality of, 274-75
formation in fishes, 277-80
vitamin A and, 282
Asthma
food allergy and, 120
Astrocytes
peptides of, 135
Ataxia
biotinidase deficiency and, 329
*Atelopus chiriquiensis*
chiriquixanthins of, 276
Atherosclerosis, 10
diabetes mellitus and, 211-12
ATP
See Adenosine triphosphate
Attention deficit disorder
caffeine and, 121
malnutrition and, 116
Attitudes
food-related behavior and, 359
Avidin
biotin and, 318-19
Azotorrhea
alcoholic malnutrition and, 468

B

*Bacillus subtilis*
histidine-deficient
growth of, 5
Bacteria
gastrointestinal lysis of, 161-62
metabolic end-products of, 160-61
*Bacteroides*
gastrointestinal, 166-67
Bartonellosis
iron overload and, 148
Basal metabolic rate, 502-6
B-cell activating factor, 140
Behavior
diet and, 113-27
iron deficiency and, 25-30
Betaine
homocystinuria and, 188
Betaine-homocysteine methyltransferase
liver and, 187-88
*Bifidobacterium*
gastrointestinal, 166-67
Bile acids
carcinogenicity of, 164
Bile steroids
intestinal absorption and, 160
Bilirubin
heme degradation and, 16
Biliverdin
heterocyclic amine mutagenicity and, 76
Biocytin, 319-20
absorption of, 320
biotinidase deficiency and, 331
Biogenic amines
binding to receptor sites, 26-27
iron deficiency and, 25-30
synthesis and catabolism of, 27-30
Biotin, 317-36
biotinidase deficiency and, 329-32
carboxylase deficiency and, 323-32
dietary deficiency of, 332-35
dietary requirements of, 321-22
germfree animals and, 162
holocarboxylase synthetase deficiency and, 324-29
metabolic role of, 319-21
Biotinidase, 320
dietary deficiency of, 329-32
Birds
carotenoid metabolism in, 284-86
B lymphocytes
biotinidase deficiency and, 329
Body mass index, 500-1
Body size
metabolism and, 6-8
Body temperature
iron deficiency and, 28-29
Body weight
metabolic adaptation and, 499-501
Bombesin
peptidyl glycine α-amidating monooxygenase and, 373
Bone
calcium balance in hypertension and, 486
vitamin D and, 548-51
Brain
biogenic amines and, 27-28
γ-butyrobetaine hydroxylase and, 43
hypoglycemia and, 212
iron deficiency and, 25
Bulimia nervosa, 309-14
differential diagnosis of, 300, 310
Bupranolol
inositol deficiency and, 576
Butyric acid
microbial metabolism and, 161
γ-Butyrobetaine
ε-*N*-trimethyllysine and, 43
γ-Butyrobetaine hydroxylase
α-ketoglutarate and, 390-91

C

Cachectin, 140-43
Caffeine
behavioral effects of, 121
elimination of
cigarette smoking and, 116
Calcitonin
peptidyl glycine α-amidating monooxygenase and, 373
Calcium
hypertension and, 475-91
osteoporosis and, 9-10
sodium-potassium pump and, 490
vitamin D and, 546-47
Calcium supplementation
animals and, 479-82
humans and, 482-83
Calmodulin
ε-*N*-trimethyllysine residues in, 43
*Caltha palustris*
epilutein of, 276
Cancer
inositol metabolism and, 587
lipotropes and, 420-24
vitamin D and, 550-51
See also specific type
Candidiasis
biotinidase deficiency and, 329

Canthaxanthin, 277, 280
  absorption in birds, 284
  vitamin A and, 282
Carbamazepine
  biotin deficiency and, 334
Carbohydrates
  behavioral effects of, 121-23
  complex
    glucose tolerance and, 215-16
  dietary requirements of, 4
  hepatic glycogen deposition and, 7
  metabolism of
    infection and, 138
Carbon dioxide
  microbial fermentation and, 161
Carboxybiotin, 319
Carboxylase deficiency
  biotin-responsive, 323-32
Carcinogens, 67-88
Cardiomyopathy
  carnitine deficiency and, 54-57
Carnitine
  absorption of, 45
  accretion and turnover of, 45-46
  biosynthesis of, 43-45, 387
  fatty acid metabolism and, 386-87
  function of, 42-43
  heart disease and, 55-57
  hydroxylases of, 386-91
  hyperlipidemia and, 57-58
  ketosis and, 58-59
  kidneys and, 46-47
  metabolism of, 41-59
    disorders of, 50-55
  perinatal energy metabolism and, 47-50
Carnitine acetyltransferase
  functions of, 56
Carnitine deficiency syndromes
  primary, 50-52
  secondary, 52-55
β-Carotene
  conversion to astaxanthin, 277
  erythropoietic protoporphyria and, 289
  ruminants and, 106
Carotenodermia, 290
Carotenoids, 273-93
  antitumor activity of, 291-92
  invertebrates and, 288
  metabolism of
    birds and, 284-86
    fishes and, 276-84
    insects and, 286-87
  photosensitization and, 289-91
  synthesis in animals, 287-88
  vertebrates and, 288-89
Casein
  requirements in ruminants, 100, 104
Catalase, 15
  neutrophils and, 31
  peptidyl glycine α-amidating monooxygenase and, 374
Catecholamines
  ascorbate and, 374
Celiac disease
  iron deficiency and, 24
  psychiatric illness and, 119
Cell-mediated immunity
  iron deficiency and, 32
  liver disease and, 421
Cerebrospinal fluid
  inositol and, 569
Ceruloplasmin
  infection and, 134-35
  interleukin-1 and, 139
*Channa micropeltes*
  nutrient requirements of, 228
Chiriquixanthins, 276
Chlorophyllin
  heterocyclic amine mutagenicity and, 76
Cholecystokinin
  peptidyl glycine α-amidating monooxygenase and, 373
Cholesterol
  biosynthesis of, 245-65
    dietary factors in, 258-65
    HMG-CoA and, 246-54
  catabolism of
    biotin and, 319
  metabolism of
    ascorbate and, 391
Cholesterol 7α-hydroxylase
  cholesterogenesis and, 264
Choline
  immune function and, 415-17
  lipotropes and, 407
  storage of, 409
Choroid plexus
  inositol and, 569
Chromium deficiency
  glucose intolerance and, 218
  vascular complications of, 217-18
*Chrysophrys major*
  nutrient requirements of, 228
Cigarette smoking
  caffeine elimination and, 116
Cirrhosis
  alcoholic, 466-70
  biotin deficiency and, 332
Citric acid cycle
  acetylcarnitine and, 56
  iron deficiency and, 21
Cobalt
  requirements in ruminants, 108
*Coccinella septempunctata*
  carotenoid metabolism in, 287
Coenzyme A
  carnitine and, 42-43
  tricarboxylic acid cycle and, 43
Coenzyme R, 318
Collagen
  glucose adducts of, 215
  prolyl and lysyl hydroxylases and, 376-83
Collagenase
  interleukin-1 and, 140
Colon cancer
  dietary fiber and, 170
  dietary habits and, 67
Coma
  3-methylcrotonyl-CoA carboxylase deficiency and, 323
  propionyl-CoA carboxylase deficiency and, 323
Compactin
  dolichol synthesis and, 252
Complement
  hydroxylation of, 384-85
Conjunctivitis
  biotin deficiency and, 332
  biotinidase deficiency and, 329
Copper
  infection and, 134
Corticotropin-releasing factor
  peptidyl glycine α-amidating monooxygenase and, 373
Corticotropin-releasing hormone
  anorexia nervosa and, 307
Cortisol
  anorexia nervosa and, 307
*Coryptiaena hippurus*
  carotenoids of, 280
C-reactive protein
  interleukin-1 and, 140
Creatine
  formation from guanidinoacetate, 183
β-Cryptoxanthin
  retinol and, 283
Crystallin
  glucose adducts of, 215
Cyclic nucleotides
  dopamine receptors and, 26
*Cyprinus carpio*
  nutrient requirements of, 228
Cystathionase
  homocysteine catabolism and, 189-90
Cystathionine synthase
  homocysteine catabolism and, 188-89
Cysteamine
  heterocyclic amine mutagenicity and, 76

Cysteine
ascorbate and, 369
heterocyclic amine mutagenicity and, 76
metabolism of, 193-99
cysteinesulfinate and, 193-96
desulfuration pathways of, 196-99
Cysteinesulfinate
cysteine metabolism and, 193-96
Cytochrome *b*
respiratory burst and, 30-31
Cytochrome $b_5$
functions of, 15
Cytochrome *c*
composition of, 15
iron deficiency and, 19
life span of, 17
ϵ-*N*-trimethyllysine residues in, 43
Cytochrome oxidase
iron deficiency and, 19, 24
Cytochrome P-450
functions of, 15
iron deficiency and, 33-34
Cytochromes
energy metabolism and, 20-25
function of, 15
heme in, 20

D

Deferoxamine
T and B lymphocytes and, 32
Dehydroascorbate
ascorbate metabolism and, 367-68
Dehydroretinol
vitamin A and, 282-83
Depression
biotin deficiency and, 332
celiac disease and, 119
tryptophan and, 125
tyrosine and, 126
vitamin deficiency and, 126
Dermatitis
biotin and, 318, 332-33
carotenoid therapy and, 289-90
Diabetes mellitus
carnitine and, 43
complications of, 211, 212
hyperglycemia and, 212
inositol metabolism and, 584-85
myocardial carnitine deficiency and, 57
Diabetic ketoacidosis
carnitine excretion and, 47
Diacetyl
mutagenicity/carcinogenicity of, 86-88
1,2-Diacylglycerol
inositol and, 582
Dicarbonyl compounds
mutagenicity/carcinogenicity of, 86-88
*Dicentrarchus labrax*
nutrient requirements of, 228, 230
Diet
behavior and, 113-27
Diet-behavior studies, 113-27
methodology in, 114-16
Dihydrolutein, 281
Dihydroparasiloxanthin, 281
1,25-Dihydroxyvitamin D
radioreceptor assay of, 540-41
Dihydrozeaxanthin, 281
Dioxygenases
ascorbate and, 369
4-hydroxyphenylpyruvate, 374-76
Diphtheria
myocardial carnitine deficiency and, 57
Disaccharide malabsorption
iron deficiency and, 24
Dithiothreitol
ascorbate and, 369
DNA
iron deficiency and, 32
nutritional evolution and, 5-6
synthesis of
lipotropes and, 407
Dolichols
cholesterol biosynthesis and, 246-48, 252
isopentenyl pyrophosphate and, 253
Dopamine
binding to receptors, 26
iron deficiency and, 26
Dopamine β-hydroxylase
ascorbate and, 372-73
Dulcitol
galactose metabolism and, 213
Dysmenorrhea
bulimia nervosa and, 312

E

Eating disorders
pathophysiology of, 299-314
Eating types
food-related behavior and, 359-60
Echinenone, 277
*Ectatosoma tiaratum*
carotenoids of, 287
Eczema
food allergy and, 120
Education
food-related behavior and, 351
Ehler-Danlos syndrome
prolyl hydroxylase and, 378
Eicosanoids
arachidonic acid and, 579-80
Elastase
interleukin-1 and, 140
Elastin
hydroxylation of, 383-84
Electron transport chain
oxidative capacity of, 21
Endocytosis
low-density lipoproteins and, 249
Endogenous pyrogen
fever and, 135
β-Endorphin
dopamine receptors and, 27
Endotoxin
interleukin-1 and, 137-38
Energy metabolism
biotin and, 319
infection and, 133
iron deficiency and, 20-25
microbial
products of, 160-61
perinatal
carnitine and, 47-50
variation in, 497
*Entamoeba histolytica*
hemochromatosis and, 148
Enterocytes
germfree animals and, 158-59
Epilutein, 276
*Epinephelus salmoides*
nutrient requirements of, 228
Epinephrine
iron deficiency and, 26
Epithelial cells
peptides of, 135
Epoxylanosterol
oxysterol and, 255
Erythrocytes
inositol pentaphosphate in, 566
*Escherichia coli*
neutrophils and, 31
Esophageal reflux
bulimia nervosa and, 312
Estrogens
osteoporosis and, 10
Ethanol
caloric value of, 460-61
metabolism of, 461-66
yeast metabolism and, 160
Ethnicity
food-related behavior and, 355-58
Evolution
nutrition and, 5-9
Exercise
respiration and, 3

## F

Failure to thrive
  propionyl-CoA carboxylase deficiency and, 323
Fanconi syndrome
  carnitine deficiency and, 53
Farnesyl pyrophosphate
  cholesterol biosynthesis and, 247
Fasting
  mental performance and, 117-18
Fats
  dietary requirements of, 4
  hepatic cholesterogenesis and, 259-60
Fatty acids
  catabolism of
    biotin and, 319
  heterocyclic amine mutagenicity and, 76
  metabolism of
    carnitine and, 386-87
  synthesis of
    enzymes and, 141
  transport of
    carnitine and, 42, 55
Fatty acid synthetase
  fatty acid synthesis and, 141
Ferritin, 15-16
  amino acid sequences of, 8
  hemoglobin and, 8-9
  iron deficiency and, 17
Fetus
  maternal iron deficiency and, 24-25
Fever
  endogenous pyrogen and, 135
  interleukin-1 and, 137
Fiber
  colon cancer and, 170
  diabetes mellitus and, 215-16
  osteoporosis and, 10
Fibronectin
  glucose adducts of, 215
Fishes
  carotenoid metabolism in, 276-84
  nutrient requirements of, 225-40
    amino acid, 229-39
    factors affecting, 228-29
    maintenance, 229
    protein, 226-28
Flavonoids
  carcinogenicity of, 68
Fluoride
  osteoporosis and, 10
Folate
  functions of, 409-11
  lipotropes and, 408
Folate deficiency
  megaloblastic anemia and, 409
Folic acid
  germfree animals and, 162
  immune function and, 411-14
  lipotropes and, 407
  storage of, 409
Food
  anorexia nervosa and, 301-2
Food additives
  childhood hyperactivity and, 119-20
Food allergy, 119
Food avoidances
  labile and stable, 447-51
  mechanisms of, 441-46
  origins of, 435-38
  taxonomy of, 438-41
Food preferences
  labile and stable, 447-51
  mechanisms of, 441-46
  origins of, 435-38
  taxonomy of, 438-41
Food-related behavior, 345-60
  psychosocial determinants in, 358-60
  sociodemographic determinants in, 348-58
  theoretical models for, 347-48
Foodways, 346
Formate
  methionine and, 411
Froelich's syndrome
  bulimia and, 300
Fructose
  metabolic effects of, 217

## G

Galactitol
  galactose metabolism and, 213
Galactose
  lactalbumin and, 8
  metabolic pathways of, 212-13
Galactosemia
  inositol metabolism and, 587
Galactosyl transferase
  lactalbumin and, 8
Galloxanthin, 285
Gastric cancer
  pernicious anemia and, 420
Gastric motility
  anorexia nervosa and, 305
Gastrin
  peptidyl glycine α-amidating monooxygenase and, 373
Gastroenteritis
  iron deficiency and, 144
Gastrointestinal microflora, 155-73
  biochemical activities of, 157
  biotin production by, 321-22
  human nutrition and, 165-72
  monogastric nutrition and, 158-65
Gastrointestinal tract
  calcium balance in hypertension and, 484-86
Gender
  food-related behavior and, 352-53
Geranyl pyrophosphate
  cholesterol biosynthesis and, 247
Globulins
  biotin and, 320
Glomerular filtration rate
  anorexia nervosa and, 304
Glomerulonephritis
  inositol reabsorption and, 586
Glomerulosclerosis
  sugar consumption and, 217
Glucagon
  release of
    interleukin-1 and, 138
Glucitol
  glucose metabolism and, 213
Glucoamylase
  acarbose and, 216
Glucocorticoids
  vitamin D and, 532
Gluconeogenesis
  carbohydrate metabolism and, 7
  hyperinsulinemia and, 142-43
  infection and, 133-34
  iron deficiency and, 23
Glucose
  homeostasis and, 212
  metabolism of
    insulin-dependent pathways of, 212-15
    iron deficiency and, 23
  premature infant and, 49-50
  synthesis of
    oxaloacetic acid and, 319
Glucose tolerance
  complex carbohydrates and, 215-16
Glucose tolerance factor
  chromium deficiency and, 218
Glucosidases
  acarbose and, 216
Glutamate
  behavioral effects of, 126
Glutamine
  muscle/viscera exchange of, 7
Glutathione
  ascorbate and, 369
Gluten sensitivity
  psychiatric illness and, 119
α-Glycerophosphate dehydrogenase, 15
Glycine methyltransferase
  methionine metabolism and, 183-84

Glycosylation
glucose metabolism and, 214-15
Glyoxal
mutagenicity/carcinogenicity of, 86-88
Gout
ethanol consumption and, 465-66
Growth-hormone-releasing factor
peptidyl glycine α-amidating monooxygenase and, 373
Growth retardation
anorexia nervosa and, 303
Guanidinoacetate
creatine formation from, 183
Günther's disease
carotenoid therapy and, 289

H

Hallucinations
biotin deficiency and, 332
Haloperidol
dopamine receptors and, 27
vitamin C and, 126
Hearing loss
biotinidase deficiency and, 330
Heart
anorexia nervosa and, 303-6
γ-butyrobetaine hydroxylase and, 43
Heart disease
carnitine and, 55-57
Heart failure
hemodialysis and, 54
myocardial carnitine deficiency and, 57
Heart muscle
iron deficiency and, 22, 25
Heme
cytochromes and, 20
degradation of, 16
Heme proteins, 14-15
life span of, 16-17
mixed-function oxidations and, 34
oxidative metabolism and, 14
Hemin
heterocyclic amine mutagenicity and, 76
Hemochromatosis
infection and, 148
Hemodialysis
biotin deficiency and, 334
carnitine deficiency and, 53-55
heart failure and, 54
Hemoglobin
diabetes mellitus and, 214
ferritin and, 8-9
function of, 14
iron deficiency and, 17, 19
life span of, 16
oxygen transport and, 20
Hemosiderin, 15-16, 135
Hepatitis
alcoholic, 466, 468
nutritional supplementation and, 469
Hepatitis V virus
liver cancer and, 427
Hepatoma
inositol metabolism and, 588
Heterocyclic amines
cooked foods and, 77
mutagenicity/carcinogenicity of, 68-81
organic syntheses of, 77
Heterocyclic imino compounds
organic syntheses of, 77
*Heteropneustes fossilis*
xanthophyll metabolism in, 281
Hexamethonium
inositol deficiency and, 576
High-density lipoproteins
carnitine and, 54
Histidine
*B. subtilis* and, 5
requirements in fishes, 233
Histones
ε-*N*-trimethyllysine residues in, 43
Holocarboxylase synthetase
biotin and, 319-20, 324-29
Homocysteine
catabolism of, 188-90
methionine synthesis and, 186-88
methylation of
vitamin $B_{12}$ and, 410
Homocystinuria
betaine and, 188
Host defense
nutritional status and, 131-32
Household size
food-related behavior and, 349-51
Humoral immunity
iron deficiency and, 33
*Hydroa aestivale*
carotenoid therapy and, 289-90
Hydrogen
gastrointestinal microflora and, 170
microbial fermentation and, 161
3-Hydroxy-3-methylglutaryl CoA reductase
cholesterol biosynthesis and, 246-54
3-Hydroxybutyrate
infection and, 134
25-Hydroxycholesterol
cholesterol biosynthesis and, 250
dolichol synthesis and, 252
oxysterol and, 255
3-Hydroxyisovaleric aciduria, 323-24
25-Hydroxylanosterol
oxysterol and, 255
Hydroxylases
carnitine pathway, 386-91
collagen metabolism and, 376-83
4-Hydroxyphenylpyruvate dioxygenase, 374-76
ascorbate and, 369
Hyperactivity
childhood
caffeine and, 121
food additives and, 119-20
Hyperalimentation
anorexia nervosa and, 307
Hyperammonemia
biotinidase deficiency and, 329
carnitine deficiency and, 51
holocarboxylase synthetase deficiency and, 327
Hypercalciuria
hypertension and, 486
Hypercarnitinemia
uremia and, 53-54
Hypercholesterolemia
inositol metabolism and, 587
Hyperferremia
infection and, 148
malaria and, 147
Hyperglobulinemia
liver disease and, 421
Hyperglycemia
diabetes mellitus and, 212
Hyperinositolemia, 586
Hyperinsulinemia
infection and, 142-43
sugar consumption and, 217
Hyperketonemia
carnitine and, 58-59
Hyperlipidemia
carnitine deficiency and, 57-58
inositol metabolism and, 587
Hyperlipoproteinemia
carnitine supplementation and, 57-58
Hypermethioninemia
S-adenosylmethionine and, 180-81
Hyperparathyroidism
vitamin D–dependent rickets and, 541
Hypersensitivity
dietary, 119-20

Hypertension
calcium and, 475-91
inositol metabolism and, 587
Hyperthyroidism
carnitine excretion and, 47
Hypertriglyceridemia
carnitine supplementation and, 54
infection and, 134
lipoprotein lipase and, 140-41
Hyperuricemia
ethanol consumption and, 465-66
Hypocalcemia
vitamin D–dependent rickets and, 541
Hypochloremia
bulimia nervosa and, 312
Hypoferremia
leukocyte endogenous mediator and, 135
Hypoglycemia
brain tissue and, 212
carnitine deficiency and, 51
3-methylcrotonyl-CoA carboxylase deficiency and, 323
Hypokalemia
bulimia nervosa and, 312
Hypoproteinemia
iron deficiency and, 24
Hypoprothrombinemia
carnitine deficiency and, 51
Hypotaurine
cysteinesulfinate pathway and, 194-95
Hypothalamic-pituitary-adrenal axis
anorexia nervosa and, 307
Hypothalamic-pituitary-gonadal axis
anorexia nervosa and, 306
Hypothalamic-pituitary-thyroid axis
anorexia nervosa and, 306-7
Hypothyroidism
anorexia nervosa and, 306-7
Hypotonia
biotinidase deficiency and, 329
3-methylcrotonyl-CoA carboxylase deficiency and, 323
Hypozincemia
leukocyte endogenous mediator and, 135

I

*Ictalurus punctatus*
nutrient requirements of, 228
Idoxanthin, 279
Imipramine
bulimia nervosa and, 313
Immune system
ascorbate and, 391
interleukin-1 and, 139-40
iron deficiency and, 30-33
lipotropes and, 411-17
vitamin D and, 548-51
Income
food-related behavior and, 348-49
Infancy
iron deficiency and, 147-48
Infection
carbohydrate metabolism and, 138
folate deficiency and, 411
interleukin-1 and, 137-39
iron deficiency and, 33, 143-49
liver cancer and, 427
metabolic responses to, 133-43
nutrition and, 131-49
Inositol, 563-89
biologic forms of, 564-66
cellular functions of, 213
dietary
effects of, 573-78
lung and, 577-78
sources of, 564-66
metabolism of, 566-73
abnormal, 584-88
Inositol deficiency
intestinal lipodystrophy and, 576-77
triacylglycerol and, 574-76
Inositol phospholipids
membranes and, 578-79
metabolism of, 566-73
abnormal, 584-88
Inositol triphosphate
degradation of, 583-84
source of, 583
Insects
carotenoid metabolism in, 286-87
Insulin
glucose metabolism and, 212-15
release of
interleukin-1 and, 138
ruminants and, 96-97
Insulin deficiency
carnitine excretion and, 47
Interleukin-1, 135-40
cachectin and, 141
hyperinsulinemia and, 142-43
immunologic effects of, 139-40
metabolic effects of, 137-39
Intestinal lipodystrophy
dietary inositol deficiency and, 576-77
Intestinal mucosa
iron deficiency and, 23-24
Invertebrates
carotenoids and, 288
Iodine
thyroid hormone biosynthesis and, 528
Iron
metabolism of
ascorbate and, 391
nutritional evolution and, 6
transport proteins and, 15-16
uteroferrin and, 8
Iron compounds
essential, 14-15
iron deficiency and, 18-19
non-heme, 15
storage, 15-16
synthesis and turnover of, 16-17
Iron deficiency, 13-35
behavior and, 25-30, 118-19
cytochrome P-450 and, 33-34
energy metabolism and, 20-25
immune response and, 30-33
infection and, 134-35, 143-49
oxygen transport and, 20
stages of, 17
tissue iron compounds and, 18-19
Iron-sulfur proteins, 15
energy metabolism and, 20-25
Isocryptoxanthin, 277
Isoleucine
catabolism of
biotin and, 319
requirements in fishes, 233-35
Isopentenyl pyrophosphate
cholesterol biosynthesis and, 247
polyisoprenoid synthesis and, 253
Isozeaxanthin
vitamin A and, 282

K

Kallikrein
interleukin-1 and, 140
Keratinocytes
peptides of, 135
Ketoconazole
lanosterol and, 256-57
α-Ketoglutarate
γ-butyrobetaine hydroxylase and, 390-91
Ketones
infection and, 134
Ketosis
carnitine and, 58-59

propionyl-CoA carboxylase deficiency and, 323
Kidney
biotin and, 321
γ-butyrobetaine hydroxylase and, 43
calcium balance and, 486
carnitine and, 46-47
inositol metabolism and, 586-87
inositol uptake in, 569
iron deficiency and, 25
Kidney disease
carnitine deficiency and, 53-55
Klein-Levine syndrome
bulimia and, 300
Kwashiorkor, 415
iron supplementation and, 146

L

Lactalbumin
lysozyme and, 8
Lactate
vascular complications of, 217
Lactic acid
bacterial metabolism and, 160
Lactic acidemia
biotinidase deficiency and, 329
holocarboxylase synthetase deficiency and, 327
Lactoferrin
hydroxyl radicals and, 31
infection and, 33
interleukin-1 and, 139
iron uptake and, 135
Lactose
malabsorption of
iron deficiency and, 24
synthesis of
lactalbumin and, 8
Lanosterol
ketoconazole and, 256-57
Leiner's disease
biotin deficiency and, 333
Leucine
requirements in fishes, 235
requirements in ruminants, 103
Leukocyte endogenous mediator
biologic effects of, 135
Leukopenia
anorexia nervosa and, 305
Leukotrienes
arachidonic acid and, 579
Linoleic acid
heterocyclic amine mutagenicity and, 76
Lipids
metabolism of
ascorbate and, 391
gram-negative sepsis and, 142
infection and, 133-34
lipotropes and, 407
tumor necrosis factor and, 143
premature infant and, 50
transport of
lipoprotein lipase and, 141
Lipoperoxidation
hepatocarcinogenesis and, 426
Lipoprotein lipase
hypertriglyceridemia and, 140-41
lipid transport and, 141
Lipotropes
cancer and, 420-24
dietary sources of, 408-9
functions of, 407-8
immune function and, 411-17
xenobiotic metabolism and, 417-19
Liver
S-adenosylmethionine and, 180
amino acid uptake by
interleukin-1 and, 138
body size/metabolism and, 7
γ-butyrobetaine hydroxylase and, 43
cholesterogenesis in, 259-60
diurnal variations in, 264-65
iron deficiency and, 25
metabolite exchange and, 7
protein synthesis in
interleukin-1 and, 140
triacylglycerol accumulation in
inositol deficiency and, 574-76
very-low-density lipoprotein production in, 263-64
Liver cancer
chemical induction of, 425-28
malnutrition and, 420-21
Liver disease
immune defects and, 421
Low-density lipoproteins
cholesterol biosynthesis and, 248-50
Lung
dietary inositol and, 577-78
Lutein
absorption in birds, 284
chirality of, 274-75
conversion to astaxanthin, 278-79
Luteinizing hormone
anorexia nervosa and, 306
Lycopene, 286-87
Lymphocytes
iron deficiency and, 19
Lymphocytosis
anorexia nervosa and, 305
Lysine
carnitine and, 42-43
requirements in fishes, 236
requirements in ruminants, 101-3
Lysosomal acid cholesteryl ester hydrolase
cholesterogenesis and, 264
Lysozyme
lactalbumin and, 8

M

Macroglobulin
interleukin-1 and, 140
Macrophages
differentiation of
vitamin D and, 529
metabolism and, 135-43
Magnesium
hypertension and, 477
Malabsorption
alcoholic malnutrition and, 468
iron deficiency and, 24
Malabsorption syndrome
developing countries and, 172
Malaria
iron deficiency and, 146-47
Malnutrition
alcoholism and, 460
cirrhosis and, 466-70
consequences of, 302-3
liver cancer and, 420-21, 427
mental retardation and, 116
Mammalian cells
phosphatidylinositol and, 578-84
pyrolysis products and, 68-69
Mammals
body size/metabolism in, 6-8
Mammary glands
development of, 8
Marasmus, 415
Megaloblastic anemia
folate deficiency and, 409
Melanotropin
peptidyl glycine α-amidating monooxygenase and, 373
Membrane proteins
glucose adducts of, 215
Membranes
inositol phospholipids and, 578-79
Meningitis
iron deficiency and, 145, 147
Mental retardation
malnutrition and, 116
propionyl-CoA carboxylase deficiency and, 323
2-Mercaptoethanol
ascorbate and, 369

Mesangial cells
peptides of, 135
Metabolic acidosis
biotin deficiency and, 334
biotinidase deficiency and, 329
holocarboxylase synthetase deficiency and, 327
3-methylcrotonyl-CoA carboxylase deficiency and, 323
propionyl-CoA carboxylase deficiency and, 323
Metabolic adaptation, 495-520
low energy intake and, 501-11
low protein intake and, 512-20
Metabolic alkalosis
bulimia nervosa and, 312
Metabolic encephalopathy
carnitine deficiency and, 51
Metabolism
body size and, 6-8
intracellular protein synthesis and, 7
macrophages and, 135-43
nitrogen balance and, 3-4
See also specific type
Metalloflavoproteins, 15
Metallothionine
infection and, 135
interleukin-1 and, 139
Methane
gastrointestinal microflora and, 170
microbial fermentation and, 161
Methemoglobin
cytochrome $b_5$ and, 15
Methionine
carnitine and, 43
catabolism of
biotin and, 319
formate conversion to CO2 and, 411
functions of, 409-11
immune function and, 415-17
lipotropes and, 407-8
metabolism of, 180-93
S-adenosylmethionine and, 180-83
polyamine pathway and, 190-92
transamination and, 192-93
transmethylation and, 179, 183-90
transsulfuration and, 179, 183-90
requirements in fishes, 238
requirements in ruminants, 99-104
storage of, 409
Methionine synthase
homocysteine metabolism and, 186-87
3-Methylcrotonyl-CoA carboxylase
biotin and, 319
3-Methylcrotonyl-CoA carboxylase deficiency, 323-24
3-Methylcrotonylglycinuria, 323-24
Methylglyoxal
mutagenicity/carcinogenicity of, 86-88
Methylmalonate
isomerization to succinate
vitamin $B_{12}$ and, 410
Methylthioribose
methionine resynthesis and, 192
Metorphamide
peptidyl glycine α-amidating monooxygenase and, 373
Mevalonic acid
cholesterol biosynthesis and, 247, 251, 253
Mianserine
bulimia nervosa and, 313
Microcytosis
iron deficiency and, 17
*Microsiphum liriodendri*
carotenoid metabolism in, 287
Microsomal ethanol oxidizing system, 462
Migraine
food allergy and, 120
Milk
breast
biotin in, 322
human
carnitine in, 48
Mineralization
vitamin D and, 548-51
Minerals
infection and, 134-35
vitamin D and, 546-47
Mitochondria
carnitine and, 42-43, 55
cytochromes in, 15
Monoamine oxidase
iron deficiency and, 26, 28
Monoclonal antibodies
vitamin D receptor and, 542-44
Monocytes
interleukin-1 and, 137
Monooxygenases
ascorbate and, 369
peptidyl glycine α-amidating, 373-74
Monosaccharides, 211-19
*Morone saxatilis*
nutrient requirements of, 228
Morphine
dopamine receptors and, 27
mRNA
interleukin-1 specific, 137
Muscle
body size/metabolism and, 7
iron deficiency and, 21-23
metabolite exchange and, 7
Mutagens, 67-88
Myalgia
interleukin-1 and, 139
Mycotoxins
carcinogenicity of, 68
Myelin
glucose adducts of, 215
Myeloperoxidase, 15
iron deficiency and, 31
oxidized halogens and, 31
Myoglobin
deficiency of, 17
function of, 14-15
iron deficiency and, 19
oxygen transport and, 20
Myoinositol
hyperglycemia and, 213-14
sorbitol and, 213
Myosin
ε-*N*-trimethyllysine residues in, 43

N

Neonate
energy production in
carnitine and, 47-50
Nephropathy
diabetic, 211-12
Neuropathy
diabetic, 211-12
Neuropeptide Y
peptidyl glycine α-amidating monooxygenase and, 373
*Neurospora crassa*
dioxygenase reactions in, 385
Neutrophilia
interleukin-1 and, 140
Neutrophils
catalase-positive bacteria and, 31
iron deficiency and, 19, 30-32
lactoferrin and, 135
Niacin deficiency
pellagra and, 369
Nicotinamide adenine dinucleotide dehydrogenase, 15
Nitrogen balance
biochemical basis of, 518-20
energy intake and, 515
metabolic adaptation and, 512-14
metabolism and, 3-4

protein turnover and, 515-18
surgery and, 5
Nitrosamides
carcinogenicity of, 68
Nitrosamines
carcinogenicity of, 68
*N*-Nitrosodiethylamine
liver cancer and, 426
Norepinephrine
body temperature and, 28-29
iron deficiency and, 26
tyrosine and, 372
Nucleosides
deoxygenase reactions of, 385-86
Nutrition
aging and, 9-10
alcohol and, 457-70
animal evolution and, 5-9
human
gastrointestinal microflora and, 165-72
infection and, 131-49
monogastric
gastrointestinal microflora and, 158-65
Nutritional deficiency
antibacterial agents and, 164
See also specific type
Nutrition knowledge
food-related behavior and, 358

O

Obesity
food oxidation and, 217
Oleic acid
heterocyclic amine mutagenicity and, 76
Oligomenorrhea
bulimia nervosa and, 312
*Oncorhynchus keta*
xanthophyll metabolism in, 281
*Oncorhynchus tshawytscha*
nutrient requirements of, 226
Optic atrophy
biotinidase deficiency and, 330
Osteomalacia
vitamin D and, 541
Osteoporosis
calcium and, 9-10
Oxaloacetic acid
glucose synthesis and, 319
Oxidative metabolism
heme proteins and, 14
iron deficiency and, 23
non-heme iron compounds and, 15
Oxidative phosphorylation
ethanol consumption and, 464
*Oxiulis californica*
oxyxanthins of, 276
Oxygen transport
iron deficiency and, 20
Oxysterols
cholesterol biosynthesis and, 254-58
Oxytocin
peptidyl glycine α-amidating monooxygenase and, 373
Oxyxanthins, 276

P

Pancreatic polypeptide
peptidyl glycine α-amidating monooxygenase and, 373
Pantothenate
germfree animals and, 162
Papilioerythrin, 287
*Papilio xuthus*
papilioerythrin of, 287
Parasiloxanthin, 281
Pellagra
niacin deficiency and, 369
vitamin deficiency and, 126
Peptides
pyrolysates of
carcinogenicity of, 68
Peritoneal dialysis
carnitine and, 55
Pernicious anemia
gastric cancer and, 420
vitamin $B_{12}$ deficiency and, 414
Peroxidase, 15
Peroxidation
aging and, 7
Phagocytosis
iron deficiency and, 30
Phenelzine
bulimia nervosa and, 313
Phenobarbital
biotin deficiency and, 334
Phenylalanine
aspartame and, 124
requirements in fishes, 236-38
requirements in ruminants, 101-4
Phenytoin
biotin deficiency and, 334
Phosphatidate
inositol and, 582
Phosphatidylcholine
methionine metabolism and, 184-85
Phosphatidylinositol
cellular levels of
alteration of, 573-74
mammalian cells and, 578-84
1-stearoyl 2-arachidonoyl
formation of, 571-72
transfer proteins and, 572-73
Phosphoenol-pyruvate-carboxykinase, 15
Phospholipase C
phosphatidylinositol and, 580-81
Phosphorus
hypertension and, 477
requirements in ruminants, 107-8
Photosensitization
carotenoids and, 289-91
Placenta
nutrient transport across, 7-8
Plasmin
interleukin-1 and, 140
*Pleuronectes platessa*
nutrient requirements of, 228
*Pneumatophorus japonicus*
xanthophyll metabolism in, 281
Pneumonia
iron deficiency and, 145
Poikilocytosis
anorexia nervosa and, 306
Polyamine pathway
methionine metabolism and, 190-92
Polyisoprenoids
cholesterol biosynthesis and, 246-48
Polymers
dietary
gastrointestinal microflora and, 167-68
Polyol pathway
glucose metabolism and, 213-15
Polyphosphoinositides
mammalian cells and, 578-84
Polysaccharides
dietary
gastrointestinal microflora and, 167-68
Porphyria cutanea tarda
carotenoid therapy and, 289-90
Potassium
hypertension and, 477
Prader-Willi syndrome
bulimia and, 300
Pregnancy
maternal iron deficiency and, 24-25
*Prognichthys agoo*
carotenoids of, 280
Propionic acid
catabolism of
biotin and, 319
microbial metabolism and, 161
Propionic acidemia
propionyl-CoA carboxylase deficiency and, 323

Propionyl-CoA carboxylase
  biotin and, 319
Propionyl-CoA carboxylase deficiency, 323
Prostaglandin $E_2$
  interleukin-1 and, 137
Prostaglandins
  arachidonic acid and, 579
Protein-calorie malnutrition
  behavior and, 116
Proteins
  dietary requirement for, 4
  hydroxylation of
    ascorbate and, 383-85
  metabolic bone disease and, 10
  metabolism of, 2-5
    infection and, 133-34
    variation in, 499
  pyrolysates of
    carcinogenicity of, 68
  requirements in fishes, 226-28
  synthesis of
    interleukin-1 and, 138-39, 140
    metabolism and, 7
    RNA and, 7
  turnover of
    body size/metabolism and, 7
    nitrogen balance and, 515-18
Proteolysis-inducing factor
  interleukin-1 and, 138
Protoporphyria
  erythropoietic
    β-carotene and, 289
Protoporphyrin
  erythrocyte
    iron deficiency and, 17
  heterocyclic amine mutagenicity and, 76
Psychiatric illnes
  dietary hypersensitivity and, 119-20
Psychosis
  vitamin deficiency and, 126
Purine nucleosides
  toxicity of
    AdoHcy hydrolase and, 185
Purple acid phosphatase
  placental iron transport and, 8
Putrescine
  AdoMet decarboxylase and, 191
Pyrimidines
  deoxygenase reactions of, 385-86
Pyrimidone
  biotin deficiency and, 334
Pyrolysates
  carcinogenicity of, 68
Pyrrolidine alkaloids
  carcinogenicity of, 68
Pyruvate
  β-sulfinylpyruvate and, 194
Pyruvate carboxylase
  biotin and, 319
Pyruvate carboxylase deficiency, 324
  biotin and, 326

R

Race
  food-related behavior and, 355-58
Respiration
  exercise and, 3
Retinoic acid
  cholesterogenesis and, 261
Retinol
  cholesterogenesis and, 261
  vitamin A and, 282-83
Retinol-binding protein
  nutritional evolution and, 6
Retinopathy
  diabetic, 211-12
  sugar consumption and, 217
Retinyl acetate
  cholesterogenesis and, 261
Reye's syndrome
  carnitine deficiency and, 51
Rhinitis
  food allergy and, 120
*Rhodotorula glutinis*
  dioxygenase reactions in, 385
Ribonucleotide reductase
  iron deficiency and, 19, 32
Rickets
  vitamin D and, 532, 541
RNA
  protein synthesis and, 7
Ruminants
  nutrient requirements of, 95-109
    amino acid, 99-106
    energy, 96-98
    inorganic, 107-8
    vitamins, 106-7

S

*Salmo gairdneri*
  nutrient requirements of, 228
*Salmo garrdneri*
  xanthophyll metabolism in, 280
*Salmo salar*
  xanthophyll metabolism in, 280
*Salmonella typhimurium*
  mutagenic activity in, 68
Salmonellosis
  iron overload and, 148
*Salvelinus fontinalis*
  nutrient requirements of, 228
Sarcosine dehydrogenase
  methionine metabolism and, 183-84
Sarcosinuria, 183
Schizophrenia
  celiac disease and, 119
  inositol metabolism and, 587
  tryptophan and, 125
*Scophtalmus maximus*
  nutrient requirements of, 228
Scurvy
  carnitine and, 388
*Sebastes flavidus*
  chiriquixanthin B of, 276
Seizures
  biotinidase deficiency and, 329
Selenium deficiency
  vascular complications of, 217
Semen
  inositol in, 565
*Seriola quinqueradiata*
  nutrient requirements of, 228
  xanthophyll formation in, 280-81
Serotonin
  binding to receptors, 26-27
  iron deficiency and, 26
Serum amyloid A
  interleukin-1 and, 140
Sickle cell anemia
  hyperferremia and, 148
Sinus bradycardia
  anorexia nervosa and, 303
Skeletal muscle
  γ-butyrobetaine hydroxylase and, 43
  carnitine deficiency and, 50-51
  iron deficiency and, 21-23
Sleep
  anorexia nervosa and, 305
Sleep latency
  tryptophan and, 125
Smoking
  See Cigarette smoking
Sodium-potassium pump
  calcium and, 490
Solar urticaria
  carotenoid therapy and, 289-90
Somnolence
  biotin deficiency and, 332
Sorbitol
  glucose metabolism and, 213
Spermidine
  synthesis of
    polyamine pathway and, 190

Spermine
  synthesis of
    polyamine pathway and, 190
*Staphylococcus aureus*
  kwashiorkor and, 146
  neutrophils and, 31
Starvation
  consequences of, 302-3
Steroid hormones
  vitamin D and, 530-32
Sterols
  cholesterol biosynthesis and, 246-48
  isopentenyl pyrophosphate and, 253
  metabolism of
    vitamin D and, 529
Stomach cancer
  dietary habits and, 67
*Streptococcus pneumoniae*
  neutrophils and, 31-32
Substance P
  peptidyl glycine α-amidating monooxygenase and, 373
Succinate
  vitamin $B_{12}$ and, 410
Succinic dehydrogenase, 15
Sucrase
  acarbose and, 216
Sucrose
  behavioral effects of, 121-23
  metabolic effects of, 217-18
Sudden infant death syndrome
  biotin deficiency and, 335
Sugars
  metabolic effects of, 217-19
β-Sulfinylpyruvate
  cysteinesulfinate and, 194
Sulfite
  β-sulfinylpyruvate and, 194
Sulfur
  metabolism of
    inorganic, 198-99
Sweat glands
  mammary gland development and, 8

T

Taraxanthin, 276
Taurine
  cysteine metabolism and, 193-96
  cysteinesulfinate pathway and, 195
  metabolism of, 196
Tetrahydrobiopterin
  ascorbate and, 369
Tetrahydrofolate
  ascorbate and, 369
  homocysteine conversion to methionine and, 410
Thalassemia
  hyperferremia and, 148
Thermogenesis
  diet-induced, 506-7
Thiamin
  requirements in ruminants, 106-7
Threonine
  catabolism of
    biotin and, 319
  requirements in fishes, 239
  requirements in ruminants, 101-4
Thrombin
  interleukin-1 and, 140
Thrombocytopenia
  anorexia nervosa and, 305
Thromboxanes
  arachidonic acid and, 579
*Thunnus orientalis*
  tunaxanthin and, 276
Thymine 7-hydroxylase, 385-86
Thyroid hormone
  biosynthesis of
    iodine and, 528
  body temperature and, 28-29
Thyroid stimulating hormone
  thermogenesis and, 29
Thyroxine
  carnitine excretion and, 47
*Tilapia aurea*
  nutrient requirements of, 228
*Tilapia mossambica*
  nutrient requirements of, 228
*Tilapia zillii*
  nutrient requirements of, 228
T lymphocytes
  biotinidase deficiency and, 329
  iron deficiency and, 32-33
Torulene, 286
Total parenteral nutrition
  biotin deficiency and, 333-34
Transamination
  methionine metabolism and, 192-93
Transferrin, 16
  glucose adducts of, 215
  infection and, 33
  nutritional evolution and, 6
  uteroferrin and, 8
Transmethylation
  S-adenosylmethionine and, 409
  methionine and, 179, 183-90
Transsulfuration
  methionine and, 179, 183-90
Triacylglycerol
  dietary inositol deficiency and, 574-76
Tricarboxylic acid cycle
  coenzyme A and, 43
  pyruvate carboxylase and, 319
ϵ-*N*-Trimethylline residues
  carnitine biosynthesis and, 43-44
Tropical sprue
  developing countries and, 172
Tryptophan
  behavioral effects of, 125
  pyrolysis products of
    mutagenicity of, 76
  requirements in fishes, 239
  requirements in ruminants, 103
  sleep latency and, 125
Tryptophan hydroxylase
  biogenic amines and, 27
Tryptophan pyrrolase, 15
Tube feeding
  anorexia nervosa and, 307
Tuberculosis
  iron supplementation and, 146
Tumor necrosis factor
  lipid metabolism and, 143
Tunaxanthin
  isolation of, 276
Tyrosine
  aspartame and, 124
  behavioral effects of, 126
  conversion to norepinephrine, 372
  metabolism of
    ascorbate and, 375
  requirements in ruminants, 101
Tyrosine hydroxylase
  biogenic amines and, 27
Tyrosinemia
  S-adenosylmethionine and, 180

U

Ubiquinones
  cholesterol biosynthesis and, 246-48, 252
  isopentenyl pyrophosphate and, 253
Urea
  metabolic adaptation and, 514-15
Uremia
  hypercarnitinemia and, 53-54
Urinary tract infection
  iron deficiency and, 144-45
*Urochordates*
  evolution of kidney in, 6
Urticaria
  food allergy and, 120
Uteroferrin
  placental iron transport and, 8

## V


Valine
  catabolism of
    biotin and, 319
  requirements in fishes, 235
  requirements in ruminants, 101-3
Vasoactive intestinal peptide
  peptidyl glycine α-amidating monooxygenase and, 373
Vasopressin
  peptidyl glycine α-amidating monooxygenase and, 373
Very-low-density lipoproteins
  cholesterogenesis and, 263-64
  lipoprotein lipase and, 140
Vitamin A
  antitumor activity of, 291
  carotenoids and, 281-83
  cholesterogenesis and, 260-61
  nutritional evolution and, 6
  requirements in ruminants, 106
Vitamin A deficiency
  vascular complications of, 217
Vitamin $B_{12}$
  functions of, 409-11
  germfree animals and, 162
  immune function and, 414-15
  lipotropes and, 407-8
  storage of, 409
Vitamin $B_{12}$ deficiency
  megaloblastic anemia and, 409
  methionine synthase and, 187
Vitamin C
  haloperidol and, 126
Vitamin D
  anticancer actions of, 550-51
  bone remodeling and, 548-51
  cholesterogenesis and, 261-63
  functions of
    calcium/mineral homeostasis and, 546-47
  immune system and, 548-51
  metabolic bone disease and, 10
  metabolism of, 529-30
    regulation of, 547-48
  mineralization and, 548-51
  receptors for, 527-52
    avian, 536-38
    evolution of, 539-40
    mammalian, 538-39
    model for, 551-52
    modification of, 544-46
    monoclonal antibodies and, 542-44
Vitamin D–resistant syndromes, 541-42
Vitamin H, 318
Vitamin K
  germfree animals and, 162
  requirements in ruminants, 106
Vitamins
  behavioral effects of, 126
  requirements in ruminants, 106-7
Vitamin supplementation
  anorexia nervosa and, 302
Volatile fatty acids
  ruminants and, 96-98
Vomiting
  3-methylcrotonyl-CoA carboxylase deficiency and, 323


## W


Werdnig-Hoffman disease
  3-methylcrotonyl-CoA carboxylase deficiency and, 323-24
Wernicke-Korsakoff syndrome
  vitamin deficiency and, 126


## X


Xanthine oxidase, 15
Xanthophylls
  metabolism in fishes, 280-81
Xenobiotics
  metabolism of
    lipotropes and, 417-19
Xylitol
  metabolic effects of, 218-19


## Y


Yeasts
  metabolic end-products of, 160-61
*Yersinia enterocolitica*
  hemochromatosis and, 148


## Z


Zeaxanthin
  absorption in birds, 284
  astaxanthin formation and, 277
  chirality of, 274-75
  conversion to astaxanthin, 279
Zinc
  infection and, 134-35

# CUMMULATIVE INDEXES

## CONTRIBUTING AUTHORS, VOLUMES 2–6


A

Alpers, D. H., 2:343–69
Anderson, T. A., 2:113–32
Andersson, B., 2:73–89
Apgar, J., 5:43–68
Asplund, J. M., 6:95–112
Atkins, F. M., 4:233–55
Avioli, L. V., 4:471–91
Axelson, M. L., 6:345–63

B

Baker, J. P., 2:179–99
Baldwin, R. L., 4:101–14
Bean, W., 2:1–20
Becker, D. J., 3:187–212
Benevenga, N. J., 4:151–81
Bengoa, J. M., 5:463–84
Bernardini, P., 2:419–54
Bier, D. M., 3:309–39
Blass, J. B., 2:201–27
Block, K. P., 4:409–54
Bloom, S. R., 5:213–39
Borum, P. R., 3:233–59
Brand, J. G., 2:249–76
Broquist, H. P., 5:391–409
Burk, R. F., 3:53–70
Bywater, A. C., 4:101–14

C

Cagan, R. H., 2:249–76
Casper, R. C., 6:299–316
Cole, S. G., 5:241–66
Combs, G. F. Jr., 4:257–80
Combs, S. B., 4:257–80
Cosman, M. P., 3:1–33
Cousins, R. J., 3:261–88
Crapo, P. A., 5:95–114

D

Dallman, P. R., 6:13–40
Danford, D. E., 2:303–22
Daniels-Kush, R., 5:411–33
Darby, W. J., 5:1–24
Dews, P. B., 2:323–41
DiSilvestro, R. A., 3:261–88
Doyle, M. P., 5:25–41

E

Elwyn, D. H., 3:433–66
Emken, E. A., 4:339–76
Englard, S., 6:365–406
Erdman, J. W. Jr., 3:213–31

F

Fant, M. E., 3:97–124
Farthing, M. J. G., 6:131–54
Fernandes, G., 2:151–77
Fiala, E. S., 5:295–321
Field, J. O., 5:143–72
Fischer, J. E., 2:419–54
Forbes, R. M., 3:213–31
Furihata, C., 6:67–94

G

Goldberg, A. C., 5:195–212
Good, R. A., 2:151–77
Goodwin, T. W., 6:273–97
Greig, P. D., 2:179–99
Grundy, S. M., 3:71–96

H

Hahn, P., 2:91–111
Halver, J. E., 6:225–44
Hansen, M. A., 2:151–77
Harper, A. E., 4:409–54
Haussler, M. R., 6:527–62
Henderson, L. M., 3:289–307; 4:455–70
Henry, H. L., 4:493–520
Herlong, H. F., 6:457–74
Heusner, A. A., 5:267–93
Himms-Hagen, J., 5:69–94
Hochstein, P., 5:365–90
Holub, B. J., 6:563–97
Horton, E. S., 5:411–33
Howard, L., 4:69–99
Hutt, P. B., 4:1–20

I

Ink, S. L., 4:455–70

J

Jansen, G. R., 4:43–67
Jarvis, W. T., 3:35–52
Jeejeebhoy, K. N., 2:179–99

K

Kagnoff, M. F., 5:241–66
Karanja, N., 6:475–94
Keusch, G. T., 6:131–54
Kinney, J. M., 3:433–66
Kissileff, H. R., 2:371–418
Klatsky, A., 2:51–71
Kruesi, M. J. P., 6:113–30

L

Lawson, D., 2:277–301
Leksell, L. G., 2:73–89
Levine, R., 6:211–24

M

MacDonald, M. L., 4:521–62
Mäkinen, K. K., 2:133–50
Matovinovic, J., 3:341–412
Matsushima, T., 6:67–94
Matthews, D. E., 3:309–39
McCarron, D. A., 6:475–94
McCay, P. B., 5:323–40
Metcalfe, D. D., 4:233–55
Mezey, E., 2:21–50
Michalek, A. V., 4:69–99
Miller, R. H., 4:409–54
Mills, C. F., 5:173–93
Mitchell, M. C., 6:457–74
Morris, J. G., 4:521–62
Munro, H. N., 3:97–124; 6:1–12

N

Naim, M., 2:249–76
Newberne, P. M., 6:407–32
Nicholl, C. G., 5:213–39
Nielsen, F., 4:21–41
Nixon, D., 2:277–301
Norman, A. W., 4:493–520
Nyhan, W. L., 6:317–43

O

Olson, R. E., 4:281–337

P

Paulson, D. J., 6:41–66
Pilistine, S. J., 3:97–124
Polak, J. M., 5:213–39
Prasad, A. S., 5:341–63

R

Rao, G. S., 4:115–36
Rapoport, J. L., 6:113–30
Rebouche, C. J., 6:41–66
Reddy, B. S., 5:295–321
Richmond, A., 2:277–301
Rogers, A. E., 6:407–32
Rogers, Q. R., 4:521–62
Rosenberg, I. H., 5:463–84
Rozin, P., 6:433–56
Rudman, D., 2:277–301
Rudney, H., 6:245–72
Rundgren, M., 2:73–89

S

Sampson, D. A., 4:43–67
Sauberlich, H. E., 4:377–407
Savage, D. C., 6:155–78
Scheinin, A., 2:133–50
Schonfeld, G., 5:195–212
Seetharam, B., 2:343–69
Seifter, S., 6:365–406
Sevanian, A., 5:365–90
Sexton, R. C., 6:245–72
Shane, B., 5:115–41
Sitrin, M. D., 5:463–84
Sommer, A., 4:183–205
Stallones, R. A., 3:155–85
Steele, R. D., 4:157–81
Stipanuk, M. H., 6:179–209
Stokstad, E. L. R., 5:115–41
Swan, P. B., 3:413–32
Sweetman, L., 6:317–43

T

Tielsch, J. M., 4:183–205

V

van Eys, J., 5:435–61
Van Itallie, T. B., 2:371–418
Visek, W. J., 4:137–55
Vollmecke, T. A., 6:433–56

W

Wagner, C., 2:229–48
Walser, M., 3:125–54
Waterlow, J. C., 6:495–526
Weisburger, J. H., 5:295–321
Wilson, R. P., 6:225–44
Woo, R., 5:411–33

Y

Young, R. C., 2:201–27

# CHAPTER TITLES, VOLUMES 2–6


PREFATORY ESSAYS

| | | |
|---|---|---|
| Personal Reflections on Clinical Investigations | W. Bean | 2:1–20 |
| A Feast for Aesculapius: Historical Diets for Asthma and Sexual Pleasure | M. P. Cosman | 3:1–33 |
| Government Regulation of the Integrity of the Food Supply | P. B. Hutt | 4:1–20 |
| Some Personal Reflections on a Half Century of Nutrition Science: 1930s–1980s | W. J. Darby | 5:1–24 |
| Back to Basics: An Evolutionary Odyssey with Reflections on the Nutrition Research of Tomorrow | H. N. Munro | 6:1–12 |

ENERGY METABOLISM

| | | |
|---|---|---|
| Nutritional Energetics of Animals | R. L. Baldwin, A. C. Bywater | 4:101–14 |
| Brown Adipose Tissue Metabolism and Thermogenesis | J. Himms-Hagen | 5:69–94 |
| Body Size and Energy Metabolism | A. A. Heusner | 5:267–93 |
| Regulation of Energy Balance | R. Woo, R. Daniels-Kush, E. S. Horton | 5:411–33 |
| Alcohol and Nutrition: Caloric Value, Bioenergetics, and Relationship to Liver Damage | M. C. Mitchell, H. F. Herlong | 6:457–74 |
| Metabolic Adaptation to Low Intakes of Energy and Protein | J. C. Waterlow | 6:495–526 |

CARBOHYDRATES

| | | |
|---|---|---|
| Recent Trends in Carbohydrate Consumption | T. A. Anderson | 2:113–32 |
| Xylitol and Dental Caries | K. K. Mäkinen, A. Scheinin | 2:133–50 |
| Simple versus Complex Carbohydrate Use in the Diabetic Diet | P. A. Crapo | 5:95–114 |
| Monosaccharides in Health and Disease | R. Levine | 6:211–24 |

LIPIDS

| | | |
|---|---|---|
| Absorption and Metabolism of Dietary Cholesterol | S. M. Grundy | 3:71–96 |
| Nutrition and Biochemistry of *Trans* and Positional Fatty Isomers in Hydrogenated Oils | E. A. Emken | 4:339–76 |
| Effects of Diet on Lipoprotein Metabolism | A. C. Goldberg, G. Schonfeld | 5:195–212 |
| Mechanisms and Consequences of Lipid Peroxidation in Biological Systems | A. Sevanian, P. Hochstein | 5:365–90 |
| Regulation of Cholesterol Biosynthesis | H. Rudney, R. C. Sexton | 6:245–72 |

PROTEINS, PEPTIDES, AND AMINO ACIDS

| | | |
|---|---|---|
| Amino Acid Imbalance and Hepatic Encephalopathy | P. Bernardini, J. E. Fischer | 2:419–54 |
| Carnitine | P. R. Borum | 3:233–59 |
| An Update of Concepts of Essential Amino Acids | W. J. Visek | 4:135–55 |
| Branched-Chain Amino Acid Metabolism | A. E. Harper, R. H. Miller, K. P. Block | 4:409–54 |

| | | |
|---|---|---|
| Metabolism of Sulfur-Containing Amino Acids | M. H. Stipanuk | 6:179–209 |
| Protein and Amino Acid Requirements of Fishes | R. P. Wilson, J. E. Halver | 6:225–44 |
| Metabolic Adaptation to Low Intakes of Energy and Protein | J. C. Waterlow | 6:495–526 |
| VITAMINS | | |
| Cellular Folate Binding Proteins | C. Wagner | 2:229–48 |
| Absorption and Transport of Cobalamin (Vitamin $B_{12}$) | B. Seetharam, D. Alpers | 2:343–69 |
| Niacin | L. M. Henderson | 3:289–307 |
| Vitamin K Metabolism | R. E. Olson | 4:281–337 |
| Vitamin $B_6$ Metabolism | S. L. Ink, L. M. Henderson | 4:455–70 |
| Vitamin D: Metabolism and Biological Actions | H. L. Henry, A. W. Norman | 4:493–520 |
| Vitamin $B_{12}$–Folate Interrelationships | B. Shane, E. L. R. Stokstad | 5:115–41 |
| Vitamin E: Interactions With Free Radicals and Ascorbate | P. B. McCay | 5:323–40 |
| The Biochemical Functions of Ascorbic Acid | S. Englard, S. Seifter | 6:365–406 |
| Vitamin D Receptors: Nature and Function | M. R. Haussler | 6:527–62 |
| INORGANIC NUTRIENTS | | |
| Biological Activity of Selenium | R. F. Burk | 3:53–70 |
| Bioavailability of Trace Mineral Elements | R. M. Forbes, J. W. Erdman, Jr. | 3:213–31 |
| Physiological Ligands for Copper and Zinc | R. A. DiSilvestro, R. J. Cousins | 3:261–88 |
| Ultratrace Elements in Nutrition | F. Nielsen | 4:21–41 |
| Dietary Intake and Bioavailability of Fluoride | G. S. Rao | 4:115–36 |
| The Nutritional Biochemistry of Selenium | G. F. Combs, Jr., S. B. Combs | 4:257–80 |
| Zinc and Reproduction | J. Apgar | 5:43–68 |
| Dietary Interactions Involving Trace Elements | C. F. Mills | 5:173–93 |
| Clinical Manifestations of Zinc Deficiency | A. S. Prasad | 5:341–63 |
| Biochemical Basis for the Manifestations of Iron Deficiency | P. R. Dallman | 6:13–40 |
| Mutagens and Carcinogens in Foods | C. Furihata, T. Matsushima | 6:67–94 |
| Metabolism, Nutrition, and Function of Carotenoids | T. W. Goodwin | 6:273–97 |
| WATER | | |
| Regulation of Water Intake | B. Andersson, L. G. Leksell, M. Rundgren | 2:73–89 |
| OTHER FOOD COMPONENTS | | |
| Naturally Occurring Anticarcinogenic Substances in Foodstuffs | E. S. Fiala, B. S. Reddy, J. H. Weisburger | 5:295–321 |
| The Indolizidine Alkaloids, Slaframine and Swainsonine: Contaminants in Animal Forages | H. P. Broquist | 5:391–409 |
| Metabolism and Function of *myo*-Inositol and Inositol Phospholipids | B. J. Holub | 6:563–97 |
| DIET, NUTRITION, AND METABOLIC REGULATION | | |
| Effects of Nutritive Factors on Metabolic Processes Involving Bioactivation and Detoxication of Chemicals | F. P. Guengerich | 4:207-31 |
| The Hormonal Regulation of Food Intake, Digestion, and Absorption | C. G. Nicholl, J. M. Polak, S. R. Bloom | 5:213–39 |
| CLINICAL NUTRITION | | |
| Liver Disease and Protein Needs | E. Mezey | 2:31–50 |
| The Relations of Alcohol and the Cardiovascular System | A. Klatsky | 2:51–71 |
| Development of Lipid Metabolism | P. Hahn | 2:91–111 |

| | | |
|---|---|---|
| Nutrition and Immunity | M. A. Hansen, G. Fernandes, R. A. Good | 2:151–77 |
| Metabolic Effects of Total Parenteral Nutrition | P. D. Greig, J. P. Baker, K. N. Jeejeebhoy | 2:179–99 |
| Iatrogenic Nutritional Deficiencies | R. C. Young, J. P. Blass | 2:201–27 |
| Chemical Senses in the Release of Gastric and Pancreatic Secretions | J. G. Brand, R. H. Cagan, M. Naim | 2:249–76 |
| Metabolic Approaches to Cancer Cachexia | D. Lawson, A. Richmond, D. Rudman, D. Nixon | 2:277–301 |
| Pica and Nutrition | D. E. Danford | 2:303–22 |
| Physiology of the Control of Food Intake | H. R. Kissileff, T. B. Van Itallie | 2:371–418 |
| The Placenta in Nutrition | H. N. Munro, S. J. Pilistine, M. E. Fant | 3:97–124 |
| Nutrition in Renal Failure | M. Walser | 3:125–54 |
| Ischemic Heart Disease and Lipids in Blood and Diet | R. A. Stallones | 3:155–85 |
| The Endocrine Responses to Protein-Calorie Malnutrition | D. J. Becker | 3:187–212 |
| Endemic Goiter and Cretinism at the Dawn of the Third Millennium | J. Matovinovic | 3:341–412 |
| Protein Metabolism and Injury | J. M. Kinney, D. H. Elwyn | 3:433–66 |
| Protein and Energy Nutrition During Lactation | D. A. Sampson, G. R. Jansen | 4:43–67 |
| Home Parenteral Nutrition | L. Howard, A.V. Michalek | 4:69–99 |
| The Epidemiology of Vitamin A Deficiency and Xerophthalmia | J. M. Tielsch, A. Sommer | 4:183–205 |
| The Diagnosis and Treatment of Food Allergy | F. A. Atkins, D. D. Metcalfe | 4:233–55 |
| Calcium and Osteoporosis | L. V. Avioli | 4:471–91 |
| Zinc and Reproduction | J. Apgar | 5:43–68 |
| Simple versus Complex Carbohydrate Use in the Diabetic Diet | P. A. Crapo | 5:95–114 |
| The Hormonal Regulation of Food Intake, Digestion, and Absorption | C. G. Nicholl, J. M. Polak, S. R. Bloom | 5:213–39 |
| Celiac Disease | S. G. Cole, M. F. Kagnoff | 5:241–66 |
| Clinical Manifestations of Zinc Deficiency | A. S. Prasad | 5:341–63 |
| Mechanisms and Consequences of Lipid Peroxidation in Biological Systems | A. Sevanian, P. Hochstein | 5:365–90 |
| Regulation of Energy Balance | R. Woo, R. Daniels-Kush, E. S. Horton | 5:411–33 |
| Nutrition and Cancer: Physiological Interrelationships | J. van Eys | 5:453–61 |
| Nutritional Aspects of Inflammatory Bowel Disease | I. H. Rosenberg, J. M. Bengoa, M. D. Sitrin | 5:463–84 |
| Carnitine Metabolism and Function in Humans | C. J. Rebouche, D. J. Paulson | 6:41–66 |
| Nutrition and Infection | G. T. Keusch, M. J. G. Farthing | 6:131–54 |
| The Pathophysiology of Anorexia Nervosa and Bulimia Nervosa | R. C. Casper | 6:299–316 |
| Inheritable Biotin-Treatable Disorders and Their Associated Phenomena | L. Sweetman, W. L. Nyhan | 6:317–43 |
| Labile Methyl Groups and the Promotion of Cancer | P. M. Newberne, A. E. Rogers | 6:407–332 |
| Calcium and Hypertension | N. Karanja, D. A. McCarron | 6:475–94 |
| Metabolic Adaptation to Low Intakes of Energy and Protein | J. C. Waterlow | 6:495–526 |
| NUTRITIONAL ANTHROPOLOGY | | |
| Food Faddism, Cultism, and Quackery | W. T. Jarvis | 3:35–52 |
| Implementing Nutrition Programs: Lessons from an Unheeded Literature | J. O. Field | 5:143–72 |
| Diet and Human Behavior: How Much Do They Affect Each Other? | M. J. P. Kruesi, J. L. Rapoport | 6:113–30 |

| | | |
|---|---|---|
| The Impact of Culture on Food-Related Behavior | M. L. Axelson | 6:345–63 |
| Food Likes and Dislikes | P. Rozin, T. A. Vollmecke | 6:433–56 |
| **NUTRITIONAL TOXICOLOGY AND PHARMACOLOGY** | | |
| Caffeine | P. B. Dews | 2:323–41 |
| Adverse Effects of Excessive Consumption of Amino Acids | N. J. Benevenga, R. D. Steele | 4:157–81 |
| Naturally Occurring Anticarcinogenic Substances in Foodstuffs | E. S. Fiala, B. S. Reddy, J. H. Weisburger | 5:295–321 |
| **NUTRITIONAL MICROBIOLOGY** | | |
| Food-borne Pathogens of Recent Concern | M. P. Doyle | 5:25–41 |
| Gastrointestinal Microflora in Mammalian Nutrition | D. C. Savage | 6:155–78 |
| **PUBLIC HEALTH NUTRITION** | | |
| Food Consumption by Individuals in the United States: Two Major Surveys | P. B. Swan | 3:413–32 |
| **COMPARATIVE NUTRITION** | | |
| Nutrition of the Domestic Cat | M. L. MacDonald, Q. R. Rogers, J. G. Morris | 4:521–62 |
| Somatic Nutrient Requirements of Ruminants | J. M. Asplund | 6:95–112 |
| Protein and Amino Acid Requirements of Fishes | R. P. Wilson, J. E. Halver | 6:225–44 |
| **SPECIAL TOPICS** | | |
| Stable Isotope Methods for Nutritional Investigation | D. E. Matthews, D. M. Bier | 3:309–39 |
| Newer Methods for Assessing Nutriture of Selected B-Complex Vitamins | H. E. Sauberlich | 4:377–407 |

| | | |
|---|---|---|
| The Impact of Culture on Food-Related Behavior | M. L. Axelson | 6:345–63 |
| Food Likes and Dislikes | P. Rozin, T. A. Vollmecke | 6:433–56 |

NUTRITIONAL TOXICOLOGY AND PHARMACOLOGY

| | | |
|---|---|---|
| Caffeine | P. B. Dews | 2:323–41 |
| Adverse Effects of Excessive Consumption of Amino Acids | N. J. Benevenga, R. D. Steele | 4:157–81 |
| Naturally Occurring Anticarcinogenic Substances in Foodstuffs | E. S. Fiala, B. S. Reddy, J. H. Weisburger | 5:295–321 |

NUTRITIONAL MICROBIOLOGY

| | | |
|---|---|---|
| Food-borne Pathogens of Recent Concern | M. P. Doyle | 5:25–41 |
| Gastrointestinal Microflora in Mammalian Nutrition | D. C. Savage | 6:155–78 |

PUBLIC HEALTH NUTRITION

| | | |
|---|---|---|
| Food Consumption by Individuals in the United States: Two Major Surveys | P. B. Swan | 3:413–32 |

COMPARATIVE NUTRITION

| | | |
|---|---|---|
| Nutrition of the Domestic Cat | M. L. MacDonald, Q. R. Rogers, J. G. Morris | 4:521–62 |
| Somatic Nutrient Requirements of Ruminants | J. M. Asplund | 6:95–112 |
| Protein and Amino Acid Requirements of Fishes | R. P. Wilson, J. E. Halver | 6:225–44 |

SPECIAL TOPICS

| | | |
|---|---|---|
| Stable Isotope Methods for Nutritional Investigation | D. E. Matthews, D. M. Bier | 3:309–39 |
| Newer Methods for Assessing Nutriture of Selected B-Complex Vitamins | H. E. Sauberlich | 4:377–407 |

| ANNUAL REVIEWS SERIES | | Prices Postpaid per volume USA/elsewhere | Regular Order Please send: | Standing Order Begin with: |
|---|---|---|---|---|
| | | | Vol. number | Vol. number |
| Annual Review of **COMPUTER SCIENCE** | | | | |
| Vol. 1 | (1986) | **$39.00/$42.00** | | |
| Vol. 2 | (avail. Nov. 1987) | **$39.00/$42.00** | Vol(s). ______ | Vol. ______ |
| Annual Review of **EARTH AND PLANETARY SCIENCES** | | | | |
| Vols. 1-10 | (1973-1982) | **$27.00/$30.00** | | |
| Vols. 11-14 | (1983-1986) | **$44.00/$47.00** | | |
| Vol. 15 | (avail. May 1987) | **$44.00/$47.00** | Vol(s). ______ | Vol. ______ |
| Annual Review of **ECOLOGY AND SYSTEMATICS** | | | | |
| Vols. 1-16 | (1970-1985) | **$27.00/$30.00** | | |
| Vol. 17 | (1986) | **$31.00/$34.00** | | |
| Vol. 18 | (avail. Nov. 1987) | **$31.00/$34.00** | Vol(s). ______ | Vol. ______ |
| Annual Review of **ENERGY** | | | | |
| Vols. 1-7 | (1976-1982) | **$27.00/$30.00** | | |
| Vols. 8-11 | (1983-1986) | **$56.00/$59.00** | | |
| Vol. 12 | (avail. Oct. 1987) | **$56.00/$59.00** | Vol(s). ______ | Vol. ______ |
| Annual Review of **ENTOMOLOGY** | | | | |
| Vols. 10-16, 18-30 | (1965-1971, 1973-1985) | **$27.00/$30.00** | | |
| Vol. 31 | (1986) | **$31.00/$34.00** | | |
| Vol. 32 | (avail. Jan. 1987) | **$31.00/$34.00** | Vol(s). ______ | Vol. ______ |
| Annual Review of **FLUID MECHANICS** | | | | |
| Vols. 1-4, 7-17 | (1969-1972, 1975-1985) | **$28.00/$31.00** | | |
| Vol. 18 | (1986) | **$32.00/$35.00** | | |
| Vol. 19 | (avail. Jan. 1987) | **$32.00/$35.00** | Vol(s). ______ | Vol. ______ |
| Annual Review of **GENETICS** | | | | |
| Vols. 1-19 | (1967-1985) | **$27.00/$30.00** | | |
| Vol. 20 | (1986) | **$31.00/$34.00** | | |
| Vol. 21 | (avail. Dec. 1987) | **$31.00/$34.00** | Vol(s). ______ | Vol. ______ |
| Annual Review of **IMMUNOLOGY** | | | | |
| Vols. 1-3 | (1983-1985) | **$27.00/$30.00** | | |
| Vol. 4 | (1986) | **$31.00/$34.00** | | |
| Vol. 5 | (avail. April 1987) | **$31.00/$34.00** | Vol(s). ______ | Vol. ______ |
| Annual Review of **MATERIALS SCIENCE** | | | | |
| Vols. 1, 3-12 | (1971, 1973-1982) | **$27.00/$30.00** | | |
| Vols. 13-16 | (1983-1986) | **$64.00/$67.00** | | |
| Vol. 17 | (avail. August 1987) | **$64.00/$67.00** | Vol(s). ______ | Vol. ______ |
| Annual Review of **MEDICINE** | | | | |
| Vols. 1-3, 6, 8-9 | (1950-1952, 1955, 1957-1958) | | | |
| 11-15, 17-36 | (1960-1964, 1966-1985) | **$27.00/$30.00** | | |
| Vol. 37 | (1986) | **$31.00/$34.00** | | |
| Vol. 38 | (avail. April 1987) | **$31.00/$34.00** | Vol(s). ______ | Vol. ______ |
| Annual Review of **MICROBIOLOGY** | | | | |
| Vols. 18-39 | (1964-1985) | **$27.00/$30.00** | | |
| Vol. 40 | (1986) | **$31.00/$34.00** | | |
| Vol. 41 | (avail. Oct. 1987) | **$31.00/$34.00** | Vol(s). ______ | Vol. ______ |